MATHEMATICAL ECONOMICS

MATHEMATICAL ECONOMICS

BY

R. G. D. ALLEN

Second Edition

MACMILLAN

ST MARTIN'S PRESS

First Edition 1956
Reprinted 1957
Second Edition 1959
Reprinted 1960
Reprinted (with alterations) 1963
Reprinted 1964, 1965, 1966, 1970, 1972

Published by
THE MACMILLAN PRESS LTD
London and Basingstoke
Associated companies in New York Toronto
Dublin Melbourne Johannesburg and Madras

SBN 333 02707 8

Reproduced and printed in Great Britain by
REDWOOD PRESS LIMITED
Trowbridge & London

PREFACE

THIS book has evolved from three strands of thought. When I was first interested in mathematical economics in the early 1930's, it seemed to me that the main need was for a grounding in calculus and I wrote my textbook, *Mathematical Analysis for Economists* (1938), for that purpose. I did not venture into the higher reaches of algebra and I made no use of the complex variable. I left such matters to be written up by those with specialist applications to economics in mind. Subsequently the uses of matrix algebra, of vectors and complex variables, of operational processes and of other such mathematical devices have been greatly developed in many parts of mathematical economics. There are in my view no mathematical texts on higher algebra and on operational methods which are really suitable for economists.

A second development of the last twenty years is the growth of econometrics. This has been so rapid that I think there is some risk that the necessary development of economic theory, formulated in a way which makes econometric sense to a statistician, will lag behind rather seriously. Such formulations of economic theory must be in mathematical terms but simplified as far as possible.

Finally, the change in the direction of economic thought over the past twenty years has involved a considerable upheaval in the structure of economic theory. This is partly, though by no means entirely, the result of the work of Keynes. I believe that there is now a real need for some synthesis of the " new " economics, for some calm survey of the form and scope of economic theory.

With these things in mind, I feel that the best contribution I can make is not to extend my 1938 book but rather to write a completely different one, a text on economic theory written in mathematical terms. The present work is not mathematics for the economist, nor is it econometrics. It aims at a fairly systematic treatment of some of the more important and simpler parts of mathematical economics. My main problem is one of selection from a vast range of economic topics, of making the book reasonably up-to-date and of keeping it down to reasonable dimensions. Even if I include only what is of particular interest to me personally, I would still find I have too much. To those who look for other topics or different methods of treatment, I can only make the familiar excuses of the anthologist.

I am sure that the book is very different from what it would have been if I had written it five years ago. How long it will remain even approximately up-to-date I cannot pretend to guess. I feel, however, that many of the techniques I attempt to describe will be relevant for some time to come ; they are now relatively new and they need to be consolidated and absorbed into the general body of economic theory. Moreover, my guiding principle is to start with, and to remain as close as possible to, economic problems of the real world, simplified as an economist might simplify them, and translated into mathematics of no more than moderate difficulty. I hope that this approach will appeal to many economists now and in the future.

I could not write a book of this kind without assistance on a scale far beyond my powers to acknowledge. I am grateful for the constant encouragement and advice of my colleagues, particularly Professor Lionel Robbins, Professor James Meade, Mr. David Knox, and Mr. Ralph Turvey. Mr. W. M. Gorman and Dr. F. H. Hahn of the University of Birmingham have kindly read through the manuscript ; they see the need for a book on the present lines, they are ideally qualified to write it, and yet they stand aside and allow me to monopolise the market. Above all, I am in debt to Dr. Helen Makower, Dr. G. Morton and Dr. A. W. Phillips ; this is clear to anyone who reads the middle and later chapters as now written.

R. G. D. ALLEN

LONDON SCHOOL OF ECONOMICS

PREFACE TO SECOND EDITION

I am glad to have this opportunity of making some changes in the text. Firstly, I have corrected errors and misprints which escaped me, all too frequently, during my original proof-reading. Secondly, I have made numerous revisions in the wording and exposition throughout the text. I hope that these will make the argument more clear and precise.

Thirdly, I have included some additional references, mainly to books and articles published since 1956. It happens that half-a-dozen books of outstanding merit have appeared in the two years 1957 and 1958. They are Goldberg : *Introduction to Difference Equations* (1958) ; Murdoch : *Linear Algebra for Undergraduates* (1957) ; Kemeny, Snell and Thompson : *Introduction to Finite Mathematics* (1957) ; Thrall and Tornheim : *Vector Spaces and Matrices* (1957) ; Luce and Raiffa : *Games and Decisions* (1957) ; and Dorfman, Samuelson and Solow : *Linear Programming and Economic Analysis* (1958). None of these can be described, mathematically, as very simple ; they vary in level from the moderately difficult to the quite advanced. But, equally, none of them can be ignored in the education of the mathematical economist.

Finally, I have completely re-written some critical sections : 1.9 and 5.8 on time lags in dynamic models ; 2.3, 10.3, 17.1 and 17.9 on general economic equilibrium ; and 16.2 on the dual problem in linear programming. Substantial parts of the chapters on vectors and matrices have been drastically re-cast. I have extended Appendix A which deals with the " practical " mathematics of operators and linear systems. I have added a completely new Appendix B on " modern " algebra to serve as an introduction to the rigorous and postulational development of algebra. In a sense, this is a complement to Appendix A. The strict, axiomatic approach of the modern algebraist should be of considerable interest in itself to the economic theorist concerned with model-building. In any case, I hope that the new Appendix provides an under-pinning for the algebra of the text, where a compromise is adopted in the interests of simplicity.

My thanks are due to a number of correspondents. I am particularly grateful for the suggestions made by Sven Danø of the University of Copenhagen ; by Lucien Foldes of the London School of Economics ;

PREFACE

by Maurice McManus of the University of Birmingham and the School of Business Administration, Minnesota ; by Peter Newman of the University College of the West Indies ; and by Ciro Tognetti of Centro per la Ricorca Economica ed Econometrica, Genoa.

R. G. D. ALLEN

UNIVERSITY OF CALIFORNIA, BERKELEY
JANUARY, 1959

CONTENTS

CONTENTS

INTRODUCTION

WHETHER mathematical techniques can be, or should be, used in economics is a much-discussed question. The proof of the pudding is in the eating. The economist must be left to determine for himself, when he reads the following chapters, whether the exposition of some important economic theories in mathematical terms assists him in appreciating the theories and in working out their implications.

The object of the text is to give a summary, and to some extent a synthesis, of what mathematical economists have written on certain economic theories. It is introductory, but it is not elementary. It is directed to the economist rather than to the mathematician, but it assumes some little mathematical background.

The order in which the economic material is developed may seem unusual ; it is not the traditional approach. The aim is to treat in mathematical form those economic problems which students of economics are required to handle and which have some bearing on the facts of economic life. It is also to start with something quite simple and to proceed later to the more difficult. The simplicity of what can be loosely described as macro-dynamic economics, the starting point here, lies in the fact that only a few broad aggregates are considered ; the relation to real problems appears through the dynamic approach. The problems of decision-taking, by the consumer, the firm, or the " economic planner ", involve whole sets of variables and they are best reserved for later treatment.

Nor is the order that of increasing complexity of the mathematics. This is an economic, not a mathematical, text-book. The nature of the mathematical techniques used is rarely allowed to dictate the order of development. The kind of mathematics set out in Allen (1938) and Tintner (1954) is assumed throughout, that is a good deal of calculus and some algebra and geometry. The main concession is that time out is taken at convenient places to introduce more advanced mathematical techniques, at the cost of disturbing the flow of the economic development.

Further, this is a book on economic theory, not on applied economics or econometrics. It is inevitable that the development verges at times on the econometric, since the concentration is always on economic theories with some relation to actual problems. Some attempt is made to frame economic theories in such a way that they can be tested against empirical data, though by no means always sufficiently for the statistician to go to work. Indeed, some of the economic analyses presented here were originally designed by their authors for immediate econometric application ; this is the case for the work of Leontief (1951, 1953) and Koopmans (1951), and perhaps also for the trade cycle theories of Hicks (1950). But the models treated here are completely *deterministic* ; econometric work generally requires that *stochastic* elements are included in the models.

Within the general field so demarcated, the method of treatment is straight-forward enough. The elements of macro-dynamic economic theory (Chapters 1, 2 and 3) show up the need for using differential and difference equations and for the description of oscillatory variation by means of complex variables and vectors (Chapters 4, 5 and 6). On this basis can be developed some fairly elaborate trade cycle theories, leading to the vital problems of economic regulation (Chapters 7, 8 and 9). General equilibrium analysis, both of the Walrasian and of the Leontief (input-output) types, is then taken up (Chapters 10 and 11). It is found that a good deal of vector and matrix algebra is needed (Chapters 12, 13 and 14) and that the theory of games is of relevance to economic problems (Chapter 15). The development of linear programming and decision-taking can then proceed (Chapters 16 and 17) with particular applications to the theory of the firm and of the consumer (Chapters 18 and 19). The concluding chapter takes up some problems in aggregation and the economics of welfare (Chapter 20).

It is evident in these chapters how much is drawn from the work of a limited number of economists of Anglo-American schools, from Hicks and Samuelson, Hansen and Harrod, Leontief and Koopmans, and (among the younger writers) from Barna, Baumol, Domar, Dorfman, Duesenberry, Goodwin, Klein, Makower, Morton, Phillips, Solow and Turvey. This is an expression of indebtedness, not of apology. For it is the work of these economists that is familiar to the present author ; and it is the work which will be in the minds of most readers of this text. Only the title of the book may be questioned, since these chapters are concerned, not so much with mathematical economics in general, but with certain economic theories of present interest, developed in mathematical terms by Anglo-American economists.

The chapters also give the impression of a very limited range of economic theories. There is little or nothing on expectations, or on international trade or sector analysis generally. Further reflection may show that the topics treated here, though limited in scope, are of central importance in the general body of economic doctrine. Other topics, dealing with expectations or international economics, can be developed from them. Moreover, the analyses both of the trade cycle and economic regulation (Chapters 7, 8 and 9), and of linear programming and decision-taking (Chapters 16, 17, 18 and 19), are largely a product of work done in the decade after the Second World War. They are coming to hold the centre of the stage in economic theory and all economists need to know at least what they are trying to achieve.

In conclusion, it must be stressed that mathematical economics is applied mathematics, a partnership between mathematics and economics. Results in mathematical economics of any interest can only be derived by an economist using mathematics. The same is true of other fields of applied mathematics such as engineering ; indeed, the economist can learn a good deal from the engineer both as regards the kind of mathematics to use and in the formulation of the technical problems.

There is a good deal of misunderstanding of the nature of mathematics and of its mode of application. Pure mathematics is sometimes described as a " language ", with the implication that it is easily translated into English. It is nothing of the kind ; rather it is a specialised form of logic, of reasoning. A mathematical proof may be quite incapable of " translation ", though the premises from which it starts and the consequences reached can be, and should be, put in " literary " form.

Further, the concentration in mathematical teaching on " proofs ", on " Q.E.D." at the bottom of the page, tends to suggest that pure mathematics proves theories. It does nothing of the kind ; it simply argues from premises to conclusions and the premises may be any self-consistent set of axioms which anyone cares to propose. Theories only arise in a particular subject matter, whether economics or electrical engineering, and so in applied mathematics. The theories then involve clothing the premises with a certain " real life " garb and in interpreting the logical or mathematical consequences in the same way. It can be said, if no slip is made in the reasoning, that the consequences hold if the premises are valid. But this is not a proof of any theory in economics or any other field. Theories are to be tested against facts, either the premises or (more usually) the consequences. The testing of a theory can lead to its rejection as inconsistent with facts ; but it can never lead to the " proof " of the theory, but only to its provisional acceptance as not inconsistent with facts. Mathematical economics is best regarded, therefore, as the process of following up the consequences of a particular set of self-consistent axioms with economic content. The proof is the establishment of the consequences of the axioms, not of the validity of the theory.

If mathematics is no more than a form of logical reasoning, the question may be asked : why use mathematics, which few understand, instead of logic which is intelligible to all? It is only a matter of efficiency, as when a contractor decides to use mechanical earth-moving equipment rather than picks and shovels. It is often simpler to use pick and shovel, and always conceivable that they will do any job ; but equally the steam shovel is often the economic proposition. Mathematics is the steam shovel of logical argument ; it may or it may not be profitable to use it. The point is that economic facts are extraordinarily complicated so that the steam shovel of mathematics is to be expected to be the most efficient way of delving into them. To maximise the relation of theory to fact, to minimise the simplification away from reality, it is usually safer to operate in mathematical terms. An economist who ventures to set up a theoretical model of empirical content is well advised to do so in explicit mathematical form. He risks failure if he does not ; or, at least, he is liable to overlook some cases or possibilities which may be important, and to make empirical testing of his model more difficult.

REFERENCES

Allais (M.) (1954) : " L'Utilisation de l'Outil Mathématique en Economique ", *Econometrica*, **22**, 58–71.

Allen (R. G. D.) (1938) : *Mathematical Analysis for Economists* (Macmillan, 1938).

Herstein (I. N.) (1953) : " Some Mathematical Methods and Techniques in Economics ", *Quarterly Journal of Applied Mathematics*, **6**, 249–62.

Hicks (J. R.) (1950) : *A Contribution to the Theory of the Trade Cycle* (Oxford, 1950).

Koopmans (T. C.) (1951) : *Activity Analysis of Production and Allocation* (Wiley, 1951).

Leontief (W. W.) (1951) : *The Structure of American Economy, 1919–39* (Oxford, Second Ed. 1951).

Leontief (W. W.) (Editor) (1953) : *Studies in the Structure of the American Economy* (Oxford, 1953).

Leontief (W. W.) (1954) : " Mathematics in Economics ", *Bulletin of the American Mathematical Society*, **60**, 215–33.

Samuelson (P. A.) (1947) : *Foundations of Economic Analysis* (Harvard, 1947).

Samuelson (P. A.) (1952) : " Economic Theory and Mathematics—An Appraisal " *American Economic Review*, **42**, 56–66.

Samuelson (P. A.) and others (1954) : " Mathematics in Economics ", *Review of Economics and Statistics*, **36**, 359–86.

Stigler (G. J.) (1949) : " The Mathematical Method in Economics ", in *Five Lectures on Economic Problems* (Longmans, 1949).

Tintner (G.) (1954) : *Mathematics and Statistics for Economists* (Constable, 1954).

Note : In a reference to an article in a Journal, the figure in bold type represents the volume number, and the following figures the pages of the article.

CHAPTER 1

THE COBWEB AND OTHER
SIMPLE DYNAMIC MODELS

1.1 Notation

ECONOMICS is concerned with quantities of goods or factors and their prices. Goods or factors are bought and sold on markets ; one group of persons or organisations is buying, another group is selling on each market. In this chapter, a market for a particular good or factor is considered and the only aggregation is of buyers into a group and of sellers into a group. Further aggregation, over different goods or factors and over different markets, is left for later chapters. Such aggregation, which raises problems of valuation, of summing the products of quantities and prices, is best avoided in a first analysis.

The variables of a single-market model are the prices and the quantities bought and sold, demanded and supplied. They are denoted by capital letters, e.g. P for the price of a good. Usually, some equilibrium value is sought and denoted by a bar over the letter, e.g. $\bar{P}$ for equilibrium price. Deviations from an equilibrium value are written with the corresponding small letters, e.g. $p = P - \bar{P}$ for the deviation of price from its equilibrium value.

The variables need to be timed. In *period analysis*, successive periods are denoted by $t = 0, 1, 2, \ldots\ldots t\ldots$ and the corresponding values of a variable by subscripts, e.g. $P_0, P_1, P_2, \ldots P_t\ldots$ for price. This is looking forward from the initial period over the whole range of periods. The perspective is easily reversed ; if t is the current period, then $(t-1)$ is the previous period, $(t-2)$ the one before that and so on back to the initial period 0. The current price is P_t, the price of the previous period P_{t-1}, and so on back to the initial price P_0.

In the alternative *continuous analysis*, assume that changes are made continuously. A variable t is taken for time and $t = 0$ is the initial moment and $t > 0$ subsequently. A variable then appears as a function of time, e.g. $P(t)$ for price at time $t (t \geqslant 0)$, with $P(0)$ as the initial value at $t = 0$. Functions such as $P(t)$ are often taken as continuous but they may not be so ; for example, they may be step-functions. The difference between period and continuous analysis is that time is chopped up into discrete segments in the former but allowed to vary continuously in the latter. In neither case is it necessarily assumed that a variable such as price changes smoothly or continuously.

The variables are connected by functional relations, which generally involve certain constants and parameters which need to be denoted with care. The parameters can be, for example, rates of growth written r or ρ, and these can be fixed or variable according to the development of the analysis. The constants are always taken as fixed throughout. In this and subsequent chapters, the relations are usually assumed to be linear, at least as an approximation over certain ranges (e.g. about an equilibrium value). A uniform notation for constants in a linear relation is adopted as far as possible, a notation which uses an English letter (with subscripts) for the coefficients of the variables and a Greek letter for the fixed term. For example, in the period case where demand depends on the price of the current period and perhaps on prices in previous periods, the demand relation is written in linear form :

$$D_t = \alpha + aP_t$$
or
$$D_t = \alpha + a_0P_t + a_1P_{t-1}$$
or
$$D_t = \alpha + a_0P_t + a_1P_{t-1} + a_2P_{t-2}$$

and so on. Note that it is generally preferable to write $D_t = \alpha + aP_t$ even if a is negative, rather than $D_t = \alpha - aP_t$ with a positive. A similar notation can be used in the continuous case ; so :

$$D(t) = \alpha + aP(t)$$
$$D(t) = \alpha + a_0P(t) + a_1\frac{d}{dt}P(t)$$

and so on.

1.2 The Cobweb Model

On a market for a single good, the demand schedule is $D = D(P)$ and the supply schedule $S = S(P)$. For equilibrium, the price must be set to clear the market :

$$D(P) = S(P)$$

An equilibrium price $\bar{P}$ is given by this equation (which may yield multiple solutions) and the corresponding purchases and sales, both written as $\bar{X}$, by :

$$\bar{X} = D(\bar{P}) = S(\bar{P})$$

A dynamic model is obtained when there are lags on the demand or supply side. The simplest model, with period analysis, has a fixed lag or *delay* of one period on the supply side :

$$D_t = D(P_t) \quad \text{and} \quad S_t = S(P_{t-1})$$

This might occur when the production of the good takes a definite period of time, chosen as the period of the analysis. The operation of the model is : given P_{t-1} in the previous period, the quantity supplied to the market is $S(P_{t-1})$ in the current period and P_t is set to clear the supply, i.e. P_t and the amount bought and sold X_t are given by :

$$X_t = D(P_t) = S(P_{t-1})$$

So, starting with an initial price P_0, the equations give P_1 and X_1 ; then given P_1, the equations give P_2 and X_2 ; and so on. In general, the course of P_t is given by a *difference equation* of the first order (one lag) :

$$D(P_t) = S(P_{t-1})$$

The solution can be illustrated in diagrammatic terms (Fig. 1). D and S are the demand and supply curves, and equilibrium ($\bar{P}$ and $\bar{X}$) corresponds to the point of intersection Q. In the dynamic model, D is interpreted as in the static case but S shows by its height the supply forthcoming in one

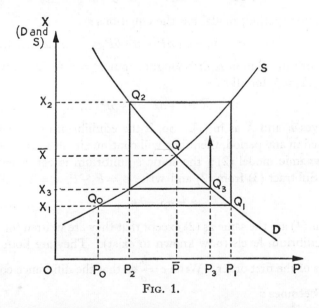

FIG. 1.

period in terms of the price ruling in the previous period. The initial price is P_0. The corresponding point Q_0 on S gives the supply in period 1 ; this supply is cleared at price P_1 given by Q_1 on D at the same height (X_1) as Q_0. In period 2, the move is from Q_1, first to the point vertically above it on S (giving X_2) and then horizontally to Q_2 on D (giving P_2). The process continues, giving the cobweb shown in Fig. 1. The prices and amounts (bought and sold) in successive periods are the co-ordinates of the points Q_1, Q_2, Q_3, ..., on the demand curve D. In the case illustrated, the sequence of points tends to Q, alternating on each side of Q. Hence the price P_t alternates but tends to $\bar{P}$ and similarly for the amount bought and sold (X_t). Suppose that D is downward and S upward sloping. Then it is clear, intuitively, that the damped oscillatory case arises when D is steeper to the OP axis than S around the point of equilibrium Q. An explosive oscillation arises when D is less steep to the OP axis than S, and a regular oscillation, neither damped nor explosive, when D and S are equally steep.

The solution can be obtained algebraically when the demand and supply schedules are linear : $D = \alpha + aP$, $S = \beta + bP$. Equilibrium values, $\bar{P}$ and $\bar{X}$, are given by :

$$\bar{X} = \alpha + a\bar{P} = \beta + b\bar{P}$$

i.e.
$$\bar{P} = \frac{\alpha - \beta}{b - a}; \quad \bar{X} = \frac{b\alpha - a\beta}{b - a} . \qquad (1)$$

The dynamic (period) model has the equations :

$$X_t = \alpha + aP_t = \beta + bP_{t-1} \qquad (2)$$

An equilibrium solution is first sought ; put $P_t = \bar{P}$ for all t, with corresponding $X_t = \bar{X}$ for all t :

$$\bar{X} = \alpha + a\bar{P} = \beta + b\bar{P} \qquad (3)$$

which gives $\bar{P}$ and $\bar{X}$ as in (1). So, if the equilibrium price and amount are realised in any period, then they will continue in all subsequent periods in the dynamic model (2) ; the static equilibrium is consistent with the model. Subtract (3) from (2) and write $p_t = P_t - \bar{P}$, $x_t = X_t - \bar{X}$. Then :

$$x_t = ap_t = bp_{t-1} \qquad (4)$$

Equations (4) are the same as (2) except that they are written for deviations from equilibrium levels (now known to exist). They are both difference equations of the first order. Write $c = \dfrac{b}{a}$ so that the difference equation for p_t in (4) becomes :

$$p_t = cp_{t-1}$$

The solution is easy, given p_0 at $t = 0$; by iteration :

$$p_t = p_0 c^t$$
or
$$P_t = \bar{P} + (P_0 - \bar{P})c^t$$

The amount bought and sold in each period follows from (4).

The usual case is a downward sloping demand curve ($a<0$) and an upward sloping supply curve ($b>0$), i.e. $c=\dfrac{b}{a}<0$. In this case, write $r=|c|=\dfrac{b}{(-a)}$ so that r is positive. Then :

$$p_t=p_0(-1)^t r^t$$

and successive values of p_t for $t=0, 1, 2, 3, \ldots$ are

$$p_0, \ -p_0 r, \ p_0 r^2, \ -p_0 r^3, \ \ldots$$

so that p_t alternates about zero. Consequently P_t alternates, being successively above and below $\bar{P}$. The three possibilities are :

(i) $b>(-a)$, S steeper than D (to OP).

Here $r>1$ and the sequence for p_t increases indefinitely in absolute value. Hence $P_t \to \pm\infty$ and there is an explosive oscillation (alternation).

(ii) $b=(-a)$, D and S equally steep.

Here $r=1$ and the sequence for p_t is simply an alternation between p_0 and $(-p_0)$. Hence P_t is successively above and below $\bar{P}$ by a fixed amount, i.e. the original discrepancy $(P_0-\bar{P})$. There is a regular oscillation (alternation).

(iii) $b<(-a)$, D steeper than S (to OP).

Here $r<1$ and the sequence for p_t decreases in absolute value. Hence $P_t \to \bar{P}$ successively from one side and from the other. There is a damped oscillation (alternation) towards the equilibrium level.

In (iii), the larger is $(-a)$ relative to b, i.e. the steeper D relative to S, the more damped is the oscillation and the more rapid is the tendency of P_t to $\bar{P}$. The initial disturbance also has its effect on the amplitude of the oscillation ; the further P_0 is away from $\bar{P}$, the larger the swings and the longer it takes for them to die away.

It is to be noted that case (ii), with its continuing and regular oscillation, is so accidental as to be almost trivial ; no theory of cyclic movements can be based on it. The interesting case is (iii), though it may be objected that oscillations dying away are " unrealistic ". There is, however, one simple development of the model, in its damped oscillatory form (iii), which gives a course of P_t with continuing oscillations over time. Instead of demand and supply curves which are fixed in time, take curves which shift over time in some exogenous manner, whether regular, cyclical, random or in some other way. Then, before the oscillation of Fig. 1 dies away, it is disturbed and started up again by some shift in D or in S. For example, Q_0 may have been at or near an equilibrium ruling before a shift in D upwards to the position shown in Fig. 1. The oscillation then starts up as illustrated, proceeds to (say) Q_3 when it is disturbed by S shifting upwards ; re-inforced oscillations then commence, dying away until another disturbance occurs. An algebraic treatment is possible in the linear case when the demand and supply lines shift parallel to themselves. Equations (2) then become :

$$X_t = \alpha_t + aP_t = \beta_t + bP_{t-1}$$

where α_t, β_t are the shifts, given for $t = 0, 1, 2, \dots$. The difference equation for price is :

$$P_t = \frac{b}{a} P_{t-1} + \frac{\beta_t - \alpha_t}{a} \quad \dots\dots\dots\dots\dots\dots\dots\dots\dots(5)$$

All that need be specified in (5) is the difference $(\beta_t - \alpha_t)$ in the shifts of supply and demand over time. Various cases have been examined by Goodwin (1947).

EXERCISES 1.2

1. Obtain (4) from (2) by using (1) to give α, β in terms of $\bar{P}$, $\bar{X}$. What is the significance of α and β in this model? If $\alpha > 0$, $a < 0$, $b > 0$ are given, what limit should be imposed on the magnitude of β?

2. Examine the course of P_t in the less usual case where both demand and supply curves are downward sloping, first in terms of a diagram like Fig. 1, and then algebraically in the linear case ($a < 0$, $b < 0$).

3. Construct and examine a dynamic model of cobweb type with a one-period lag on the demand side and no supply-lag. There is nothing to choose between this and the supply-lag model from the mathematical angle ; are there any economic considerations leading to a preference?

4. The demand and supply lines shift in a regular (and linear) way over time, with $\alpha_t = \alpha_0 + \alpha_1 t$ and $\beta_t = \beta_0 + \beta_1 t$ ($t = 0, 1, 2, \dots$) in equation (5). Is there a possible solution for price in the form $P_t = \lambda_0 + \lambda_1 t$, i.e. a regular (and linear) growth over time?

1.3 A Simple Continuous Model

In a continuous model, price is a function of time $P(t)$ while demand and supply (flows per unit of time) are also functions of time. The cobweb of 1.2 above takes the lag on the supply side. A roughly corresponding assumption is to take price variation into account in demand but not in supply. The model is then equivalent to one in which a continuous lag is taken on the supply side, the lag being that described in 1.9 as of simple exponential type (see 1.9, Ex. 2, below). $D(t)$ depends on P and $\frac{dP}{dt}$ but

$S(t)$ depends only on P. The operation of the model, as before, is that P is set at each point of time to clear supply, i.e. $X(t)$ and $P(t)$ satisfy :

$$X=D\left(P,\frac{dP}{dt}\right)=S(P)$$

When the schedules are linear :

$$X=\alpha+aP+a_1\frac{dP}{dt}=\beta+bP \quad\dotfill(1)$$

Try $P(t)=\bar{P}$ and $X(t)=\bar{X}$ for all t, i.e. for a consistent equilibrium position :

$$\bar{X}=\alpha+a\bar{P}=\beta+b\bar{P} \quad\dotfill(2)$$

So the equilibrium values, given by (1) of 1.2 above, are again consistent with the model. Subtract (2) from (1) and write $p=P-\bar{P}$ and $x=X-\bar{X}$. Since $\dfrac{dp}{dt}=\dfrac{dP}{dt}$:

$$x=ap+a_1\frac{dp}{dt}=bp \quad\dotfill(3)$$

Equations (1) and (3) are differential equations of the first order. Write $c=\dfrac{b-a}{a_1}$ and the differential equation for $p(t)$ is :

$$\frac{dp}{dt}=cp$$

To solve, note that $\dfrac{1}{p}\dfrac{dp}{dt}=\dfrac{d}{dt}(\log p)$. So :

$$\frac{d}{dt}(\log p)=c$$

i.e. $\qquad\qquad\qquad \log p=\text{constant}+ct$

i.e. $\qquad\qquad\qquad p=p_0e^{ct}$

or $\qquad\qquad\qquad P=\bar{P}+(P_0-\bar{P})e^{ct}$

The usual case has $a<0$, $a_1<0$, $b>0$, so $c<0$. Hence the course of price over time, $P(t)$, is a steady progression towards equilibrium $\bar{P}$, since $p\to0$ like e^{-t}. The less usual case, with $b<0$ also, leads to the same result, provided that $(-b)<(-a)$, i.e. provided that D is steeper than S when referred to the OP axis in the OPX plane (see Ex. 1 below). The differential equation of this model is less rich in solutions than the corresponding difference equation of 1.2 above.

EXERCISES 1.3

1. Show that, if $a<0$, $a_1<0$, $b<0$, there are two possibilities for $P(t)$ in this model, i.e. if $(-b)>(-a)$ then $P\to\infty$ steadily, and if $(-b)<(-a)$ then $P\to\bar{P}$ steadily. Interpret diagrammatically.

2. Construct and examine a similar dynamic model in which price variation is taken into account on the supply but not on the demand side.

3. Generalise the model so that D and S each depend on P and on $\dfrac{dP}{dt}$ and solve in the linear case where $D=\alpha+a_0P+a_1\dfrac{dP}{dt}$, $S=\beta+b_0P+b_1\dfrac{dP}{dt}$. What economic interpretations may be put on this model? See Evans (1930), Chapter IV.

1.4 General Features of the Models

The cobweb model of 1.2 and the continuous model of 1.3 are very simple and well-known. They are in the field of partial dynamics, since they relate to the market for a single good and take account only of the price of the good, and not of other prices or income. However, they are basic dynamic formulations and they disclose some of the main features of all dynamic models. A closer examination of these features will go far in indicating the ways of handling more complex dynamic models. The following observations apply specifically to the cobweb (period) model of 1.2 ; a separate note is added on the continuous model of 1.3

First, the model assumes some functional relations, here the demand of the buyers on the market and the supply of the sellers, each related to price. These functions are essentially *ex ante* constructions. The price is either given to the buyers and sellers or expected by them. The demand is then what buyers plan or intend to purchase, supply what sellers plan or intend to sell and the intentions are those at the beginning of the period t. The sellers expect the price to be as in the previous period P_{t-1} and plan to sell $S_t=S(P_{t-1})$ accordingly ; the buyers take the price P_t as they find it and plan their purchases $D_t=D(P_t)$ to match.

Second, the form of the functions is a datum. The problem may be simplified by taking a particular case where the functions assume a certain form (e.g. linear : $D=\alpha+aP$), or by taking an approximation to the given form, e.g. a linear approximation for a limited range about an equilibrium position. This may be done by a Taylor expansion :

$$D(P)=D(\bar{P})+D'(\bar{P})(P-\bar{P})=\alpha+aP$$

for the demand function with $(P-\bar{P})$ small. The linear (or any other) form assumed in the problem is incidental, either a convenient simplification or an approximation. For example, the coefficient written a above may be *either* the coefficient of P in a linear demand law, *or* the slope of the demand curve at the equilibrium point and used approximately for small variations of P around $\bar{P}$.

Third, the conditions under which the model operates need to be carefully described. This step involves the translation from *ex ante* expectations and plans to *ex post* realisation. The precise nature of *ex post* relations between variables is to be specified, and how *ex ante* variables become *ex post*. Here, since the model is of a single market on which a given good changes hands, the *ex post* relation is that purchases equal sales (X_t by definition). Further, in the present instance, the " equilibrium method " of translation from *ex ante* to *ex post* is followed, with price as the " equilibrating " variable. At the beginning of period t sellers expect the price to be P_{t-1} and so bring forward the supply S_t for sale. No allowance for stock changes is made (the good may be a perishable) and so this supply must turn out to be X_t (sales = purchases). Demand is then made equal to supply (= sales = purchases) by the processes of market equilibrium, the price being settled to clear supply. Everything expected or intended is realised, with one exception : the price expected by the sellers (P_{t-1}) is not realised in the price ruling (P_t) in the period.

Only a slight variation of this period model need be made to bring in quite different conditions of operation, the step-by-step (or disequilibrium) method. In the period ($t-1$), producers turn out a quantity of the good appropriate to the price P_{t-1} ruling in the period, and this quantity passes into the hands of merchants at the end of the period and is available for sale (as S_t) in the next period t. At the beginning of period t, the merchants fix their selling price P_t in the light of all the data known to them. Buyers then decide how much (D_t) they will take at the price. What is assumed, in the model of 1.2, is that the merchants always guess right and fix the price which will clear what they have for sale : $S_t = D_t =$ amount bought and sold. The variation needed in the model is a provision for the merchants to guess wrong. Suppose the price P_t set by them is such that D_t exceeds the supply S_t available for sale. If merchants hold stocks, the demand can be met (= sales = purchases) by drawing upon stocks. Then, *ex ante* supply S_t is short of *ex post* sales and the deficiency made up out of stocks, i.e. buyers realise their plans (*ex ante* demand = *ex post* purchases), but sellers have an unintended disinvestment in stocks. On the other hand, if no or insufficient stocks are held (e.g. a perishable good), demand cannot be met and an enforced reduction by rationing or otherwise takes place. Then, *ex ante* demand is cut down to *ex post* purchases, buyers having an unintended saving, whereas sellers realise their plans. It is usually assumed, in most models, that purchase plans are realised (*ex ante* demand

=*ex post* purchases) with any " slack " being taken up by investment. This may be reasonable or convenient, but it is certainly not necessary as the present illustration shows ; see also Bent Hansen (1951).

Fourth, the condition of operation of the model, to be satisfied *ex post*, is written as an equation in the variable concerned, here price as the equilibrating variable. The procedure is to get rid of other variables (D_i, S_t and the common *ex post* value X_t) and to concentrate on the one (P_t) of most interest. Other variables (e.g. X_t) can always be got once the variable of interest (P_t) is found. The equation of the cobweb model is a simple form of a *difference equation* involving one lag, P_t and P_{t-1} both appearing. The solution of the equation is sought. In equilibrium without lags, this is a matter of finding a value (or values) of P consistent with the equilibrium condition. With a lag in the difference equation, the solution is that some initial values or conditions must be given and specified, here the initial price P_0. The equation represents the working of the model from one time to another, but the complete result over time depends on the configuration at the start—before the penny is inserted to make the model work. The model can only " start up " from some initial position. In economic terms the course of price over time can only be determined given an initial disturbance or divergence from equilibrium. The fact that, in this instance, only one initial value is required is incidental, a result of the fact that there is only one lag, that the difference equation is of the first order. With multiple or distributed lags, the difference equation is of higher order and more than one initial value is needed.

Fifth, the techniques of solving the difference equation is a matter of mathematics. It is simplified, in this and many other cases, in that the model is of a type described by Wold (1951) as *recursive*, i.e. given all variables up to period ($t-1$), the model provided the variables in period t, and provides them one by one. Here, given P_{t-1}, then $X_t(=S_t)$ follows, and then P_t.

There are, however, some general points which can be made about the solution, points which are not only mathematically helpful but which make economic sense. The first question to raise is always : is there an equilibrium level consistent with the equation? The question is put by testing the equation with $P_t = \bar{P}$ for all t. In the present case, there is a $\bar{P}$ and it is the static level ; in other cases, no $\bar{P}$ may exist. The next trick, with a $\bar{P}$ found, is to switch the variable from the original P_t to a deviation from equilibrium, $p_t = P_t - \bar{P}$. This is economic sense for it is a divergence from equilibrium which is of interest. The best way of effecting the switch is the mathematical device of subtracting the equation in $\bar{P}$ from that in P_t, e.g. subtracting (3) from (2) in 1.2 above.

Finally, the model makes it quite clear that statics and dynamics are not cases separated off in water-tight compartments. A dynamic model, like the cobweb, is concerned with divergences from or movements around some equilibrium position. Note, however, that the existence of an equilibrium consistent with the model (once reached, always maintained) does not imply that any divergence is followed by a movement back to the static position. The movement may be away from the static position, or towards some position different from the static one. Conversely, the question of the " stability " of a position of equilibrium in the static case is one which is to be considered—indeed it can only be considered—in the light of a dynamic model. An equilibrium position is stable if an initial disturbance leads to a (dynamic) movement back to equilibrium, and not away from it or towards some other position. This question is taken up for consideration in 1.8 below.

The continuous model of 1.3 above has the same general features, with some differences mainly of emphasis or detail. The functions of the model represent demand and supply as dependent on price and the rate of change of price. They represent the plans or intentions of buyers and sellers, as continuously adjusted over time in relation to the movement of prices. These intentions, as before, need to be meshed together, to be made consistent. The operation of the model, which relates intended supply and demand, again follows the equilibrium method ; the forces of the market are allowed continuously to adjust prices to clear supply. Price is the equilibrating variable, changing from one moment to another to make and keep demand and supply equal, the common value being purchases and sales (flows at the moment of time concerned). The main difference lies in the interpretation in terms of decisions by buyers and sellers. In period analysis, the period chosen is that of taking decisions or of revising plans ; an essential feature is the distinction between *ex ante* (intentions) and *ex post* (realisations). All this largely disappears in continuous analysis, since decisions, revisions and adjustments are assumed to take place continuously. However, many of the features of period analysis, e.g. time lags, or changes in stocks, can be introduced also into the continuous analysis.

On the mathematical side, the conditions of the continuous model lead to a differential equation in the variable, here $P(t)$, and not a difference equation. The general technique of solution is much the same but with considerable variation in detail. For example, the solution of 1.3 involves the exponential function e^{ct} instead of the power function c^t of 1.2, and the model is consequently less rich in the range of different cases comprised within the solution. The two techniques of solution, of difference and of differential equations, are examined in subsequent chapters, as is the economic relevance of the period and continuous methods of analysis to various types of problems.

1.5 The Econometric Problem

It is not the purpose of the present text to examine problems of econometrics. The simple cobweb model, however, does serve to bring out the essential problems, as described by Leontief (1948), and it merits a brief digression. Consider first the equilibrium of the market with no time lags. In terms of a diagram in the OPX plane, equilibrium price and amount (bought and sold) are given by the point of intersection of demand and supply curves. As the curves shift over time, the equilibrium point describes some historical path, price and amount follow some historical course. The question is: given price and amount as observed time series, can the slopes (or parameters) of the demand and supply curves be deduced? The answer in general is no; the historical path depends essentially on the shifts in the curves, whether these are regular or random. With linear functions and shifts which always move the curves parallel to themselves:

$$X_t = \alpha + aP_t + u_t = \beta + bP_t + v_t$$

where u_t and v_t are the shifts, given (but not known) over time, which may be regular (e.g. $u_t = \alpha_0 t$, $v_t = \beta_0 t$) or which may be " stochastic " variates with a joint probability distribution. Without loss of generality, let u_t and v_t have zero means and let p_t and x_t be deviations from means over any range of observations. Then:

$$x_t = ap_t + u_t = bp_t + v_t \quad \dots\dots\dots\dots\dots\dots\dots\dots(1)$$

So: $$p_t = \frac{u_t - v_t}{b - a}; \quad x_t = \frac{bu_t - av_t}{b - a}$$

These are the observed paths of p_t and x_t, dependent on u_t and v_t which are given but not known. To get a and b, u_t and v_t would need to be known. An attempt to eliminate u_t and v_t by (e.g.) taking the regression of x_t on p_t will fail in general. Only in cases so special as to be almost trivial will anything of economic significance emerge. Such a case is when $u_t = 0$ (demand curve fixed) so that:

$$p_t = -\frac{v_t}{b - a}; \quad x_t = -\frac{av_t}{b - a}$$

i.e., $$x_t = ap_t$$

and a (the slope of the fixed demand curve) can be determined.

The problem is different when a lag is introduced on the supply side but not on the demand side, as in the cobweb model. The relations (1) then become:

$$x_t = ap_t + u_t = bp_{t-1} + v_t \quad \dots\dots\dots\dots\dots\dots(2)$$

These equations can be re-arranged:

$$x_t = bp_{t-1} + v_t \; ; \quad p_t = \frac{b}{a}p_{t-1} + \frac{v_t - u_t}{a} \quad \dots\dots\dots\dots(3)$$

The observed x_t and p_t each have a " systematic " part depending on p_{t-1} and an " error " or " shift " part depending on u_t, v_t. If the latter are random the regression of x_t on p_{t-1} gives b and that of p_t on p_{t-1} gives $\frac{b}{a}$. Consequently, both a and b can be estimated from the observations.

To summarise, model (1) is not identifiable ; a and b cannot be estimated from the observations. Model (2) is a variant in which p_t appears in one relation and another variable p_{t-1} in the second. This makes all the difference. The equations (2) are transferred into (3), the so-called " reduced form ", and the coefficients in (3) can be estimated and identified in terms of the parameters a and b sought. Further, if prediction of x_t and p_t is required, then the regression equations derived as in the " reduced form " (3) are all that is needed.

1.6 Extensions of the Cobweb Model

The cobweb model of 1.2, in the usual case of a downward sloping demand curve and an upward sloping supply curve, gives a solution in which price alternates, above and below equilibrium in successive periods. This is an oscillation which completes itself in two periods, i.e. twice the lag on the supply side ; the speed of adjustment decreases in proportion as the time lag increases.

The expectation on the supply side is that the price of the previous period will continue. This expectation is continually disappointed ; if the price in one period is above equilibrium, then suppliers expect it to be above in the next period whereas it turns out to be below equilibrium. The model assumes in effect that suppliers never learn. It can be extended, however, to allow for an expectation on the supply side which is modified by experience, as analysed by Goodwin (1947).

The price in period $(t-1)$ is P_{t-1}. Let the price in period t expected by suppliers be:

$$P_{t-1} - \rho \varDelta P_{t-2}$$

where $\varDelta P_{t-2}$ is the price increase from period $(t-2)$, i.e. $\varDelta P_{t-2} = P_{t-1} - P_{t-2}$, and where ρ is a given constant. Usually, in this kind of situation, ρ can be taken as a positive fraction $(0 \leqslant \rho \leqslant 1)$ in which case the price is expected to move in the direction opposite to that of the previous period ; suppliers are expecting an alternation in price. Less usually, ρ may be negative and suppliers then expect that the price movement will continue in the same direction. The size of ρ indicates what weight suppliers attach to the tendency of price movements to be reversed (or continued). If $\rho=0$, no price movement is expected ; if $\rho=1$, a complete reversal is expected.

The equation of the cobweb model of 1.2, with linear functions, becomes :

$$X_t = \alpha + aP_t = \beta + b(P_{t-1} - \rho \Delta P_{t-2})$$

i.e.
$$X_t = \alpha + aP_t = \beta + b(1-\rho)P_{t-1} + b\rho P_{t-2} \quad \dots\dots\dots\dots\dots(1)$$

Try $P_t = \bar{P}$, $X_t = \bar{X}$ for all t :

$$\bar{X} = \alpha + a\bar{P} = \beta + b(1-\rho)\bar{P} + b\rho\bar{P} \quad \dots\dots\dots\dots(2)$$

This gives
$$\bar{P} = \frac{\alpha - \beta}{b - a}; \quad \bar{X} = \frac{b\alpha - a\beta}{b - a}$$

Equilibrium of the static situation is again consistent with the model.

Subtract (2) from (1) and write $p_t = P_t - \bar{P}$, $x_t = X_t - \bar{X}$, and $c = \dfrac{b}{a}$:

$$x_t = ap_t = b(1-\rho)p_{t-1} + b\rho p_{t-2} \quad \dots\dots\dots\dots\dots(3)$$

which are the difference equations in terms of deviations from equilibrium. For price :

$$p_t = c(1-\rho)p_{t-1} + c\rho p_{t-2} \quad \dots\dots\dots\dots\dots(4)$$

and the corresponding x_t is given by (3). The difference equation (4), to be solved for the course of price over time, reduces to the simple (first order) equation of 1.2 when $\rho=0$. For $\rho \neq 0$, (4) is a difference equation of the second order, involving a two-fold distributed lag. Two initial values, say P_0 and P_1 at $t=0, 1$, must be given to " start up " the system represented by (4) ; all succeeding values $P_2, P_3, P_4 \dots$ then follow by iteration. To write the general solution for p_t or P_t in explicit form requires a knowledge of the theory of difference equations. The equation (4) is left for further examination (Chapter 6 below).

EXERCISES 1.6

1. In the difference equation (4) take $c = -\frac{3}{4}$, $\rho = \frac{1}{2}$. Given the two initial values $p_0 = 0$, $p_1 = 1$, write down the subsequent course of the price deviations, $p_2, p_3, p_4, \dots$, by repeated use of (4) and carry far enough to see the nature of the variation. Interpret the result.

2. In the previous exercise, suppose that $\rho = -\frac{1}{2}$ instead of $\rho = \frac{1}{2}$. Now obtain $p_2, p_3, p_4 \dots$; interpret and contrast with the previous solution.

1.7 Models with Stocks

In the models of 1.2 and 1.3 the price is set to clear supply ; either there are no stocks of the good (e.g. a perishable) or stocks are maintained at a constant level. The models can be extended to allow for changing stocks. (A) In the *period case*, with the notation of 1.2, let Q_t be stocks at end of period t. Then :

$$\Delta Q_t = Q_t - Q_{t-1} = S_t - D_t$$

is the increase in stocks over the period t. In the present analysis, stocks need only be taken in the *ex post* sense of realised stocks (like realised purchases and sales). *Ex ante* S_t and D_t may be different, planned supply and demand. *Ex post* S_t and D_t may also be different ; realised supply feeds into stocks and realised demand comes out of stocks. Purchases and sales are still (by definition) equal on the market, and their common value is realised demand, i.e. $X_t = D_t$ *ex post*. Buyers' intentions are realised in purchases (=sales) ; suppliers' intentions are also realised in sales to merchants who are assumed to hold stocks and to sell to buyers. Hence a third group must be considered, the merchants who hold stocks and make sales ; they are to be distinguished in their functions from buyers and suppliers. (The merchants can be the same people as the suppliers, in which case the group has a double function.) The operation of the model turns on the way in which merchants make sales, on how they set prices in relation to stocks. Two cases will be considered ; prices are set according to stock changes in one case and according to the level of stocks in the other. In each case linear demand and supply functions are taken without lags and, for simplicity, it is assumed that merchants always buy and sell at the same price.

Model I. Merchants set P_t in period t according to the condition : the price is set higher if stocks in the previous period fall and the amount of the increase is proportional to the fall in stocks. So :

$$P_t = P_{t-1} - \lambda \Delta Q_{t-1} \quad \dots\dots\dots\dots\dots\dots(1)$$

where λ is given and positive. Now :

$$D_t = \alpha + aP_t ; \quad S_t = \beta + bP_t$$

and $\quad \Delta Q_{t-1} = Q_{t-1} - Q_{t-2} = S_{t-1} - D_{t-1} = (\beta - \alpha) + (b - a)P_{t-1}$

The equation (1) then reduced to :

$$P_t = P_{t-1} + \lambda(\alpha - \beta) - \lambda(b - a)P_{t-1}$$

i.e. $\quad P_t = \lambda(\alpha - \beta) + \{1 - \lambda(b - a)\}P_{t-1} \quad \dots\dots\dots\dots(2)$

Try $P_t = \bar{P}$ for all t :

$$\bar{P} = \lambda(\alpha - \beta) + \{1 - \lambda(b - a)\}\bar{P} \quad \dots\dots\dots\dots\dots\dots\dots(3)$$

i.e. $\qquad \bar{P} = \dfrac{\alpha - \beta}{b - a}$ the usual equilibrium level.

Subtract (3) from (2) and write $p_t = P_t - \bar{P}$, $c = 1 - \lambda(b - a)$:

$$p_t = c p_{t-1}$$

The solution is :

$$p_t = p_0 c^t$$
or $\qquad P_t = \bar{P} + (P_0 - \bar{P})c^t \quad \dots\dots\dots\dots\dots\dots\dots(4)$

The amount bought (and sold by merchants) is then $X_t = \alpha + aP_t$.

The usual case is $a < 0$, $b > 0$, so that $(b - a) > 0$. There are three possibilities for λ, with the corresponding variation in P_t given by (4) :

(i) $\lambda < \dfrac{1}{b - a}$, so that $0 < c < 1$ and $P_t \to \bar{P}$ steadily.

(ii) $\dfrac{1}{b - a} < \lambda < \dfrac{2}{b - a}$, so that $-1 < c < 0$ and P_t alternates and $\to \bar{P}$, i.e. damped oscillation.

(iii) $\lambda > \dfrac{2}{b - a}$, so that $c < -1$ and P_t alternates and $\to \pm\infty$, i.e. explosive oscillation.

The size of λ is the determinant of the course of P_t ; the larger the value of λ the more unstable does the course become, first oscillating in damped form and then exploding. Instability arises when, in setting prices, the response of merchants to stock changes is strong.

Model II. Merchants set P_t in period t, raising the price if the level of stocks in the previous period fell below a given amount $\bar{Q}$, and by an amount proportional to the deficit in stocks below $\bar{Q}$. So :

$$P_t = P_{t-1} - \lambda(Q_{t-1} - \bar{Q}) \quad \dots\dots\dots\dots\dots\dots(5)$$

where λ is given and positive.

As before $\qquad D_t = \alpha + aP_t ; \quad S_t = \beta + bP_t.$

To get the level of stocks Q_t, summation back to an initial period ($t = 0$) is needed, i.e.

$$Q_t = Q_0 + \sum_{i=1} \Delta Q_i = Q_0 + \sum_{i=1}(S_i - D_i)$$

$$= Q_0 + \sum_{i=1}^{t} \{(\beta - \alpha) + (b - a)P_i\}$$

The equation (5) thus involves all prices back to the initial period. But this dependence on the whole course of past prices can be put differently :

$$P_t = P_{t-1} - \lambda(Q_{t-1} - \bar{Q})$$

and
$$P_{t-1} = P_{t-2} - \lambda(Q_{t-2} - \bar{Q})$$

Subtract :
$$(P_t - P_{t-1}) = (P_{t-1} - P_{t-2}) - \lambda(Q_{t-1} - Q_{t-2}) \qquad \dots\dots\dots(6)$$

So equation (5) can be written by re-arranging and developing (6) :

$$P_t = 2P_{t-1} - P_{t-2} - \lambda(S_{t-1} - D_{t-1})$$

i.e.
$$P_t = \lambda(\alpha - \beta) + \{2 - \lambda(b-a)\}P_{t-1} - P_{t-2} \qquad \dots\dots\dots\dots(7)$$

This is the difference equation of the model ; it is of the second order since prices in two previous periods are involved.

The condition of the model can be interpreted in the light of (6). The change in price, as set by merchants, depends on the level of stocks. But the change in the rate of change of price depends on changes in stocks, i.e. on the difference between supply and demand. Stock changes give rise to an " acceleration " in price movement. Prices rise because the stock level is low ; a decrease in stocks is followed by an accelerated increase in the price set.

In solving the difference equation (7), try $P_t = \bar{P}$ for all t :

$$\bar{P} = \lambda(\alpha - \beta) + \{2 - \lambda(b-a)\}\bar{P} - \bar{P} \qquad \dots\dots\dots\dots(8)$$

i.e. $\bar{P} = \dfrac{\alpha - \beta}{b - a}$ which is again the usual equilibrium level. Subtract (8) from (7) and write $p_t = P_t - \bar{P}$. The difference equation then becomes :

$$p_t = \{2 - \lambda(b-a)\}p_{t-1} - p_{t-2} \qquad \dots\dots\dots\dots(9)$$

The general solution of (9), with two initial values (say P_0 and P_1) must again be left for further examination (Chapter 6 below).

(B) In the *continuous case*, stocks vary continuously over time like the other variables D, S and P. By definition, if stocks are $Q(t)$ at time t,

$$\frac{dQ}{dt} = S - D$$

and
$$Q = Q_0 + \int_0^t (S - D)\,dt$$

Model III. Merchants set P at each moment of time so that the rate of increase of price is proportional to the rate of decrease of stocks :

$$\frac{dP}{dt} = -\lambda\frac{dQ}{dt} = -\lambda(S - D)$$

where λ is given and positive. With linear functions and no lags, $D = \alpha + aP$, $S = \beta + bP$. So:

$$\frac{dP}{dt} = \lambda(\alpha - \beta) - \lambda(b - a)P$$

Try $P(t) = \bar{P}$, for all t:

$$0 = \lambda(\alpha - \beta) - \lambda(b - a)\bar{P}$$

i.e. $\bar{P} = \dfrac{\alpha - \beta}{b - a}$ which is again the usual equilibrium level.

Subtract and write $p(t) = P(t) - \bar{P}$:

$$\frac{dp}{dt} = -\lambda(b - a)p$$

This is the differential equation of the model. The solution follows exactly as in 1.3 above:

$$p = p_0 e^{-\lambda(b-a)t}$$

or

$$P = \bar{P} + (P_0 - \bar{P})e^{-\lambda(b-a)t}$$

In the usual case, $a < 0$, $b > 0$, so that $(b - a) > 0$. Hence the course of price over time $P(t)$ is a steady progression towards equilibrium $\bar{P}$, since $p \to 0$ like e^{-t}. This is true for all (positive) values of λ. The size of λ simply determines the speed of response or adjustment; the larger the value of λ, the faster does P approach $\bar{P}$.

Model IV. Merchants set P at each moment of time so that the rate of increase of price is proportional to the amount by which stocks fall short of a given level $\bar{Q}$:

$$\frac{dP}{dt} = -\lambda(Q - \bar{Q}) = -\lambda\left\{Q_0 - \bar{Q} + \int_0^t (S - D)\,dt\right\}$$

where λ is given and positive. So:

$$\frac{d^2P}{dt^2} = -\lambda\frac{dQ}{dt} = -\lambda(S - D)$$

and the acceleration of the price increase is proportional to the rate of decrease of stocks. With linear functions and no lags:

$$\frac{d^2P}{dt^2} = \lambda(\alpha - \beta) - \lambda(b - a)P$$

Try $P(t) = \bar{P}$ for all t:

$$0 = \lambda(\alpha - \beta) - \lambda(b - a)\bar{P}$$

i.e. $\bar{P} = \dfrac{\alpha - \beta}{b - a}$ which is again the usual equilibrium level.

Subtract and write $p(t) = P(t) - \bar{P}$:

$$\frac{d^2p}{dt^2} = -\lambda(b-a)p$$

This is the differential equation of the model; it is of the second order and requires two initial conditions, e.g. the values of P and $\dfrac{dP}{dt}$ at $t=0$. Equations of this type are examined later (Chapter 5 below).

EXERCISES 1.7

1. Examine the course of P_t in model I above in the case where both demand and supply curves are downward sloping, and where the demand curve is steeper than the supply curve, i.e. with linear functions, $a<0$, $b<0$ and $(-b)<(-a)$. Show that the conclusions are effectively those given above in the usual case $(a<0, b>0)$. Are they changed if the supply curve is the steeper, i.e. if $(-b)>(-a)$?

2. Construct the dynamic models corresponding to I and II above when there is a one-period lag on the supply side $(S_t = \beta + bP_{t-1})$ and no lag on the demand side $(D_t = \alpha + aP_t)$. Show that the difference equations for price deviations p_t are both of second order, i.e.

   I. $p_t = (1+\lambda a)p_{t-1} - \lambda b p_{t-2}$
   II. $p_t = (2+\lambda a)p_{t-1} - (1+\lambda b)p_{t-2}$

3. What (limiting) forms do the models I and II of the previous exercise take when $\lambda=0$ and when $\lambda \to \infty$.

4. Examine the course of $P(t)$ in model III above when $a<0$ and $b<0$. Show that P progresses steadily towards $\bar{P}$ if $(-b)<(-a)$, and that the course of P is explosive only if $(-b)>(-a)$. Interpret in terms of demand and supply curves.

5. Construct the dynamic models corresponding to III and IV above when the demand function is $D = \alpha + a\left(P + \dfrac{dP}{dt}\right)$ and supply $S = \beta + bP$. Show that the differential equations in price deviations $p(t)$ are

   III. $(1-\lambda a)\dfrac{dp}{dt} + \lambda(b-a)p = 0$
   IV. $\dfrac{d^2p}{dt^2} - \lambda a \dfrac{dp}{dt} + \lambda(b-a)p = 0$

6. In the models of the previous exercise, what are the limiting forms when $\lambda=0$? When $\lambda \to \infty$, show that both models become $\dfrac{dp}{dt} = \left(\dfrac{b-a}{a}\right)p$, solve for p and interpret the result.

1.8 Stability of Market Equilibrium

The price and amount of a good (bought and sold) in market equilibrium are given by the equation of demand and supply, by the intersection of demand and supply curves. When the question of stability, as opposed to existence, of equilibrium is considered, it is inevitable that dynamic processes must be introduced. The question must be put in a form somewhat as follows : there is an equilibrium price which, once set on the market, would always clear supply ; but if some other price happens to be set, will the subsequent movement of price over time be towards the equilibrium value and how quickly is the adjustment made? There may however be more than one equilibrium price and a large initial disturbance may swing the whole system from one equilibrium to another. To avoid this possibility, the question of stability can be examined in terms of a *small* initial disturbance.

A small deviation from the equilibrium position is thus the starting point. What happens over time then involves something more than knowledge of equilibrium ; it requires the setting up of a suitable dynamic model, operating under certain assumed conditions, allowing for a lack of agreement between demand and supply either *ex ante* or *ex post*. The model might assume that sellers or merchants hold stocks of the good and that variations in stocks influence the setting of prices (e.g. the models of 1.7 above). Or, the model might assume that there are lags in demand or in supply (e.g. that of 1.2 or 1.3 above). These are only two of the possibilities ; there is a large number of them. In short, the problem of stability is a dynamic one and it is not unique. The prospect must be faced that a given market equilibrium may be judged stable under certain (dynamic) conditions, and unstable under other conditions.

Since only small movements or deviations from equilibrium are considered, there is little or no loss of generality in taking demand and supply as linear functions, i.e. as approximations over a small range around equilibrium. So, $D = \alpha + aP$, $S = \beta + bP$ will be taken, with equilibrium at $\bar{P} = \dfrac{\alpha - \beta}{b - a}$, $\bar{X} = \dfrac{b\alpha - a\beta}{b - a}$. The constants a and b are the slopes (to OP) of the demand and supply curves at their (equilibrium) point of intersection. It will be assumed that a is negative ; b can be either positive or negative. The demand curve is taken as downward sloping, the supply curve as either upward or downward sloping.

The argument on stability is often crudely framed. If price is set too low, demand exceeds supply and price rises to equilibrium. Or, if the amount offered for sale is too low, buyers offer higher prices than sellers would be willing to accept and supply rises to equilibrium. Such arguments need to be refined and made more explicit. They are not only crude as expressed ; they are also different. The first is Walrasian, the second Marshallian. They can lead to different conclusions on stability.

The Walrasian argument can be expressed in terms of a continuous dynamic model. If at any time price differs from equilibrium, $p = P - \bar{P} \neq 0$, then *ex ante* demand and supply are not equal. Assume in the dynamic model that price rises if supply falls short of demand and with a rate of increase proportional to the deficit. The motive force here may be decreasing stocks (see Model III of 1.7 above). Hence:

$$D = \alpha + aP, \quad S = \beta + bP$$

and
$$\frac{dP}{dt} = -\lambda(S - D) = \lambda(\alpha - \beta) - \lambda(b - a)P$$

where λ is to be interpreted as the *speed of response*. The larger λ, the more rapid is the price reaction to a given deficit in supply. It was found (in 1.7, Model III, above) that P progresses steadily towards $\bar{P}$ if $(b - a)$ is positive, and equilibrium is then stable. P moves steadily away from $\bar{P}$ if $(b - a)$ is negative, and equilibrium is then unstable.

The Marshallian argument is different. If at any time the amount on offer differs from equilibrium, $x = X - \bar{X} \neq 0$, then the *ex ante* price buyers are willing to pay is different from the price acceptable to sellers. Assume a dynamic model in which the amount on offer rises if the sellers' price falls short of the buyers' price and with a rate of increase proportional to the deficit. So:

$$\text{Buyers' price} = \frac{X - \alpha}{a}, \quad \text{Sellers' price} = \frac{X - \beta}{b}$$

and $\frac{dX}{dt} = -\lambda(\text{Sellers' price} - \text{Buyers' price}) = \lambda\left(\frac{\beta}{b} - \frac{\alpha}{a}\right) - \lambda\left(\frac{1}{b} - \frac{1}{a}\right)X$ where λ is again the speed of response. The solution follows as in the previous case. X progresses steadily towards $\bar{X}$ if $\left(\frac{1}{b} - \frac{1}{a}\right)$ is positive (stable equilibrium), and X progresses steadily away from $\bar{X}$ if $\left(\frac{1}{b} - \frac{1}{a}\right)$ is negative (unstable equilibrium).

The results are different. Walrasian stability occurs when $(b - a) > 0$; Marshallian stability when $\left(\frac{1}{b} - \frac{1}{a}\right) > 0$. So, with slopes measured with respect to OP, the possibilities are:

	S upward sloping $(b > 0)$	S downward sloping $(b < 0)$	
		D steeper $(-b) < (-a)$	S steeper $(-b) > (-a)$
Walras model	Stable	Stable	Unstable
Marshall model	Stable	Unstable	Stable

The demand curve is taken as downward sloping $(a < 0)$ throughout.

The results are illustrated in Fig. 2. Here, the initial position Q_0 corresponds to a previous position of equilibrium, before an upward shift in the demand curve to the position D shown, with Q as the new equilibrium. If the new equilibrium is stable, the price and amount should

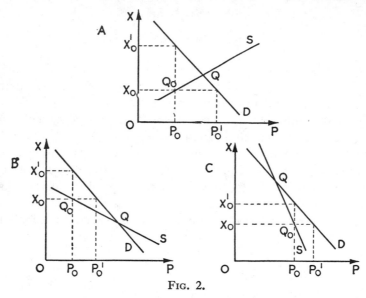

FIG. 2.

move from the values at Q_0 towards those at Q. At price P_0 (given by Q_0), demand exceeds supply *ex ante*, i.e. $X_0' > X_0$, and price rises in the Walras model. With an amount X_0 on offer (given by Q_0), buyers' price exceeds sellers' price, i.e. $P_0' > P_0$, and the amount rises in the Marshall model. In Fig. 2a, the movement in each case is towards Q, which is a stable equilibrium in the Walras and in the Marshall sense. In Fig. 2b, the price rises towards equilibrium at Q but the amount rises away from Q; the equilibrium position Q is one of Walrasian stability, but of Marshallian instability. The converse holds in Fig. 2c.

A third dynamic model for stability takes stocks into account (as the Walrasian and Marshallian models do implicitly) but in a different way. The rate of increase of price is assumed, for example, to be proportional to the excess of stocks over a " normal " level $\bar{Q}$ at any time. This is Model IV of 1.7 above. To anticipate the solution of the differential equation of this model, P moves with a regular (unchanged) oscillation about $\bar{P}$ if $(b - a)$ is positive. This can be described as stability, but in a different sense. The equilibrium position is not unstable since P does not move away from $\bar{P}$. But it does not move towards $\bar{P}$ either; it oscillates regularly and continuously around $\bar{P}$. Otherwise, the results are the same as in the Walras case.

The feature of these dynamic models for stability is that they allow for non-equality of demand and supply, i.e. for changing stocks ; they are also of the continuous type. A completely different model can be constructed with time lags and period analysis. The speed of adjustment is now expressed, not as a multiple λ, but as a lag of greater or less extent in the reaction of demand or supply. Assume that there is a one-period lag on the supply side. Then the dynamic model is the cobweb of 1.2, as illustrated in Fig. 1. Again, Q_0 is the initial position, corresponding to a previous equilibrium before an upward shift in demand. The movement of P_t and X_t over successive periods after the initial disturbance is described in 1.2. It is more varied in its possibilities than in the Walrasian and Marshallian models. If the supply curve is downward sloping (like the demand curve), then the Walrasian case is reproduced. But, if the supply curve is upward sloping, it does *not* follow that the equilibrium is stable (the point on which Walras and Marshall agree). P_t now oscillates and the oscillation is explosive (unstable) if S is the steeper curve, damped (stable) if D is the steeper curve. In short, for stability in the lagged dynamic model, the demand curve must be steeper (to OP) than the supply curve, whether the latter is upward or downward sloping.

1.9 Time Lags in Dynamic Models

It is already clear that time lags must generally be included in the relations of an economic model in dynamic form. It is usually appreciated that time lags occur, less often that the forms they take are important. The time-paths followed by the variables of the model depend, not only on the fact that lags exist, but also on the particular forms they take, see Koyck (1954) and Phillips (1956). Some attention can usefully be paid at this early stage to the various types and forms which time lags can assume.

(A) *Period Analysis.* If the unit of time is taken for convenience as the period of the analysis, two variables X and Y can be timed by the addition of a subscript t ($t=0, 1, 2, \ldots$). Let Y be related linearly to X. Then :

$$Y_t = \alpha + aX_t$$

in the absence of lag. A lag is a *fixed-time delay* of T periods, where the *time-constant* of the lag T is a given positive integer :

$$Y_t = \alpha + aX_{t-T} \qquad \ldots\ldots\ldots\ldots\ldots\ldots\ldots\ldots\ldots(1)$$

gives Y in terms of the value of X of T periods ago. As a particular case $(T=1)$, the lag can be a delay of one period : $Y_t = \alpha + aX_{t-1}$.

A more general case is that of a *distributed lag* giving :

$$Y_t = \alpha + a_1X_{t-1} + a_2X_{t-2} + a_3X_{t-3} + \ldots \quad \Big\}$$
with $\qquad a = a_1 + a_2 + a_3 + \ldots \qquad \qquad \qquad \Big\} \quad \ldots\ldots\ldots\ldots(2)$

as dependent not on one prior value of X but on a whole sequence of such values. The fixed-time delay is then a particular case : $a_T = a$, other a's $= 0$. Note that, in (2) as well as in (1), $X_t = $ constant (all t) corresponds to $Y_t = \alpha + aX_t = $ constant (all t), i.e. the basic relation without lag.

The fixed coefficients $a_1, a_2, a_3, \ldots$, summing to a of the linear relation, represent the *time-form* of the lag (2). They can also be described as the *weighting coefficients*. They may be finite or infinite in number.

An important case of distributed lag is the *geometric lag* :

$$Y_t = \alpha + a(1-r)(X_{t-1} + rX_{t-2} + r^2X_{t-3} + \ldots) \quad \ldots\ldots\ldots\ldots(3)$$

in which the weighting coefficients decrease in a given ratio $r(0 < r < 1)$ in an infinite geometric series. The first coefficient is fixed as $a(1-r)$ in order that the sum of the infinite geometric series of coefficients is a :

$$a(1-r)(1 + r + r^2 + \ldots) = a(1-r)\frac{1}{1-r} = a$$

As a useful device, introduce the intermediate variable :
$$Z_t = \alpha + aX_t$$

which is the *potential value* of the dependent variable, that realised in the absence of lag. The actual value Y_t arises from the X's through the operation of the lag. In fact, Z_t is the variable behind which Y_t lags. If X is constant over time, $Y_t = Z_t = $ constant ; otherwise, if X_t varies, Y_t lags behind Z_t. A simple linear transformation relates Y_t to Z_t instead of X_t. In particular, it is easily seen that :

Fixed-time delay (1) $Y_t = Z_{t-T}$

Distributed lag (2) $Y_t = \lambda_1 Z_{t-1} + \lambda_2 Z_{t-2} + \lambda_3 Z_{t-3} + \ldots$
$\qquad\qquad\qquad$ where $\lambda_1 + \lambda_2 + \lambda_3 + \ldots = 1$

Geometric lag (3) $Y_t = (1-r)(Z_{t-1} + rZ_{t-2} + r^2Z_{t-3} + \ldots)$

The last of these can be further developed. Write the first difference $\Delta Y_t = Y_{t+1} - Y_t$:

$$\frac{\Delta Y_t}{1-r} = (Z_t + rZ_{t-1} + r^2Z_{t-2} + r^3Z_{t-3} + \ldots) - (Z_{t-1} + rZ_{t-2} + r^2Z_{t-3} + \ldots)$$

$$= Z_t - (1-r)(Z_{t-1} + rZ_{t-2} + r^2Z_{t-3} + \ldots) = Z_t - Y_t$$

Put $\lambda = 1 - r$ where $0 < \lambda < 1$. Then:

$$\Delta Y_t = -\lambda(Y_t - Z_t) \quad \text{or} \quad (\Delta + \lambda)Y_t = \lambda Z_t$$

if Δ is treated as an operator (see Appendix A). Hence (3) is:

$$\left. \begin{aligned} \Delta Y_t = -\lambda(Y_t - Z_t) \quad &\text{or} \quad Y_t = \frac{\lambda}{\Delta + \lambda} Z_t \\ Z_t = \alpha + aX_t \end{aligned} \right\} \quad \ldots \ldots \ldots \ldots (4)$$

where

This is for a fixed period, taken as the unit of time. To allow the period to vary, take it as Δt instead of unity. Then:

$$\frac{\Delta Y_t}{\Delta t} = -\lambda(Y_t - Z_t) \quad \text{where} \quad Z_t = \alpha + aX_t \quad \ldots \ldots \ldots \ldots (5)$$

is the *geometric lag with period* Δt and with increment $\Delta Y_t = Y_{t+\Delta t} - Y_t$.

The geometric lag, in form (4) or (5), is capable of a simple interpretation. It is defined as a particular case of a distributed lag in which the weighting coefficients decrease in a geometric series (fixed ratio r). Further it appears that the increase ΔY_t in the unit period, or the average rates of increase $\Delta Y_t / \Delta t$ over period Δt, is always proportional to the deficit $-(Y_t - Z_t)$ of the actual as compared with the potential value at the beginning of the period. The lagged value of Y_t tends to catch up with the potential (or unlagged) value Z_t and in steps proportional to the outstanding deficit. The proportion $\lambda = 1 - r$ is the *speed of response*.

(B) *Continuous Analysis.* The variables are $X(t)$ and $Y(t)$, functions of time. In a linear relation without lag:

$$Y = \alpha + aX$$

With a lag, denote $Z = \alpha + aX$ as the potential value of the dependent variable and Y lags behind Z by the operation of whatever lag is taken.

The simplest case of a *fixed-time delay* extends at once:

$$Y(t) = Z(t - T) = \alpha + aX(t - T) \quad \ldots \ldots \ldots \ldots (6)$$

where the *time-constant* T is any given positive (not necessarily integral) value. The more general case of a *continuously distributed lag* is obtained by analogy with the distributed (period) lag (2). The infinite series of coefficients $a_1, a_2, a_3, \ldots$ is replaced in the limit by a continuous set of ordinates of some function $f(\tau)$ of a continuous variable τ, and the sum is similarly replaced by an integral. Hence:

$$\left. \begin{aligned} Y(t) &= \alpha + a \int_0^\infty f(\tau)X(t - \tau)\,d\tau \\ \int_0^\infty f(\tau)\,d\tau &= 1 \end{aligned} \right\} \quad \ldots \ldots \ldots \ldots (7)$$

where

is a continuous lag in which $f(\tau)$ is the *time-form* or the *weighting function*. Hence Y depends, not on X at a discrete set of prior points of time, but on the values of X over all past (continuous) time. The function $f(\tau)$ represents the dependence of Y at time t on the value of X at time $(t-\tau)$, a period τ ago. Shift to $Z=\alpha+aX$, so that (7) becomes:

$$Y(t)=\int_0^\infty f(\tau)Z(t-\tau)\,d\tau \quad \text{where} \quad \int_0^\infty f(\tau)\,d\tau=1 \quad \dots\dots\dots(8)$$

The fixed-time delay (6) is a particular case of (7) or (8) in which $f(\tau)=1$ at $\tau=T$ and is zero elsewhere.

There is considerable difficulty in handling the integrals in (7) or (8). However, it can be shown that, under certain conditions, (8) is equivalent to a differential equation in the operator D (see Appendix A):

$$Y=\frac{F(D)}{G(D)}Z \quad \text{where} \quad Z=\alpha+aX \quad \dots\dots\dots\dots\dots(9)$$

where F and G are polynomials, F being of lower order than G (see 5.8 below). The differential equation (9) is generally easier to handle.

An important case of continuous lag is the *exponential lag*, the continuous version of the geometric lag in period analysis. The time-form of the latter is a descending geometric series; for the exponential lag it is:

$$f(\tau)=\lambda e^{-\lambda\tau} \quad (\lambda \text{ a positive constant})$$

i.e. a continuous set of ordinates of a decreasing exponental function. It can be checked that $\int_0^\infty f(\tau)\,d\tau$ is unity (as required):

$$\int_0^\infty \lambda e^{-\lambda\tau}\,d\tau = \left[-e^{-\lambda\tau}\right]_0^\infty = -(0-1)=1$$

Hence, in the form (8) with $Z=\alpha+aX$, the exponental lag is:

$$Y(t)=\lambda\int_0^\infty e^{-\lambda\tau}Z(t-\tau)\,d\tau \quad \dots\dots\dots\dots\dots(10)$$

In this particular case, the differential equation (9) is obtained easily. With a simple transformation of the variable of integration $x=t-\tau$:

$$Y(t)=\lambda\int_{-\infty}^t e^{-\lambda(t-x)}Z(x)\,dx=\lambda e^{-\lambda t}\int_{-\infty}^t e^{\lambda x}Z(x)\,dx$$

So:

$$Y(t)e^{\lambda t}=\lambda\int_{-\infty}^t e^{\lambda x}Z(x)\,dx \quad \text{and on differentiation:}$$

$$\lambda Ye^{\lambda t}+\frac{dY}{dt}e^{\lambda t}=\lambda\frac{d}{dt}\left\{\int_{-\infty}^t e^{\lambda x}Z(x)\,dx\right\}=\lambda e^{\lambda t}Z(t)$$

i.e. $$\frac{dY}{dt} = -\lambda(Y-Z) \quad \text{or} \quad (D+\lambda)Y=\lambda Z$$

Hence, the differential equation of the exponential lag is :

$$\frac{dY}{dt} = -\lambda(Y-Z) \quad \text{or} \quad Y=\frac{\lambda}{D+\lambda}Z \quad \text{where } Z=\alpha+aX \quad ......(11)$$

This makes use of the operator D. The parallel with the geometric lag, (4) or (5), is obvious. Indeed, (11) comes from (5) by taking $\Delta t \to 0$.

The interpretation of (11) for the exponental lag is exactly similar to that of (4) or (5) for the geometric lag. The rate of increase of Y is always proportional to the deficit $-(Y-Z)$ of the actual as compared with the potential value of Y. The proportion λ is the *speed of response*.

As an alternative parameter to the speed of response λ, both for the geometric and for the exponental lag, take the reciprocal $T=1/\lambda$, the *time-constant* of the lag. This is consistent with the use of the same term for the fixed-time delay; in this case the parameter T is the length of the delay. Two limiting cases are of interest : when $T=0$ $(\lambda \to \infty)$, (11) gives $Y=Z=\alpha+aX$ and there is no lag; when $T \to \infty$ $(\lambda=0)$ then $\frac{dY}{dt}=0$, Y is constant, and there is no response.

(C) *Response of Y to a step-change in X.* Assume that X changes by a single jump at $t=0$ and choose units so that $Z=\alpha+aX$ jumps from $Z=0$ ruling for $t<0$ to $Z=Z_0$ for $t \geqslant 0$. Three types of lagged response in Y, in particular cases, are then illustrated in Fig. 3.

(i) *Fixed-time delay* of time-constant T :
$$Y(t)=Z(t-T)=0 \text{ for } t<T \quad \text{and} \quad =Z_0 \text{ for } t \geqslant T$$

(ii) *Geometric lag* with speed of response $\lambda=\frac{1}{T}$ and period $\Delta t=\frac{1}{3}T$:

$$\Delta Y_t = -\frac{1}{3}(Y_t-Z_0) \quad \text{for } t \geqslant 0 \quad \text{from (5)}$$

i.e. $$Y_{t+(T/3)} - \frac{2}{3}Y_t = \frac{1}{3}Z_0 \quad \text{and} \quad Y_t=0 \text{ at } t=0$$

By iteration : $$Y_{n(T/3)} = \left\{1-\left(\frac{2}{3}\right)^n\right\}Z_0 \quad \text{for} \quad n=0, 1, 2, ...$$

(iii) *Exponential lag* with speed of response $\lambda=\frac{1}{T}$:

$$Y(t)=\lambda\int_0^\infty e^{-\lambda\tau}Z(t-\tau)\,d\tau = \lambda\int_0^t e^{-\lambda\tau}Z(t-\tau)\,d\tau + \lambda\int_t^\infty e^{-\lambda\tau}Z(t-\tau)\,d\tau$$

with $Z(t-\tau)=Z_0$ for $\tau \leqslant t$ and $=0$ for $\tau > t$

So : $$Y(t)=\lambda Z_0 \int_0^t e^{-\lambda \tau}\, d\tau = Z_0 \left[-e^{-\lambda \tau} \right]_0^t$$

i.e. $$Y(t)=(1-e^{-\lambda t})Z_0$$

The same time-path $Y(t)=(1-e^{-\lambda t})Z_0$ is obtained for the exponential lag by solving (5.8 below) the differential equation (11) which is now :

$$\frac{dY}{dt}+\lambda Y=\lambda Z_0 \quad \text{subject to } Y=0 \text{ at } t=0$$

The three particular responses of Y, in cases (i), (ii) and (iii), are shown by the three time-paths of Fig. 3. The basic case can be taken as (ii), a discrete distributed lag (geometric form) ; Y is here a step-function approaching the potential value Z_0 in the limit $t \to \infty$. The number of steps taken by Y depends on the period of the geometric lag, here $T/3$ where T is the time-constant of lag. Case (iii) can be regarded as the limiting continuous form of (ii), i.e. a continuously distributed (exponential) lag, again with Y approaching Z_0 asymptotically. Case (i) is a very special case of the step-function of (ii), Y achieving Z_0 in one step at $t=T$.

More generally, (i) can be taken as representative of any fixed-time delay ; (ii) as representative of any distributed (period) lag with time-form given by a series of coefficients $a_1, a_2, a_3, \ldots$; and (iii) as representative of any continuously distributed lag with time-form given by a function $f(\tau)$. The shape of the curve (iii) is given by $Y=Z_0 \int_0^t f(\tau)\, d\tau$, or $\frac{dY}{dt}=f(t)Z_0$, instead of the particular exponential curve illustrated (see Ex. 5 below).

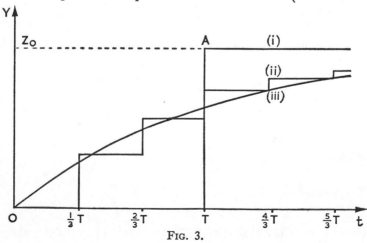

FIG. 3.

The question remains : what is a "realistic" lag to assume in an economic model? A fixed-time delay may be appropriate, e.g. when considering the reactions of a single firm with a decision period of length T. It is clearly less appropriate when the variables are aggregates over the total market for a commodity or for the whole economy. There are also particular features of fixed-time delays which serve to stress their lack of realism, e.g. the fact that a whole range of short-period oscillations can arise, each within the period T of the delay (Chapter 9 below).

When a distributed lag is taken, it may be argued that a step-function response is realistic, like case (ii) of Fig. 3 appropriate to period analysis. However, it is by no means obvious that the continuous form, e.g. the exponential response of case (iii) of Fig. 3, is inappropriate. The continuous lag, so convenient for the mathematician, may well be the case to take in macro-economic models where there are many individuals and firms, all with differing decision periods ; aggregate variables are then likely to show responses which are approximately continuous.

EXERCISES 1.9

1. In Fig. 3, show that the line OA is the tangent to the curve (iii) at O. Hence give an interpretation of the time-constant T of the exponential lag.

2. In the problem of 1.3 above, take demand $=\alpha + aP$ without lag, and supply $=\dfrac{\lambda}{D+\lambda}(\beta + bP)$ with exponential lag. Show that P satisfies

$$\alpha + aP + \frac{a}{\lambda}\frac{dP}{dt} = \beta + bP$$

and hence that the "roughly corresponding assumption" of 1.3 is in effect the assumption of an exponential lag on the supply side.

3. Y_1 is related to its potential value Z with an exponential lag (speed of response λ) and Y_2 is related to its potential value Y_1 with another exponential lag (speed μ). Write $\dfrac{dY_1}{dt} = -\lambda(Y_1 - Z)$ and $\dfrac{dY_2}{dt} = -\mu(Y_2 - Y_1)$ and get :

$$\frac{d^2Y_2}{dt^2} + (\lambda + \mu)\frac{dY_2}{dt} + \lambda\mu Y_2 = \lambda\mu Z$$

by eliminating Y_1. Get the same differential equation from :

$$Y_1 = \frac{\lambda}{D+\lambda}Z, \quad Y_2 = \frac{\mu}{D+\mu}Y_1 \quad \text{so that} \quad Y_2 = \frac{\lambda\mu}{(D+\lambda)(D+\mu)}Z.$$

4. As a particular case of the double exponential lag of the previous exercise, take

$$Y = \left(\frac{2\lambda}{D+2\lambda}\right)^2 Z \quad \text{with } Z = Z_0 \text{ for } t \geqslant 0 \quad \text{and} \quad Y = \frac{dY}{dt} = 0 \text{ at } t = 0.$$

Plot the response of Y and compare with the single exponential lag, curve (iii) of Fig. 3. Show that each of the successive lags has time-constant $1/2\lambda$ so that the total time-constant of the double lag is again $T = 1/\lambda$. Generalise by considering the lagged variable $Y = \left(\dfrac{n\lambda}{D+n\lambda}\right)^n Z.$

5. For the lagged variable Y of (8) above, take $Z(t) = 0 \, (t < 0)$ and $Z(t) = Z_0 \, (t \geqslant) 0$.

Show: $$Y = Z_0 \int_0^t f(\tau) \, d\tau \quad \text{and} \quad \frac{dY}{dt} = f(t) Z_0.$$

REFERENCES

Baumol (W. J.) (1951) : *Economic Dynamics* (Macmillan, 1951), Chapter 7.

Evans (G. C.) (1930) : *Mathematical Introduction to Economics* (McGraw-Hill, 1930), Chapter IV.

Ezekiel (M.) (1938) : " The Cobweb Theorem ", *Quarterly Journal of Economics*, **52**, 255–80.

Goodwin (R. M.) (1947) : " Dynamical Coupling with Especial Reference to Markets Having Production Lags ", *Econometrica*, **15**, 181–204.

Hansen (Bent) (1951) : *A Study in the Theory of Inflation* (Allen and Unwin, 1951).

Hooton (F. G.) (1950) : " Risk and the Cobweb Theorem ", *Economic Journal* **60**, 69–80.

Koyck (L. M.) (1954) : *Distributed Lags and Investment Analysis* (North-Holland, Amsterdam, 1954), Chapter II.

Leontief (W. W.) (1934) : " Verzögerte Angebotanpassung und Partielles Gleichgewicht ", *Zeitschrift für Nationalökonomie*, **5**, 670–76.

Leontief (W. W.) (1948) : " Econometrics " in *A Survey of Contemporary Economics* (Edited by Howard S. Ellis) (Vol. I, Blakiston, 1948).

Phillips (A. W.) (1954) : " Stabilisation Policy in a Closed Economy ", *Economic Journal*, **64**, 290–323.

Phillips (A. W.) (1956) : " Some Notes on the Estimation of Time-Forms of Reactions in Interdependent Dynamic Systems ", *Economica*, **23**, 99–113.

Samuelson (P. A.) (1941) : " The Stability of Equilibrium : Comparative Statics and Dynamics ", *Econometrica*, **9**, 97–120.

Samuelson (P. A.) (1947) : *Foundations of Economic Analysis* (Harvard, 1947), Chapter IX.

Wold (H. O. A.) (1951) : " Dynamic Systems of the Recursive Type ", *Sankhyā*, **11**, 205–16.

Wold (H. O. A.) and Jureen (L.) (1953) : *Demand Analysis* (Wiley, 1953.)

CHAPTER 2

KEYNES AND THE CLASSICS: THE MULTIPLIER

2.1 Macro-economic Variables and Relations

THE dynamic models of the previous chapter are simple but of basic construction. They are simple because they are *partial dynamics*. The market for a single good is considered and the behaviour or decision relations of the models are concerned with price formation—the fixing of the price of the good. The prices of other goods, the incomes of consumers, the production techniques of firms are all ignored. There is no aggregation over different markets or different goods. It is only because of the partial analysis—the neglect of the multiplicity of inter-related variables or of aggregation—that results are obtained immediately, i.e. the movement through time of prices and of amounts bought and sold on the market.

Generalisation can proceed in either of two directions. More variables can be introduced into a demand or supply relation, e.g. other prices and consumer income in a demand function. More goods and markets can be taken and considered in all their inter-connections. This is a generalisation to a system of micro-economics, very detailed and inter-related in complex ways. Alternatively, the number of variables and relations can be kept down by a process of aggregation, by assuming relations between broad aggregates. This generalisation leads to macro-economics. The second method is followed in the present and succeeding chapters. A first approach to reality is best made through heroic aggregation; the alternative is to go into such detail as to risk failing to see the wood for the trees.

The method of macro-economics, however, is always beset with the difficulty of handling aggregates. It is easy enough to take the demand or supply functions of the previous chapter and to say simply that they relate to the aggregate of all goods as a function of the general price level. But the simple quantity-price relation has then disappeared. Amounts demanded or supplied, bought or sold, cannot be aggregated in quantitative units of any general significance. Aggregations can be made, in general, only in value terms, in money. If the values over time are at current prices—as recorded—then " real " and " price " movements do not show up separately, but only in combination. A separation can be attempted in terms of index numbers, but it will not be uniquely determined. For example, " real " demand or consumption can be written as the value of demand or consumption at certain fixed prices. There is the arbitrary choice to be made of the base prices, and a base-weighted index of volume of demand or consumption is used. The corresponding price index, i.e. the price index which multiplies out to recorded value changes, is then of current-weighted form. The " real " variable, in effect, is obtained by deflating recorded values with a current-weighted price index. The whole process could be carried through the other way round, i.e. the " real " variable obtained by deflating values with a base-weighted price index.

Aggregation keeps down the number of variables and relations. But it must not be over-done. Total demand, supply or output can be taken as money aggregates and deflated to " real " terms by division by a price index. Macro-economics would then be of little interest. At least a distinction between consumption and saving, between output for consumption and for investment, must be made. A further problem then arises when deflation to " real " terms is attempted. Is output for consumption to be deflated with the same price index as output for investment, or with a different price index? In many models, the same index is used for simplicity. In this case, changes in relative prices, i.e. the " terms of trade " between the consumption goods sector and the investment goods sector, are ignored.

Macro-economic models of the most heroic kind must still distinguish consumption, saving and investment. Moreover, except in the simplest Keynesian model, there is more than one market; for example, one market for goods and one for factors. This complicates the question of what variables become equal *ex post* and by definition, in a way which is not always appreciated. If attention is directed to the market and to the goods or factors being traded, then purchases and sales are equal *ex post*. On the other hand, there are two groups (persons, firms, etc.) on each market, one buying and the other selling; a given group appears twice as buying on one market and selling on another. *Ex post* equality of purchases and sales on various markets does not necessarily imply that anyone's receipts from one market equal expenditures on another market.

The analysis of the present chapter proceeds in period terms; the corresponding continuous analysis is given later. The basic variable of macro-economics is income, as a money aggregate over the whole economy and as a flow or rate in a period. The aggregate is best thought of as it is used in national income accounting in a closed economy. Income then includes the amounts actually paid out to factors as wages, salaries, profits and other forms of receipts, together with business saving which, though not paid out to and then saved by factors, can be conveniently imputed as income. This point is developed in 2.9 below.

National income is also equal, on the customary definitions, to national product or output, i.e. the money aggregate of the net output of all industries producing goods and services. From the point of view of producers, output is both produced and distributed (or imputed) to factors. When the economy is looked at broadly, as in macro-economic theory, it is legitimate to take income and output as equal, *ex post* and by definition. The same letter Y is used here for aggregate income and output.

Though income is not planned by anyone, being equal to output *ex post*, there can be *expected* income. The notation makes this clear when the case arises ; e.g. expected income may be Y_{t-1} (the actual income of the previous period) whereas actual income is Y_t in period t. This is one way in which lags may enter. Another kind of lag is that between income as earned (the variable Y equal to output *ex post*) and income for spending by recipients ; for example, with a one-period lag, output and income earned is Y_t whereas income spendable in period t is Y_{t-1}. The notation is flexible enough to allow for such differences in interpretation.

The rate of interest, denoted by i, is another variable beyond the influence of individuals. It is to be used and interpreted as a price, a rate ruling at any moment of time or set during any period. There is here no question of any aggregation in money and other terms. On the other hand, the assumption of a single rate i does abstract from reality. It must be taken as representative of a whole complex or system of different rates, the yields of all things sold on capital account.

The main relations of macro-economics relate to consumers as a group and to producers as a group. For consumers, if income for spending in any period is Y, the decision is to divide Y into so much consumed (C) and the balance saved ($Y - C$). Intended or planned consumption is a function of income ; this *ex ante* consumption function is written $C = C(Y)$. Then, by definition, saving is :

$$S = Y - C(Y)$$

also an *ex ante* function of income. Though two functions (consumption and saving) appear, one follows by definition when the other is specified. In the following analysis, the usual assumption will be that planned consumption is realised, i.e. C is both *ex ante* and *ex post* consumption, while saving follows by difference. For this reason, the consumption function is usually the one written, as above. The analysis, however, can be the other way round and the assumption can be that planned saving is realised. Then, the saving function can be written $S = S(Y)$ with consumption following by difference : $C = Y - S(Y)$.

For producers, the main interest lies in the distribution of output Y between investment (I) and the balance produced for or sold to consumers ($Y - I$). Intended or planned investment is a function of the rate of interest, an *ex ante* function which is written $I = I(i)$. Investment *ex ante* also depends on the level of output or on changes in output, but on a first analysis this is ignored in order to concentrate attention on the relation between i and I. This function is the marginal efficiency of capital schedule.

All variables (except i) are money aggregates : Y, C, S and I. They are best interpreted in terms of national income accounting. They are flows of income or outlay per period or unit of time. So, C represents consumption *outlays*, not decisions to consume nor deliveries of consumer goods, and similarly for I. At first, the analysis proceeds in terms of current values, i.e. " real " and " price " changes will appear in combination. Later, with no change in notation, the analysis handles " real " values of output, consumption, saving and investment. The assumption then is that the money aggregates are at fixed prices, or deflated with some price index.

Other variables, and relations between them, will be introduced below, according to the problem considered. In macro-economics, however, the main variables are Y, C, S, I and i and the main relations are between these variables.

2.2 A Formulation of Keynesian Liquidity Preference

There is no general agreement among economists on the theory of interest, despite (or perhaps because of) the work of Keynes. A good analysis of the position is given by Hahn (1955). Much of the dispute arises because of the partial analysis adopted ; out of a whole system of supply-and-demand relations, one particular relation is selected as the determinant of the rate of interest. But which relation is the question?

According to a simple kind of theory the rate of interest is determined by the equation of demand and supply on the money market. Apart from transactions balances, constant as long as money values of income and output do not change, the demand for money is for money as an asset, i.e. to hold in idle balances. The demand depends on the rate of interest —the reward for not holding money and so the price paid for holding it.

This is the liquidity preference schedule. If the supply of money is fixed, then the schedule determines the rate of interest as that rate for which demand equals the given supply.

This approach is too simple. According to the loanable funds theory, the demand and supply of money cannot be considered except as part of the whole capital market, i.e. money, securities and investment. The basic fact is then the balance of financing ; the flow of all transactions on the capital market must balance out in each period. This is Walras' Law and it can be put in terms of demand and supply, taking all the possible flows on each side (assuming that the factor market is in balance) :

Demand for money + demand for securities + investment
= supply of money + supply of securities + saving............(1)

The demand and supply of money then appear as part of an identical relation which holds *ex ante* as well as *ex post*.

The rate of interest is not so much the reward for not holding money— a negative definition at best—as the yield on all things bought on capital account. It is in fact not a single rate, but a complex of rates. As a representative rate, take the Keynesian bond-rate. A bond can be assumed to be a perpetuity paying a fixed amount (say £1 per year) and its price (P) is the reciprocal of the bond rate of interest (i). The determination of the bond price $P = \frac{1}{i}$, and hence of the bond rate of interest, is a matter of the demand and supply of bonds, in the setting of the capital market generally.

The identity (1) now provides the essential clue. Suppose that the rate of interest is such as to equate demand and supply of securities (of which bonds are representative). It still does not follow that this is also the rate of interest to equate demand and supply of money, for saving need not equal investment. It is possible, for example, to finance part of investment by reducing money holdings. To put the same point another way, suppose that saving is not equal to investment in (1) at some particular rate of interest. Then an excess in the demand for money is not exactly matched by an excess in the supply of bonds, and no adjustment in the rate of interest will simultaneously wipe out each excess.

The conclusion is that the use of the liquidity preference schedule, in determining the rate of interest by equation of demand and supply of money, is valid only if saving and investment are equal *ex ante*. The identity (1) is then : excess demand for money = excess supply of securities. The rate of interest which balances demand and supply of securities does the same thing for money. The following development therefore starts by laying down the condition that saving and investment are to be kept equal and then turns to the liquidity preference schedule.

Saving is a function of income : $S = Y - C(Y)$. The marginal efficiency of capital schedule gives investment as a function of the rate of interest : $I = I(i)$. Hence, however Y and i vary, they must satisfy :

$$Y - \dot{C}(Y) = I(i) \quad ....(2)$$

The possible values of Y and i lie on a curve in the OYi plane, the curve SI of Fig. 4b. The curve can be taken as downward sloping ; an *increase*

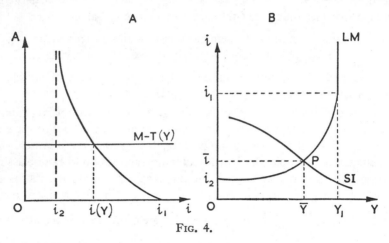

Fᵢ₉. 4.

in Y gives rise to increased saving to be matched, on (2), by an increased investment associated with a *decrease* in the rate of interest i. Following Hicks (1950), the SI curve can be flattened off for low and for high values of Y as shown in Fig. 4b.

Next take the supply of money M as fixed. The demand for money is in two parts, i.e. for transactions balances and for idle balances. The transactions demand depends on income or output : $T(Y)$. The demand for idle balances, for money to hold instead of securities or other capital assets, is now taken for reasons already given as dependent on the rate of interest : $A(i)$. With little loss of generality the two elements can be taken as independent and additive. The demand for money, or the liquidity preference schedule, is then :

$$L(i, \ Y) = T(Y) + A(i)$$

For equilibrium, with demand equal to the given supply M :

$$L(i, \ Y) = M$$

i.e. $\quad A(i) \quad = M - T(Y) \quad ....(3)$

The equation (3) is put in this particular way to show that i is determined when Y (as well as M) is given. It represents the simplest form of the liquidity preference construction. Various extensions or modifications are possible ; for example, Smithies (1942) would have the demand A for idle balances depend on saving S as well as the rate of interest i.

The general form of the demand for idle balances $A(i)$ is shown by the curve of Fig. 4a. This assumes that $A(i)=0$ for high rates of interest $(i \geqslant i_1)$ and that there is an effective minimum rate $i=i_2$ dictated by institutional factors. For various Y, the rate of interest determined by (3) can be written $i=i(Y)$, as illustrated in Fig. 4a. As Y increases, the level $M - T(Y)$ falls and $i(Y)$ increases, in the range $i_2 \leqslant i \leqslant i_1$. For $i > i_1$, the given supply of money can finance no increases in Y beyond the value Y_1 reached at $i=i_1$. Hence the dependence of i on Y, given by (3), is shown by the curve LM in the plane OYi, Fig. 4b.

The conditions (2) and (3) together serve to determine Y and i for equilibrium, the co-ordinates of the point of intersection (P) of the SI and LM curves in Fig. 4b. There are two limiting cases of particular interest :

" *Classical* " *Case* : Y is at a high level, at or near the maximum Y_1 permitted by the supply of credit. An upward shift in the inducement to invest $I(i)$, which moves the SI curve upwards and to the right, has the effect of increasing the rate of interest, with little or no increase in income (and employment). The " Classics " might also say that the same result would follow at lower levels of income and employment, provided that prices and wages are freely variable.

Keynes " *Special* " *Case* : Y is at a low level and the rate of interest at or near the minimum i_2. An upward shift in the inducement to invest corresponds to a movement of P to the right along the nearly horizontal part of the LM curve in Fig. 4b. Income (and employment) increase with little or no effect on the rate of interest.

EXERCISES 2.2

1. Take linear functions : $C = \gamma + cY$, $I = \beta + bi$ and $L = \lambda_1 Y + \lambda_2 i$. Show that the equilibrium values are :

$$Y = \frac{bM + \lambda_2(\beta + \gamma)}{\lambda_1 b + \lambda_2(1 - c)} \quad \text{and} \quad i = \frac{(1 - c)M - \lambda_1(\beta + \gamma)}{\lambda_1 b + \lambda_2(1 - c)}$$

Interpret the constants b, c, λ_1 and λ_2 (which are usually $b < 0$, $0 < c < 1$, $\lambda_1 > 0$ and $\lambda_2 < 0$).

2. In the linear case of the previous exercise, show that an upward shift in the inducement to invest corresponds to an increase in β, raising Y and i in the ratio

$$\frac{dY}{di} = \frac{(-\lambda_2)}{\lambda_1}.$$ Interpret in terms of the " classical " and of the Keynes " special " case.

3. Modify the equations by taking the supply of money $M = M(i, Y)$, where the monetary authorities expand credit when Y and i increase. Show that the LM curve of Fig. $4b$ is " stretched " to the right. What can be said now in the " classical " case? Examine also the inflationary possibility that the SI curve becomes horizontal. See Hicks (1950) and Modigliani (1944).

2.3 General Equilibrium : Modigliani Model

The partial analysis of 2.2 above can be put in a more general setting. The idea is to add the determinants of " real " output and employment and to link with money through the price level. The approach is essentially that of Modigliani (1944), taking account of objections by Patinkin as assessed by Hahn (1955) and of some unpublished work by Papandreou.

There are seven variables : aggregate output Y in money and y in " real " terms ; employment n in man-hours ; the rate of interest i, price level P, hourly wage rate W in money and w in " real " terms. The given data are the money supply and a minimum wage rate, either W_0 in money or w_0 in " real " terms. In practice, the variables are generally index numbers. So, y may be a base-weighted index of output, P and W corresponding current-weighted indexes of prices and wage rates. The index numbers must be such that the simple relations hold : $y = Y/P$ and $w = W/P$.

Classical Model. There are seven relations, grouped as in the table below. (1) and (2) equate saving and investment and put the demand for money equal to the given supply M_0. These are familiar but now generalised so that each function involves both i and Y (whether elastic or inelastic need not concern us here). (3) is a production function, relating output to employment ; (4) and (5) are the links from " real " to money values. On the labour market, the demand side is simple : labour is demanded to the point where marginal product $y'(n)$ equals the " real " wage rate w. The difficulty in models of the present type lies in the speci-

Classical Model : Modigliani		
Monetary :	(1)	$S(i, Y) = I(i, Y)$
	(2)	$L(i, Y) = M_0$
Technical :	(3)	$y = y(n)$
	(4)	$Y = Py$
	(5)	$W = Pw$
Labour Market :	(6)	$w = y'(n)$
	(7)	$w - w_0 = w(n)$

fication of the labour supply. In this classical case, assume a given minimum w_0 for " real " wages, below which no labour is on offer and above which the " real " wage w determines the supply n. Write $w - w_0 = w(n)$ where the form of $w(n)$ is : zero for n below some value n_0, then increasing and tending to infinity as n tends to some higher value n_1. The supply curve, relating w to n, has the same shape as the LM curve shown in Fig. 4b.

The system is determinate with a complete dichotomy between the " real " and monetary parts. On the " real " side, (6) and (7) of the labour market fix w and n and the production function (3) gives y. The monetary equations (1) and (2) fix i and Y. This means that, since " real " income is given on the " real " side, money income from the monetary side serves to fix P so that $Y = Py$. In this classical case, the scale of activity (employment) is determined on the labour market and the supply of money fixes the price level.

Keynesian Model. In the Modigliani version shown in the table below, the only change from the classical case is in the specification of labour supply. The institutional minimum W_0 is now given for *money* wages. The supply of labour, with the same $w(n)$ as before, is then :

$$w - \frac{W_0}{P} = w(n) \quad \text{or} \quad W - W_0 = Pw(n)$$

There are still seven relations but the simple dichotomy of the classical model is lost. On the monetary side, (1) and (2) fix i and Y exactly as in Fig. 4b. The labour market, (6) and (7) on substitution of W from (5), together with the production function (3), gives w, n and y—but only in terms of P. Hence, Y is given in terms of P by (4) and P must be such that this is consistent with Y from the monetary side. In this Keynesian model, it is not altogether clear how the price level is determined but it is certainly not only on the monetary side.

A model suggested by Papandreou, also shown in the table, is perhaps a closer representation of the Keynesian position, certainly a sharper

Keynesian Model		Modigliani	Papandreou
Monetary :	(1)	$S(i, Y) = I(i, Y)$	$S(i, y) = I(i, y)$
	(2)	$L(i, Y) = M_0$	$L(i, y) = m_0$
Technical :	(3)	$y = y(n)$	$y = y(n)$
	(4)	$Y = Py$	$Y = Py$
	(5)	$W = Pw$	$W = Pw$
Labour Market :	(6)	$w = y'(n)$	$w = y'(n)$
	(7)	$W - W_0 = Pw(n)$	$W - W_0 = W(n)$

distinction from the classical case. There are two differences. Firstly, the marginal efficiency of capital and liquidity schedules are applied to " real " output in (1) and (2). The given money supply may still be taken as M_0, with M_0/P on the right of (2). Or, as a different assumption here, it may be taken that the authorities adjust the money supply to keep it fixed at m_0 in " real " terms. Secondly, the supply of labour is taken as influenced only by the *money* wage rate (above the minimum W_0). The supply curve $W(n)$, relating $W - W_0$ to n, has the same J-shaped form as $w(n)$. This version of the Keynesian system gives i and y from (1) and (2) and n from (3). So, without reference to the labour market, employment and output are fixed on the money and product markets. All that is left to the labour market, i.e. (6) and (7) with (5) substituted, is to fix W and P. The labour market determines money wage rates and the price level.

A limitation of these models is that they are short-run in a special sense. The production function $y=y(n)$ assumes capital equipment unchanged, i.e. investment is in working capital. It is possible to extend the models, as suggested by Fort (1945), but without completely overcoming the difficulty.

2.4 A Dynamic Monetary Model

So far only the conditions for macro-economic equilibrium have been given and it remains to devise dynamic models on the general lines indicated in Chapter 1. Such models will show, as their solution, the path over time of a variable such as income Y, starting from a specified initial position or disturbance. It is to be expected that many different dynamic models can be constructed upon the same equilibrium position ; they will vary according to what is assumed about the dynamic operation of the system, e.g. about the response to a disturbance or deviation. As a particular application of such dynamic models, attention can be given to the question of the stability or instability of the basic equilibrium position, and there will be as many interpretations of stability and instability as there are dynamic models.

The main analysis of economic dynamics in the following chapters is in real terms, and the rate of interest will be ignored just as the prices of goods and factors are. As an initial digression—though perhaps not a very satisfactory one—a dynamic model will be suggested, based on the monetary conditions of equilibrium already given in 2.2 and 2.3 above. They relate to the marginal efficiency of capital and the liquidity preference schedules and they take saving equal to investment *ex ante* at all interest rates considered. The equilibrium position, for income Y and the rate of interest

i, is obtained from the intersection of the *SI* and *LM* curves of Fig. 4b. A rather general form is taken for the equilibrium conditions :

$$Y - C(Y) = I(i) \quad \text{and} \quad L(i, Y) = M(i, Y) \quad \dots\dots\dots\dots(1)$$

The supply of money or credit, M, is not necessarily fixed ; it can be adjusted by the monetary authorities according to changes in income and the rate of interest.

Period analysis is adopted in the dynamic version, and the subscript t indicates the period ($t = 0, 1, 2, \dots$). The first equilibrium condition of saving equal to investment is maintained in each period so that the first equation of (1) is simply re-written :

$$Y_t - C(Y_t) = I(i_t) \quad \dots\dots\dots\dots\dots\dots\dots(2)$$

The variables Y_t and i_t have no lag or advance on each other. This may be because of offsetting lags, with saving lagging behind income and investment behind the rate of interest, as suggested by Hicks (1950).

The second equation of (1), relating to the demand and supply of credit, is taken with lags in the dynamic version. It is assumed that both demand and supply, though influenced by the current rate of interest, depend on income after a one-period lag. For example, transactions demand for money depends on the transactions of the previous period and the monetary authorities expand credit in response to income changes of one period before. The equation is then :

$$L(i_t, Y_{t-1}) = M(i_t, Y_{t-1}) \dots(3)$$

The dynamic model operates according to (2) and (3). Given Y_{t-1}, (3) determines i_t and (2) then gives Y_t. Elimination of i_t between (2) and (3) results in a first order difference equation involving Y_t and Y_{t-1}. The course of Y_t over time follows at once. It is shown graphically in

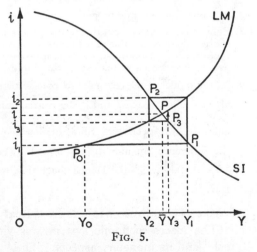

Fig. 5.

Fig. 5 in the form of the familiar cobweb model. The initial position is P_0, say a position of equilibrium before a small upward shift in the inducement to invest (and so in the curve *SI*). The new equilibrium position is P. Given Y_0 at P_0, i_1 in the first period is determined from the *LM* curve at

P_0 and Y_1 from the SI curve at the same height (saving = investment persisting). In the second period, i_1 adjusts to i_2 on LM and the cycle is repeated. The course of Y_t (and of i_t) is an oscillation or alternation; it is damped and tends to the equilibrium value provided that SI is steeper to OY than LM at P.

On this model, the monetary equilibrium of Fig. 4*b* is stable at any point P when the SI curve cuts the LM curve at a steeper angle to OY. This is to be expected for low levels of income and employment, e.g. in the Keynes " special " case, but only at higher levels if the supply of credit is expanded by the monetary authorities. The LM curve is then " stretched " out to the right (see 2.2, Ex. 3, above). This is not altogether a " realistic " result and it indicates that this dynamic model is not fully adequate or complete. The difficulty is probably that the concept of liquidity preference requires that expectations be included among the dynamic conditions.

EXERCISES 2.4

1. Consider $Y_t - C(Y_{t-1}) = I(i_t)$ and $L(i_t Y_{t-1}) = M$ as a possible dynamic model in which consumers expect income to continue at Y_{t-1} in period t. Show that saving is not equal to investment *ex ante* and therefore that the liquidity preference construction is not appropriate.

2. Do the same strictures as in the previous exercise apply to :
$$Y_t - C(Y_t) = I(i_{t-1}) \quad \text{and} \quad L(i_{t-1}, Y_t) = M$$
as a possible dynamic model?

3. Show that, in the model of the text, there is unintended liquidity, but that, in those suggested in the two previous exercises, there is unintended saving or investment. Again illustrate the importance of the fact that saving = investment *ex ante* is essential to the use of the liquidity preference schedule.

4. In the model of the text take M constant and linear functions as in 2.2, Ex. 1, above. Show that SI and LM are straight lines with slopes (to OY) of $\left(\dfrac{1-c}{b}\right)$ and $\left(-\dfrac{\lambda_1}{\lambda_2}\right)$ respectively. Show further that the conditions of the model lead to the difference equation in $y_t = Y_t - \bar{Y}$ (where $\bar{Y}$ is the equilibrium value) : $\left(\dfrac{1-c}{b}\right)y_t + \dfrac{\lambda_1}{\lambda_2}y_{t-1} = 0$. Hence check that, for stability, SI must be steeper than LM.

2.5 Macro-economic Models in " Real " Terms

The macro-economic system was viewed in 2.3 above in both its " real " and its monetary aspects. The " real " side, e.g. the production function and the condition that marginal product must equal the " real " wage rate, was not stressed. It was introduced to supplement the monetary side in a broad description of general equilibrium. This is not the only " real " contribution of the Keynesian theory, nor is it the main contribution. What the equilibrium of 2.3 above ignores is the inter-action between output and investment, between capital equipment and the goods produced. It is just this inter-action, both through the " multiplier " and through the " accelerator ", which dominates all macro-economic models expressed in " real " and dynamic forms.

Here, and in subsequent chapters, dynamic models are developed in " real " terms ; monetary factors including the rate of interest drop out of the picture. It is indeed possible to re-introduce them later, e.g. by adding a dynamic monetary mechanism, on some such lines as in 2.4 above, to the " real " model ; this is what is done by Hicks (1950). It will become clear, however, that the interest in macro-economic dynamics centres on the operation of " real " (and not on monetary) factors, and in particular on the multiplier and accelerator.

The variables are now : (i) income and output (Y), (ii) consumption (C) and its complement saving (S) and (iii) investment (I). Each is a " real " aggregate over the whole economy. As in national income accounting, each aggregate may be obtained by revaluing the corresponding money aggregate in some fixed prices, or by the equivalent procedure of deflating the money aggregate by an index of prices (or by a complex of such indices). Strictly speaking, each aggregate, and indeed various sub-aggregates within it, should be deflated by a different index of prices, e.g. consumption by various indices of the prices of consumers' goods and services, investment by various indices of prices of capital goods. In this case, one factor in the analysis would be relative price movements, changes in the " terms of trade " between different sectors. To simplify the model without reducing its essential significance, the assumption is that all sector prices move in parallel so that each aggregate can be regarded as deflated with one and the same price index. In addition, it is assumed that the economy is closed, with no government budget, and that there are sufficient unemployed resources (labour and other factors) to permit the necessary variations in output.

Hence, again as in national income accounting, Y can stand for income and output, equal by definition. This is so in " real " terms as in money terms because the " terms of trade " effect is assumed away. Income Y is a variable which is not planned. The *ex post* conditions which govern the problem are :

$$Y = C + S \quad \text{and} \quad Y = C + I \quad \text{................(1)}$$

The first expresses the fact that income is divided into consumption and saving, by definition *ex post* ; what is not consumed is saved. The second represents the similar division of output into output for consumption and output for investment *ex post*. The link between the two is consumption C, which is bought out of income and sold out of output. It follows, by definition *ex post*, that $S = I$, saving equals investment.

In the models developed in the following analysis, $Y = C + I$ is the usual condition written for the equation and hence for the solution of the model. The other condition (1) is used to determine, incidentally, what has happened to saving.

The formulation is different on the *ex ante* side. There is no reason why conditions such as (1) should hold *ex ante*, why saving and investment should be equal or indeed related in any way *ex ante*. What needs to be specified is the set of basic relations or functions which hold *ex ante*. The first such relation is the consumption function :

$$C = C(Y) = \gamma + cY$$

if a linear form is taken. The complement is the saving function :

$$S = Y - C(Y) = (1 - c)Y - \gamma$$

Either relation is *ex ante*, giving planned or intended consumption (or saving) in terms of income, current or expected. The second *ex ante* relation sets out whatever factors are taken as determining investment. Investment *ex ante* is no longer taken as a function of the rate of interest, through the marginal efficiency of capital schedule. It remains to specify, in each model constructed, the influences assumed to affect investment. For the present, in this first analysis, investment is taken as given and fixed :

$$I = A \quad \text{(autonomous investment)}$$

is the *ex ante* relation assumed. As an extension, autonomous investment can be taken as given but varying in a specified way (e.g. oscillatory) over time. A is then a given function of time, but it remains autonomous investment.

To complete the formulation of the present type of model, it is assumed that consumption and investment plans are both realised, i.e. that *ex post* and *ex ante* values are the same. Hence C and A can be written *ex post* and *ex ante*. The same is not necessarily true of saving ; saving *ex post* will appear (as a residual) in the model, equal to investment *ex post* and *ex ante*, but having no necessary relation to saving *ex ante*. The model is one in which unintended saving can appear. It is possible to formulate a model in which saving but not consumption plans are realised, with unintended consumption arising ; the point is that this would be a different model.

2.6 The Static Multiplier

With the general type of model formulated as above, the static multiplier arises at once from the condition for equilibrium:

$$Y = C + I$$

i.e. $$Y - C(Y) = A \quad (A \text{ given}) \quad \dots\dots\dots\dots\dots\dots(1)$$

This is an equation which gives Y in terms of A; it specifies the equilibrium income and output, with due allowance for the possibility of multiple solutions. As a matter of comparative statics, let A shift and determine the corresponding change in equilibrium income. Differentiate (1)

$$\frac{dY}{dA} - \frac{dC}{dY}\frac{dY}{dA} = 1$$

i.e. $$\frac{dY}{dA} = \frac{1}{1-c} = \frac{1}{s}$$

where $c = c(Y) = \dfrac{dC}{dY}$ and $s = s(Y) = \dfrac{dS}{dY}$ with $s = 1 - c$.

In terms of small finite increments, the relation is approximately:

$$\Delta Y \doteq \frac{\Delta A}{1-c} = \frac{\Delta A}{s} \quad \dots\dots\dots\dots\dots\dots\dots(2)$$

This is the multiplier.

By definition, c is the *marginal propensity to consume* $\left(\dfrac{dC}{dY}\right)$ and it varies in general with the level of income and consumption. Equally, and as an alternative, s is the *marginal propensity to save* $\left(\dfrac{dS}{dY}\right)$, again varying with income. The two are complements since, at each income, $s = 1 - c$ and $c = 1 - s$. In general, provided only that C and S are increasing functions of income, c and s are both positive and hence both less than unity (since $s = 1 - c > 0$ gives $c < 1$). It will always be assumed that this is so:

$$0 < c < 1 \text{ and } 0 < s < 1$$

The relation (2) is now to be interpreted:

If autonomous investment changes by a small amount ΔA, then equilibrium income changes by an amount which is a multiple of ΔA, the multiple being greater than unity, i.e.

$$\Delta Y = \frac{1}{1-c}\Delta A$$

where c is the marginal propensity to consume $\dfrac{dC}{dY}$.

The position is even simpler if linear forms are assumed for the consumption and saving functions. The marginal propensities (c and s) then become constants, unchanged at all income levels, i.e. the coefficients of Y in the linear relations :

$$C=\gamma+cY \qquad S=(1-c)Y-\gamma=-\gamma+sY$$

The constant γ remains to be interpreted ; it can be taken as positive ($\gamma>0$) and it is that part of consumption which is not influenced by income. It is because of γ that saving can be negative at low incomes. Further, as an extension, γ can be allowed to vary in a specified way over time to give " trends " in consumption. The curve $C=cY+\gamma_t$ in the OYC plane then shifts parallel to itself over time.

The equilibrium condition (1) is now :

$$Y-(\gamma+cY)=A$$

i.e.
$$Y=\frac{A+\gamma}{1-c}=\frac{A+\gamma}{s} \quad \dots\dots\dots\dots\dots\dots\dots\dots\dots(3)$$

This is the multiplier in the linear case.

The linear multiplier (3) seems similar to the general case (2). The difference is that the relation is between income and investment in the linear case, but only between changes in income and changes in investment in the general case. This is in addition to the fact that c and s are constants in (3) but not in (2).

One further point emerges in the linear case. In the multiplier relation (3), A and γ appear together ; they are additive. This is to be expected for A is autonomous expenditure on investment, i.e. not dependent on income, and γ is that part of consumption expenditure which does not depend on income. From the point of view of the determination of income, these two expenditures simply supplement each other. Therefore, it is often convenient to absorb γ into A and to call the total *autonomous expenditure*. The consumption function is then $C=cY$ (and saving $S=sY$), representing that part of consumption (or saving) which depends on income. The formulation of the multiplier is then as follows. The condition for equilibrium is :

$$Y=C+I+A$$

where C and I are consumption and investment expenditures which are not autonomous and where A is autonomous expenditure of all kinds. Here $C=cY$ and $I=0$:

$$Y=cY+A$$

i.e.
$$Y=\frac{A}{1-c}=\frac{A}{s} \quad \dots\dots\dots\dots\dots\dots\dots\dots\dots(4)$$

The multiplier (4) is only a variant of (3) with γ absorbed into A. The interpretation in this linear case is :

If the marginal propensity to consume is constant $(0 < c < 1)$, then equilibrium income is a multiple (greater than unity) of autonomous expenditure on consumption and investment, i.e.

$$Y = \frac{1}{1-c} A$$

It is important to realise that autonomous expenditure, as well as all forms of investment, gets " multiplied up " to income in the operation of the multiplier.

The static multiplier is illustrated on a diagram in Fig. 6. The line OS in the plane OAY has equation $Y = \dfrac{A}{1-c}$; it can be called the S line since it corresponds to equilibrium in which saving equals investment. The

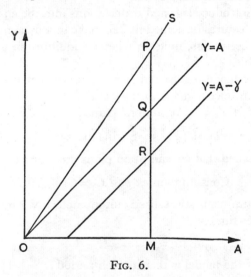

Fig. 6.

diagram also shows the line $Y = A$, which would represent income without the multiplier effect, and the line $Y = A - \gamma$, which represents autonomous investment alone. Given any level of autonomous expenditure (OM), the " multiplier " income in equilibrium is MP, where P is on the S line. If Q and R are corresponding points on the other two lines, then equilibrium income is divided into saving (equal to autonomous investment, MR) *plus* autonomous consumption (RQ) *plus* consumption dependent on income (QP).

M.E.

EXERCISES 2.6

1. Let Y be the equilibrium income corresponding to autonomous expenditure A and given by $Y - C(Y) = A$; let Y_0 be an initial equilibrium income corresponding to A_0. Show that:

$$(Y - Y_0) - (A - A_0) = \left(\frac{dC}{dY}\right)_0 (Y - Y_0) + \tfrac{1}{2}\left(\frac{d^2C}{dY^2}\right)_0 (Y - Y_0)^2 + \dots$$

and deduce that $Y - Y_0 = \dfrac{1}{1-c}(A - A_0)$, where $c = \left(\dfrac{dC}{dY}\right)_0$ approximately when $(Y - Y_0)$ is small. Identify with the multiplier (2) above.

2. Define average propensity to consume (save) as consumption (saving) in proportion to income. In the linear case, show that the average propensity to consume is $c + \dfrac{\gamma}{Y}$, decreasing as income increases; and that the average propensity to save is $s - \dfrac{\gamma}{Y}$, increasing with income. This result depends on $\gamma > 0$; is it at all " realistic " to take $\gamma < 0$?

2.7 A Dynamic Multiplier Model

It remains to introduce lags and expectations into the analysis and so to make use of the features described in 2.5 above in a dynamic model which will, amongst other things, indicate whether equilibrium under the static multiplier is stable.

The particular model developed here assumes that consumers expect income to remain unchanged from one period to the next. In period t, expected income is Y_{t-1}. Consumers' plans in period t are:

$$\text{Consumption } ex\ ante = C(Y_{t-1}); \quad \text{Saving } ex\ ante = Y_{t-1} - C(Y_{t-1}) \dots(1)$$

It is further assumed that consumption plans are realised:

$$\text{Consumption } ex\ post\ C_t = C(Y_{t-1})$$

and that investment plans are realised, autonomous investment being given and constant over time:

$$\text{Investment } I_t = A$$

The condition of the model is that in each period:

$$Y_t = C_t + I_t$$

which gives a difference equation of the first order:

$$Y_t - C(Y_{t-1}) = A \quad \dots \dots \dots \dots(2)$$

If the initial income Y_0 is specified, equation (2) serves by iteration to give the subsequent course of Y_t for $t = 1, 2, 3, \dots$.

Consumption and investment are realised; what of saving? Saving *ex ante* is given by (1) and this has not been used in deriving (2) and the path of Y_t. However, once Y_t is determined, then realised saving follows from $Y_t = C_t + S_t$:

$$\text{Saving } ex \text{ } post \text{ } S_t = Y_t - C(Y_{t-1}) \quad \ldots\ldots\ldots\ldots\ldots\ldots(3)$$

A comparison of (1) and (3) shows that saving *ex ante* and *ex post* are different, unless income happens to remain unchanged from one period to another. The model with difference equation (2) has income varying over time and it is characterised by the fact that there can be unintended saving.

In the linear case, absorb autonomous consumption into investment A and take $C = cY$ for consumption dependent on income. Then:

$$Y_t = C_t + I_t + A_t$$

where $C_t = cY_{t-1}$, $I_t = 0$ and $A_t = A$ (given autonomous expenditure, both consumption and investment). The difference equation is:

$$Y_t - cY_{t-1} = A \quad \ldots\ldots\ldots\ldots\ldots\ldots\ldots\ldots\ldots(4)$$

Try $Y_t = \overline{Y}$ for all t:

$$\overline{Y} - c\overline{Y} = A \quad \text{i.e. } \overline{Y} = \frac{A}{1-c}$$

which is the equilibrium income with the static multiplier. Write

$$y_t = Y_t - \overline{Y}$$

so that (4) becomes:

$$y_t = cy_{t-1}$$

with solution

$$y_t = y_0 c^t$$

or

$$Y_t = \overline{Y} + (Y_0 - \overline{Y})c^t \quad \ldots\ldots\ldots\ldots\ldots\ldots(5)$$

Since $0 < c < 1$, the solution (5) represents a path of Y_t tending steadily to the equilibrium level $\overline{Y}$. Hence the equilibrium level under the static multiplier is stable; if there is any initial disturbance, income will tend to return to the equilibrium level. The *speed of response*, or the rate at which Y_t tends to $\overline{Y}$ over time, depends on two things: the length of the period lag and the magnitude of the marginal propensity to save $s = 1 - c$. If the lag becomes shorter (e.g. from 6 to 3 months) then each step in the process of Y_t tending to $\overline{Y}$ takes less time. If s becomes larger, then the smaller value of c in (5) implies that there is a larger change in Y_t from one period to the next.

The model specified here represents the dynamic operation of the simple or Kahn multiplier. It can be developed and extended in a number of ways, some of which are referred to now and then taken up in the next chapter. A diagrammatic version of the Kahn multiplier, in the linear form (4) and (5) above, is given by Hicks (1950). This is shown in terms of the S line in Fig. 7. The initial income is $Y_0 = MP_0 = M'Q_0$; this may have been an equilibrium income at autonomous expenditure OM'.

Autonomous expenditure shifts to OM and the new equilibrium income is $\overline{Y}=MP$. In period 1, income becomes $Y_1=MP_1$ where by (4) :

$$Y_1 - \overline{Y} = c(Y_0 - \overline{Y})$$

i.e. $$Y_1 - Y_0 = (1-c)(\overline{Y} - Y_0)$$

i.e. $$P_0P_1 = (1-c)P_0P$$

The slope of the S line is $\dfrac{1}{1-c}$ so that $\dfrac{P_0P}{Q_0P_0} = \dfrac{1}{1-c}$, or $Q_0P_0 = (1-c)P_0P$.

Hence $P_0P_1 = Q_0P_0$ and the line Q_0P_1 is at 45° to the horizontal. The same result holds in subsequent periods so that Q_1P_2, Q_2P_3, ... are all at 45° to the horizontal. This gives an obvious graphical method of constructing the steps from P_0 to P_1, to P_2, to P_3, ... tending to P.

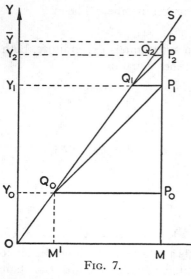

Fig. 7.

In the linear model (4) A is assumed to be constant over time. This can be extended to the case where autonomous expenditure varies over time, provided only that the variation is given and specified. All that needs to be done is to replace A by A_t, a specified time variation. This may be, for example, a progressive expansion or a given type of oscillation. Take the case where autonomous expenditure expands progressively at a rate $r(r>0)$:

$$A_t = A_0(1+r)^t$$

The difference equation is :

$$Y_t - cY_{t-1} = A_0(1+r)^t \quad \dots\dots\dots\dots\dots\dots\dots(6)$$

No static position of equilibrium is now possible—nor can one be expected ; this can be checked by trying $Y_t = \overline{Y}$ for all t in (6). As an alternative, take income as expanding *at the same rate* as autonomous investment and try $Y_t = \overline{Y}_0(1+r)^t$ in (6) :

$$\overline{Y}_0(1+r)^t - c\overline{Y}_0(1+r)^{t-1} = A_0(1+r)^t$$

i.e. $$\overline{Y}_0 = A_0 \Big/ \left(1 - \frac{c}{1+r}\right) \quad \dots\dots\dots\dots\dots\dots\dots(7)$$

Hence, provided that income starts from the particular level (7), the expanding path of income $\overline{Y}_0(1+r)^t$ is consistent with the model.

This is not the complete story. The path of Y_t from any other initial level (or disturbance) $Y_0 \neq \overline{Y}_0$ has still to be found. It is easily obtained, as in 6.6 below, in the form :

$$Y_t = \overline{Y}_0(1+r)^t + (Y_0 - \overline{Y}_0)c^t \quad \dots\dots\dots\dots\dots(8)$$

The first term in (8) is the steady expansion ; the second term is damped steadily to zero. In fact, the solution is the same as before, (5) above, except that the steady approach of Y_t is not to a fixed equilibrium level $\overline{Y}$ but to an expanding level $\overline{Y}_0(1+r)^t$ set by the assumed expansion in autonomous investment.

Results of a similar nature arise when the path of A_t, as given over time, takes other forms. The general conclusion is that, given any course for A_t, there is a corresponding course for Y_t over time, the effect of " multiplying up " the autonomous expenditure. If Y_t is disturbed from this course, then it tends to return to it and the speed of adjustment depends on the magnitude of $s = 1 - c$.

This conclusion has a certain limited interest. The multiplier reproduces in income or output, suitably " multiplied up ", whatever autonomous expenditure there is. But, from the economic point of view, there is something missing. Even if autonomous investment did expand progressively, it is not economically sensible to expect income to expand at precisely the same rate. This case might have some relevance to population growth—which can be handled otherwise and more simply—but, as Alexander (1951) points out, a progressive growth in autonomous expenditure is not a realistic economic possibility. It is more likely that autonomous investment proceeds in " spurts " in a Schumpeterian manner. Hence, the appropriate path of A_t to substitute in (4) is not some regular mathematical formula but rather an empirical time series. All the simple multiplier gives is the information that, whatever autonomous expenditure may be, it is " multiplied up " by the factor $\dfrac{1}{1-c}$ in income or output, and that this is a stable result in dynamic terms.

One extension of the simple multiplier can be made at once. So far the consumption function has been taken $C_t = C(Y_{t-1})$, dependent only on the income of the previous period ; the lag involved is a simple *delay* of one period. More generally there is a *distributed lag* in which C_t depends on income in several past periods (1.9 above). In the linear case, $C_t = \gamma + cY_{t-1}$ is replaced by :

$$\left. \begin{array}{l} C_t = \gamma + c_1 Y_{t-1} + c_2 Y_{t-2} + c_3 Y_{t-3} + \dots \\ \text{where} \qquad c_1 + c_2 + c_3 + \dots = c \end{array} \right\} \quad \dots\dots\dots\dots(9)$$

There is now a sequence of marginal propensities to consume ($c_1, c_2, c_3, \dots$)

adding to the over-all marginal propensity c. In particular, the coefficients may decrease in geometric series, the case of a geometric lag.

Many more possibilities are now covered. It is to be noted that C_t relates to consumption *outlays* in period t, not to decisions to consume, nor even to deliveries of consumer goods. One kind of case included under (9) arises when income fluctuates over time and consumers " average out " their outlays in some way. More important is the fact that consumption outlay is on a mixed collection of goods and services ; the decisions to buy (as influenced by current or recent income) may give rise to outlays at all kinds of future times. Hire purchase is just one illustration. A decision taken now, on the basis of current income, to buy on hire purchase is followed by payments made over several periods ahead ; the delivery of the goods is irrelevant for it is outlay which matters.

The additional flexibility in the multiplier model is seen even in the case of a lag distributed over two periods. With $C_t = c_1 Y_{t-1} + c_2 Y_{t-2}$ where $c_1 + c_2 = c$, the difference equation (4) becomes

$$Y_t - c_1 Y_{t-1} - c_2 Y_{t-2} = A$$

Again $Y_t = \overline{Y} = \dfrac{A}{1-c}$, as in the static multiplier, is a solution. Write $y_t = Y_t - \overline{Y}$ and the equation becomes

$$y_t = c_1 y_{t-1} + c_2 y_{t-2}$$

which is a difference equation of the second order. A complete and general solution is given in 6.7 below. However the fact that there are more possibilities, including oscillation or alternation, can be checked by trial and error, by inserting various pairs of initial values of y_t and writing the subsequent values from the difference equation.

EXERCISES 2.7

1. Consider an alternative model in which saving (rather than consumption) is realised. Write saving in period t as $S(Y_{t-1})$ *ex ante* and show that the condition of the model is that $S(Y_{t-1}) =$ investment *ex post*. If investment plans are realised (e.g. fixed autonomous investment only), then $S(Y_{t-1}) = A$. Show that no dynamic model results ; equilibrium income $\dfrac{A}{1-c}$ alone is consistent with the system. Why is the double assumption of saving and investment plans realised such a rigid one?

2. In the dynamic model represented by equation (2) above, take an actual time lag between income and spending so that Y_{t-1} is what is spendable in period t. Show that the same equation (2) serves and that the only difference in interpretation is that saving *ex post* can be divided :

$$Y_t - C(Y_{t-1}) = (Y_t - Y_{t-1}) + \{Y_{t-1} - C(Y_{t-1})\}$$

Interpret these two terms.

3. Use Fig. 7 to illustrate that, given the period lag, the speed of response in the adjustment of Y_t to equilibrium $\bar{Y}$ varies with $s = 1 - c$.

4. In the dynamic model of the text show that the *ex ante* difference of (investment − saving) equals $(Y_t - Y_{t-1})$. Interpret. Use this result to specify a corresponding model in continuous terms :

$$\frac{dY}{dt} = (\text{investment} - \text{saving}) = A - Y + C(Y)$$

In the linear case show that the solution in $y = Y - \bar{Y}$ is

$$y = y_0 e^{-(1-c)t}$$

which represents a convergence of Y to $\bar{Y}$ with speed dependent on $s = 1 - c$.

5. In the equation (6) for progressive expansion, the solution $Y_t = \dfrac{A_0}{1-c}(1+r)^t$ might be expected, the coefficient being A_0 " multiplied up ". The actual coefficient is $\bar{Y}_0 = A_0 / \left(1 - \dfrac{c}{1+r}\right)$. Show that, for $0 < c < 1$ and $r > 0$, $\bar{Y}_0 < \dfrac{A_0}{1-c}$. See Fig. 3 of Hicks (1950).

2.8 The Relation between Saving and Investment

A dynamic analysis in period terms involves the relation between saving and investment both *ex ante* and *ex post*. The relation is sometimes a source of confusion in interpreting dynamic models. The following may be the clearest approach to the question.

As a matter of definition, saving and investment are equal *ex post*. This is a consequence of the identity of income and output, an identity which is basic to the analysis developed here, as it is in national income accounting. As *ex ante* concepts, however, neither saving nor investment need be equal, or in any way related to, their *ex post* values. A dynamic analysis must make provision for the possibility of unintended saving, e.g. in the form of unplanned additions to balances held by consumers or by firms. Equally, it must provide for unintended investment, e.g. in the guise of accumulation of stocks beyond what was planned. If there is no unintended saving (or investment), then it must be because the dynamic model is built on the *assumption*, to be made explicitly, that saving (or investment) plans are realised, so equating the *ex post* to the *ex ante* value. The model of 2.7 above, for example, assumed investment plans realised but allowed for unintended saving.

It is possible also to set saving equal to investment *ex ante* as well as (by definition) *ex post*, i.e. to *assume* a link of equality between saving and investment from the beginning. The link is not at all necessary ; all turns on whether the assumption is a " realistic " one in the sense that it gives rise to a dynamic model of economic significance. There may be elaborate models where the assumption of *ex ante* equality of saving and investment is a great simplification. Such may be the case in models involving monetary factors in which it is desired to use the concept of liquidity preference (see 2.2 above). Saving equals investment *ex ante* may then be both a necessary and a useful assumption ; unintended saving and unintended investment are ruled out, but only because it is unintended liquidity which is of interest. The dynamic element in the cobweb model of Fig. 5 above is not in the *SI* curve (which is an equilibrium relation between saving and investment) but in the *LM* curve.

No such justification can be made in models based on the multiplier and of the relatively simple and broad form of 2.7 above. Here, it can be maintained that setting saving equal to investment *ex ante* assumes away the real problem. Either the variables of interest are always just right—in which case they are not explained—or there is the rather trivial or accidental case of two schedules being the same (as demand=supply at all prices).

Consider the *ex ante* relations appropriate to a model of the multiplier (and accelerator), as set out in 2.5 above. Consumption and saving are each a function of income Y, one being the complement of the other. Investment is a function of whatever factors are chosen as determinants. These are plans or schedules, very much like demand and supply curves. The question is : which of the plans are realised? This is a matter of assumption, with an eye on economic significance. The usual assumption —and, it is maintained, the most significant assumption in economic terms—is that consumption and investment plans are realised. Hence *ex post* and *ex ante* consumption (or investment) are equal. There is here an implicit shift from a schedule to a value. What is involved, e.g. in consumption plans realised, is that income is anticipated and the purchases appropriate (on the schedule) to that income are actually made, whether or no anticipation of income is correct. No such assumption is made for saving—unintended saving is the element of flexibility in the models. The situation can be summarised :

$$S_t^a \neq S_t = I_t = I_t^a$$

when the superscript a denotes *ex ante* values and the other variables are *ex post*.

As an alternative type of model, saving *and* investment plans may be assumed realised, leaving room only for unintended consumption. The scheme is then :

$$S_t^a = S_t = I_t = I_t^a$$

The implication is that saving and investment are equal from the beginning, that the separate plans for saving and for investment are consistent. Whatever may be the case in more elaborate models, this leaves too little flexibility in a dynamic analysis based on the multiplier (see 2.7, Ex. 1, above). This is the difficulty in the particular formulation adopted by Harrod and Domar in their growth theory (see 3.6 below).

There is one other possibility as an alternative to unintended saving as the flexible element—to allow for unintended investment by refraining from assuming that investment plans are realised. The scheme would then be :

$$S_t^a = S_t = I_t \neq I_t^a$$

There is also room in such a model for unintended consumption. However, more elaborate cases of investment planning than that of 2.7 above (only autonomous investment taken) would be necessary in constructing models on this line.

Considerations of these kinds will recur as the subsequent analysis proceeds. What is here described as the " usual " assumption (consumption and investment plans realised) will be tried out in practice. Later (in Chapter 9 below) various dynamic models are represented schematically and it then appears that investment is an essential link, but not saving, in the *ex ante* relations. It is perhaps not entirely accidental that saving tends to be a residual in national income accounting ; it does appear that it is not such a vital link in the structure of the economy.

2.9 Markets for Goods and Factors

The analysis so far has taken consumption, and hence saving, as directly dependent on income. This ignores the fact that only part of total saving is by persons (i.e. consumers) and the balance by business in the form of undistributed profits. Similarly, in the dynamic model of 2.7 above, the only lag assumed is between the earning and the spending of income by consumers. Two other types of lag are ignored, i.e. lags between spending and production by business, and between production and income earned by factors. The analysis is easily extended to take account of these facts ; all that needs to be done is to separate two markets, that for goods and that for factors of production. There are then two sectors, one composed of persons (consumers), the other of firms (business).

One further variable needs to be taken in addition to those used so far. This is personal income, or income earned and spendable by factors of production, which is denoted by F. As with other variables, F is here considered in " real " terms.

The consumption function is now $C = C(F)$, dependent *ex ante* on personal income. A second *ex ante* function, relating to the business sector, is needed. This expresses the demand for the factors by business, dependent on output: $F=F(Y)$. It is, in effect, the inverse of a simple form of production function; Y is dependent on F in a manner which expresses the technical conditions of production and the inverse gives F in terms of Y. Hence $C=C(F)$ where $F=F(Y)$, and the dependence of consumption on output is indirect.

The condition for equilibrium, with given autonomous investment A, is unchanged:

$$Y=C+A \quad \text{where } C=C(F) \text{ and } F=F(Y)$$

The condition reduces, by substitution, to a single equation in Y, giving Y in terms of A. Saving can now be split into two parts: business saving $(Y-F)$ and personal saving $(F-C)$. The condition for equilibrium can, therefore, be written:

$$(Y-F)+(F-C)=A \quad \text{where } C=C(F) \text{ and } F=F(Y)$$

Here Y is a function of A and by differentiation:

$$dY-\frac{dC}{dF}\frac{dF}{dY}dY=dA$$

i.e.
$$dY=\frac{1}{1-\dfrac{dC}{dF}\dfrac{dF}{dY}}\,dA$$

The multiplier is now the factor on the right-hand side; it involves the marginal propensity of consumers to spend $\left(\dfrac{dC}{dF}\right)$ and the marginal propensity of business to spend $\left(\dfrac{dF}{dY}\right)$. In the linear case:

$$C=\gamma+cF \quad \text{for consumers' spending}$$
$$F=\beta+bY \quad \text{for business spending}$$
so that
$$C=(\beta c+\gamma)+bcY$$

which is a consumption function of Keynesian form. Then, for equilibrium:

$$Y=\frac{A+\beta c+\gamma}{1-bc}$$

The main difference is that the Keynesian marginal propensity to consume now appears as the product of two marginal propensities to spend, one for business (b) and one for consumers (c). Autonomous expenditure, moreover, now has three elements: expenditure on investment, by business and by consumers.

In a dynamic model, three lags can be introduced. If each lag is of one period, they are:

(1) *Production-income lag* : $F_t = F(Y_{t-1})$ where receipts from output Y_{t-1} in period $(t-1)$ are used by business to provide factor incomes in period t.

(2) *Income-spending lag* : $C_t = C(F_{t-1})$ where personal income F_{t-1} in period $(t-1)$ is the basis of consumer spending in period t.

(3) *Spending-production lag* : $Y_t = C_{t-1} + A$ where production in period t is made up of production for autonomous investment A and production for consumption based on the actual spending by consumers C_{t-1} in period $(t-1)$.

Condition (3), in conjunction with the lagged functions of (1) and (2), gives a relation between Y_t and Y_{t-3}, i.e. a first order difference equation involving a lag which is of three periods. The lag of 2.7 is thus seen to be of triple form : it is the sum of the three separate lags distinguished here. In the linear case :

$$Y_t = C_{t-1} + A$$

where
$$C_t = \gamma + cF_{t-1} \quad \text{and} \quad F_t = \beta + bY_{t-1}$$

On substitution :

$$Y_t = \gamma + cF_{t-2} + A = c(\beta + bY_{t-3}) + A + \gamma$$

i.e.
$$Y_t - bcY_{t-3} = A + \beta c + \gamma$$

which is the same as (4) of 2.7 above, with the triple lag and with constants in the extended form.

The lags can be interpreted entirely in terms of expectations. In (1), firms expect their receipts to be Y_{t-1} in period t whereas they turn out to be different (Y_t). In (2), consumers expect their income to be F_{t-1}, instead of the actual F_t, in period t. In (3), business expects sales to be C_{t-1} in period t but actual sales are C_t. Denote expected or *ex ante* values by means of a superscript a, leaving actual or *ex post* values without a superscript. Then :

$$\text{(1) } Y_t^a = Y_{t-1} \quad \text{(2) } F_t^a = F_{t-1} \quad \text{(3) } C_t^a = C_{t-1}$$

The nature of the model can be seen by setting out the relation of saving to investment (given as A) :

	Expected	Realised
Business saving	$Y_t^a - F_t$	$Y_t - F_t$
Personal saving	$F_t^a - C_t$	$F_t - C_t$
Total saving	$Y_t^a + (F_t^a - F_t) - C_t$	$Y_t - C_t$
Investment	$Y_t - C_t^a$	$Y_t - C_t$
Saving – Investment	$(Y_t^a - Y_t) + (F_t^a - F_t) + (C_t^a - C_t)$	Zero

Hence, the difference between saving and investment *ex ante* is :

$$(Y_t{}^a - Y_t) + (F_t{}^a - F_t) + (C_t{}^a - C_t)$$
$$= \text{Output gap} + \text{Factor gap} + \text{Goods gap}$$

Each gap represents an excess of demand, i.e. the excess of the expected value over the actual value. So the factor gap is the excess of the income expected by consumers over what they actually get $(F_t{}^a - F_t = F_{t-1} - F_t)$.

There are now three lags in the circular flow of income around the cycle : production-income-spending-production. To match this, instead of one possible gap between outputs in successive periods $(Y_t{}^a - Y_t = Y_{t-1} - Y_t)$, there are three gaps. The two additional gaps appear on the factor market and on the market for consumers' goods. The lags are to be interpreted in terms of the sector concerned (persons or firms), the gaps in terms of the markets on which an excess of demand has developed. The position can be summarised :

(1) *Production-income lag* : the payment (F_t) to factors lags behind the output (Y_{t-1}) which provides the receipts of firms ; the lag arises because of the output gap $Y_t{}^a - Y_t = Y_{t-1} - Y_t$. In a Robertsonian expectation scheme, this gap would be zero since expected and actual output are equal.

(2) *Income-spending lag* : Consumption spending (C_t) lags behind the personal income (F_{t-1}) from which it is made ; the lag corresponds to the factor gap $F_t{}^a - F_t = F_{t-1} - F_t$. The lag here is Robertsonian, due to expectations by persons (consumers).

(3) *Spending-production lag* : production for consumption lags behind the actual purchasing of consumers ; the lag corresponds to the goods gap $C_t{}^a - C_t = C_{t-1} - C_t$. This lag is Lundbergian and represents expectations by firms (business).

In the one-period form of lag adopted here, the circular flow of income takes three periods to work itself out. Total output in one period (Y_{t-3}) is taken as business receipts and laid out (in part) as payments to factors in the next period (F_{t-2}). Next, the personal incomes of consumers (F_{t-2}) are spent (in part) on purchases of consumers' goods in the following period (C_{t-1}). Finally the sales to consumers (C_{t-1}) leads in the third period to production of consumers' goods by firms and hence to total output (Y_t).

EXERCISES 2.9

1. The model with all three lags, as above, implies that no plans for saving or investment are realised. Show that business saving is realised as planned if there is no production-income lag, i.e. if firms plan their output correctly. Show further that planned investment is realised if the spending-production lag disappears, i.e. if firms do not have to revise their plans in meeting demand for consumers' goods.

2. Assume no production-income lag in the above model. Show that, if firms anticipate correctly the sales of goods, then investment is realised as planned, unintended personal saving arises and the multiplier is Robertsonian. On the other hand, if consumers anticipate correctly, show that personal saving is realised as planned, there is unintended investment and the multiplier is Lundbergian. See Turvey and Brems (1951).

3. The model with triple lag has a difference equation relating Y_t to Y_{t-3}. Show that *one* initial value Y_0 fixes every third value of Y_t thereafter, but that *three* initial values are required for a complete solution.

REFERENCES

Alexander (S. S.) (1951): " Issues of Business Cycle Theory Raised by Mr. Hicks ", *American Economic Review*, **41**, 861–78.

Fort (D. M.) (1945): " A Theory of General Short-run Equilibrium ", *Econometrica*, **13**, 293–310.

Hahn (F. H.) (1955): " The Rate of Interest and General Equilibrium Analysis ", *Economic Journal*, **65**, 52–66.

Hicks (J. R.) (1937): " Mr. Keynes and the ' Classics ' ", *Econometrica*, **5**, 147–59.

Hicks (J. R.) (1950): *A Contribution to the Theory of the Trade Cycle* (Oxford, 1950), Chapters II, III and XI.

Lange (O.) (1943): " The Theory of the Multiplier " *Econometrica*, **11**, 227–45.

Metzler (L. A.) (1948): " Three Lags in the Circular Flow of Income ", in *Income, Employment and Public Policy* (Essays in Honor of Alvin H. Hansen) (Norton, 1948).

Modigliani (F.) (1944): " Liquidity Preference and the Theory of Interest and Money ", *Econometrica*, **12**, 45–88.

Smithies (A.) (1942): " Process Analysis and Equilibrium Analysis ", *Econometrica*, **10**, 26–38.

Solow (R.) 1951): " A Note on Dynamic Multipliers ", *Econometrica*, **19**, 306–16.

Turvey (R.) and Brems (H.) (1951): " The Factor and Goods Markets ", *Economica*, **18**, 57–68.

Turvey (R.) (1953): " Some Notes on Multiplier Theory ", *American Economic Review*, **43**, 275–95.

CHAPTER 3

THE ACCELERATION PRINCIPLE

3.1 Autonomous and Induced Investment

THE development of the previous chapter takes investment as given, i.e. *autonomous investment* denoted by A. The effect of a given rate of investment was examined by means of the multiplier. This is one-sided and it ignores the reciprocal relations between investment and output. Investment does influence output, but output affects investment. More strictly, it is a change in output over time, or from one period to another, which influences net investment as the addition to capital stock in a period. Investment which arises because of a change in output is called *induced investment*, denoted by I. A number of preliminary points must be made; the relation of output to induced investment is both complicated and indirect, and the distinction between induced and autonomous investment is never clear-cut.

First, the formulation of dynamic models must provide for both autonomous and induced investment. It might be argued, in strict terms, that all investment is induced by changes in output right back in time. In practice, however, the past time span considered in the model must be limited and there must be some investment which is so slightly influenced by recent changes in output as to be effectively autonomous. Investment by public authorities, e.g. in roads and buildings, is one type of autonomous investment; investment which arises because of inventions and innovations is another type.

Secondly, there is the distinction between fixed and working capital. Fixed capital consists of land, buildings, plant and equipment; working capital comprises both stocks of end products and stocks of intermediate products or work in progress. The effect of an increase in demand is to increase output and to induce investment. But the first reaction may be a *reduction* in working capital (stocks of end products) followed by a more or less rapid build-up of working capital, first stocks of intermediate goods and then stocks of final goods. Meanwhile, orders are placed for fixed capital goods which take time for delivery and installation. The emphasis here will be largely on fixed capital and the interim period when working capital is changing will be ignored. In period analysis, this is relatively simple ; the period is chosen long enough to comprise within itself all the first effects of an increase in output on working capital.

Thirdly, investment in fixed capital is to be taken net, i.e. gross investment less provision for depreciation. Generally speaking, it is net investment, positive or negative, which is induced by a change in output. Even here, there can be complications since a rise in output may encourage earlier replacement. Moreover, new capital assets come from the industries making capital goods and the output of these industries is gross. This leads to a consideration of an essential lack of symmetry in the process of investment in fixed assets. Following an *increase* in output, orders can be placed and deliveries taken of new capital goods up to the capacity of the capital goods industries. The expansion of net investment is only limited by this capacity ; even this limit may appear as an extension of the time of delivery rather than as a reduction in the amount of investment. On the other hand, a *decrease* in output cannot result in a large or rapid contraction of investment, i.e. in large negative figures for net investment. Orders for capital goods may be cancelled or withheld, but the output of the capital goods industries cannot sink below zero. Net investment cannot then fall below a certain negative figure, representing the effective scrapping rate.

Finally, net investment is the derivative of the stock of capital (fixed and working). Capital stock is measured at a moment of time net investment is the rate of increase of the stock, or the increase in a period. The level of output influences the stock of capital required to produce it ; changes in output influence changes in capital stock and hence net investment. An analysis which may be better suited to the distinction between autonomous and induced investment, in terms of capital stock, will not be made until later (Chapter 8 below) ; the emphasis now is on net investment without explicit reference to the stock of capital goods. The general position, however, is clear. If the flow of output is constant (like a velocity), then capital stock is constant and net investment zero. If the flow of output changes (like an acceleration), then the required capital stock also changes and there is (positive or negative) net induced investment. This is the acceleration principle—an increasing flow of output calls for a greater stock of capital and induces investment.

The multiplier is a relation between output and investment. Even in its dynamic form (2.7 above) it is clearly defective as a description of economic reality. Output can reproduce the course of autonomous investment, suitably " multiplied up ", but otherwise it tends steadily to its equilibrium level. This is because the multiplier uses only one *ex ante* relation, the consumption function ; it ignores completely the other *ex ante* considerations on the side of investment. The various determinants of investment need to be specified and added to the multiplier model. The investment relation can be given various forms but one particular version is now taken for detailed consideration, that which involves the acceleration principle, linking induced investments to changes in output.

The acceleration principle—the " relation " of Harrod—has long been used in the theory of investment and of the trade cycle, see Knox (1952). Early references are J. M. Clark (1917), Frisch (1931), Harrod (1936) and Lundberg (1937). Formulations stressing the inter-action between multiplier and accelerator are in Samuelson (1939 *a*, *b*), following Hansen, and developed by Hicks (1950) and others. The combination of the multiplier and accelerator leads to quite elegant mathematical models. The emphasis here is on the nature of such models rather than on various objections which can be made against the accelerator from the economic point of view. The models tend to ignore, for example, the fact that there may be excess capacity to be brought in before an increase in output requires new investment. Many of these objections are bound up with the question of " non-linearities " in the system, a question which will be postponed for later consideration.

3.2 The Accelerator

The formulation of the accelerator depends on whether continuous or period analysis is employed, particularly in the matter of the introduction of time lags (see 1.9 above). Both types of analysis are now adopted— they represent different approaches to economic " realism "—whereas the previous chapter was confined to period analysis. As before, the general functional relation of investment to changes in output is usually replaced by the particular linear form, at least as an approximation over limited ranges of the variables.

The simplest expression of the accelerator is the continuous form without lags :

$$I(t) = I\left\{\frac{d}{dt}Y(t)\right\} \quad \dots\dots\dots\dots\dots\dots\dots\dots\dots(1)$$

where $\frac{d}{dt}Y(t)$ is the rate of output (income) and $I(t)$ the rate of induced investment, each as a flow at time t. In linear form:

$$I(t) = v\frac{d}{dt}Y(t) \quad \dots\dots\dots\dots\dots\dots\dots\dots\dots(2)$$

where v is a positive constant, the *investment coefficient* indicating the *power of the accelerator*. There is no need to have an additive constant since this would be absorbed into autonomous investment. Hence induced investment is here a constant proportion of the current rate of change of output.

In continuous analysis the simplest way in which lags can be introduced is to take a continuously distributed lag of exponential form (1.9 above). If the rate of response is κ, so that the time-constant of the lag is $T = \dfrac{1}{\kappa}$, the rate of induced investment depends on output according to the relation:

$$\frac{d}{dt} I(t) = -\kappa \left\{ I(t) - v \frac{d}{dt} Y(t) \right\} \quad \dots\dots\dots\dots\dots (3)$$

The interpretation is as follows. The potential rate of investment at time t is fixed by the unlagged accelerator $J(t) = v \dfrac{d}{dt} Y(t)$. The actual rate of investment $I(t)$ lags behind and its increase $\dfrac{d}{dt} I(t)$ is proportional to the deficit $- \{ I(t) - J(t) \} = - \left\{ I(t) - v \dfrac{d}{dt} Y(t) \right\}$. The proportion κ indicates the speed of response.

The lagged relation (3) of the exponential form is conveniently expressed with the differential operator $D = \dfrac{d}{dt}$ (see Appendix A). It is:

$$DI = -\kappa (I - v\,DY)$$

i.e.
$$I = \frac{\kappa}{D + \kappa} v\,DY \quad \dots\dots\dots\dots\dots\dots (4)$$

is the expression of the accelerator.

If the simple exponential form is regarded as too specific, it can be replaced by two or more such lags operating in sequence. For two lags, each of speed 2κ (or time constant $\frac{1}{2}T$), the accelerator (4) is replaced by:

$$I = \left(\frac{2\kappa}{D + 2\kappa} \right)^{2} v\,DY$$

See 1.9, Ex. 4, above.

In period analysis, the accelerator without lags is to be written:

$$I_t = I\{(Y_t - Y_{t-1})\} = v(Y_t - Y_{t-1}) \quad \dots\dots\dots\dots (5)$$

in linear form. This is the " match " of (2) above; induced investment depends on the current change in output. The simplest form of the lagged accelerator is then:

$$I_t = I\{(Y_{t-1} - Y_{t-2})\} = v(Y_{t-1} - Y_{t-2}) \quad \dots\dots\dots\dots (6)$$

which has a single lag of one period. This takes account of the fact that, in the *ex ante* relation which gives investment plans, the most " recent " change in output which can usually be considered is that recorded in the previous period, $(Y_{t-1} - Y_{t-2})$. The adoption of (6) rather than (5) seems consistent with the use of the lagged consumption function $C_t = C(Y_{t-1})$, as in 2.7 above. If planned consumption is taken as dependent, not on the current level of income, but on that of the previous period, it is just as important to take planned investment as dependent on the change in output recorded in the previous period, rather than on the change being currently made.

The extension of the period accelerator (6) to the case of a lag distributed over any number of periods is easily made. In the linear form :

$$I_t = v_1(Y_{t-1} - Y_{t-2}) + v_2(Y_{t-2} - Y_{t-3}) + \dots \left.\right\}$$

where $\qquad\qquad v_1 + v_2 + \dots = v.$ $\qquad$ ....(7)

There is now a series of investment coefficients $(v_1, v_2, \dots)$ adding to v the over-all power of the accelerator. In particular, the coefficients may decrease in geometric series, the case of a geometric lag and that corresponding most closely to the exponential lag of (4).

In the interpretation of the distributed lag case, represented by (7) as well as by (3) or (4), it is to be noted that I is investment outlay—not investment decisions nor the deliveries of equipment. To say that investment outlay in period t depends on output changes in a series of past periods is equivalent to saying that the output change in period t gives rise to investment outlays in a series of future periods. There may be a lag between the output change and the decision to invest but, in any case, once the decision is made there will still be time taken in placing orders and in making out-payments, whether on delivery of equipment or as progress payments. Add to this the fact that the investment induced by a given output is a " mixed bag " of different kinds of plant, machinery and inventories and it becomes very reasonable to assume a distribution of outlays over a whole series of periods.

3.3 Harrod-Domar Growth Theory

The static multiplier is a stable relation ; the accelerator principle is to be expected to have an explosive tendency. The question is : what results from a combination of the two? A first answer is obtained in a model in which no lags, either in the multiplier or in the accelerator, are assumed. The multiplier and accelerator are then found to act together to produce a steady and progressive growth in income or output over time. This proposition was stated by Lundberg (1937), and developed by Harrod (1936, 1948) and Domar (1946).

The underlying idea is easily expressed. If autonomous investment A rises, e.g. because of a " spurt " in inventions, the multiplier gives a corresponding rise $\frac{A}{1-c}$ in output, where c is the marginal propensity to consume ($0 < c < 1$). The expansion of output then brings the accelerator into play and leads to further (induced) investment. The extra investment in its turn is " multiplied up " by the operation of the multiplier and another round begins. The net result is that output expands progressively.

Continuous analysis is better suited than period analysis to a development of the multiplier-accelerator inter-action with no lags present, with the accelerator in the simplest form of 3.2 above. All the variables are taken as continuous functions of time and relations are assumed linear. If autonomous expenditure, both consumption and investment, is separated off, the basic condition is :

$$Y = C + I + A$$

where
$$C = cY \text{ and } I = v\frac{dY}{dt}$$

are the consumption function and accelerator relation respectively ($0 < c < 1$, $v > 0$). Hence :

$$Y = cY + v\frac{dY}{dt} + A$$

i.e.
$$\frac{dY}{dt} = \rho \left(Y - \frac{A}{s} \right) \quad \dots\dots\dots\dots\dots\dots\dots(1)$$

is the differential equation satisfied by the path of output $Y(t)$ over time. Here $\rho = \frac{s}{v}$, where $s = 1 - c$ is the marginal propensity to save.

The solution of (1) depends on what is assumed about the course of autonomous expenditure A over time. Two cases merit particular attention.

Case : $A =$ constant. Fixed autonomous expenditure. Let y be the deviation of income from the fixed level $\frac{A}{s}$, i.e. $y = Y - \frac{A}{s}$ and $\frac{dy}{dt} = \frac{dY}{dt}$.

Then (1) is :

$$\frac{dy}{dt} = \rho y \quad \text{where } \rho = \frac{s}{v} > 0 \quad \dots\dots\dots\dots\dots(2)$$

Since $\dfrac{d}{dt}(\log y) = \dfrac{1}{y}\dfrac{dy}{dt}$, (2) is $\dfrac{d}{dt}(\log y) = \rho$ and so

$$\log y = \rho t + \text{constant}$$

i.e. $$y = Be^{\rho t}$$

where B is a constant to be found in terms of the initial income level. Write $y = y_0$ at $t = 0$ so that $B = y_0$. The solution of (2) is :

$$y = y_0 e^{\rho t} \quad\dots\dots\dots\dots\dots\dots\dots\dots\dots\dots\dots(3)$$

There is a steady and progressive expansion in income or output over time, the constant rate of growth being $\rho = \dfrac{s}{v} > 0$. Generally the marginal propensity to save $s = 1 - c$ is quite small in comparison with the investment coefficient v ; in this case ρ is a positive fraction which may be quite small. For example, with a year as the time unit, suppose $s = 0.05$ (marginal propensity to save of 5%) and $v = 2.5$, then $\rho = 0.02$ and income grows steadily at the compound rate of 2% per year.

The result throws a clear light on the accelerator. Even when autonomous expenditure is fixed, the multiplier-accelerator reaction produces a progressive expansion in output. The rate of growth is fixed by the structural constants, s and v, of the system. The accelerator is evidently an explosive factor.

Case : $A = A_0 e^{rt}$. Progressive growth in autonomous expenditure. The rate of growth in A is r, a given constant $(r > 0)$. Equation (1) becomes :

$$\frac{dY}{dt} = \rho\left(Y - \frac{A_0}{s}e^{rt}\right) \quad\dots\dots\dots\dots\dots\dots\dots\dots(4)$$

where $\rho = \dfrac{s}{v} > 0$ as before. Try $Y = \overline{Y}_0 e^{rt}$ as a solution of (4), i.e. a progressive growth in Y at the same rate as in A. On substitution in (4) :

$$r\overline{Y}_0 e^{rt} = \rho\left(\overline{Y}_0 e^{rt} - \frac{A_0}{s}e^{rt}\right) \quad\dots\dots\dots\dots\dots\dots(5)$$

i.e. $$\overline{Y}_0 = A_0/v(\rho - r)$$

Hence, provided that $\overline{Y}_0$ has this particular value (fixed by the structure of the system), a progressive expansion in Y at rate r is possible.

It remains to trace the path of Y from *any* initial value or disturbance $Y_0 \neq \overline{Y}_0$. Write $y = Y - \overline{Y}_0 e^{rt}$ so that $y_0 = Y_0 - \overline{Y}_0$ initially at $t = 0$. Subtract (5) from (4) and note that $\dfrac{dy}{dt} = \dfrac{dY}{dt} - r\overline{Y}_0 e^{rt}$. Then :

$$\frac{dy}{dt} = \rho y$$

with solution as before :

$$y = y_0 e^{\rho t}$$

This is similar to (3) of the case of fixed autonomous expenditure. The difference is that y is a deviation of output from a path of progressive growth, rather than a fixed level. Consequently the solution of (4) is a progressive growth away from a progressive growth of output. In full, the solution is :

$$\left. \begin{array}{l} Y = \overline{Y}_0 e^{rt} + (Y_0 - \overline{Y}_0) e^{\rho t} \\ \overline{Y}_0 = A_0 / v(\rho - r) \end{array} \right\} \quad \dots\dots\dots\dots\dots\dots(6)$$

where

The solution (6) needs to be interpreted with care. There is what may be described as an " equilibrium " rate of growth in output, $Y = \overline{Y}_0 e^{rt}$, i.e. an expansion at the same rate as autonomous expenditure. If output starts at the right level $\overline{Y}_0$, then its subsequent course is according to the " equilibrium " path. This is a familiar result, for the present " equilibrium " path is exactly similar to that under the dynamic multiplier in the same circumstances (2.7 above). If the initial level of output is not right, $Y_0 \neq \overline{Y}_0$, then the subsequent course of output is steadily and progressively away from the " equilibrium " path. The rate of divergence is the structural constant $\rho = \dfrac{s}{v}$. Compare this with the corresponding result for the dynamic multiplier (2.7 above) where there is a steady return to the " equilibrium " path. Again the accelerator comes in to provide the explosive element.

Whichever case is considered, there is a progressive growth in output at a rate $\rho = \dfrac{s}{v}$ which is inherent in the system. It represents the anti-damping or explosive operation of the accelerator (constant v), modified by the damping effect of the multiplier (constant $s = 1 - c$). This is Harrod's " warranted " rate of growth, warranted because it arises from a continued equation of saving and investment over time. There are no lags in the model so that the basic equation (1) derives from the condition $Y = C + I + A$ and this is the same as saving equal to investment. Nowhere, is there any divergence between saving and investment ; unintended saving and unintended investment are equally ruled out.

In writing the basic equation (1), the term $v \dfrac{dY}{dt}$ is the accelerator, relating induced investment to changes in output. It is put equal to $(Y - C - A)$ on the other side of the equation, i.e. saving less autonomous investment. This interpretation follows Harrod. Domar gets the same relation (1) but with a different interpretation; or, rather, he provides alternative interpretations. In his main approach, Domar (1946) (p. 141), the constant v is taken as the reciprocal of the average investment productivity. Hence $1/v$ is the ratio of the additional output from investment to the amount of the investment :

$$\frac{1}{v} = \frac{dY}{dt} \Big/ I$$

This is to be written $\frac{dY}{dt} = \frac{1}{v} I$ rather than the formally equivalent $I = v \frac{dY}{dt}$.

I is not taken as dependent on $\frac{dY}{dt}$ as in the acceleration principle; it is $\frac{dY}{dt}$ which is dependent on I through productivity of investment. Domar's theory appears as a requirement of full employment or capacity; for this output and investment must grow at a progressive (or warranted) rate. As Yeager (1954) puts it : the relation $\frac{dY}{dt} = \frac{1}{v} I$ expresses that " the increase in income necessary to make full use of an increase in production capacity is proportional to the intended investment that makes this extra income possible ".

In the alternative approach, Domar (1946) (p. 145), the treatment is reversed. If output does grow at a progressive rate, then the question is whether sufficient investment will be induced; the answer is " yes " if the rate of growth is the warranted rate. It is in this approach that Domar, in effect, introduces the accelerator.

The Harrod-Domar growth theory is open to many objections. It is not so much that the theory represents an undue simplification—a criticism of all theoretical models in macro-economic dynamics—but rather that it appears with " illegitimate precision ", to quote Yeager (1954) again. Among the simplifications which can be accepted for the moment are that there are two simple constants (c and v) in the system, with consumption proportional to output and investment to change in output. What cannot be accepted is the complete absence of time lags; and with this is associated the assumption of equality of saving and investment, not only *ex post*, but also *ex ante*.

The theory, in fact, is dynamic only in a limited sense. It is already known (2.7 above) that the multiplier alone is stable or damping in its effect; it can make output follow the time-path of autonomous expenditure, whether this is progressive, oscillatory or proceeding in " fits and starts ". The Harrod-Domar theory adds, what is generally to be expected, that the accelerator is explosive in its operation. The essential thing to be established is that the multiplier-accelerator system is inherently oscillatory. It is not enough for trade cycle theory that an oscillation in autonomous expenditure results in an oscillation in income and output. It is the accelerator which is required to produce a structural oscillation, i.e. to " explode " the damping of the multiplier into an oscillation about equilibrium. It may, of course, over-do it by making the oscillation explosive in itself ; but this is anticipating. The Harrod-Domar theory has no oscillatory feature—because it has no lags and is consequently not fully dynamic.

EXERCISES 3.3

1. Compare the paths of Y given by (1) when autonomous expenditure is (i) $A(t)$ and (ii) $A(t) + a_0$, where a_0 is a constant. Show that path (ii) is higher than path (i) by $\dfrac{a_0}{1-c}$, as given by the multiplier.

2. In equation (1), take $A = at$, i.e. a steady (but not progressive) growth. Show that $Y = \overline{Y}_0 + \dfrac{at}{1-c}$ is a steady growth in output which satisfies the equation provided that $\overline{Y}_0 = \dfrac{av}{(1-c)^2}$. Interpret this result.

3. Take $A = A_0 e^{rt} + a_0$ as, for example, the case where there is a progressive autonomous investment and a constant autonomous consumption expenditure. Show that the solution of equation (1) is unaltered (as compared with $a_0 = 0$) provided that $\left(Y - \dfrac{a_0}{1-c} \right)$ is written for Y. See Ex. 1 above.

4. In case $A = A_0 e^{rt}$, with $Y = \overline{Y}_0 e^{rt}$ as a solution, show that $\overline{Y}_0 = \dfrac{A_0}{s-rv} > \dfrac{A_0}{s}(s = 1 - c)$. In what sense does this imply that Y is above what the multiplier would suggest?

5. Take equation (4) in case $A = A_0 e^{rt}$, write $\eta = \dfrac{Y - \overline{Y}_0 e^{rt}}{\overline{Y}_0 e^{rt}}$ and show that the equation becomes $\dfrac{d\eta}{dt} = (\rho - r)\eta$ with solution $\eta = \eta_0 e^{(\rho - r)t}$. Show that this is identical with solution (6) of text. Interpret in terms of *proportional* deviations from " equilibrium ". Indicate the usefulness of the solution in η by representing the solution for Y as a function of time on a graph with semi-logarithmic scales.

3.4 Phillips' Model of the Multiplier

The next step is to introduce lags in the multiplier-accelerator model. If the analysis is to remain in continuous terms and to produce differential equations, then an appropriate lag is the continuously distributed (exponential) form. Such a model has been constructed by Phillips (1954).

It might be thought that the introduction of one or more delays, instead of the continuously distributed lags, would give rise to simpler models.

This is not so since the equations which result are of the awkward mixed type involving both differentials and differences. This is clear from Ex. 1 below and it will be illustrated further in some of the models of Chapter 8 below.

The accelerator is ignored at first and the analysis confined to the operation of the dynamic multiplier with a continuous (exponential) lag. This is, in effect, a continuous version of the previous model of 2.7 above. All variables are functions of a continuously varying time so that, for example, income or output Y stands for $Y(t)$. Linear relations are assumed throughout.

No lags are taken on the demand side ; planned consumption is $C = cY$ and autonomous expenditure (investment and consumption) is A, so that the total demand without lags is :

$$Z = C + A = cY + A$$

Take A as given and constant and use $s = 1 - c$, the marginal propensity to save rather than the marginal propensity to consume. Indeed, following Phillips, s can be interpreted rather more widely as the " marginal leakage ", see Ex. 2 below. In either case, the unlagged total demand is :

$$Z = (1 - s)Y + A \quad \dotfill (1)$$

On the supply side, the response of output Y to demand Z is not taken as instantaneous (as in 3.3 above) but as lagged according to the continuous (exponential) form. Let λ be the speed of response, or $T = \dfrac{1}{\lambda}$ the time-constant of lag, so that :

$$\frac{dY}{dt} = -\lambda(Y - Z) \quad \dotfill (2)$$

is the variation of output over time.

The relations of the model are (1) and (2), from which is derived a differential equation in output Y :

$$\frac{dY}{dt} + \lambda Y = \lambda Z = \lambda(1 - s)Y + \lambda A$$

i.e.
$$\frac{dY}{dt} + \lambda s Y = \lambda A \quad \dotfill (3)$$

The equilibrium level $Y = \overline{Y} = \dfrac{A}{s}$ of the static multiplier is again a solution of (3). Write $y = Y - \overline{Y}$ so that (3) becomes :

$$\frac{dy}{dt} + \lambda s y = 0 \quad \dotfill (4)$$

As before, using $\dfrac{1}{y}\dfrac{dy}{dt} = \dfrac{d}{dt}(\log y)$, the solution of (4) is obtained :

$$\frac{d}{dt}(\log y) = -\lambda s$$

i.e. $\qquad\qquad\qquad \log y = -\lambda st + \text{constant}$

i.e. $\qquad\qquad\qquad y = y_0 e^{-\lambda st}$

The solution in full is :

$$Y = \overline{Y} + (Y_0 - \overline{Y})e^{-\lambda st} \quad\dotfill(5)$$

Given any initial output Y_0 at $t=0$, the course of output over time is given by (5) as a steady and progressive approach to the equilibrium level $\overline{Y} = \dfrac{A}{s}$. The approach is like e^{-t} and it is only assumed that λ and s are positive. The speed of adjustment is given by λs, a combination of the marginal propensity to save (as in 2.7 above) and of the speed of response in the lag of production.

One particular application, involving particular initial conditions, is made by Phillips. Assume there is equilibrium initially. Measure Y from this equilibrium level ($Y=0$, $t=0$). A single shift in demand, represented by A, then takes place, e.g. because of an increase in autonomous investment. The new equilibrium level is $\overline{Y} = \dfrac{A}{s}$. The path of Y towards the new equilibrium is given by the equation (3) with $Y=0$ at $t=0$; the solution (5) has $Y_0 = 0$. Hence, following a shift A in demand, the path of output from one equilibrium ($Y=0$) to the second $\left(Y = \dfrac{A}{s}\right)$ is :

$$Y = \frac{A}{s}(1 - e^{-\lambda st}) \quad\dotfill(6)$$

It is shown graphically by curve (iii) of Fig. 3 above, with $T = \dfrac{1}{\lambda s}$ and $Z_0 = \dfrac{A}{s}$. In fact the path of Y in this form of the dynamic multiplier is that in an exponential lag with speed of response λs (see Ex. 3 below). It is to be compared with the dynamic multiplier in the case of the single period lag (2.7 above). The solution (5) of 2.7, with $Y_0 = 0$ and $\overline{Y} = \dfrac{A}{1-c}$, is

$$Y_t = \frac{A}{1-c}(1 - c^t)$$

i.e. $$Y_t = \frac{A}{s}\{1 - (1-s)^t\} \quad\dotfill(7)$$

which compares directly with (6) above. The continuous solution involves an exponential function of time of form e^{-at} (with $a = \lambda s$ here) while the period solution has a power function of form a^t (with $a = c = 1 - s$ here); this is characteristic of the two types of analysis, as will be seen in Chapters 5 and 6 below. The more important difference—a property of the models as constructed—is that the speed of response depends on the magnitude of λs in (6) but only of s in (7).

EXERCISES 3.4

1. The differential equation (1) of 3.3 above represents the multiplier-accelerator with no lags present. Take delays of length θ_1 in the consumption function and of length θ_2 in the accelerator and show that the equation becomes

$$v \frac{d}{dt} Y(t - \theta_2) = Y(t) - c Y(t - \theta_1) - A$$

This is of mixed form, even in the simplest case $(\theta_1 = \theta_2 = 1)$. Show, however, that $Y = \bar{Y}$ constant for all time is still a solution, with $\bar{Y} = \dfrac{A}{1 - c}$ from the static multiplier.

2. Write aggregate demand $Z = C + A$ where *both* C and A are linearly dependent on income Y. Show that it can be written $Z = (1 - l) Y + \delta$ where l can be interpreted as " marginal leakage " and δ is autonomous demand. Then show that the dynamic multiplier remains exactly as in the text above.

3. The differential equation of the dynamic multiplier is (3) above. Write this as $\dfrac{dY}{dt} = -\lambda s \left(Y - \dfrac{A}{s} \right)$ and interpret as the operation of a continuous lag.

4. The dynamic model of the text does not mention saving. Show that *ex ante* consumption is $(1 - s) Y$, saving $s Y$ and investment A (assuming no autonomous consumption expenditure); hence show that consumption and saving add to Y and consumption and investment add to Z *ex ante*. Deduce that there is unintended investment, except when consumption plans are not realised and exactly balanced by unintended saving.

5. In the path (6) from one equilibrium to another, show that $\dfrac{dY}{dt} = \lambda A$ at $t = 0$ and interpret on curve (iii) of Fig. 3 above.

3.5 Phillips' Model of the Multiplier-Accelerator

The model of 3.4 above has only autonomous investment; there is no accelerator. A lagged version of the accelerator is now added, the lag being of continuous exponential form, (3) of 3.2 above, with investment coefficient v and speed of response κ. Hence, if I is actual induced investment at time t in response to changes in output, I is given by :

$$\frac{dI}{dt} = -\kappa \left(I - v \frac{dY}{dt} \right) \quad \dots\dots\dots\dots\dots\dots\dots(1)$$

Total demand is now $Z = C + I + A$ with $C = cY = (1 - s) Y$ without lags as before, i.e.

$$Z = (1 - s) Y + I + A \quad \dots\dots\dots\dots\dots(2)$$

The supply side is taken as before with a continuous lag, speed of response λ:

$$\frac{dY}{dt} = -\lambda(Y - Z) \quad\dotfill(3)$$

The relations of the model are (1), (2) and (3). There are two continuously distributed lags, one on the supply side (output responding to demand with speed λ) and the other on the side of the accelerator (induced investment responding to changes in output with speed κ). A differential equation in Y is obtained by eliminating Z and I from (1), (2) and (3). First substitute from (2) into (3):

$$\frac{dY}{dt} = -\lambda Y + \lambda\{(1-s)Y + I + A\}$$

i.e.

$$I = \frac{1}{\lambda}\frac{dY}{dt} + sY - A$$

and so

$$\frac{dI}{dt} = \frac{1}{\lambda}\frac{d^2Y}{dt^2} + s\frac{dY}{dt}$$

Substitute into (1):

$$\frac{1}{\lambda}\frac{d^2Y}{dt^2} + s\frac{dY}{dt} = -\kappa\left(\frac{1}{\lambda}\frac{dY}{dt} + sY - A\right) + \kappa v\frac{dY}{dt}$$

i.e.

$$\frac{1}{\lambda}\frac{d^2Y}{dt^2} + \left(s + \frac{\kappa}{\lambda} - \kappa v\right)\frac{dY}{dt} + \kappa sY = \kappa A$$

The differential equation in Y is of second order:

$$\left.\begin{array}{l}\dfrac{d^2Y}{dt^2} + a\dfrac{dY}{dt} + bY = \kappa\lambda A \\[2mm] a = \lambda s + \kappa - \kappa\lambda v \quad\text{and}\quad b = \kappa\lambda s\end{array}\right\} \quad\dotfill(4)$$

where

A solution of (4) is $Y = \bar{Y}$, constant all t, where $\bar{Y} = \dfrac{A}{s}$. The static multiplier level is again consistent with the model. Write $y = Y - \bar{Y}$ and (4) becomes:

$$\frac{d^2y}{dt^2} + a\frac{dy}{dt} + by = 0 \quad\dotfill(5)$$

with the same values of a and b. The solution of (5) gives the path of y, and hence of Y, over time. It is examined in Chapter 8 below, where it is found in general to be an oscillatory path (which may well be explosive) around $Y = \bar{Y} = \dfrac{A}{s}$.

With suitable initial conditions the differential equation (4) can represent the path of output from one equilibrium level to another. At $t = 0$, $Y = 0$

is assumed to be the first equilibrium level, immediately prior to a shift A in demand. The path from $Y=0$ to the new equilibrium level $\overline{Y}=\dfrac{A}{s}$ is given by (4), except that now *two* initial conditions are needed (see 5.2 below). One condition is $Y=0$ at $t=0$. The other is that the initial value of $\dfrac{dY}{dt}$ (at $t=0$) is that given by the multiplier, since the accelerator will not then have come into operation. This value is $\dfrac{dY}{dt}=\lambda A$, see 3.4, Ex. 5, above. Hence the path from one equilibrium to the other is given by the differential equation (4) subject to $Y=0$, $\dfrac{dY}{dt}=\lambda A$ at $t=0$.

EXERCISES 3.5

1. If consumption plans are realised, show that the multiplier-accelerator model has no unintended saving ; all the lack of realisation of plans, due to the lags in the model, is in unintended investment.

2. Illustrate the fact that two initial conditions are needed to go with the differential equation (4) by showing that, if $Y=0$ and $\dfrac{dY}{dt}=\lambda A$ at $t=0$, then $\dfrac{d^2Y}{dt^2}$ is also known at $t=0$. What is the value of $\dfrac{d^2Y}{dt^2}$ and what does it mean in terms of the the graph of the path of Y over time?

3. Show that the equations (1), (2) and (3) of the model can be written in terms of the operator $D=\dfrac{d}{dt}$: $Y=\dfrac{\lambda}{D+\lambda}Z$,

where $Z=C+I+A$, $C=(1-s)Y$, $I=\dfrac{\kappa}{D+\kappa}v\,DY$.

Deduce that $Y=\dfrac{\lambda}{(D+\kappa)(D+\lambda)}\{(\kappa v+1-s)DY+\kappa(1-s)Y+\kappa A\}$

and show that this reduces to the differential equation (4) of the text.

4. The model of the text assumes no lag in consumption demand. Introduce a continuously distributed consumption lag by writing $\dfrac{dC}{dt}=-\gamma(C-cY)$, where γ is the speed of response. Show that the model is only changed by replacing $C=cY$ in equation (2) by the value of C given here, and indicate that a differential equation of the third order is obtained. Show that, in the notation of the previous exercise :

$$Y=\dfrac{\lambda}{D+\lambda}Z \text{ where } Z=C+I+A,\quad C=\dfrac{\gamma}{D+\gamma}cY,\quad I=\dfrac{\kappa}{D+\kappa}v\,DY$$

and hence derive the third-order differential equation in Y.

3.6 Harrod-Domar Growth Theory in Period Form

In 3.3 above, a version of the Harrod-Domar theory was given in continuous terms and with no lag either in consumption and saving or in investment. A warranted and progressive growth of output is obtained, the rate of growth being $\rho = \dfrac{s}{v}$. The objection to this theory is that it is not fully dynamic, having no lags. The condition of the model is that saving and investment are never different even when *ex ante* plans are considered.

An attempt can now be made to translate the theory into period terms which will lay more stress on *ex ante* and *ex post* values, on plans and the extent to which they are realised. If no lags are introduced, the same simple or formally dynamic, result is obtained as in 3.3 above (see Ex. 1 below). It is more realistic to assume lags and so to break the rigidity of the model and permit a genuine dynamic version to appear. The simplest case is considered in which a lag of one period is introduced in the consumption and saving relation ; no lag is assumed on the investment side, in the accelerator. This is the case which seems most in keeping with Harrod's own exposition. The following analysis is based on the work of Baumol (1948, 1949) and Alexander (1950).

Harrod's two conclusions can be stated at the outset. The first is that there is a warranted rate of growth in output which, once achieved, will be maintained. The second is that if any other rate of growth is attained, then the adjustment within the system will move the rate, not towards, but further away from the warranted rate.

The main assumption made by Harrod is that saving plans, rather than consumption plans, are realised. This is one possible assumption when a lag is introduced. In the linear case, and excluding any autonomous expenditure, the saving relation is $S_t = s Y_{t-1}$ where s is the constant marginal propensity to save. This is an *ex ante* relation but, with saving plans realised, S_t is also saving *ex post*. Consumption is $(1-s)Y_{t-1}$ *ex ante* but $C_t = Y_t - S_t = Y_t - s Y_{t-1}$ *ex post* ; there can be unintended consumption.

The *ex post* condition as before is $Y_t = C_t + I_t + A_t$, where I_t is induced investment and A_t is autonomous investment. Hence :

$$S_t = I_t + A_t$$

is the *ex post* equality of saving and investment. The main case to be considered is that in which there is no autonomous investment. With $A_t = 0$, *ex post* investment (all induced) is :

$$I_t = S_t = s Y_{t-1}$$

Induced investment *ex ante* is the accelerator relation, without lag :

$$I_t' = v(Y_t - Y_{t-1})$$

The development of the model now turns on the relation between investment *ex ante* and *ex post*, between I_t' and I_t.

The warranted rate of growth in Y_t is given by the equilibrium condition that investment plans are always realised, $I_t' = I_t$ for all t. Since saving plans are assumed realised in the first place, this is the special type of situation in which saving and investment happen always to be the same, *ex ante* as well as *ex post*. The condition is:

$$v(Y_t - Y_{t-1}) = s Y_{t-1}$$

i.e.
$$Y_t = \left(1 + \frac{s}{v}\right) Y_{t-1}$$

Write $\rho = \dfrac{s}{v}$ and the solution of this simple difference equation (by iteration) is:

$$Y_t = Y_0(1 + \rho)^t$$

Hence Y_t expands progressively at the warranted rate $\rho = \dfrac{s}{v}$.

Now assume some disturbance, i.e. some rate of growth other than ρ has occurred in period $(t-1)$. In this period, investment *ex ante* is not realised in investment *ex post*; $I'_{t-1} \neq I_{t-1}$. The question is: what adjustment is made in period t? This is a matter of further assumption, or a further condition of operation of the model. Write:

$$\bar{U}_t = I_t' - I_t = v(Y_t - Y_{t-1}) - s Y_{t-1} = v Y_t - (v+s) Y_{t-1} \quad \ldots\ldots\ldots(1)$$

for the excess of planned over realised investment in period t. If $\bar{U}_t > 0$, there is some planned investment not realised; if $\bar{U}_t < 0$, there is unintended investment. The additional condition needed concerns the effect of a given $\bar{U}_{t-1} \neq 0$ in period $(t-1)$ on the output Y_t of period t.

A first possibility is to assume that output increases in period t by just enough to make good the deficiency $\bar{U}_{t-1}$ (or decreases if $\bar{U}_{t-1}$ is negative):

$$Y_t = Y_{t-1} + \bar{U}_{t-1} \quad \ldots\ldots\ldots\ldots\ldots\ldots\ldots\ldots\ldots\ldots(2)$$

From (1):
$$Y_t = Y_{t-1} + v Y_{t-1} - (v+s) Y_{t-2}$$

A difference equation of the second order is obtained:

$$Y_t = (1+v) Y_{t-1} - (v+s) Y_{t-2} \quad \ldots\ldots\ldots\ldots\ldots(3)$$

The solution is given in 6.6. below. Given s, generally a small positive fraction, the nature of the path of Y_t depends on the size of the investment coefficient v. For likely values of v, between $1-s$ and $1+2\sqrt{s}$, the course of Y_t given by (3) is an explosive oscillation. For example, if $s = \frac{1}{4}$, a value of v between $\frac{3}{4}$ and 2 gives the explosive and oscillatory case. The difficulty about this apparently reasonable result—which is in line with the Samuelson-Hicks model of 3.7 below—is that the condition (2) is not consistent with the maintenance of the warranted rate of growth. If $\rho = \frac{s}{v}$ is the rate of growth in period $(t-1)$ so that $\bar{U}_{t-1} = 0$, then (2) gives $Y_t = Y_{t-1}$, i.e. output remains unchanged and so does not continue at the warranted rate.

The second possibility allows for this; the condition assumed is that output increases in period t by the warranted rate with an adjustment for the deficiency $\bar{U}_{t-1}$:

$$Y_t = (1+\rho)Y_{t-1} + \bar{U}_{t-1} \quad \dots\dots\dots\dots\dots\dots(4)$$

From (1) and $\rho = \frac{s}{v}$:

$$Y_t = Y_{t-1} + \frac{s}{v}Y_{t-1} + vY_{t-1} - (v+s)Y_{t-2}$$

The difference equation is again of second order:

$$Y_t = \left(1 + v + \frac{s}{v}\right)Y_{t-1} - (v+s)Y_{t-2} \quad \dots\dots\dots\dots\dots\dots(5)$$

which differs from (3) in the extra term $\frac{s}{v}$ in the coefficient of Y_{t-1}. The path of Y_t given by (5) is now a steady and indefinite increase, at least for all likely values of $v > 1 - s$ (see 6.6 below). This is the explosive and non-oscillatory case of variation of Y_t. It does, in fact, lead to Harrod's two conclusions. If the warranted rate of growth is once achieved, and so $\bar{U}_{t-1} = 0$, then the condition (4) implies that it will continue. However, if some other rate rules, the path of Y_t given by (5) is a progressive deviation away from the warranted rate, at least for $v > 1 - s$.

A still more general condition can be corresponding rate of growth shown in period $(t-1)$, with the condition assumed now is that $\bar{U}_{t-1}$. So $Y_{t-1} = Y_{t-2}(1+r_{t-1})$. The rate of growth of output is stepped fixed for period t: Y ment is not realised. Hence the condition is: the rate of growth and decrease up as l

$$\begin{array}{ll} r_t > r_{t-1} & \text{if } \bar{U}_{t-1} > 0 \\ r_t = r_{t-1} & \text{if } \bar{U}_{t-1} = 0 \\ r_t < r_{t-1} & \text{if } \bar{U}_{t-1} < 0 \end{array} \left.\right\} \quad \dots\dots\dots\dots\dots(6)$$

It follows from (6) that once the warranted rate of growth is achieved ($\bar{U}_{t-1}=0$) then it is continued ($r_t=r_{t-1}$); this is Harrod's first conclusion. Next suppose that a rate of growth greater than the warranted rate is achieved: $r_{t-1}=\dfrac{s}{v}+\epsilon$ where $\epsilon>0$. Then $Y_{t-1}=Y_{t-2}\left(1+\dfrac{s}{v}+\epsilon\right)$ and from (1):

$$\bar{U}_{t-1}=v\left(1+\frac{s}{v}+\epsilon\right)Y_{t-2}-(v+s)Y_{t-2}=v\epsilon Y_{t-2}>0$$

Hence by (6) $\qquad\qquad r_t>r_{t-1}>\dfrac{s}{v}$

and the rate of growth continues to diverge from the warranted rate. This is Harrod's second conclusion.

The reasons why the Harrod-Domar type of growth theory is not a satisfactory dynamic model are now clear. They are to be sought particularly in Harrod's assumption that saving plans are realised. If it is also assumed that investment plans are realised, then the whole system becomes restricted to what is essentially a moving equilibrium. Output grows progressively at the warranted rate $\rho=\dfrac{s}{v}$. As long as investment plans continue to be realised, this is all that is possible. The system is not a dynamic model in the full sense, e.g. it does not fix the time-path of a variable from one equilibrium to another, following a disturbance. The difficulty is that the double assumption of saving and investment plans fulfilled is a rigid one; it implies that saving equals investment *ex ante*, that plans always happen to be in agreement.

The alternative explored here is to keep the assumption of saving plans realised, but to allow investment plans to go unfulfilled. An extra condition is then required in the model, to specify the response of output to a deficiency in investment. The condition can be assumed in many ways, of which (2), (4) and ... are examples. The resulting path of Y_t can then take various for...

... ceases to ... main point now is that the warranted rate of growth $\rho=\dfrac{s}{v}$ ... equilibrium condition (saving ... relevance at all; it arises when the dynamic models such as those ju... *ex ante*) is imposed, not in results from condition (2) or (4), for ... explosive ... The path of Y_t which right; it may be oscillatory or explosive ... action in ... judged in its own the multiplier-accelerator inter-action in ... the expression of The common feature of the models is that there ... ic model. ment (leading to adjustments) but never uninten... invest-
... the

models seems satisfactory for there is little economic reason why conditions like (2) or (4) are assumed.

The present conclusion, therefore, is that the warranted rate of growth has little, if anything, to do with a macro-economic model in dynamic terms. Further, dynamic models with simple lags and based on the assumption that saving plans are realised do not appear economically very sensible, even when divorced from the concept of a warranted rate of growth. A more profitable approach is to go back to the beginning and to make a different basic assumption, i.e. that consumption plans are realised, leaving open the possibility of unintended saving. The model of Samuelson-Hicks in period terms, to be considered next, assumes that consumption and investment are both realised. This does not have the rigidity, found in Harrod's theory, that the double assumption of saving and investment plans has; there is plenty of room for flexibility in the possibility of unintended saving.

EXERCISES 3.6

1. Show that, in the model of the text, the assumption of no lags leads to :
$$I_t = s Y_t \quad \text{and} \quad I_t' = v(Y_t - Y_{t-1})$$
and that consumption as well as saving plans are realised. If investment plans are also realised, show that $Y_t = \dfrac{v}{v-s} Y_{t-1}$ and that Y_t expands progressively at the rate $\rho' = \dfrac{s}{v-s}$. Why is this " warranted " rate of growth greater than Harrod's $\rho = \dfrac{s}{v}$ (provided that $v > s$)?

2. Examine the case of an accelerator so weak that $v < s$, both in the lagged model of the text, and in that of the previous exercise without lags. Comment on the further difficulties with the Harrod-Domar type of model disclosed in this case.

3.7 Samuelson-Hicks Model of the Multiplier-Accelerator

The most complete formulation of the multiplier-accelerator inter-action in period terms is that first given by Samuelson (1939a, b) and later developed by Hicks (1950). The basic assumption is that consumption plans are realised ; with lags in the *ex ante* consumption and saving functions, this leaves room for unintended saving. The condition is then imposed that, in the operation of the model, investment plans are realised, so that investment *ex ante* is equal to the common *ex post* value of saving and investment. The *ex ante* investment relation is the accelerator with lags. The formulation differs from that of Harrod (3.6 above) on two counts ; consumption (and not saving) plans are realised and lags are an essential feature of both *ex ante* relations of consumption and investment.

M.E.

In general, the model takes the consumption function in linear form with a distributed lag, as indicated at the end of 2.7 above :

$$C_t = \gamma + c_1 Y_{t-1} + c_2 Y_{t-2} + c_3 Y_{t-3} + \ldots \Big\}$$
where $\qquad c_1 + c_2 + c_3 + \ldots = c$ $\qquad$ ....(1)

The over-all marginal propensity to consume is assumed to be a positive fraction $(0 < c < 1)$, as is each of the series of coefficients $(c_1, c_2, c_3, \ldots)$. The accelerator relation is similarly taken as linear with a distributed lag (as in 3.2 above) :

$$I_t = v_1(Y_{t-1} - Y_{t-2}) + v_2(Y_{t-2} - Y_{t-3}) + \ldots \Big\}$$
where $\qquad v_1 + v_2 + \ldots = v$ $\qquad$ ....(2)

The over-all investment coefficient v is assumed positive ; the series of coefficients $(v_1, v_2, \ldots)$ can also be taken as all positive.

The *ex ante* plans represented by (1) and (2) cover all kinds of possibilities. The current level of income leads to decisions by consumers to spend and the corresponding outlays are spread or averaged over several periods ahead, e.g. in hire purchase. Even more important, the current change in output is followed by decisions to invest and the necessary outlays are planned over future periods. The relations (1) and (2) are for consumption and investment expenditure or outlays. They may depend on prior decisions to consume or invest ; the actual deliveries of consumer and capital goods may follow, accompany or indeed precede the outlays. All that is needed here is that the outlays should be timed. The actual distribution of lags, as written in (1) and (2), can be of various forms, e.g. " humped " or spread, which will be considered later.

The Samuelson-Hicks model on this basis is to be compared with the corresponding model of Phillips in continuous terms (3.5 above). Both models make, or can make, full use of lags. Phillips takes continuously distributed lags in consumption and investment demand ; it is only to simplify the mathematical development that the case of no consumption lag is analysed (see 3.5, Ex. 4, above). The Samuelson-Hicks model has distributed lags in consumption and investment outlays as planned ; these correspond to Phillips' type of lag if the coefficients decrease in geometric progression but otherwise they are rather more general. The difference between the Phillips and Samuelson-Hicks models lies in the conditions under which they operate. Phillips considers demand and supply separately ; lagged consumption and investment plans add up to total demand, and supply is adjusted to demand with a further lag. The emphasis is on unintended investment because of the supply lag ; consumption and saving alike may be realised. In the Samuelson-Hicks model consumption and investment as planned are again added but both are assumed realised. Hence the lagged consumption and investment plans *ex ante* become actual outlays *ex post* adding to total output. There is no unintended investment (or consumption); the emphasis is on unintended saving. All this is partly a matter of the convenience of the continuous and period approaches, and partly a question of economic interpretation. In Phillips' construction, the lag in the operation of the accelerator (giving investment demand) is followed by another lag in the adjustment of the supply of capital goods. In the Samuelson-Hicks case, the whole complex of lags on the investment side is incorporated in the single accelerator relation (2); it is therefore all the more important to be flexible in formulating and interpreting this relation.

The simplest Samuelson-Hicks case is considered first, that in which all investment outlays are concentrated or " humped " in the period immediately after the originating change in output. The period can be chosen long enough to absorb initial effects on working capital but not so long as to include outlays on new fixed capital. The investment induced by output changes is net of replacement. The " echo " effect is ignored, i.e. the replacement of fixed capital originally introduced in a " hump " in one period at roughly the same subsequent time.

Only the first term in the accelerator (2) is taken. But this involves two past periods in Y_{t-1} and Y_{t-2}. Hence there is little to be gained in simplicity by taking a Kahn-type multiplier and only one term (in Y_{t-1}) in the consumption function (1). Two terms are taken, involving Y_{t-1} and Y_{t-2}, and there is a distributed lag in consumption. As a special case, c_2 can later be put zero giving the Kahn-type multiplier and the " elementary case " of Hicks (1950).

The condition of the model is:

$$Y_t = C_t + I_t + A_t$$

where $C_t = \gamma + c_1 Y_{t-1} + c_2 Y_{t-2}$ is consumption, $I_t = v(Y_{t-1} - Y_{t-2})$ is induced investment and A_t is autonomous investment, all realised *ex post*. The condition is equivalent to the equation of *ex ante* investment to saving and investment *ex post*. Nothing is said about *ex ante* saving which is not necessarily or generally equal to saving and investment *ex post*; unintended saving can arise.

The condition reduces to a difference equation of the second order in Y_t:

$$Y_t = \gamma + c_1 Y_{t-1} + c_2 Y_{t-2} + v(Y_{t-1} - Y_{t-2}) + A_t$$

i.e.
$$Y_t = (v + c_1) Y_{t-1} - (v - c_2) Y_{t-2} + (A_t + \gamma)$$

Absorb γ into A_t and call A_t autonomous expenditure. Write $c=c_1+c_2$ and use c and c_2 with $c_1=c-c_2$ kept in mind. Then:

$$Y_t=(v+c-c_2)\,Y_{t-1}-(v-c_2)\,Y_{t-2}+A_t$$

i.e.
$$Y_t=cY_{t-1}+(v-c_2)(\,Y_{t-1}-Y_{t-2})+A_t \quad\ldots\ldots\ldots\ldots(3)$$

This is to be solved for the path of Y_t, given A_t over time. If $A_t=A$ (constant), one solution is $Y_t=\bar{Y}$ (constant) where $\bar{Y}=A/(1-c)$, as is seen by substituting in (3). The static multiplier level is consistent with the model. Write $y_t=Y_t-\bar{Y}$ and (3) becomes:

$$y_t=cy_{t-1}+(v-c_2)(y_{t-1}-y_{t-2}) \quad\ldots\ldots\ldots\ldots(4)$$

A general solution of (4) is found later (Chapter 7) and a usual path of Y_t is seen to be an explosive oscillation around $\bar{Y}=A/(1-c)$.

Hicks' *elementary case* has the simplest relations: $C_t=cY_{t-1}$ and $I_t=v(\,Y_{t-1}-Y_{t-2})$. The difference equation is (4) with $c_2=0$:

$$y_t=cy_{t-1}+v(y_{t-1}-y_{t-2}) \quad\ldots\ldots\ldots\ldots(5)$$

where c is the marginal propensity to consume and v is the power of the accelerator. The effect of a distributed lag in consumption, shown by c_2, is simply to reduce the power of the accelerator from v in (5) to $(v-c_2)$ in (4). The effect of a distributed lag in investment can be explored by taking a non-zero v_2 in the relation (2). A particularly interesting case, not worked out by Hicks, arises when there is a *geometric lag* in investment. Then, if $Z_t=v(\,Y_t-Y_{t-1})$ is unlagged investment:

$$I_t=\lambda\{Z_{t-1}+(1-\lambda)Z_{t-2}+(1-\lambda)^2Z_{t-3}+\ldots\}$$

where λ is the speed of response $(0<\lambda<1)$. As shown in 1.9 above:

$$I_t=\frac{\lambda}{\varDelta+\lambda}Z_t=\frac{\lambda}{\varDelta+\lambda}(v\varDelta Y_{t-1})$$

Substitute this and $C_t=cY_{t-1}$ in $Y_t=C_t+I_t+A$ (A constant):

$$Y_t=cY_{t-1}+\frac{\lambda}{\varDelta+\lambda}(v\varDelta Y_{t-1})+A$$

i.e. $\varDelta Y_t+\lambda Y_t=c\varDelta Y_{t-1}+c\lambda Y_{t-1}+\lambda v\varDelta Y_{t-1}+\lambda A$ (since $\varDelta A=0$)

Write $\varDelta Y_t=Y_{t+1}-Y_t$ and $\varDelta Y_{t-1}=Y_t-Y_{t-1}$ and collect terms:

$$Y_{t+1}=(1+c-\lambda+\lambda v)\,Y_t-(c-\lambda c+\lambda v)\,Y_{t-1}+\lambda A$$

The static level $Y_t=\bar{Y}=A/(1-c)$ is again a solution. Write $y_t=Y_t-\bar{Y}$ and shift back from $(t+1)$ to t for convenience:

$$y_t=(1+c-\lambda+\lambda v)y_{t-1}-(c-\lambda c+\lambda v)y_{t-2}$$

i.e.
$$y_t = c'y_{t-1} + v'(y_{t-1} - y_{t-2})$$
$$\text{where } c' = (1-\lambda) + \lambda c \quad \text{and} \quad v' = (1-\lambda)c + \lambda v \Big\} \quad \ldots\ldots\ldots\ldots\ldots\ldots(6)$$

Notice that c' is a weighted mean of 1 and c, the weights being $(1-\lambda)$ and λ where $0 < \lambda < 1$: v' is a similar weighted mean of c and v. Hence, if $c < v$, the usual case : $c < c' < 1$ and $c < v' < v$. Comparison of (6) with (5) shows that the effect of the distributed (geometric) lag in investment is again to reduce the power of the accelerator.

The accelerator of the simple Hicks model, with difference equation (4) or (5), is $I_t = v(Y_{t-1} - Y_{t-2})$. The interpretation given here is essentially that of Hicks (1950) : a change in total output in period $(t-1)$ leads to investment which is *planned and realised* in period t because of the lags involved. Samuelson (1939a) gives a rather different interpretation in which induced investment is related only to changes in output of consumer goods (Ex. 1 below). Smithies (1942) obtains the same difference equation in yet another way, by eliminating the variable rate of interest in his loanable-funds theory (2.2 above).

EXERCISES 3.7

1. Ignore autonomous expenditure and write investment as $I_t = k(C_t - C_{t-1})$, induced without lag by the change in output of consumer goods. Take a lagged consumption function $C_t = \iota Y_{t-1}$ and deduce the accelerator in the form $I_t = kc(Y_{t-1} - Y_{t-2})$. Interpret the investment coefficient $v = kc$. This is in effect the version of Samuelson (1939a).

2. Consider the " elementary case " with $s = 0$ and show that the difference equation is then $Z_t = vZ_{t-1} + A_t$ where $Z_t = Y_t - Y_{t-1}$. Solve for Z_t given $A_t = A$ (constant) and interpret. Why is there no equilibrium level $Y_t = \overline{Y}$?

3. Extend the case of the previous exercise to allow for a distributed consumption lag ($c_2 \neq 0$) but still with $s = 0$. What can be said of the unusual case of a **very** weak accelerator with $v < c_2$?

3.8 The Possibility of Progressive Equilibrium

It has already been shown that, under certain circumstances, a progressive expansion of income and output is possible in the form $Y_t = \overline{Y}_0(1+\rho)^t$, where ρ is the rate of growth. This is so in the multiplier model of 2.7 above, if autonomous expenditure is expanding at the rate ρ ; the effect is simply to " multiply up " autonomous expenditure. It is also the case in a multiplier-accelerator model even when autonomous expenditure is fixed, the rate ρ then being Harrod's warranted rate of growth $\dfrac{s}{v}$ (3.6 above). This is a demonstration of the explosive effect of the accelerator. In both cases, the path of Y_t is an equilibrium concept and not a fully dynamic solution of a dynamic model, i.e. once Y_t starts off along the path, it can be maintained on it by the operation of the model.

The same possibility of progressive growth of income exists in the Samuelson-Hicks model. It is again a particular solution, of equilibrium rather than dynamic form, and it shows up the power of the accelerator. In the difference equation of the model, (4) of 3.7 above, with fixed autonomous expenditure A :

$$y_t = cy_{t-1} + (v - c_2)(y_{t-1} - y_{t-2})$$

try $y_t = \bar{y}_0(1 + r)^t$ as a particular solution. Then :

$$\bar{y}_0(1 + r)^t = c\bar{y}_0(1 + r)^{t-1} + (v - c_2)\{\bar{y}_0(1 + r)^{t-1} - \bar{y}_0(1 + r)^{t-2}\}$$

must be satisfied for all t. Any value of $\bar{y}_0$ will serve provided that r satisfies :

$$(1 + r)^2 = c(1 + r) + (v - c_2)(1 + r - 1)$$

which is obtained by dividing through by $\bar{y}_0(1 + r)^{t-2}$. Hence, any value $r = \rho$ which is an admissible (real and positive) root of the quadratic :

$$R = r^2 - (v - c_2 - s - 1)r + s = 0 \qquad (s = 1 - c)$$

gives a progressive growth of income $y_t = \bar{y}_0(1 + \rho)^t$ at rate ρ.

The roots of the quadratic $R = 0$ can be examined in graphical terms (Fig. 8). Since the constant term s in R is positive, the curve of Fig. 8

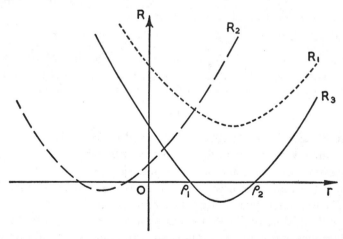

Fig. 8.

cuts OR above O. Hence the two roots are *either* not real (R_1), *or* real and negative (R_2), *or* real and positive (R_3). It is only the last case which is relevant here ; it gives two possible rates of growth, ρ_1 and ρ_2. The solution of a quadratic is easily obtained in algebraic terms. Here, the roots of $R=0$ are real if:

$$(v - c_2 - s - 1)^2 \geqslant 4s$$

and they are then positive if:

$$(v - c_2 - s - 1) \geqslant 2\sqrt{s}$$

i.e. if
$$v - c_2 \geqslant (1 + \sqrt{s})^2$$

Hence, a progressive growth in output is possible, at a suitable rate of growth ρ, provided that the accelerator is powerful enough; all that is necessary is that $v \geqslant c_2 + (1 + \sqrt{s})^2$. There are then two suitable values of ρ, one only in the case $v = c_2 + (1 + vs)^2$:

$$\rho_1, \rho_2 = \tfrac{1}{2}\{(v - c_2 - s - 1) \pm \sqrt{(v - c_2 - s - 1)^2 - 4s}\}$$

Each of these values provides a suitable rate of growth, depending only on the structural constants of the system. One of them is generally quite small (the root with the − rather than the + sign) and this is the one which may be taken as " realistic ".

This serves, once again, to demonstrate the explosive power of the accelerator. Even with fixed autonomous investment, an accelerator of only moderate power (see Ex. 1 below) can produce enough induced invest-ment to make a progressive economy possible. Further, if there is an expansion in autonomous expenditure, then the multiplier alone will give an expanding level of output and the accelerator merely adds to it, very much on the lines of 3.3 above (see also Ex. 3 and 4 below).

Hicks (1950) pays a considerable amount of attention to the possibility of progressive expansion and he has been criticised for it, e.g. by Alexander (1951). It is true that economic growth should be consistent with a dynamic model. But, as before, in 2.7 and 3.6 above, the progressive case remains only a particular solution of the dynamic model. The main interest in the model remains with the fully dynamic solution of the differ-ence equation of the system, and particularly whether the path of output Y_t over time is oscillatory or not and whether it is damped or explosive. This question is left for examination later (Chapter 7 below).

EXERCISES 3.8

1. Show that the critical value of v for the progressive case is smaller the lower the marginal propensity to save. Illustrate by showing that (in the case $c_2 = 0$) the progressive case arises for $v > 1 \cdot 44$ when $s = 0 \cdot 04$, but for $v > 2 \cdot 25$ when s is as large as $0 \cdot 25$. What is the influence of c_2 on this result?

2. If $s = 0$, show that there is only one suitable rate of growth, provided only that $v > 1 + c_2$.

3. Consider the case of progressive expansion in autonomous expenditure. Write $A_t = A_0(1+r)^t$ in equation (3) of 3.7 above and try $Y_t = \overline{Y}_0(1+r)^t$. Show that this path of Y_t is a solution provided that $\overline{Y}_0 = \dfrac{A_0(1+r)^2}{R}$ where R has the value shown above.

4. The result of the previous exercise has one limitation : r must be such that $R > 0$. Examine in terms of Fig. 8. If v, s and c_2 are all given, then show that any r will serve in cases of curves R_1 and R_2 but only small $r < \rho_1$ (or large $r > \rho_2$) in case of curve R_3. Conclude that, with a strong accelerator, r must be small enough ($r < \rho_1$) to make progressive growth in output possible with progressive growth in autonomous expenditure at the given rate r.

5. Interpret the condition $R > 0$ of the previous exercise in the case $c_2 = 0$ by showing that $s > r\left(\dfrac{v}{1+r} - 1\right)$ is its equivalent. Deduce that, if $v > 0$ is given and if r is a given positive fraction, then this is so if saving is large enough to cover investment. See Hicks (1950), p. 184.

3.9 Distributed Investment ; Period and Continuous Analysis

The development of 3.7 above proceeded in the simplest case where $I_t = v(Y_{t-1} - Y_{t-2})$ and induced investment was all " humped " in the first period after the originating change in output. It needs to be extended to the more general case of a distributed lag in investment, as shown by (2) of 3.7 above. At the same time a wider spread in the consumption lags can be taken, according to (1) of 3.7.

The nature of the extension is sufficiently illustrated by taking :

$$C_t = c_1 Y_{t-1} + c_2 Y_{t-2} + c_3 Y_{t-3} \quad \text{where} \quad c_1 + c_2 + c_3 = c \quad \dots\dots\dots\dots(1)$$
$$\text{and} \quad I_t = v_1(Y_{t-1} - Y_{t-2}) + v_2(Y_{t-2} - Y_{t-3}) \quad \text{where} \quad v_1 + v_2 = v \quad \dots\dots(2)$$

The condition of the model, $Y_t = C_t + I_t + A_t$, then gives a difference equation of third order :

$$Y_t = (v_1 + c_1)Y_{t-1} - (v_1 - v_2 - c_2)Y_{t-2} - (v_2 - c_3)Y_{t-3} + A_t$$

This can also be re-arranged into the form :

$$Y_t = cY_{t-1} + (v_1 - c')(Y_{t-1} - Y_{t-2}) + (v_2 - c'')(Y_{t-2} - Y_{t-3}) + A_t \quad \dots(3)$$
$$\text{where} \quad c = c_1 + c_2 + c_3, \quad c' = c_2 + c_3 \quad \text{and} \quad c'' = c_3$$

which can be described as cumulative marginal propensities to consume in the distributed consumption lag (1).

The most important features of the model are those of the accelerator (2). There is now a distributed lag ; investment outlays in period t depend on the output changes of periods $(t-1)$ and $(t-2)$, e.g. on two sets of earlier decisions to invest. Alternatively, each investment decision results in outlays in two future periods. The two extremes are : $v_1 = v$, $v_2 = 0$ when investment outlays are " humped " in the first following period ; and $v_1 = 0$, $v_2 = v$ when outlays are further postponed, to be

" humped " in the second following period. In between, there are various cases where $v_1>0$ and $v_2>0$, i.e. where outlays are made in both periods, either evenly or more or less " humped " in one or other of the periods. The accelerator lag can be described, like an average and a dispersion or spread, by two constants ; these can be v the over-all power of the accelerator, and the magnitude of v_2 (relative to v_1 or to v) which indicates to what extent the lag is spread.

The effect of the distributed consumption lags is more easily assessed. They are described by the cumulated marginal propensities : c, c' and c''. The effect of the first appears also in terms of the marginal propensity to save $s=1-c$. The other two, which reflect the distribution of lags, simply serve to reduce the power of the accelerator. In the difference equation (3), v_1 is reduced by c' and v_2 by c''.

Various particular solutions of (3) can be obtained as before. If A_t is constant (A), then $Y_t=\overline{Y}$ is a solution with $\overline{Y}=\dfrac{A}{1-c}$ from the static multiplier. Then, write $y_t=Y_t-\overline{Y}$ and (3) becomes :

$$y_t=cy_{t-1}+(v_1-c')(y_{t-1}-y_{t-2})+(v_2-c'')(y_{t-2}-y_{t-3}) \ldots\ldots\ldots(4)$$

to be solved for the path of y_t, i.e. Y_t about $\overline{Y}$.

Again, with constant autonomous expenditure, there is the possibility of progressive growth of income. Put $y_t=\bar{y}_0(1+r)^t$ in (4) and a suitable rate of growth r is found to be any real positive root of :

$$(1+r)^3=c(1+r)^2+(v_1-c')r(1+r)+(v_2-c'')r$$

which is a cubic equation in r :

$$R=r^3-(v-v_2-s-c'-2)r^2-(v-2s-c'-c''-1)r+s=0 \ \ \ldots\ldots(5)$$

Graphical considerations, like those of Fig. 8 above, indicate that, of three possibilities, only one is of interest, i.e. that in which the three roots of (5) are all real, one being negative and two positive. In this case, there are again two possible rates of progressive growth of Y_t.

The general solution of the difference equation must be left over. However, to anticipate, it can be said that the variety of types of paths for Y_t over time is greater with this third order equation than with the second order equation of 3.7 above. Moreover, as a wider distribution of lags is introduced in the consumption and investment functions (i.e. in the multiplier and the accelerator), the order of the resulting difference equation increases, and with it the variety of possible paths of Y_t as its solution.

The conclusion is that, in a " realistic " period model which takes account of all the various delays and lags which arise in practice, the path of Y_t is to be found from a high order difference equation. There is then a great wealth of possibilities. The richness of the range of solutions is both an advantage and an embarrassment in interpreting the result in economic terms. It is most difficult to see, among the rich variety of solutions of an equation even of moderate order, which are the usual or important cases—and which are odd possibilities to ignore. This is a mathematical reflection of the economic realities of period analysis. For example, if consumption responds after a short delay while investment decisions take longer and variable periods to work themselves out, then quite odd things can happen to output, stocks and working capital in the short run ; moreover these odd happenings are later " echoed " in subsequent periods and mask the real operation of the accelerator.

One possibility is to simplify by severe assumptions on the lengths and uniformities of the lags involved in the system, as is done in the present chapter. The risk here is that the unit period taken—always somewhat arbitrary—may be so long as to sweep into it much that is of interest, e.g. short-run variations in stocks or working capital.

The characteristic of period analysis is the awkward choice between arbitrary simplification in the interests of mathematical convenience, and the complexities of a " realistic " model with widely distributed lags and a rich variety of solutions from which to pick and choose what is more and what is less important. There remains another possibility : since " realism " indicates many and various lags, it seems more appropriate to use continuous analysis, as in Phillips' model of 3.5 above. A widely distributed lag (e.g. in the accelerator) then becomes in the limit a continuously distributed lag, which can be handled with differentials rather than differences. It might be expected that the continuous case, as the limit to which the period case tends as the lags become more widely spread, would involve even higher order equations with an even greater range of possible solutions. This is not so, as the analysis of 3.5 indicates, at least when the continuous lags are taken in the special exponential form. The advantage of the continuous analysis is that it deals with differential equations of relatively low order, less rich in solutions than the corresponding difference equations and more easily solved by well-established techniques. Different types of models will be explored later (Chapter 7, 8 and 9 below) and it will then appear that the greater range of solutions presented in period analysis, as compared with a continuous model, does not correspond to greater economic " reality ". Among the solutions will be found many oscillations which take place *within* the fixed lags or delays assumed ; these are of little interest, if not completely spurious.

EXERCISES 3.9

1. Show that, as long as a distributed lag is taken for the accelerator, it is no real simplification to take a short or no lag at all in consumption, when period analysis is used. Contrast this with the simplification of no consumption lags in continuous analysis (see 3.5, and particularly Ex. 4, above).

2. Consider the cubic equation $R=0$ of (5) above in terms of the graph of R as a function of r. Show first that the graph cuts OR above 0. Deduce that there are only three possibilities for the roots of $R=0$, i.e. (i) only one real root which is negative, (ii) three real and negative roots, and (iii) three real roots, two positive and one negative.

REFERENCES

Alexander (S. S.) (1950) : " Mr. Harrod's Dynamic Model ", *Economic Journal*, 60, 724–39.

Alexander (S. S.) (1951) : " Issues of Business Cycle Theory Raised by Mr Hicks ", *American Economic Review*, 41, 861–78.

Baumol (W. J.) (1948) : " Notes on Some Dynamic Models ", *Economic Journal*, 58, 506–21.

Baumol (W. J.) (1949) : " Formalisation of Mr. Harrod's Model ", *Economic Journal*, 59, 625–29.

Baumol (W. J.) (1951) : *Economic Dynamics* (Macmillan, 1951), Chapters 4, 10, 12.

Clark (J. M.) (1917) : " Business Acceleration and the Law of Demand ", *Journal of Political Economy*, 25, 217–35.

Domar (E. D.) (1946) : " Capital Expansion, Rate of Growth, and Employment ", *Econometrica*, 14, 137–47.

Frisch (R.) (1931) : " The Interrelation between Capital Production and Consumer-Taking ", *Journal of Political Economy*, 39, 646–54.

Goodwin (R. M.) (1948) : " Secular and Cyclical Aspects of the Multiplier and the Accelerator ", in *Income, Employment and Public Policy* (Essays in Honor of Alvin H. Hansen), (Norton, 1948).

Hamberg (D.) (1952) : " Full Capacity vs. Full Employment Growth ", *Quarterly Journal of Economics*, 66, 444–49.

Harrod (R. F.) (1936) : *The Trade Cycle* (Oxford, 1936), Chapter 2.

Harrod (R. F.) (1948) : *Towards a Dynamic Economics* (Macmillan, 1948), Lecture Three.

Hicks (J. R.) (1950) : *A Contribution to the Theory of the Trade Cycle* (Oxford, 1950), Chapters IV, V, VI.

Knox (A. D.) (1952) : " The Acceleration Principle and the Theory of Investment : A Survey ", *Economica*, 19, 269–97.

Lundberg (E.) (1937) : *Studies in the Theory of Economic Expansion* (King, 1937), Chapter IX.

Phillips (A. W.) (1954) : " Stabilisation Policy in a Closed Economy ", *Economic Journal*, 64, 290–323.

Pilvin (H.) (1953) : " Full Capacity vs. Full Employment Growth ", *Quarterly Journal of Economics*, 67, 545–52.

Samuelson (P. A.) (1939*a*) : "Interactions between the Multiplier Analysis and the Principle of Acceleration ", *Review of Economic Statistics*, **21**, 75–8.

Samuelson (P. A.) (1939*b*) : "A Synthesis of the Principle of Acceleration and the Multiplier ", *Journal of Political Economy*, **47**, 786–97.

Smithies (A.) (1942) : "Process Analysis and Equilibrium Analysis ", *Econometrica*, **10**, 26–38.

Yeager (L. B.) (1954) : "Some Questions about Growth Economics ", *American Economic Review*, **44**, 53–63.

CHAPTER 4

MATHEMATICAL ANALYSIS: COMPLEX NUMBERS

4.1 The Description of Oscillations

THE number system of ordinary algebra, comprising the so-called " real numbers ", is not sufficient to describe oscillatory movements in variables. In particular, it does not provide solutions of differential or difference equations, except in special cases. An extension of the number system is needed to include what are called complex numbers.

The adjective " complex " is unfortunate, and the alternative " imaginary ", which is sometimes applied to the same number concept, is even more so. Certainly, complex numbers are less well-known than real numbers. But they are not more complicated in any mathematical sense, once it is realised that complex numbers are *pairs* of real numbers. Neither are they more unreal or mysterious than real numbers, once a method of representing the square root of (-1) is devised. The mystery is the result of the accident of historical development ; since (-1) turns up equally with $(+1)$ and since $(+1)$ has a square root, it became convenient to *pretend* that (-1) also has a square root. In fact, though $\sqrt{1}$ is a simple concept, $\sqrt{2}$ is much more involved and $\sqrt{-1}$ is no worse. Many people are willing to accept $\sqrt{2}$ as obvious, but not $\sqrt{-1}$. They are wrong on both counts for, in algebra, $\sqrt{-1}$ is a much simpler concept than $\sqrt{2}$.

The algebra of complex numbers, though conventional, is both simple in development and very workable in practice. It is a formal construction based on certain rules of behaviour imposed on complex numbers. It is found, however, that the familiar formulae of algebra apply to complex as to real numbers and, for the most part, in the familiar way.

Complex numbers are of very wide application. They appear even in some very elementary problems, e.g. in the solution of a quadratic equation. Their main use in the present text is in the description of oscillations. To the extent that macro-economic theory deals with oscillatory movements in income, output and other variables, which is largely the case, then the mathematical formulation must involve the use of the algebra of complex numbers.

The most obvious kinds of oscillations are those expressed by means of trigonometric functions. These are defined and handled in elementary trigonometry with a variety of uses in mind, e.g. in surveying. A particular extension or development of the functions is needed to make them appropriate to the description of oscillations. The present text is concerned with this development, and the functions are perhaps better described as " circular " or " sinusoidal " functions. They are to be related to exponential functions and they involve complex as well as real variables. The exposition of the present chapter, therefore, starts with the trigonometric functions, proceeds to introduce complex numbers and develops the circular or sinusoidal functions which are to be so useful in the analysis of oscillations.

4.2 Trigonometric Functions

The definition of the trigonometric functions is best framed in terms of the unit circle, the circle of radius unity, as shown in Fig. 9. All angles are

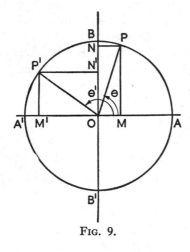

FIG. 9.

measured in degrees from some radius OA fixed in the unit circle. The radius OP makes an angle $\theta°$ and the radius OP' an angle of $\theta'°$ with OA. As P moves round the unit circle in the positive or anti-clockwise direction, the angle takes all values from 0° to 360°. For example, at B the angle is 90°, at A' it is 180°, at B' it is 270° ; and finally back at A after one complete revolution the angle is 360°.

Drop perpendiculars from P on the two fixed diameters, $A'OA$ and $B'OB$ at right angles, obtaining the points M and N. Similarly, from P' points M' and N' are obtained. Measure all distances either along $A'OA$ or along $B'OB$, with the convention that positive distances are to the right along $A'OA$ and upwards along $B'OB$ (as represented in Fig. 9) and negative distances in the opposite directions. So, in Fig. 9, OM is positive while OM' is negative.

Define the *sine* and the *cosine* of the angle $\theta°$ as follows :

DEFINITION : $\sin \theta° = \dfrac{ON}{OP} = ON$ $\cos \theta° = \dfrac{OM}{OP} = OM$

since OP is here taken as 1. The signs of OM and ON, on the above convention, must be taken into account. So, in Fig. 9, $\sin \theta°$ and $\cos \theta°$

are both positive, while sin θ'° is positive and cos θ'° negative. A third trigonometric ratio is also useful, the *tangent* of the angle θ° defined as the ratio of the sine to the cosine:

DEFINITION: $\tan \theta^\circ = \dfrac{\sin \theta^\circ}{\cos \theta^\circ} = \dfrac{ON}{OM}$

Two developments are now made; first a change of measurement of angles from degrees to units called radians, which are more convenient from the theoretical point of view, and second the extension from angles between zero and four right angles (360°) to angles of any size. The new measure (in radians) of the angle AOP is the distance AP taken counterclockwise round the circumference of the unit circle. So, the angle θ° is also measured as x radians, where x is the length of the arc AP. A wellknown geometric result (that the arc of a circle is proportional to the angle at the centre) shows that the relation between degrees and radians is one of direct proportion; it is of exactly the same kind as the relation between inches and feet, or between seconds and minutes. The numerical value of the proportion is fixed since, by definition, the whole circumference of the unit circle of length 2π corresponds to four right angles (360°). Hence to transform from degrees to radians or conversely:

$$2\pi \text{ radians} = 360°$$

So $x \text{ radians} = \dfrac{180}{\pi} x^\circ; \quad \theta^\circ = \dfrac{\pi}{180} \theta \text{ radians}$

It is useful to remember certain particular angles, e.g.

$$45° = \frac{\pi}{4} \text{ radians}; \qquad 90° = \frac{\pi}{2} \text{ radians}$$

$$180° = \pi \text{ radians}; \qquad 360° = 2\pi \text{ radians}$$

Next, angles larger than $360° = 2\pi$ radians are defined by lettering OP rotate more than once round the circle. So, for the position OP, the angle is θ°, $(360+\theta)^\circ$, $(720+\theta)^\circ$, ... according as the radius is on the first, the second, the third, ... round. In radians, the angle is x, $(2\pi+x)$, $(4\pi+x)$, ... where $AP=x$. Further, negative values can be assumed on the convention that a clockwise rotation cf OP is negative. So, for the position OP reached clockwise from OA, the angle is $(\theta-360)^\circ$, $(\theta-720)^\circ$, ... or $(x-2\pi)$, $(x-4\pi)$, ... radians, according as the radius is on the first, the second, ... round in the negative (clockwise) direction.

In all theoretical work, the radian measure of angles is used and denoted by a variable (such as x) without specific reference to the unit. The trigonometric functions are then $\sin x$, $\cos x$, $\tan x = \dfrac{\sin x}{\cos x}$. The next stage is to table the values taken by these functions and to represent them graphically as in Fig. 10. The values follow from Fig. 9 where $\sin x$ is ON

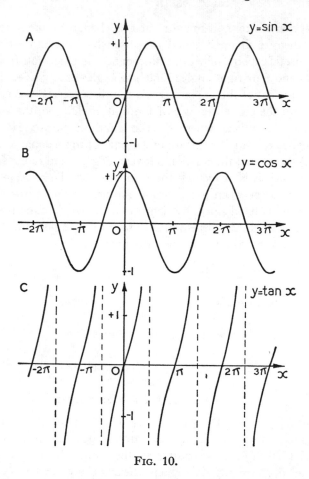

FIG. 10.

and $\cos x$ is OM. Hence, for $y = \sin x = ON$, the value of y increases from 0 to 1 as x goes from 0 to $\dfrac{\pi}{2}$; decreases from 1 back to 0 for x from $\dfrac{\pi}{2}$ to π; decreases further through negative values from 0 to -1 for x from π to $\dfrac{3\pi}{2}$; increases again, through negative values, from -1 to 0 for x from

$\dfrac{3\pi}{2}$ to 2π. There is a whole cycle of $y=\sin x$ from 0 to 1, to 0, to -1, and back to 0 in the range of x from 0 to 2π. By the definition of positive and negative angles of all sizes, this cycle repeats itself in every range of length 2π. The graph of $y=\sin x$ follows as shown in Fig. 10a. The variation of $y=\cos x$ is very similar, from OM in Fig. 9 ; the only difference is that y now starts from 1 when $x=0$. The graph of $y=\cos x$ is shown in Fig. 10b ; that of $y=\tan x=\dfrac{\sin x}{\cos x}$ follows from the other two and is shown in Fig. 10c. Certain particular values of the functions can be remembered :

Angle x	0	$\dfrac{\pi}{2}$	π	$\dfrac{3\pi}{2}$	2π
$\sin x$	0	1	0	-1	0
$\cos x$	1	0	-1	0	1
$\tan x$	0	∞	0	∞	0

For other values, tables are available covering the range $x=0$ to $\dfrac{\pi}{2}$; these values repeat themselves, with appropriate signs, in other ranges of x. In particular :

$$\sin(-x) = -\sin x \qquad \cos(-x) = \cos x$$
$$\sin(\pi-x)= \sin x \qquad \cos(\pi-x)= -\cos x$$
$$\sin(\pi+x)= -\sin x \qquad \cos(\pi+x)= -\cos x$$

Such relations can be read off the graphs of Fig. 10.

There are many properties of the trigonometric functions, to be found in the standard text-books. The following are among the more important and they are quoted here without proof :

(i) *Relation between sin x and cos x* :

$$\sin^2 x + \cos^2 x = 1$$

(ii) *Addition formulae* :

$$\sin(x+y)=\sin x \cos y + \cos x \sin y$$
$$\cos(x+y)=\cos x \cos y - \sin x \sin y$$

In particular, with y put equal to x :

$$\sin 2x = 2\sin x \cos x$$
$$\cos 2x = \cos^2 x - \sin^2 x$$

(iii) *Derivatives* :

$$\frac{d}{dx}(\sin x) = \cos x$$

$$\frac{d}{dx}(\cos x) = -\sin x$$

$$\frac{d}{dx}(\tan x) = 1 + \tan^2 x$$

Note that, as a matter of convenience of notation, $(\sin x)^2$ is written $\sin^2 x$. Similarly $(\sin x)^3 = \sin^3 x$, and so on ; corresponding notations are used for powers of the other functions.

EXERCISES 4.2

1. What is the radian measure of 45°? For this angle, show that

$$\sin x = \cos x = \frac{1}{\sqrt{2}} = 0\cdot7071$$

Check these values in tables of the trigonometric functions.

2. For $x = 60° = \frac{\pi}{3}$ radians, show that

$$\sin x = \frac{\sqrt{3}}{2} = 0\cdot8660 ; \quad \cos x = \tfrac{1}{2} = 0\cdot5 ; \quad \tan x = \sqrt{3} = 1\cdot7321$$

and check from tables. Show that the same values are obtained for $x = 120° = \frac{2\pi}{3}$ radians except that $\cos x$ and $\tan x$ are negative. What are the values for $x = \frac{4\pi}{3}, \frac{5\pi}{3}, \frac{7\pi}{3}$ radians?

3. Apply Pythagoras' theorem to the right-angled triangle *OPM* of Fig. 9 to prove that $\sin^2 x + \cos^2 x = 1$. If $\cos x$ is given, show that $\sin x = \pm\sqrt{1 - \cos^2 x}$ and $\tan x = \pm\sqrt{\frac{1}{\cos^2 x} - 1}$. How is the $\pm$ to be interpreted?

4. Use the results $\sin(-x) = -\sin x$ and $\cos(-x) = \cos x$, and the addition formulae (ii), to show that

$$\sin(x - y) = \sin x \cos y - \cos x \sin y ;$$
$$\cos(x - y) = \cos x \cos y + \sin x \sin y$$

Check when $y = x$.

5. Interpret the derivatives of $\sin x$ and $\cos x$ diagrammatically and check the formulae (iii) above from the graphs of Fig. 10.

6. From the derivatives of $\sin x$ and $\cos x$ show that

$$\frac{d}{dx}(\tan x) = 1 + \tan^2 x = \frac{1}{\cos^2 x}$$

When $x = \frac{\pi}{2}$, show that both $\tan x$ and $\frac{d}{dx}(\tan x)$ are infinite. Interpret in terms of Fig. 10c.

4.3 Vectors and Complex Numbers

A complex number is a concept which appears in a number of disguises and there are several possible definitions from which choice can be made. Once one definition is adopted, the others are to be derived as properties. The most convenient definition is to take the complex number z as an *ordered pair* of real numbers (x, y), where the real number x is written first and y second. Hence, (y, x) is also a complex number, but a different one since the order of the real numbers is switched. The convenience of this definition is that the complex number z can be represented as a *point P* in plane Oxy, that with co-ordinates (x, y). Better still, z can be represented as the *vector OP*, joining O to P with co-ordinates (x, y) in the plane Oxy (see Fig. 11). Hence :

DEFINITION : The complex number z is the ordered pair of real numbers (x, y), represented in the plane Oxy by the vector OP, where P is the point with co-ordinates (x, y).

A complex number is to be regarded as a single entity ; it is the *pair* of real numbers, not the real numbers themselves. It is clearly a two-dimensional concept. The complex number z may be fixed or constant, i.e. if x and y are constants. It can also be a variable, if x and y are variable real numbers. The two-dimensional aspect of z is illustrated by its (unrestricted) variation ; the point P which corresponds moves over the whole plane Oxy. The convenience of the vector representation is that it stresses the fact that the complex number is a single entity (the line OP) and shows up the simplest form of its two-dimensional variation. The vector OP has *length* and it has *direction*; either or both can vary. All this is clear

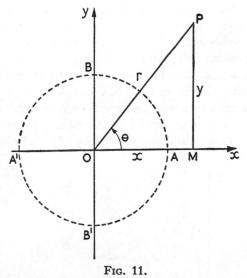

FIG. 11.

in Fig. 11 which is the kind of representation known as an *Argand diagram*. The unit circle is shown in Fig. 11 to fix the scale used. The particular vectors OA and OB are of considerable use ; they are *unit vectors* measured respectively along Ox and along Oy.

The next stage is to construct an algebra for operating with complex numbers. An algebra is a set of rules (definitions or axioms) which are arbitrary except that they must be consistent in themselves. The rules specify certain operations like " addition " or " multiplication " performed on the entities, here complex numbers. The practical trick in designing a new algebra is to make the operations useful and to keep as close as possible to the familiar rules of ordinary algebra. By analogy, then, the operations of the new rules are called by the familiar names, e.g. " addition " and " multiplication ". This may be a source of confusion, for they are different operations and some of the properties of ordinary algebra may not in fact hold for the new algebra. A more complete account of this problem is given later in connection with vectors and matrices in Chapter 13 and very generally in Appendix B. However, if suitable care is taken in interpretation, the use of familiar terms for new operations is to be preferred to the introduction of a strange terminology.

In the following rules of the new algebra $z = (x, y)$, $z_1 = (x_1, y_1)$ and $z_2 = (x_2, y_2)$ all represent complex numbers, and OP, OP_1 and OP_2 are the corresponding vectors. First, a *zero* is required since it is not yet clear what $z = 0$ means. The definition is $z = 0$ when $x = y = 0$, and the vector OP reduces to the point O. Next, the *equality* of complex numbers is defined, i.e. $z_1 = z_2$ when $x_1 = x_2$ *and* $y_1 = y_2$; the vectors OP_1 and OP_2 are exactly co-incident. The two most important rules are then defined, those of addition and multiplication. The rules appear arbitrary, but they work in practice. For the non-mathematician, the only advice can be : wait and see. However, the addition rule at least can be expressed in terms of vectors in a way which will be very familiar indeed to anyone with some knowledge of applied mathematics (elementary mechanics).

Addition is illustrated in Fig. 12a. The two complex numbers z_1 and z_2,

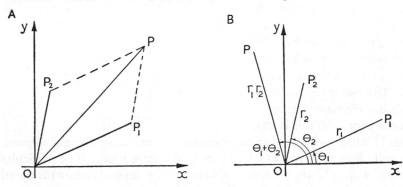

FIG. 12.

or the two vectors OP_1 and OP_2, are to be added. Complete the parallelogram and call the diagonal vector OP the sum. This is what is done when the resultant of two forces is taken in mechanics. From Fig. 12a, the translation into (x_1, y_1) and (x_2, y_2), the co-ordinates of P_1 and P_2, is simple :

$$z = z_1 + z_2 = (x_1 + x_2, y_1 + y_2) \qquad ....(1)$$

i.e. the separate co-ordinates are added.

Multiplication is less easy. It can be taken in two stages :

(i) *Scalar multiplication* is the product of a complex number z_1 by a scalar (real number) a, giving the complex number $z = az_1$ as product. The definition is to take the vector OP_1 and " blow up " by the factor a, i.e. adjust its length in the ratio $a : 1$ and leave its direction unchanged. This also translates at once into x's and y's :

$$z = az_1 = (ax_1, ay_1) \qquad ....(2)$$

(ii) *Multiplication generally* is the product of one complex number z_1 by another z_2, giving the complex number $z = z_1 z_2$. The definition is illustrated in Fig. 12b. The product vector OP is taken such that $OP = OP_1 \times OP_2$ in length and such that its direction

$$\angle POx = \angle P_1 Ox + \angle P_2 Ox.$$

The product of lengths is much the same as in scalar multiplication (2). The new fact of the definition is the rule for change of direction : the angles the two vectors OP_1 and OP_2 make with the horizontal (Ox) are *added* to give the angle for the product vector OP. The translation of the definition into x's and y's, as in (1) and (2), is postponed until another line of approach is pursued.

The reference to length and direction of a vector suggests an alternative specification of a complex number z. When $z = (x, y)$ is written, x and y are the *cartesian co-ordinates* of P in Oxy. As x and y vary, the point P moves in two dimensions over the plane. The alternative is to use *polar co-ordinates* of P ; these are respectively r the *length* of OP and θ radians the *angle* OP makes with Ox. The complex number may then be conveniently represented $z = r/\theta$. The two degrees of freedom in z now show up as the variable length of the vector OP and its variable direction. As r varies (θ fixed), the length OP expands and contracts. As θ varies (r fixed), the vector OP rotates around O. This is very convenient, e.g. because it links up complex numbers and the trigonometric functions. In the complex number $z = (x, y) = r/\theta$, the relation between the two specifications is :

$$x = r \cos \theta, \quad y = r \sin \theta \qquad ....(3)$$

These follow at once from the Argand diagram (Fig. 11).

No improvement on the addition rule (1) is made by the introduction of polar co-ordinates. By (1) and (3), all that can be written for $z = z_1 + z_2$ is :

$$r \cos \theta = r_1 \cos \theta_1 + r_2 \cos \theta_2 \quad \text{and} \quad r \sin \theta = r_1 \sin \theta_1 + r_2 \sin \theta_2$$

The multiplication rule, expressed in vectors as in Fig. 12b, is very much simpler in polar co-ordinates than in cartesian. For $z = z_1 z_2$ the definition gives :

$$r = r_1 r_2 \quad \text{and} \quad \theta = \theta_1 + \theta_2$$

Hence the product of r_1/θ_1 and r_2/θ_2 is $r_1 r_2/\theta_1 + \theta_2$. This is both simple and sensible.

The multiplication rule can now be translated into x's and y's. For $z = z_1 z_2$:

$$x = r_1 r_2 \cos (\theta_1 + \theta_2) = r_1 r_2 (\cos \theta_1 \cos \theta_2 - \sin \theta_1 \sin \theta_2)$$
$$= x_1 x_2 - y_1 y_2$$

and
$$y = r_1 r_2 \sin (\theta_1 + \theta_2) = r_1 r_2 (\cos \theta_1 \sin \theta_2 + \sin \theta_1 \cos \theta_2)$$
$$= x_1 y_2 + x_2 y_1$$

Here the relations (3) have been used both for the product $r_1 r_2/\theta_1 + \theta_2$ and for the separate complex numbers r_1/θ_1 and r_2/θ_2.

The *general multiplication rule* is :

$$z = z_1 z_2 = (x_1 x_2 - y_1 y_2, \; x_1 y_2 + x_2 y_1) \quad \ldots\ldots\ldots\ldots\ldots(4)$$

A simplification of the notation can be effected, one which makes the rule (4) look less involved and artificial. Some particular cases need to be examined. Two special complex numbers are :

$$(1, 0) = 1/0 = \text{unit vector } OA \text{ in Fig. 11}$$
$$(0, 1) = 1/\frac{\pi}{2} = \text{unit vector } OB \text{ in Fig. 11}$$

Call the first the complex number 1 (unity), to be identified now with a real number. Call the other the complex number i; here i is just a notation for a particular complex number, the unit vector OB along Oy. Scalar multiplication, for any real numbers a and b whatever, gives by virtue of (2) :

$$a \times 1 = (a, 0) \quad \text{and} \quad b \times i = (0, b)$$

These can be called a and ib respectively, two particular complex numbers or vectors (one along Ox, the other along Oy). Now use (1) to add :

$$a + ib = (a, 0) + (0, b) = (a, b)$$

Here a and b are any real numbers and so (a, b) is the general complex number. The result can be written :

$$z=(x, y)=x+iy \quad \dots\dots\dots\dots\dots\dots\dots(5)$$

The interpretation of (5) is that any complex number $z=(x, y)$ can be written as the sum of two complex numbers, the first being the complex number 1 (vector OA) scaled up by x and the other the complex number i (vector OB) scaled up by y.

The new notation is (5) ; a complex number is $x+iy$. Here x and y are real numbers (scalars) ; the " + " and " i " refer to complex numbers or vectors. It remains to show that " + " and " i " can be treated by elementary algebraic processes. Take any complex number z and multiply first by 1 and then by i, by rule (4) :

$$1 \times z=(1, 0) \times (x, y)=(x, y)=z$$
$$i \times z=(0, 1) \times (x, y)=(-y, x)$$

The first shows that the vector 1 is really unity and identifies it as a real number. The second gives an interpretation of i, the vector OB. The result is shown in Fig. 13, where OP is the vector $z=(x, y)$. The vector OQ is at right angles to OP and of the same length ; hence OQ is the vector $(-y, x)$, to be identified as $i \times z$. The result is important: multiplication by i turns the vector of the complex number through a right angle. This is

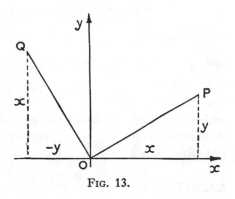

FIG. 13.

also seen from the facts that i is the complex number $1/\frac{\pi}{2}$ and that multiplication involves the addition of the angles, here the addition of $\frac{\pi}{2}$ or a right angle.

The final particular case is the one which identifies i with $\sqrt{-1}$, or rather i^2 with -1, and which is so often the cause of misunderstanding. Multiply the complex number i by itself, again by (4) :

$$i^2=(0, 1) \times (0, 1)=(-1, 0)=(-1) \times 1$$

where (-1) is the scalar and 1 is the (complex) number unity. Hence $i^2=-1$. To see this in vectors will clarify. Start with the complex number 1, the unit vector OA. Multiply by i, giving a rotation through a right angle, i.e. to the unit vector OB which is i. Multiply by i again, another rotation through a right angle to the negative unit vector OA' of Fig. 11. Hence i^2 is a complex number ; as a vector it is OA' and this is -1. To sum up all that need be known about i :

By definition i is a complex number, represented by the unit vector OB along Oy in the Argand diagram ; multiplication of any complex number (vector) by i rotates the vector through a right angle ; algebraically i follows the rule $i^2 = -1$.

The complex number $z=(x, y)=r/\theta$ can now be denoted $z=x+iy$. From what has been said, everything in $x+iy$ can be treated according to the operations of elementary algebra, provided only that i^2 is written as -1 whenever it appears. The fact that this new notation works in practice is illustrated by the addition and multiplication rules, (1) and (4) above. Let $z_1=x_1+iy_1$ and $z_2=x_2+iy_2$ be two complex numbers. Then :

$$z_1+z_2=(x_1+iy_1)+(x_2+iy_2)=(x_1+x_2)+i(y_1+y_2)$$

which is rule (1),

and
$$\begin{aligned} z_1z_2 &=(x_1+iy_1)(x_2+iy_2)=x_1x_2+x_1iy_2+iy_1x_2+i^2y_1y_2 \\ &=x_1x_2+ix_1y_2+ix_2y_1-y_1y_2 \\ &=(x_1x_2-y_1y_2)+i(x_1y_2+x_2y_1) \end{aligned}$$

which is rule (4). These rules can now be forgotten ; all that need be done is to operate with $(x+iy)$ according to the laws of elementary algebra and with $i^2 = -1$.

EXERCISES 4.3

1. Use the relations $x=r\cos\theta$, $y=r\sin\theta$ to check that $1=(1, 0)=1/0$ and that $i=(0, 1)=1/\frac{\pi}{2}$.

2. Show that $(1, \sqrt{3})=2/\frac{\pi}{3}$ and $(-1, -\sqrt{3})=2/\frac{4\pi}{3}$. Represent on an Argand diagram.

3. Show that the order of z_1 and z_2 in z_1+z_2, and in z_1z_2, as sum and product of complex numbers, is immaterial. Why does this kind of result need proof at all?

4. Define division as the inverse of multiplication, i.e. $z=\frac{z_1}{z_2}$ if $z_1=z\times z_2$. Hence show that :

$$\frac{z_1}{z_2}=\frac{(x_1, y_1)}{(x_2, y_2)}=\left(\frac{x_1x_2+y_1y_2}{x_2^2+y_2^2}\ \frac{x_2y_1-x_1y_2}{x_2^2+y_2^2}\right)$$

and that it is equivalent to :

$$\frac{z_1}{z_2}=\frac{r_1/\theta_1}{r_2/\theta_2}=\frac{r_1}{r_2}\bigg/(\theta_1-\theta_2)$$

5. Obtain the division result of the previous exercise, by use of $z_1=x_1+iy$, and $z_2=x_2+iy_2$.

6. Show that $\sqrt{x^2-y^2+2ixy}=\pm(x+iy)$.

4.4 Polar and Exponential Forms of Complex Numbers

The complex number $z=x+iy$ can be written in polar co-ordinates (r and θ) with the aid of the transformation $x=r\cos\theta$, $y=r\sin\theta$ from the Argand diagram. Hence, in polars, write :

$$z=r/\theta=r(\cos\theta+i\sin\theta) \quad\dots\dots\dots\dots\dots\dots(1)$$

The notation r/θ is no longer needed to indicate z through the length (r) and direction (θ) of the corresponding vector. It can be replaced by (1), or by still a further representation to be developed now. This new form of z makes use of exponentials and it will be found to be particularly useful, e.g. in describing oscillations.

The exponential function $y=e^{ax}$ has a constant and

$$e=\operatorname*{Lim}_{n\to\infty}\left(1+\frac{1}{n}\right)^n=2{\cdot}71828\dots$$

The expansion by Taylor's series is :

$$e^{ax}=1+ax+\frac{(ax)^2}{2!}+\frac{(ax)^3}{3!}+\dots \quad\dots\dots\dots\dots\dots(2)$$

The sign of a is critical ; if $a>0$, $e^{ax}\to\infty$ and if $a<0$, $e^{ax}\to0$ as $x\to\infty$. The " speed " of these tendencies is also very important. It is evident from the expansion (2) that $e^x\to\infty$ faster than any positive power of x, so that :

$$\frac{e^x}{x},\frac{e^x}{x^2},\frac{e^x}{x^3},\ \dots\ \text{all}\to\infty\quad\text{as}\quad x\to\infty$$

Equally, $e^{-x}\to0$ faster than any negative power of x, i.e.

$$xe^{-x},\ x^2e^{-x},\ x^3e^{-x},\ \dots\ \text{all}\to0\ \text{as}\ x\to\infty$$

Similar remarks apply to e^{ax} in the two cases $a>0$ and $a<0$ respectively.

The exponential function and its expansion (2) can be written with complex numbers. Two particular cases are of great interest :

$$e^{ix}=1+ix-\frac{x^2}{2!}-i\frac{x^3}{3!}+\dots$$

$$e^{-ix}=1-ix-\frac{x^2}{2!}+i\frac{x^3}{3!}+\dots$$

making use of $i^2 = -1$ as usual. Add and subtract these results in complex number form and two results in real numbers only emerge :

$$\left.\begin{aligned}
\tfrac{1}{2}(e^{ix} + e^{-ix}) &= 1 - \frac{x^2}{2!} + \frac{x^4}{4!} - \frac{x^6}{6!} + \cdots \\
\frac{1}{2i}(e^{ix} - e^{-ix}) &= x - \frac{x^3}{3!} + \frac{x^5}{5!} - \frac{x^7}{7!} + \cdots
\end{aligned}\right\} \quad \cdots\cdots\cdots\cdots(3)$$

The expressions on the left of (3), though written in complex form with i, are in fact real values. They are now to be identified with oscillations, i.e. with the trigonometric functions $\cos x$ and $\sin x$.

Taylor's series can be used to expand $y = \cos x$ and $y = \sin x$. The successive derivatives of $y = \cos x$ are :

$$\frac{dy}{dx} = -\sin x \quad \frac{d^2y}{dx^2} = -\cos x \quad \frac{d^3y}{dx^3} = \sin x \quad \cdots$$

The values at $x = 0$ are :

$$y = 1 \quad \frac{dy}{dx} = 0 \quad \frac{d^2y}{dx^2} = -1 \quad \frac{d^3y}{dx^3} = 0 \quad \cdots$$

so that, by Taylor's series :

$$\cos x = 1 - \frac{x^2}{2!} + \frac{x^4}{4!} - \frac{x^6}{6!} + \cdots$$

Similarly

$$\sin x = x - \frac{x^3}{3!} + \frac{x^5}{5!} - \frac{x^7}{7!} + \cdots$$

These are the expansions (3) above. Hence the basic relations between the exponential and trigonometric functions are :

$$\left.\begin{aligned}
\cos x &= \tfrac{1}{2}(e^{ix} + e^{-ix}) \; ; \quad \sin x = \frac{1}{2i}(e^{ix} - e^{-ix}) \\
\cos x &+ i \sin x = e^{ix} \; ; \quad \cos x - i \sin x = e^{-ix}
\end{aligned}\right\} \quad \cdots\cdots\cdots\cdots(4)$$

or

by addition and subtraction. In the derivation of (4) given here it is assumed (without proof) that all the series written are convergent and so valid.

The polar form (1) of a complex number can be written with the aid of exponentials :

$$z = r(\cos \theta + i \sin \theta) = re^{i\theta} \quad \cdots\cdots\cdots\cdots\cdots(5)$$

which holds whether θ is positive or negative. The notation $z = re^{i\theta}$ effectively replaces r/θ. Its use in the rule for multiplication of complex numbers (vectors) is apparent :

$$z_1 z_2 = r_1 e^{i\theta_1} \times r_2 e^{i\theta_2} = r_1 r_2 e^{i(\theta_1 + \theta_2)}$$

The product of the r's and the sum of the θ's come naturally ; in multiplying exponentials the indices are added. The rotation of vectors, which corresponds to addition of the θ components, is taken care of by the index in $z=re^{i\theta}$.

The unit vector OA or complex number $1=(1, 0)=1/0$ is shown as $z=re^{i\theta}$ with $r=1$ and $\theta=0$, i.e. $z=1$. The other unit vector OB or complex number $i=(0, 1)=1/\dfrac{\pi}{2}$ is now :

$$i=re^{i\theta} \text{ with } r=1 \text{ and } \theta=\frac{\pi}{2}$$

i.e. $$e^{i\pi/2}=i \quad\dotfill(6)$$

The result (6) is to be remembered ; it is often used. It can be checked from (5), $re^{i\theta}=r(\cos\theta+i\sin\theta)$, with $r=1$ and $\theta=\dfrac{\pi}{2}$. Also note that $e^{-i\pi/2}=-i$ so that $e^{i\pi/2}+e^{-i\pi/2}=0$; this can also be checked from the fact that $\cos\dfrac{\pi}{2}=\frac{1}{2}(e^{i\pi/2}+e^{-i\pi/2})$ and $\cos\dfrac{\pi}{2}=0$.

Another particular case of (5), with $r=1$ and $\theta=\pm\pi$, is :

$$e^{i\pi}=e^{-i\pi}=-1 \quad\dotfill(7)$$

Another version of $i^2=-1$ now appears from (6) and (7) since :

$$(e^{i\pi/2})^2=e^{i\pi} \quad \text{i.e. } i^2=-1$$

Finally, the effect of multiplication by i, equivalent to rotation of a vector through a right angle $\left(\dfrac{\pi}{2}\right)$, is also to be seen in the exponential form. For any complex number (vector) z :

$$iz=e^{i\pi/2}\,re^{i\theta}=re^{i(\theta+\pi/2)} \quad\dotfill(8)$$

The rotation through a right angle appears in the addition of $\dfrac{\pi}{2}$ in the index in (8). For example, (6) and (7) represent two such rotations, starting from the unit vector OA and getting first OB and then OA' (Fig. 11 above) :

$$1\times i=e^{i0}\times e^{i\pi/2}=e^{i\pi/2}=i$$
$$1\times i\times i=i\times i=e^{i\pi/2}\times e^{i\pi/2}=e^{i\pi}=-1$$

As a footnote to this development, the results (3) and (4) above suggest similar results in real variables only. Two particular cases of the exponential expansion are :

$$e^{x}=1+x+\frac{x^2}{2!}+\frac{x^3}{3!}+\dots$$

and $$e^{-x}=1-x+\frac{x^2}{2!}-\frac{x^3}{3!}+\dots$$

Hence $\qquad \frac{1}{2}(e^x + e^{-x}) = 1 + \frac{x^2}{2!} + \frac{x^4}{4!} + \cdots$

and $\qquad \frac{1}{2}(e^x - e^{-x}) = x + \frac{x^3}{3!} + \frac{x^5}{5!} + \cdots$

It is convenient to have a notation for these expansions, so similar to (3) above. The trigonometric functions $\cos x$ and $\sin x$ are used in (4). The new notation, by analogy, is written $\cosh x$ and $\sinh x$:

$$\cosh x = \tfrac{1}{2}(e^x + e^{-x}) \; ; \; \sinh x = \tfrac{1}{2}(e^x - e^{-x})$$

These are called *hyperbolic functions*. It is to be noted, however, that $\cosh x$ and $\sinh x$ have no such connection with trigonometric functions as was found before ; they are just convenient shorthand for the exponential expressions shown, nothing more than a matter of notation.

EXERCISES 4.4

1. From (4) above, check that $\cos x = 1$ and $\sin x = 0$ when $x = 0$.

2. In the notation $z = re^{i\theta}$, the vector $OA = 1$ (with $\theta = 0$), $OB = e^{i\pi/2}$ and $OA' = e^{i\pi}$ (Fig. 11). What is the vector OB'? What does $e^{2i\pi}$ represent?

3. Use (4) above to check that $\cos^2 x + \sin^2 x = 1$ and show that the corresponding result for hyperbolic functions is
$$\cosh^2 x - \sinh^2 x = 1.$$

4. From the exponential form of $\cos x$, write $\cos \left(\frac{\pi}{2} - x \right)$, use $e^{i\pi/2} = i$ and $i^2 = -1$ and show that $\cos \left(\frac{\pi}{2} - x \right) = \frac{1}{2i}(e^{ix} - e^{-ix}) = \sin x$.

4.5 The Algebra of Complex Numbers

The analytical results obtained for complex numbers, as opposed to the representation in vector form, can now be assembled, applied and extended into the algebra of complex numbers. First, as a matter of *notation*, a complex number z can be written in equivalent cartesian, polar and exponential forms :

$$z = x + iy = r(\cos \theta + i \sin \theta) = re^{i\theta} \quad \dots\dots\dots\dots\dots(1)$$

Next, in (1) the *transformation* from x and y to r and θ, or conversely, is needed. The direct transformation is easy :

$$x = r \cos \theta \quad \text{and} \quad y = r \sin \theta \quad \dots\dots\dots\dots\dots(2)$$

The inverse transformation relates r and θ to x and y and it serves to determine r and θ for a complex number, given x and y. The value of r is readily obtained since from (2) :

$$x^2 + y^2 = r^2(\cos^2 \theta + \sin^2 \theta) = r^2$$

Further, since $r>0$, it follows that $r=+\sqrt{x^2+y^2}$. Difficulties emerge in deriving the angle θ radians. From (2) the tangent of the angle is :

$$\tan\theta=\frac{y}{x}$$

Hence, given x and y, $\tan\theta$ is known and θ is required.

Consider the function $\tau=\tan\theta$. The graph of the function (see Fig. 10c) shows that there is only one value of τ for each given θ, but that there are many values of θ corresponding to a given value of τ. Hence, the inverse function $\theta=\tan^{-1}\tau$ is not single-valued. Even if θ is restricted to the range $0\leqslant\theta<2\pi$, there are still *two* values of θ for each τ. If $\tau>0$, the two values of θ lie respectively between 0 and $\pi/2$ and between π and $3\pi/2$. If $\tau<0$, they lie between $\pi/2$ and π, and between $3\pi/2$ and 2π, respectively. There is no way, except through additional information, of distinguishing between them. The value $\theta=\tan^{-1}\tau$, which can be obtained from tables, is conventionally taken in the range $-\pi/2$ to $\pi/2$, for which it is unique. To get the two values of θ in the range 0 to 2π, either θ, $(\theta+\pi)$ or $(\theta+2\pi)$ may need to be used.

To obtain θ in the range 0 to 2π from (2), $\tan\theta=\frac{y}{x}$ is not enough. Given $\frac{y}{x}$, there are two values of θ. But given x and y separately, there is only one θ. The reason for this is that x and y give one θ and $(-x)$ and $(-y)$ give the second θ, the ratio $\frac{y}{x}$ being the same. Hence θ is to be sought from $\tan\theta=\frac{y}{x}$ together with the sign of $x=r\cos\theta$ (or of $y=r\sin\theta$). In other words, in $\theta=\tan^{-1}\frac{y}{x}$, there are two values of θ ($0\leqslant\theta<2\pi$) but only one of them gives the right sign for x or $\cos\theta$. This is the one value sought. With $\tan^{-1}\frac{y}{x}$ found from tables in the range $-\frac{\pi}{2}$ to $\frac{\pi}{2}$, it may be necessary to add π or 2π to it according to the signs of x and y (see Ex. 1 below). To sum up, the inverse transformation is :

$$r=\sqrt{x^2+y^2}\quad\text{and}\quad\theta=\tan^{-1}\frac{y}{x}\quad\dots\dots\dots\dots\dots\dots(3)$$

where the positive square root is taken for r and where the $\tan^{-1}\frac{y}{x}$ value from tables needs an addition (of zero, π or 2π) according to the signs of x and y. This is for θ between 0 and 2π; any multiple of 2π can also be added.

In the polar form of z, as given by (3), the terms often used are :

$$r = |z| = \textit{modulus of } z$$
$$\theta = \arg z = \textit{argument of } z$$

The modulus can also be described as the *absolute value* of z.

The next step is to specify the *rules* of algebra obeyed by the complex number (1). These are the ordinary rules of elementary algebra, provided that i^2 is written (-1) wherever it appears. There are some special features to notice. There is, first, the *equation* of two complex numbers, $z_1 = z_2$. The two real components need to be equated separately, i.e.

$$x_1 = x_2 \quad \text{and} \quad y_1 = y_2$$
or
$$r_1 \cos\theta_1 = r_2 \cos\theta_2 \quad \text{and} \quad r_1 \sin\theta_1 = r_2 \sin\theta_2$$

This is because a complex number is two-dimensional. The process is sometimes called " equating the real and imaginary parts ". In $x + iy$, x is sometimes described as the " real part " and y as the " imaginary part ", corresponding on the Argand diagram to Ox as the " real " axis (on which real numbers x appear) and to Oy as the " imaginary " axis (on which numbers iy appear).

The rules of *addition* and *multiplication* are generally a matter of ordinary algebra with the $x + iy$ form (and $i^2 = -1$). So:

$$(x_1 + iy_1) + (x_2 + iy_2) = (x_1 + x_2) + i(y_1 + y_2)$$
$$(x_1 + iy_1)(x_2 + iy_2) = x_1 x_2 + i(x_1 y_2 + x_2 y_1) + i^2 y_1 y_2$$
$$= (x_1 x_2 - y_1 y_2) + i(x_1 y_2 + x_2 y_1)$$

However, multiplication is much simpler in the polar and exponential forms :

$$r_1 e^{i\theta_1} \times r_2 e^{i\theta_2} = r_1 r_2 e^{i(\theta_1 + \theta_2)}$$

i.e. $r_1(\cos\theta_1 + i\sin\theta_1)$ times $r_2(\cos\theta_2 + i\sin\theta_2)$ gives
$$r_1 r_2 (\cos\overline{\theta_1 + \theta_2} + i\sin\overline{\theta_1 + \theta_2})$$

There remain the processes of *subtraction* and *division*. These introduce nothing new, since they are the inverses of addition and multiplication; subtract reverses or " undoes " addition and similarly for division and multiplication. First, the negative $(-z)$ of z is such that $z + (-z) = 0$ which gives :

$$-z = -(x + iy) = (-x) + i(-y)$$

Then, the difference z between z_1 and z_2 is such that $z + z_2 = z_1$ which gives :

$$z = z_1 - z_2 = (x_1 - x_2) + i(y_1 - y_2)$$

Finally, the quotient $z = \dfrac{z_1}{z_2}$ (where $z_2 \neq 0$) is defined so that $z \times z_2 = z_1$.

The consequence of this definition is easily seen to be that the ordinary algebraic processes apply. In cartesian form, with x_2 and y_2 not zero :

$$\frac{z_1}{z_2} = \frac{x_1 + iy_1}{x_2 + iy_2} = \frac{(x_1 + iy_1)(x_2 - iy_2)}{(x_2 + iy_2)(x_2 - iy_2)} = \frac{x_1 x_2 - i(x_1 y_2 - x_2 y_1) - i^2 y_1 y_2}{x_2^2 - i^2 y_2^2}$$

$$= \frac{(x_1 x_2 + y_1 y_2)}{x_2^2 + y_2^2} - i \frac{x_1 y_2 - x_2 y_1}{x_2^2 + y_2^2}$$

which could be made, if thought fit, into a " rule " for division. However, it is usually best to " slog " it out as shown. Notice the first step—to multiply both parts of the ratio by $(x_2 - iy_2)$—which is the standard way of getting rid of the " imaginary " part in the denominator. However, division, like multiplication, is much simpler with r and θ :

$$\frac{z_1}{z_2} = \frac{r_1 e^{i\theta_1}}{r_2 e^{i\theta_2}} = \frac{r_1}{r_2} e^{i(\theta_1 - \theta_2)}$$

The moduli (or absolute values) are divided ; the arguments are subtracted. Compare with multiplication, where moduli are multiplied and arguments added.

The two related numbers, $x + iy$ and $x - iy$, are called *conjugate complex numbers* and they frequently appear together. They are particularly useful in polar and exponential form :

$$r(\cos \theta + i \sin \theta) = re^{i\theta}$$

and
$$r(\cos \theta - i \sin \theta) = re^{-i\theta}$$

The main feature of conjugate complex numbers is that they add and multiply to real numbers :

$$\text{Sum} = r(e^{i\theta} + e^{-i\theta}) = 2r \cos \theta = 2x$$
$$\text{Product} = r^2 = x^2 + y^2$$

The difference and quotient are also relatively simple (see Ex. 3 below).

The exponential form of the complex number enables powers of z to be handled very easily :

$$z^n = (re^{i\theta})^n = r^n e^{in\theta} = r^n(\cos n\theta + i \sin n\theta)$$

and similarly for the conjugate. The result is known as *De Moivre's Theorem* :

$$\{r(\cos \theta \pm i \sin \theta)\}^n = r^n(\cos n\theta \pm i \sin n\theta)$$

It is true for any value of n, e.g. for $n=\frac{1}{2}$ or $-\frac{3}{2}$, as well as for integral values.

The algebra of complex numbers is often used when the interest is confined to real numbers. In operating with real numbers it is found to be an advantage to have the extra dimension of complex numbers ; it provides additional room for manoeuvre. In terms of the Argand diagram, real numbers lie on the single axis Ox but, in dealing with them, it is convenient to go out into the plane Oxy of complex numbers. For example, multiplication of x by i and then by i again gives $(-x)$; the starting and final points are real numbers. The main examples of pairs of complex numbers which combine by addition or by product to give real numbers are conjugate complex numbers and the exponentials e^{ix} and e^{-ix}. For example, the product of $(x+iy)$ and $(x-iy)$ is $r^2=x^2+y^2$; the sum of e^{ix} and e^{-ix} is $2\cos x$. It is on properties such as these that the formulation of oscillations depends ; this is the reason for using complex variables in a theory involving oscillatory movements.

EXERCISES 4.5

1. Show that $\tan^{-1}\dfrac{y}{x}$ from tables is negative $\left(-\dfrac{\pi}{2} \text{ to } 0\right)$ if $\dfrac{y}{x}<0$, positive $\left(0 \text{ to } \dfrac{\pi}{2}\right)$ if $\dfrac{y}{x}>0$. Show further that $\theta=\arg z$ is obtained as follows in four different cases :

Signs of x and y		Range of θ	Value of θ
$x>0$	$y>0$	0 to $\dfrac{\pi}{2}$	$\tan^{-1}\dfrac{y}{x}$
$x<0$	$y>0$	$\dfrac{\pi}{2}$ to π	$\pi+\tan^{-1}\dfrac{y}{x}$
$x<0$	$y<0$	π to $\dfrac{3\pi}{2}$	$\pi+\tan^{-1}\dfrac{y}{x}$
$x>0$	$y<0$	$\dfrac{3\pi}{2}$ to π	$2\pi+\tan^{-1}\dfrac{y}{x}$

2. Show that $z=0$ is a particular case of equating $z_1=z_2$ and that the " real " and " imaginary " parts of z are put separately equal to zero.

3. Show that, for the conjugate complex numbers $r(\cos\theta \pm i\sin\theta)$, the difference is $2ir\sin\theta$ and the quotient is $\cos 2\theta+i\sin 2\theta$.

4. If a real number is the sum of squares of two other real numbers, show that it can be expressed as the product of two conjugate complex numbers. Indicate that this is a way of " factorising " some prime numbers, but illustrate that it is not unique by showing that :
$$13=(2+3i)(2-3i)=(3+2i)(3-2i)$$

5. By straight-forward multiplication show that the square of $r(\cos\theta+i\sin\theta)$ is $r^2(\cos 2\theta+i\sin 2\theta)$; hence extend to a proof of De Moivre's Theorem for n a

positive integer. In this case, indicate that De Moivre's Theorem is another manifestation of the fact that arguments of complex numbers cumulate in multiplication.

4.6 Polynomials and Equations

A polynomial is the sum of integral powers of a variable x with constant coefficients, the highest power being the *degree* of the polynomial. An equation is formed by equating the polynomial to zero ; the values of x which satisfy the equation are sought, the *roots* of the equation. In general a polynomial of nth degree can be written with the coefficient of x^n equal to unity (since this coefficient cannot be zero) :

$$f(x) = x^n + a_1 x^{n-1} + a_2 x^{n-2} + \ldots + a_{n-1} x + a_n \quad \ldots\ldots\ldots\ldots(1)$$

The corresponding equation of degree n is $f(x) = 0$. Some of the roots of such an equation may be real values of x ; but others may be complex values, in conjugate pairs, as will be seen.

There are few hard and fast rules to assist in the solution of an equation ; it is very largely an empirical, trial and error matter. Graphical representation is a great help and the general ideas can be explained in terms of Fig. 14, which shows the graph of a hypothetical polynomial

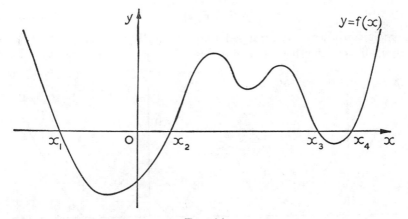

FIG. 14.

function $y = f(x)$. First, the real roots of $f(x) = 0$ are those values of x where the graph cuts Ox, values like x_1, x_2, x_3, ... in Fig. 14. Secondly, if $f(x)$ is specified numerically and if the graph is drawn accurately, the number and actual numerical values of the real roots can be found to a high accuracy. Thirdly, even if $f(x)$ involves certain unspecified parameters, the general form of $y = f(x)$ can often be indicated sufficiently for the graph to indicate how many real roots there are and where they are located in various cases. Finally, once the real roots (x_1, x_2, x_3, ...) of $f(x)=0$ are found or located, the ranges of x for which the polynomial $f(x)$ is positive, and those for which it is negative, follow at once. The function $y=f(x)$ is continuous and crosses Ox (i.e. y changes sign) *only* at a root of $f(x)=0$. Between any two consecutive roots, $f(x)$ has a constant sign, e.g. between x_2 and x_3 in Fig. 14 when $f(x)>0$.

It frequently happens in mathematical problems (e.g. in 3.8 above) that the various possibilities of location of the roots of $f(x)=0$ are to be examined for different values of the parameters of $f(x)$; or alternatively that the ranges of values of x for which $f(x)>0$ are required. This is the type of problem considered now, with the aid of graphical representation as in Fig. 14.

The simplest cases of linear, quadratic and cubic polynomials and equations are examined first. The *linear equation* is $x+a_1=0$ which has always just one real root: $x=-a_1$. The quadratic equation can be written from (1):

$$x^2+a_1x+a_2=0$$

However, it is more usual to show it with a coefficient of x^2 and in the form:

$$ax^2+bx+c=0 \quad \dots\dots\dots\dots\dots\dots\dots\dots\dots\dots(2)$$

where it can always be arranged that $a>0$. The curve $y=ax^2+bx+c$, with $a>0$, is of the shape shown in Fig. 15a; $y\to+\infty$ as $x\to\pm\infty$. There

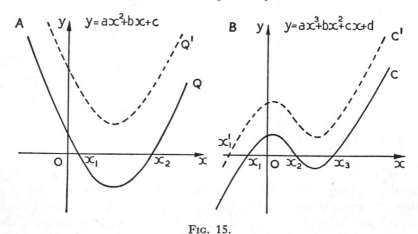

Fig. 15.

are two main cases: two real roots (x_1 and x_2) of the quadratic as with curve Q; no real roots at all as with curve Q'. In Fig. 15a, Q' is merely an upward shift of Q, representing a change in the constant c (intercept on Oy). There is an intermediate case where the curve touches Ox and there are still two real roots, but they coincide in value. The position is not very tidy ; there may be two roots or none. It can be tidied up by use of complex numbers.

The algebraic solution of the quadratic (2) is simple ; by the process of " completing the square ", two roots are found :

$$x_1, \ x_2 = \frac{1}{2a} \left(-b \pm \sqrt{b^2 - 4ac} \right) \quad \dots\dots\dots\dots\dots\dots (3)$$

If $b^2 > 4ac$, x_1 and x_2 are real and distinct. If $b^2 = 4ac$, x_1 and x_2 are real but coincide in the single value, $x_1 = x_2 = -\dfrac{b}{2a}$. If $b^2 < 4ac$, x_1 and x_2 do not exist (as real roots) since the value under the square root in (3) is negative. However, allow complex values of x and the third case has two distinct roots ; they are conjugate complex :

$$x_1, \ x_2 = \frac{1}{2a} \left(-b \pm i\sqrt{4ac - b^2} \right)$$

Notice that, both in the case of real and in that of conjugate complex roots, the sum of the roots is $\left(-\dfrac{b}{a} \right)$ and the product is found to be $\dfrac{c}{a}$:

$$x_1 + x_2 = -\frac{b}{a} \quad \text{and} \quad x_1 x_2 = \frac{c}{a} \quad \dots\dots\dots\dots\dots\dots (4)$$

in all cases. The algebra of quadratic equations is complete, once conjugate complex roots are allowed ; results (3) and (4) sum up all that need be said.

The *cubic equation* is $x^3 + a_1 x^2 + a_2 x + a_3 = 0$, more usually written :

$$ax^3 + bx^2 + cx + d = 0 \quad \dots\dots\dots\dots\dots\dots\dots (5)$$

where again $a > 0$ can be taken. The corresponding curve is of the form shown in Fig. 15b ; $y \to +\infty$ as $x \to +\infty$ and $y \to -\infty$ as $x \to -\infty$. There are again two main cases : three real roots (x_1, x_2 and x_3) as curve C ; one real root (x'_1) as curve C', which is again only an upward shift of C. Intermediate cases exist when two or all three roots, in the first main case, happen to coincide. The position is once more tidied up by the provision of two (conjugate) complex roots in the second main case.

No complete algebraic solution of the cubic (5) can be given in general terms. The method of approach, however, is easily described. There *must* be one real root, say $x = x_1$. It can be found by graphical methods or by numerical approximation, e.g. by Newton's or Horner's method, see Durell and Robson (1937) (p. 164). Since $(x - x_1)$ is a factor of (5):

$$(x - x_1)(ax^2 + b'x + c') = 0$$

The other two roots then follow from the quadratic, $ax^2 + b'x + c' = 0$, either as two real roots or as conjugate complex roots. Hence the solution of the cubic gives *either* three real roots *or* one real and two (conjugate) complex roots. Two or three of the roots may happen to coincide in value. Hence the equation can always be written : $(x - x_1)(x - x_2)(x - x_3) = 0$. It is only necessary to allow x_2 and x_3 to be conjugate complex. By multiplying out this form and comparing with (5), it follows that

$$x_1 + x_2 + x_3 = -\frac{b}{a}; \quad x_1 x_2 + x_2 x_3 + x_3 x_1 = \frac{c}{a} \quad \text{and} \quad x_1 x_2 x_3 = -\frac{d}{a} \quad ....(6)$$

in all cases. Result (6) is an extension of (4) for the quadratic.

No complete treatment of the general case (1) can be attempted here ; indeed a rigorous algebra of polynomials is far from easy (see Appendix B). Enough has been said, however, to indicate the main outlines. First, if $a_n = 0$ in (1), then $x = 0$ is a root of $f(x) = 0$; the factor x can be removed, leaving an equation of degree $(n - 1)$ for the other roots. Hence it can be taken that $a_n \neq 0$, i.e. that the curve $y = f(x)$ in Fig. 14 does not go through the origin O. The problem is to locate the roots of $f(x) = 0$, allowing for complex as well as real values. The basic results are that there are precisely n roots and that, if x_1, x_2, ... x_k are the real roots, then :

$$f(x) = (x - x_1)(x - x_2) \dots (x - x_k)g(x)$$

where *either* $k = n$ and $g(x) = 1$, *or* $k = n - 2$ and $g(x)$ is a quadratic factor, *or* $k = n - 4$ and $g(x)$ is the product of two quadratic factors, and so on. Hence, if x_1, x_2, ... x_k are all the real roots of $f(x) = 0$, each quadratic factor in $g(x)$ gives two (conjugate) complex roots ; there are no other possibilities. The complex roots, which make up the complete tally of n, always occur in conjugate pairs. The possibilities in $f(x) = 0$ of degree n are *either* n real roots, *or* $(n - 2)$ real roots and one conjugate complex pair, *or* $(n - 4)$ real roots and two conjugate complex pairs, and so on. If n is even, there may be no real roots ; if n is odd there must be one real root at least.

The next step is to show how the roots can be located, and particularly how to determine the number of real roots which are positive and the number which are negative. Reference to Fig. 14 again gives the clue. Take two points on the curve $y = f(x)$, one above and one below Ox ; then the curve must cross the axis Ox at least once, and in general an odd number of times, between the two points. If the points are both above (or both below) Ox, then the curve may not cross Ox at all between the points and, if it does, it makes an even number of crossings. Interpreted in terms of roots of $f(x)=0$, the result is, for any two values $x=a$ and $x=b$ whatever:

If $f(a)$ and $f(b)$ are of *opposite sign*, an *odd number* of real roots of $f(x)=0$ exist between $x=a$ and $x=b$.

If $f(a)$ and $f(b)$ are of the *same sign*, an *even number* of real roots of $f(x)=0$ exist between $x=a$ and $x=b$.

An odd number implies at least one root; an even number is taken as including the case of no roots.

The simplest application of the result takes a and b as $\pm\infty$ and zero. Then $f(\infty)$ and $f(-\infty)$ are determined in sign by the degree of the equation; $f(0)=a_n$ and so fixed in sign by a_n. Take the case of *an equation of even degree* (n even); the other case is similar (see Ex. 1 below). The signs are:

$$f(-\infty)>0 \quad f(0)=\text{sign of } a_n \quad f(\infty)>0$$

Hence:

Case	Number of:	
	Positive roots	Negative roots
$a_n>0$	Even	Even
$a_n<0$	Odd	Odd

For example, if a_n is negative, there must be at least one negative real root and at least one positive real root of $f(x)=0$. Other tricks of this kind are available as indicated in Exs. 3 and 5 below.

In conclusion, the relation between the *sign* of the polynomial $f(x)$ and the *roots* of $f(x)=0$ is clear from Fig. 14. Since a change of sign of $f(x)$ occurs only at a real root of $f(x)=0$, the sign of $f(x)$ remains the same between any two consecutive real roots of $f(x)=0$. The degree of the polynomial, and particular values of it, are usually sufficient to determine which sign rules. For example, if $f(x)$ is of even degree, then $f(x)$ is positive for very large x (both positive and negative); hence if the real roots are x_1, x_2, x_3, ... in ascending order, $f(x)$ is only negative between x_1 and x_2, between x_3 and x_4, ... If there are no real roots (which is possible for an even degree), then $f(x)>0$ all x. The case of $f(x)$ of odd degree is similar (see Ex. 2 below). The quadratic and cubic equations of Fig. 15 illustrate both cases.

EXERCISES 4.6

1. If $f(x) = 0$ is of odd degree, show that :

Case	Number of :	
	Positive roots	Negative roots
$a_n > 0$	Even	Odd
$a_n < 0$	Odd	Even

When can it be said that there is at least one positive root, one negative root?

2. For an equation $f(x) = 0$ of odd degree, there is at least one real root. Let the roots be $x_1, x_2, x_3 \ldots$ in ascending order. Show that $f(x)$ is only negative below x_1, between x_2 and x_3, and so on ; and that $f(x) > 0$ for large x.

3. From Fig. 14 show that, if a and b are consecutive real roots of $f(x) = 0$, then $f'(x) = 0$ has at least one real root between a and b (*Rolle's Theorem*). Indicate how knowledge of the real roots of $f'(x) = 0$ of degree $(n-1)$ help to locate real roots of $f(x) = 0$ of degree n.

4. Apply the result of the previous exercise to determine the values of k for which $x^3 - 3x + k = 0$ has three unequal real roots. Check graphically.

5. Consider the series of coefficients $(1, a_1, a_2, \ldots a_n)$ in $f(x)$. If there are exactly k changes of sign in this series, show that the number of real positive roots of $f(x) = 0$ is either k, or $(k - 2)$, or $(k - 4)$, ... (*Descartes' Rule of Signs*). Deduce that, if $a_n < 0$, k is odd and $f(x) = 0$ has at least one real positive root, which is otherwise obvious.

4.7 Sinusoidal Functions and Oscillatory Motion

The trigonometric functions, $y = \cos x$ and $y = \sin x$, have regular oscillations each of length 2π in x as x increases (see Fig. 10 above). The two functions are the same from this point of view, except for the " phase " or choice of origin. Beginning at $x = \dfrac{\pi}{2}$, $y = \sin x$ is exactly the same as $y = \cos x$ beginning at $x = 0$; one lags $\left(\text{by } x = \dfrac{\pi}{2}\right)$ behind the other. Hence, for the analysis of oscillations, only one of the two functions need be taken. The preference is for $y = \cos x$, since it is symmetrical with respect to positive and negative x and since it displays its peak at $x = 0$.

The function $y = \cos x$ can be extended to show a greater variety of regular oscillations. It can then be called a *circular or sinusoidal function* rather than a trigonometric function. In the present context, regular oscillations are those which repeat themselves always in the same length (of x), which show the same range of variation up and down in every cycle, and which have the symmetrical shape of the cosine function within the cycle. There are then three features of the regular oscillation to distinguish and specify. The first is the *period* or the range of x in which one complete oscillation appears; alternatively the same feature is shown by the *frequency*, the reciprocal of the period, as the number of oscillations per unit of x. The second feature is the *amplitude* or the peak (and trough) of the oscillation measured from its average level; the third is the *phase* as indicated by a value of x at which a peak is attained.

For $y = \cos x$, the period is 2π, the amplitude is ± 1 and the phase is indicated by a peak at $x = 0$. These are particular values; what is required is a more general function in which the period, amplitude and phase can be any specified values. It must have three parameters for the three features and a suitable form is found to be:

$$y = A \cos(\omega x + \epsilon) \quad\quad\quad\quad\quad\quad \dots\dots\dots\dots\dots\dots(1)$$

where ω, A and ϵ are the parameters.

To show that (1) is the general sinusoidal function for regular oscillations, it is only necessary to locate its series of peaks and troughs. The peaks occur at any value of x for which $\cos(\omega x + \epsilon) = 1$, i.e. whenever $(\omega x + \epsilon)$ is zero, plus or minus any multiple of 2π. The whole range of peaks are at:

$$x = \dots -\frac{4\pi + \epsilon}{\omega}, \ -\frac{2\pi + \epsilon}{\omega}, \ -\frac{\epsilon}{\omega}, \ \frac{2\pi - \epsilon}{\omega}, \ \frac{4\pi - \epsilon}{\omega}, \ \dots$$

The range of troughs occur at the midway points. It follows that the period is fixed and of value $\dfrac{2\pi}{\omega}$, given by the parameter ω; and that the phase is then specified by ϵ since a peak occurs at $x = -\dfrac{\epsilon}{\omega}$. In each period the shape of the oscillation of y is that of the cosine function and the amplitude is fixed at $\pm A$. Hence $y = A \cos(\omega x + \epsilon)$ is a regular sinusoidal variation, with period $\left(\dfrac{2\pi}{\omega}\right)$, amplitude $(\pm A)$ and phase $\left(\text{peak at } x = -\dfrac{\epsilon}{\omega}\right)$ fixed by the three parameters.

A useful variant of (1) can be given in which the two parameters A and ϵ are replaced by a different pair:

$$y = A \cos(\omega x + \epsilon) = A(\cos \epsilon \cos \omega x - \sin \epsilon \sin \omega x)$$

i.e. $$y = a \cos \omega x + b \sin \omega x$$

when $a = A \cos \epsilon$ and $b = -A \sin \epsilon$. Conversely, $y = a \cos \omega x + b \sin \omega x$ where a and b are any constants, can always be put in the form

$$y = A \cos(\omega x + \epsilon)$$

Write $a = A \cos \epsilon$ and $(-b) = A \sin \epsilon$; this is a general device and it can always be done. In fact, the transformation from a and $(-b)$ to A and ϵ

is simply the change from a complex number $a - ib$ in cartesian co-ordinates to $Ae^{i\epsilon} = A(\cos \epsilon + i \sin \epsilon)$ in polars. Then :

$$y = a \cos \omega x + b \sin \omega x = A \cos \epsilon \cos \omega x - A \sin \epsilon \sin \omega x = A \cos (\omega x + \epsilon)$$

Hence the regular sinusoidal function can be shown in equivalent forms :

$$y = A \cos (\omega x + \epsilon) = a \cos \omega x + b \sin \omega x \quad \dots\dots\dots\dots\dots(2)$$
where $\qquad\qquad a = A \cos \epsilon \quad \text{and} \quad b = - A \sin \epsilon$

To express A and ϵ in terms of a and b, the inverse transformation of 4.5 is used.

In (1) it is assumed that A is fixed, i.e. that the oscillation is regular in the sense of fixed amplitude. This is not necessary. The value of A can be made to vary with x in any way, according to some function $A(x)$. The oscillation is the same as before, except that, over the different periods, the amplitude changes in some specified way, e.g. it may decrease (damped), increase (anti-damped or explosive), vary up and down (or indeed in any way). The case of particular interest is when $A(x) = Ae^{\alpha x}$, for some constant α ; the amplitude is then damped when $\alpha < 0$ and anti-damped or explosive when $\alpha > 0$. Hence a sinusoidal function with damped, regular or explosive oscillations is :

$$y = Ae^{\alpha x} \cos (\omega x + \epsilon) \quad \dots\dots\dots\dots\dots\dots\dots(3)$$

There are now four parameters, three of them (ω, A and ϵ) as before, and the fourth (α) indicating the degree of damping or anti-damping. The general form of the oscillation (3), in the three typical cases of $\alpha < 0$, $\alpha = 0$ and $\alpha > 0$, is shown in Fig. 16. Notice that the oscillation of Fig. 16b ($\alpha = 0$) is that of the form (1) and it is to be compared with the graph of $y = \cos x$ of Fig. 10b above.

The independent variable x in (1) or (3) can be anything ; y depends on some variable x and does so by oscillating in value as x increases. The most important, and the usual, case is when x is time. This case of temporal oscillation is the one now taken for analysis. Write x as t, take $t = 0$ as the initial position and $t > 0$ for subsequent oscillation. Occasionally, " prior " time periods for which $t < 0$ may be taken as well. The *period* of the oscillation $T = \dfrac{2\pi}{\omega}$ is now the length of the complete oscillation in units of time, e.g. $T = 3$ months or 10 years. The reciprocal is very useful, the *frequency* of the oscillation $f = \dfrac{\omega}{2\pi}$, or the number of complete oscillations per unit of time, e.g. $f = 4$ times a year when $T = 3$ months $= \frac{1}{4}$ year. The period and frequency of an oscillation are alternatives ; one may be more appropriate than the other according to circumstances. Generally, T is preferred for long periods and f for short periods (high frequency).

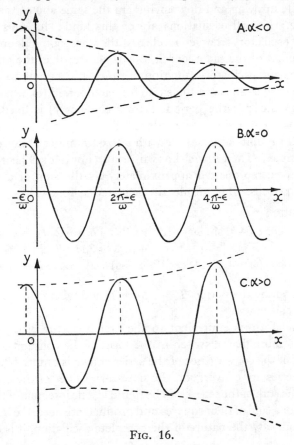

Fig. 16.

The general sinusoidal variation, of cosine form, and its properties can therefore be described as follows :

The sinusoidal function $y = Ae^{\alpha t} \cos(\omega t + \epsilon)$ represents damped, regular or explosive oscillations over time, in the symmetrical (cosine) form. Its features are indicated by the four parameters ω, A, α, and ϵ:

PERIOD $T = \dfrac{2\pi}{\omega}$ or FREQUENCY $f = \dfrac{\omega}{2\pi}$

INITIAL AMPLITUDE $= A$

DAMPING FACTOR for subsequent amplitudes $= \alpha$

PHASE given by peak at $t = -\dfrac{\epsilon}{\omega}$

With the sinusoidal function the oscillation is limited to that of cosine form. Within any one period—apart from the effect of damping or anti-damping—the upswing and downswing are the same and of the particular cosine shape. Not all oscillations are of this kind ; for most economic variables of oscillatory character, clearly they are not. Booms and depressions are not of the same length, one is shorter than the other.

Let $F(t)$ be any oscillatory function of time, subject only to the restrictions that the oscillations are the same for each period (of whatever shape they may be) and that the period T (or frequency f) is fixed. In $F(t)$, the oscillations repeat themselves identically, with each taking place in a fixed interval (T units of time), or with a fixed number (f) of oscillations per unit of time. Then a well-known result (Fourier's Theorem) shows that $F(t)$ can be represented approximately by the sum of a number of sinusoidal functions. The result can be stated as follows.

FOURIER SERIES :

$$\left.\begin{aligned}
F(t) = a_0 &+ (a_1 \cos \omega t + b_1 \sin \omega t) + (a_2 \cos 2\omega t + b_2 \sin 2\omega t) \\
&+ (a_3 \cos 3\omega t + b_3 \sin 3\omega t) + \ldots \\
= a_0 &+ A_1 \cos (\omega t + \epsilon_1) + A_2 \cos (2\omega t + \epsilon_2) + A_3 \cos (3\omega t + \epsilon_3) + \ldots
\end{aligned}\right\} \ldots(4)$$

when ω is given by the period $T = \dfrac{2\pi}{\omega}$ of $F(t)$ and where the a's, b's, or the A's, ϵ's, are constants.

The second form is equivalent to the first in virtue of (2) above ; it represents no more than a switch in the form of the constants.

The proof of the convergence of the series shown is omitted here. However, if the series are convergent, the necessary values of the constants, to give $F(t)$ as the sum of the series, can be found. The integrals of the sine and cosine functions, and of their squares and product, are needed over the range of their period. By the nature of the complete oscillation, it is clear that :

$$\int_0^{2\pi} \sin t \, dt = \int_0^{2\pi} \cos t \, dt = \int_0^{2\pi} \sin t \cos t \, dt = 0$$

But

$$\int \sin^2 t \, dt = \int \tfrac{1}{2}(1 - \cos 2t) \, dt = \tfrac{1}{2}t - \tfrac{1}{4} \sin 2t$$

so that

$$\int_0^{2\pi} \sin^2 t \, dt = \left[\tfrac{1}{2}t - \tfrac{1}{4} \sin 2t \right]_0^{2\pi} = \pi$$

and similarly

$$\int_0^{2\pi} \cos^2 t \, dt = \pi$$

This uses the property : $\cos 2t = \cos^2 t - \sin^2 t = 1 - 2 \sin^2 t = 2 \cos^2 t - 1$.

In (4), multiply through by $\cos \omega t$ and integrate from 0 to $T = \dfrac{2\pi}{\omega}$:

$$\int_0^T F(t) \cos \omega t \, dt = a_0 \int_0^T \cos \omega t \, dt + a_1 \int_0^T \cos^2 \omega t \, dt + b_1 \int_0^T \sin \omega t \cos \omega t \, dt + \ldots$$

$$= a_1 \int_0^T \cos^2 \omega t \, dt \quad \text{since all the other integrals are zero.}$$

Now $\displaystyle \int_0^T \cos^2 \omega t \, dt = \frac{1}{\omega} \int_0^{2\pi} \cos^2 \tau \, d\tau \quad$ where $\tau = \omega t$

$$= \frac{\pi}{\omega} \quad \text{by the result above.}$$

Hence $\displaystyle \int_0^T F(t) \cos \omega t \, dt = a_1 \frac{\pi}{\omega}$

i.e. $$a_1 = \frac{\omega}{\pi} \int_0^T F(t) \cos \omega t \, dt$$

The other constants are found similarly and, in general,

$$a_n = \frac{\omega}{\pi} \int_0^T F(t) \cos n\omega t \, dt, \quad b_n = \frac{\omega}{\pi} \int_0^T F(t) \sin n\omega t \, dt$$

The interpretation of Fourier series is that any type of oscillation with given period $\dfrac{2\pi}{\omega}$ can be approximated by the sum of *sinusoidal* oscillations by taking a sufficient number of terms in the series (4). The first of the sinusoidal oscillations has the *same* period or frequency as $F(t)$, the fundamental frequency. The later sinusoidal oscillations in the sum have shorter periods, or higher frequencies in multiples of the fundamental frequency. Hence, in expressing $F(t)$ as a sum of sinusoidal functions, there is a range of decreasing periods $\left(\dfrac{2\pi}{n\omega}\right)$, or of increasing frequencies $\left(\dfrac{n\omega}{2\pi}\right)$, for $n = 1, 2,$ 3, ... Where the series is stopped is a matter of convenience or closeness of approximation. It is to be noticed that terms can be added without affecting those already written.

The general conclusion is that an analysis of sinusoidal functions is more generally useful than might appear. The sinusoidal oscillation is a particular kind of oscillation. But a series of such oscillations, with a range of increasing frequencies, can be used to approximate any kind of oscillation with a given frequency.

EXERCISES 4.7

1. Show that $y = A \sin(\omega t + \epsilon)$ differs from $y = A \cos(\omega t + \epsilon)$ only in phase, and that $y = A \sin(\omega t + \epsilon) = A \cos\left(\omega t + \epsilon - \dfrac{\pi}{2}\right)$.

2. Show that $\quad \cos \omega x + \sin \omega x = \sqrt{2} \cos \left(\omega x - \dfrac{\pi}{4} \right)$

$$\cos \omega x - \sin \omega x = \sqrt{2} \cos \left(\omega x + \dfrac{\pi}{4} \right)$$

$$\cos \omega x + \sqrt{3} \sin \omega x = 2 \cos \left(\omega x - \dfrac{\pi}{3} \right)$$

$$\cos \omega x - \sqrt{3} \sin \omega x = 2 \cos \left(\omega x + \dfrac{\pi}{3} \right)$$

and check by (2) above.

3. In what sense is $y = \tan t$ an oscillatory variable? Show that its period is π. Examine and draw a diagram for $y = A \tan (\omega t + \epsilon)$.

4.8 Vector Components of a Sinusoidal Function

Consider first the regular sinusoidal function with no damping factor :

$$y = A \cos (\omega t + \epsilon)$$

The initial value of y at $t = 0$ is :

$$y_0 = A \cos \epsilon$$

There are three parameters, ω for the period or frequency of oscillation, A for the amplitude and ϵ for the phase. The last two go together ; between them, *A and ϵ fix the initial position* of y. The other parameter is different ; ω is the *determinant of the subsequent motion* of y.

Take the initial position and the parameters A and ϵ, and leave ω on one side for the moment. A and ϵ can be combined into a vector or complex number $Ae^{i\epsilon}$; the vector has length A and direction ϵ and these are the polar co-ordinates of the complex number. The initial position y_0 is the " real " component of $Ae^{i\epsilon} = A(\cos \epsilon + i \sin \epsilon)$. Hence, in describing the starting point, the vector $Ae^{i\epsilon}$ can be used ; it is to be remembered only that y_0 is the " real " part of it.

The vector $Ae^{i\epsilon}$ can be represented by OP in the usual type of Argand diagram, as on the left in Fig. 17. For a reason which will appear later,

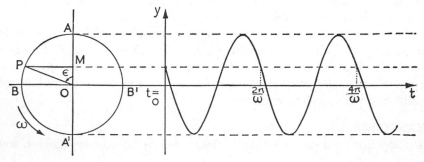

Fig. 17.

the Argand diagram is drawn with its " real " axis $A'OA$ vertical (instead of horizontal) ; and the circle of Fig. 17 is of radius A. The initial vector OP is of length A and makes an angle ϵ (measured anti-clockwise) with OA. the initial value y_0 is shown by the length OM on the " real " axis.

Now let OP rotate over time, anti-clockwise around O, at the *angular speed* ω, defined as an angle ω radians covered per unit of time. This means $\dfrac{\omega}{2\pi}$ complete revolutions per unit of time or one complete revolution in time $\dfrac{2\pi}{\omega}$. The length OM then oscillates up and down the " real " axis between A and A'. After time t, the angle covered by OP is ωt, and OP then makes an angle $(\omega t + \epsilon)$ with OA. Hence, the position of OP after time t indicates the value of y at that time ; the actual value of y is read off as the length $OM = A \cos(\omega t + \epsilon)$ at the time concerned. The oscillation of OM up and down the " real " axis $A'OA$ is the oscillation of y. The varying length OM can be stretched out over time, as shown on the right of Fig. 17 ; all that is necessary is to plot the height of OM at time t over the appropriate point t on the time axis. In Fig. 17, the oscillation of y is shown on the left as a movement up and down $A'OA$ and on the right as a time graph of y plotted against time. The two correspond as indicated by the broken horizontal lines. To fix the scale of t on the right of the figure, it is only necessary to note that y returns to its initial value y_0 after the lapse of time $t = \dfrac{2\pi}{\omega}$, which is the period of the oscillation.

The initial vector OP is $Ae^{i\epsilon}$; after time t it has revolved through an angle ωt. In terms of vectors, this is multiplication by $e^{i\omega t}$. Hence the vector after time t is $Ae^{i\epsilon} \times e^{i\omega t}$ and y is the " real " part of the product. This can be checked :

$$Ae^{i\epsilon} \times e^{i\omega t} = Ae^{i(\omega t + \epsilon)} = A\{\cos(\omega t + \epsilon) + i \sin(\omega t + \epsilon)\}$$

with " real " part, $y = A \cos(\omega t + \epsilon)$.

The result of the analysis is that the value $y = A \cos(\omega t + \epsilon)$ of the sinusoidal function after time t is the " real " part of a vector product :

$$Ae^{i\epsilon} \times e^{i\omega t}$$

The first vector $Ae^{i\epsilon}$ fixes the initial position, and it involves the parameters A for amplitude and ϵ for phase ; all this is shown by the vector OP of Fig. 17. The second vector $e^{i\omega t}$ represents the subsequent motion through time, and it involves the frequency ω ; this is covered in Fig. 17 by the rotation of OP at angular speed ω since $e^{i\omega t}$ as a vector represents an advance in the angle by ωt. As a matter of notation and terminology, care must be taken to interpret ω correctly. The angular frequency is ω, the angular speed of rotation of OP; from this is derived $f = \dfrac{\omega}{2\pi}$, the frequency per unit of time, and $T = \dfrac{2\pi}{\omega}$, the period of the oscillation in units of time. With this understood, it is convenient to speak of the " frequency ω ".

It is a simple matter to extend the result to the case of the damped (or anti-damped) sinusoidal function

$$y = A e^{\alpha t} \cos (\omega t + \epsilon)$$

In terms of Fig. 17, the vector OP expands or contracts (according to the factor $e^{\alpha t}$) as it rotates, as does the length OM which represents y. This is covered by multiplication by $e^{\alpha t}$, a " real " vector. Since it relates to the subsequent motion, $e^{\alpha t}$ is to be combined with the vector $e^{i\omega t}$, used for the motion above, to give the extended form of the vector : $e^{\alpha t}e^{i\omega t} = e^{(\alpha + i\omega)t}$. Write :

$$p = \alpha + i\omega$$

as the complex number which combines the two parameters (α and ω) of motion. The vector of the motion is e^{pt}. The value $y = A e^{\alpha t} \cos (\omega t + \epsilon)$ is the " real " part of the vector product :

$$A e^{i\epsilon} \times e^{pt}$$

This can be checked :

$$A e^{i\epsilon} \times e^{pt} = A e^{i\epsilon} \times e^{\alpha t + i\omega t} = A e^{\alpha t} e^{i(\omega t + \epsilon)}$$
$$= A e^{\alpha t} \{ \cos (\omega t + \epsilon) + i \sin (\omega t + \epsilon) \}$$

with " real " part $y = A e^{\alpha t} \cos (\omega t + \epsilon)$.

The complete result can now be summarised and interpreted as follows :

The sinusoidal function $y = A e^{\alpha t} \cos (\omega t + \epsilon)$ has a value after time t given by the " real " part of the vector product $A e^{i\epsilon} \times e^{pt}$, where the vector $A e^{i\epsilon}$ represents the initial position and the vector e^{pt} describes the subsequent motion ($p = \alpha + i\omega$).

The diagrammatic interpretation, as in Fig. 17, is that $A e^{i\epsilon}$ is the initial vector OP (A and ϵ being the polar co-ordinates of P), and that e^{pt} (or $e^{\alpha t} \times e^{i\omega t}$) is the combined effect of expanding or contracting OP (according to the damping factor) and of rotating it at angular speed ω over time. The projection of OP as OM on the " real " axis gives y. A similar sinusoidal function $y = A e^{\alpha t} \sin (\omega t + \epsilon)$ is obtained as the " imaginary " part of $A e^{i\epsilon} \times e^{pt}$, with a corresponding interpretation in Fig. 17 (see Ex. 1 and 2 below).

It is important to see how the four parameters fall into two pairs, A and

ϵ going together for the initial value y_0 and α and ω going together for the subsequent motion of y. There is a complete separation in two vectors, which are multiplied to give the value of y. The *initial position* is fixed by A and ϵ (amplitude and phase) in the initial vector $OP = Ae^{i\epsilon}$. The *subsequent motion* is described by α and ω (damping and frequency of oscillation) in the multiplying vector $e^{pt} = e^{\alpha t} \times e^{i\omega t}$. Here $e^{\alpha t}$ serves to expand or contract OP (and hence y) according to the damping factor α; $e^{i\omega t}$ serves to advance OP (and hence y) with speed ω.

EXERCISES 4.8

1. Show that $\sin(\omega t + \epsilon) = \cos\left(\omega t + \epsilon - \dfrac{\pi}{2}\right)$ and deduce that $y = Ae^{\alpha t} \sin(\omega t + \epsilon)$ is a sinusoidal function of exactly the same time path as the cosine function of the text, except for the initial phasing which is an advance of $\dfrac{\pi}{2}$.

2. Illustrate the sinusoidal variation $y = Ae^{\alpha t} \sin(\omega t + \epsilon)$ in terms of vectors and Fig. 17. Show that y is the " imaginary " part of $y = Ae^{i\epsilon}e^{pt}$ and the projection of the moving vector of Fig. 17 on the axis $B'OB$. Check that, if OP' is the vector obtained by turning OP through a right angle, then the sine path from OP' is identical with the cosine path obtained from OP.

4.9 Derivatives, Integrals and Combinations of Sinusoidal Variables

The result just obtained, that the function $y = Ae^{\alpha t} \cos(\omega t + \epsilon)$ is the " real " part of the vector product $Ae^{i\epsilon} \times e^{pt}$ where $p = \alpha + i\omega$, is of fundamental importance in handling oscillations which are of the particular symmetric shape represented by the trigonometric (sinusoidal) function. The damping (shown by α) of the oscillation, and its frequency (ω) or period $\left(\dfrac{2\pi}{\omega}\right)$, can be given any values whatever. As a particular case, write $\omega = \epsilon = 0$ and the steady (damped or explosive) exponential variation $y = Ae^{\alpha t}$ is obtained. Sinusoidal variation includes a steady exponential growth as well as an oscillatory path.

From the basic sinusoidal variable, $y = Ae^{\alpha t} \cos(\omega t + \epsilon)$, many other variables also of sinusoidal form can be obtained. Consider, first, derivatives and integrals of y. Straight-forward differentiation or integration can be used; the work is laborious but it is worth while as an exercise. Later a much simpler process is devised, with the aid of the vector notation. The particular case ($\alpha = 0$) of a regular oscillation is taken first. Write:

$$y = A \cos(\omega t + \epsilon)$$

so that $\qquad \dfrac{dy}{dt} = -\omega A \sin(\omega t + \epsilon) = \omega A \cos\left(\omega t + \epsilon + \dfrac{\pi}{2}\right)$

and $\qquad \displaystyle\int y\, dt = \dfrac{1}{\omega} A \sin(\omega t + \epsilon) = \dfrac{1}{\omega} A \cos\left(\omega t + \epsilon - \dfrac{\pi}{2}\right)$

Hence, the derivative or integral of y is also a sinusoidal variable with the same frequency (ω) as y. The difference lies only in the initial amplitude and phasing. The derivative $\dfrac{dy}{dt}$ has amplitude which is A multiplied by ω and phase advanced by $\dfrac{\pi}{2}$; the integral $\int y\, dt$ has amplitude A multiplied by $\dfrac{1}{\omega}$ and phase retarded by $\dfrac{\pi}{2}$. Similar results obtain for successive differentiation or integration of y (see Ex. 1 below).

There is more difficulty in handling the general case $(\alpha \neq 0)$ of an oscillation which can be damped or explosive. Write:

$$y = Ae^{\alpha t} \cos(\omega t + \epsilon)$$

so that

$$\frac{dy}{dt} = Ae^{\alpha t}\{\alpha \cos(\omega t + \epsilon) - \omega \sin(\omega t + \epsilon)\}$$

$$= A\sqrt{\alpha^2 + \omega^2}\, e^{\alpha t}\left\{\frac{\alpha}{\sqrt{\alpha^2 + \omega^2}} \cos(\omega t + \epsilon) - \frac{\omega}{\sqrt{\alpha^2 + \omega^2}} \sin(\omega t + \epsilon)\right\}$$

$$= \rho Ae^{\alpha t}\{\cos \eta \cos(\omega t + \epsilon) - \sin \eta \sin(\omega t + \epsilon)\}$$

$$= \rho Ae^{\alpha t} \cos(\omega t + \epsilon + \eta)$$

where

$$\rho = \sqrt{\alpha^2 + \omega^2} \quad \text{and} \quad \tan \eta = \frac{\omega}{\alpha}$$

Again $\dfrac{dy}{dt}$ is a sinusoidal variable with the same frequency (ω) and damping (α) as y, but with amplitude A multiplied by ρ and phase advanced by η. The amplitude ratio ρ and the phase shift η are to be obtained from α and ω; if the point P is plotted with cartesian co-ordinates (α, ω) on an Argand diagram, then ρ and η are the polar co-ordinates of P, i.e. ρ is the length OP and η is the angle POx.

The integral of y is to be obtained by application of the rule of " integration by parts ". Write the two integrals:

$$\int e^{\alpha t} \cos(\omega t + \epsilon)\,dt = \frac{1}{\alpha} e^{\alpha t} \cos(\omega t + \epsilon) + \frac{\omega}{\alpha} \int e^{\alpha t} \sin(\omega t + \epsilon)\,dt$$

and

$$\int e^{\alpha t} \sin(\omega t + \epsilon)\,dt = \frac{1}{\alpha} e^{\alpha t} \sin(\omega t + \epsilon) - \frac{\omega}{\alpha} \int e^{\alpha t} \cos(\omega t + \epsilon)\,dt$$

Eliminate the integral involving the sine function and collect terms:

$$\left(1 + \frac{\omega^2}{\alpha^2}\right) \int e^{\alpha t} \cos(\omega t + \epsilon)\,dt = \frac{1}{\alpha} e^{\alpha t}\left\{\cos(\omega t + \epsilon) + \frac{\omega}{\alpha} \sin(\omega t + \epsilon)\right\}$$

i.e. $\displaystyle \int y\, dt = A \int e^{\alpha t} \cos(\omega t + \epsilon)\, dt$

$$= \frac{A}{\sqrt{\alpha^2 + \omega^2}}\, e^{\alpha t} \left\{ \frac{\alpha}{\sqrt{\alpha^2 + \omega^2}} \cos(\omega t + \epsilon) + \frac{\omega}{\sqrt{\alpha^2 + \omega^2}} \sin(\omega t + \epsilon) \right\}$$

$$= \frac{1}{\rho}\, A e^{\alpha t} \cos(\omega t + \epsilon - \eta)$$

where ρ and η have the same values as before. $\int y\, dt$ is a sinusoidal variable with the same frequency (ω) and damping (α) as y, but with amplitude A multiplied by $\dfrac{1}{\rho}$ and phase retarded by η.

Repeated differentiation and integration give similar results. As shown in Ex. 2 below, the second derivative and integral are :

$$\frac{d^2 y}{dt^2} = \rho^2 A e^{\alpha t} \cos(\omega t + \epsilon + 2\eta) \; ; \; \iint y\, dt\, dt = \frac{1}{\rho^2} A e^{\alpha t} \cos(\omega t + \epsilon - 2\eta)$$

The general result is now sufficiently clear. In terms of the differential operator $D = \dfrac{d}{dt}$ and $D^{-1} = \int$, the derivative or integral of $y = A e^{\alpha t} \cos(\omega t + \epsilon)$ of any order is given by :

$$D^n y = \rho^n A e^{\alpha t} \cos(\omega t + \epsilon + n\eta) \quad \dots\dots\dots\dots\dots\dots(1)$$

where n is any (positive or negative) integer, $\rho = \sqrt{\alpha^2 + \omega^2}$ and $\tan\eta = \dfrac{\omega}{\alpha}$.

So far straight-forward methods have been used. They can now provide the justification for the following much simpler derivation. Write the sinusoidal variable y as the " real " part of the complex variable or vector product :

$$z = A e^{i\epsilon} e^{pt} \quad \text{where} \quad p = \alpha + i\omega$$

Proceed to differentiate (or integrate) z according to the ordinary rules :

$$\frac{dz}{dt} = A e^{i\epsilon} (p e^{pt}) = p z$$

and

$$\int z\, dt = A e^{i\epsilon} \left(\frac{1}{p} e^{pt} \right) = \frac{1}{p} z$$

Quite generally : $\qquad\qquad D^n z = p^n z \quad \dots\dots\dots\dots\dots\dots(2)$

for any (positive or negative) integer n. The sinusoidal variable $y = A e^{\alpha t} \cos(\omega t + \epsilon)$ is the " real " part of z ; what is now suggested is that $D^n y$ as a sinusoidal variable is the " real " part of $D^n z = p^n z$. This can be checked by showing that (1) is obtained as the " real " part of (2). For example, if $n=1$, the " real " part of :

$$Dz = pz = A(\alpha + i\omega)e^{i\epsilon}e^{(\alpha + i\omega)t}$$
$$= Ae^{\alpha t}(\alpha + i\omega)\{\cos(\omega t + \epsilon) + i \sin(\omega t + \epsilon)\}$$

is : $\qquad Ae^{\alpha t}\{\alpha \cos(\omega t + \epsilon) - \omega \sin(\omega t + \epsilon)\} = \rho Ae^{\alpha t} \cos(\omega t + \epsilon + \eta)$

which is (1) with $n=1$.

The simplicity of the result (2) is that the operator D, when applied to the vector product z for a sinusoidal variable with $p = \alpha + i\omega$, is to be replaced by the value p. It is just easier to use (2) than (1), and it covers all derivatives and integrals of a sinusoidal variable.

Another result of the same nature can be added, the treatment of a delay of fixed time θ. If $y(t) = Ae^{\alpha t} \cos(\omega t + \epsilon)$ is a sinusoidal variable, the delayed variable is :

$$y(t - \theta) = Ae^{\alpha(t-\theta)} \cos\{\omega(t - \theta) + \epsilon\}$$

i.e. $\qquad y(t - \theta) = (e^{-\alpha\theta}A)e^{\alpha t} \cos(\omega t + \epsilon - \omega\theta) \quad \dots\dots\dots\dots\dots(3)$

The frequency and damping are unchanged ; the delayed variable only differs in that its amplitude is A multiplied by $e^{-\alpha\theta}$ and its phase is retarded by $\omega\theta$. In terms of $z(t) = Ae^{i\epsilon}e^{pt}$, the delayed variation is given by :

$$z(t - \theta) = Ae^{i\epsilon}e^{p(t-\theta)}$$

i.e. $\qquad z(t - \theta) = e^{-p\theta}z(t) \quad \dots\dots\dots\dots\dots\dots\dots\dots(4)$

Again, as can easily be checked, (3) is the real part of (4). It is simpler to use (4) than (3). The operator for " delay θ " is to be replaced by $e^{-p\theta}$ for a sinusoidal variable with $p = \alpha + i\omega$.

The results (2) and (4) can be pulled together and summarised in the following general statement :

If $z = Ae^{i\epsilon}e^{pt}$ (where $p = \alpha + i\omega$) is a complex variable (vector) then :

$\qquad D^n z = p^n z \quad$ *(n any positive or negative integer)*

and $\qquad z(t - \theta) = e^{-p\theta}z(t) \quad$ *(θ any given delay)*

i.e. the operator D is written p and the operator for " delay θ " is written $e^{-p\theta}$. These results give, as their " real " parts, the sinusoidal variable $y = Ae^{\alpha t} \cos(\omega t + \epsilon)$, its derivatives, integrals and delayed values, all as oscillations with the same damping (α) and frequency (ω).

What has now been established is, first, that the derivatives, integrals and delayed values of a sinusoidal variable all have sinusoidal oscillation of the same frequency and damping, and, second, that the relation between the different oscillations (i.e. their differing amplitude and phase) is best handled in terms of operators applied to the corresponding vector products.

Now suppose that a number of sinusoidal variables is given :

$$y_n = A_n e^{\alpha_n t} \cos(\omega_n t + \epsilon_n) \qquad n = 1, 2, 3, \ldots$$

Form the linear combination of them :

$$y = \Sigma \lambda_n y_n = \lambda_1 y_1 + \lambda_2 y_2 + \lambda_3 y_3 + \ldots$$

where the λ's are constants. Since each λ can be absorbed into the corresponding amplitude A, there is no loss of generality in taking :

$$y = \Sigma y_n = y_1 + y_2 + y_3 + \ldots$$

What kind of variable is y? In other words, what results when different sinusoidal variables are added?

The answer is not obvious. Indeed, as long as the frequencies (ω_n) and damping factors (α_n) of the variables are different, almost anything can be produced by the addition. It is only in the very important case when all variables have the same frequency (ω) and damping (α) that a useful result emerges. It is then very simple : the sum of the variables is an oscillation with the same frequency and damping as the variables themselves. It then remains to determine the amplitude and phase of y in terms of those of y_n.

The result appears clearly in terms of the vector products, of which the sinusoidal variables are the " real " parts. Write $p = \alpha + i\omega$ for the common oscillation of frequency (ω) and damping (α), and let :

$$z_n = A_n e^{i\epsilon_n} e^{pt} \quad (n = 1, 2, 3, \ldots)$$

be the variations to be added. Then :

$$z = \Sigma z_n = (\Sigma A_n e^{i\epsilon_n}) e^{pt}$$

and z has the same p, i.e. the same frequency and damping. Its amplitude and phasing are given by :

$$A e^{i\epsilon} = \Sigma A_n e^{i\epsilon_n}$$

This is a process of adding the initial vectors according to the ordinary rules. It is equivalent to :

$$A \cos \epsilon = \Sigma A_n \cos \epsilon_n \quad \text{and} \quad A \sin \epsilon = \Sigma A_n \sin \epsilon_n$$

The result can be made clear, and a diagrammatic illustration can be given, in the case of the addition of two variables. If y_1 and y_2 are the sinusoidal variables represented by :

$$z_1 = A_1 e^{i\epsilon_1} e^{pt} \quad \text{and} \quad z_2 = A_2 e^{i\epsilon_2} e^{pt}$$

then $y = y_1 + y_2$ is represented by :

$$z = z_1 + z_2 = (A_1 e^{i\epsilon_1} + A_2 e^{i\epsilon_2}) e^{pt}$$

Let $z = Ae^{i\epsilon}e^{pt}$ so that :

$$Ae^{i\epsilon} = A_1 e^{i\epsilon_1} + A_2 e^{i\epsilon_2}$$

i.e. $A(\cos \epsilon + i \sin \epsilon) = A_1(\cos \epsilon_1 + i \sin \epsilon_1) + A_2(\cos \epsilon_2 + i \sin \epsilon_2)$

Hence A and ϵ for $y = y_1 + y_2$ are obtained from :

$$A \cos \epsilon = A_1 \cos \epsilon_1 + A_2 \cos \epsilon_2$$

and $$A \sin \epsilon = A_1 \sin \epsilon_1 + A_2 \sin \epsilon_2$$

This is simply the " parallelogram rule " for adding vectors. It is illustrated by Fig. 18 in the case $\alpha = 0$. On the left of the diagram, the two

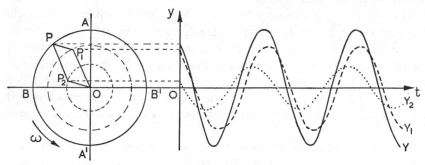

FIG. 18.

initial vectors OP_1 and OP_2 for y_1 and y_2 are added to give OP for $y = y_1 + y_2$ by the " parallelogram rule ". On the right of the diagram is shown the generation of the two given sinusoidal variables y_1 and y_2 from OP_1 and OP_2, and the generation of the sinusoidal variable $y = y_1 + y_2$ from OP, the rate of rotation (ω) being the same for all. It is easily checked, from the diagram, that the ordinate y is the sum of the separate ordinates y_1 and y_2 at each point of time. The point is that, to compound two sinusoidal variables as on the right of Fig. 18, all that need be done is to compound the initial vectors as on the left of Fig. 18.

The result obtained can be expressed in full in the following terms :

A number of sinusoidal variables y_n with the same frequency and damping ($p = \alpha + i\omega$) is given and the sum $y = \Sigma y_n$ is formed. Then y is a sinusoidal variable with the same frequency and damping. If y_n is the " real " part of $A_n e^{i\epsilon_n}e^{pt}$, then y is the " real " part of $Ae^{i\epsilon}e^{pt}$ where in vectors :

$$Ae^{i\epsilon} = \Sigma A_n e^{i\epsilon_n}$$

or in full :

$$A \cos \epsilon = \Sigma A_n \cos \epsilon_n \quad A \sin \epsilon = \Sigma A_n \sin \epsilon_n$$

The importance of this result lies in the fact that, as already established, derivatives, integrals and delayed values of any sinusoidal variable all have the same frequency and damping and so can be added to give a compound variable which is also sinusoidal with the same frequency and damping. Hence, if $y = Ae^{\alpha t} \cos(\omega t + \epsilon)$ is a sinusoidal variable, then an expression such as

$$\frac{d^2 y}{dt^2} + a\frac{dy}{dt} + by$$

or

$$\lambda_1 y(t) + \lambda_2 \frac{d}{dt} y(t - \theta) + \lambda_3 \int y(t) dt$$

has a sinusoidal variation with the same frequency (ω) and damping (α), but with different amplitude and phasing to be found by addition of appropriate vectors.

EXERCISES 4.9

1. If $y = A \cos(\omega t + \epsilon)$. show that $\dfrac{d^2 y}{dt^2} = \omega^2 A \cos(\omega t + \epsilon + \pi)$ and that

$$\iint y \, dt \, dt = \frac{1}{\omega^2} A \cos(\omega t + \epsilon - \pi)$$

2. From the values of $\dfrac{dy}{dt}$ and $\int y \, dt$ obtained in the text from $y = Ae^{\alpha t} \cos(\omega t + \epsilon)$, obtain by further differentiation and integration :

$$\frac{d^2 y}{dt^2} = \rho^2 Ae^{\alpha t} \cos(\omega t + \epsilon + 2\eta)$$

$$\iint y \, dt \, dt = \frac{1}{\rho^2} Ae^{\alpha t} \cos(\omega t + \epsilon - 2\eta)$$

3. If $y = Ae^{\alpha t} \cos(\omega t + \epsilon)$, then $\dfrac{dy}{dt} = \rho Ae^{\alpha t} \cos(\omega t + \epsilon + \eta)$ indicates that the amplitude of the oscillation is multiplied by $\rho = \sqrt{\alpha^2 + \omega^2}$, and the phase advanced by $\eta = \tan^{-1}\dfrac{\omega}{\alpha}$, in passing from y to $\dfrac{dy}{dt}$. Write $\alpha = 0$ and show that the amplitude is multiplied by ω and the phase advanced by $\dfrac{\pi}{2}$ if the oscillation is regular.

4. From $y = Ae^{\alpha t} \cos(\omega t + \epsilon)$ obtain $\dfrac{d}{dt} y(t - \theta)$. Show that it is the " real " part of $pe^{-p\theta} z$, where $z = Ae^{i\epsilon}e^{pt}$. As a particular case, show that, if

$$y = A \cos(\omega t + \epsilon),$$

then $\dfrac{d}{dt} y\left(t - \dfrac{\pi}{2\omega}\right)$ is a sinusoidal variable with no lag or lead on $y(t)$.

5. If $y_1, y_2, y_3, \dots y_n, \dots$ are sinusoidal variables with the same frequency and damping, *and* with the same phase, show that $y = \Sigma y_n$ is a similar variable and that its amplitude is the sum of the amplitudes of the y_n. Illustrate in terms of Fig. 18.

6. Take $y_1 = Ae^{\alpha t} \cos(\omega t + \epsilon)$ and $y_2 = Ae^{\alpha t} \cos\left(\omega t + \epsilon + \dfrac{\pi}{2}\right)$ as two sinusoidal variables which differ only in that one leads the other in phase $\left(\text{by } \dfrac{\pi}{2}\right)$. Show that, if $y = y_1 + y_2$, then

$$y = \sqrt{2}\, Ae^{\alpha t} \cos\left(\omega t + \epsilon + \dfrac{\pi}{4}\right)$$

and interpret in Fig. 18 . What happens to $y = y_1 + y_2$ if y_1 is as above but $y_2 = Ae^{\alpha t} \cos(\omega t + \epsilon + \pi)$?

REFERENCES

Allen (R. G. D.) (1938) : *Mathematical Analysis for Economists* (Macmillan, 1938), Chapters IX and XVII.

Courant (R.) and Robbins (H.) (1941) : *What is Mathematics?* (Oxford, 1941), Chapter II.

Durell (C. V.) and Robson (A.) (1937) : *Advanced Algebra* (Bell, 1937), Chapter VIII and XIII.

Littlewood (D. E.) (1949) : *The Skeleton Key of Mathematics* (Hutchinson, 1949), Chapters V and VI.

Titchmarsh (E. C.) (1949) : *Mathematics for the General Reader* (Hutchinson, 1949), Chapter IX.

Tustin (A.) (1953) : *The Mechanism of Economic Systems* (Heinemann, 1953), Chapter III.

CHAPTER 5

MATHEMATICAL ANALYSIS:
LINEAR DIFFERENTIAL EQUATIONS

5.1 Differential Equations

THERE are many ways in which differential equations arise in practice but they all involve continuous variation. Among the simpler forms of differential equations are those representing a cumulative growth when the addition is made continuously and in a specified way. Continuity here is a concept obtained from finite processes by proceeding to the limit, just as the derivative of a function is defined from finite changes. This is illustrated by considering a sum of money accumulating at compound interest at the rate of $100r\%$ per year. Let $\pounds Y_0$ be the initial sum, amounting to $\pounds Y_x$ at the end of x years. If interest is compounded annually, then $Y_{x+1}=(1+r)Y_x$ where x takes the values, 0, 1, 2, 3, ... ; if compounding is twice a year, then $Y_{x+\frac{1}{2}}=(1+\frac{1}{2}r)Y_x$ where $x=0, \frac{1}{2}, 1, \frac{3}{2}, ...$ Generally, if interest is compounded n times a year and x runs through the values $0, \dfrac{1}{n}, \dfrac{2}{n}, \dfrac{3}{n}, ...,$ then :

$$Y_{x+\frac{1}{n}}=\left(1+\frac{r}{n}\right)Y_x$$

i.e.
$$\frac{Y_{x+\frac{1}{n}}-Y_x}{1/n}=rY_x$$

i.e.
$$\frac{Y_{x+h}-Y_x}{h}=rY_x \quad \text{where } h=\frac{1}{n}$$

The concept of interest compounded continuously is a limiting one where n increases indefinitely ($n\to\infty$, $h\to0$). The law of growth then takes the limiting form :

$$\frac{dY_x}{dx}=rY_x$$

The variation of x is continuous and the law of growth is represented by a differential equation in the derivative of the function Y_x under investigation. The solution of the differential equation is an explicit expression of the function Y_x in terms of x. In this instance, the solution (see 5.3 below) is :

$$Y_x=Y_0e^{rx}$$

An *ordinary differential equation* is a relation in which appear a function of one variable and its various derivatives. The form of the function is not given; it is to be found in solving the equation. There are other types of differential equations involving functions of more than one variable but these are not considered here. The general expression of an ordinary differential equation in a function Y of an independent variable x can be written:

$$\phi\left(x,\ Y, \frac{dY}{dx},\ \frac{d^2Y}{dx^2},\ \dots\ \frac{d^nY}{dx^n}\right)=0 \quad\dots\dots\dots\dots\dots(1)$$

The *order* of the equation is that of the highest derivative in it. A first order equation, like that representing growth at compound interest, contains $\dfrac{dY}{dx}$ but no higher derivatives. A second order equation includes $\dfrac{d^2Y}{dx^2}$ but no derivatives of higher order. The general form (1) is of order n.

The solution of ordinary differential equations of various orders and types is a technical matter not pursued here. There are text books on the subject such as Piaggio (1920) and the solutions of some types (mainly of the first order) of interest to economists are given in Allen (1938). Here one particular type of differential equation is treated in some detail, the type known as the linear equation with constant coefficients.

The ordinary differential equation (1) is *linear* if Y and all its derivatives enter in linear combination; there are no squares or higher powers, nor any other algebraic or analytical forms. The independent variable x, however, can appear in any way, both in the coefficients of $Y, \dfrac{dY}{dx}, \dfrac{d^2Y}{dx^2}, \dots$ and in the term which does not involve Y and its derivatives. The equation is *linear with constant coefficients* if, in addition, the coefficients of Y, $\dfrac{dY}{dx}, \dfrac{d^2Y}{dx^2}, \dots$ are all constants not involving x. It is only the term not involving Y and its derivatives which contains the variable x and this term can still take any form whatever.

The general linear differential equation with constant coefficients and of order n is:

$$a_0\frac{d^nY}{dx^n}+a_1\frac{d^{n-1}Y}{dx^{n-1}}+\dots+a_{n-1}\frac{dY}{dx}+a_nY=f(x) \quad\dots\dots\dots\dots(2)$$

where $a_0, a_1, \dots a_{n-1}, a_n$ are constants ($a_0\neq0$) and where $f(x)$ is any expression in x. The particular case in which $f(x)$ is absent is called the *homogeneous* form:

$$a_0\frac{d^ny}{dx^n}+a_1\frac{d^{n-1}y}{dx^{n-1}}+\dots+a_{n-1}\frac{dy}{dx}+a_ny=0 \quad\dots\dots\dots\dots(3)$$

Equations of the form (2) or (3) are considered here. There is no limitation on the order n of the equations though particular attention is paid to those of low order, e.g. $n=1, 2$. As will be seen, it is a matter of convenience in economic applications to denote the dependent variable or function by Y in the non-homogeneous form (2) and by y in the homogeneous form (3).

Examples of linear differential equations with constant coefficients are:

$$\text{(i)} \quad \frac{dY}{dx} = \frac{1}{ax+b}$$

$$\text{(ii)} \quad \frac{dY}{dx} + Y = \sin x + \cos x$$

$$\text{(iii)} \quad \frac{d^2y}{dx^2} + \lambda(b-a)y = 0$$

$$\text{(iv)} \quad \frac{d^2Y}{dx^2} + 2\frac{dY}{dx} + Y = x + 2$$

$$\text{(v)} \quad 4\left(\frac{d^2Y}{dx^2} + \frac{dY}{dx} - 1\right) = 5(x - Y)$$

$$\text{(vi)} \quad \frac{d^3y}{dx^3} - \frac{d^2y}{dx^2} + 2y = 0$$

EXERCISES 5.1

1. If Y is the distance travelled by a moving object in time x, show that $\frac{dY}{dx} = $ constant, and $\frac{d^2Y}{dx^2} = $ constant, represent a constant velocity, and a constant acceleration, respectively. Re-interpret when Y is national income or output at time x.

2. Show that the amount of $£Y_0$ at the end of x years at compound interest at $100r\%$ per year compounded n times a year is $£Y_x$ where:

$$Y_x = Y_0\left(1 + \frac{r}{n}\right)^{nx}$$

Check for $n=1$, $n=2$. Deduce that, with continuous compounding $Y_x = Y_0e^{rx}$ and check that $\frac{dY_x}{dx} = rY_x$.

5.2 Basic Results; Initial Conditions and Arbitrary Constants

The solution of a differential equation is essentially a practical matter. It is to find, in one way or another, by trial and error, a function which satisfies the given equation. The assumption is that there is such a function, that the solution exists. This avoids complicated questions of existence, of whether there is any function in a certain range of types (algebraic, trigonometric, and so on) which satisfies the equation. If the practical attempt fails, it may be because it has not been pursued far enough—or because there is no solution to find.

The practical guides are some basic results which can be formulated quite simply. The first is a theorem on ordinary differential equations in general ; it is offered here without formal proof but with an explanation which is plausible enough.

The general solution of an ordinary differential equation of order n gives Y as a function of x involving exactly n arbitrary constants :

$$Y = Y(x ;\ A_1, A_2, \dots A_n)$$

The following consideration makes this a plausible result. An arbitrary constant can always be made to disappear by one process of differentiation. So, if a function contains two arbitrary constants, the first derivative eliminates one and the second derivative eliminates the other. The solution of a differential equation reverses the process of differentiation and the arbitrary constants re-appear.

The theorem relates to the *general solution* of the equation. There is a great variety of *particular solutions* of any given equation. The significance of the theorem is that all particular solutions are included within the general solution, each corresponding to some particular values of the constants $A_1, A_2, \dots A_n$. There are no solutions other than particular instances of the general solution. Particular solutions are obtained by specifying or determining the constants, and the usual way of interpreting (and hence of determining) the constants to suit particular circumstances is in terms of initial conditions.

The other basic results are rules relating to a linear differential equation with constant coefficients. In non-homogeneous form of order n it is :

$$a_0 \frac{d^n Y}{dx^n} + a_1 \frac{d^{n-1} Y}{dx^{n-1}} + \dots + a_{n-1} \frac{dY}{dx} + a_n Y = f(x) \ \dots\dots\dots\dots(1)$$

and the corresponding homogeneous form is :

$$a_0 \frac{d^n y}{dx^n} + a_1 \frac{d^{n-1} y}{dx^{n-1}} + \dots + a_{n-1} \frac{dy}{dx} + a_n y = 0 \ \dots\dots\dots\dots(2)$$

RULES : (i) If the homogeneous equation (2) has solutions $y = y_1(x)$ and $y = y_2(x)$, then $y = y_1(x) + y_2(x)$ is also a solution.

(ii) If the homogeneous equation (2) has a solution $y = y(x)$, then $y = Ay(x)$ is also a solution for any constant A.

(iii) If $Y = \overline{Y}(x)$ is any particular solution whatever of the general equation (1) and if $y = y(x ;\ A_1, A_2, \dots A_n)$ is the general solution of the corresponding homogeneous form (2), then the general solution of (1) is $Y = \overline{Y}(x) + y(x ;\ A_1, A_2, \dots A_n)$.

The proofs of these rules are quite simple ; it is a matter of substituting the suggested solutions in the equation and of checking that they satisfy it.

The rules provide a practical procedure for solving any given equation of form (1). The homogeneous form (2) is tackled first, with the aid of Rules (i) and (ii) in combination. Attempt to find n particular and different solutions of (2) and let them be $y_1(x)$, $y_2(x)$, ... $y_n(x)$. Then, by the rules, a solution of (2) is :

$$y = A_1 y_1(x) + A_2 y_2(x) + ... + A_n y_n(x) \quad ....(3)$$

Since this contains exactly n arbitrary constants A_1, A_2, ... A_n, it is the general solution of (2). Rule (iii) then provides the general solution of the original equation (1), once any particular solution of the equation is found. The general solution is :

$$Y = \overline{Y}(x) + A_1 y_1(x) + A_2 y_2(x) + ... + A_n y_n(x) \quad ....(4)$$

In (4), $\overline{Y}(x)$ is called the *particular integral* and the remainder makes up the *complementary function*, the general solution (3) of the corresponding homogeneous form. This practical procedure fails if n particular solutions of (2) which are all different cannot be found to write in (3) or (4). The case of failure does arise in practice and a way round the difficulty will be devised when it is met.

The procedure seeks the general solution of the homogeneous form first, and then adds a particular solution of the original equation to give the general solution of the given non-homogeneous form. The reverse procedure is often preferable and it is usually more appropriate in solving differential equations arising in economic problems. The practical steps are then as follows. The given equation (1) is expressed in terms of the function Y (e.g. income or output) under investigation. Some particular solution $Y = \overline{Y}(x)$ is first sought. Any particular solution will serve but the most relevant, from the point of view of interpreting the result, is a solution which represents the *trend* or equilibrium variation of Y. Interest is usually concentrated on the path of Y as x increases indefinitely, e.g. the time path of Y if x is time. The particular solution $Y = \overline{Y}(x)$ sought then describes that path which is consistent with the given equation (1) and which is in some sense a norm or equilibrium. The next step is to write $y = Y - \overline{Y}$ as the deviation of Y from the trend or equilibrium value. It follows that y must satisfy the homogeneous form (2), as is seen by substituting Y and $\overline{Y}$ in (1)—both being solutions—and subtracting. The last step is to obtain the general solution of the homogeneous form (2) in the way indicated in (3). The solution is now both complete and ready

for interpretation. The deviations y of Y from $\overline{Y}$ are given by (3);
translating back into the original variables gives the solution (4). Of the
two terms in this solution, one is the trend or equilibrium path (the particular integral) and the other is the deviation from trend or equilibrium
(the complementary function). An example of this practical procedure has
already been worked out in an economic problem, see equation (4) of
3.3 above.

There are some troublesome sources of confusion about the arbitrary
constants which appear (in number equal to the order of the equation) in
the general solution (4). One arises from the fact that the constants, being
arbitrary, can appear in various disguises. The general solution can be
written in two or more ways which appear to be different or conflicting;
in fact, they differ because of a re-arrangement and they are identical. The
same difficulty is met when, as is often convenient, the solution is written
first with one set of arbitrary constants and then with another—apparently
transforming the nature of the solution.

For example, the solution of $\dfrac{dY}{dx} = \dfrac{1}{ax+b}$ is $Y = \dfrac{1}{a} \log (ax+b)$ plus an
arbitrary constant (see 5.3 below). This can be written in various ways in
which arbitrary constants are swapped according to convenience. So:

$$Y = \frac{1}{a} \log (ax+b) + A$$

$$= \log A' \, (ax+b)^{\frac{1}{a}} \qquad \text{where } A = \log A'$$

$$= \frac{1}{a} \log A'' \, (ax+b) \qquad \text{where } A' = (A'')^{\frac{1}{a}}$$

The arbitrary constant can be A, A' or A'' as desired.

The most usual way of interpreting arbitrary constants is through initial
conditions imposed on Y or its derivatives. To each arbitrary constant
there can correspond one initial condition which " determines " the
constant. A differential equation of the first order has a general solution
of the form $Y = Y(x ; A)$ with one arbitrary constant A. Suppose that
the equation is subject to the single initial condition $Y = Y_0$ when $x = 0$.
Then :

$$Y(0 ; \ A) = Y_0$$

which gives A in terms of Y_0. In fact, $Y = Y(x ; A) = F(x ; Y_0)$ is the
solution, switching the arbitrary constant from A to Y_0. This is a very
useful form of the general solution; given Y_0 at $x = 0$, the differential
equation then provides the value of $\dfrac{dY}{dx}$ at $x = 0$ and so the initial *variation*

in Y from the starting value Y_0. The general idea is that the solution needs to be " started up " by specifying one initial value.

Similarly, a differential equation of the second order has a general solution $Y = Y(x; A_1, A_2)$. Let the equation be subject to two initial conditions, e.g.

$$Y = Y_0 \quad \text{and} \quad \frac{dY}{dx} = Y_0' \quad \text{at} \quad x = 0$$

Then, on substituting $Y = Y(x; A_1, A_2)$, two equations are obtained relating A_1 and A_2 to Y_0 and Y_0'. From these, A_1 and A_2 can be expressed in terms of Y_0 and Y_0' and the arbitrary constants can be switched in the solution : $Y = F(x; Y_0, Y_0')$. Given Y_0 and Y_0' at $x = 0$, the differential equation fixes the value of $\frac{d^2Y}{dx^2}$ at $x = 0$ and " starts up " the variation of Y.

Two initial conditions are needed to generate the solution of a differential equation of the second order. The extension of higher order equations is clear.

From one point of view, therefore, initial values like Y_0 and Y_0' are just arbitrary constants. However, if specific initial conditions are imposed, then the arbitrary constants take specific values and the general solution becomes a particular solution—that appropriate to specific initial conditions. Two cases will illustrate :

Ex. (a). $\dfrac{dY}{dx} = \dfrac{1}{ax + b}$ subject to $Y = 0$ at $x = 0$.

The general solution is $\quad Y = \dfrac{1}{a} \log(ax + b) + A \quad$ (5.3 below)

At $x = 0$ $\qquad\qquad\qquad 0 = \dfrac{1}{a} \log b + A$

i.e. $\qquad\qquad\qquad\qquad A = -\dfrac{1}{a} \log b$

The particular solution is $Y = \dfrac{1}{a}\{\log(ax + b) - \log b\} = \dfrac{1}{a} \log \dfrac{ax + b}{b}$.

Ex. (b). $\dfrac{d^2y}{dx^2} - a^2 y = 0$ subject to $y = y_0$ and $\dfrac{dy}{dx} = 0$ at $x = 0$.

The general solution is $y = A_1 e^{ax} + A_2 e^{-ax}$ (5.4, Ex. 1, below).

So $\qquad\qquad\qquad \dfrac{dy}{dx} = a(A_1 e^{ax} - A_2 e^{-ax})$

The initial conditions then give at $x = 0$:

$$y_0 = A_1 + A_2 \quad \text{and} \quad 0 = a(A_1 - A_2)$$

i.e. $\qquad\qquad\qquad\qquad A_1 = A_2 = \tfrac{1}{2} y_0$

The particular solution is $y = \tfrac{1}{2} y_0(e^{ax} + e^{-ax})$.

Here y_0 can be regarded as arbitrary ; but the solution is still a particular one since the other arbitrary constant has been given a specified value.

EXERCISES 5.2

1. Prove the Rules (i), (ii) and (iii) above.

2. Consider the solution (4) of equation (1) as giving the variation of Y about a trend or equilibrium $\bar{Y}$. As x increases indefinitely, distinguish between " explosive " and " damped " variations and show that one y_r of " explosive " form is sufficient for " explosive " Y. What can be said of the " damped " case? Express in terms of a concept of a " dominant " term among $y_r (r=1, 2, \dots n)$

5.3 Linear Differential Equations : First Order

The equation $\dfrac{dY}{dx}=f(x)$ is the simplest form of a linear differential equation with constant coefficients ; it is of first order and the term in Y is missing. The solution is the indefinite integral of $f(x)$ with an additive constant :

$$Y=\int f(x)dx + A$$

Integration here is simply reverse differentiation. The more common and useful cases can be tabled in relation to the standard forms of differentiation, e.g.

Derivatives : Standard forms	Differential Equations	
	Equation	Solution
$\dfrac{d}{dx}\left(\dfrac{x^{n+1}}{n+1}\right)=x^n$	$\dfrac{dY}{dx}=x^n$	$Y=\dfrac{x^{n+1}}{n+1}+A \quad (n \neq -1)$
$\dfrac{d}{dx}(e^x)=e^x$	$\dfrac{dY}{dx}=e^x$	$Y=e^x+A$
$\dfrac{d}{dx}(\log x)=\dfrac{1}{x}$	$\dfrac{dY}{dx}=\dfrac{1}{x}$	$Y=\log x+A$
$\dfrac{d}{dx}(\sin x)=\cos x$	$\dfrac{dY}{dx}=\cos x$	$Y=\sin x+A$

These results are easily extended to the case where $(ax+b)$ appears instead of x in the function $f(x)$. So, $\dfrac{dY}{dx}=e^{ax+b}$ has solution $Y=\dfrac{1}{a}e^{ax+b}+A$ and

$\dfrac{dY}{dx}=\dfrac{1}{ax+b}$ has solution $Y=\dfrac{1}{a}\log(ax+b)+A$.

A feature of the solution here is that the single arbitrary constant is an additive one. It will be seen later (5.5 below) that any linear differential equation with constant coefficients has a solution with an additive constant if the term in Y is missing from the equation, as it is in $\dfrac{dY}{dx}=f(x)$.

From equation (1) of 5.2, the general linear differential equation (constant coefficients) of the first order is :

$$a_0 \frac{dY}{dx} + a_1 Y = f(x)$$

Since $a_0 \neq 0$, the equation can be written with a change of notation :

$$\frac{dY}{dx} - aY = f(x) \quad \dots\dots\dots\dots\dots\dots\dots\dots(1)$$

and the corresponding homogeneous form is :

$$\frac{dy}{dx} = ay \quad \dots\dots\dots\dots\dots\dots\dots\dots\dots(2)$$

According to the practical method of 5.2, two steps need to be taken. First, some particular solution $Y = \overline{Y}(x)$ must be found for equation (1). This is generally a matter of trial and error, depending on the particular form of $f(x)$ specified. Second, write $y = Y - \overline{Y}$ and note that Y and $\overline{Y}$ both satisfy (1) :

$$\frac{dY}{dx} - aY = f(x) \quad \text{and} \quad \frac{d\overline{Y}}{dx} - a\overline{Y} = f(x)$$

Subtract :
$$\frac{dy}{dx} = ay$$

i.e. $y = Y - Y$ satisfies the homogeneous form (2). A general solution of (2) must be found to give y. This is something which can be tackled in general terms.

The equation (2) can be written:

$$\frac{d}{dx}(\log y) = \frac{1}{y}\frac{dy}{dx} = a$$

The solution is $\log y = ax + A'$ (A' arbitrary constant)

i.e. $y = e^{ax+A'}$

i.e. $y = Ae^{ax}$ ($A = e^{A'}$, arbitrary constant)

The general solution of (1) is then:

$$Y = Y(x) + Ae^{ax} \quad \dots\dots\dots\dots\dots\dots(3)$$

The arbitrary constant can be found from one initial condition, e.g. $Y = Y_0$ when $x = 0$.

There is an alternative way of solving (2) which proves to be more easily extended to cases of higher order equations. Try $y = e^{px}$ as a solution of (2), where p is some constant to be found. Then :

$$\frac{d}{dx}(e^{px}) = ae^{px}$$

i.e. $$pe^{px} = ae^{px}$$

i.e. $$p = a \quad \text{(since } e^{px} \neq 0\text{)}$$

Hence, a solution of (2) is $y = e^{ax}$. By 5.2, the general solution is :

$$y = Ae^{ax}$$

where A is an arbitrary constant. The solution is that already obtained.

The constant a is given ; it represents the " structure " of the equation (1). The behaviour of the solution (3) as x increases depends on the magnitude and particularly on the sign of a. If $a > 0$, the term Ae^{ax} in (3) increases steadily as x increases—the " explosive " case. If $a < 0$, the term Ae^{ax} decreases steadily towards zero as x increases—the " damped " case. The term $\overline{Y}(x)$, whatever form it may have, is the trend or equilibrium path on which is super-imposed an explosive or damped variation. The nature of the variation depends on the initial disturbance (which determines A) and on the magnitude of a. The larger the numerical value of a, the more explosive or damped is the variation.

The solution of linear differential equations generally involves exponential functions and the properties of these functions need to be known. See Allen (1938), Chapter IX, and 4.4 above. The following properties are frequently required :

(i) $e^x = 1$ when $x = 0$ \qquad (ii) $\dfrac{d}{dx}(e^{ax+b}) = ae^{ax+b}$

(iii) e^{ax+b} varies at a constant proportionate rate a, increasing to infinity as x increases if $a > 0$ and decreasing to zero as x increases if $a < 0$.

The term $\overline{Y}(x)$ in the solution (3) depends on the form of $f(x)$ in (1). An important case arises when $f(x) = \alpha$ (constant). A particular solution is sought for :

$$\frac{dY}{dx} - aY = \alpha$$

Try $Y = \mu$, where μ is some constant to be found. Then :

$$-a\mu = \alpha \quad \text{i.e. } \mu = -\frac{\alpha}{a}$$

The general solution of $\dfrac{dY}{dx} - aY = \alpha$ is $Y = Ae^{ax} - \dfrac{\alpha}{a}$. The variation

(Ae^{ax}) is from a constant level $\overline{Y} = -\dfrac{\alpha}{a}$. Other forms of $f(x)$ are examined in Ex. 6 below.

Linear differential equations of the first order appear in simple economic models based on continuous analysis. They have been found above for variation in price P over time in cobweb-type models. In 1.3, the equation is :

$$\frac{dP}{dt} = \left(\frac{b-a}{a_1}\right) P - \frac{\alpha - \beta}{a_1} \quad\dots\dots\dots\dots\dots\dots\dots\dots\dots(4)$$

and, in 1.7 Model III, it is :

$$\frac{dP}{dt} = -\lambda(b-a)P + \lambda(\alpha - \beta)\dots\dots\dots\dots\dots\dots\dots(5)$$

where $D = \alpha + aP$ and $S = \beta + bP$ are the static demand and supply relations and λ is a speed of response (of price changes to stock changes). There is a steady return of price towards equilibrium $\left(\overline{P} = \dfrac{\alpha - \beta}{b - a}\right)$ provided that the coefficients of P in the differential equations (4) and (5) are negative. This is so in the usual case, i.e. $a < 0$, $a_1 < 0$, $b > 0$, $\lambda > 0$. In the cobweb of 1.3, the numerical value of the coefficient is $\dfrac{b + (-a)}{(-a_1)}$ and the approach to equilibrium is fast if a_1 is small. In the stocks model of 1.7, the speed of approach depends on λ.

The simplest versions of macro-economic models also give linear differential equations of the first order, for the variation of income or output Y over time. In the simple multiplier model of 3.4 the equation is :

$$\frac{1}{\lambda}\frac{dY}{dt} = -sY + A$$

which represents a steady return of Y to equilibrium $\left(\overline{Y} = \dfrac{A}{s}\right)$, the speed of approach depending on s, the marginal propensity to save. In the Harrod-Domar growth theory of 3.3, however, the effect of the accelerator is to give a progressive expansion in Y according to the equation :

$$\frac{dY}{dt} = \rho\left(Y - \frac{A}{s}\right)$$

where the coefficient of Y is now $\rho = \dfrac{s}{v} > 0$.

As a further problem, suppose that income Y increases at a constant (proportionate) rate ρ and that deficit spending by the government is a constant proportion k of Y. The national debt D is increased by deficit spending. Hence, for continuous variation :

$$\frac{dY}{dt}=\rho Y \quad \text{and} \quad \frac{dD}{dt}=kY$$

with initial values $Y=Y_0$ and $D=D_0$ at $t=0$. The solution for Y is the constant (proportionate) growth :

$$Y=Y_0 e^{\rho t}$$

and

$$\frac{dD}{dt}=kY_0 e^{\rho t}$$

Hence

$$D=\frac{k}{\rho} Y_0 e^{\rho t}+A$$

where the constant A is found from initial values :

$$D_0=\frac{k}{\rho} Y_0+A$$

On substituting A, national debt is found to increase at the same proportionate rate ρ as national income :

$$D=D_0+\frac{k}{\rho}Y_0(e^{\rho t}-1)$$

and

$$\frac{D}{Y}=\left(\frac{D_0}{Y_0}-\frac{k}{\rho}\right)e^{-\rho t}+\frac{k}{\rho} \to \frac{k}{\rho} \text{ as } t\to\infty$$

The conclusion is that national debt tends to become a fixed proportion of income. This problem is due to Domar (1944), as quoted by Baumol (1951).

EXERCISES 5.3

1. If $\frac{dY}{dx}=a^x$, show that $Y=\frac{a^x}{\log a}+A$ when a is positive $(a\neq 1)$. Examine the case $a=1$.

2. If $\frac{dY}{dx}=\sin(ax+b)$, show that $Y=-\frac{1}{a}\cos(ax+b)+A$.

3. If $\frac{dY}{dx}=\sin(ax+b)$, show that $Y=\frac{1}{a}\sin\left(ax+b-\frac{\pi}{2}\right)+A$ and check that the result is the same as in the previous exercise.

4. Show that the homogeneous differential equation $\frac{dy}{dx}=0$ has $y=1$ as a particular solution and $y=A$ as the general solution. Hence solve $\frac{dY}{dx}=f(x)$ by the method of 5.2 above.

5. Show that the solution of $\frac{dy}{dx}+y=0$ is $y=Ae^{-x}$.

6. Illustrate the determination of particular integrals by showing that the solutions of (i) $\dfrac{dY}{dx} + Y = 1 + x$, (ii) $\dfrac{dY}{dx} + Y = \sin x + \cos x$ are (i) $Y = x + Ae^{-x}$ and (ii) $Y = \sin x + Ae^{-x}$. Represent the solutions graphically (for $x \geqslant 0$) and comment on their nature.

7. When $a = 0$, show that the solution (3) above reduces to $Y = \int f(x)dx + A$. What can then be said about the trend and variation from trend in Y?

8. Combine the models represented by (4) and (5) above as indicated in 1.7, Ex. 5, above, and show that the coefficient of P in the differential equation is $-\lambda \dfrac{b-a}{1-\lambda a}$. What can be said about the speed of approach of P to $\bar{P}$ now?

5.4 Linear Differential Equations : Second Order

Without loss of generality, the linear differential equation of second order, and its corresponding homogeneous form, can be written :

$$\frac{d^2Y}{dx^2} + a\frac{dY}{dx} + bY = f(x) \quad \dots\dots\dots\dots\dots(1)$$

$$\frac{d^2y}{dx^2} + a\frac{dy}{dx} + by = 0 \quad \dots\dots\dots\dots\dots(2)$$

The two constants a and b can be given any specific values (including zero) ; they represent the " structure " of the equation.

The same two steps need to be taken. A particular solution $Y = \bar{Y}(x)$ must be found for (1). Write $y = Y - \bar{Y}$ so that y satisfies (2). The essential problem is then to find the general solution of (2). The device already used in 5.3 works again in this case. Try $y = e^{px}$ as a solution of (2). Substitute in (2) and note that $\dfrac{dy}{dx} = pe^{px}$ and $\dfrac{d^2y}{dx^2} = p^2 e^{px}$:

$$(p^2 + ap + b)e^{px} = 0$$

Since $e^{px} \neq 0$, the appropriate values of p are given by the *auxiliary equation* :

$$p^2 + ap + b = 0 \quad \dots\dots\dots\dots\dots(3)$$

This is a quadratic in p with roots

$$p_1, p_2 = \tfrac{1}{2}(-a \pm \sqrt{a^2 - 4b}) \quad \dots\dots\dots\dots(4)$$

The roots may be real and different $(a^2 > 4b)$, real and equal $(a^2 = 4b)$ or conjugate complex $(a^2 < 4b)$, as shown in 4.6 above. In each case the general solution of (2) is obtained and, with $\bar{Y}(x)$, provides the general solution of (1).

Case : $a^2 > 4b$. The roots of (3) are real and different, given by (4). The general solution of (1) is then :

$$Y = \bar{Y}(x) + A_1 e^{p_1 x} + A_2 e^{p_2 x} \quad \dots\dots\dots\dots(5)$$

where A_1 and A_2 are arbitrary constants which can be determined from two initial conditions, e.g. $Y = Y_0$ and $\dfrac{dY}{dx} = Y_0'$ at $x = 0$. The solution is analogous to that of the first order equation of 5.3.

The nature of the solution depends on the signs and magnitudes of p_1 and p_2 which in their turn depend on a and b in the original equation. Interest usually centres on the deviation of Y from the trend of equilibrium $\bar{Y}$, and on what happens to this deviation as x increases. If the deviation increases indefinitely, through positive or negative values, then the variation of Y is " explosive " from the trend $\bar{Y}$. On the other hand, if the deviation decreases towards zero (with or without oscillations), then Y has a " damped " variation about the trend $\bar{Y}$. In this case, the deviation is composed of two terms, $A_1 e^{p_1 x}$ and $A_2 e^{p_2 x}$. The question is : which is the *dominant term*, i.e. which effectively determines the course of $y = Y - \bar{Y}$ as x increases.

The answer in this case is simple ; the greater of the two roots of the auxiliary equation gives the dominant term in the solution. Suppose that this greater or *dominant root* is p_1. If p_1 is positive, then $A_1 e^{p_1 x}$ increases indefinitely and the variation of Y is " explosive ". The other term matters little ; it may increase $(p_2 > 0)$ or decrease $(p_2 < 0)$ without effecting the " explosive " nature of the variation of Y as x increases. If p_1 is negative, then p_2 must also be negative and both terms $A_1 e^{p_1 x}$ and $A_2 e^{p_2 x}$ decrease towards zero, i.e. the variation of Y is " damped " towards $\bar{Y}$.

Case : $a^2 = 4b$. The roots of (3) are real but equal and, from (4), the common value is $p_1 = p_2 = -\tfrac{1}{2}a$. The homogeneous equation is now :

$$\frac{d^2y}{dx^2} + a\frac{dy}{dx} + \tfrac{1}{4}a^2 y = 0 \quad \dotfill (6)$$

and the auxiliary equation is $p^2 + ap + \tfrac{1}{4}a^2 = (p + \tfrac{1}{2}a)^2 = 0$

One solution of (6) is found : $y = e^{-\frac{1}{2}ax}$. The method of 5.2 breaks down unless a second and different solution of (6) can be found. The " trick " which works now is to try $y = xe^{px}\ (p = -\tfrac{1}{2}a)$ as a solution of (6). On substitution of

$$y = xe^{px} ; \quad \frac{dy}{dx} = (1 + px)e^{px} ; \quad \frac{d^2y}{dx^2} = (2p + p^2x)e^{px} :$$
$$\{2p + p^2x + a(1 + px) + \tfrac{1}{4}a^2x\}e^{px} = \{2(p + \tfrac{1}{2}a) + (p + \tfrac{1}{2}a)^2x\}e^{px} = 0$$

since $p = -\tfrac{1}{2}a$. Hence $y = xe^{-\frac{1}{2}ax}$ is a solution of (6) as well as $y = e^{-\frac{1}{2}ax}$. The general solution of (6) is $y = (A_1 + A_2x)e^{-\frac{1}{2}ax}$ where A_1 and A_2 are arbitrary constants. The general solution of the original equation (1) is then :

$$Y = \overline{Y}(x) + (A_1 + A_2 x)e^{-\frac{1}{2}ax} \quad \dots\dots\dots\dots\dots\dots(7)$$

A_1 and A_2 can again be determined by initial conditions.

This is almost the same as the solution of the first order equation of 5.3. The difference is that, instead of a single arbitrary constant, there are now two arbitrary constants combined in the factor $(A_1 + A_2 x)$ multiplying the exponential $e^{-\frac{1}{2}ax}$ in (7). The difference is appreciable for moderate values of x but becomes unimportant as x increases indefinitely. This is because the exponential $e^{-\frac{1}{2}ax}$ swamps the factor $(A_1 + A_2 x)$. The exponential function increases or decreases more rapidly than any power of x ; for example xe^x increases like e^x, and xe^{-x} decreases to zero like e^{-x}, as x tends to infinity. The variation of Y from $\overline{Y}$ is given by $(A_1 + A_2 x)e^{-\frac{1}{2}ax}$ and the *dominant term* is $e^{-\frac{1}{2}ax}$. If $a < 0$, the variation is " explosive " ; if $a > 0$, the variation is " damped " to zero.

Case : $a^2 < 4b$. The roots of (3) are conjugate complex numbers which can be written :

$$p_1, p_2 = \alpha \pm i\omega = \tfrac{1}{2}(-a \pm i\sqrt{4b - a^2})$$

so that
$$\alpha = -\tfrac{1}{2}a \quad \text{and} \quad \omega = \tfrac{1}{2}\sqrt{4b - a^2}$$

The general solution of (1) is then :

$$Y = \overline{Y}(x) + B_1 e^{p_1 x} + B_2 e^{p_2 x}$$

i.e.
$$Y = \overline{Y}(x) + B_1 e^{(\alpha + i\omega)x} + B_2 e^{(\alpha - i\omega)x}$$

where B_1 and B_2 are arbitrary constants. From the properties of complex numbers (Chapter 4 above), the solution can be developed as follows :

$$\begin{aligned}
Y - \overline{Y}(x) &= e^{\alpha x}(B_1 e^{i\omega x} + B_2 e^{-i\omega x}) \\
&= e^{\alpha x}\{B_1(\cos \omega x + i \sin \omega x) + B_2(\cos \omega x - i \sin \omega x)\} \\
&= e^{\alpha x}(A_1 \cos \omega x + A_2 \sin \omega x)
\end{aligned}$$

where $A_1 = B_1 + B_2$ and $A_2 = i(B_1 - B_2)$ are also arbitrary constants. The first arbitrary constants (B_1 and B_2) must be conjugate complex to give real A_1 and A_2.

A further switch of arbitrary constants can be made. Write :

$$A_1 = A \cos \epsilon \quad \text{and} \quad A_2 = A \sin \epsilon$$

which is equivalent to transformation from cartesian co-ordinates (A_1, A_2) to polar co-ordinates (A, ϵ). The two constants A and ϵ are arbitrary and given in terms of A_1 and A_2 by :

$$A = +\sqrt{A_1^2 + A_2^2} \quad \text{and} \quad \tan \epsilon = \frac{A_2}{A_1}$$

where ϵ is to be obtained from tan ϵ with due regard to the signs of A_1 and A_2 as well as their ratio (see 4.5 and 4.7 above). The solution now appears :

$$Y - \overline{Y}(x) = e^{\alpha x}(A \cos \omega x \cos \epsilon + A \sin \omega x \sin \epsilon)$$
$$= A e^{\alpha x} \cos (\omega x - \epsilon)$$

Hence the general solution of (1) can be written equally as :

$$\left. \begin{array}{l} Y = \overline{Y}(x) + e^{\alpha x}(A_1 \cos \omega x + A_2 \sin \omega x) \\ Y = \overline{Y}(x) + A e^{\alpha x} \cos (\omega x - \epsilon) \end{array} \right\} \quad \dots \dots \dots \dots (8)$$

or

The " structural " constants are α and ω, given by a and b of equation (1). The arbitrary constants are A_1 and A_2, or A and ϵ. The term $\overline{Y}(x)$ is some particular solution of (1) depending on the form of $f(x)$; it can be determined so that it is the trend or equilibrium path of Y. On this is super-imposed a variation $(y = Y - \overline{Y})$ given by the second term in (8).

The variation $y = Y - \overline{Y}$ now takes the form of the general sinusoidal function $A e^{\alpha x} \cos (\omega x - \epsilon)$ and it is of an oscillatory nature (see 4.7 above). The *amplitude* and the *damping factor* of the oscillation are given by $A e^{\alpha x}$; the level is fixed by the arbitrary constant A, e.g. by initial conditions, but the change in amplitude as x increases depends on the " structural " constant $\alpha = -\frac{1}{2}a$. The *period* of the oscillation is $\dfrac{2\pi}{\omega}$ which depends on the other " structural " constant $\omega = \frac{1}{2}\sqrt{4b - a^2}$. The phase of the oscillation, or the particular starting point, depends on the arbitrary constant ϵ and is fixed by initial conditions. Hence, as x increases, the oscillation has changing amplitude (depending on α) but always the same period (given by ω). Of the arbitrary constants, one (A) fixes the initial amplitude and the other (ϵ) fixes the initial phase of the oscillation.

Since the amplitude changes, the oscillatory variation of Y about $\overline{Y}$ can be explosive, regular or damped. This depends solely on the sign of $\alpha = -\frac{1}{2}a$. If $\alpha > 0$, the variation is explosive as x increases ; if $\alpha = 0$, it is a regular oscillation of fixed amplitude A ; if $\alpha < 0$, it is a damped oscillation. The three cases are illustrated in Fig. 16 above. The idea of the *dominant term* in the solution (8) is again appropriate. It is $e^{\alpha x}$, so that, if $\alpha > 0$, the variation of Y is explosive and the oscillation is incidental, whereas if $\alpha < 0$, the variation is damped and the oscillation is the main feature.

In all cases, the term $\overline{Y}(x)$ in the solution of (1) depends on the form of $f(x)$. The case where $f(x) = \beta$ (constant) is easily handled. A particular solution is required for :

$$\frac{d^2 Y}{dx^2} + a \frac{dY}{dx} + b Y = \beta$$

Try $Y = \mu$ where μ is a constant to be found. Then $b\mu = \beta$, or $\mu = \dfrac{\beta}{b}$. The general solution of the equation is now :

$$Y = \frac{\beta}{b} + y(x \, ; \, A_1, A_2)$$

where $y(x \, ; \, A_1, A_2)$ is the general solution of the corresponding homogeneous equation and includes two arbitrary constants. The variation of Y is about a constant level $\overline{Y} = \dfrac{\beta}{b}$. Other cases of $f(x)$ are considered in the Exercises below.

A simple economic application of linear differential equations of the second order is provided by the cobweb-type model with stocks (1.7, Model IV, above) in which the rate of change of price P depends on the level of stocks. With linear demand and supply relations ($D = \alpha + aP$ and $S = \beta + bP$), and with λ as the speed of response of prices changes, the equation is :

$$\frac{d^2P}{dt^2} + \lambda(b - a)P = \lambda(\alpha - \beta)$$

The particular solution $P = \overline{P} = \dfrac{\alpha - \beta}{b - a}$ (equilibrium price) is obtained, and $p = P - \overline{P}$ then satisfies :

$$\frac{d^2p}{dt^2} + \lambda(b - a)p = 0 \quad \dotfill (9)$$

A solution of (9) completes the analysis of the problem. The auxiliary equation (written in q, since p is used for price) is :

$$q^2 + \lambda(b - a) = 0$$

In the usual case ($a < 0, b > 0, \lambda > 0$), the term $\lambda(b - a)$ is positive. Write $\omega = \sqrt{\lambda(b - a)}$ so that the roots of the auxiliary equations are :

$$q_1, q_2, = \pm i\omega$$

and the general solution of (9) is

$$p = A \cos(\omega t - \epsilon)$$

where A and ϵ are constants to be given by initial conditions. Hence, the path of P over time is obtained by adding $\overline{P}$:

$$P = \overline{P} + A \cos(\omega t - \epsilon) \quad \dotfill (10)$$

Notice that the damping factor (α) of the general case of the oscillatory solution, (8) above, is here zero.

The path of P over time given by (10) is a regular oscillation around the equilibrium level. The period of the oscillation is $\dfrac{2\pi}{\omega} = \dfrac{2\pi}{\sqrt{\lambda(b-a)}}$, fixed by the structure of the system. The amplitude and phase (A and ϵ) are determined by initial conditions. The conclusion is that, in this model, an initial disturbance sets price oscillating regularly around equilibrium with a period $\dfrac{2\pi}{\omega}$ independent of the type of disturbance. The equilibrium level of prices cannot be described as unstable, since there is no progressive movement away from it ; on the other hand, the tendency is not to return to equilibrium but rather to oscillate regularly about it. The period of oscillation is short if λ and $(b-a)$ are large, i.e. for a rapid response of prices to stock changes and for steep demand and supply curves of slopes $(-a)$ and b respectively.

EXERCISES 5.4

1. If $\dfrac{d^2y}{dx^2} = a^2y$, show that $y = A_1e^{ax} + A_2e^{-ax}$. Indicate that the sign of a is immaterial and that the dominant term in the solution is always explosive ($a \neq 0$).

2. Check that $Y = x + A_1e^{ax} + A_2^{-ax}e$ is the general solution of $\dfrac{d^2Y}{dx^2} + a^2(x - Y) = 0$; and $Y = e^{-x} + A_1e^{ax} + A_2e^{-ax}$ of $\dfrac{d^2Y}{dx^2} = a^2Y + (1 - a^2)e^{-x}$.

3. Solve $\dfrac{d^2y}{dx^2} + 2\dfrac{dy}{dx} + y = 0$ subject to $y = 1$ and $\dfrac{dy}{dx} = 0$ when $x = 0$. Draw a graph of the solution and comment.

4. Show that the solution of $\dfrac{d^2Y}{dx^2} + 2\dfrac{dY}{dx} + Y = x + 2$, subject to $Y = Y_0$ and $\dfrac{dY}{dx} = 0$ when $x = 0$, is :
$$Y = x(1 - e^{-x}) + Y_0(1 + x)e^{-x}$$

5. By differentiating and eliminating A and ϵ, find the two differential equations with (i) $y = Ae^x \cos(x - \epsilon)$ and (ii) $y = Ae^{-x} \cos(x - \epsilon)$ as solutions. Check by solving the equations by the methods of 5.4. Represent the solutions graphically and comment on their main features.

6. Check that $Y = x + Ae^{-\frac{1}{2}x} \cos(x - \epsilon)$ is the general solution of
$$4\left(\dfrac{d^2Y}{dx^2} + \dfrac{dY}{dx} - 1\right) = 5(x - Y)$$
Find A and ϵ under the initial conditions (i) $Y = 1$, $\dfrac{dY}{dx} = \frac{1}{2}$ at $x = 0$, (ii) $Y = 1$ at $x = 0$, $Y = \dfrac{\pi}{2}$ at $x = \dfrac{\pi}{2}$. Why are these the same?

7. In case : $a^2 = 4b$ of the text, try $y = ue^{-\frac{1}{2}ax}$ as a solution of the homogeneous equation (6), where u is some function of x to be found. Show that $u = A_1 + A_2x$ as in the solution (7).

8. In the economic problem represented by the equation (9) and solution (10) above, take both demand and supply as downward sloping lines ($a<0$, $b<0$). Show that price still oscillates regularly if $(-a)>(-b)$ but that it is an explosive variation from equilibrium if $(-a)<(-b)$. Interpret these conditions. What happens when the demand and supply curves have the same slope?

9. Extend the economic problem by replacing (9) by :

$$\frac{d^2p}{dt^2} - \lambda a \frac{dp}{dt} + \lambda(b-a)p = 0$$

as in 1.7, Ex. 5, above. Find the solution and interpret.

10. In the problem of the national debt and income, end of 5.3 above, eliminate Y to obtain:

$$\frac{d^2D}{dt^2} - \rho \frac{dD}{dt} = 0 \quad \text{subject to} \quad D = D_0, \frac{dD}{dt} = kY_0 \text{ at } t = 0$$

Show that the solution is $D = D_0 + \dfrac{k}{\rho}Y_0(e^{\rho t} - 1)$ as before.

5.5 Linear Differential Equations Generally

The methods of 5.4 indicate, sufficiently clearly, the lines on which any linear differential equation with constant coefficients is to be solved. The nth order equation and corresponding homogeneous form are :

$$a_0 \frac{d^n Y}{dx^n} + a_1 \frac{d^{n-1} Y}{dx^{n-1}} + \ldots + a_{n-1} \frac{dY}{dx} + a_n Y = f(x) \quad \ldots\ldots\ldots\ldots(1)$$

$$a_0 \frac{d^n y}{dx^n} + a_1 \frac{d^{n-1} y}{dx^{n-1}} + \ldots + a_{n-1} \frac{dy}{dx} + a_n y = 0 \quad \ldots\ldots\ldots\ldots\ldots(2)$$

Some particular solution $Y = \overline{Y}(x)$ of (1) must be found ; this can be done so as to set the trend or equilibrium path of Y as x increases. The deviation $y = Y - \overline{Y}$ then satisfies (2) and the general solution

$$y = y(x; \ A_1, A_2, \ldots A_n)$$

must be found. The complete solution of (1) is then :

$$Y = \overline{Y}(x) + y(x; \ A_1, A_2, \ldots A_n)$$

The essential step is the general solution of (2) and a device is available for the purpose. Try $y = e^{px}$ where p is a constant to be found. Then :

$$\frac{dy}{dx} = pe^{px}; \quad \frac{d^2y}{dx^2} = p^2 e^{px}; \quad \ldots \frac{d^n y}{dx^n} = p^n e^{px}$$

On substituting in (2), the appropriate values of p are found to be those satisfying the *auxiliary equation* :

$$a_0 p^n + a_1 p^{n-1} + \ldots + a_{n-1}p + a_n = 0 \quad \ldots\ldots\ldots\ldots\ldots(3)$$

This equation always has exactly n roots $p_1, p_2, \ldots p_n$, either real or conjugate complex values in pairs (4.6 above). The general solution of (2) is then :

$$y = A_1 e^{p_1 x} + A_2 e^{p_2 x} + \dots + A_n e^{p_n x} \quad\dots\dots\dots\dots\dots(4)$$

The solution can be developed into alternative forms involving sinusoidal functions when there are pairs of complex roots of the equation (3).

The solution is comprehensive except for provision for the possibility that two or more of the roots of (3) are equal in value. In this case, (4) fails to give the general solution since it lacks the full complement of terms. The way round this difficulty is on the lines indicated in the second case of 5.4 above.

If all the roots of (3) are real, the *dominant term* in the solution (4) is that in the largest root p_1. If $p_1 > 0$, the variation of y is explosive as x increases. If $p_1 < 0$ (as are all the other p's), y is damped to zero. Though y may have turning points, there are no regular oscillations in either case.

If there are complex roots of (3), they occur in pairs $p = \alpha \pm i\omega$ and two of the terms of (4) reduce to $A e^{\alpha x} \cos(\omega x - \epsilon)$ for such a pair of complex roots, A and ϵ being arbitrary constants. Which is the *dominant term* of (4) now turns on the relative magnitudes of p_1 the largest real root, and α_1 the largest value of α among the complex pairs $p = \alpha \pm i\omega$. There are then always oscillations in the variation of y. The oscillations can be explosive in themselves ($\alpha_1 > 0$) or they can be added to a steady explosive term ($p_1 > 0$). However, if both α_1 and p_1 are negative, there is no explosive element and the main component of the solution (4) is a damped oscillation. The possibility of equal roots of (3) adds some complications to this analysis.

The roots of the auxiliary equation (3) are never easy to find for orders greater than the second. For example, in the third order case, the auxiliary equation is the cubic $a_0 p^3 + a_1 p^2 + a_2 p + a_3 = 0$. *Either* all three roots (p_1, p_2, p_3) are real, though two or more may be equal in value. *Or* one root is real and the others are conjugate complex ($p_1, \alpha \pm i\omega$). In all cases there must be at least one real root (p_1); if it can be found, then ($p - p_1$) is a factor of the cubic auxiliary equation which reduces to :

$$a_0 (p - p_1)(p^2 + a p + b) = 0$$

The coefficients a and b are found from those in the original auxiliary equation. The other two roots, whether real or conjugate complex, are derived at once as the roots of the quadratic $p^2 + a p + b = 0$. Once one real root of the cubic auxiliary equation is located, the other two roots follow. The devices for finding the necessary first root include various methods of graphical and numerical approximation (see 4.6 above).

There is one particular case where a root of the auxiliary equation can always be found, the case where the term in Y is missing from the differential equation. Such an equation of first order is examined in 5.3 above. The corresponding equation of second order, in homogeneous form, is

$\dfrac{d^2y}{dx^2} + a\dfrac{dy}{dx} = 0$ The auxiliary equation $p^2 + ap = 0$ has roots $p = -a$ and $p = 0$

and the general solution is :

$$y = A_1 e^{-ax} + A_2$$

The corresponding third-order equation is $\dfrac{d^3y}{dx^3} + a\dfrac{d^2y}{dx^2} + b\dfrac{dy}{dx} = 0$ and the

auxiliary equation $p^3 + ap^2 + bp = 0$ has roots p_1, $p_2 = \frac{1}{2}(-a \pm \sqrt{a^2 - 4b})$ and $p_3 = 0$. The general solution is :

$$y = A_1 e^{p_1 x} + A_2 e^{p_2 x} + A_3$$

In each case there is an *additive constant* which corresponds to a zero root of the auxiliary equation. This is clearly a general property (see Ex. 2 below).

This " classical " method of solution of linear differential equations (with constant coefficients) can be summed up as follows. The general solution of (1) is :

$$Y = \overline{Y}(x) + A_1 e^{p_1 x} + A_2 e^{p_2 x} + \ldots + A_n e^{p_n x} \quad \ldots\ldots\ldots\ldots\ldots(5)$$

where the A's are arbitrary constants, given by initial conditions, and the p's are the roots of the auxiliary equation :

$$a_0 p^n + a_1 p^{n-1} + \ldots + a_{n-1} p + a_n = 0 \quad \ldots\ldots\ldots\ldots\ldots(6)$$

The n roots of (6) may include real or conjugate complex values and they may not be all different. For a real root, the term in (5) is a simple exponential. For a conjugate complex pair, $p = \alpha \pm i\omega$, two terms in (5) amalgamate to give $Ae^{\alpha x} \cos(\omega x - \epsilon)$ where A and ϵ are arbitrary constants replacing two of the A's in (5). The treatment of two or more equal roots is illustrated by the pair of real roots $p_1 = p_2 = p$, when two terms in (5) are replaced by $(A_1 + A_2 x)e^{px}$.

Nothing has been said about $\overline{Y}(x)$, the particular integral, in (5) ; except that, since *any* solution of (1) will do, there is the general recommendation to " fish around " for a particular $\overline{Y}(x)$. As a simple illustration, let $f(x) = \beta$ (constant) in (1) and try $Y = \overline{Y}$ (constant) as a solution. Then $a_n \overline{Y} = \beta$,

i.e. $\overline{Y} = \dfrac{\beta}{a_n}$ is a particular integral for insertion in (5). In this case, Y varies about a constant level.

One further device remains to be added to facilitate the " classical " method of solution, i.e. the use of the operator $D = \dfrac{d}{dx}$ (see Appendix A).

This does not help much in finding the complementary function. The homogeneous form (2) is :

$$(a_0 D^n + a_1 D^{n-1} + \ldots + a_{n-1}D + a_n)y = 0$$

Try $y = e^{px}$ for which $Dy = pe^{px} = py$ i.e. $D = p$. On substitution of p for D and on dropping the y, the auxiliary equation (6) is obtained. The operator D is of great help, however, in finding the particular integral $\overline{Y}(x)$. Write :

$$F(D) = a_0 D^n + a_1 D^{n-1} + \ldots + a_{n-1}D + a_n$$

so that (1) is $F(D)Y = f(x)$. This suggests :

$$Y = \frac{1}{F(D)} f(x)$$

might help in finding a particular integral. It does—provided that D is treated algebraically and according to certain rules set out in Appendix A. Two examples of second and third order equations illustrate.

Ex. (a). $$\frac{d^2 Y}{dx^2} - Y = -x. \quad \ldots\ldots\ldots\ldots\ldots\ldots\ldots(7)$$

The complementary function, from the auxiliary equation $p^2 - 1 = 0$ with p_1, $p_2 = \pm 1$, is :

$$y = A_1 e^x + A_2 e^{-x} \quad (A_1 \text{ and } A_2 \text{ arbitrary})$$

A particular integral is sought from :

$$Y = \frac{1}{D^2 - 1}(-x) = (1 - D^2)^{-1} x$$
$$= (1 + D^2 + D^4 + \ldots)x$$
$$= x$$

The complete solution of (7) is : $Y = x + A_1 e^x + A_2 e^{-x}$ (see 5.4, Ex. 2, above).

Ex. (b). $$\frac{d^3 Y}{dx^3} - \frac{d^2 Y}{dx^2} + 2Y = xe^x \quad \ldots\ldots\ldots\ldots\ldots\ldots\ldots(8)$$

The auxiliary equation, $p^3 - p^2 + 2 = 0$, or $(p+1)(p^2 - 2p + 2) = 0$, has roots $(1 \pm i)$ and -1. Hence the complementary function is :

$$y = Ae^x \cos(x - \epsilon) + Be^{-x} \quad (A, B \text{ and } \epsilon \text{ arbitrary})$$

A particular integral is sought from :

$$Y = \frac{1}{D^3 - D^2 + 2}(xe^x)$$

Now $\dfrac{1}{D^3 - D^2 + 2} = \dfrac{1}{(D+1)(D^2 - 2D + 2)} = \dfrac{1}{5}\left(\dfrac{1}{D+1} - \dfrac{D-3}{D^2 - 2D + 2}\right)$ in partial fractions. Hence, for the particular integral Y :

$$5Y = \frac{1}{D+1}(xe^x) - \frac{D-3}{D^2 - 2D + 2}(xe^x)$$
$$= e^x \frac{1}{(D+1)+1}(x) - e^x \frac{(D+1)-3}{(D+1)^2 - 2(D+1)+2}(x) \quad \text{(see Appendix A)}$$

$$\therefore \frac{5}{e^x} Y = \tfrac{1}{2}(1 + \tfrac{1}{2}D)^{-1}(x) + (2 - D)(1 + D^2)^{-1}(x)$$
$$= \tfrac{1}{2}(1 - \tfrac{1}{2}D + \tfrac{1}{4}D^2 + \ldots)x + (2 - D)(1 - D^2 + D^4 + \ldots)x$$
$$= \tfrac{1}{2}(x - \tfrac{1}{2}) + (2 - D)x$$
$$= \frac{2x - 1}{4} + 2x - 1 = \tfrac{5}{4}(2x - 1)$$

$$\therefore \quad Y = \tfrac{1}{4}(2x - 1)e^x$$

This can be checked as a particular integral. Substitute :

$$Y = \tfrac{1}{4}(2x - 1)e^x, \frac{dY}{dx} = \tfrac{1}{4}(2x + 1)e^x, \frac{d^2Y}{dx^2} = \tfrac{1}{4}(2x + 3)e^x \text{ and } \frac{d^3Y}{dx^3} = \tfrac{1}{4}(2x + 5)e^x$$

in the left-hand side of (8) :

$$\tfrac{1}{4}(2x + 5)e^x - \tfrac{1}{4}(2x + 3)e^x + \tfrac{1}{2}(2x - 1)e^x = xe^x = \text{right-hand side of (8)}.$$

Hence the complete solution of (8) is : $Y = \{A \cos(x - \epsilon) + \tfrac{1}{4}(2x - 1)\}e^x + Be^{-x}$ which is an explosive oscillation super-imposed on a progressive trend $\tfrac{1}{4}(2x - 1)e^x$.

EXERCISES 5.5

1. Show that the solution of $\dfrac{d^2y}{dx^2} = a\dfrac{dy}{dx}$, subject to $y = y_0$ and $\dfrac{dy}{dx} = k$ at $x = 0$, can be expressed in the form $y = y_0 + \dfrac{k}{a}(e^{ax} - 1)$.

2. Show that the nth order homogeneous equation with y term missing :

$$a_0 \frac{d^ny}{dx^n} + a_1 \frac{d^{n-1}y}{dx^{n-1}} + \ldots + a_{n-1}\frac{dy}{dx} = 0 \qquad \ldots\ldots\ldots\ldots\ldots\ldots(i)$$

has general solution of the form $y = \int z(x)\,dx + A$ where $z(x)$ is the general solution of the $(n-1)$th order equation :

$$a_0 \frac{d^{n-1}z}{dx^{n-1}} + a_1 \frac{d^{n-2}z}{dx^{n-2}} + \ldots + a_{n-1}z = 0 \qquad \ldots\ldots\ldots\ldots\ldots\ldots(ii)$$

and where A is an additive arbitrary constant.

3. As a substitute for the operator method, try $Y = (ax + b)e^x$ in differential equation (8) and find a and b. Show that $Y = \tfrac{1}{4}(2x - 1)e^x$ is a particular integral.

4. If $\dfrac{d^3y}{dx^3} - 3\dfrac{d^2y}{dx^2} + 4\dfrac{dy}{dx} - 2y = 0$ show that $y = \{A \cos(x - \epsilon) + B\}e^x$ where A, B and ϵ are arbitrary constants. Is there now a dominant term?

5. In the light of the previous exercise and of the example in the text, what can be said generally about the solution (and particularly about its dominant term) of third-order differential equation when the auxiliary equation has a pair of conjugate complex roots?

5.6 The Laplace Transform

The solution of differential equations, and especially the finding of the particular integral, is greatly facilitated by employing one of the general " tricks " of the mathematician. The underlying idea is easily explained and, indeed, a simple form of the method has already been used. If the solution of a problem in a certain variable cannot be found easily and directly, the " trick " is to transform the variable into another one, to try to solve for the new variable and then to go back to the original variable by the inverse transformation. The example already used is the familiar one of a logarithmic transform. The first order differential equation $\frac{dy}{dx} = cy$ is most easily solved by writing $z = \log y$ so that $\frac{dz}{dx} = \frac{1}{y}\frac{dy}{dx}$ and the equation becomes $\frac{dz}{dx} = c$ with solution $z = cx + \text{constant}$. The inverse of the transformation is $y = e^z$. Hence, the solution in the original variable is $y = Ae^{cx}$, where A is the arbitrary constant (see 5.3 above).

The same general idea, in a much wider context and with a more complicated transformation, lies behind the use of the Laplace Transform. In addition to its application in the solution of differential equations—where it is the most powerful method available—the Laplace Transform serves to link up many results which are apparently unconnected. In particular, it is connected with the sinusoidal variable $y = Ae^{\alpha t} \cos(\omega t + \epsilon)$, and the vector product $Ae^{i\epsilon}e^{pt}$ ($p = \alpha + i\omega$), as analysed in 4.8 and 4.9 above. The " p " of the Laplace Transform can be identified with $p = \alpha + i\omega$ of the sinusoidal variable.

The Laplace Transform can be applied to a function $y = y(x)$ of any independent variable x. However, since its main applications are to time variation, it will be defined and used here in relation to a function of continuously variable time t. Let $y = y(t)$ be a function of time ($t \geqslant 0$) with initial value y_0 at $t = 0$. Assume that y and its derivatives up to any desired order are continuous ; the analysis can be extended to handle discontinuous functions (e.g. a step function) but this is not considered here. Denote the derivatives :

$$\frac{dy}{dt} = y'(t); \quad \frac{d^2y}{dt^2} = y''(t); \quad \dots \frac{d^ny}{dt^n} = y^{(n)}(t) \dots$$

with initial values at $t = 0$:

$$y_0'; \quad y_0''; \quad \dots y_0^{(n)} \dots$$

Consider the integral :

$$\int_0^\infty e^{-pt}y(t)\,dt = \underset{T\to\infty}{\text{Lim}} \int_0^T e^{-pt}y(t)\,dt \quad \dots\dots\dots\dots\dots(1)$$

where p is any given real or complex number. The first task is to see whether the limit (and hence the integral) exists at all. This is no easy matter but it is not pursued here. Two things can be noted. The first is that $e^{-pt} \to 0$ very strongly as $t \to \infty$ (see 4.4 above) so that either p must be small or $y(t)$ must increase very fast if (1) fails to exist; the other is that, even so, there are functions $y(t)$ for which (1) does not exist for small p or indeed for any p at all (e.g. the function e^{t^2}). It is simply assumed here that, for the function $y(t)$ and for the values of p considered, the limit and integral of (1) exist. This is certainly true of ordinary functions, e.g. a polynomial in t.

Next, the integral (1) depends in value on the given value of p as well as on the form of $y(t)$. In other words, (1) defines a function of p, a real or complex variable. Denote it by $\bar{y}(p)$ to indicate that it is derived from $y(t)$ for various values of p. It is therefore a transformation from a given function of time $y(t)$ to a new function $\bar{y}(p)$ of a real or complex variable p.

DEFINITION : The Laplace Transform from $y(t)$ to $\bar{y}(p)$ is

$$\bar{y}(p) = \int_0^\infty e^{-pt} y(t) \, dt$$

The Laplace Transform has many properties but only three are needed here. The first is the basic result that the correspondence between $y(t)$ and $\bar{y}(p)$ is unique both ways. The definition gives $\bar{y}(p)$ uniquely, given $y(t)$; what is difficult to establish is the converse, that given $\bar{y}(p)$ a unique $y(t)$ corresponds. The result is here stated but not proved; see Carslaw and Jaeger (1941, 1948), Appendix I on Lerch's Theorem. The other two properties are concerned with the Laplace Transform of the derivatives of $y(t)$ and they are proved without much difficulty.

PROPERTY (i) : To a given $y(t)$ there corresponds by definition a unique $\bar{y}(p)$; conversely, given $\bar{y}(p)$, then if one continuous $y(t)$ exists it is the only continuous $y(t)$ satisfying the Laplace Transform.

PROPERTY (ii) : If the Laplace Transform of $y(t)$ is $\bar{y}(p)$, then the Laplace Transform of the nth derivative $y^{(n)}(t)$ is

$$\int_0^\infty e^{-pt} y^{(n)}(t) \, dt = p^n \bar{y}(p) - (p^{n-1} y_0 + p^{n-2} y_0' + \ldots + p y_0^{(n-2)} + y_0^{(n-1)})$$

PROPERTY (iii) : If $y(t)$ satisfies the linear differential equation :

$$a_0 \frac{d^n y}{dt^n} + a_1 \frac{d^{n-1} y}{dt^{n-1}} + \ldots + a_{n-1} \frac{dy}{dt} + a_n y = f(t) \quad \ldots\ldots\ldots\ldots(2)$$

subject to $y = y_0, \frac{dy}{dt} = y_0', \frac{d^2 y}{dt^2} = y_0'', \ldots \frac{d^{n-1} y}{dt^{n-1}} = y_0^{(n-1)}$ at $t = 0$

and if $\bar{f}(p)$ is the Laplace Transform of $f(t)$, then the Laplace Transform $\bar{y}(p)$ of $y(t)$ is given by the *subsidiary equation* :

$$
\left.
\begin{aligned}
(a_0 p^n &+ a_1 p^{n-1} + \ldots + a_{n-1} p + a_n)\bar{y}(p) \\
&= \bar{f}(p) + a_0 (p^{n-1} y_0 + p^{n-2} y_0' + \ldots + p y_0^{(n-2)} + y_0^{(n-1)}) \\
&\quad + a_1 (p^{n-2} y_0 + p^{n-3} y_0' + \ldots + p y_0^{(n-3)} + y_0^{(n-2)}) \\
&\quad + \ldots \\
&\quad + a_{n-2} (p y_0 + y_0') \\
&\quad + a_{n-1} y_0
\end{aligned}
\right\} \quad \ldots (3)
$$

Property (i) is the basic result which permits the Laplace Transform to be inverted. The inversion—on the continuity assumptions made here—is unique. There is one good reason for this ; the Laplace transform from $y(t)$ to $\bar{y}(p)$ involves an integral, so that the inverse from $\bar{y}(p)$ to $y(t)$ is a reversal of integration and no additive or other constants " re-appear " in reversing integration. Integration as the reverse of differentiation produces additive constants ; but differentiation as the reverse of integration does not.

Property (ii) is the " rule " for Laplace Transforms of derivatives of $y(t)$. It is easily established from the definition stage by stage (see Ex. 1 and 2 below). For the successive derivatives, the " rule " is :

$$
\left.
\begin{aligned}
\int_0^\infty e^{-pt} y'(t)\, dt &= p\bar{y}(p) - y_0 \\
\int_0^\infty e^{-pt} y''(t)\, dt &= p^2 \bar{y}(p) - (p y_0 + y_0') \\
\int_0^\infty e^{-pt} y'''(t)\, dt &= p^3 \bar{y}(p) - (p^2 y_0 + p y_0' + y_0'')
\end{aligned}
\right\} \quad \ldots \ldots \ldots (4)
$$

and so on. The second term in each Laplace Transform is a polynomial in p with coefficients given by the series of initial values $(y_0, y_0', y_0'', \ldots)$ and of degree one less than the order of the derivatives concerned.

Property (iii) provides the basis for the solution of differential equations by means of Laplace Transforms. It makes use of the derivative " rules " of Property (ii) to provide the Laplace Transform of a function $y(t)$ satisfying a linear differential equation. The subsidiary equation (3) which gives the Laplace Transform $\bar{y}(p)$ is derived as follows. Multiply (2) through by e^{-pt} and integrate :

$$
a_0 \int_0^\infty e^{-pt} y^{(n)}\, dt + a_1 \int_0^\infty e^{-pt} y^{(n-1)}\, dt + \ldots + a_{n-1} \int_0^\infty e^{-pt} y'\, dt + a_n \int_0^\infty e^{-pt} y\, dt
$$

$$
= \int_0^\infty e^{-pt} f(t)\, dt
$$

By Property (ii)

$$\int_0^\infty e^{-pt} y^{(n)} dt = p^n \bar{y}(p) - (p^{n-1} y_0 + p^{n-2} y_0' + \ldots + p y_0^{(n-2)} + v_0^{(n-1)})$$

for any $n = 1, 2, 3, \ldots$. The particular expressions for low values of n are (4). Further :

$$\int_0^\infty e^{-pt} y \, dt = \bar{y}(p) \quad \text{and} \quad \int_0^\infty e^{-pt} f(t) dt = \bar{f}(p)$$

Substituting and collecting terms together give the subsidiary equation (3).

Two vital points are to be noticed about Property (iii). The first is that the solution $y(t)$ is sought for the differential equation (2), but *subject to particular initial conditions* which specify the values of y and its first $(n-1)$ derivatives at $t = 0$. It is limited to this particular, though very common, case. On the other hand, when the solution is obtained, it has the initial conditions " built in " ; there is none of the bother about a solution with n arbitrary constants, to be " fitted " or evaluated with great labour from the initial conditions.

The second point is that the subsidiary equation (3), though it does not give $y(t)$ directly (as required), does give $\bar{y}(p)$. Apart from the term $\bar{f}(p)$, the expression for $\bar{y}(p)$ is in the form of the ratio of one polynomial in p (generally of degree $n-1$) to another polynomial in p (of degree n). Hence $\bar{y}(p)$ is completely specified in terms of the constants of the differential equation $(a_0, a_1, \ldots a_n)$, of the initial values $(y_0, y_0', \ldots y_0^{(n-1)})$ and of the Laplace Transform of the given function $f(t)$. The form of (3) looks a little complicated but it is less so than it appears. There is nothing to be done about the form of the Laplace Transform of a derivative, as in (4) for $n = 1, 2, 3, \ldots$ and generally by Property (ii) ; these must be looked up or remembered. The right-hand side of (3) contains (reading up from the bottom) the successive polynomials (4) of the Laplace Transforms of the derivatives, multiplied by $a_{n-1}, a_{n-2}, \ldots$.

Hence the differential equation (2), subject to the specified initial conditions, is nearly solved, but not quite. What is given by (3) is $\bar{y}(p)$, not $y(t)$ as required. The Laplace Transform of the solution of the differential equation is provided. To complete the solution, all that is needed is the inverse of the Laplace Transform, to get $y(t)$ from $\bar{y}(p)$. This is where Property (i) comes in ; if any (continuous) $y(t)$ can be found to give

$$\bar{y}(p) = \int_0^\infty e^{-pt} y(t) dt,$$

then it is the unique solution of the differential equation subject to its initial conditions. The last step is to devise a set of *standard forms* which associate particular $y(t)$ with $\bar{y}(p)$ and a set of *rules* to give combinations of $y(t)$ or $\bar{y}(p)$, a process similar to that of getting standard forms and rules for derivatives or integrals. The standard forms and rules will enable the $\bar{y}(p)$ of (3) to be turned into the solution $y(t)$ of (2); they also serve to turn the given $f(t)$ of (2) into the $\bar{f}(p)$ which appears in (3).

A short list of *standard forms* can be set out:

	$\bar{y}(p)$	$y(t)$
(1)	$1/p$	1
(2)	$1/p^2$	t
(3)	$1/p^{n+1}$	$t^n/n!$
(4)	$1/(p+\omega)$	$e^{-\omega t}$
(5)	$\omega/(p^2+\omega^2)$	$\sin \omega t = \dfrac{1}{2i}(e^{i\omega t} - e^{-i\omega t})$
(6)	$p/(p^2+\omega^2)$	$\cos \omega t = \frac{1}{2}(e^{i\omega t} + e^{-i\omega t})$
(7)	$\omega/(p^2-\omega^2)$	$\sinh \omega t = \frac{1}{2}(e^{\omega t} - e^{-\omega t})$
(8)	$p/(p^2-\omega^2)$	$\cosh \omega t = \frac{1}{2}(e^{\omega t} + e^{-\omega t})$

They are given this way round, i.e. given $\bar{y}(p)$, determine $y(t)$, since they are more often used so. Further standard forms are to be found in the text-books, such as Carslaw and Jaeger (1941, 1948), Appendix III. To prove them, substitute $y(t)$ in $\int_0^\infty e^{-pt} y(t)\,dt$ and evaluate to give $\bar{y}(p)$, see Ex. 3 and 4 below.

Still other standard forms can be obtained by taking forms such as (4)–(8) above and differentiating with respect to ω. For example:

Given (6) $\displaystyle \int_0^\infty e^{-pt} \cos \omega t \, dt = \frac{p}{p^2+\omega^2}$

then $\displaystyle \frac{d}{d\omega}\int_0^\infty e^{-pt} \cos \omega t \, dt = \int_0^\infty e^{-pt}\left(\frac{d}{d\omega}\cos \omega t\right) dt = -\int_0^\infty e^{-pt}\, t \sin \omega t \, dt$

and $\displaystyle \frac{d}{d\omega}\left(\frac{p}{p^2+\omega^2}\right) = -\frac{2\omega p}{(p^2+\omega^2)^2}$

Hence the Laplace Transform of $(t \sin \omega t)$ is found to be $\dfrac{2\omega p}{(p^2+\omega^2)^2}$, i.e.

if $\displaystyle \bar{y}(p) = \frac{p}{(p^2+\omega^2)^2}$ then $\displaystyle y(t) = \frac{t}{2\omega}\sin \omega t$

Four *rules* can be easily obtained and set out:

RULES: (i) If $\bar{y}(p)$ is the Laplace Transform of $y(t)$ and a is a constant, then $a\bar{y}(p)$ is the Laplace Transform of $ay(t)$.

(ii) If $\bar{y}_1(p)$, $\bar{y}_2(p)$, ... are the Laplace Transforms of $y_1(t)$, $y_2(t)$, ... and

a_1, a_2, ... are constants, then $a_1\bar{y}_1(p) + a_2\bar{y}(p) + ...$ is the Laplace Transform of $a_1 y_1(t) + a_2 y_2(t) + ...$.

(iii) If $\bar{y}(p)$ is the Laplace Transform of $y(t)$ and ω is a constant, then

$\dfrac{1}{\omega}\, \bar{y}\left(\dfrac{p}{\omega}\right)$ is the Laplace Transform of $y(\omega t)$.

(iv) If $\bar{y}(p)$ is the Laplace Transform of $y(t)$ and α is a constant, then $\bar{y}(p - \alpha)$ is the Laplace Transform of $e^{\alpha t} y(t)$ and $\bar{y}(p + \alpha)$ of $e^{-\alpha t} y(t)$.

The proofs are straight-forward applications of the definition, see Ex. 6–8 below.

Rule (iv) is a very useful one. It serves to extend the standard forms to cover cases where some expression $y(t)$ is multiplied by $e^{\alpha t}$. In particular, note :

	$\bar{y}(p)$	$y(t)$
(2a)	$1/(p - \alpha)^2$	$te^{\alpha t}$
(5a)	$\omega/(p - \alpha)^2 + \omega^2$	$e^{\alpha t} \sin \omega t$
(6a)	$(p - \alpha)/(p - \alpha)^2 + \omega^2$	$e^{\alpha t} \cos \omega t$

A simple development of these and many other properties and uses of Laplace Transforms is given in Jaeger (1949), particularly Chapter I.

EXERCISES 5.6

1. By differentiating both sides with respect to t, establish the following particular case of " integration by parts " :

$$\int e^{-pt} y'(t)\, dt = y(t) e^{-pt} + p \int y(t) e^{-pt}\, dt$$

Deduce that the Laplace Transform of $y'(t)$ is $p\bar{y}(p) - y_0$.

2. Extend the result of the previous exercise to show that the Laplace Transforms of $y''(t)$ and $y'''(t)$ are $p^2\bar{y}(p) - (py_0 + y_0')$ and $p^3\bar{y}(p) - (p^2 y_0 + p y_0' + y_0'')$.

3. By evaluating the integrals, show that :

$$\int_0^\infty e^{-pt}\, dt = \frac{1}{p},\ \int_0^\infty e^{-pt} t\, dt = \frac{1}{p^2},\ \int_0^\infty e^{-pt} t^n\, dt = \frac{n!}{p^{n+1}},\ \int_0^\infty e^{-pt} e^{-\omega t}\, dt = \frac{1}{p + \omega}$$

and hence prove the standard forms (1) to (4) above.

4. Show that $\quad \int e^{-pt} \sin \omega t\, dt = -\dfrac{1}{\omega} e^{-pt} \cos \omega t - \dfrac{p}{\omega} \int e^{-pt} \cos \omega t\, dt$

and $\qquad \int e^{-pt} \cos \omega t\, dt = \dfrac{1}{\omega} e^{-pt} \sin \omega t + \dfrac{p}{\omega} \int e^{-pt} \sin \omega t\, dt$

Hence deduce standard forms (5) and (6) above.

5. Take standard form (5) above : $\int_0^\infty e^{-pt} \sin \omega t\, dt = \dfrac{\omega}{p^2 + \omega^2}$. Differentiate with respect to ω and show that the Laplace Transform of $(\sin \omega t - \omega t \cos \omega t)$ is $2\omega^3/(p^2 + \omega^2)^2$.

6. From the definition, establish Rules (i) and (ii) above.

7. Show that $\int_0^\infty e^{-pt} y(\omega t)\,dt = \dfrac{1}{\omega}\int_0^\infty e^{-\frac{p}{\omega}\tau} y(\tau)\,d\tau$, by putting $\tau = \omega t$. Deduce that $y(\omega t)$ has Laplace Transform $\dfrac{1}{\omega}\,\bar{y}\left(\dfrac{p}{\omega}\right)$, i.e. Rule (iii).

8. Show that $\int_0^\infty e^{-pt} e^{\alpha t} y(t)\,dt = \int_0^\infty e^{-(p-\alpha)t} y(t)\,dt = \bar{y}(p-\alpha)$ and deduce that $e^{\alpha t} y(t)$ has Laplace Transform $\bar{y}(p-\alpha)$, i.e. Rule (iv). Show that standard form (4) can then be deduced from standard form (1) above. Show also that $\dfrac{t^n}{n!}\,e^{\alpha t}$ has Laplace Transform $\dfrac{1}{(p-\alpha)^{n+1}}$.

5.7 Solution of Differential Equations by Laplace Transforms

The given differential equation in $y(t)$ is :

$$a_0 \frac{d^n y}{dt^n} + a_1 \frac{d^{n-1} y}{dt^{n-1}} + \ldots + a_{n-1} \frac{dy}{dt} + a_n y = f(t)$$

subject to
$$\left. y = y_0,\ \frac{dy}{dt} = y_0',\ \frac{d^2 y}{dt^2} = y_0'',\ \ldots\ \frac{d^{n-1} y}{dt^{n-1}} = y_0^{(n-1)}\ \text{at } t=0 \right\} \quad \ldots\ldots\ldots\ldots(1)$$

The solution by Laplace Transforms is obtained in two stages. At the *first stage*, the Laplace Transform of the solution $y(t)$ is written down from the *subsidiary equation* as set out in 5.6 above. It is of the form :

$$\bar{y}(p) = \frac{\bar{f}(p) + \text{polynomial in } p \text{ of degree less than } n}{a_0 p^n + a_1 p^{n-1} + \ldots + a_{n-1} p + a_n} \quad \ldots\ldots\ldots\ldots(2)$$

At the *second stage*, the Laplace Transform is inverted to get $y(t)$ from $\bar{y}(p)$ as specified in (2). The first stage can be regarded as complete ; the present problem—and it is beset with all the practical difficulties—is to complete the solution by getting back from $\bar{y}(p)$ to $y(t)$.

The problem is not an easy one, but the difficulties are all practical, not theoretical. It is very much like the practical problem of evaluating integrals, using standard forms, a set of rules and a good many tricks. The standard forms and rules for Laplace Transforms exist ; some of them are given in 5.6 above and others can be devised. Equally, there are many tricks, the main one involving the expression of a ratio of polynomials in terms of " partial fractions ", as explained in text-books on elementary algebra.

However, when the practical problem is solved and $y(t)$ obtained, it is the unique solution of the differential equation (1) subject to the specified initial conditions. The solution $y(t)$ contains the initial values $(y_0, y_0', y_0'', \ldots)$ automatically ; there is nothing further to be done. Unlike the " classical " method of solution of 5.5 above, there is no question of fitting arbitrary constants to the initial conditions.

Some simple observations serve to clear the ground. The standard forms of 5.6 indicate that, for many of the common forms of $y(t)$, the Laplace Transform $\bar{y}(p)$ is the ratio of polynomials of low degree in p, e.g. the ratio of $(\alpha p + \beta)$ to $(ap^2 + bp + c)$. This has two consequences. The first is that, in the expression (2) for $\bar{y}(p)$, the entry $\bar{f}(p)$ is usually obtained from the given $f(t)$ in the ratio-of-polynomials form. It can be absorbed, therefore, into the other polynomials of (2) and $\bar{y}(p)$ is to be expected to be itself the ratio of two polynomials. The other consequence is that the standard forms and their various combinations are well designed to turn $\bar{y}(p)$ as the ratio of polynomials back into $y(t)$ of various common forms like t^n, $e^{\alpha t}$ or $\cos \omega t$. The process is to be facilitated by splitting $\bar{y}(p)$ up into simpler factors, i.e. into the sum of very simple ratios of polynomials to each of which the standard forms apply directly. This is, in fact, the process of writing $\bar{y}(p)$ in " partial fractions ".

Hence, assume that (2) can be written :

$$\bar{y}(p) = \frac{F(p)}{G(p)} \dots\dots\dots\dots\dots(3)$$

where $F(p)$ and $G(p)$ are two polynomials in p, F being of lower degree than G. It is to be particularly noted that $G(p)$ *either* is identical with the polynomial $(a_0 p^n + a_1 p^{n-1} + \dots + a_{n-1} p + a_n)$ *or* is this polynomial together with other factors :

$$G(p) = (a_0 p^n + a_1 p^{n-1} + \dots + a_{n-1} p + a_n) g(p) \dots\dots\dots\dots(4)$$

where $g(p)$ is either unity or another polynomial in p. The importance of (4) is that the polynomial of degree n shown, when equated to zero, gives the auxiliary equation of the differential equation (1). Its factors, corresponding to the roots of the auxiliary equation, are therefore both needed and known.

The method of " partial fractions " applied to (3) consists of finding all the roots of $G(p) = 0$, i.e. p_1, p_2, p_3, ..., which contain real values and conjugate complex values. Amongst these roots are all those of the auxiliary equation. So :

$$G(p) = a_0 (p - p_1)(p - p_2)(p - p_3) \dots \dots\dots\dots\dots(5)$$

Substitute (5) into (3), then split up into the sum of fractions like $A_1/(p - p_1)$, $A_2/(p - p_2)$, ... and (3) is ready for inversion into $y(t)$. However, there are two ways of allowing for complex values, e.g. p_1, $p_2 = \alpha \pm i\omega$. They can be left in (5) as two factors $(p - \alpha - i\omega)(p - \alpha + i\omega)$, in which case the constants $A_1, A_2, \ldots$ of the partial fractions are also complex. Or, they can be taken together in (5) in the form of a quadratic $\{(p-\alpha)^2 + \omega^2\}$, in which case one of the partial fractions takes the form $\dfrac{A_1(p-\alpha)+B_1}{(p-\alpha)^2+\omega^2}$.

If $G(p)$ is written as (5) and if all the roots $(p_1, p_2, p_3, \ldots)$ are left whether real or complex, then a general result of partial fractions is :

$$\bar{y}(p) = \frac{F(p)}{G(p)} = \sum_r \frac{F(p_r)}{G'(p_r)} \frac{1}{p-p_r} \quad \ldots\ldots\ldots\ldots\ldots\ldots(6)$$

where $\sum\limits_r$ is taken over all the roots $p_1, p_2, p_3 \ldots$. Here $G'(p) = \dfrac{d}{dp} G(p)$ and $F(p_r)$ and $G'(p_r)$ are the results of substituting $p = p_r$ in $F(p)$ and $G'(p)$. All that (6) says, in effect, is that the coefficient of the particular partial fraction $\dfrac{1}{p-p_r}$ is $\dfrac{F(p_r)}{G'(p_r)}$. When p_r is a complex root, the coefficient is also complex ; in fact, for a pair of conjugate complex roots, there is a pair of complex coefficients which are also conjugate.

Given (6), together with standard form (4) and Rule (ii) of 5.6, the inversion from $\bar{y}(p)$ to $y(t)$ is immediate :

$$y(t) = \sum_r \frac{F(p_r)}{G'(p_r)} e^{p_r t} \quad \ldots\ldots\ldots\ldots\ldots\ldots\ldots(7)$$

Hence, as long as $\bar{y}(p)$ of (2) can be written as in (3), the inversion to $y(t)$ can always be done by formula. The formula is (7).

In practice, however, it is generally preferable to avoid the complex p_r and the corresponding complex coefficients which arise in the use of (7). The alternative is to take complex roots in pairs and to deal with partial fractions like :

$$\frac{A_1(p-\alpha)+B_1}{(p-\alpha)^2+\omega^2}$$

But $\bar{y}(p)$ of this form can easily be inverted to $y(t)$ with the aid of standard forms (5a) and (6a) of 5.6 above. The corresponding $y(t)$ is:

$$e^{\alpha t}\left(A_1 \cos \omega t + \frac{B_1}{\omega} \sin \omega t\right) = A e^{\alpha t} \cos(\omega t + \epsilon)$$

which is the familiar sinusoidal component, equivalent in (7) to two exponentials (with conjugate complex indices) knocked together.

Two illustrations are given of the method in practice. If $f(t) = 0$ and the equation (1) is homogeneous, it is seen that the solution (7) is equivalent to that obtained easily by the " classical " method of 5.5 above (see Ex. 1 below). The two illustrations, therefore, take particular forms of $f(t)$;

the method gets the complementary function and particular integral together and incorporates the initial conditions. This is where the "classical" method, even with the aid of the operator $D = \dfrac{d}{dt}$, is particularly weak.

Ex. (a). $\dfrac{d^2y}{dt^2} - y + t = 0$ subject to $y = \dfrac{dy}{dt} = 0$ at $t = 0$.

The subsidiary equation is :

$$(p^2 - 1)\bar{y}(p) = -\text{Laplace transform of } t$$
$$= -\frac{1}{p^2}$$

The simple form of this equation arises, in part, because $y_0 = y_0' = 0$ eliminates so many terms. Hence :

$$\bar{y}(p) = -\frac{1}{p^2(p^2 - 1)} = \frac{1}{p^2} - \frac{1}{2}\left(\frac{1}{p-1} - \frac{1}{p+1}\right)$$

in partial fractions. By standard forms (2) and (4) of 5.6 :

$$y(t) = t - \tfrac{1}{2}(e^t - e^{-t})$$

which is the solution of the differential equation. It can be shown (Ex. 2 below) to be equivalent to the solution obtained by "classical" methods :

$$y(t) = t + A_1 e^t + A_2 e^{-t} \quad \text{(see 5.5, Ex. (a), above)}$$

when A_1 and A_2 are fitted to the initial conditions $y = \dfrac{dy}{dt} = 0$ at $t = 0$.

Ex. (b) $\dfrac{d^3y}{dt^3} - \dfrac{d^2y}{dt^2} + 2y = te^t$ subject to $y = 4$, $\dfrac{dy}{dt} = \dfrac{d^2y}{dt^2} = 7$ at $t = 0$.

Since, for $f(t) = te^t$, $\bar{f}(p) = \dfrac{1}{(p-1)^2}$ by standard form (2a) of 5.6, the subsidiary equation is :

$$(p^3 - p^2 + 2)\bar{y}(p) = \frac{1}{(p-1)^2} + (4p^2 + 7p + 7) - (4p + 7)$$
$$= \frac{1 + p(p-1)^2(4p+3)}{(p-1)^2}$$

i.e.

$$\bar{y}(p) = \frac{1 + p(p-1)^2(4p+3)}{(p-1)^2(p+1)(p^2 - 2p + 2)}$$
$$= \frac{4p-1}{p^2 - 2p + 2} - \frac{p-3}{4(p-1)^2} + \frac{1}{4(p+1)} \quad \text{in partial fractions}$$
$$= \frac{4(p-1) + 3}{(p-1)^2 + 1} - \frac{1}{4}\frac{(p-1) - 2}{(p-1)^2} + \frac{1}{4}\frac{1}{p+1}$$
$$= 4\frac{(p-1)}{(p-1)^2 + 1} + 3\frac{1}{(p-1)^2 + 1} - \frac{1}{4}\frac{1}{p-1} + \frac{1}{2}\frac{1}{(p-1)^2} + \frac{1}{4}\frac{1}{p+1}$$

Hence, by various standard forms :

$$y(t) = 4e^t \cos t + 3e^t \sin t - \tfrac{1}{4}e^t + \tfrac{1}{2}te^t + \tfrac{1}{4}e^{-t}$$
$$= e^t(4\cos t + 3\sin t) + \frac{2t-1}{4}e^t + \tfrac{1}{4}e^{-t}$$

i.e.

$$y(t) = \{5\cos(t - \epsilon) + \tfrac{1}{4}(2t - 1)\}e^t + \tfrac{1}{4}e^{-t} \quad \text{where } \tan \epsilon = \tfrac{3}{4}$$

This is the solution of the differential equation subject to the specified initial conditions. It is equivalent to that obtained by the " classical " method in 5.5, Ex. (b), above :

$$y(t) = \{A \cos(t - \epsilon) + \tfrac{1}{4}(2t - 1)\}e^t + Be^{-t}$$

when the constants A, B and ϵ are fitted to the given initial conditions.

EXERCISES 5.7

1. Put $f(t) = 0$ in the differential equation (1) and show that :

$$\bar{y}(p) = \frac{F(p)}{a_0(p - p_1)(p - p_2) \cdots (p - p_n)}$$

where $p_1, p_2, \ldots p_n$ are the n roots of the auxiliary equation of (1). Hence show that the solution of (1) is :

$$y(t) = \frac{F(p_1)}{a_0(p_1 - p_2) \cdots (p_1 - p_n)} e^{p_1 t} + \frac{F(p_2)}{a_0(p_2 - p_1) \cdots (p_2 - p_n)} e^{p_2 t} + \ldots$$

Identify with the general solution of the (homogeneous) equation (1) given by " classical " methods as (4) of 5.5 above, when the appropriate initial conditions are added.

2. In the solution $y(t) = t + A_1 e^t + A_2 e^{-t}$ of 5.4, Ex. (2), above, find A_1 and A_2 for initial conditions $y = \dfrac{dy}{dt} = 0$ at $t = 0$. Hence obtain the solution as in Ex. (a) above.

3. If $\dfrac{d^2 y}{dt^2} + 2 \dfrac{dy}{dt} + y = t + 2$, show that

$$\text{(i)} \quad y = t(1 - e^{-t}) \quad \text{given } y = \frac{dy}{dt} = 0 \text{ at } t = 0$$

and $\quad$ (ii) $\quad y = t - (1 + 2t)e^{-t} \quad$ given $y = -1$, $\dfrac{dy}{dt} = 0$ at $t = 0$.

4. Solve

$$\frac{d^2 y}{dt^2} + \frac{dy}{dt} + \frac{5}{4} y = 1 + \frac{5}{4} t$$

subject to $y = 1$, $\dfrac{dy}{dt} = \tfrac{1}{2}$ at $t = 0$. (See 5.4, Ex. 6, above.)

5.8 Continuously Distributed (Exponential) Lags

A variable $Y(t)$ is related linearly and with a continuously distributed lag to another variable $X(t)$. It is convenient to relate $Y(t)$ to its potential value :

$$Z(t) = \alpha + aX(t) \qquad \text{(see 1.9 above)}$$

The general case of a continuously distributed lag has a time-form, or weighting function, $f(\tau)$ where $\displaystyle\int_0^\infty f(\tau)d\tau = 1$. It is :

$$Y(t) = \int_0^\infty f(\tau)Z(t - \tau)\, d\tau \qquad \ldots\ldots\ldots\ldots\ldots\ldots(1)$$

In view of the difficulty of handling integrals, it would be useful to express (1) in an alternative form, e.g. as a differential equation.

Take $Z(t)$ as a sinusoidal variable with $p = \alpha + i\omega$ (see 4.8 above):

$$Z(t) = Ae^{\alpha t} \cos(\omega t + \epsilon) = \text{real part of vector product } Ae^{i\epsilon}e^{pt}$$

This includes cases of undamped variation ($\alpha = 0$) and of steady exponential growth ($\omega = 0$). The results obtained in 4.9 above now apply:

$$Z(t - \tau) = e^{-p\tau}Z(t) \qquad (\text{Delay } \tau = e^{-p\tau})$$

So: $\qquad Y(t) = \displaystyle\int_0^\infty f(\tau)e^{-p\tau}Z(t)\, d\tau = Z(t)\int_0^\infty e^{-p\tau}f(\tau)\, d\tau = \bar{f}(p)Z(t)$

where $\bar{f}(p)$ is the Laplace Transform of the time-form $f(\tau)$. Finally, replace p by the operator $D = \dfrac{d}{dt}$ (since $D = p$, from 4.9 above) and so:

$$\left.\begin{aligned} Y(t) &= \bar{f}(D)Z(t) \\ \bar{f}(p) &\text{ is the Laplace Transform of } f(\tau) \end{aligned}\right\} \quad \dots\dots\dots\dots(2)$$

where

is the differential equation to which the continuous lag (1) is reduced. $\bar{f}(p)$ is also the " transfer function " of the lag (9.3 below).

It commonly happens (see 5.7 above) that $\bar{f}(p) = F(p)/G(p)$ where F and G are two polynomials, F being of lower degree than G. The continuous lag (1) then corresponds to a linear differential equation with constant coefficients:

$$Y(t) = \frac{F(D)}{G(D)}Z(t) \quad \text{or} \quad G(D)Y(t) = F(D)Z(t) \quad \dots\dots\dots\dots(3)$$

The order of the differential equation in Y is the degree of the polynomial G. The solution of (3) proceeds by the " classical " method of 5.5 or by Laplace Transforms as in 5.7. It provides the time-path of $Y(t)$ for given $Z(t)$.

The case of the *exponential lag* can now be reviewed. The time-form is $f(\tau) = \lambda e^{-\lambda\tau}$ with Laplace Transform $\bar{f}(p) = \lambda/p + \lambda$. Hence the differential equation of the exponential lag is that already given (1.9 above):

$$Y(t) = \frac{\lambda}{D + \lambda} \cdot Z(t) \quad \dots\dots\dots\dots\dots\dots\dots\dots(4)$$

A further case is the *double exponential lag* with time-form:

$$f(\tau) = 4\lambda^2\tau e^{-2\lambda\tau} \quad \text{and} \quad \bar{f}(p) = \left(\frac{2\lambda}{p + 2\lambda}\right)$$

The differential equation of the lag in this case is:

$$Y(t) = \left(\frac{2\lambda}{D + 2\lambda}\right)^2 Z(t) \quad \dots\dots\dots\dots\dots(5)$$

A comparison of (4) and (5) shows that the double exponential lag is obtained from two single exponential lags, each with speed of response 2λ, applied in succession. The time-constant of the double lag is the sum of the time-constants (each $\frac{1}{2}T$ where $T=1/\lambda$) of the single lags. Hence (4) and (5) have the same time-constant T. Various other cases of multiple lags can be defined, see Exs. 1 and 2 below.

The response of Y to a step-change in Z from zero to Z_0 at $t=0$ can be got by solving the differential equation (2) or (3) on putting $Z(t)=Z_0$ for $t \geqslant 0$ and on specifying initial conditions :

$$Y=\frac{dY}{dt}=\frac{d^2Y}{dt^2}=\ldots=0 \quad \text{at } t=0$$

For the single *exponential lag* (4) :

$$\frac{dY}{dt}+\lambda Y=\lambda Z_0 \quad \text{with } Y=0 \text{ at } t=0$$

and the solution by " classical " methods is :

$$\left. \begin{aligned} Y(t)&=(1-e^{-\lambda t})Z_0 \\ Y'(t)&=\lambda e^{-\lambda t}Z_0 \end{aligned} \right\} \quad \ldots\ldots\ldots\ldots\ldots\ldots\ldots(6)$$

and so

Again, for the *double exponential lag* (5) :

$$\frac{d^2Y}{dt^2}+4\lambda\frac{dY}{dt}+4\lambda^2 Y=4\lambda^2 Z_0 \quad \text{with } Y=\frac{dY}{dt}=0 \text{ at } t=0$$

By " classical " methods, a particular integral is $Y=Z_0$ and the complementary function is obtained from the auxiliary equation $p^2+4\lambda p+4\lambda^2=0$ with two equal roots $p_1=p_2=-2\lambda$. Hence :

$$Y(t)=Z_0+(A+Bt)e^{-2\lambda t}$$

and the constants, from the initial conditions, are $A=-Z_0$ and $B=-2\lambda Z_0$

Hence :
and so :

$$\left. \begin{aligned} Y(t)&=\{1-(1+2\lambda t)e^{-2\lambda t}\}Z_0 \\ Y'(t)&=4\lambda^2 te^{-2\lambda t}Z_0 \end{aligned} \right\} \quad \ldots\ldots\ldots\ldots\ldots(7)$$

Both in (6) and in (7), the time-form of the lag is reproduced in $Y'(t)$; this is a general property (see 1.9, Ex. 5, above). The response of Y can be shown graphically either in *cumulative form* $Y(t)=\left(\int_0^t f(\tau)\,d\tau\right)Z_0$ or in *time-form* $Y'(t)=f(t)Z_0$ as in Fig. 19. Here, case (i) is the single exponential lag plotted from (6) and case (ii) is the double exponential lag from (7). The greater " realism " of the response of case (ii) is clear ; even more " realistic " forms are to be got from multiple lags.

The response of Y to other types of (given) variation in Z is to be found similarly. To illustrate, take a sinusoidal variation $Z(t)=e^{\alpha t}\cos \omega t$. The potential value of Y has an oscillatory time-path ; what of the actual (lagged) value of Y? It is to be expected that Y will have the same

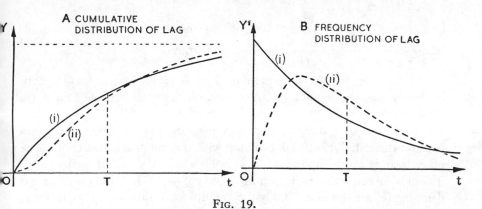

FIG. 19.

frequency (ω) and damping (α) as Z, but different amplitude and phase. This is to be investigated by solving the differential equation of the lag. For the single *exponential lag* (4) :

$$\frac{dY}{dt} + \lambda Y = \lambda e^{\alpha t} \cos \omega t \quad \text{with } Y = 0 \text{ at } t = 0 \quad \dots\dots\dots\dots(8)$$

Though this is easily solved by " classical " methods (see Ex. 4 below), it is instructive here to use Laplace Transforms. The function $e^{\alpha t} \cos \omega t$ has Laplace Transform :

$$\frac{p - \alpha}{(p - \alpha)^2 + \omega^2} \qquad \text{(standard form (6a) of 5.6 above)}$$

Hence, the differential equation (8) has subsidiary equation (since $Y = 0$ at $t = 0$) :

$$(p + \lambda)\overline{Y}(p) = \lambda \frac{p - \alpha}{(p - \alpha)^2 + \omega^2}$$

i.e.
$$\overline{Y}(p) = \lambda \frac{p - \alpha}{(p + \lambda)\{(p - \alpha)^2 + \omega^2\}} \qquad \dots\dots\dots\dots(9)$$

is the Laplace Transform of the solution of (8). Put (9) into partial fractions :

$$\overline{Y}(p) = \frac{\lambda}{(\lambda + \alpha)^2 + \omega^2} \frac{(\lambda + \alpha)(p - \alpha) + \omega^2}{(p - \alpha)^2 + \omega^2} - \frac{\lambda(\lambda + \alpha)}{(\lambda + \alpha)^2 + \omega^2} \frac{1}{p + \lambda}$$

and use the standard forms of Laplace Transforms to give :

$$Y(t) = \frac{\lambda}{(\lambda+\alpha)^2 + \omega^2} e^{\alpha t}\{(\lambda+\alpha)\cos\omega t + \omega\sin\omega t\} - \frac{\lambda(\lambda+\alpha)}{(\lambda+\alpha)^2 + \omega^2} e^{-\lambda t}$$

i.e.

$$\left.\begin{array}{c} Y(t) = \rho e^{\alpha t}\cos(\omega t - \phi) - \rho\cos\phi\, e^{-\lambda t} \\[2mm] \text{where} \quad \rho = \dfrac{\lambda}{\sqrt{(\lambda+\alpha)^2 + \omega^2}} \quad \text{and} \quad \tan\phi = \dfrac{\omega}{\lambda+\alpha} \end{array}\right\} \quad \dots\dots\dots(10)$$

The solution for the time-path of $Y(t)$ is given in two ways : both explicitly as a function of t in (10) and indirectly as the Laplace Transform (a function of p) in (9). The time-path of $Y(t)$ in (10) has two terms. One of them is a damped variation proportional to $e^{-\lambda t}$; this arises because the initial $Y=0$ is out of step with the initial $Z=1$ at $t=0$. The other term is more important : it is $\rho e^{\alpha t}\cos(\omega t - \phi)$, i.e. an oscillation in Y following the given oscillation in $Z = e^{\alpha t}\cos\omega t$. The frequency (ω) and damping (α) are the same. Only the amplitude, multiplied by the factor ρ, and the phase, given by $\dfrac{\phi}{\omega}$, are different.

EXERCISES 5.8

1. Show that $Y = \left(\dfrac{3\lambda}{D+3\lambda}\right)^3 Z$ is a triple exponential lag of Y on Z, being three equal lags in sequence, total time constant $T = \dfrac{1}{\lambda}$. If Z is given as the constant Z_0 and if $Y = \dfrac{dY}{dt} = \dfrac{d^2Y}{dt^2} = 0$ at $t = 0$, show that

$$Y = \left\{1 - \left(1 + 3\lambda t + 9\lambda^2\frac{t^2}{2}\right)e^{-3\lambda t}\right\} Z_0$$

and represent graphically on Fig. 19.

2. Generalise the double lag, (5) above, to allow for different speeds of response in the separate lags and show that it can be represented by :

$$Y = \frac{\lambda_1\lambda_2}{(D+\lambda_1)(D+\lambda_2)} Z$$

Solve for $Z = Z_0$ (constant) given $Y = \dfrac{dY}{dt} = 0$ at $t = 0$.

3. Give the differential equation which defines an n-fold exponential lag (a) when all lags are of equal speed of response $\left(\text{total time constant } T = \dfrac{1}{\lambda}\right)$, and (b) generally when the lags are of different speeds of response.

4. Obtain the solution (10) of (8) by " classical " methods, using the operator D to provide a particular integral, as at the end of 5.5 above.

5.9 The Use of $p = \alpha + i\omega$

The variable p, generally representing the complex number $\alpha + i\omega$, has now made several appearances and they would seem to have no connection with each other. This is not so ; in fact, all the uses of $p = \alpha + i\omega$ have a common thread and hang together. It is time that all this is made clear. The different uses can be assembled in the following manner.

(i) $p = \alpha + i\omega$ *relates to sinusoidal variables.* The general sinusoidal function is $y = Ae^{\alpha t} \cos(\omega t + \epsilon)$; it is the " real " part of the complex variable $z = Ae^{i\epsilon} e^{pt}$ where $p = \alpha + i\omega$, and z can be represented as a product of vectors. Of the four parameters, A and ϵ (amplitude and phase) concern the initial position at $t = 0$ and they are separated off as the term $Ae^{i\epsilon}$ in z, as the first of the vectors in the product. The other two parameters are ω and α (period and damping) and they serve to describe the sinusoidal variation over time. The purpose of $p = \alpha + i\omega$ is to string them together so that p, or more strictly the complex number or vector e^{pt}, describes the movement over time. On this, see 4.7—4.9 above.

(ii) p *is the variable used in the auxiliary equation of a linear differential equation.* For the general (nth order) differential equation, linear with constant coefficients, the auxiliary equation is

$$a_0 p^n + a_1 p^{n-1} + \ldots + a_{n-1} p + a_n = 0$$

If $p_1, p_2, \ldots p_n$ are the roots, the complementary function, part of the solution of the differential equation, is

$$A_1 e^{p_1 t} + A_2 e^{p_2 t} + \ldots + A_n e^{p_n t}$$

Suppose p_1 and p_2 are conjugate complex ($\alpha \pm i\omega$). Then the first two terms in the solution combine to give $Ae^{\alpha t} \cos(\omega t + \epsilon)$, A and ϵ being arbitrary. So again $p = \alpha + i\omega$ has the same meaning—sinusoidal variation over time, as given by a differential equation. A real root of the auxiliary equation is merely a particular case, $\omega = 0$. The use of p in the auxiliary equation is justified ; when oscillations arise, $p = \alpha + i\omega$ with the interpretation of (i) above.

(iii) p *is written for the operator* $D = \dfrac{d}{dt}$ *applied to sinusoidal variables.* This has been worked out and justified in 4.9 above. It is the *same* $p = \alpha + i\omega$ as in (i), i.e. ω and α are the two parameters of the sinusoidal variable which relate to motion over time and so concern $\dfrac{d}{dt}$. Hence, to deal with $y = Ae^{\alpha t} \cos(\omega t + \epsilon)$, write $z = Ae^{i\epsilon} e^{pt}$ with $Dz = pz$, and Dy comes by taking the " real " part of pz.

(iv) p *is the variable of the Laplace Transform* : $\bar{y}(p) = \displaystyle\int_0^\infty e^{-pt} y(t) \, dt$.

This does appear to be something quite different. Indeed, p is any real or complex number, the independent variable in $\bar{y}(p)$ obtained from $y(t)$, provided only that the integral converges. The point, however, is that in most uses p is again $\alpha + i\omega$, where α and ω are to be interpreted as the damping and frequency of a sinusoidal component of $y(t)$. This is the matter to be examined further ; it is the critical link in the chain.

A linear differential equation defines $y(t)$:

$$a_0 \frac{d^n y}{dt^n} + a_1 \frac{d^{n-1} y}{dt^{n-1}} + \ldots + a_{n-1} \frac{dy}{dt} + a_n y = f(t) \quad \ldots\ldots\ldots\ldots\ldots(1)$$

where $f(t)$, or a component of $f(t)$, is taken as a sinusoidal variable :

$$f(t) = A e^{\alpha t} \cos(\omega t + \epsilon) \quad \ldots\ldots\ldots\ldots\ldots\ldots\ldots(2)$$

Assume further that the structure of the differential equation (the a's) is such that $y(t)$ has an inherent sinusoidal oscillation. Hence, part of $y(t)$, as obtained from (1) with $f(t)$ dropped, is a sinusoidal variable :

$$\text{Oscillation inherent in } y(t) = A' e^{\alpha' t} \cos(\omega' t + \epsilon') \quad \ldots\ldots\ldots\ldots(3)$$

There are now two sinusoidal variations to consider, given by (2) and by (3). They are described, as regards their motion over time (damping and period) by :

$$p = \alpha + i\omega \quad \text{and} \quad p' = \alpha' + i\omega'$$

Now consider the analysis of (1). If the inherent oscillation is in question, drop $f(t)$ and write (1) as $(a_0 D^n + a_1 D^{n-1} + \ldots + a_{n-1} D + a_n) y = 0$. Since, for the variation (3) considered, $D = p' = \alpha' + i\omega'$:

$$a_0 p'^n + a_1 p'^{n-1} + \ldots + a_{n-1} p' + a_n = 0$$

which is just the auxiliary equation, already known to have a root $p' = \alpha' + i\omega'$, together with the conjugate $\alpha' - i\omega'$. There is nothing new here. But, if the other oscillation (2) is considered, the question is : can $y(t)$ oscillate like $f(t)$? If so, the equation (1) with $D = p = \alpha + i\omega$ is :

$$(a_0 p^n + a_1 p^{n-1} + \ldots + a_{n-1} p + a_n) Y = Z$$

where Z is $A e^{i\epsilon} e^{pt}$, or $f(t)$ written in complex variable form, and Y is a corresponding complex variable for $y(t)$. This is new ground ; it needs to be explored. It is also quite close to the subsidiary equation of (1) in the Laplace Transform, with Y and Z replaced by the transforms $\bar{y}(p)$ and $\bar{f}(p)$.

The equation (1) has a subsidiary equation which gives the Laplace Transform of the solution $y(t)$ as :

$$\bar{y}(p) = \frac{\bar{f}(p) + \text{polynomial in } p}{a_0 p^n + a_1 p^{n-1} + \ldots + a_{n-1} p + a_n}$$

where the polynomial in the numerator includes the initial conditions. In this case, $\bar{f}(p)$ is the Laplace Transform of (2); apart from the phase ϵ, it is:

$$\bar{f}(p) = \frac{p - \alpha}{(p - \alpha)^2 + \omega^2}$$

On substituting:

$$\left.\begin{array}{l} \bar{y}(p) = \dfrac{\text{Polynomial in } p}{(a_0 p^n + a_1 p^{n-1} + \ldots + a_{n-1} p + a_n)(\overline{p - \alpha^2 + \omega^2})} \\[3mm] \quad = \displaystyle\sum_{r=1}^{n+2} A_r \frac{1}{p - p_r} \text{ in partial fractions} \end{array}\right\} \quad \ldots\ldots\ldots(4)$$

where the A_r are certain coefficients and p_1, p_2, $\cdots$ p_n, p_{n+1}, p_{n+2} (assumed all different) comprise the roots to be obtained by equating the denominator of $\bar{y}(p)$ to zero.   From the two factors equated to zero—the auxiliary equation and $(p - \alpha)^2 + \omega^2 = 0$—it follows that p_1, p_2, $\ldots p_n$ are the roots of the auxiliary equation of (1) and p_{n+1}, $p_{n+2} = \alpha \pm i\omega$.   Hence the p_r of (4) include *both* $p = \alpha + i\omega$ (and conjugate) *and* $p' = \alpha' + i\omega'$ (and conjugate), since p' comes from the auxiliary equation.

Result (4) now inverts directly into the complete solution of (1):

$$y(t) = \sum_{r=1}^{n+2} A_r e^{p_r t} \quad \ldots\ldots\ldots\ldots\ldots\ldots\ldots\ldots\ldots(5)$$

Two pairs of terms in (5), corresponding to $p = \alpha \pm i\omega$ and $p' = \alpha' \pm i\omega'$ included among the p_r, amalgamate into two sinusoidal components of $y(t)$:

$$y(t) = B e^{\alpha t} \cos(\omega t + \eta) + B' e^{\alpha' t} \cos(\omega' t + \eta') + \ldots \quad \ldots\ldots\ldots\ldots(6)$$

where B, B', η and η' are certain constants.   The conclusion is that $y(t)$ contains, in additive form, both the *forced* oscillation of (2) and the *inherent* oscillation of (3).   This is expected; the first is the particular integral from $f(t)$, the second one of the structural oscillations of the complementary function.   What is now clear is the way in which the Laplace Transform gives them, and the fact that $p = \alpha + i\omega$ and $p' = \alpha' + i\omega'$ are the values of p in the Laplace Transform.

Laplace Transforms, switching from $y(t)$ to $\bar{y}(p)$ and back, make for great flexibility in interpretation and use.   When sinusoidal oscillations, both forced and inherent, are concerned, the solution of the differential equation is written equally well as (4) or as (6).   In the latter case, $y(t)$ is the function of time, or the solution itself.   In the former case, $\bar{y}(p)$ is a corresponding function of p, to be interpreted as $\alpha + i\omega$; the function of time has been transformed into a function of frequency (ω) and damping (α) of oscillation.

The simple case of the exponential lag, considered at the end of **5.8** above, is an illustration; the differential equation is

$$Y = \frac{\lambda}{D+\lambda} Z \quad \text{where } Z = e^{\alpha t} \cos \omega t$$

The Laplace Transform of the solution, (9) of 5.8, is

$$\overline{Y}(p) = \lambda \frac{p - \alpha}{(p+\lambda)(p - \alpha^2 + \omega^2)}$$

which is a function of frequency and damping. The solution as a function of time, (10) of 5.8, is

$$Y(t) = \rho e^{\alpha t} \cos (\omega t - \phi) - \rho \cos \phi e^{-\lambda t}$$

The *forced oscillation* is that of Z, $p = \alpha + i\omega$; it is to be seen in $\overline{Y}(p)$ in the quadratic factor $(p - \alpha)^2 + \omega^2$, giving $p = \alpha \pm i\omega$ when equated to zero. There is *no inherent oscillation* in this case, only a steady damping shown by the $e^{-\lambda t}$ term in $Y(t)$ and by the value $p = -\lambda$ or the factor $(p+\lambda)$ in $\overline{Y}(p)$.

The interpretation of a solution such as (6) above can vary according to the type of problem. Sometimes the emphasis is on the *inherent oscillations*, those with frequencies such as ω' given by the structure of the system (1) and arising no matter what outside influence $f(t)$ is at work. If further oscillations are introduced by $f(t)$, these are incidental. On other occasions, the emphasis is on the *forced oscillations* set up in $y(t)$ by the given oscillations in $f(t)$, the frequency being ω. In this case, it is any inherent oscillations which are incidental. Indeed, they are not only incidental; they can be actually eliminated if the initial conditions are suitable. Herein lies the difference between forced oscillations, which *must* arise in $y(t)$ if injected by $f(t)$, and the inherent oscillations, which *may* never arise if there is no initial disturbance.

The case of the exponential lag illustrates. The inherent variation of Y is the steady and damped component involving $e^{-\lambda t}$; this may be the main interest, e.g. if Z is given as a constant. However, if an oscillation is injected by taking $Z = e^{\alpha t} \cos \omega t$, then attention is directed to the corresponding variation in Y, the component $\rho e^{\alpha t} \cos (\omega t - \phi)$. The other component, the inherent variation involving $e^{-\lambda t}$, can be taken as dying away over time. Indeed it may not arise at all. Take $\alpha = -\lambda$ so that $\phi = \frac{\pi}{2}$ and $\cos \phi = 0$. The second term in $Y(t)$ disappears and the solution is simply:

$$Y(t) = \frac{\lambda}{\omega} e^{-\lambda t} \cos \left(\omega t - \frac{\pi}{2} \right)$$

corresponding to:
$$Z(t) = e^{-\lambda t} \cos \omega t.$$

The oscillation in Z gives rise to a corresponding oscillation in Y, the amplitude being modified by the factor $\dfrac{\lambda}{\omega}$ and the phase shift being $\dfrac{\pi}{2}$.

EXERCISES 5.9

1. In the double exponential lag $Y = \left(\dfrac{\lambda}{D+\lambda}\right)^2 Z$, take $Z = \cos \omega t$. Solve for Y and show that the lag of Y behind Z is given by $\phi = \tan^{-1} \dfrac{2\omega\lambda}{\lambda^2 - \omega^2}$.

2. The expansion of $\bar{y}(p)$ in partial fractions in (4) above depends on p_r being all different. What modification is needed when $p_1 = p_2$? Hence examine the case of resonance where the forced oscillation agrees in frequency and damping with one of the inherent oscillations.

3. Illustrate the case of resonance by solving $\dfrac{d^2y}{dt^2} + y = \cos \omega t$ and by taking ω nearly equal to unity.

REFERENCES

Allen (R. G. D.) (1938) : *Mathematical Analysis for Economists* (Macmillan, 1938), Chapter XVI.

Baumol (W. J.) (1951) : *Economic Dynamics* (Macmillan, 1951), Chapter 12.

Carslaw (H. S.) and Jaeger (J. C.) (1941, 1948) : *Operational Methods in Applied Mathematics* (Oxford, First Ed. 1941, Second Ed. 1948), Chapter I.

Domar (E. D.) (1944) : " The 'Burden of the Debt' and the National Income ", *American Economic Review*, **34**, 798–827.

Gardner (M. F.) and Barnes (J. L.) (1942) : *Transients in Linear Systems* (Wiley, 1942).

Jaeger (J. C.) (1949) : *An Introduction to the Laplace Transformation* (Methuen, 1949), Chapter I.

Piaggio (H. T. H.) (1920) : *An Elementary Treatise on Differential Equations* (Bell, 1920), Chapter III.

CHAPTER 6

MATHEMATICAL ANALYSIS: LINEAR DIFFERENCE EQUATIONS

6.1 Difference Equations

SIMPLE forms of difference equations arise in practice when a cumulative total $Y_x (x = 0, 1, 2, ...)$ is defined from a specific law of cumulation, e.g. when Y_x increases by a specified amount at each stage. This is illustrated by the cumulative growth of a sum of money at compound interest. Interest at $100r\%$ per year is compounded annually and an original sum of £Y_0 amounts to £Y_x at the end of x years $(x = 0, 1, 2, ...)$. Then:

$$Y_x = (1+r)Y_{x-1} \quad \text{subject to} \quad Y_x = Y_0 \text{ at } x = 0$$

This is a difference equation involving both Y_x and the lagged value Y_{x-1}. The solution of the equation is an explicit expression of Y_x as a function of x valid for $x = 0, 1, 2, ...$ In this case, it is $Y_x = Y_0(1+r)^x$ (see 6.3 below).

As a variant, suppose £Y_0 is invested each year. Then:

$$Y_x = (1+r)Y_{x-1} + Y_0 \quad \text{subject to } Y_x = Y_0 \text{ at } x = 0.$$

This slightly different equation has solution (see 6.3, Ex. 10, below):

$$Y_x = \frac{Y_0}{r} \left\{ (1+r)^{x+1} - 1 \right\}$$

Rather more generally, the sum S_x of the first x terms of a series satisfies a difference equation which is the expression of the general term of the series. The xth term u_x of the series is the amount to be added to S_{x-1} to get S_x: $S_x - S_{x-1} = u_x$. Once u_x is specified in terms of $x (x = 0, 1, 2, ...)$, this is a difference equation, to be solved to give S_x in terms of x. An instance is given in 6.3, Ex. 5, below.

In general, an *ordinary difference equation* relates to a function $Y = Y(x)$ considered for a series of *equally-spaced* values of x. The interval between successive values of x can be taken, without loss of generality, as the unit for measuring x. From any value x as a starting point, a series of equally-spaced values is $x, (x+1), (x+2), ...$ Alternatively, the series read in the other direction is $x, (x-1), (x-2), ...$ The corresponding values of Y are $Y(x), Y(x+1), Y(x+2), ...$ or $Y(x), Y(x-1), Y(x-2), ...$ A slightly different notation is adopted here: $Y_x, Y_{x+1}, Y_{x+2}, ...$ or $Y_x, Y_{x-1},$

Y_{x-2}, ...   This is a compact and convenient notation which emphasises sufficiently that only isolated and equally-spaced values of x are considered.

Successive *differences* of Y are defined :

First differences	*Second differences*	*Third differences* ....
$\Delta Y_x = Y_{x+1} - Y_x$	$\Delta^2 Y_x = \Delta Y_{x+1} - \Delta Y_x$	$\Delta^3 Y_x = \Delta^2 Y_{x+1} - \Delta^2 Y_x$ ......
$\Delta Y_{x+1} = Y_{x+2} - Y_{x+1}$	$\Delta^2 Y_{x+1} = \Delta Y_{x+2} - \Delta Y_{x+1}$	$\Delta^3 Y_{x+1} = \Delta^2 Y_{x+2} - \Delta^2 Y_{x+1}$ ...
$\Delta Y_{x+2} = Y_{x+3} - Y_{x+2}$	$\Delta^2 Y_{x+2} = \Delta Y_{x+3} - \Delta Y_{x+2}$	....
$\Delta Y_{x+3} = Y_{x+4} - Y_{x+3}$	....	
....		

So, from the value x, ΔY_x is the first difference, $\Delta^2 Y_x$ the second difference, $\Delta^3 Y_x$ the third difference, and so on.   By analogy with differential equations, an ordinary difference equation is a relation between x, Y_x and successive differences $\Delta Y_x, \Delta^2 Y_x, \Delta^3 Y_x, \ldots$.   It can be written, in general, as :

$$\phi(x, Y_x, \Delta Y_x, \Delta^2 Y_x, \ldots \Delta^n Y_x) = 0 \quad\ldots\ldots\ldots\ldots\ldots(1)$$

The *order* of the equation is that of the highest difference contained.   A first order equation includes ΔY_x but no higher differences, a second order equation contains $\Delta^2 Y_x$ but no higher differences.   The general form (1) is of order n.

Though the difference equation (1) is in a form closely analogous to a differential equation, it is often more convenient to express it in other ways.   The first order equation $\phi(x, Y_x, \Delta Y_x) = 0$ can be written $\psi(x, Y_x, Y_{x+1}) = 0$ when $\Delta Y_x = Y_{x+1} - Y_x$ is substituted.   In the second order equation $\phi(x, Y_x, \Delta Y_x, \Delta^2 Y_x) = 0$ substitute :

$$\Delta Y_x = Y_{x+1} - Y_x$$

and $\Delta^2 Y_x = \Delta Y_{x+1} - \Delta Y_x = (Y_{x+2} - Y_{x+1}) - (Y_{x+1} - Y_x) = Y_{x+2} - 2Y_{x+1} + Y_x$ and it becomes $\psi(x, Y_x, Y_{x+1}, Y_{x+2}) = 0$ Equally, $\chi(x, Y_x, Y_{x-1}) = 0$ is a first order, and $\chi(x, Y_x, Y_{x-1}, Y_{x-2}) = 0$ a second order difference equation, the equally spaced values of x running backwards instead of forwards. Generally :

$$\psi(x, Y_x, Y_{x+1}, Y_{x+2}, \ldots Y_{x+n}) = 0 \quad\ldots\ldots\ldots\ldots\ldots(2)$$

and

$$\chi(x, Y_x, Y_{x-1}, Y_{x-2}, \ldots Y_{x-n}) = 0 \quad\ldots\ldots\ldots\ldots\ldots(3)$$

are two forms of a difference equation of order n alternative to (1).

The fact that one and the same difference equation can be written in the alternative forms (1), (2) and (3) is illustrated by the following simple case. A first order equation can be defined by $\Delta Y_x = Y_x + x + 1$.   Write $\Delta Y_x = Y_{x+1} - Y_x$ and the equation becomes $Y_{x+1} = 2Y_x + x + 1$.   Replace $(x+1)$ by x and x by $(x-1)$ and the equation is then $Y_x = 2Y_{x-1} + x$. Hence :

(1) $\Delta Y_x = Y_x + x + 1$ (2) $Y_{x+1} = 2Y_x + x + 1$ (3) $Y_x = 2Y_{x-1} + x$

are three forms of one and the same relation.

Which form is used is a matter of convenience. Here, the third form is generally adopted since difference equations arise in this way in economic problems, as illustrated by the first order equations expressing growth at compound interest. The general case, in this form, is given by (3) where Y_x and its values lagged 1, 2, ... n periods all appear. The highest lag fixes the order of the difference equation.

As in Chapter 5, the treatment of difference equations is here confined to one particular type, the equation which is *linear with constant coefficients*. Such a difference equation, of order n, is written :

$$a_0 Y_x + a_1 Y_{x-1} + \ldots + a_{n-1} Y_{x-n+1} + a_n Y_{x-n} = f(x) \quad \ldots\ldots\ldots\ldots(4)$$

together with the corresponding *homogeneous form* :

$$a_0 y_x + a_1 y_{x-1} + \ldots + a_{n-1} y_{x-n+1} + a_n y_{x-n} = 0 \quad \ldots\ldots\ldots\ldots(5)$$

The coefficients on the left-hand side are all constants, not involving the independent variable x, and $a_n \neq 0$ if the equation is of order n. In the general form (4), $f(x)$ is any expression in the variable x ; hence x appears explicitly only in an expression which is separate from the dependent variable. In the homogeneous form (5), x does not appear explicitly at all.

The following are examples of linear difference equations with constant coefficients in form (4) or (5), together with the equivalent form in terms of differences in each case :

(i) $Y_x - Y_{x-1} = \alpha^{x-1}$ or $\Delta Y_x = \alpha^x$

(ii) $Y_x - a Y_{x-1} = \alpha^{x-1}$ or $\Delta Y_x - (a-1) Y_x = \alpha^x$

(iii) $y_x = y_{x-1} - y_{x-2}$ or $\Delta^2 y_x + \Delta y_x + y_x = 0$

(iv) $8y_x - 6y_{x-1} + y_{x-2} = 0$ or $8\Delta^2 y_x + 10\Delta y_x + 3y_x = 0$

(v) $Y_x - a^2 Y_{x-2} = \alpha x + \beta$ or $\Delta^2 Y_x + 2\Delta Y_x - (a^2 - 1) Y_x = \alpha(x+2) + \beta$

(vi) $y_x - 3y_{x-1} + 4y_{x-2} - 2y_{x-3} = 0$ or $\Delta^3 y_x + \Delta y_x = 0$

EXERCISES 6.1

1. Check that the successive differences of $y = x^3$ for $x = 0, 1, 2, \ldots$ are :

x	y_x	Δy_x	$\Delta^2 y_x$	$\Delta^3 y_x$	$\Delta^4 y_x$
0	0	1	6	6	0
1	1	7	12	6	0
2	8	19	18	6	...
3	27	37	24	...	
4	64	61	...		
5	125	...			
...	...				

Write the corresponding table for $y = x^4$.

2. Generalise the results of the previous exercise by indicating that the nth differences of a polynomial of degree n are all equal and all higher differences zero.

3. Write the table of successive differences of $y = \cos x$ for $x = 0$, π, 2π, 3π, ... and show that the differences of any one order are constant but alternating in sign all down the table.

4. Express Δy_x, $\Delta^2 y_x$ and $\Delta^3 y_x$ in terms of y_x, y_{x+1}, y_{x+2} and y_{x+3}. Conversely, express y_{x+1}, y_{x+2} and y_{x+3} in terms of y_x, Δy_x, $\Delta^2 y_x$ and $\Delta^3 y_x$. In the examples (i) to (vi) above, translate the first form into the second in each case ; check by translating the second form into the first.

6.2 Discrete Solution ; Basic Results

There is no doubt about the nature of the solution of a differential equation ; it is a function of the independent variable x which is subject itself to continuous variation. The matter is a little more complicated when a difference equation is to be solved. The equation relates to a function $Y = Y(x)$ of a variable x which is not changed continuously but which jumps over successive terms in a series of equally-spaced values. From the formulation of the difference equation, however, it is seen that the series of equally-spaced values can start from any value x whatever, and the starting value can be varied, and varied continuously. So, as will be indicated in 6.8 below, it is quite in order to seek a continuous solution of a difference equation.

It is convenient to develop the analysis, first and primarily, in terms of a particular type of solution. The series of equally-spaced values of x is taken as starting from one definite point, so that the only values of x considered make up the particular equally-spaced series which stems from a fixed starting value. No other values of x are taken into account ; there is no question of continuous variation. Any solution obtained under these conditions is a *discrete solution* of the difference equation. It is important to concentrate on discrete solutions, not only because they are more easily obtained and interpreted, but also because they are sufficient for a wide variety of problems, including those in economics. Such a discrete solution applies, for example, to the course of price or output over time when only year-end values, or yearly averages, are considered. This ignores what happens within a year, e.g. the seasonal variation in price or output.

Since the unit of measuring x is already selected as the interval between equally-spaced values, it is only necessary now to select the starting point and this can be done, without loss of generality, by taking $x = 0$. The particular series for a discrete solution is then :

$$x = 0, 1, 2, 3, \ldots \; n \ldots$$

So, x takes only positive integral values with zero as the starting point.

The methods of obtaining discrete solutions of difference equations are very similar to those adopted for differential equations. There are some differences and these will be summarised later. One of the most important of the differences arises at the outset and it merits detailed consideration. In solving differential equations, the usual procedure is to seek the general solution and then to derive particular solutions by specifying (e.g.) definite initial conditions. The position is the reverse with difference equations. A particular (discrete) solution is easily obtained ; indeed it comes automatically. The general solution is more difficult to derive.

This can be illustrated by a first-order difference equation, written generally as $\chi(x, Y_x, Y_{x-1}) = 0$, considered for $x = 0, 1, 2, \ldots$. Let Y_0 be the initial value of Y_x at $x = 0$. Then, given Y_0, substituting $x = 1$ in the difference equation gives Y_1. Given Y_1, substituting $x = 2$ gives Y_2 ; and so on. The whole series, $Y_0, Y_1, Y_2, \ldots$, is obtained numerically by a process of iteration, of repeated use of the difference equation, provided only that the initial value Y_0 is specified. This is a particular discrete solution of the equation.

Take, for example, the first-order equation $Y_x = 2Y_{x-1} + x$, subject to $Y_0 = \frac{1}{2}$. Successive values of Y_x are then found :

$$Y_1 = 2 \cdot \tfrac{1}{2} + 1 = 2$$
$$Y_2 = 2 \cdot 2 + 2 = 6$$
$$Y_3 = 2 \cdot 6 + 3 = 15$$

A particular discrete solution is $Y_x = \frac{1}{2}, 2, 6, 15, \ldots$ for $x = 0, 1, 2, 3, \ldots$. Other particular solutions are obtained equally easily, e.g.

$$Y_x = 1, 3, 8, 19, \ldots \quad \text{or} \quad Y_x = 2, 5, 12, 27, \ldots$$

It may be said that the general discrete solution corresponds to the assignment of an *arbitrary* initial value Y_0—and this is indeed the case. The difficulty is to express it explicitly in terms of x for $x = 0, 1, 2, \ldots$. With Y_0 as the starting value in this case, successive values of Y_x are obtained from the difference equation :

$$Y_x = Y_0, (2Y_0 + 1), (4Y_0 + 4), (8Y_0 + 11), (16Y_0 + 26), \ldots$$

This is the general discrete solution, produced automatically from the equation. But what is Y_x explicitly in terms of x? Fairly evidently, the first term in Y_x is $Y_0 2^x$; the second term is more difficult (see below).

Difference equations of the second (or higher) order are handled similarly. Particular discrete solutions are obtained once two (or more) initial values of Y_x are specified to " start up " the whole series, e.g. Y_0 and Y_1 for a second order equation. The process is automatic and the only difficulty is the weight of numerical calculation involved. The main trouble, again, is to get a general discrete solution and to get it explicitly in terms of x.

The problem is tackled, as with differential equations, on an entirely practical level. Complicated questions of whether there exists a solution within a certain range of function types are avoided; the assumption is that a solution is there to be found. The practical guides are, again, some basic results in the form of a theorem about discrete solutions of difference equations in general, and rules for solving difference equations which are linear with constant coefficients. The basic theorem is:

The general discrete solution of an ordinary difference equation of order n gives Y_x as a function of x ($x = 0, 1, 2, \ldots$) involving exactly n arbitrary constants:

$$Y_x = Y(x; A_1, A_2, \ldots A_n)$$

From what has been said, this result is at least plausible. It takes one arbitrary constant (e.g. the initial value Y_0) to " start up " the solution of a first order difference equation; it takes two arbitrary constants (e.g. Y_0 and Y_1) to " start up " a second-order equation; and so on. In the *general solution*, the constants or initial values are arbitrary; in a *particular solution*, they are given definite and specified values. All particular solutions, however, are comprised within the general solution.

The rules which serve as guides in the practical task of obtaining a general solution explicitly in terms of x are given here for linear difference equations with constant coefficients. The general form of order n and the corresponding homogeneous form are:

$$a_0 Y_x + a_1 Y_{x-1} + \ldots + a_{n-1} Y_{x-n+1} + a_n Y_{x-n} = f(x) \ldots\ldots\ldots\ldots(1)$$
$$a_0 y_x + a_1 y_{x-1} + \ldots + a_{n-1} y_{x-n+1} + a_n y_{x-n} = 0 \ldots\ldots\ldots\ldots(2)$$

RULES: (i) If the homogeneous equation (2) has discrete solutions $y_1(x)$ and $y_2(x)$, then $y_1(x) + y_2(x)$ is also a discrete solution.

(ii) If the homogeneous equation (2) has a discrete solution $y(x)$, then $Ay(x)$ is also a discrete solution for any constant A.

(iii) If $\overline{Y}(x)$ is any particular discrete solution whatever of the general equation (1) and if $y(x; A_1, A_2, \ldots A_n)$ is the general discrete solution of the corresponding homogeneous form (2), then the general discrete solution of (1) is:

$$\overline{Y}(x) + y(x; A_1, A_2, \ldots A_n)$$

The rules are similar to those for differential equations and the proofs are equally straight-forward.

The practical method of finding a discrete solution of (1) now follows. An attempt can be made first to find n particular and different solutions of the homogeneous form (2) and then to combine them into :

$$y_x = A_1 y_1(x) + A_2 y_2(x) + \ldots + A_n y_n(x) \quad \ldots\ldots\ldots\ldots\ldots(3)$$

Since this contains exactly n arbitrary constants, A_1, A_2, $\ldots A_n$, it is the general discrete solution of (2). Finally, once any particular discrete solution $\overline{Y}(x)$ is found for (1), the general discrete solution of (1) follows :

$$Y_x = \overline{Y}(x) + A_1 y_1(x) + A_2 y_2(x) + \ldots + A_n y_n(x) \quad \ldots\ldots\ldots\ldots(4)$$

Here, $\overline{Y}(x)$ is called the *particular integral* and the remainder is the *complementary function*, the general solution (3) of the corresponding homogeneous form. It is not always easy to find n different solutions to combine into the complementary function and, as will be seen, various " tricks " may need to be employed.

As with differential equations, it is often preferable, particularly in solving difference equations arising in economic problems, to adopt an alternative procedure in which the order of the main steps is reversed. The original variable Y_x considered (e.g. income or output) satisfies the difference equation (1). First attempt to find a particular solution $\overline{Y}(x)$; any particular solution will do but the easiest to interpret is a solution which represents the *trend* or *equilibrium* variation of Y_x as x increases indefinitely. If x is time, for example, then $\overline{Y}(x)$ is a time path of Y_x consistent with (1) and, at the same time, a norm or equilibrium variation over time. Next write $y_x = Y_x - \overline{Y}(x)$ as the deviation of Y from the trend or equilibrium. Both Y_x and $\overline{Y}(x)$ satisfy (1) ; substitute and subtract, so that y_x is seen to satisfy the homogeneous form (2). Finally, y_x is found as the general solution of (2) as shown in (3). The method is now complete and the result readily interpreted. The variation y_x from trend or equilibrium is given by (3) ; switching back to the original variable Y_x gives the solution (4). An example of this procedure in practice has already been given in the economic problem of 2.7 above.

The remarks about arbitrary constants and initial conditions in 5.2 above apply equally well to difference equations. Initial conditions for the discrete solution of a difference equation are (almost always) a sufficient number of the first values of Y_x ; Y_0, Y_1, Y_2, $\ldots$. The number required is the order of the equation, i.e. Y_0 is sufficient to " start up " the solution of a first-order equation, Y_0 and Y_1, are needed for a second-order equation, and so on.

Take as an illustration the first-order equation already examined :

$Y_x = 2Y_{x-1} + x$. Following the practical procedure given here, the general discrete solution is :

$$Y_x = A2^x - (x+2) \quad \text{(6.3, Ex. 9, below)}$$

where A is an arbitrary constant. The initial condition is $Y_x = Y_0$ at $x=0$. So :

$$Y_0 = A - 2 \quad \text{i.e.} \quad A = Y_0 + 2$$

The general discrete solution is now :

$$Y_x = Y_0 2^x + (2^{x+1} - x - 2)$$

This is still a *general* solution, since the initial value Y_0 is an arbitrary one. A *particular* solution follows if Y_0 is specified, e.g. $Y_0 = \frac{1}{2}$ giving :

$$Y_x = \frac{5}{2} 2^x - x - 2$$

i.e. $\quad\quad Y_x = \frac{1}{2}, 2, 6, 15, \ldots \quad$ for $x = 0, 1, 2, 3, \ldots$

This is one of the particular solutions already written from the equation itself. It is now seen to fit into a general solution in which Y_x is expressed explicitly in terms of x.

EXERCISES 6.2

1. Prove the rules (i), (ii) and (iii) above.

2. By repeated applications of the equation, obtain the particular solution of $y_x = \frac{1}{2} y_{x-1}$ subject to $y_x = 1$ at $x = 0$, and the general solution when $y_x = y_0$ at $x = 0$ (y_0 being arbitrary). Guess the form of y_x explicitly in terms of x in each case.

3. In the same way, solve $y_x = y_{x-1} - y_{x-2}$ given the initial values y_0 and y_1. Write the particular solution when $y_0 = y_1 = 1$. Indicate that, as x increases, the path of y_x is a regular oscillation of period 6 intervals of x, i.e. y_0 is repeated at $x = 6$, 12, ..., and similarly for y_1, y_2, y_3, y_4 and y_5.

4. The solution (3) of equation (2) above gives the deviation y_x from trend or equilibrium. Indicate that the path of y_x as x increases is " explosive " if at least one y_r is of " explosive " form. When is the path of y_x of " damped " form? Express in terms of a concept of a " dominant " term among y_r ($r = 1$, 2, ...n).

6.3 Linear Difference Equations : First Order

The solution of the differential equation $\dfrac{dY}{dx} = f(x)$ is the indefinite integral of $f(x)$ with an additive constant, i.e. it is the reversal of a standard form of differentiation (5.3 above). In the same way, $\Delta Y_x = f(x)$ has a discrete solution which reverses the standard forms of differences, again with an additive and arbitrary constant (which disappears on differencing). The standard differences for particular functions are not as well-known as standard derivatives and they must be worked out from first principles.

The functions x^n and e^{ax} are among those with the simplest derivatives:

$$\frac{d}{dx}(x^n)=nx^{n-1} \quad \text{and} \quad \frac{d}{dx}(e^{ax})=ae^{ax}$$

This is not so for differences. Instead of x^n it is found that the "factorial" expression denoted by $x^{(n)}=x(x-1)(x-2) \dots (x-n+1)$ is easy to handle in differencing:

$$\begin{aligned}
\Delta x^{(n)} &=(x+1)^{(n)} - x^{(n)}\\
&=(x+1)x(x-1) \dots +(x+1-n+1) - x(x-1) \dots (x-n+2)(x-n+1)\\
&=x(x-1) \dots (x-n-1+1)\{(x+1)-(x-n+1)\}\\
&=nx^{(n-1)}
\end{aligned}$$

Again, instead of e^{ax}, it is a^x which has a simple difference:

$$\begin{aligned}
\Delta a^x &=a^{x+1} - a^x\\
&=(a-1)a^x
\end{aligned}$$

Broadly, $x^{(n)}$ and a^x play the roles in differencing that x^n and e^{ax} play in differentiation.

Rules for differences of sums and products of functions are obtained just as are the well-known rules for derivatives. The simplest rules are:

$$\Delta a=0 \; ; \; \Delta (ay_x+bz_x)=a\Delta y_x+b\Delta z_x \; ; \; \Delta (y_x z_x)=z_{x+1}\Delta y_x+y_x\Delta z_x$$

where a and b are constants, y_x and z_x functions of x. The proofs are quite straight-forward.

On this basis the standard differences can be tabled and hence the discrete solutions of $\Delta Y_x=f(x)$ for various forms of $f(x)$:

Differences : Standard forms	Difference Equations	
	Equation	Solution
$\Delta \dfrac{x^{(n+1)}}{n+1}=x^{(n)}$	$\Delta Y_x=x^{(n)}$	$Y_x=\dfrac{x^{(n+1)}}{n+1}+A \quad (n \neq -1)$
$\Delta \left(\dfrac{a^x}{a-1}\right)=a^x$	$\Delta Y_x=a^x$	$Y_x=\dfrac{a_x}{a-1}+A \quad (a \neq 1)$
$\Delta (\log x)=\log \left(1+\dfrac{1}{x}\right)$	$\Delta Y_x=\log \left(1+\dfrac{1}{x}\right)$	$Y_x=\log x +A$
$\Delta \left(\dfrac{\sin ax}{2 \sin \frac{1}{2}a}\right)=\cos a(x+\frac{1}{2})$	$\Delta Y_x=\cos a(x+\frac{1}{2})$	$Y_x=\dfrac{\sin ax}{2 \sin \frac{1}{2}a}+A$

In all cases there is an additive arbitrary constant A.

A first-order difference equation which is linear with constant coefficients can always be written in the form:

$$Y_x - aY_{x-1}=f(x) \quad \dots\dots\dots\dots\dots\dots\dots(1)$$

and the corresponding homogeneous form is :

$$y_x = a y_{x-1} \quad \dots\dots\dots\dots\dots\dots\dots\dots\dots\dots (2)$$

To obtain the general discrete solution, the practical method of 6.2 is used and the steps are as follows. First, some particular solution $Y_x = \overline{Y}(x)$ must be found for (1) ; this is a matter of trial and error and it depends on the form of $f(x)$. Next, write $y_x = Y_x - \overline{Y}(x)$. Since Y_x and $\overline{Y}$ both satisfy (1) :

$$Y_x - a Y_{x-1} = f(x) \quad \text{and} \quad \overline{Y}(x) - a \overline{Y}(x-1) = f(x)$$

Subtract :
$$y_x = a y_{x-1}$$

i.e. $y_x = Y_x - \overline{Y}(x)$ satisfies (2). Finally, a general discrete solution of (2) must be found to give y_x. This is achieved by repeated application of the equation :

$$y_x = a y_{x-1} = a^2 y_{x-2} = \dots$$

i.e.
$$y_x = A a^x$$

where A is the arbitrary initial value. The general discrete solution of (1) is :

$$Y_x = \overline{Y}(x) + A a^x \quad \dots\dots\dots\dots\dots\dots\dots (3)$$

There is an alternative way of solving (2) which is applicable also to the solution of difference equations of higher orders. Try $y_x = \lambda^x$, where λ is some constant to be found. Then :

$$\lambda^x = a \lambda^{x-1}$$

Hence $\lambda = a$, $y_x = a^x$ is a solution of (2) and $y_x = A a^x$ is the general discrete solution as before. Note that $\lambda = 0$ is also a possibility, but this leads only to the particular solution $Y_x = \overline{Y}(x)$ with $y_x = 0$ for all x.

The " structure " of the equation (1) is represented by the constant a, and the variation of the solution (3) as x increases depends on the sign and magnitude of a. There are four possibilities for the variation of $y_x = Y_x - \overline{Y}$ as x increases :

$1 < a$	y_x increases steadily and without limit
$0 < a < 1$	y_x decreases steadily towards zero
$-1 < a < 0$	y_x alternates and decreases towards zero
$a < -1$	y_x alternates and increases without limit

The range of possibilities is wider than for the corresponding differential equation (see 5.3 above). The new feature is the possibility of alternation. When a is negative, y_x takes positive and negative values alternatively as x runs through the values $x = 0, 1, 2, \dots$. When a is positive, y_x progresses steadily. In both cases, the numerical magnitude of a distinguishes between the " explosive " variation $(a>1$ numerically) and the " damped " variation $(a<1$ numerically).

The term $\bar{Y}(x)$ in the solution (3) depends on the form of $f(x)$ in the original equation. $\bar{Y}$ is easily found in the case $f(x)=\alpha$ (constant). It is then a particular solution of $Y_x-aY_{x-1}=\alpha$. Try $Y_x=\mu$, where μ is some constant to be found :

$$\mu-a\mu=\alpha \quad \text{i.e. } \mu=\frac{\alpha}{1-a}$$

The general discrete solution of $Y_x-aY_{x-1}=\alpha$ is $Y_x=\dfrac{\alpha}{1-a}+Aa^x$. The variation is now from or around a constant level $\bar{Y}=\dfrac{\alpha}{1-a}$. Other forms of $f(x)$ are considered in Ex. 7 and 8 below.

EXERCISES 6.3

1. Show that $\varDelta(y_xz_x)=z_{x+1}\varDelta y_x+y_x\varDelta z_x$. Also show that the same difference can be expressed $y_{x+1}\varDelta z_x+z_x\varDelta y_x$.

2. Show that $\varDelta(\log x)=\log\left(1+\dfrac{1}{x}\right)$.

3. Deduce that $\varDelta(\sin ax)=2\sin\dfrac{a}{2}\cos a(x+\tfrac{1}{2})$ by showing first that :

$$\sin x-\sin y=2\sin\frac{x-y}{2}\cos\frac{x+y}{2}$$

4. If $\varDelta Y_x=a_0x^{(n)}+a_1x^{(n-1)}+\ldots+a_{n-1}x^{(1)}+a_n$, show that

$$Y_x=\frac{a_0}{n+1}x^{(n+1)}+\frac{a_1}{n}x^{(n)}+\ldots+\frac{a_{n-1}}{2}x^{(2)}+a_nx^{(1)}+A$$

Indicate how this result provides the solution of $\varDelta Y_x=$ polynomial in x, by showing that a polynomial in x can be written in terms of " factorials ", e.g.

$$x^2+2x+1=x^{(2)}+3x^{(1)}+1$$

Hence, if $\varDelta Y_x=x^2+2x+1$, show that $Y_x=\tfrac{1}{6}x(x+1)(2x+1)+A$.

5. Let Y_x be the sum of the squares of the first x integers. Show that

$$\varDelta Y_x=(x+1)^2 \text{ subject to } Y_0=0$$

Hence show that

$$Y_x=\tfrac{1}{6}x(x+1)(2x+1)$$

6. Show that, for the linear equation (1), the case $a=0$ is trivial but that the case $a=1$ gives a solution $Y_x=\bar{Y}(x)+A$ and is effectively the case $\varDelta Y_x=f(x)$. Why can $a=1$ be regarded as the dividing line between the " explosive " and the " damped " cases?

7. If $Y_x-aY_{x-1}=\alpha^x$ (α constant), show that $Y_x=\dfrac{\alpha^{x+1}}{\alpha-a}+Aa^x$. Why is $\alpha=a$ not possible?

8. If $Y_x - aY_{x-1} = \alpha x + \beta$ (α and β constants), show that :

$$Y_x = \frac{\alpha x + \beta}{1 - a} - \frac{a\alpha}{(1-a)^2} + Aa^x$$

9. Use the result of the previous exercise to show that the general discrete solution of $Y_x = 2Y_{x-1} + x$ is $Y_x = A2^x - (x+2)$ (see 6.2 above).

10. As a particular case of Ex. 8, check that the general discrete solution of

$$Y_x - aY_{x-1} = \alpha \ (\alpha \text{ constant}) \quad \text{is} \quad Y_x = \frac{\alpha}{1-a} + Aa^x$$

Hence solve the equation $Y_x = aY_{x-1} + Y_0$ subject to $Y_x = Y_0$ at $x=0$, as obtained for the problem of accumulation at compound interest (6.1 above).

6.4 Linear Difference Equations : Second Order

The difference equation and its homogeneous counterpart are now :

$$Y_x + aY_{x-1} + bY_{x-2} = f(x) \quad \dots\dots\dots\dots\dots(1)$$
$$y_x + ay_{x-1} + by_{x-2} = 0 \quad \dots\dots\dots\dots\dots(2)$$

where a and b are " structural " constants $(b \neq 0)$

The same method of solution is followed. A particular solution $Y_x = \overline{Y}(x)$ must be found for (1). Write $y_x = Y_x - \overline{Y}(x)$ and y_x satisfies (2). The problem is then to find the general discrete solution of (2) and the device introduced in 6.3 above again applies. Try $y_x = \lambda^x$ in (2) :

$$\lambda^x + a\lambda^{x-1} + b\lambda^{x-2} = 0$$

Since λ is not zero (except as giving the particular solution $Y_x = \overline{Y}$), divide through by λ^{x-2} and the appropriate values of λ are the roots of the *auxiliary equation* :

$$\lambda^2 + a\lambda + b = 0 \quad \dots\dots\dots\dots\dots\dots(3)$$

i.e. $$\lambda_1, \lambda_2 = \tfrac{1}{2}(-a \pm \sqrt{a^2 - 4b}) \quad \dots\dots\dots\dots(4)$$

The roots may be real and different $(a^2 > 4b)$, real and equal $(a^2 = 4b)$ or conjugate complex $(a^2 < 4b)$, as shown in 4.6 above. In each case, the general solution of (2) can be written and hence the general solution of (1).

Case : $a^2 > 4b$. The roots of (3) are real and different, given by (4). The general discrete solution of (1) is then :

$$Y_x = \overline{Y}(x) + A_1\lambda_1^x + A_2\lambda_2^x \quad \dots\dots\dots\dots(5)$$

where A_1 and A_2 are arbitrary constants which can be found in terms of the initial values Y_0 and Y_1. The solution is very similar to that of the first-order equation of 6.3.

The solution (5) depends on the signs and magnitudes of λ_1 and λ_2 and these involve the " structural " constants a and b of the difference equation. The deviation $y_x = Y_x - \overline{Y}$ from the trend or equilibrium is made up of two terms, $A_1\lambda_1{}^x$ and $A_2\lambda_2{}^x$, and the main interest lies in what happens to this deviation as x increases without limit ($x=0, 1, 2, ...$). Each term can be " explosive " or " damped " (according as the λ is greater or less than unity numerically) and each can vary steadily or alternate (according as the λ is positive or negative). The range of possibilities is great. What matters, however, is the *dominant root* λ_1 or λ_2 and the corresponding *dominant term* in (5), if the deviation is considered not for early values in the series $x=0$, 1, 2, ... but as x increases indefinitely through these integral values. The numerically greater value λ_1 of the two given by (4) is the dominant root. If $\lambda_1>1$ numerically, then the variation of y_x is " explosive ", though it may be either steadily so or alternating. If $\lambda_1<1$ numerically (and λ_2 also), then the variation of y_x is " damped " towards zero, either steadily or alternating, i.e. Y_x is " damped " towards $\overline{Y}$.

Case : $a^2=4b$. The roots of (3) are real but equal with $\lambda_1=\lambda_2=-\frac{1}{2}a$. The homogeneous equation is now :

$$y_x+ay_{x-1}+\tfrac{1}{4}a^2y_{x-2}=0 \quad\dots\dots\dots\dots\dots\dots(6)$$

and the auxiliary equation is $\lambda^2+a\lambda+\tfrac{1}{4}a^2=(\lambda+\tfrac{1}{2}a)^2=0$

One solution of (6) is $y_x=\lambda^x(\lambda=-\tfrac{1}{2}a)$. A second solution is needed and the trick is to try $y_x=x\lambda^x(\lambda=-\tfrac{1}{2}a)$ in (6) :

$$x\lambda^x+a(x-1)\lambda^{x-1}+\tfrac{1}{4}a^2(x-2)\lambda^{x-2}$$
$$=(-\tfrac{1}{2}a)^{x-2}\{\tfrac{1}{4}a^2x+a(-\tfrac{1}{2}a)(x-1)+\tfrac{1}{4}a^2(x-2)\}$$
$$=\tfrac{1}{4}a^2(-\tfrac{1}{2}a)^{x-2}\{x-2(x-1)+x-2\}$$
$$=0$$

Hence λ^x and $x\lambda^x$ ($\lambda=-\tfrac{1}{2}a$) are both solutions of (6) and the general discrete solution is $y_x=(A_1+A_2x)(-\tfrac{1}{2}a)^x$. The general discrete solution of (1) is :

$$Y_x=\overline{Y}(x)+(A_1+A_2x)(-\tfrac{1}{2}a)^x \quad\dots\dots\dots\dots\dots(7)$$

where A_1 and A_2 are arbitrary constants which can be found in terms of initial values Y_0 and Y_1.

The solution (7) is little different from that of the first-order difference equation of 6.3. The single arbitrary constant of the first-order form is now replaced by (A_1+A_2x) with two arbitrary constants, but this factor is swamped by $(-\tfrac{1}{2}a)^x$ as x increases indefinitely through integral values. The variation of $y_x=Y_x-\overline{Y}$ is given by $(A_1+A_2x)(-\tfrac{1}{2}a)^x$ and the dominant term is $(-\tfrac{1}{2}a)^x$. The four possibilities of 6.3 are again to be distinguished. If $a<0$, the variation is steady ; if $a>0$, it alternates between positive and negative values. The numerical magnitude of a then determines whether the variation is " explosive " ($a>2$ numerically) or " damped " to zero ($a<2$ numerically).

Case : $a^2<4b$. The roots of (3) are conjugate complex:

$$\alpha \pm i\beta = \tfrac{1}{2}(-a \pm i\sqrt{4b-a^2})$$

so that $\qquad \alpha = -\tfrac{1}{2}a \quad$ and $\quad \beta = \tfrac{1}{2}\sqrt{4b-a^2}$

The general discrete solution of (1) is then :

$$Y_x = \overline{Y}(x) + B_1(\alpha + i\beta)^x + B_2(\alpha - i\beta)^x$$

where B_1 and B_2 are arbitrary constants. The properties of complex numbers (Chapter 4 above) can be used to develop the solution into more useful forms. Write $\alpha \pm i\beta = r(\cos\theta \pm i\sin\theta) = re^{\pm i\theta}$ so that :

$$\begin{aligned}
Y_x - \overline{Y}(x) &= r^x(B_1 e^{i\theta x} + B_2 e^{-i\theta x}) \\
&= r^x\{B_1(\cos\theta x + i\sin\theta x) + B_2(\cos\theta x - i\sin\theta x)\} \\
&= r^x(A_1 \cos\theta x + A_2 \sin\theta x)
\end{aligned}$$

where $A_1 = B_1 + B_2$ and $A_2 = i(B_1 - B_2)$ are also arbitrary constants. A_1 and A_2 are generally to be taken as having real values (expressible in terms of initial values Y_0 and Y_1) so that the first arbitrary constants, B_1 and B_2, must be conjugate complex.

A further switch of arbitrary constants can be made by writing :

$$A_1 = A\cos\epsilon \quad \text{and} \quad A_2 = A\sin\epsilon$$

or $\qquad A = +\sqrt{A_1{}^2 + A_2{}^2} \quad$ and $\quad \tan\epsilon = \dfrac{A_2}{A_1}$

with due regard to the signs of $\cos\epsilon$ and $\sin\epsilon$ (i.e. of A_1 and A_2). This is equivalent to a transformation from cartesian co-ordinates (A_1, A_2) to polar co-ordinates (A, ϵ), see 4.5 above. The solution is then :

$$\begin{aligned}
Y_x - \overline{Y}(x) &= Ar^x(\cos\theta x \cos\epsilon + \sin\theta x \sin\epsilon) \\
&= Ar^x \cos(\theta x - \epsilon) \quad \text{(5.2 above)}
\end{aligned}$$

Hence the general discrete solution of (1) can be written alternatively :

$$\left.\begin{aligned}
Y_x &= \overline{Y}(x) + r^x(A_1 \cos\theta x + A_2 \sin\theta x) \\
Y_x &= \overline{Y}(x) + Ar^x \cos(\theta x - \epsilon)
\end{aligned}\right\} \quad \dots\dots\dots\dots(8)$$

or

The arbitrary constants are A_1 and A_2, or A and ϵ, and these are to be found from the initial values Y_0 and Y_1. The " structural " constants are r and θ, given by a and b of the original equation :

$$r\cos\theta = \alpha = -\tfrac{1}{2}a \quad \text{and} \quad r\sin\theta = \beta = \tfrac{1}{2}\sqrt{4b-a^2} \quad \dots\dots(9)$$

or $\qquad r^2 = \alpha^2 + \beta^2 = b \quad$ and $\quad \tan\theta = \dfrac{\beta}{\alpha} = -\dfrac{\sqrt{4b-a^2}}{a} \quad \dots\dots(10)$

In determining θ from (10), the signs of $\sin \theta$ and $\cos \theta$ to satisfy (9) must be taken into account. Since r is positive, it follows that $\sin \theta$ is always positive whereas the sign of $\cos \theta$ depends on that of a. Consequently, θ lies between 0 and π, being between 0 and $\dfrac{\pi}{2}$ if $a<0$ and between $\dfrac{\pi}{2}$ and π if $a>0$.

The variation of $y_x = Y_x - \overline{Y}$ is described by the general sinusoidal function $Ar^x \cos(\theta x - \epsilon)$ and it is of an oscillatory form (4.7 above). The *amplitude* and *damping* of the oscillation is given by $Ar^x = Ae^{\gamma x}$ (where $r = e^\gamma$, $\gamma = \log r$). Here A fixes the initial amplitude (depending on initial conditions) and the magnitude of the (positive) " structural " constant $r = \sqrt{b}$ determines whether the amplitude grows ($r>1$) or declines ($r<1$) as x increases. The " explosive " case is $r>1$ and the " damped " case $r<1$; the border-line case $r=1$ corresponds to a regular oscillation of constant amplitude. The *period* of the oscillation is $\dfrac{2\pi}{\theta}$ where θ is the other " structural " constant given by (10). Since θ lies between 0 and π, the period is at least 2 intervals of x. Hence, unlike the amplitude, the period is fixed once and for all by the structure of the original equation ; it does not change from one oscillation to another as x increases. The value of y_x always describes a complete oscillation in the same number of intervals of x. The smallest possible is 2 intervals (when $\theta = \pi$) and the oscillation is then an alternation. The smaller the value of θ, the longer the period ; as θ approaches the value zero, the period becomes very long and the oscillation tends to be ironed out completely. The *phase* of the oscillation, i.e. the particular starting point at $x=0$, depends on the arbitrary constant ϵ as fixed by initial conditions.

The oscillatory variation of y_x is " started up " by two initial values (Y_0 and Y_1) which between them fix the initial amplitude and the phase of the oscillation. The subsequent path of the oscillation as x increases is a consequence of the structure of the difference equation, and it depends only on r and θ as given from a and b by (10). The period depends on θ and it is longer the smaller the value of θ. The oscillation can be explosive, regular or damped according as r is greater than, equal to or less than unity. The *dominant term* in the solution (8) is r^x which determines whether there are explosive or damped oscillations.

The trend or equilibrium term $\overline{Y}(x)$ in the solution depends on the form of $f(x)$ in (1). An important case arises when $f(x)$ is a constant :

$$Y_x + aY_{x-1} + bY_{x-2} = \alpha$$

As a particular solution, try $Y_x = \mu$ where μ is a constant to be found. Then $(1+a+b)\mu = \alpha$ or $\mu = \dfrac{\alpha}{1+a+b}$. The general discrete solution is:

$$Y_x = \frac{\alpha}{1+a+b} + y(x;\ A_1, A_2)$$

where $y(x;\ A_1, A_2)$ is the general solution of (2) already examined in detail. The variation of Y_x is about a constant trend or equilibrium level $\dfrac{\alpha}{1+a+b}$. Other forms of $f(x)$ are included in Ex. 7 below.

EXERCISES 6.4

1. Solve $y_x - \frac{1}{4}y_{x-2} = 0$ subject to $y_0 = 1$, $y_1 = 0$. Express the solution in the form $y_x = \{1 + (-1)^x\}(\frac{1}{2})^{x+1}$ and show that y_x alternates between a positive (but decreasing) value and zero. Draw a graph to illustrate.

2. Generalise by showing that $y_x - a^2 y_{x-2} = 0$ has the alternating solution

$$y_x = \{A_1 + (-1)^x A_2\}a^x.$$

When is the variation of y_x damped?

3. Compare and contrast the solutions of

(i) $y_x - \frac{5}{2}y_{x-1} + y_{x-2} = 0$ (ii) $y_x - y_{x-1} + \frac{1}{4}y_{x-2} = 0$ and (iii) $y_x - \frac{3}{4}y_{x-1} + \frac{1}{8}y_{x-2} = 0$

4. Show that the solution of $y_x - y_{x-1} + \frac{1}{2}y_{x-2} = 0$ is a damped oscillation of y_x, with a period of 8 intervals of x. Show that $y_x + y_{x-1} + \frac{1}{2}y_{x-2} = 0$ has the same solution except that the period is shorter.

5. If $y_x = y_{x-1} - y_{x-2}$ show that y_x oscillates regularly with period equal to 6 intervals of x (see 6.2, Ex. 3).

6. Show that the second-order difference equation with $b = 1$:

$$y_x + a y_{x-1} + y_{x-2} = 0$$

gives certain border-line or limiting cases of solution. Specifically, if $a^2 = 4$, show that y_x has a linear growth, either steady $(a = -2)$ or alternating $(a = 2)$. If $a^2 < 4$, show that y_x oscillates regularly and check that the equation of the previous exercise is a particular instance. What can be said when $a^2 > 4$?

7. If $Y_x = \overline{Y}(x) + y(x;\ A_1, A_2)$ is the general solution of $Y_x + a Y_{x-1} + b Y_{x-2} = f(x)$ show that (i) $\overline{Y}(x) = \dfrac{\alpha^2}{\alpha^2 + a\alpha + b}\alpha^x$ when $f(x) = \alpha^x$ and

(ii) $\overline{Y}(x) = \dfrac{\alpha x + \beta}{1+a+b} + \alpha\dfrac{a+2b}{(1+a+b)^2}$ when $f(x) = \alpha x + \beta$

8. Why can the auxiliary equation of a second-order difference equation never have a root $\lambda = 0$? Check by seeing what happens to the solution (5) above when one of λ_1, λ_2 is put equal to zero. It is possible to have a root $\lambda = 1$; what happens to the solution then?

9. A time series u_t is generated by the *autoregressive scheme* represented by the second-order difference equation:

$$u_t = \alpha u_{t-1} + \beta u_{t-2} + \epsilon_t$$

where α and β are constants and ϵ_t is a given series of random terms with zero mean. Examine the solution and write the condition in α and β for intrinsic oscillations in u_t. How is the " trend " path in u_t defined and in what sense is it random?

10. In the previous exercise, examine the case $\beta=0$, when the autoregression is a simple *Markoff process*, and show that u_t cannot oscillate.

11. For what values of a and b does the autoregressive time series u_t oscillate, when the law of generation is :

$$u_t = au_{t-1} + b(u_{t-1} - u_{t-2}) + \epsilon_t$$

In the case $a=1$, show that the first differences $v_t = u_t - u_{t-1}$ are generated by a simple Markoff process. Examine the particular law

$$u_t = 1 \cdot 3u_{t-1} - 0 \cdot 3u_{t-2} + \epsilon_t$$

which Orcutt (1948) shows is an autoregressive scheme appropriate to many economic time series.

6.5 Linear Difference Equations Generally

The general method of finding discrete solutions is now evident. The nth order linear difference equation with constant coefficients and its corresponding homogeneous form are :

$$a_0 Y_x + a_1 Y_{x-1} + \ldots + a_{n-1} Y_{x-n+1} + a_n Y_{x-n} = f(x) \quad \ldots \ldots \ldots \ldots (1)$$
$$a_0 y_x + a_1 y_{x-1} + \ldots + a_{n-1} y_{x-n+1} + a_n y_{x-n} = 0 \quad \ldots \ldots \ldots \ldots (2)$$

Some particular solution $Y_x = \overline{Y}(x)$ is first sought for (1), usually that giving the trend or equilibrium path of Y_x as x increases. The deviation $y_x = Y_x - \overline{Y}$ then satisfies (2) and the general discrete solution

$$y_x = y(x ; A_1, A_2, \ldots A_n)$$

is required. Finally, the complete solution of (1) is

$$Y_x = \overline{Y}(x) + y(x ; A_1, A_2, \ldots A_n).$$

The device for solving (2) is to try $y_x = \lambda^x$, where λ is a constant found to satisfy the *auxiliary equation* :

$$a_0 \lambda^n + a_1 \lambda^{n-1} + \ldots + a_{n-1} \lambda + a_n = 0 \quad \ldots \ldots \ldots \ldots \ldots (3)$$

There are n roots of (3), $\lambda_1, \lambda_2, \ldots \lambda_n$, which may be real or conjugate complex in pairs (see 4.6 above). The general discrete solution of (2) is

$$y_x = A_1 \lambda_1{}^x + A_2 \lambda_2{}^x + \ldots + A_n \lambda_n{}^x \quad \ldots \ldots \ldots \ldots \ldots (4)$$

When (3) has pairs of conjugate complex roots, the corresponding terms of the solution (4) can be developed into alternative forms involving sinusoidal functions. It is possible that two or more of the roots of (3) are equal in value, in which case the solution (4) is defective since it does not have the requisite number of different terms. The device of the second case of 6.4 is then to be employed.

If all the roots of (3) are real, the *dominant term* in the solution (4) is that containing the numerically largest root, say $A_1\lambda_1^x$. If $\lambda_1 > 1$ numerically, then the solution for y_x is explosive as x increases ; if $\lambda_1 < 1$ numerically, then the variation is damped to zero. In both cases the variation of y_x can alternate in sign, but y_x does not oscillate in the ordinary sense (i.e. with period greater than two intervals of x).

If there are complex roots of (3), they occur in pairs of form $r(\cos\theta \pm \sin\theta)$. For each such pair, two terms of (4) combine to give $Ar^x \cos(\theta x - \epsilon)$ where A and ϵ are arbitrary constants. The *dominant term* of (4) then depends on the largest value of r (say r_1) for complex roots and the numerically largest value of λ (say λ_1) for real roots. The path of y_x includes an oscillation with period $\dfrac{2\pi}{\theta}$, or several such oscillations. The oscillation may be explosive in itself (if $r_1 > 1$) and may be added to a separate non-oscillatory term which is explosive (if $\lambda_1 > 1$ numerically). However, if r_1, $\lambda_1 < 1$ numerically, there are damped oscillations and no explosive element. There are added complications if (3) has equal roots.

As in 5.5 above, it is not easy to find the roots of the auxiliary equation for orders greater than the second. Even for a third-order equation, one root must be located (e.g. graphically) before the other two can be derived. In some particular cases it is possible to guess one or more particular roots of the auxiliary equation (3). Suppose that the coefficients of the difference equation add to zero :

$$a_0 + a_1 + \ldots + a_n = 0$$

Then $\lambda = 1$ is a root of (3) and one of the terms in the solution (4) is an additive constant. This corresponds to the case of a differential equation with terms in Y missing (5.5 above). Again, suppose that the coefficients are such that :

$$a_0 - a_1 + a_2 - a_3 + \ldots = 0$$

Then $\lambda = -1$ is a root of (3) and the solution (4) includes an additive but alternating constant $(-1)^x A_1$.

Nothing has been said about the particular integral $\overline{Y}(x)$ which appears in the complete solution of (1). It depends on the form of $f(x)$ and it is to be found by trial and error, since *any* particular solution of (1) will serve for $\overline{Y}(x)$. For example, in the simplest case, take $f(x) = \alpha$ (constant). Try $Y_x = \overline{Y}$ (constant) as a solution of (1) so that $(a_0 + a_1 + \ldots + a_n)\overline{Y} = \alpha$. Hence, the particular integral is :

$$\overline{Y} = \frac{\alpha}{a_0 + a_1 + \ldots + a_n}$$

and the solution of (1) in complete form is a variation about this constant level.

One further device can be tried in practice; as with the corresponding device for differential equations, it is based on the use of operators (see Appendix A). The operator now is the shift operator E such that $EY_x = Y_{x+1}$, or the corresponding difference operator Δ such that $\Delta Y_x = Y_{x+1} - Y_x$, where $\Delta = E - 1$. One or other of these operators is of help in finding the particular integral $\overline{Y}(x)$ of (1). Write:

$$F(E) = a_0 E^n + a_1 E^{n-1} + \ldots + a_{n-1} E + a_n$$

The equation (1), with $E^{-1} Y_x = Y_{x-1}$, $E^{-2} Y_x = Y_{x-2}$, and so on, is:

$$(a_0 + a_1 E^{-1} + \ldots + a_{n-1} E^{-(n-1)} + a_n E^{-n}) Y_x = f(x)$$

i.e.
$$\frac{1}{E^n} F(E) Y_x = f(x)$$

which suggests
$$Y_x = \frac{E^n}{F(E)} f(x)$$

for the particular integral. The way in which E can be treated algebraically, as in this expression for the particular integral, is described in Appendix A. Two examples illustrate the method with actual difference equations.

Ex. (a). $Y_x - a^2 Y_{x-2} = \alpha^x$.
From the auxiliary equation $\lambda^2 - a^2 = 0$ is derived the complementary function:

$$y_x = \{A_1 + (-1)^x A_2\} a^x \quad (A_1 \text{ and } A_2 \text{ arbitrary})$$

For the particular integral:

$$Y_x = \frac{E^2}{E^2 - a^2} \alpha^x$$

$$= \frac{\alpha^2}{\alpha^2 - a^2} \alpha^x \quad (\text{Appendix } A, (4))$$

The complete solution is:

$$Y_x = \{A_1 + (-1)^x A_2\} a^x + \frac{\alpha^{x+2}}{\alpha^2 - a^2}$$

which has an alternating element, represented by the term in $(-1)^x$, and which is damped or explosive according to the magnitudes of a and α.

Ex. (b). $Y_x - Y_{x-1} + 2 Y_{x-3} = x + 2^x$.
The auxiliary equation, $\lambda^3 - \lambda^2 + 2 = 0$, is of the form with a root $\lambda = -1$.

It is
$$(\lambda + 1)(\lambda^2 - 2\lambda + 2) = 0$$

with roots
$$\lambda = 1 \pm i \text{ and } -1$$

The complex roots are $re^{\pm i\theta} = r(\cos\theta \pm i \sin\theta)$ where $r = \sqrt{2}$ and $\theta = \frac{\pi}{4}$, from (10) of 6.4 above. Hence the complementary function is

$$y_x = A(\sqrt{2})^x \cos\left(\frac{\pi}{4} x - \epsilon\right) + (-1)^x B \quad (A, B \text{ and } \epsilon \text{ arbitrary})$$

The particular integral is :

$$Y_x = \frac{E^3}{E^3 - E^2 + 2}(x + 2^x)$$

$$= \frac{E^3}{E^3 - E^2 + 2}(x) + \frac{2^3}{2^3 - 2^2 + 2}2^x \quad \text{(Appendix } A \text{ (4))}$$

The second term is simply $\frac{4}{3}2^x$. The first term is handled by switching from E to $\Delta = E - 1$. Substitute $E = \Delta + 1$:

$$\frac{E^3}{E^3 - E^2 + 2} = \frac{(\Delta + 1)^3}{(\Delta + 1)^3 - (\Delta + 1)^2 + 2} = \frac{(\Delta + 1)^3}{(\Delta + 2)(\Delta^2 + 1)}$$

$$= \frac{(\Delta + 1)^3}{5}\left(\frac{1}{\Delta + 2} - \frac{\Delta - 2}{\Delta^2 + 1}\right) \text{ in partial fractions.}$$

This is to be expanded in powers of Δ. So :

$$\frac{1}{\Delta + 2} = \frac{1}{2}(1 + \frac{1}{2}\Delta)^{-1} = \frac{1}{2}(1 - \frac{1}{2}\Delta + \frac{1}{4}\Delta^2 - \ldots)$$

$$-\frac{\Delta - 2}{\Delta^2 + 1} = (2 - \Delta)(1 + \Delta^2)^{-1} = (2 - \Delta)(1 - \Delta^2 + \ldots) = 2 - \Delta - 2\Delta^2 + \ldots$$

and $\qquad \text{sum} = \frac{5}{2}(1 - \frac{1}{2}\Delta - \frac{3}{4}\Delta^2 + \ldots)$

The first term in Y_x is then :

$$\frac{1}{2}(1 + \Delta)^3(1 - \frac{1}{2}\Delta - \frac{3}{4}\Delta^2 + \ldots)x = \frac{1}{2}(1 + 3\Delta + 3\Delta^2 + \Delta^3)(x - \frac{1}{2})$$

$$= \frac{1}{2}(x - \frac{1}{2} + 3) = \frac{1}{4}(2x + 5)$$

since $\Delta x = 1$ and $\Delta^2 x = \Delta^3 x = \ldots = 0$.

The particular integral is $\qquad Y_x = \frac{1}{4}(2x + 5) + \frac{4}{3}2^x$

and the complete solution :

$$Y_x = A(\sqrt{2})^x \cos\left(\frac{\pi}{4}x - \epsilon\right) + (-1)^x B + \frac{1}{4}(2x + 5) + \frac{4}{3}2^x$$

EXERCISES 6.5

1. Check that $y_x = A(\sqrt{2})^x \cos\left(\frac{\pi}{4}x - \epsilon\right) + B$ is the solution of

$$y_x - 3y_{x-1} + 4y_{x-2} - 2y_{x-3} = 0.$$

Show that y_x has explosive oscillations of period 8 in this case and in that of Ex. (b) above. What is the difference between the two solutions?

2. A linear difference equation is expressed in terms of successive differences, Y_x, ΔY_x, $\Delta^2 Y_x$, ... Examine the case where the term in Y_x is missing, e.g. $\Delta Y_x = f(x)$; $\Delta^2 Y_x + a\Delta Y_x = f(x)$; and so on. Translate into equations in Y_x, Y_{x-1}, Y_{x-2}, ... and show that $\lambda = 1$ is a root of the auxiliary equation and that the solution for Y_x has an additive constant in each case. (Cf. the result for differential equations, 5.5 above.)

3. The equation $a_0 Y_x + a_1 Y_{x-1} + \ldots + a_n Y_{x-n} = \alpha$ has particular solution

$$\overline{Y} = \frac{\alpha}{a_0 + a_1 + \ldots + a_n}$$

Show that this solution fails when $a_0 + a_1 + \ldots + a_n = 0$ and that the particular solution is then $\overline{Y} = -\frac{\alpha x}{a_1 + 2a_2 + \ldots + na_n}$. What is the solution if, in addition, $a_1 + 2a_2 + \ldots + na_n = 0$?

4. If $y_x - 3\alpha y_{x-1} + 3\alpha^2 y_{x-2} - \alpha^3 y_{x-3} = 0$, show that one solution is $y_x = \alpha^x$ and that two others are $x\alpha^x$ and $x^{(2)}\alpha^x$. Hence write the general solution and indicate an extension to higher order difference equations of this type.

5. The auxiliary equation of a difference equation has two conjugate complex roots $r(\cos\theta \pm i \sin\theta)$. What happens when $\theta = \pi$ and the period of the solution reduces to 2? Show that the solution tends to $(A_1 + A_2 x)(-r)^x$, i.e. that the smallest period of oscillation (2 intervals of x) is equivalent to alternation.

6. A fourth-order linear difference equation has an auxiliary equation with two *equal* pairs of complex roots $r(\cos\theta \pm i \sin\theta)$. Show that the solution is :

$$y_x = r^x \{(A_1 + A_2 x)\cos x\theta + (B_1 + B_2 x)\sin x\theta\}$$

6.6 Economic Illustrations

In the cobweb model of 1.2 above, the difference equation for price (as a deviation from the equilibrium level) is : $p_t = \dfrac{b}{a} p_{t-1}$. The solution is $p_t = p_0 \left(\dfrac{b}{a}\right)^t$, where p_0 is the initial disturbance. The critical factor is $\left(\dfrac{b}{a}\right)$, the ratio of the slopes of the supply and demand curves. A similar equation is obtained in 1.7, Model I, where price changes depend on changes in stocks (the extent of response being indicated by λ) ; the critical factor is then $1 - \lambda(b - a)$.

In the extended cobweb model of 1.6 above, the deviation of price from static equilibrium, $p_t = P_t - \bar{P}$, is given by :

$$p_t = c(1 - \rho)p_{t-1} + c\rho p_{t-2} \quad \ldots\ldots\ldots\ldots\ldots\ldots(1)$$

where $c = \dfrac{b}{a}$ is the ratio of the slopes of supply and demand curves and where ρ (usually $0 \leqslant \rho \leqslant 1$) represents the expectation of suppliers about price reversal. Assume the usual case with $a < 0$ and $b > 0$ so that $c < 0$. Write $\gamma = (-c) = \dfrac{b}{(-a)}$. The auxiliary equation is :

$$\lambda^2 + \gamma(1 - \rho)\lambda + \gamma\rho = 0$$

and the roots are conjugate complex $\lambda_1, \lambda_2 = r(\cos\theta \pm i \sin\theta)$ if :

$$\gamma < \frac{4\rho}{(1 - \rho)^2} \quad \ldots\ldots\ldots\ldots\ldots\ldots\ldots\ldots\ldots(2)$$

This is satisfied if ρ is of moderate size (about $\frac{1}{2}$) and unless the supply slope is quite large compared with the demand slope. For example, if $\rho = \frac{1}{2}$, the condition is $\gamma < 8$ i.e. $b < 8(-a)$. If (2) is satisfied, then from 6.4 above :

$$r = \sqrt{\gamma\rho} \quad \text{and} \quad \tan\theta = -\sqrt{\frac{4\rho}{\gamma(1 - \rho)^2} - 1} \quad \ldots\ldots\ldots\ldots(3)$$

and the solution of (1) is :

$$p_t = A r^t \cos(\theta t - \epsilon) \quad \ldots\ldots\ldots\ldots\ldots\ldots(4)$$

where A and ϵ are fixed by initial conditions.

In the usual case of upward sloping supply curve and downward sloping demand curve, and with ρ of moderate size, it is practically certain that (2) is satisfied and hence that the course of price is oscillatory. It is not necessary that the supply curve be less steep than the demand curve (as for a simple cobweb model of damped form) ; the supply curve can be much steeper than the demand curve without violating (2).

In the oscillatory solution (4), the period is $\frac{2\pi}{\theta}$ and the oscillations are damped if $r<1$, where r and θ are given by (3). The interesting comparison is with the simple cobweb, where price alternates (oscillation of period 2) and is damped if $b<(-a)$.

Since $\tan \theta$ is negative, θ lies between $\frac{\pi}{2}$ and π, being near the lower limit $\frac{\pi}{2}$ if γ is small and near the upper limit π if γ is large. Hence, the period of oscillation lies between 2 and 4, and it increases and approaches 4 as γ gets smaller (for given ρ). So, if the supply curve is steep compared with the demand curve, the period of oscillation is a little above 2 and the price variation is not much different from the simple cobweb. For less steep supply curves, the period lengthens and many approach 4, double the simple cobweb. Further, for a damped oscillation, $r^2=\gamma\rho<1$, i.e. γ must be less than $\frac{1}{\rho}$ which has a value above unity. Hence, a damped oscillation can occur even if b is greater than $(-a)$, i.e. even if the supply curve is steeper than the demand curve. The damped case is more usual than in the simple cobweb. This model, as compared with the simple cobweb, has greater damping and a longer period of oscillation.

In the problem of price variation with stocks (1.7, Model II, above), the deviation of price from equilibrium is given by :

$$p_t=\{2-\lambda(b-a)\}\,p_{t-1}-p_{t-2} \quad\ldots\ldots\ldots\ldots\ldots\ldots\ldots(5)$$

where $\lambda>0$. Assume the usual case of upward sloping supply and downward sloping demand curves so that $a<0$, $b>0$ and $(b-a)>0$. Write $c=1-\frac{1}{2}\lambda(b-a)$ so that $c<1$.

The difference equation (5) is of the type which leads to border-line solutions (see 6.4, Ex. 6, above). The auxiliary equation, written in μ, is :

$$\mu^2-2c\mu+1=0$$

with roots $\qquad\qquad \mu_1,\mu_2=c\pm\sqrt{c^2-1}$

The value of λ is the determining factor and the cases are:

$$\text{(i)}\ \lambda>\frac{4}{b-a},\ c<-1\,;\quad \text{(ii)}\ \frac{2}{b-a}<\lambda<\frac{4}{b-a},\ -1<c<0\,;$$

$$\text{(iii)}\ \lambda<\frac{2}{b-a},\ 0<c<1$$

Unless λ is large $\left(\text{greater than }\dfrac{4}{b-a}\right)$, the value of c is a positive or negative fraction and the roots of the auxiliary equation are conjugate complex:

$$r(\cos\theta\pm i\sin\theta)=c\pm i\sqrt{1-c^2}$$

so that
$$r=1 \quad\text{and}\quad \tan\theta=\pm\sqrt{\frac{1}{c^2}-1}\quad\ldots\ldots\ldots\ldots\ldots(6)$$

The solution of (5), from 6.4 above, is:

$$p_t=A\cos(\theta t-\epsilon)\quad\ldots\ldots\ldots\ldots\ldots\ldots\ldots(7)$$

when A and ϵ are fixed by initial conditions.

The course of price, with $\lambda<\dfrac{4}{b-a}$, is always a regular oscillation of period $\dfrac{2\pi}{\theta}$. In (6), which gives θ, the $+$ sign for $\tan\theta$ is to be taken when $\lambda<\dfrac{2}{b-a}$ and c is positive; θ is then between 0 and $\dfrac{\pi}{2}$. The $-$ sign for $\tan\theta$ is to be taken when $\dfrac{2}{b-a}<\lambda<\dfrac{4}{b-a}$ and c is negative; θ is then between $\dfrac{\pi}{2}$ and π. Hence, as λ takes larger values from 0 through $\dfrac{2}{b-a}$ to $\dfrac{4}{b-a}$, θ increases from 0 through $\dfrac{\pi}{2}$ to π and the period shortens from indefinitely long through 4 to 2. Though the oscillation is always regular, its period depends on the value of λ. As λ increases, the period shortens and eventually tends to 2 (i.e. alternation of price) as λ approaches the critical value $\dfrac{4}{b-a}$.

Difference equations also appear in period analysis of the multiplier and accelerator in dynamic terms, as in 2.7, 3.6 and 3.7 above. The dynamic multiplier model of 2.7 has the difference equation in income Y: $Y_t-cY_{t-1}=A_t$, where c is the constant marginal propensity to consume. A_t represents autonomous expenditure; take it as growing progressively over time so that the difference equation is:

$$Y_t-cY_{t-1}=A_0(1+r)^t\quad\ldots\ldots\ldots\ldots\ldots(8)$$

The complementary function of (8) is $y_t = Ac^t$ and the particular integral is :

$$Y_t = \overline{Y}_0(1+r)^t \quad \text{where} \quad \overline{Y}_0 = A_0 \Big/ \left(1 - \frac{c}{1+r}\right)$$

as is checked by substituting in (8). The complete solution in the case of progressive growth is :

$$Y_t = \overline{Y}_0(1+r)^t + Ac^t$$

The arbitrary constant $A = Y_0 - \overline{Y}_0$ when it is given that $Y_t = Y_0$ at $t = 0$.

In the development of the Harrod-Domar growth theory of 3.6 above, various dynamic versions are suggested. One leads, in (3) of 3.6, to the difference equation :

$$Y_t = (1+v)Y_{t-1} - (v+s)Y_{t-2}$$

where $s = 1 - c =$ marginal propensity to save and v is the power of the accelerator. The auxiliary equation is :

$$\lambda^2 - (1+v)\lambda + (v+s) = 0 \quad \dots\dots\dots\dots\dots\dots(9)$$

The path of Y_t over time is oscillatory if the roots of (9) are conjugate complex ; the condition is : $(1+v)^2 - 4(v+s) < 0$. Hence, $(1-v)^2 < 4s$, which gives :

$$1 - 2\sqrt{s} < v < 1 + 2\sqrt{s}$$
or
$$(1 - \sqrt{s})^2 < v + s < (1 + \sqrt{s})^2$$

This is usually the case if v is around unity and s is small. If the roots of (9) are $re^{\pm i\theta}$, then $r^2 = (v+s)$ by (10) of 6.4 above and the size of r determines whether the oscillation is damped or explosive. It is likely that $v + s > 1$ so that the explosive case is to be expected. The exact condition for explosive oscillation is $1 < v + s < (1 + \sqrt{s})^2$ or $1 - s < v < 1 + 2\sqrt{s}$ (see Ex. 5 below).

A second dynamic version leads to (5) of 3.6 above :

$$Y_t = \left(v + \frac{v+s}{v}\right)Y_{t-1} - (v+s)Y_{t-2}$$

with auxiliary equation :

$$\lambda^2 - \left(v + \frac{v+s}{v}\right)\lambda + (v+s) = 0 \quad \dots\dots\dots\dots\dots(10)$$

This only differs from (9) by the addition of $\frac{s}{v}$ in the coefficient of λ, a difference which is enough to change the picture. The roots of (10) **are** real if a positive value is taken by the expression :

$$\left(v+\frac{v+s}{v}\right)^2 - 4(v+s) = v^2 + 2(v+s) + \left(\frac{v+s}{v}\right)^2 - 4(v+s)$$

$$= v^2 - 2(v+s) + \left(\frac{v+s}{v}\right)^2$$

$$= \left(v - \frac{v+s}{v}\right)^2$$

which is the case for all v and s. It follows that the path of Y_t over time is *not* oscillatory. The only question is whether it is damped or explosive. As shown in 4.6 above, the two real roots λ_1 and λ_2 of (10) satisfy :

$$\lambda_1 + \lambda_2 = v + \frac{v+s}{v} > 0 \quad \lambda_1\lambda_2 = v + s > 0$$

Hence both values are positive and the path of $Y_t = A_1\lambda_1{}^t + A_2\lambda_2{}^t$ is a steady progression. In the likely case, $v+s>1$ and so $\lambda_1\lambda_2>1$ and at least one of the two real roots is above unity. In this case, Y_t is explosive.

EXERCISES 6.6

1. Examine the solution of the extended cobweb problem, equation (1) above, when $\rho<0$ and suppliers expect the price movement to continue in the same direction. In the usual case ($a<0$, $b>0$) show that the auxiliary equation has real roots, the numerically larger being negative. Deduce that the dominant movement of p_t is an alternation as in the simple cobweb but amplified by the suppliers' expectation.

2. In the extended cobweb model, examine the case where $a<0$ and $b<0$ such that $(-a)>(-b)$. What can be said of this model in the limiting cases where $\rho=0$ and $\rho=1$?

3. In the problem with stocks, equation (5) above, still assuming $(b-a)>0$, take λ large and greater than $\frac{4}{b-a}$. Show that $p_t = A_1\mu_1{}^t + A_2\mu_2{}^t$ where μ_1, $\mu_2 = c \pm \sqrt{c^2 - 1}$. Show also that the dominant term has μ_1 negative and numerically greater than unity. Describe the path of p_t. Then examine the case $(b-a)<0$; is this a genuine possibility in the economic sense?

4. Extend the stocks problem, equation (5) above, in the way specified in 1.7, Ex. 2. Solve and interpret in the usual case $a<0$, $b>0$.

5. Complete the analysis of the possibilities of equation (9) above and show that :

Value of $v+s$	Course of Y_t
$v+s<(1-\sqrt{s})^2$	Damped, non-oscillatory
$(1-\sqrt{s})^2<v+s<1$	Damped oscillation
$1<v+s<(1+\sqrt{s})^2$	Explosive oscillation
$(1+\sqrt{s})^2<v+s$	Explosive, non-oscillatory

If s is given (usually small), interpret in terms of the power of the accelerator.

Compare with the results for the Samuelson-Hicks model of the multiplier-accelerator (7.1 and Fig. 21 below).

6. In the previous exercise, put $s=0$ and show that oscillations in Y_t are no longer possible. Deduce that $v<1$ implies a damped variation and $v>1$ an explosive variation in Y_t.

6.7 Delays, Distributed Lags and the Multiplier-Accelerator

A continuous lag has the advantage that, for particular cases of its time-form $f(\tau)$ (e.g. single or multiple exponential lags), it can be represented by a differential equation, (3) of 5.8 above, which can be of low order and easily solved. The disadvantage is that it is not easy to handle lags of " realistic " or empirical time-forms. A distributed lag in period analysis has these features reversed (see 3.9 above). It is easily specified in any form, as is done for the multiplier-accelerator in 3.7 above. Moreover, the effect of changes in the form of the lag are easily seen (through the coefficients concerned) in the solution of a problem using the lag. On the other hand, for a widely distributed and hence " realistic " lag (like those of Fig. 19 but in period terms), the problem involves difference equations of a high order which are not easily solved and interpreted.

The simplest kind of lag is the *delay*, i.e. a single lag of θ units of time or periods, where θ can often be taken (by choice of time unit) as $\theta=1$. A delay can be used in period or continuous analysis alike. In *period analysis*, it is very simple indeed ; a delay is the special case of a distributed lag in which only the first term is used. So, for the consumption function of the multiplier, to write $C_t=C(Y_{t-1})$ implies a delay of one period—a special case of the distributed lag $C_t=C(Y_{t-1}, Y_{t-2}, Y_{t-3}, \ldots)$. In *continuous analysis*, the formal introduction of a delay of θ units of time only involves replacing t by $(t-\theta)$ in the appropriate function or relation ; but this simple step serves to " gum up " the whole process. The result is usually, not a differential equation, but a mixed difference-differential equation. For example, the unlagged multiplier-accelerator relation (with no autonomous expenditure) is specified by :

$$Y=cY+v\,\frac{dY}{dt}$$

which gives the differential equation $\dfrac{dY}{dt}=\dfrac{1-c}{v}\,Y$ of Harrod-Domar. Introduce a delay of one period in the consumption and investment relations and the equation becomes :

$$Y(t)=cY(t-1)+v\,\frac{d}{dt}\,Y(t-1)$$

giving the mixed difference-differential equation :

$$\frac{d}{dt} Y(t-1) = \frac{1}{v} \{Y(t) - cY(t-1)\}$$

Delays can be handled in continuous analysis (see Chapters 8 and 9 below) but they do cause difficulty. Consider a sinusoidal variable with damping α and frequency ω defined by the complex variable $z = Ae^{i\epsilon}e^{pt}$ ($p = \alpha + i\omega$). Then $D^n z = p^n z$ is a similar sinusoidal variation (5.9 above). Now introduce a delayed variable $u(t) = z(t - \theta)$:

$$u(t) = Ae^{i\epsilon}e^{p(t-\theta)} = e^{-p\theta}z(t)$$

The effect of the factor $e^{-p\theta}$ is to modify the amplitude and to lag the phase of z :

$$u(t) = Ae^{i\epsilon}e^{-\alpha\theta}e^{-i\omega\theta}e^{pt}$$
$$= (Ae^{-\alpha\theta})e^{i(\epsilon-\omega\theta)}e^{pt}$$

where the amplitude is modified by $e^{-\alpha\theta}$ and the phase ϵ reduced by $(-\omega\theta)$. It remains true, however, that $u(t)$ is a sinusoidal variable of the same damping and frequency as $z(t)$; the e^{pt} term is unchanged. The same is true of $D^n u = p^n u = p^n e^{-p\theta}z$.

The general *distributed lag* in *period analysis* is fully illustrated by its introduction in the multiplier-accelerator model. Here :

$$C_t = c_1 Y_{t-1} + c_2 Y_{t-2} + c_3 Y_{t-3} + \ldots \quad \text{where } c = c_1 + c_2 + c_3 + \ldots$$
$$I_t = v_1(Y_{t-1} - Y_{t-2}) + v_2(Y_{t-2} - Y_{t-3}) + \ldots \quad \text{where } v = v_1 + v_2 + \ldots$$

are the consumption (multiplier) and investment (accelerator) relations to put in the condition of the model : $Y_t = C_t + I_t + A_t$ (A_t being autonomous expenditure).

In the distributed consumption lag, the coefficients (c_1, c_2, c_3, ...) can take any values, provided only that they add to c, the over-all marginal propensity to consume. The shape of the lag can be varied at will and it is described by the coefficients. It is not necessary, for example, that c_1, c_2, c_3, ... should decrease in geometric progression—the corresponding assumption to that of the continuous exponential lag. Similar remarks apply to the investment lag. When the lagged expressions C_t and I_t are substituted in the condition of the model, the resulting difference equation is solved for Y_t and the effect of the coefficients of the lags (the c's and the v's) is to be seen in the solution. In the problem of the multiplier-accelerator, the lag on the investment side is the more important ; a preliminary treatment is given in 3.7–3.9 above but the more general problem is left over to Chapter 7 below.

Meanwhile, and to clear the ground, the effect of the consumption lag can be seen in the simpler multiplier model of 2.7 above, i.e. the model of the multiplier-accelerator with $I_t = 0$. The difference equation is

$$Y_t = C_t + A_t \quad \text{with} \quad C_t = c_1 Y_{t-1} + c_2 Y_{t-2} + c_3 Y_{t-3} + \ldots$$

With a *single lag* (delay) $C_t = c Y_{t-1}$ and with A_t constant, the equation is

$$Y_t - c Y_{t-1} = A$$

with solution $\quad y_t = y_0 c^t \quad \left(y_t = Y_t - \overline{Y}, \ \overline{Y} = \dfrac{A}{1-c} \right)$

The corresponding equation with a *lag distributed over two periods* is :

$$Y_t - c_1 Y_{t-1} - c_2 Y_{t-2} = A$$

The particular integral is again $\overline{Y} = \dfrac{A}{1-c}$ so that, with $y_t = Y_t - \overline{Y}$:

$$y_t - c_1 y_{t-1} - c_2 y_{t-2} = 0$$

Since $c = c_1 + c_2$, put $c_1 = c - c_2$ and write the equation :

$$y_t - (c - c_2) y_{t-1} - c_2 y_{t-2} = 0 \quad \ldots\ldots\ldots\ldots\ldots\ldots(1)$$

The solution is $\quad y_t = A_1 \lambda_1{}^t + A_2 \lambda_2{}^t \quad (A_1 \text{ and } A_2 \text{ arbitrary}) \ldots\ldots\ldots\ldots(2)$

where λ_1 and λ_2 are the roots of the auxiliary equation :

$$\lambda^2 - (c - c_2)\lambda - c_2 = 0 \quad \ldots\ldots\ldots\ldots\ldots\ldots(3)$$

If the c's have specified values, and if the initial disturbance y_0 and y_1 are given, a numerical solution can be found for (1).

Ex. Take $c = \frac{3}{4}$, $c_2 = \frac{1}{4}$, i.e. $C_t = \frac{1}{2} Y_{t-1} + \frac{1}{4} Y_{t-2}$
The auxiliary equation (3) is $\lambda^2 - \frac{1}{2}\lambda - \frac{1}{4} = 0$
with roots $\qquad\qquad \lambda_1, \lambda_2 = \frac{1}{4}(1 \pm \sqrt{5}) = 0.809, \ -0.309$
The solution of (2) is $\quad y_t = A_1 (0.809)^t + A_2 (-0.309)^t.$
If the initial values are $y_0 = 0$ and $y_1 = 1$, then by substituting $t = 0$ and $t = 1$ the values $A_1 = 0.895$ and $A_2 = -0.895$ are obtained. The solution is then :
$$y_t = 0.895 \, (0.809)^t - 0.895 \, (-0.309)^t$$
The first term is dominant and the second soon dies away ; hence $y_t \to 0$ through positive values.

The general problem is to locate λ_1 and λ_2 from (3), whatever the values of c and c_2 of the consumption lag. The roots are :

$$\lambda_1, \lambda_2 = \frac{1}{2}\{c - c_2 \pm \sqrt{(c - c_2)^2 + 4c_2}\}$$

The usual assumption on the c's is $0 \leqslant c_2 \leqslant c \leqslant 1$, since all coefficients (c_1, c_2 and $c = c_1 + c_2$) are taken as positive fractions. Hence λ_1 and λ_2 are real ;

one (λ_1) is positive and the other (λ_2) negative, the positive root being numerically larger. To locate more precisely, on the method of 4.6 above, changes in sign of $f(\lambda) = \lambda^2 - (c - c_2)\lambda - c_2$ are sought. By substitution :

$\lambda =$	-1	$-c_2$	0	c	1
$f(\lambda) = $	$1 + c - 2c_2$	$-c_2(1-c)$	$-c_2$	$-c_2(1-c)$	$1-c$
	$+ve$	$-ve$	$-ve$	$-ve$	$+ve$

This is illustrated by the graph of $f(\lambda)$ shown in Fig. 20. Hence, the positive root λ_1 lies between c and 1, the negative root λ_2 between -1 and $-c_2$

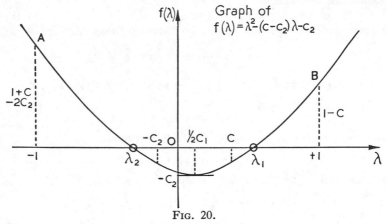

Fig. 20.

The larger root numerically (λ_1) is a positive fraction ; the other root (λ_2) is a negative fraction.

The conclusion is that, whatever the actual values of c and c_2 ($0 \leqslant c_2 \leqslant c \leqslant 1$), the solution for y_t given by (2) has a dominant term $A_1\lambda_1^t$ which converges steadily to zero. The other term $A_2\lambda_2^t$ introduces an alternating element which dies away.

Some of the more extreme cases are to be noted. The size of c, over-all marginal propensity to consume, can be considered first. If c is small (and so c_1 and c_2 also), then the graph of Fig. 20 only just dips below 0 ; hence λ_1 and λ_2 are both small and the convergence of y_t to zero is rapid. If c is large, then the point B on the curve of Fig. 20 is only just above 0 ; hence the dominant root λ_1 is near 1 and the convergence of y_t is slow. The convergence is slower the larger the value of c, or the smaller the value of $s = 1 - c =$ marginal propensity to save. Secondly, given the value of c, the size of c_2 (which fixes the distribution of the lag) becomes important and affects the convergence of y_t through the second (negative) root λ_2. If c_2 is small, then the point A on the curve of Fig. 20 is well above 0 and ($-\lambda_2$) is small ; the alternating term in y_t dies away quickly. If c_2 is large, then A is only just above 0 and $(-\lambda_2)$ is also near 1 ; the alternating term as well as the dominant term decreases slowly. There is a wide distribution of the lag, and the average lag is large, when c_2 is large. Hence, the convergence is slower the larger the average lag.

In the *general case* of a distributed lag, the difference equation is :

$$Y_t - (c_1 Y_{t-1} + c_2 Y_{t-2} + \ldots + c_n Y_{t-n}) = A$$

where all the c_r and $c = c_1 + c_2 + \ldots + c_n$ are positive fractions. The particular integral is again $= \dfrac{A}{1-c}$ and, with $y_t = Y_t - \overline{Y}$, the difference equation is :

$$y_t = c_1 y_{t-1} + c_2 y_{t-2} + \ldots + c_n y_{t-n}$$

and the general discrete solution :

$$y_t = A_1 \lambda_1{}^t + A_2 \lambda_2{}^t + \ldots + A_n \lambda_n{}^t$$

Here, λ_1, λ_2, ... λ_n are the n roots of the auxiliary equation

$$f(\lambda) = \lambda^n - c_1 \lambda^{n-1} - c_2 \lambda^{n-1} - \ldots - c_n = 0$$

and A_1, A_2, ... A_n are arbitrary constants which can be expressed in terms of n initial disturbances.

The auxiliary equation must have a real root (λ_1) which is positive and between c and 1 in value. Substituting in $f(\lambda)$:

$$\begin{aligned}
f(c) &= c^n - c_1 c^{n-1} - c_2 c^{n-2} - \ldots - c_n \\
&= c^{n-1}(c - c_1) - c_2 c^{n-2} - \ldots - c_n \\
&= c_2 c^{n-2}(c - 1) + c_3 c^{n-3}(c^2 - 1) + \ldots + c_n(c^{n-1} - 1) < 0
\end{aligned}$$

since $c - c_1 = c_2 + c_3 + \ldots + c_n$ and $c < 1$

and $\qquad f(1) = 1 - c_1 - c_2 - \ldots - c_n = 1 - c > 0 \quad$ since $c < 1$

Hence $f(\lambda)$ changes sign between $\lambda = c$ and $\lambda = 1$ and there is a root λ_1 of the auxiliary equation in this range.

It can also be established, though with some difficulty as shown by Hicks (1950), that the root λ_1 is the only positive root and that it is the largest root in absolute magnitude. Of the other $(n-1)$ roots, some may be real and negative and others may occur in pairs of conjugate complex values. Each negative root, however, is numerically less than λ_1. If there is a pair of conjugate complex roots $r(\cos \theta \pm i \sin \theta)$ then the modulus r (or absolute magnitude) must be less than λ_1. Consequently, the dominant root is λ_1 and the dominant term in y_t is $A_1 \lambda_1{}^t$. Since $c < \lambda_1 < 1$, the path of y_t converges to zero. The speed of convergence depends primarily on λ_1, and, in general, the convergence is slower the larger the value of c.

Though the term $A_1 \lambda_1{}^t$ dominates in y_t, the other terms are also of interest. Since $\lambda_2, \lambda_3, \ldots \lambda_n$ have either negative or conjugate complex values, these other terms give rise either to alternations or to oscillations in y_t (or both). Hence, in general, y_t converges to zero, and Y_t to $\overline{Y}$, but with alternations in sign and with oscillations super-imposed on the main path. The subsidiary movements serve to slow up (or to speed up) the convergence. As shown by Solow (1951), it is the distribution of lags given by $c_1 : c_2 : \ldots : c_n$ as opposed to the over-all marginal propensity c, which is important here. In general, other things being equal, the speed of convergence of Y_t to $\overline{Y}$ is slower the larger the average lag and the wider the dispersion of the distributed lag.

EXERCISES 6.7

1. Examine the multiplier model with two-period lag in the case $c_1 = 0$. In what respects does the solution now differ from the single lag case?

2. In the multiplier model with two-period lag, let $c \rightarrow 1$ with c_1 and c_2 still positive fractions and examine the form taken by the solution for y_t. What can be said about saving (*ex ante* and *ex post*) in this case?

3. In the solution y_t given by (2) above, let initial values be y_0 at $t = 0$ and y_1 at $t = 1$, and show that

$$A_1 = \frac{-\lambda_2 y_0 + y_1}{\lambda_1 - \lambda_2} \quad \text{and} \quad A_2 = \frac{\lambda_1 y_0 - y_1}{\lambda_1 - \lambda_2}$$

What effects do different values and signs of y_0 and y_1 have on the path of y_t?

6.8 Continuous Solutions of Difference Equations

A difference equation in Y_x relates to any series of equally-spaced values of the independent variable x. The discrete solutions considered so far apply to one particular series of values of x denoted by $x = 0, 1, 2, 3, \ldots$. The difference equation, however, is not limited in this way ; the starting point for x can be any value whatever. If $x = 0$ is the starting point, the difference equation generates the discrete solution $Y_0, Y_1, Y_2, \ldots$. If $x = \frac{1}{2}$ is selected, then a completely different discrete solution is obtained and involves $Y_{\frac{1}{2}}, Y_{\frac{3}{2}}, Y_{\frac{5}{2}}, \ldots$. There is evidently no limit to the number of different discrete solutions which can be written. Any value of x between 0 and 1 can serve as the starting point, and x can be made to vary continuously. The question is whether all the discrete solutions can be put together into a single continuous solution, giving Y_x in terms of x for any series of equally-spaced values of x whatever.

For example, suppose the difference equation relates to the price level Y_x at various points of time x and that the interval of x involved is a year. Then $x = 0, 1, 2, \ldots$ may represent the end of each year and the discrete solution Y_x then shows the variation in end-of-year prices from one year to another. But $x=\frac{1}{2}$, $\frac{3}{2}$, $\frac{5}{2}$, ... will give another discrete solution, Y_x showing the variation in mid-year prices. In both cases, and in others like them, the variation of prices within a year (e.g. the seasonal variation) is ignored. The question is whether a continuous solution for Y_x can be obtained to show the whole variation of prices over time, within the year as well as year by year.

A first-order equation $\chi(x, Y_x, Y_{x-1})=0$ has a discrete solution $Y_x = Y(x ; A)$ with one arbitrary constant A. Whatever the particular series of x considered, A can be found in terms of the initial value of Y. Given Y_0, the solution relates to Y_x for $x=0, 1, 2, ...$; given $Y_{\frac{1}{2}}$, it gives Y_x for $x=\frac{1}{2}$, $\frac{3}{2}$, $\frac{5}{2}$, ... ; and so on for any given Y_x, $0 \leqslant x < 1$. Now extend the arbitrary element from *one* given Y_x such as Y_0 or $Y_{\frac{1}{2}}$, to the *whole range* of given Y_x for $0 \leqslant x < 1$. More precisely, instead of taking an arbitrary initial value, an arbitrary *function* is specified in the range $0 \leqslant x < 1$; the function can start from any value Y_0, varies in any way from $x=0$ to $x=1$, but returns to the initial value at $x=1$. The arbitrary function is of period 1. In terms of the illustration where Y_x is the price level, the element which is to be specified arbitrarily is the whole range of prices over a year, expressed in the form of a seasonal variation, starting and finishing at the same level. Once this is done, the difference equation gives Y_x for any value of x, varying continuously.

Denote by $W(x)$ any function of period 1 so that all values of W separated by unit intervals of x are equal. Hence $\varDelta W = 0$ for unit intervals. Just as the derivative of a constant is zero, so the difference of a function of period 1 is zero. The constant appears on differentiation ; the function of period 1 disappears on differencing. The general continuous solution of $\chi(x, Y_x, Y_{x-1})=0$ is then $Y_x = Y(x ; W)$. Here W is an arbitrary function of period 1 which can be identified in terms of the initial conditions for Y_x in the interval $0 \leqslant x < 1$.

The concept of a continuous solution is easily generalised. A second-order difference equation $\chi(x, Y_x, Y_{x-1}, Y_{x-2})=0$ has discrete solution $Y_x = Y(x ; A_1, A_2)$ for $x=0, 1, 2, ...$ where A_1 and A_2 are arbitrary values which can be identified with Y_0 and Y_1. It has continuous solution $Y_x = Y(x ; W_1, W_2)$ for any x, where W_1 and W_2 are arbitrary functions of period 1 which can be expressed in terms of initial conditions for Y_x in the two intervals $0 \leqslant x < 1$ and $1 \leqslant x < 2$. The extension to any difference equation is evident. All that has been said above about arbitrary constants or initial values in a discrete solution now applies equally well to arbitrary functions of period 1 in the continuous solution.

M.E.

The solutions of difference and differential equations have distinctive features ; for example, the range of possibilities for the solution of a linear difference equation (depending on a power function like a^x) is generally much wider or richer than for a linear differential equation (depending on the exponential e^{ax}). This is clear from the analysis of 6.3–6.5 above. However, a comparison of the present and the previous chapter shows that the methods of handling linear differential and difference equations are very much the same ; they happen to be more familiar, and much more developed, for differential equations.

Finally, difference equations can be solved by methods analogous to that of Laplace Transforms for differential equations (5.7 above). The particular discrete solution $Y_x(x=0, 1, 2, ...)$ becomes a particular continuous solution by putting $Y_x = Y_0$ throughout the range $0 \leqslant x < 1$. The solution is then a step-function of a continuous variable :

$$Y(x) = Y_0(0 \leqslant x < 1) ; \quad = Y_1(1 \leqslant x < 2) ; \quad ...$$

and the method of Laplace Transforms applies, see Gardner and Barnes (1942). Alternatively, a transform can be defined for the discrete series Y_x in terms of a sum—analogous to the integral of the Laplace Transform for a function of a continuous variable. A simple transform of this kind is the *generating function* :

$$\bar{Y}(s) = \sum_{x=0}^{\infty} Y_x s^x = Y_0 + Y_1 s + Y_2 s^2 + ...$$

in which the coefficients of successive powers of s generate the sequence Y_x. The solution of difference equations by transforming Y_x into $\bar{Y}(s)$ is very similar to that of the differential equation by Laplace Transforms, See Goldberg (1958), particularly his example (p. 194).

REFERENCES

Baumol (W. J.) (1951) : *Economic Dynamics* (Macmillan, 1951), Chapters 9–11.

Baumol (W. J.) (1958) : " Topology of Second Order Linear Difference Equations with Constant Coefficients ", *Econometrica*, **26**, 258–85.

Durell (C. V.) and Robson (A.) (1937) : *Advanced Algebra* (Bell, 1937), Chapter XI.

Gardner (M. F.) and Barnes (J. L.) (1942) : *Transients in Linear Systems* (Wiley 1942), Chapter IX.

Goldberg (S.) (1958) : *Introduction to Difference Equations* (Wiley, 1958).

Hicks (J. R.) (1950) : *A Contribution to Theory of the Trade Cycle* (Oxford, 1950).

Milne (W. E.) (1949) : *Numerical Calculus* (Princeton, 1949), Chapter XI.

Orcutt (G. H.) (1948) : " A Study of the Autoregressive Nature of the Time Series used for Tinbergen's Model of the Economic System of the United States, 1919–1932 ", *Journal Royal Statistical Society*, Series B, **10**, 1–45.

Solow (R.) (1951) : " A Note on Dynamic Multipliers ", *Econometrica*, **19**, 306–16.

CHAPTER 7

TRADE CYCLE THEORY: SAMUELSON-HICKS

7.1 The Simple Multiplier-Accelerator Model with Humped Investment

AUTONOMOUS consumption and investment expenditure (A_t) is specified over successive periods $t = 0, 1, 2, \ldots$. There are no limitations on the time profile of A_t but it is assumed given as a datum. Income or output in period t is Y_t. A change in output from period $(t-2)$ to period $(t-1)$ induces investment, spread out in some way over period t and subsequent periods. In the simple model (as in 3.7 above), it is assumed that induced investment is humped in the period t immediately following the output change. The relation is taken as a proportional one so that:

Induced investment $\qquad I_t = v(Y_{t-1} - Y_{t-2})$

A linear consumption function is assumed with distributed lag:

Consumption $\qquad C_t = c_1 Y_{t-1} + c_2 Y_{t-2}$

The condition of the model is that investment and consumption plans are realised so that $Y_t = C_t + I_t + A_t$. This condition implies that saving and investment are equal *ex post*, i.e. $(Y_t - C_t) = (I_t + A_t)$. Nothing is said about saving *ex ante*, which depends on what Y_t is anticipated by consumers; the model allows for unintended saving but not unintended investment.

The condition of the model gives a second-order difference equation (3.7 above) which can be written:

$$\left. \begin{array}{l} Y_t = (v + c_1) Y_{t-1} - (v - c_2) Y_{t-2} + A_t \\ Y_t = c Y_{t-1} + (v - c_2)(Y_{t-1} - Y_{t-2}) + A_t \end{array} \right\} \quad \ldots\ldots\ldots\ldots\ldots(1)$$

or

The structural constants are v, c_1 and c_2; $c = c_1 + c_2$ is the over-all marginal propensity to consume, and $s = 1 - c$ is the over-all marginal propensity to save. The only restrictions imposed are $v > 0$, $0 < c_1, c_2, c, s < 1$.

The first step is to find a particular integral of (1) which should be, if possible, the trend path or equilibrium level of Y_t over time. It will depend on the course assumed for autonomous expenditure A_t.

The possibility of progressive equilibrium $\overline{Y}_t = \overline{Y}_0 (1 + \rho)^t$, where ρ is some fixed rate of growth, has already been examined (3.8 above). When autonomous expenditure is fixed, $A_t = A$ for all t, there is progressive equilibrium at rate ρ provided that $r = \rho$ is a root of :

$$R = r^2 - (v - c_2 - s - 1)r + s = 0$$

In general, there is such a progressive trend, consistent with the model even when autonomous expenditure is fixed.

When there is a given progressive expansion in autonomous expenditure, i.e. when $A_t = A_0(1+r)^t$ for given r, then $\overline{Y}_t = \overline{Y}_0(1+r)^t$ is a particular (equilibrium) solution of (1) if :

$$\overline{Y}_0 = \frac{A_0(1+r)^2}{R} \quad \text{provided that } R > 0.$$

Here, r is given and $\overline{Y}_t$ must expand at the same rate (r) as A_t (see 3.8, Ex. 3 and 4, above). A progressive trend in output generally exists and the rate of growth is that given for autonomous investment. As a particular case ($r = 0$), $A_t = A = $ constant (all t) and there is an equilibrium level $\overline{Y} = \dfrac{A}{1-c}$ as given by the multiplier.

Other given paths of autonomous investment give rise to other equilibrium movements $\overline{Y}_t$ in output. For example, A_t may oscillate over time in a given way; the equilibrium path $\overline{Y}_t$ then oscillates also (see 7.6 below).

Now assume that, given the course of autonomous investment A_t, some corresponding trend or equilibrium path $\overline{Y}_t$ is determined for output. Write $y_t = Y_t - \overline{Y}_t$ as the deviation of output from equilibrium. Then, since Y_t and $\overline{Y}_t$ both satisfy (1), the difference equation becomes :

i.e.
$$\left. \begin{array}{l} y_t = (v + c_1)y_{t-1} - (v - c_2)y_{t-2} \\ y_t = cy_{t-1} + w(y_{t-1} - y_{t-2}) \\ \text{where } w = v - c_2 \end{array} \right\} \quad \ldots\ldots\ldots\ldots\ldots(2)$$

The final, and most important, step is to solve (2) to obtain the time path of y_t, given any initial disturbance. This solution will answer such questions as : does Y_t oscillate about $\overline{Y}_t$ and, if so, is the variation explosive or damped as t increases indefinitely?

The structural constants are the investment coefficient v, the over-all marginal propensity to consume c and the second partial marginal propensity to consume c_2. It is not usually necessary to look at the other partial marginal propensity $c_1 = c - c_2$. Given the value of c, the distribution of the consumption lag is indicated by c_2.

It is clear from (2), however, that there are effectively only two structural constants, c and $w = v - c_2$. The effect of distributed consumption lag is simply to reduce the size of v, i.e. to make the accelerator less power-ful. The constant $w = v - c_2$ can be called the *reduced investment coefficient*. In the " elementary case " of Hicks ($c_2 = 0$), w is the investment coefficient v; as the consumption lag gets longer, the value of w decreases for any given investment coefficient v, or more powerful accelerators correspond to a given value of w. The other constant c is conveniently replaced by $s = 1 - c =$ marginal propensity to save, when the solution of (2) comes up for interpretation.

It will be established (7.2 below) that there are four cases :

Structural constants, s and $w = v - c_2$	Path of y_t over time
(i) $w < (1 - \sqrt{s})^2$	Non-oscillatory and damped
(ii) $(1 - \sqrt{s})^2 < w < 1$	Oscillatory and damped
(iii) $1 < w < (1 + \sqrt{s})^2$	Oscillatory and explosive
(iv) $(1 + \sqrt{s})^2 < w$	Non-oscillatory and explosive

Fig. 21 shows the nature of the solution for all combinations of s and w. The curve AB is $w = (1 - \sqrt{s})^2$ and BC is $w = (1 + \sqrt{s})^2$.

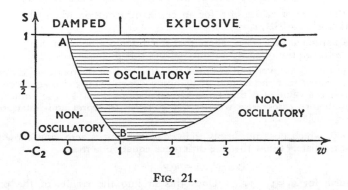

Fig. 21.

Whether the path of y_t is damped ($w < 1$) or explosive ($w > 1$) depends only on w. The influence of s is in the determination of the range of values of w required for y_t to oscillate. If s is very small, oscillations arise only if w is close to 1. As s takes larger values, there is a wider range of oscilla-tory solutions. Or, what comes to the same thing, any value of w sign-ificantly above 1 makes y_t steadily explosive if s is small ; larger values of w are required as s increases.

More precisely, as shown in Ex. 4 below, the condition for oscillations is that $s>(1-\sqrt{w})^2$. Hence, if w is between 0 and 4, there is always a (positive fractional) value of s sufficiently large for oscillations in y_t.

The influence of c_2, the indicator of distributed lags in consumption, is always to reduce the power of the accelerator. In the " elementary case " ($c_2=0$), the range of values of v for oscillations is $(1-\sqrt{s})^2 < v < (1+\sqrt{s})^2$ and $v=1$ corresponds to a regular oscillation. With a distributed lag, as c_2 increases, the range is shifted upwards to $(1-\sqrt{s})^2+c_2 < v < (1+\sqrt{s})^2+c_2$ and $v=1+c_2$ is the case of regular oscillation. An accelerator of given power works less strongly the greater the value of c_2 and the longer the average lag. A more powerful accelerator is required for explosive variations in y_t; damped variations arise over a wider range of the power of the accelerator. The existence of distributed lags in consumption makes for convergence and stability in y_t.

EXERCISES 7.1

1. If A_t expands at a given progressive rate r, so that a progressive equilibrium $\bar{Y}_t$ exists provided that $R>0$, show that this is so for any value of r when :
$$(1-\sqrt{s})^2 < v - c_2 < (1+\sqrt{s})^2$$
i.e. the oscillatory case. Follow up by showing that there is only difficulty when $v-c_2 > (1+\sqrt{s})^2$ and that, in this case of a powerful accelerator, progressive equilibrium still exists if r is sufficiently small (see 3.8, Ex. 4, above).

2. Find the range of values of v for an oscillatory solution when (i) $s=c_2=0\cdot25$ and when (ii) $s=0\cdot04$, $c_2=0\cdot06$.

3. In the particular case $v=c_2$, show that the difference equation for y_t is of first order with solution damped to zero. Does this fit into cases (i)–(iv) above?

4. Take $w=v-c_2$ as given and examine the effect of s on the nature of the solution for y_t. Show that the degree of damping depends on the magnitude of $\sqrt{w}$ whatever the value of s, that there are oscillations if $s>(1-\sqrt{w})^2$ and that the non-oscillatory cases arise when $s<(1-\sqrt{w})^2$. Interpret and illustrate when $v=1$, $c_2=0\cdot25$.

5. Put $s=0$, which does not imply that *ex post* saving is zero, and show that y_t cannot oscillate. Show that the difference equation is then
$$(y_t-y_{t-1})=w(y_{t-1}-y_{t-2})$$
and solve for $z_t=y_t-y_{t-1}$. Does this fit into the results of the previous exercise? Interpret and check with 3.7, Ex. 3 and 4, above.

7.2 Detailed Solution of the Simple Model

The general solution is sought for :
$$y_t=cy_{t-1}+w(y_{t-1}-y_{t-2}) \quad \text{where } w=v-c_2 \quad \dots\dots\dots\dots(1)$$

It depends on the roots of λ_1 and λ_2 of the auxiliary equation :
$$f(\lambda)=\lambda^2-(w-s+1)\lambda+w=0 \quad \text{where } s=1-c \quad \dots\dots\dots\dots(2)$$

The solution is then :
$$y_t=A_1\lambda_1{}^t+A_2\lambda_2{}^t \quad \dots\dots\dots\dots\dots\dots(3)$$

where A_1 and A_2 are arbitrary constants fixed by initial disturbances. The roots of (2) may be real and the solution (3) is non-oscillatory ; or the roots of (2) may be conjugate complex and the solution (3) has oscillations. In either case, the solution may be damped or anti-damped according to the magnitude of the dominant root and term in (3). The method followed is that of 6.4 above.

The location of the roots of (2) can be found by considering the sign of $f(\lambda)$ for particular values of λ :

$\lambda =$	$-\infty$	-1	0	1	∞
$f(\lambda) =$	positive	$2(v+c_1)+s$ positive	w	s positive	positive

...............(4)

Notice also that : $\lambda_1 + \lambda_2 = w - s + 1 = v + c_1 > 0$ ....(5)

Hence, if $w < 0$, then one root (λ_1) is a positive fraction and one root (λ_2) a negative fraction, since the value of $f(\lambda)$ in (4) is negative when $\lambda = 0$. By (5), the larger root numerically is the positive root λ_1. However, in the more usual case where $w > 0$, all the signs of $f(\lambda)$ in (4) are positive, so that

$$f(\lambda) = \lambda^2 - (w-s+1)\lambda + w$$

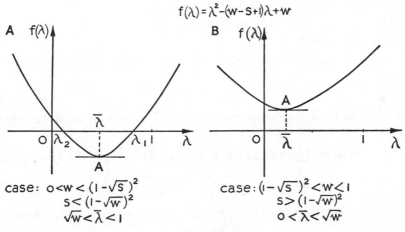

A $f(\lambda)$

$\bar{\lambda}$

$O \; | \lambda_2$ $\lambda_1 \; |$ λ

A

case: $o < w < (1-\sqrt{s})^2$
$s < (1-\sqrt{w})^2$
$\sqrt{w} < \bar{\lambda} < 1$

B $f(\lambda)$

A

O $\bar{\lambda}$ 1 λ

case: $(1-\sqrt{s})^2 < w < 1$
$s > (1-\sqrt{w})^2$
$0 < \bar{\lambda} < \sqrt{w}$

Fig. 22.

both roots, if real, occur in one of the four ranges $(-\infty, -1)$, $(-1, 0)$, $(0, 1)$, $(1, \infty)$. But, by (5), they can only occur in one of the two positive ranges.

Further progress can be made graphically, by plotting the graph of $f(\lambda)$. Fig. 22 illustrates two of the cases. If $\dfrac{d}{d\lambda} f(\lambda) = 2\lambda - (w-s+1) = 0$

then $\lambda = \frac{1}{2}(w - s + 1) = \frac{1}{2}(v + c_1) > 0$. Hence, the graph has a minimum point at A, where $\bar{\lambda} = \frac{1}{2}(w - s + 1)$ and :

$$f(\bar{\lambda}) = -\tfrac{1}{4}\{w - (1 + \sqrt{s})^2\}\{w - (1 - \sqrt{s})^2\}$$

Hence the minimum point is *above* the axis $O\lambda$ if $(1 - \sqrt{s})^2 < w < (1 + \sqrt{s})^2$, in which case there are no real roots of (2). Otherwise there are two real roots and $(w > 0)$ they are *either* both in the range $(0, 1)$ *or* both in the range $(1, \infty)$. The value of $\lambda_1 + \lambda_2$ in (5) is sufficient to decide. If $w < (1 - \sqrt{s})^2$, $\lambda_1 + \lambda_2 = w - s + 1 < 2(1 - \sqrt{s}) < 2$, i.e. λ_1 and λ_2 are in the range $(0, 1)$. Similarly, if $w > (1 + \sqrt{s})^2$, $\lambda_1 + \lambda_2 = w - s + 1 > 2(1 + \sqrt{s}) > 2$ i.e. λ_1 and λ_2 are in the range $(1, \infty)$.

The different cases can be put together as in 7.1 above :

(i) (a) $w < 0$. λ_1 a positive fraction, λ_2 a negative fraction and λ_1 numerically larger, i.e. by (3) y_t is damped to zero, non-oscillatory but with some alternation of sign possible.

    (b) $0 < w < (1 - \sqrt{s})^2$. λ_1 and λ_2 positive fractions, i.e. y_t damped to zero and non-oscillatory.

(ii)
(iii) $\Bigg\}$ $(1 - \sqrt{s})^2 < w < (1 + \sqrt{s})^2$. λ_1 and λ_2 conjugate complex, i.e. y_t has oscillations.

(iv) $(1 + \sqrt{s})^2 < w$. λ_1 and λ_2 positive and greater than 1, i.e. y_t is explosive and non-oscillatory.

It remains to examine cases (ii) and (iii) further. Here, w is in the range :

$$(1 - \sqrt{s})^2 < w < (1 + \sqrt{s})^2 \quad \dots\dots\dots\dots\dots\dots(6)$$

and the roots of (2) are conjugate complex. Let them be $r(\cos\theta \pm i \sin\theta)$ so that :

$$r\cos\theta = \tfrac{1}{2}(w - s + 1) \quad \text{and} \quad r\sin\theta = \tfrac{1}{2}\sqrt{4w - (w - s + 1)^2} \dots\dots\dots(7)$$

i.e. $\qquad\qquad r = \sqrt{w} \qquad\qquad \text{and} \qquad \cos\theta = \dfrac{w - s + 1}{2\sqrt{w}} \quad \dots\dots\dots\dots\dots(8)$

Here, both $\cos\theta$ and $\sin\theta$ are positive, so that θ can be taken between 0 and $\dfrac{\pi}{2}$. The structural coefficients are now r and θ given in terms of w and s by (7) or (8).

The general solution of (1) is now :

$$y_t = Ar^t \cos(\theta t - \epsilon) \quad \dots\dots\dots\dots\dots\dots\dots(9)$$

where A and ϵ are arbitrary constants given by initial disturbances.

The oscillations of (9) are *damped* if $r < 1$ and *explosive* if $r > 1$, i.e. if

$w<1$ or $w>1$. The border-line case of regular oscillations is $w=1$. Hence the distinction between cases (ii) and (iii) in the range (6):

(ii) $(1-\sqrt{s})^2<w<1$; damped oscillations
(iii) $1<w<(1+\sqrt{s})^2$; explosive oscillations.

The *period* of the oscillations of (9) is $\dfrac{2\pi}{\theta}$ where $\cos\theta$ is given by (8) and θ is between 0 and $\dfrac{\pi}{2}$. The period is at least 4 time intervals (periods) and there is no upper limit. If s is given, the period depends on the magnitude of w in range (6). Differentiate $\cos\theta$ in (8) with respect to w:

$$\frac{d}{dw}(\cos\theta)=\frac{w+s-1}{4w\sqrt{w}}$$

Hence
$$\frac{d}{dw}(\cos\theta)<0 \quad \text{for } w<1$$
$$=0 \quad \text{for } w=1-s$$
$$>0 \quad \text{for } w>1-s$$

i.e. the value of $\cos\theta$ is a minimum when $w=1-s$. At the lower end of the range (6), $w=(1-\sqrt{s})^2$ and $\cos\theta=\dfrac{w-s+1}{2\sqrt{w}}=1$. At $w=1-s$ within the range (6), $\cos\theta=\sqrt{1-s}$ and this is the minimum value. At the upper end of the range (6), $w=(1+\sqrt{s})^2$ and $\cos\theta=1$ again. Since $\cos\theta$ decreases from 1 to 0 as θ increases from 0 to $\dfrac{\pi}{2}$, it follows that θ increases from 0 to a maximum θ_m (where $\cos\theta_m=\sqrt{1-s}$) and then decreases to 0 again as w increases over the range (6). The period of oscillation, therefore, is infinitely long at the lower end of the range of w, decreases to a minimum of $\dfrac{2\pi}{\theta_m}$ at $w=1-s$ and then increases again, becoming infinitely long at the upper end of the range w.

The initial *amplitude* and the *phasing* of the oscillations of (9) depend on the two arbitrary constants A and ϵ. These are the features of the oscillation which are fixed by the initial disturbances.

Hence, given s, the oscillatory solution (9) arises when $w=v-c_2$ lies between $(1-\sqrt{s})^2$ and $(1+\sqrt{s})^2$. For low values of w, the oscillations are damped; when $w=1$, the oscillations become regular; for higher values of w, the oscillations are explosive. Within the range there is a point, $w=1-s$, where the oscillations are damped and with the smallest possible period $\dfrac{2\pi}{\theta_m}$ (where $\cos\theta_m = \sqrt{1-s}$). The length of this minimum period depends solely on s. In the usual case where s is small, θ_m is small and even the minimum period is a long one. A small value of s implies both that the range of values of w for oscillations is narrow and that, when oscillations do occur, they are of long period.

EXERCISES 7.2

1. Write and interpret the solution for y_t when $v = 0.05$, $s = 0.04$ and $c_2 = 0.06$.

2. Since s is a positive fraction, show that $(1 - \sqrt{s})^2 < 1 - s < 1$ and hence establish that the value of w for shortest period does fall within the range for damped oscillations. If $s = c_2 = 0.25$, show that the shortest period is 12 time intervals and arises when $v = 1$.

3. If $s = 0$, show that the solution is $y_t = A_1 + A_2 w^t$, which converges to a constant $(w < 1)$ or explodes $(w > 1)$ without oscillations.

4. In the border-line cases $w = (1 \pm \sqrt{s})^2$, show that the solution is

$$y_t = (A_1 + A_2 t)(1 \pm \sqrt{s})^t \quad \text{where } A_1 \text{ and } A_2 \text{ are arbitrary.}$$

5. The border-line cases $w = (1 \pm \sqrt{s})^2$ also correspond to the ends of the range (6) above, i.e. to oscillations with infinitely long period. Is there any inconsistency between this and the result of the previous exercise? On either method of approach, show that the solution for y_t is damped to zero when $w = (1 - \sqrt{s})^2$ and explosive when $w = (1 + \sqrt{s})^2$.

6. If the equilibrium path of output is $\overline{Y}_t = \overline{Y}_0(1+\rho)^t$, ρ given and positive, write $\eta_t = \dfrac{Y_t - \overline{Y}_t}{\overline{Y}_t}$ so that $\eta_t = \dfrac{c}{1+\rho}\eta_{t-1} + \dfrac{w}{1+\rho}\left(\eta_{t-1} - \dfrac{\eta_{t-2}}{1+\rho}\right)$. Examine the solution of this difference equation for η_t. Show that it oscillates in the same range of w (given $s = 1 - c$) as for y_t but that $w = (1+\rho)^2$ for a regular oscillation. Why is the distinction between damped, regular and explosive oscillations different for η_t than for y_t?

7.3 Interpretation of the Solution

The solution of the multiplier-accelerator model may be required to satisfy one of two quite different conditions. It may be desired that y_t *converges* to zero, i.e. Y_t converges to $\overline{Y}_t$, whether over an oscillatory path or otherwise. This is so provided only that the power of accelerator is low enough, $w = v - c_2 < 1$. The condition does not depend on the over-all marginal propensity to consume or save.

On the other hand, it may be desired that y_t *oscillates* about zero, and Y_t about $\overline{Y}_t$, whether damped or anti-damped. The condition for this depends on the combination of values of w and s. It can be expressed: given s, then w must lie in the range $(1 - \sqrt{s})^2$ to $(1 + \sqrt{s})^2$ which is narrow or wide according as s is small or large. It can also be expressed: given w, then s must exceed a certain value $(1 - \sqrt{w})^2$. It is this rather complex condition which is of more interest in trade cycle theory.

Some numerical illustrations are relevant, to get some idea of the orders of magnitude of the structural constants necessary for oscillations. Usually s can be taken as quite small. If $s = 0\cdot04$, then the range of values of w for oscillations is $0\cdot64 < w < 1\cdot44$, so that a value of w in the neighbourhood of unity will serve. If s is as large as $0\cdot25$, the range widens to $0\cdot25 < w < 2\cdot25$ and almost any moderate value of w will give oscillations. These are ranges for the reduced investment coefficient w; to get corresponding ranges for v, the power of the accelerator, they need to be shifted upwards by the value of c_2. For example, if $s = 0\cdot04$ and $c = 0\cdot96$, then the range of v shifts from $0\cdot64 < v < 1\cdot44$ when $c_2 = 0$ to $1\cdot6 < v < 2\cdot4$ when $c_2 = 0\cdot96$ and all consumption is postponed. More powerful accelerators are needed for oscillations as the average lag in consumption increases.

The magnitude of the reduced power of the accelerator, $w = v - c_2$, is critical. If w is near unity, then oscillations will arise almost irrespective of the value of s. The oscillations will be mildly damped or explosive according as $w < 1$ or $w > 1$. Values of w further removed from unity will give oscillations only if s is sufficiently large, and the oscillations will be more strongly damped or explosive. What evidence there is suggests that w is likely in practice to be less than unity rather than greater than unity; this is the conclusion of Fisher (1952) for the United States. Oscillatory solutions of the multiplier-accelerator model are likely; they may well be damped though explosive cases are not by any means ruled out.

The magnitude of the marginal propensity to save s is of no relevance to the question of damping and of importance in the condition for oscillations only when w diverges from unity. Where s becomes critical is in the length of the period of oscillations. The period depends on both structural constants w and s, but the shortest period possible in the model is $\dfrac{2\pi}{\theta_m}$ where $\cos \theta_m = \sqrt{1-s}$, dependent only on s. If s is small, there is only a fairly narrow range of values of w for oscillations and even the shortest period is quite long. As s takes larger values, oscillations of shorter period become possible. An alternating variable (as in the cobweb model) has a period of 2 time intervals. In the multiplier-accelerator model, even if s is as large as $0\cdot25$, no oscillations of shorter period than 12 time intervals are possible; if s is only $0\cdot04$, then the period of oscillation must be more than 30 time intervals.

The oscillatory path of Y_t is endogenous or intrinsic in the model. Oscillations arise because of the structure of the model, as a result of the interaction of the multiplier and the accelerator. The main features of the oscillations are determined by the structural constants $w = v - c_2$ and s.

Specifically, the degree of damping or anti-damping in the oscillation is fixed by the magnitude of $r = \sqrt{w}$, i.e. by the power of the accelerator, reduced by the distributed lags in consumption. The period of the oscillation is fixed by θ, which depends on both w and s. The shortest period possible in the model, however, depends solely on the value of s, i.e. on the over-all marginal propensity to consume or save. These features of the oscillations intrinsic in the model remain fixed and unchanged whatever extraneous factors may operate. In particular, they are independent of the initial disturbances which set off the oscillations and of any later disturbances which may keep them going.

On the other hand, the influence of exogenous factors is not to be ignored. To start up an oscillatory movement in Y_t about its trend, there must be some " initial " disturbances, i.e. something extraneous to the model. These disturbances fix the starting point, or the phase, of the oscillation ; even more important, they determine the amplitude of the first oscillation—which is then damped or magnified according to the intrinsic properties of the model. In particular, if the structure of the model gives an oscillation in Y_t which is approximately regular (i.e. if $w = 1$ approximately), then the amplitude of the oscillation is not an intrinsic feature ; rather it depends on the disturbances which set the oscillation going.

7.4 Application in Trade Cycle Theory

The multiplier-accelerator described above is not in itself a theory of the trade cycle, nor can it be applied in any simple or mechanical way. The question is whether it is a useful ingredient in trade cycle theory. It is to be noticed, first, that the model represents the inter-action of multiplier and accelerator, but the inter-action can be taken as operating in various ways (3.7 above). However derived, the multiplier-accelerator model displays intrinsic oscillations in Y_t, provided that the constants w and s appear in suitable combination. The phenomena to be explained in trade cycle theory are also characterised by oscillations in income or output, The similarity does not imply any close connection, causal or otherwise, between the oscillations. On the contrary, there are important differences :

(i) Trade cycles are more or less regular, not obviously damped or explosive. The oscillations of the model are regular only in the border-line case where $w = v - c_2 = 1$. A theory cannot rest on the accident that the accelerator has a power of just the right magnitude.

(ii) Trade cycles, though regular, are not symmetrical. The upswing differs in form and nature from the downswing, e.g. the boom tends to be

longer than the depression. In the model, apart from their damped or
explosive nature, oscillations are essentially symmetrical as represented by
the sinusoidal variation.

(iii) Trade cycles have an amplitude which appears to be intrinsic, or at
least as needing explanation. The model does not determine the amplitude
of oscillations in endogeneous terms ; it is arbitrary in the sense that it
depends on extraneous factors or initial conditions.

As a basis for a trade cycle theory, therefore, the multiplier-accelerator
model needs to be modified or supplemented. There are several possible
modifications to consider. The *period analysis* of the model may be too
rigid and it may be better to have continuous variation. The *linear
assumptions* may be the reason for the " unrealistic " features of the model
and a non-linear accelerator may be the answer.

It can be noted here that the conditions for a dynamic relation or model
to be linear are not altogether obvious ; they are not as simple, for example,
as assuming linear demand or supply functions in static analysis. A
dynamic relation can involve derivatives, integrals, lags and delays in all
kinds of ways and still be linear. As defined in Appendix A, 9, a *linear
model* is such that any variable Y included has a variation of which only
the damping and frequency of oscillation are determined by the structure
of the model. The amplitude and phase of any oscillation in Y are fixed
by extraneous factors, e.g. by initial conditions. Hence, for an inherent
oscillation within a linear system, the period and damping are structural
features—the amplitude and phase are not. Further, if Y is the " output "
arising from some " input ", then a forced oscillation in " input " gives
rise to an oscillation in " output " of the same period and damping but
with different amplitude and phase (according to initial conditions). For
example, in the present case, the " output " Y_t depends on autonomous
expenditure A_t as an " input ". A forced oscillation in A_t produces an
oscillation in Y_t of the same period and damping but with amplitude and
phase fixed by extraneous factors (see 7.6 below). The Samuelson-Hicks
model, as developed so far, is clearly linear. Goodwin's accelerator model
is not (see 8.3 and Fig. 28 below). These matters are developed in
Chapters 8 and 9 below.

Meanwhile, a brief account can be given of ways to supplement the
Samuelson-Hicks model, as it stands, in a theory of the trade cycle. One
critical point is whether the constant v of the accelerator is fairly small and
the oscillations in Y_t damped—or whether v is rather larger and Y_t intrinsically explosive. Even if the damping or anti-damping is mild, the
oscillations become " unrealistic " in time. The intrinsic oscillation needs

to be supplemented by exogeneous influences. A damped oscillation may be kept going by outside disturbances of the " erratic shock " type. Or, an explosive oscillation can be kept within bounds by exogeneous factors of the " ceiling " and " floor " type.

Another critical point is how to introduce the necessary element of assymmetry in the oscillations of the model. This may be a matter only of suitable " erratic shocks " or appropriate " ceilings " and " floors ". Or there may be some basic assumption of symmetry which needs to be relaxed, e.g. the assumption that the accelerator works in the same way if output is high or low, increasing or decreasing.

Hicks (1950) chooses to supplement his multiplier-accelerator model by exogeneous factors of the " ceiling " and " floor " type and to relax the assumption of a reversible accelerator. He assumes that v is large enough for oscillations which are intrinsically explosive, but symmetrical. The other influences introduced are not symmetrical. A " ceiling " on output is imposed so that, when reached, output remains constant and the accelerator ceases to be effective. There is no accelerator unless there are changes in output. On the other hand, as the downswing approaches a " floor ", the accelerator is taken out of operation altogether because of excess capacity and because disinvestment is limited by the scrapping rate. The accelerator in the form $I_t = v(Y_{t-1} - Y_{t-2})$ is reversible ; this assumption is given up in the downswing.

There remains the difficulty that, though the degree of damping or anti-damping is intrinsic, the amplitude of the oscillations in this as in any linear model is fixed only by extraneous or initial conditions. But, once the accelerator is allowed to go out of operation in each downswing, these " initial " conditions are not remote economic history. They are re-imposed after the downswing in each and every cycle. When the accelerator comes in again, with excess capacity eliminated, it does so from new initial conditions and starts off a new oscillation with its own amplitude. To the extent that each set of initial conditions (depending on actual disinvestment in the downswing) is more or less the same, the amplitude tends to be constant.

On pursuing this point, as Duesenberry (1950) does, it is seen that the explosive nature of the oscillations is largely irrelevant and no " ceiling " is needed. A first intrinsic oscillation occurs, the accelerator goes out in the downswing, and a second oscillation starts up when the accelerator comes back with new initial conditions. The explosive element never has time to be effective—and the oscillations do not necessarily hit a " ceiling "—because each oscillation is on its own and started up from the bottom of each downswing. The amplitude can be fairly constant, not because of any property of the multiplier-accelerator interaction, but because of similarities in starting-up successive oscillations.

On this interpretation, Hicks' application of the multiplier-accelerator model has two important features. Firstly, the power of the accelerator v can vary within quite wide limits ; any value of v will serve as long as it corresponds to oscillations, perhaps with the qualification that they should not be very strongly damped or anti-damped. Secondly, though the mathematical formulation of the model is linear, the break in the operation of the accelerator in its application to the downswing introduces a non-linear element. Indeed, if $I_t = v(Y_{t-1} - Y_{t-2})$ for some ranges, while I_t is an arbitrary (negative) amount for other ranges, then the accelerator is non-linear. In short, Hicks' theory of the trade cycle is an example of a non-linear accelerator. See Baumol (1958), pp. 281–4.

This brief account suffices to illustrate the part a multiplier-accelerator model can play in a theory of the trade cycle. There are, however, some further features of the model which are of relevance and which need to be examined.

7.5. Inventory Cycles

A multiplier-accelerator model of the form of 7.1 above can be constructed for investment in stocks or inventories (i.e. working capital). A simple version, based on the work of Lundberg (1937) and Metzler (1941), is obtained on the following lines.

Autonomous investment expenditure A_t is given and specified over successive periods $t = 0, 1, 2, \ldots$. Sales of consumers' goods are C_t in period t and the stock held by producers is K_t at the end of period t. It is assumed that the aim of producers is to relate stock to the level of sales and that the relation is a proportional one. In period t it is assumed that producers expect sales to be C_{t-1}, as in the previous period. Hence kC_{t-1} is the level of stocks planned in period t. The actual level of stocks K_t differs from the planned level by the amount that actual sales C_t diverges from expected sales C_{t-1}. So :

$$K_t = kC_{t-1} - (C_t - C_{t-1}) \quad \ldots\ldots\ldots\ldots\ldots\ldots(1)$$

The consumption function giving sales C_t is assumed to be linear in income or output Y_t and without lag :

$$C_t = cY_t \quad \ldots\ldots\ldots\ldots\ldots\ldots(2)$$

Output Y_t in period t is made up of three elements as planned by producers, i.e. production for sale C_{t-1}, production for stock $(kC_{t-1} - K_{t-1})$ and autonomous investment A_t.

So :
$$Y_t = C_{t-1} + (kC_{t-1} - K_{t-1}) + A_t \quad \dots\dots\dots\dots\dots(3)$$

On substitution of (1) and (2) in (3), the condition of the model is expressed in terms of a second-order difference equation in Y_t :

$$Y_t = cY_{t-1} + c(1+k)(Y_{t-1} - Y_{t-2}) + A_t \quad \dots\dots\dots\dots(4)$$

The multiplier in this model operates through an unlagged consumption function (2). Both consumption and saving are realised as planned. The accelerator appears because of the effect of changing sales on stocks and the planned investment in stocks. Plans for inventory investment, however, are not realised as indicated by (1). The model allows for unintended investment or disinvestment in inventories.

The difference equation (4) is of exactly the same form as in the Samuelson-Hicks model of 7.1 above, in the "elementary case" of no distributed lag in consumption. This model is $Y_t = cY_{t-1} + v(Y_{t-1} - Y_{t-2}) + A_t$. The inventory model (4) is the same, with the constant of the accelerator v taking the form $c(1+k)$. Here, c is a positive fraction and $k>0$. Hence the accelerator constant, $c(1+k)$, is positive but it can be greater or less than unity.

The solution of (4) follows as in 7.2 above. $\overline{Y}_t$ is a particular integral of (4), depending on the form at A_t. For example if $A_t = A = $ constant, $\overline{Y} = \dfrac{A}{1-c}$, the level given by the multiplier. Then $y_t = Y_t - \overline{Y}_t$ satisfies :

$$y_t = cy_{t-1} + c(1+k)(y_{t-1} - y_{t-2})$$

The solution has oscillations in y_t if :

$$(1 - \sqrt{s})^2 < c(1+k) < (1 + \sqrt{s})^2$$

i.e.
$$\frac{(1 - \sqrt{s})^2}{1-s} < 1 + k < \frac{(1 + \sqrt{s})^2}{1-s} \quad \dots\dots\dots\dots\dots\dots(5)$$

The oscillations are damped if $c(1+k)<1$, i.e. if :

$$1 + k < \frac{1}{1-s} \quad \dots\dots\dots\dots\dots\dots\dots(6)$$

They are regular if $1+k = \dfrac{1}{1-s}$ and explosive if $1+k > \dfrac{1}{1-s}$.

For usual values of s, the condition (5) is satisfied by the values of k which may be expected. The condition (6), however, implies that k is small. For example, if $s = 0.04$, $k < \frac{1}{2}$ is sufficient for oscillations from (5), but the oscillations are damped only when $k < \dfrac{1}{24}$ from (6).

The conclusion is that oscillations in output Y_t about some equilibrium path (depending on autonomous investment) are to be expected ; these are inventory cycles. The cycles may be damped or explosive according as the constant k, relating desired stocks to sales, is small or large.

This model can be combined with that of 7.1 above, by adding the accelerator in Hicks' sense of induced fixed investment to the accelerator in the present sense of induced inventory investment. As indicated by Baumol (1948), the model then becomes more complicated and it involves a difference equation of the third or higher order.

EXERCISES 7.5

1. If s is as large as 0.25, show that $k < 2$ for oscillations and $k < \frac{1}{3}$ for damping in the inventory model above.

2. Given k, find the value of s needed for convergence of y_t and explain how increasing s is a factor making for stability in this model.

3. Interpret the model in the case $k = 0$. Show that y_t satisfies :

$$y_t = 2cy_{t-1} - cy_{t-2}$$

and that there are always damped oscillations in y_t.

4. In period t, income or output is Y_t, consumer demand is cY_t and desired investment is $v(Y_t - Y_{t-1}) + kY_t + A$, all without lags. Producers' estimates of consumer demand C_t and investment demand I_t are lagged and based on experiences of the previous period :

$$C_t = cY_{t-1} \quad \text{and} \quad I_t = v(Y_{t-1} - Y_{t-2}) + kY_{t-1} + A + R_t$$

where R_t is investment demand left unsatisfied (through inventory changes) at the end of period $(t-1)$. The condition of the model is $Y_t = C_t + I_t$. Show that :

$$R_t - R_{t-1} = \text{desired investment less actual investment in period } (t-1)$$
$$= v(Y_{t-1} - Y_{t-2}) + kY_{t-1} - (1-c)Y_{t-1} + A$$

Hence, derive the third-order difference equation in Y_t :

$$Y_t = (k+c)(2Y_{t-1} - Y_{t-2}) + v(2Y_{t-1} - 3Y_{t-2} + Y_{t-3}) + A$$

5. In the model of the previous exercise, show that there is unintended investment but no unintended saving. Modify by taking consumer demand as cY_{t-1} and show that the difference equation is still of third-order, but that there is unintended saving as well as unintended investment. See Baumol (1948).

7.6 Oscillations in Autonomous Investment

Some further consideration can now be given to autonomous expenditure A_t, always assumed given over time. The cases so far examined are those in which A_t is either constant or expanding at a fixed progressive rate. Equally important is the possibility that A_t follows a given oscillatory path over time. It remains to determine the trend path of Y_t in this case and to examine its relation to the intrinsic oscillations (or other variations of Y_t.

The difference equation of any model employing the simple accelerator can be written :

$$Y_t - aY_{t-1} + bY_{t-2} = A_t \quad \ldots\ldots\ldots\ldots\ldots\ldots\ldots(1)$$

where a and b are constants generally to be taken as positive. For the simple model of 7.1, $a = w + c$ and $b = w$. For the inventory model of 7.5, $a = c(2+k)$ and $b = c(1+k)$.

Attention is now concentrated on the important case where the solution for Y_t given by (1) has inherent oscillations which are mildly damped (or mildly explosive) and with period greater than 4 intervals of time. Hence $a^2 < 4b$ and the oscillatory term in the solution is $Ar^t \cos(\theta t - \epsilon)$ where r and θ are given in terms of a and b :

$$r \cos \theta = \tfrac{1}{2}a \quad \text{and} \quad r \sin \theta = \tfrac{1}{2}\sqrt{4b - a^2}$$

or
$$r = \sqrt{b} \quad \text{and} \quad \cos \theta = \frac{a}{2\sqrt{b}}$$

Conversely, a and b can be expressed in terms of r and θ :

$$a = 2r \cos \theta \quad \text{and} \quad b = r^2 \quad \ldots\ldots,\ldots\ldots\ldots\ldots\ldots(2)$$

It is taken that r, the damping factor, is in the neighbourhood of unity. Further, for a period $\frac{2\pi}{\theta} > 4$, θ lies between 0 and $\frac{\pi}{2}$ so that $\sin \theta$, $\cos \theta$ and $\tan \theta$ are all positive. The limitations on a and b are :

$$a^2 < 4b; \quad a > 0 \quad \text{and} \quad b = 1 \text{ approximately} \quad \ldots\ldots\ldots\ldots(3)$$

These are satisfied in quite usual cases of the models of 7.1 and 7.5 above.

So much for the inherent oscillations of the model. Now assume that autonomous expenditure A_t oscillates regularly according to a given sinusoidal function

$$A_t = A_0 \cos(kt - k_0) \quad \ldots\ldots\ldots\ldots\ldots\ldots\ldots(4)$$

This is a forced (or exogeneous) oscillation of fixed period $\frac{2\pi}{k}$; it is regular, neither damped or explosive, and with fixed amplitude A_0. The phasing is indicated by the constant k_0, i.e. a peak of the oscillation occurs at $t = \frac{k_0}{k}$.

To fix ideas and to concentrate on what is the more important case in practice, take $k < \theta$. The period of the forced oscillation $\left(\frac{2\pi}{k}\right)$ is longer than that of the inherent oscillation of the model $\left(\frac{2\pi}{\theta}\right)$. The trend path of Y_t corresponding to the forced oscillation is to be determined. This is a particular integral of (1) and the form which suggests itself is :

$$Y_t = \overline{Y}_0 \cos (kt - \kappa_0) \quad \dots\dots\dots\dots\dots\dots\dots (5)$$

i.e. an oscillation of the same period $\dfrac{2\pi}{k}$ as that of the forced oscillation.

The amplitude and phasing of the oscillation in Y_t, determined by $\overline{Y}_0$ and κ_0, are different and remain to be found. The expression (5) for Y_t must satisfy the difference equation for all t.

In handling this condition with sinusoidal functions, use can be made of the methods involving complex variables and vectors described in 4.8 and 4.9 above. However, in this period analysis, it is better to stick to elementary methods and to use trigonometric relations such as :

$$\cos (\phi_1 - \phi_2) = \cos \phi_1 \cos \phi_2 + \sin \phi_1 \sin \phi_2$$

So $\quad \cos (kt - \kappa_0) \qquad\qquad\qquad = \cos (kt - \kappa_0)$

$\cos (\overline{kt - 1} - \kappa_0) = \cos (kt - \kappa_0 - k) \quad = \cos (kt - \kappa_0) \cos k$
$$\qquad\qquad\qquad\qquad\qquad\qquad\qquad\qquad + \sin (kt - \kappa_0) \sin k$$

$\cos (\overline{kt - 2} - \kappa_0) = \cos (kt - \kappa_0 - 2k) \quad = \cos (kt - \kappa_0) \cos 2k$
$$\qquad\qquad\qquad\qquad\qquad\qquad\qquad\qquad + \sin (kt - \kappa_0) \sin 2k$$

$\cos (kt - k_0) \quad = \cos (kt - \kappa_0 - \overline{k_0 - \kappa_0}) = \cos (kt - \kappa_0) \cos (k_0 - \kappa_0)$
$$\qquad\qquad\qquad\qquad\qquad\qquad\qquad\qquad + \sin (kt - \kappa_0) \sin (k_0 - \kappa_0)$$

Substitute (5) into (1) with A_t given by (4) and use the above results. Then, since the result is true for all t, the coefficients of $\cos (kt - \kappa_0)$ and of $\sin (kt - \kappa_0)$ in the equation found must be separately zero. Hence :

$$\left. \begin{aligned} \overline{Y}_0(1 - a \cos k + b \cos 2k) &= A_0 \cos (k_0 - \kappa_0) \\ \overline{Y}_0(- a \sin k + b \sin 2k) \;\;&= A_0 \sin (k_0 - \kappa_0) \end{aligned} \right\} \dots\dots\dots\dots (6)$$

The equations (6) serve to determine $\overline{Y}_0$ and κ_0, given the structural constants a and b shown in (2) subject to (3), and given the constants A_0, k and k_0 of the exogeneous oscillation of A_t shown by (4).

The complete solution of the difference equation (1) is :

$$Y_t = \overline{Y}_0 \cos (kt - \kappa_0) + Ar^t \cos (\theta t - \epsilon) \quad \dots\dots\dots\dots\dots (7)$$

The path of Y_t over time is an inherent oscillation super-imposed on a forced oscillation fixed by the given oscillation in autonomous expenditure. If the initial conditions are suitable (giving $A = 0$), the " output " Y_t simply oscillates in tune with the forced oscillation in the " input " A_t, i.e. with the same frequency but different amplitude and phase. More generally, the inherent oscillation has period $\dfrac{2\pi}{\theta}$ and it is taken as mildly damped or explosive (the value of r being near unity); it is set going by some initial disturbances which determine, through the arbitrary constants A and ϵ, the amplitude and phasing of the oscillation. The forced oscillation in Y_t is regular (undamped) and with the same period $\dfrac{2\pi}{k}$ as in the given oscillation of A_t; it is taken that this period is longer than the inherent period. However, when the forced oscillation of A_t is translated into a corresponding oscillation in Y_t, the amplitude and phasing are different and to be determined by (6). In general, they depend on the nature of the inherent oscillation as well as on the forced (or exogeneous) oscillation. All turns, therefore, on the values of $\overline{Y}_0$ and κ_0 which fix the amplitude and phasing of the forced oscillation in Y_t.

The equations (6) are easily handled when $r=1$ exactly and the inherent oscillation is regular (undamped). From (2), $a=2\cos\theta>0$ and $b=1$. In this particular case, the equations (6) are:

$$\left.\begin{aligned}\overline{Y}_0(1-2\cos k\cos\theta+\cos 2k)&=A_0\cos(k_0-\kappa_0)\\ \text{and}\qquad \overline{Y}_0(-2\sin k\cos\theta+\sin 2k)&=A_0\sin(k_0-\kappa_0)\end{aligned}\right\}\ \ \dots\dots\dots\dots(8)$$

Substituting $\cos 2k=2\cos^2 k-1$ and $\sin 2k=2\sin k\cos k$ into (8):

$$\overline{Y}_0\cos k=\frac{A_0}{2(\cos k-\cos\theta)}\cos(k_0-\kappa_0)$$

and

$$\overline{Y}_0\sin k=\frac{A_0}{2(\cos k-\cos\theta)}\sin(k_0-\kappa_0)$$

Since k and θ are both between 0 and $\pi/2$ and since $k<\theta$, we have:

(i) $k_0-\kappa_0=k>0$ and (ii) $\overline{Y}_0=\dfrac{A_0}{2(\cos k-\cos\theta)}>0$

The economics of the model require that the forced oscillation in Y_t lags behind that in A_t. A peak in A_t occurs at $t=k_0/k$. Y_t has successive peaks at

$$t=\frac{\kappa_0}{k},\ \frac{\kappa_0+2\pi}{k},\ \dots=\frac{k_0}{k}-1,\ \frac{k_0}{k}+\left(\frac{2\pi}{k}-1\right),\ \dots\ \text{ by result (i)}$$

The second of these is the earliest to follow the peak $t=k_0/k$ in A_t, i.e. Y_t peaks $[(2\pi/k)-1]>3$ time intervals later than A_t. Result (ii) shows that the amplitude of the forced oscillation in Y_t is a multiple λ of that in A_t, where $1/\lambda=2(\cos k-\cos\theta)$ and λ increases as k increases from 0 to θ. When $k=0$, the A_t oscillation is indefinitely long and $\lambda = \dfrac{1}{2(1 - \cos \theta)}$. In the model of 7.1 when $a = 2 \cos \theta = 1 + c$,

$\lambda = \dfrac{1}{1 - c}$. The amplitude of the Y_t oscillation is approximately $\dfrac{A_0}{1 - c}$, as

given by the multiplier, when k is small and the forced oscillation is of long period. On the other hand, as $k \to \theta$ and the forced and inherent oscillations tend to have the same period, the value of $\lambda \to \infty$. Hence, the amplitude of the Y_t oscillation increases indefinitely when the forced oscillation agrees (in period) with the inherent oscillation. They re-inforce each other to produce large swings in the path of Y_t; this is the " resonance " effect well known in physics.

The results obtained here are for the case where $r = 1$ exactly, e.g. the case where the reduced coefficient of the accelerator is exactly 1 in the model of 7.1. It can be shown (see Ex. 3 below) that much the same results hold when r is a little different from unity and the intrinsic oscillation is mildly damped or explosive. The amplitude $\overline{Y}_0$ of the forced oscillation in Y is then somewhat damped. The results also relate to forced oscillations of the particular or sinusoidal form (4). Bennion (1945) has examined the effect of taking types of forced oscillations which are not sinusoidal.

The analysis suggests that a theory of the trade cycle can take account of oscillations of different lengths. There can be a relatively long and regular oscillation in output of the trend type, associated with oscillations of the same period in autonomous expenditure. Super-imposed on this can be one or more shorter oscillations in output which are structural and inherent and which arise (e.g.) from the interaction of the multiplier and accelerator or from inventory movements. The shorter oscillations may be intrinsically damped or explosive and they are started up by initial disturbances. However, the amplitude of the long oscillation in output is not independent of the intrinsic oscillations. As the period of the given oscillations in autonomous expenditure approaches that of the inherent oscillations in output, the " resonance " effect is found and the path of output is characterised by larger and larger swings.

EXERCISES 7.6

1. In the multiplier-accelerator model of 7.1, show that the particular case $r = 1$ arises when $w = 1$ so that $a = 2 - s$, $b = 1$. Show also that $\cos \theta = 1 - \frac{1}{2}s$ so that the period of the intrinsic oscillation is fixed by s.

2. The construction of Fig. 23 is a geometrical representation of the particular case of the previous exercise. Show that

$$\text{Projection of } OP \text{ on } OX = 1 - (2 - s) \cos k + \cos 2k$$
$$\text{Projection of } OP \text{ on } OY = \quad - (2 - s) \sin k + \sin 2k$$

From equations (8) above, deduce that, if the angle POX is α,

$$OP \cos \alpha = \frac{A_0}{Y_0} \cos (k_0 - \kappa_0) \quad \text{and} \quad OP \sin \alpha = \frac{A_0}{Y_0} \sin (k_0 \cdot \kappa_0)$$

and so $\qquad \alpha = k_0 - \kappa_0 \qquad$ and $\qquad OP = \dfrac{A_0}{Y_0}$

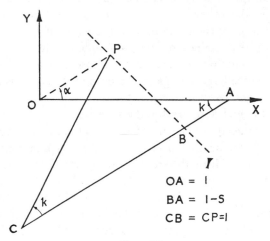

$$
\begin{aligned}
OA &= 1 \\
BA &= 1 - s \\
CB &= CP = 1
\end{aligned}
$$

Fig. 23.

Note that, in this construction, $\alpha = k$. Hence interpret the results (for $r = 1$) obtained in the text above, in particular the effect of the inherent period (fixed by s) on $\overline{Y}_0$.

3. The model of 7.1 ($w \neq 1$) has $a = w - s + 1$ and $b = w$; in the case of oscillations, $a = 2r \cos \theta$ and $b = r^2$. In the previous exercise, generalise Fig. 23 by making $BC = CP = w$ and show that the results still hold. Show that, as w varies from unity in either direction, P moves along the line BP of Fig. 23 ; hence determine what happens to the value of $\overline{Y}_0$. See Hicks (1950), Appendix, pp. 197–9.

7.7 A More General Model with Distributed Investment

A generalisation of the multiplier-accelerator model of 7.1 allows for the distribution of induced investment over several periods and, at the same time, for a wider spread of the consumption lag. Generally, the functions in linear form are :

Induced investment $I_t = v_1(Y_{t-1} - Y_{t-2}) + v_2(Y_{t-2} - Y_{t-3})$
$$+ v_3(Y_{t-3} - Y_{t-4}) + \ldots$$

Consumption $\qquad C_t = c_1 Y_{t-1} + c_2 Y_{t-2} + c_3 Y_{t-3} + c_4 Y_{t-4} + \ldots$

Autonomous expenditure A_t is again specified over successive periods, $t = 0, 1, 2, \ldots$. The condition of the model is unchanged: $Y_t = C_t + I_t + A_t$. The order of the resulting difference equation depends on the distribution of the lags taken in investment and consumption.

The structural constants are v_1, v_2, v_3, ... and c_1, c_2, c_3, ... Some switching of the constants is again found useful. The over-all investment coefficient, or power of the accelerator, is $v = v_1 + v_2 + v_3 + ...$. It is often convenient to take v as a structural constant (instead of v_1) and to leave v_2, v_3, ... to fix the distribution of the investment lag. The c's can be cumulated :

$$c = c_1 + c_2 + c_3 + c_4 + ... ; \quad c' = c_2 + c_3 + c_4 + ... ; \quad c'' = c_3 + c_4 + ... ; \quad ...$$

The over-all marginal propensity to consume is c and the marginal propensity to save is $s = 1 - c$. The other cumulated propensities fix the distribution of the consumption lag. The only restrictions are that all the v's are positive and all the c's positive fractions.

A model sufficiently general for most purposes is that with a distributed lag of two terms for investment and of three terms for consumption. The third-order difference equation :

$$Y_t = cY_{t-1} + (v_1 - c')(Y_{t-1} - Y_{t-2}) + (v_2 - c'')(Y_{t-2} - Y_{t-3}) + A_t \quad ...(1)$$

is obtained (see 3.9 above). This can be reduced to homogeneous form and re-arranged. A particular integral $\overline{Y}_t$ is derived from the given form of A_t and interpreted as the trend path. On writing $y_t = Y_t - \overline{Y}_t$, the equation (1) becomes homogeneous in y_t with the A_t term missing. The effect of the distributed lag in consumption is to diminish the power of the accelerator. Write $w_1 = v_1 - c'$ and $w_2 = v_2 - c''$ as the *reduced investment coefficients* and $w = w_1 + w_2 = v - c' - c''$ as the *reduced power* of the accelerator. The equation (1) is then :

$$y_t = cy_{t-1} + w_1(y_{t-1} - y_{t-2}) + w_2(y_{t-2} - y_{t-3}) \quad ....(2)$$

It is possible that w_1 and w_2, and also w, take negative values. The structural constants in (2) are c, w_1 and w_2. It is often convenient to write $c = 1 - s$ and $w_1 = w - w_2$ so that the structural constants are s and w for the over-all marginal propensity to save and power of the accelerator, together with w_2 to indicate distributed investment.

The solution of (2) requires the roots, λ_1, λ_2, and λ_3, of the auxiliary equation :

$$\lambda^3 - (w_1 + c)\lambda^2 + (w_1 - w_2)\lambda + w_2 = 0$$

or $\quad\quad\quad \lambda^3 - (w - w_2 - s + 1)\lambda^2 + (w - 2w_2)\lambda + w_2 = 0 \quad ....(3)$

The solution is :

$$y_t = A_1\lambda_1{}^t + A_2\lambda_2{}^t + A_3\lambda_3{}^t \quad ....(4)$$

where A_1, A_2 and A_3 are arbitrary constants fixed by initial disturbances.

The extra feature, as compared with the simple model, is the constant w_2. It is useful to distinguish two extreme cases as well as the general case :

(i) Extreme case : $w_1=w$, $w_2=0$. Investment is *humped*, exactly as in the simple model, except that just enough investment is distributed $(v_2=c_3)$ to allow for the effect of the distributed lag in consumption.

(ii) Extreme case : $w_1=0$, $w_2=w$. Investment is *postponed and humped* in the second period, apart from the effect $(v_1=c_2+c_z)$ of the consumption lag.

(iii) General case : $w_1\neq0$, $w_2\neq0$. Investment is *distributed*, part in the first period and part postponed until the second period.

In the following analysis, w is taken as given and $w<1$ is assumed— the case of a damped or convergent solution in the simple model. The explosive possibility with $w>1$ is handled on similar lines. The value of s, the other feature of the simple model, is usually quite small, but some attention is paid to its influence on the solution (4). There remains the effect of the value of w_2, the new constant indicating distributed investment, on the solution.

7.8 Analysis for Humped Investment

Since the present approach is rather different, it is convenient to summarise the nature of the solution in case (i), humped investment as in the simple model $(w_2=0)$. Let $s=0$ so that the marginal propensity to save is zero (though not *ex post* saving). The solution is then $y_t=A_1+A_2w$ converging to a constant (see 7.2, Ex. 4). An alternating element is possible in unusual cases $(w<0)$ but the convergence is generally steady $(0<w<1)$. As s takes larger values, oscillatory solutions become more possible. Oscillations arise when s becomes sufficiently large, given w ; the condition is $s>(1-\sqrt{w})^2$ (see 7.1, Ex. 5). Whether the solution oscillates or not, the variation of y_t is convergent and the damping factor is fixed by w.

Case (ii), postponed and humped investment, is new. The auxiliary equation (3) of 7.7, with $w_1=0$ and $w_2=w$, becomes :

$$\lambda^3-(1-s)\lambda^2-w\lambda+w=0$$

or
$$(\lambda-1)(\lambda^2-w)+s\lambda^2=0 \quad\dots\dots\dots\dots\dots\dots(1)$$

If $s=0$ and if $0<w<1$, the roots of (1) in descending order are :

$$\lambda_1=1, \quad \lambda_2=\sqrt{w}, \quad \lambda_3=-\sqrt{w}$$

The first is the dominant root and the solution (4) of 7.7 becomes :

$$y_t=A_1+A_2(\sqrt{w})^t+A_3(-\sqrt{w})^t\dots\dots\dots\dots\dots(2)$$

which converges to a constant as in case (i). The difference is the presence of an alternating term $(-\sqrt{w})^t$. Though not dominant, it is an important addition. Further, if $s=0$ and $w<0$, a weak accelerator, it is found that the roots λ_2 and λ_3 are complex and y_t has an oscillatory element which can be taken as quite heavily damped (see Ex. 1 below).

As s takes larger values in case (ii), the effect on the three roots of (1)

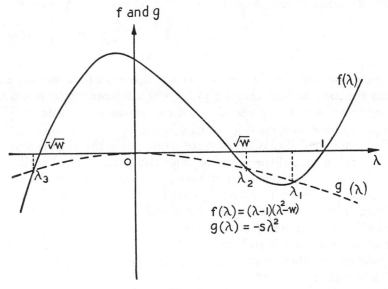

FIG. 24.

is most easily seen in the graphical terms of Fig. 24. The roots are given by the intersections of the graphs of $f(\lambda)$ and $g(\lambda)$:

$$f(\lambda)=(\lambda-1)(\lambda^2-w) \quad \text{and} \quad g(\lambda)=-s\lambda^2$$

The illustration of Fig. 24 applies when $0<w<1$. (The unusual case, $w<0$, is taken up in Ex. 2 below.) The graph of $f(\lambda)$ cuts $O\lambda$ in the points $\lambda=1$, $\sqrt{w}$ and $-\sqrt{w}$, which are the roots when $s=0$. The graph of $g(\lambda)$ is a parabola, with a maximum (vertex) at O; it is flat if s is small, more convex if s is larger. It follows, from Fig. 24, that for increasing (but sufficiently small) values of s the positive roots λ_1 and λ_2 draw together and lie between $\sqrt{w}$ and 1 while the negative root λ_3 gets numerically larger. As long as $(-\lambda_3)<1$, all three roots are fractions, two being positive and one negative. The solution then converges to zero, with a damped alternating term represented by λ_3.

The value of s increases to certain critical points when two things happen. The first possibility is that the curve $g(\lambda)$ misses the curve $f(\lambda)$ altogether in the range of positive λ. The roots λ_1 and λ_2 become complex and the solution includes an oscillatory element. This happens for quite small values of s, certainly for s rather smaller than in the simple model when the condition is $s > (1 - \sqrt{w})^2$ (see Ex. 3 below). For conjugate complex roots, $\lambda_1, \lambda_2 = r(\cos \theta \pm i \sin \theta)$, the product remains real, i.e. $\lambda_1 \lambda_2 = r^2$. From the auxiliary equation (1):

$$\lambda_1 \lambda_2 \lambda_3 = -w \quad \text{i.e.} \quad \lambda_1 \lambda_2 = \frac{w}{(-\lambda_3)}$$

whatever the roots may be. As s increases, $(-\lambda_3)$ increases from the value $\sqrt{w}$ as shown in Fig. 24, and so $\lambda_1 \lambda_2$ decreases from the value $\sqrt{w}$. When the roots become complex $(\lambda_1 \lambda_2 = r^2)$, it follows that r^2 is less than $\sqrt{w}$ and decreases as s increases. The oscillations in the solution y_t are damped and the damping is greater for larger s.

The other possibility is equally interesting ; it is that the negative root λ_3 becomes greater than unity in numerical value : $(-\lambda_3) > 1$. The critical value of s is now that $f(\lambda) = g(\lambda)$ at $\lambda = -1$, i.e. $s = 2(1 - w)$ on substitution. Hence, $(-\lambda_3) > 1$ if $s > 2(1 - w)$. This is possible if s is sufficiently large (and still a positive fraction) provided that $\frac{1}{2} < w < 1$. Generally, in the quite usual cases where w is not far from unity, a value of s of moderate size is sufficient for $(-\lambda_3) > 1$. The dominant term in the solution y_t is then an alternating element, i.e. a short cycle of period 2 which is explosive.

The solution for y_t is given by (2) above when $s = 0$. For quite small values of s, the solution is modified slightly to :

$$y_t = A_1 \lambda_1{}^t + A_2 \lambda_2{}^t + A_3 \lambda_3{}^t \quad\quad\quad\quad\quad\ldots\ldots\ldots\ldots\ldots\ldots(3)$$

when λ_1 and λ_2 are positive fractions and λ_3 is a negative fraction. The form (3) corresponds to a convergence to zero without oscillations. For larger values of s, the solution becomes :

$$y_t = Ar^t \cos(\theta t - \epsilon) + B(-\lambda)^t \quad\quad\ldots\ldots\ldots\ldots\ldots(4)$$

where A, B and ϵ are the arbitrary constants. The form (4) arises when, of the roots of the auxiliary equation, two are complex $r(\cos \theta \pm i \sin \theta)$ and the third is the negative value $(-\lambda)$. The solution (4) consists of a damped oscillatory element with period $\dfrac{2\pi}{\theta}$ and damping factor given by r, together with an alternating element fixed by $(-\lambda)$. As s increases, the oscillations are increasingly damped, but the alternations may be magnified until they become dominant and explosive. When investment is postponed, w not far from 1 and s fairly large, there can be a dominating and explosive short cycle (of period 2) in output y_t.

Apart from the short cycle, the solution is one of damped oscillations. This is because the cases examined are those for which $0 < w < 1$. The analysis is similar for cases where w is given and $w > 1$; the oscillations are then explosive. It is still true that the value of w, the reduced power of the accelerator, determines the convergence, or degree of damping, in the solution. The qualification is that, whatever the value of w (not far from unity), there may arise a short cycle or alternation of explosive nature.

The new possibilities—and particularly that of an explosive short cycle—are not to be dismissed lightly. Postponed investment may be the rule rather than the exception. The unit period is chosen to coincide with the (shortest) lag on the consumption side. The period for decision-taking for investment may be longer and the lags in investment outlays and in production of capital equipment longer still. It must, therefore, be expected that induced investment outlays will not be made until the second period after an output change. A moderately large marginal propensity to save can then produce an explosive alternation, or short cycle, in output.

EXERCISES 7.8

1. Examine case (ii), $w_1 = 0$, $w_2 = w$ and $s = 0$, when $w < 0$. Show that the roots (other than unity) of the auxiliary equation are complex, $r(\cos \theta \pm i \sin \theta)$, where

$$r = \sqrt{-w} \quad \text{and} \quad \theta = \frac{\pi}{2}.$$

Deduce that the oscillations in y_t are of period 4 and usually heavily damped.

2. Follow up the previous exercise ($w < 0$) by considering larger s ($\neq 0$). Re-draw Fig. 24 to meet the new situation and show that the auxiliary equation generally has one real root (a positive fraction) and two complex roots.

3. Show that $f(\lambda)$ has a minimum value $-\frac{2}{27}\{(1 + 3w)^{3/2} + 1 - 9w\}$ at

$$\lambda = \tfrac{1}{3}(\sqrt{1 + 3w} + 1)$$

When $w = \frac{16}{27}$, show that the minimum is $-\dfrac{16}{(27)^2}$ and that $g(\lambda) = -\frac{16}{27}s$ at the lower end of the range ($\lambda = \sqrt{w}$) in which $f(\lambda)$ is negative, Fig. 24. Deduce that, for this w, there will certainly be oscillations in y_t in the postponed investment model if $s > \frac{1}{27} = 0.037$. Compare with the simple model, where for oscillations

$$s > (1 - \sqrt{w})^2 = 0.044.$$

4. Carry through the analysis of the test above when $w > 1$, showing that the case of postponed investment is then characterised (for sufficiently large s) by an oscillation in y_t, combined with an alternation or short cycle both of which are explosive.

7.9 Analysis for Distributed Investment

The general case of distributed investment when there are two lags and $w_1 \neq 0$, $w_2 \neq 0$ can be investigated on the lines of 7.8 above, from the starting point of the situation when $s=0$. This is done by Hicks (1950). There is, however, an alternative method which can be usefully pursued. The difference equation is :

$$y_t = cy_{t-1} + w_1(y_{t-1} - y_{t-2}) + w_2(y_{t-2} - y_{t-3}) \quad \ldots\ldots\ldots\ldots(1)$$

when $w_1 \neq 0$, $w_2 \neq 0$. The case examined in detail here is that in which $w = w_1 + w_2$ is given and $0 < w < 1$; this is, generally speaking, the case of convergence or damping of y_t. The other cases, where the accelerator is so weak that $w < 0$, or so strong that $w > 1$, can be easily examined on the same lines.

Even with $w = w_1 + w_2$ positive, it is still possible that one or other of w_1 and w_2 is negative, since each coefficient is of the " reduced " type. If investment is mainly humped in the first period, then w_2 can be negative and $w_1 > w$; if investment is mainly postponed to the second period, then w_1 can be negative and $w_2 > w$. The coefficients used here are w and w_2 ; the usual case is $0 < w_2 < w$, but exceptionally $w_2 < 0$ or $w_2 > w$.

The solution for the distributed case is $y_t = A_1\lambda_1{}^t + A_2\lambda_2{}^t + A_3\lambda_3{}^t$ where λ_1, λ_2 and λ_3 are the roots of :

$$\lambda^3 - (w - w_2 - s + 1)\lambda^2 + (w - 2w_2)\lambda + w_2 = 0 \quad \ldots\ldots\ldots\ldots(2)$$

This is to be compared with the solution of the corresponding simple model (7.2 above) with the same w and s but no distribution of investment, i.e. $y_t = A_1\lambda_1{}^t + A_2\lambda_2{}^t$ where λ_1 and λ_2 are the roots of:

$$\lambda^2 - (w - s + 1)\lambda + w = 0 \quad \ldots\ldots\ldots\ldots\ldots\ldots(3)$$

Since $\lambda \neq 0$ as long as w_2 is not zero, the equation (2) can be arranged :

$$\left.\begin{array}{c}\lambda^2 - (w - s + 1)\lambda + w = -w_2\dfrac{(\lambda-1)^2}{\lambda}\\[2mm] f(\lambda) = g(\lambda)\end{array}\right\} \quad \ldots\ldots\ldots\ldots(4)$$

i.e.

Here $f(\lambda) = \lambda^2 - (w - s + 1)\lambda + w$ equated to zero is the auxiliary equation (3) of the simple model ; $g(\lambda) = -w_2\dfrac{(\lambda-1)^2}{\lambda}$ introduces the constant w_2 of the distributed investment.

The roots of (4) can be located graphically by finding the intersections of the graphs of $f(\lambda)$ and $g(\lambda)$ plotted to the same axes. The graph of $f(\lambda)$ in the present case of $0 < w < 1$ is plotted in Fig. 22. Its intersections with $O\lambda$ gives the roots of (3) for the solution of the simple model. The curve moves upwards and to the left as s increases, given w. When s is small and $s < (1 - \sqrt{w})^2$, the curve is shown in Fig. 22a and the simple model has a damped but non-oscillatory solution.   When s is larger and

$$s > (1 - \sqrt{w})^2,$$

the curve is shown in Fig. 22b and the simple model has damped oscillations in y_t.

The graph of $g(\lambda)$ is the hyperbola shown in Fig. 25 when $w_2 > 0$. (For $w_2 < 0$, see Ex. 2 below.) The curve depends on the value of w_2 and two

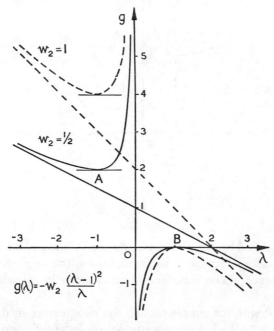

FIG. 25.

cases are illustrated. The minimum point A has value $4w_2$ at $\lambda = -1$; the maximum point B has value 0 at $\lambda = 1$. As w_2 increases, the curve becomes steeper everywhere; to the left of O it also shifts upwards, but to the right of O it remains anchored to the point B.

In Fig. 26, the graphs of $f(\lambda)$ and $g(\lambda)$ are put together. Though w is taken as fixed, s and w_2 can take various values. Increasing s shifts $f(\lambda)$ upwards and to the left; increasing w_2 shifts $g(\lambda)$ as illustrated in Fig. 25. For small values of s, and almost independently of w_2, the curve $f(\lambda)$ dips below $O\lambda$ between 0 and 1 and cuts $g(\lambda)$ in two points in this range, and in another point between 0 and -1. The equation (4) has three fractional roots, two positive (λ_1 and λ_2) and one negative (λ_3), and the solution y_t is damped to zero without oscillations.

However, as s increases or as w_2 increases, the curves so shift that they miss each other in the range $(0, 1)$ for λ. The positive fractional roots of

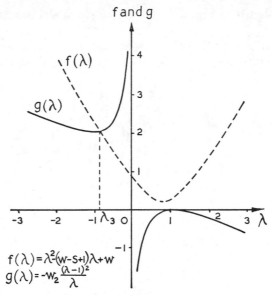

$$f(\lambda) = \lambda^2 - (w-s+1)\lambda + w$$
$$g(\lambda) = -w_2 \frac{(\lambda-1)^2}{\lambda}$$

FIG. 26.

(4) are then replaced by complex roots and the solution y_t has an oscillatory term. Again, as s increases or as w_2 increases, the negative root λ_3 gets numerically larger. The solution y_t has a term in $\lambda_3{}^t$ which becomes more important.

As compared with the simple model, the new feature in the solution y_t is the term in $\lambda_3{}^t$,which gives an alternation or short cycle of period 2. From Fig. 26, it appears that $(-\lambda_3)$ may well be a fraction, but that

$$(-\lambda_3) > 1$$

is quite possible. If $f(\lambda) < g(\lambda)$ at $\lambda = -1$, then the (negative) intersection of the curves is to the left of $\lambda = -1$. Hence, the condition that $(-\lambda_3) > 1$ is :

$$1 + (w - s + 1) + w < 4w_2$$

i.e. $s > 2(1 + w - 2w_2)$ or $w_2 > \frac{1}{2}(1 + w - \frac{1}{2}s)$

Large enough values of s, or large enough values of w_2, or any suitable combination, give $(-\lambda_3) > 1$ and the alternation in y_t is explosive. In particular, if so much investment is postponed that w_2 is not only greater than w, but greater than $w + \frac{1}{2}(1 - w)$, then the condition for $(-\lambda_3) > 1$ is satisfied for all s. For smaller w_2, it is still possible to have s large enough for $(-\lambda_3) > 1$.

In the distributed as in the simple model, there are oscillations in y_t if s is sufficiently large, given w. In the simple model, $s > (1 - \sqrt{w})^2$ for oscillations and the curve $f(\lambda)$ is above $O\lambda$. In the distributed model, a rather lower range of s gives oscillations, since it is possible for the curve $f(\lambda)$ to dip below $O\lambda$ and still miss the curve $g(\lambda)$. From the auxiliary equation (2), the product of the three roots λ_1, λ_2 and λ_3 is $(-w_2)$,

i.e.
$$\lambda_1 \lambda_2 = \frac{w_2}{(-\lambda_3)}$$

whether λ_1 and λ_2 are real or complex. As s increases, $(-\lambda_3)$ increases and the product $\lambda_1 \lambda_2$ decreases. When these two roots are real, they are both positive fractions. When they are complex, $r(\cos \theta \pm i \sin \theta)$, the value of $\lambda_1 \lambda_2$ is r^2. Hence, r^2 is less than unity and decreases as s increases. The oscillations are increasingly damped for larger values of s.

Hence, for distributed investment with w given $(0 < w < 1)$ and with s not very small, the solution y_t is of the form :

$$y_t = Ar^t \cos (\theta t - \epsilon) + B(-\lambda)^t$$

where A, B and ϵ are arbitrary constants and λ stands for the numerical value of the negative root λ_3. There is an oscillatory term of the damped type, as in the simple model of humped investment, except that it arises for rather smaller s and that the damping increases as s gets larger (instead of remaining constant). There is, in addition, an alternating (or short-cycle) term which arises because of the postponement of part of the investment. The more investment is postponed, and the larger the value of s, the more important does the alternating term become, and the more likely is the case where the short cycle is explosive and dominates the solution. A small or negative value of w_1, and hence w_2 near or greater than w, makes for a dominant short cycle. A large value of the marginal propensity to save s, while damping down the oscillation in y_t, also re-inforces the possibility of a dominant short-cycle. All this is very similar to, and extends, the results obtained in 7.8 above for postponed investment.

EXERCISES 7.9

1. Establish that $g(\lambda) = -w_2 \dfrac{(\lambda - 1)^2}{\lambda}$ for $w_2 > 0$ has a maximum 0 at $\lambda = 1$ and a minimum $4w_2$ at $\lambda = -1$. See graph, Fig. 25. What are the corresponding results when $w_2 < 0$?

2. When $w_2 < 0$ and $0 < w < 1$, show that the graph of $g(\lambda)$ is as shown in Fig. 25 but reflected in $O\lambda$. Hence modify Fig. 26 and show that the solution y_t, generally has a steadily damped term added to an oscillatory term. Compare with the simple model ($w_2 = 0$).

3. Show that the auxiliary equation (2) above has a root $\lambda = -1$ when

$$w_2 = \tfrac{1}{2}(1 + w - \tfrac{1}{2}s),$$

and that the other two roots are given by :

$$\lambda^2 + (w - 3w_2)\lambda + w_2 = 0$$

Interpret this case in terms of Fig. 26 and indicate that the " short cycle " is now a constant but alternating term.

4. Show that the case $s = 0$ corresponds to a root $\lambda = 1$ of the auxiliary equation (2) and conversely. How does this root appear in the solution y_t? Further, show that the other two roots are given by $\lambda^2 - w_1\lambda - w_2 = 0$ and examine this equation (when w_1 and w_2 are positive).

5. Again in the case $s = 0$ ($\lambda = 1$), show that the difference equation (1) reduces to a second-order equation in $z_t = y_t - y_{t-1}$, solve for z_t and check with the results of the previous exercise.

6. Arrange the auxiliary equation (2) in the form $f(\lambda) = g(\lambda)$, where :

$$f(\lambda) = \lambda^2 - (w_1 - s + 1)\lambda + w_1 \quad \text{and} \quad g(\lambda) = w_2\left(1 - \frac{1}{\lambda}\right)$$

and locate the roots from graphs of $f(\lambda)$ and $g(\lambda)$. Compare with Fig. 26.

7. Put the auxiliary equation (2) into the form :

$$(\lambda - 1)(\lambda^2 - w_1\lambda - w_2) = -s\lambda^2$$

Examine first the case $s = 0$ (see Ex. 4 and 5 above). Then, for $s \neq 0$, $\lambda \neq 1$, arrange the equation as $f(\lambda) = g(\lambda)$ where $f(\lambda) = \lambda^2 - w_1\lambda - w_2$, $g(\lambda) = -s\dfrac{\lambda^2}{\lambda - 1}$ and locate the roots by a graphical method similar to Fig. 26. Hence deduce the effect of s increasing from the value zero.

8. Examine the case $w_1 = w_2 = \tfrac{1}{2}w$, i.e. an even distribution of investment over two periods. Show that the difference equation (1) becomes :

$$y_t = cy_{t-1} + \tfrac{1}{2}w(y_{t-1} - y_{t-3})$$

with auxiliary equation :

$$F(\lambda) = \lambda^3 - (\tfrac{1}{2}w + c)\lambda^2 + \tfrac{1}{2}w = 0$$

Show that there are *either* (a) two real values of λ greater than 1 (and one negative λ), *or* (b) two real values of λ which are positive fractions, *or* (c) no real and positive values of λ. Interpret (a) as a non-oscillatory explosive growth and (c) as an oscillatory path of income over time. How is case (b) to be interpreted?

9. In the case of the previous exercise, show that $F(\lambda)$ has a minimum value at $\lambda = \tfrac{2}{3}(\tfrac{1}{2}w + c)$. Examine the sign of $F(\lambda)$ at $\lambda = 1$, λ and $(\tfrac{1}{2}w + c)$ and show that the explosive case, (a) of the previous exercise, occurs when $\tfrac{2}{3}(\tfrac{1}{2}w + c)$ exceeds both 1 and $\sqrt[3]{w}$. Illustrate by showing that, when $w = 2$, c must exceed 0·9 for explosive growth ; but that, when $w = 1$, the explosive case cannot arise.

10. Extend the case of the previous two exercises to allow for investment distributed evenly over n periods with $w_1 = w_2 = w_3 = \ldots = w_n = \dfrac{1}{n} w$ and difference equation :

$$y_t = cy_{t-1} + \frac{1}{n} w(y_{t-1} - y_{t-n-1}) \quad \text{See Alexander (1949).}$$

REFERENCES

Alexander (S. S.) (1949) : " The Accelerator as a Generator of Steady Growth ", *Quarterly Journal of Economics*, **63**, 174–97.

Alexander (S. S.) (1951) : " Issues of Business Cycle Theory Raised by Mr. Hicks ", *American Economic Review*, **41**, 861–78.

Baumol (W. J.) (1948) : " Notes on Some Dynamic Models ", *Economic Journal*, **58**, 506–21.

Baumol (W. J.) (1958) : " Topology of Second Order Linear Difference Equations with Constant Coefficients ", *Econometrica*, **26**, 258–85.

Bennion (E. G.) (1945) : " The Multiplier, the Acceleration Principle, and Fluctuating Autonomous Investment ", *Review of Economic Statistics*, **27**, 85–92.

Duesenberry (J. S.) (1950) : " Hicks on the Trade Cycle ", *Quarterly Journal of Economics*, **64**, 464–76.

Fisher (G. H.) (1952) : " Hicks' Elementary Case Economic Model for the United States, 1929–1941 ", *Journal of the American Statistical Association*, **47**, 541–49.

Hansen (A. H.) (1941) : *Fiscal Policy and Business Cycles* (Norton, 1941), Chapter 12.

Hansen (A. H.) (1951) : *Business Cycles and National Income* (Norton, 1951) Chapter 11.

Hicks (J. R.) (1950) : *A Contribution to the Theory of the Trade Cycle* (Oxford, 1950), Chapter VI and Appendix.

Lundberg (E.) (1937) : *Studies in the Theory of Economic Expansion* (King, 1937), Chapter IX.

Metzler (L. A.) (1941) : " The Nature and Stability of Inventory Cycles ", *Review of Economic Statistics*, **23**, 113–29.

Samuelson (P. A.) (1939) : " Interactions between the Multiplier Analysis and the Principle of Acceleration ", *Review of Economic Statistics*, **21**, 75–8.

Samuelson (P. A.) (1947) : *Foundations of Economic Analysis* (Harvard, 1947), Chapter XI.

CHAPTER 8

TRADE CYCLE THEORY : GOODWIN, KALECKI AND PHILLIPS

8.1 Introduction

THE Samuelson-Hicks theory of Chapter 7 is an example of the treatment of oscillations in macro-economic quantities in period terms. The period analysis is particularly well developed in this model and full advantage is taken—or can be taken—of the many kinds of distributed lags which can arise in the operation of the multiplier and accelerator. There are, however, certain disadvantages in this approach. Consumption and investment outlays are related to levels and changes in income over past periods —distributed according to the kind of lag assumed. The two outlays, together with any autonomous expenditures, are then added to give total output and income as the condition of the model. There is one (distributed) lag on the consumption side and one on the investment side. But things are not quite as simple as this. On the investment side, for example, there is a lag between a change in income and the decision to invest (or the demand for investment goods) and a further lag between the decision to invest and the disbursements made on equipment produced (or the supply of investment goods). There may also be additional lags or leads between the investment outlays and the physical delivery or installation of equipment ; but, as long as outlays are considered as in national income accounting, differences in timing between disbursements and deliveries are either ignored or treated as an additional or subsidiary matter. The accelerator of period analysis, however distributed the lag may be, rolls all these up into one relation. It is possible to separate the different lags, but it does not come easily in period terms.

With continuous analysis, though lags may be of more specific (exponential) form, it is quite easy to distinguish lags on the demand side and on the supply side. This is well illustrated by Phillips' theory, 3.4 and 3.5 above. Demand is made up of consumption and investment demand separately (together with autonomous expenditures). Consumption demand can lag behind the income levels which determine it, i.e. the decision to consume may depend on earlier income levels. Similarly, even more important, investment demand or the decision to invest can lag behind the originating output changes. Against this, the supply of consumer and investment goods can respond to demand with a quite different and separable lag. Even without consumption lags (as Phillips assumes for convenience), there are still two lags ; investment demand is a lagged response to output changes and supply is a lagged response to demand.

The present chapter develops some models of dynamic processes in which time is taken as varying continuously. Economic quantities such as income and output Y then vary as functions of time. This does not necessarily mean that the functions are continuous. Though Y usually varies continuously with time, it is still possible to have such discontinuities as jumps in the level or direction of change of Y, and to allow for non-linear features such as " ceilings " and " floors " for Y. Lags are introduced, perhaps not with the great range of distributed period lags, but still with a good deal of choice. It is particularly important to distinguish between a *delay* and a *continuously distributed lag*. In a delay of time θ, one variable influences another after the lapse of precisely θ units of time. For example, orders and payments for ships may both vary continuously over time, but the ship ordered today may be paid for on delivery in exactly 15 months' time. However, in most cases of lagged responses, a continuously distributed lag is a more " realistic " assumption ; the response becomes gradually effective over time as with the various disbursements made between the ordering and delivery of a ship. If Y is determined by Z but with a lagged response, then the adjustment of Y works itself out over time even if there is only one shift in Z. If Z is also changing, then Y varies over time for two reasons : to catch up with the response to past changes in Z and to keep up with current changes. Whether the continuously distributed lag is taken of the exponential form —so amenable to analysis—or in some more " realistic " form such as several exponential lags in sequence, is a matter partly of convenience in simplifying the mathematical analysis.

The models treated here are a selection of various types which have appeared in the literature since the 1930's. Three particular models are taken for examination, partly because they illustrate different treatments of the economic problems of the trade cycle.

There is first the model developed by Goodwin (1951), in many ways similar to the theory of Samuelson and Hicks, but developed independently and incorporating some of the features of the Phillips model. A characteristic feature is Goodwin's treatment of the non-linear element in the multiplier-accelerator inter-action. The basic construction of Samuelson-Hicks is an oscillation, generally of mildly explosive form ; a non-linear

element is later introduced. This may be in the form of " floors " and
" ceilings ", or of an assumption of alternative demand relations for investment in the up and down swings. The advantage of Goodwin's model is
that the non-linear element is " built in " at the outset ; the resulting
oscillation maintains itself without any dependence on outside factors or
on particular initial (or historical) conditions. Goodwin's lags are of two
kinds ; there is a fixed-time delay in the operation of the accelerator on
the side of investment demand, and a continuously distributed response
on the side of supply.

Next, there is the model of Kalecki (1935) and its various later developments (1943, 1954). This model was first proposed before the work of
Keynes had its profound effect on the direction in which trade cycle
theory was developed. Consequently, it has a number of distinctive
features, particularly as regards the relation between investment and the
stock of capital assets. As with Goodwin's model, it is of mixed form since
Kalecki has chosen to introduce a fixed-time delay (between decisions to
invest and deliveries of equipment) as well as continuous variation represented by derivatives and integrals. The resulting equation of the model,
though of quite simple form, is of the mixed difference-differential type.
Such an equation is not easy to solve mathematically and, when solved,
it is not easy to interpret. In particular, the possible oscillations are found
to comprise a whole range of cycles of increasing frequency (decreasing
period). The reason for these is to be sought in the assumption of the
fixed delay, difficult enough in the period analysis of Samuelson-Hicks,
but more so when combined with continuous development over time.

These difficulties suggest that the multiplier-accelerator model of
Phillips (1954) may be the more profitable one to pursue. The basic
construction of the model is already described in 3.4 and 3.5 above. The
lags are all of the continuously distributed kind leading to low-order differential equations ; there is an inherent element of explosive nature
which needs to be kept in check through the operation of other factors ;
the accelerator alone sees to that. Whereas the Samuelson-Hicks and
Goodwin models introduce non-linear elements for the purpose, while
Kalecki has a " damping " factor in the form of the growth of capital
equipment, Phillips is led to consider economic regulation and stabilisation
in a wider context.

8.2 Goodwin Model : Simple Version

The non-linear form of Goodwin's accelerator is most easily interpreted
in his simplest model with " crude allowance for technological progress ",

see Goodwin (1951), pp. 4–8. All variables are functions of continuously varying time and the condition of the model is the familiar relation for income and output Y:

$$Y = C + I + A$$

where $C = cY$ is the consumption function without lags, where I is all net investment (however determined) and where A is autonomous consumption expenditure. This relation corresponds to the multiplier without lags:

$$Y = \frac{I + A}{1 - c} \quad \dots\dots\dots\dots\dots\dots\dots\dots\dots(1)$$

on substituting for C. A is taken as constant over time.

The accelerator is introduced, in non-linear form, in explaining net investment I. At any time, let K be the actual and $\bar{K}$ the desired stock of capital assets. Then, by definition, $I = \dfrac{dK}{dt}$. Assume:

$$\left.\begin{aligned} \bar{K} &= vY + at \\ \frac{d\bar{K}}{dt} &= v\frac{dY}{dt} + a \end{aligned}\right\} \quad \dots\dots\dots\dots\dots\dots(2)$$

i.e.

Here a is a positive constant representing technological progress over time; the positive value v is to be interpreted as the marginal desired capital-income ratio, assumed to be constant.

It remains to link up desired and actual capital stock. There are two limits for actual investment, one set by the (constant) replacement or scrapping rate M of existing capital equipment and the other by the (constant) capacity $L + M$ of the capital goods industries. The gross output of capital goods must be between 0 and $(L + M)$ and net output $\left(I = \dfrac{dK}{dt}\right)$ between $-M$ and L. The non-linear relation assumed is that investment is at its upper limit as long as $K < \bar{K}$, that it equals the trend value (a) when $K = \bar{K}$ and that it is at its lower limit if $K > \bar{K}$:

$$I = \frac{dK}{dt} = L,\ a \text{ or } -M \quad \text{according as } K <, = \text{ or } > \bar{K} \dots\dots\dots(3)$$

The non-linear accelerator assumed in (2) and (3) gives an indirect dependence of I on changes in output $\left(\dfrac{dY}{dt}\right)$. A change in output alters the desired capital stock $\bar{K}$ by (2) and this in turn determines the rate of actual investment by (3).

The equations (1), (2) and (3) describe the system. With $I=\dfrac{dK}{dt}$, the first two become

$$Y=\frac{1}{1-c}\left(\frac{dK}{dt}+A\right) \quad \text{and} \quad \bar{K}=\frac{v}{1-c}\left(\frac{dK}{dt}+A\right)+at \dots\dots\dots(4)$$

In *any one phase* of (3), $I=\dfrac{dK}{dt}$ remains constant (i.e. L, a or $-M$) and consequently, from (4), the different phases can be specified:

Phase	$\dfrac{dK}{dt}$	Y	$\bar{K}$	$\dfrac{d\bar{K}}{dt}$	$\dfrac{d(K-\bar{K})}{dt}$
$K-\bar{K}<0$	L	$\dfrac{A+L}{1-c}$	$\dfrac{v}{1-c}(A+L)+at$	a	$L-a$
$K-\bar{K}=0$	a	$\dfrac{A+a}{1-c}$	$\dfrac{v}{1-c}(A+a)+at$	a	0
$K-\bar{K}>0$	$-M$	$\dfrac{A-M}{1-c}$	$\dfrac{v}{1-c}(A-M)+at$	a	$-(M+a)$

$$\dots\dots\dots\dots(5)$$

Apart from the trend term (a), the only changes occur when the system shifts from one phase to another. The operation of the system is shown most conveniently in the " phase diagram " of Fig. 27, in which $\dfrac{d(K-\bar{K})}{dt}$ is plotted against $(K-\bar{K})$.

There is a position of (moving) equilibrium, represented by the point O of Fig. 27, when $\dfrac{dK}{dt}=\dfrac{d\bar{K}}{dt}=a$ and $Y=\dfrac{A+a}{1-c}$ as given by the multiplier.

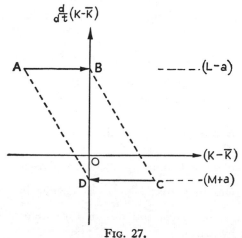

Fig. 27.

Investment proceeds at the desired trend rate and, once achieved, the equilibrium is maintained. It is, however, unstable. Given any initial disturbances, the system does not tend towards equilibrium; instead it describes a regular oscillation defined by the cycle $ABCDA$ of Fig. 27. The following argument makes use of the features of the different phases set out in (5).

Suppose initially $K > \bar{K}$ so that $\dfrac{d(K - \bar{K})}{dt} = -(M + a) < 0$. Hence $(K - \bar{K})$ is positive but decreases to zero over time; this is a movement from C to D in Fig. 27. When D is reached, $K = \bar{K} = \dfrac{v}{1-c}(A - M) + at$; but then $\dfrac{d(K - \bar{K})}{dt}$ becomes zero and $\bar{K}$ rises to $\dfrac{v}{1-c}(A + a) + at$. At once $K < \bar{K}$, so that $\dfrac{d(K - \bar{K})}{dt}$ becomes $(L - a) > 0$ and $\bar{K}$ rises to $\dfrac{v}{1-c}(A + L) + at$. Hence, once D is reached, there is no stopping at O and a jump to A is made immediately. The phase $(K - \bar{K})$ negative but increasing to zero over time is then in operation, a movement from A to B. When B is reached, an immediate return to D follows by the reverse process, and the cycle begins over again.

The regular oscillation is a cycle of alternative boom (AB) and depression (CD). It is important to notice that boom and depression are not of equal time duration. During boom:

$$\frac{dK}{dt} = L, \quad \frac{d\bar{K}}{dt} = a \quad \text{and} \quad \bar{K} = \frac{v}{1-c}(L + A) + at$$

i.e. $\bar{K}$ is increasing so that the increase in K (at rate L) must go on until K catches up with a rising $\bar{K}$. During depression:

$$\frac{dK}{dt} = -M, \quad \frac{d\bar{K}}{dt} = a \quad \text{and} \quad \bar{K} = \frac{v}{1-c}(-M + A) + at$$

i.e. $\bar{K}$ is at a lower level but increasing as before; the decrease in K (at rate M) goes on until falling K and rising $\bar{K}$ come together. Booms tend to be longer than depressions, as shown by the course of K and $\bar{K}$ over time (Fig. 28), and by the corresponding course of Y (Fig. 30a below). From (5), Y is seen to alternate in value between $\dfrac{A+L}{1-c}$ and $\dfrac{A-M}{1-c}$, while $I = \dfrac{dK}{dt}$ alternates between L and $-M$. Such alternations are discontinuous variations in Y and I, and quite unrealistic. They are the result of taking a very special form for the accelerator, with no lags ; a more general and " realistic " version of the model is given in 8.3 below.

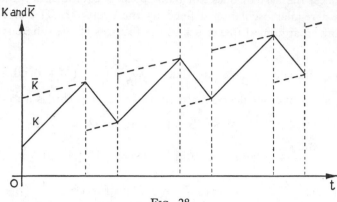

FIG. 28.

The model, crude though it is, has three desirable features. *First*, there is an inherent and self-sustained oscillation in the system. The explosive nature of the accelerator is kept in check by the indirect (or non-linear) dependence of investment $\left(\dfrac{dK}{dt}\right)$ on change in output $\left(\dfrac{dY}{dt}\right)$. There is need neither for the " ceiling " of the Samuelson-Hicks model nor for a series of " erratic shocks " to keep a damped oscillation going. The oscillation, moreover, is in no way dependent on initial conditions (see Ex. 2 below). *Second*, the lengths of the boom and of the depression are not equal, except by accident. In Fig. 28 the desired capital stock $\bar{K}$ (though subject to jumps) increases at the fixed rate a ; the actual capital stock K increases at the rate L during boom and decreases at the rate M during depression. The boom is longer relative to depression for high rates of technological progress (a) and for a high capital scrapping rate relative to the capacity of the capital goods trades. *Third*, a distinction is made between induced and autonomous changes in the desired level of the stock of capital. The change in the desired stock of capital is the sum of the induced change (vY) and the cumulative change resulting from the technological, or autonomous, progress. In this way, much of the objection to the distinction is avoided and, at the same time, the model is easily adapted to a Schumpeterian theory of innovations. Technological improvements may occur fairly regularly over time, as reflected in the steady increase in desired capital stock ; the actual stock, however, rises in a lagged and irregular way.

EXERCISES 8.2

1. Show that the fall in $\bar{K}$ at point B of Fig. 27 is the same, $\dfrac{v}{1-c}(L+M)$, as the rise in $\bar{K}$ at point D. Deduce that the excess of capital equipment to be "worked off" during depression is the same as the deficit to be made good during boom. Interpret in terms of Fig. 28 and of the length of boom and depression.

2. Use Fig. 27 to show that the same cycle is obtained if initially $K < \bar{K}$ (instead of $K > \bar{K}$) and that it is not dependent on the amount of the initial difference between K and $\bar{K}$.

3. Show that autonomous consumption expenditure can be permitted to increase steadily over time without changing the nature of the model.

8.3 Extensions of the Goodwin Model

The simple version of Goodwin's model, analysed in 8.2 above, represents the inter-action between the multiplier and a non-linear accelerator, but without lags. The model can be extended in two ways. A more general form of the non-linear accelerator is introduced, and it is assumed to operate with a lag, taken as a fixed-time delay by Goodwin. The multiplier is put into dynamic form by adding a lag on the supply side, i.e. a delayed response to demand very much on the lines of Phillips' multiplier (3.4 above).

The demand side is represented by :

$$Z = C + I + A \quad \dotfill (1)$$

where Z is total demand, made up of consumption demand (C), investment demand (I) and autonomous expenditure, all in terms of outlays. The consumption function is taken in the simple (unlagged) form $C = cY$ as before. Investment outlays are assumed to follow decisions to invest (B) after a delay of a fixed interval, θ units of time : $I(t) = B(t - \theta)$. The accelerator appears as a relation between decisions to invest $B(t)$ and the current rate of change of output $\dfrac{d}{dt}Y(t)$. In general, it can be written :

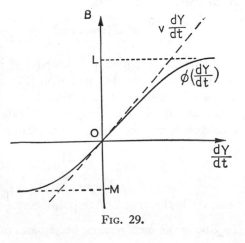

Fig. 29.

$$B(t) = \phi\left\{\frac{d}{dt}Y(t)\right\}$$

where ϕ is some function of non-linear form. A suitable form for the function ϕ is shown in Fig. 29. For small changes in output, either increases or decreases, the ordinary accelerator relation $B = v \dfrac{dY}{dt}$ is taken as operative. For large increases in output, B levels off to a limit (L) set by the capacity of the capital goods industries. For large decreases in output, B again levels off to the negative limit $(-M)$ set by the scrapping rate.

As compared with the " crude " accelerator represented by relations (2) and (3) of 8.2 above, there is now a lag between investment $\left(I = \dfrac{dK}{dt}\right)$ and decisions to invest and the investment decisions vary smoothly according to output changes $\left(\dfrac{dY}{dt}\right)$ but with the same two limits as before (L and $-M$). In (2) and (3) of 8.2, $I = \dfrac{dK}{dt} = B$ was allowed to take only the values L and $-M$ (apart from an unstable intermediate position) and hence to jump between them.

The position on the demand side is that $C = cY$ and :

$$I(t) = B(t - \theta) = \phi \left\{ \frac{d}{dt} Y(t - \theta) \right\}$$

are to be substituted in (1), together with given autonomous expenditure A, to give :

$$Z(t) = cY(t) + \phi \left\{ \frac{d}{dt} Y(t - \theta) \right\} + A \quad \dots\dots\dots\dots\dots\dots(2)$$

Technological progress is allowed for, with any autonomous consumption expenditure, in the term A in (2) ; A can be given in any form, e.g. a steady increase $A = at$ over time.

On the supply side, output Y is taken as lagging behind demand Z according to the continuously distributed (exponential) lag :

$$\frac{dY}{dt} = -\lambda(Y - Z) \quad \dots\dots\dots\dots\dots\dots\dots\dots(3)$$

where λ is the speed of response and $\dfrac{1}{\lambda}$ is the time-constant of the lag. In Goodwin's own version, he equates output Y to the expression (2) for consumption and investment with the addition of a term $\left(-\epsilon \dfrac{dY}{dt}\right)$ which he notes is " analogous to the lag in the usual time period analysis ", Goodwin (1951), p. 9. Hence, he takes in effect :

$$Y = Z - \epsilon \frac{dY}{dt}$$

or

$$\frac{dY}{dt} = -\frac{1}{\epsilon}(Y - Z)$$

and ϵ is the time-constant of the ordinary exponential lag (3).

A combination of the demand and supply sides, equations (2) and (3), gives :

$$\frac{1}{\lambda} \frac{d}{dt} Y(t) = -Y(t) + cY(t) + \phi \left\{ \frac{d}{dt} Y(t - \theta) \right\} + A$$

i.e.

$$Y(t) = \frac{1}{1 - c} \left[\phi \left\{ \frac{d}{dt} Y(t - \theta) \right\} - \frac{1}{\lambda} \frac{d}{dt} Y(t) \right] + \frac{A}{1 - c} \quad \ldots\ldots\ldots(4)$$

This is the equation of Goodwin's general model and it is of mixed difference-differential form. If autonomous expenditure A is constant over time, then $Y(t) = \bar{Y}$ (constant) is consistent with (4) provided that $\bar{Y} = \frac{A}{1 - c}$. The model represented by (4) has an equilibrium level, that given by the static multiplier. It remains to determine the path of $Y(t)$ given any initial disturbance and this is obtained as a solution of (4).

A comparison of this model with that arising from the " crude " accelerator of 8.2 above can be made in the special case where $\theta = 0$ and there is no lag in the operation of the accelerator. Equation (4) then becomes a differential equation :

$$Y = \frac{1}{1 - c} \left\{ \phi \left(\frac{dY}{dt} \right) - \frac{1}{\lambda} \frac{dY}{dt} \right\} + \frac{A}{1 - c} \quad \ldots\ldots\ldots\ldots\ldots(5)$$

which can be solved, by analytical or graphical methods, once a definite form is taken for the function ϕ, i.e. either an analytical expression or an empirical (graphical) form. The corresponding equation of the model of 8.2, from table (5) of that section, is

$$Y = \frac{1}{1 - c} \frac{dK}{dt} + \frac{A}{1 - c} \quad \ldots\ldots\ldots\ldots\ldots\ldots(6)$$

where $\frac{dK}{dt} = L$ during boom and $\frac{dK}{dt} = -M$ during depression. A comparison of (6) with (5) shows up clearly the special form of the non-linear accelerator of 8.2 above. The variation of Y given by (6) (for A constant) is the step function of Fig. 30a. The path of Y specified by (5) is shown by Goodwin to be of the form of Fig. 30b, with A constant and the function ϕ as in Fig. 29. Income Y no longer proceeds by jumps; it has a

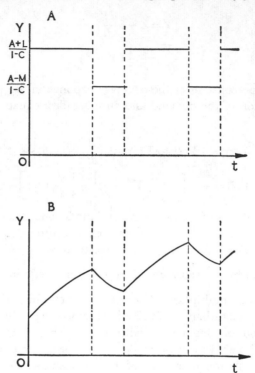

Fig. 30.

continuous path, though with discontinuous changes in direction at the crises. The time duration of the boom is lengthened relative to that of depression ; the increase in income Y is most rapid at the beginning of the boom, tailing off later, and similarly for the decrease during depression.

The mixed difference-differential form (4) arises because of the assumption of a fixed-time delay in the function of the accelerator. Goodwin introduces this as a simplification, not as an expression of economic " reality ". In fact, θ is an *average* lag between decisions to invest and investment outlays, equal to " approximately one half the length of time required for fabrication ", Goodwin (1951), p. 12. The delay would be better replaced by a continuous (exponential) lag—probably preferable from the economic point of view and certainly for ease of mathematical analysis (see 3.5 above).

Goodwin gives a graphical integration (or solution) of (4), based on methods which have been developed by electrical engineers in similar problems in their own field and described in Le Corbeiller (1936). This will be taken up in Chapter 9 below, from a rather different angle and making use of the approach of Tustin (1953). Goodwin's graphical representation can be compared with analogue and analytical solutions, worked out by Strotz, McAnulty and Naines (1953), and quoted in Tustin (1953). The main result is that, apart from a range of high frequency (short period) oscillations which arise within the fixed-time delay (see 8.5 below), the oscillation in $Y(t)$ given by (4) settles down to a definite type of cycle. This " limit cycle " depends on the limits L and M imposed on the accelerator (Fig. 29) but it is not of sinusoidal form. Consequently, the upswing and the downswing are not of the same form or duration ; in particular high levels of income are maintained longer (in boom), and low levels of income are more sustained (in depression), than is given in the simple sinusoidal form.

8.4 Kalecki Model : Early Version

The dynamic model of Kalecki (1935, 1943 and 1954) was first proposed in the pre-Keynesian period and it has since been considerably elaborated. The equation to which the model leads is of mixed difference-differential type, little changed between successive versions of the model in general form but varying in interpretation. The analysis of the present section is basically that of Kalecki (1935) with only minor variations.

The variables are again functions of continuously varying time. No lags are taken for the multiplier, i.e. for the consumption function or on the supply side. Attention is concentrated on the determinants of investment decisions and outlays.

The condition of the model is the familiar split of income and output Y into consumption (C), investment (I) and autonomous expenditure (A) :

$$Y = C + I + A$$

where $C = cY$ and A is given. Consequently income is determined from investment according to the unlagged multiplier :

$$Y = \frac{I + A}{1 - c} \quad \dots\dots\dots\dots\dots\dots\dots\dots\dots\dots(1)$$

On the investment side, the decision to invest $B(t)$ at time t is the central variable. It is assumed that, following the decision to invest (i.e. to order capital equipment), deliveries are made after a fixed interval of time θ, and disbursements are spread throughout the period of production and installation of the equipment. $I(t)$ represents investment outlays or disbursements, defined net of replacement. To distinguish deliveries, again net of replacement, write $K(t)$ for stock of capital assets at time t so that $\dfrac{dK}{dt}$ is the rate of deliveries of new equipment. The assumption on lags on the investment side gives:

$$I(t) = \frac{1}{\theta} \int_{t-\theta}^{t} B(t)\, dt \quad \dots\dots\dots\dots\dots\dots\dots(2)$$

and

$$\frac{d}{dt} K(t) = B(t - \theta) \quad \dots\dots\dots\dots\dots\dots\dots(3)$$

The determination of $B(t)$ is a relation, similar to the accelerator in other models, but here taken in different form. The assumption is that $B(t)$ is influenced directly by the *rate* of saving $S(t) = (1-c)Y(t)$ and inversely by the existing *stock* of capital assets $K(t)$. If the relations are taken as proportional and without lags, then:

$$B = aS - kK + \epsilon$$

where a and k are positive constants and ϵ is a trend term taken as constant here, but capable of variation over time in the long-run. Hence:

$$B = a(1-c)Y - kK + \epsilon \quad \dots\dots\dots\dots\dots\dots(4)$$

It would appear that investment decisions depend, not on the change in income $\dfrac{dY}{dt}$ as in the accelerator, but on the level of income Y. If the coefficient a is at all large, this dependence can be an unstable influence. But the decision to invest also depends (inversely) on the stock of capital and, with a large coefficient k, there is a moderating influence of considerable importance in the system. In fact, the joint effect of Y and K on investment decisions B is to be expected to be similar to an accelerator, and a rather weak one.

It is important to see that, if there is no delay θ in the system, equations (2), (3) and (4) above, then the relation between investment and income is precisely that of a lagged accelerator. The equations are ($\theta = 0$):

$$I = B, \quad \frac{dK}{dt} = B \quad \text{and} \quad B = a(1-c)Y - kK + \epsilon$$

Differentiate the last of these, and substitute the others:

$$\frac{dB}{dt} = a(1-c)\frac{dY}{dt} - k\frac{dK}{dt}$$

i.e.

$$\frac{dI}{dt} + kI = kv\frac{dY}{dt} \qquad \text{where } v = \frac{a(1-c)}{k}$$

In terms of the operator $D = \dfrac{d}{dt}$:

$$I = \frac{k}{D+k}\, vDY$$

which is an accelerator with continuous exponential lag. The power of the accelerator is $v = \dfrac{a(1-c)}{k}$ and its time-constant of lag is $T = \dfrac{1}{k}$.

The constant k depends on the unit taken for time; it arises in the relation of the *rate* of investment decisions to the *stock* of capital. It fixes the time-constant of the lag in the accelerator. The constant a is independent of the time unit. It is usually a fraction and, if small, the accelerator relation implied in the Kalecki model is a weak one. In support of a small value of a, notice that the investment of the model is made mainly out of the internal savings of business, which are considerably less than the total savings in the economy.

The system is completely described by the relations (1), (2), (3) and (4). There are four variable quantities: $Y(t)$, $I(t)$, $K(t)$ and $B(t)$. The relations suffice for the elimination of three of them and for the derivation of a single equation in the fourth. The variable $K(t)$, representing the capital stock at time t, is selected for the purpose here; a similar equation can be derived for one of the other variables, e.g. $Y(t)$ or $I(t)$. From (2) and (3):

$$I(t) = \frac{1}{\theta} \int_{t-\theta}^{t} \frac{d}{dt} K(t+\theta)\, dt = \frac{1}{\theta} \int_{t}^{t+\theta} \frac{d}{d\tau} K(\tau)\, d\tau \quad (\tau = t + \theta)$$

$$= \frac{1}{\theta} \Big[K(\tau) \Big]_{t}^{t+\theta}$$

i.e.
$$I(t) = \frac{1}{\theta}\{K(t+\theta) - K(t)\} \quad \dots\dots\dots\dots\dots(5)$$

Then, from (1):

$$Y(t) = \frac{I(t) + A}{1-c} = \frac{1}{\theta(1-c)}\{K(t+\theta) - K(t)\} + \frac{A}{1-c} \quad \dots\dots\dots(6)$$

Substitute this and $B(t) = \dfrac{d}{dt} K(t+\theta)$ in (4):

$$\frac{d}{dt} K(t+\theta) = \frac{a}{\theta}\{K(t+\theta) - K(t)\} - kK(t) + (aA + \epsilon)$$

i.e.
$$\frac{d}{dt} K(t+\theta) = \frac{a}{\theta} K(t+\theta) - \left(k + \frac{a}{\theta}\right) K(t) + (aA + \epsilon)$$

This is the equation in $K(t)$; it is of mixed difference-differential form. There is an equilibrium level $\bar{K} = \dfrac{aA + \epsilon}{k}$, on the assumption that A and ϵ are both constant over time. If K is measured as a deviation from K, and if t is switched to $(t - \theta)$, the equation becomes:

$$\frac{dK(t)}{dt} = \frac{a}{\theta} K(t) - \left(k + \frac{a}{\theta} \right) K(t - \theta) \quad \ldots\ldots\ldots\ldots\ldots(7)$$

The path of $K(t)$ over time is to be obtained by solving (7). The other variables follow from (3), (5) and (6); if $Y(t)$ is also measured from its equilibrium level $\bar{Y} = \dfrac{A}{1 - c}$, then:

$$Y(t) = \frac{K(t + \theta) - K(t)}{\theta(1 - c)}$$

EXERCISES 8.4

1. Consider the case where saving and capital stock influence gross (not net) investment so that (4) above gives gross investment decisions. Show that the model is unchanged provided that the replacement rate $R(t)$ can be taken as constant over the cycle. Is this justifiable? If not, what difficulties arise in making $R(t)$ proportional to $K(t)$?

2. Show that $Y(t)$ satisfies exactly the same equation (7) as $K(t)$ and hence that the path of $Y(t)$ only differs for that of $K(t)$ in initial conditions.

3. Examine the effect on the equation (7) of introducing a term $\left(+ v \dfrac{dY}{dt} \right)$ in the determinants of investment decisions as set out in (4). Interpret in terms of the accelerator and its explosive character.

8.5 Solution of the Difference-Differential Equation

Without loss of generality, the unit of time can be chosen so that $\theta = 1$, i.e. to equal the fixed time interval between orders and deliveries of capital equipment. The equation to be solved for variation in capital stock in the Kalecki model is then:

$$\frac{dK(t)}{dt} = aK(t) - bK(t - 1)\ldots\ldots\ldots\ldots\ldots\ldots(1)$$

where $0 < a < 1$ and $b = a + k > 0$. The solution for $Y(t)$ follows at once from:

$$Y(t) = \frac{K(t + 1) - K(t)}{1 - c}$$

A complete solution of a mixed difference-differential equation of type (1) is given by Frisch and Holme (1935) on the lines indicated below.

As a solution, try $K = K_0 e^{\rho t}$, $\dfrac{dK}{dt} = \rho K_0 e^{\rho t}$ for some values of ρ to be found.   Substitute in (1):

$$\rho = a - b e^{-\rho} \dots\dots\dots\dots\dots\dots\dots(2)$$

Any value of ρ satisfying (2) provides a solution $K = K_0 e^{\rho t}$ of (1). If ρ is real, then there is a steady (exponential) variation in K which could be explosive ($\rho > 0$) or damped to zero ($\rho < 0$). If ρ is complex, then it is easily checked that the conjugate value also satisfies (2). The two solutions of form $K = K_0 e^{\rho t}$ then add to a single solution :

$$K = K_0 e^{\alpha t} \cos (\omega t + \epsilon) \dots\dots\dots\dots\dots\dots(3)$$

where $\rho = \alpha \pm i\omega$ is a solution of (2) and where K_0 and ϵ are arbitrary constants given by initial values. There is then an oscillation of frequency ω in K which may be explosive ($\alpha > 0$) or damped ($\alpha < 0$).

Possible real roots of (2) need to be checked first.   A graphical method (Fig. 31) is appropriate, plotting the two functions :

$$z_1 = e^{-\rho} \quad \text{and} \quad z_2 = \frac{a - \rho}{b}$$

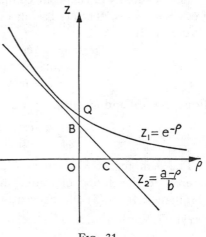

as an exponential curve and straight line in the plane $O\rho z$. Real roots of (2) correspond to intersections of the line and curve. The curve z_1 cuts Oz at Q where $OQ = 1$. The line is BC, where the intercepts $OB = \dfrac{a}{b}$ and $OC = a$ are both positive and less than unity. Hence there

Fig. 31.

is certainly no intersection for positive ρ, and probably not for negative ρ. The latter point needs to be made quite definite.

Consider the condition needed for the line BC to *touch* the exponential curve at some point P where $\rho < 0$ (only one such point is possible). At P, the ordinates and slopes are equal, i.e.

$$e^{-\rho} = \frac{a - \rho}{b} \quad \text{and} \quad -e^{-\rho} = -\frac{1}{b}$$

Hence $\rho = \log b$ from the second condition. Substitute in the first and write $A = a - \log b$. Then $A = 1$ is the condition for tangency. Consider a fixed and b decreasing, so that the line BC swings clockwise around C

B rising but remaining short of Q. If the line BC starts as a tangent to the curve ($A = a - \log b = 1$), then as it swings round there are two points of intersection. Conversely, if the line BC swings the other way, a fixed and b increasing, then there are no points of intersection. Further, $A = a - \log b$ increases as b decreases (and so $A > 1$) and decreases as b increases ($A < 1$). It follows that (2) has two real and different roots, two real and equal roots or no real roots, according as $A > 1$, $A = 1$ or $A < 1$. The condition for no real roots is :

$$A = a - \log b < 1 \quad\dots\dots\dots\dots\dots\dots\dots\dots(4)$$

This is the usual case ; a is a fraction and k is usually large enough to make $b = a + k > 1$ (or at least near to 1), i.e. to make $\log b$ positive (or at least small and negative). The case (4) is here assumed ; there are then no real roots of (2) and no non-oscillatory solutions of (1).

The possibility of conjugate complex roots of (2) is next to be examined. Let $\rho = \alpha \pm i\omega$ so that (1) has an oscillatory solution of form (3). Substitute in (2) :

$$\alpha \pm i\omega = a - be^{-\alpha}e^{\mp i\omega}$$
$$= a - be^{-\alpha}(\cos \omega \mp i \sin \omega)$$
$$= (a - be^{-\alpha}\cos \omega) \pm ibe^{-\alpha}\sin \omega$$

Equating real and imaginary parts

$$\left.\begin{array}{l} \alpha = a - be^{-\alpha}\cos \omega \\ \omega = be^{-\alpha}\sin \omega \end{array}\right\} \quad\dots\dots\dots\dots\dots\dots\dots(5)$$

The damping of K given by (3) depends on α ; this is of subsidiary interest to the period of frequency of oscillation given by ω. Hence, eliminate α from (5) and concentrate attention on ω. From the second equation of (5) :

$$e^{\alpha} = b \frac{\sin \omega}{\omega}$$

i.e.
$$\alpha = \log b + \log \frac{\sin \omega}{\omega} \quad\dots\dots\dots\dots\dots(6)$$

Substitute in the first equation of (5) :

$$\log b + \log \frac{\sin \omega}{\omega} = a - \omega \frac{\cos \omega}{\sin \omega}$$

Hence ω is given by :

$$\frac{\omega}{\tan \omega} + \log \frac{\sin \omega}{\omega} = a - \log b = A < 1 \quad \text{by (4)}$$

Write
$$f(\omega) = \frac{\omega}{\tan \omega} + \log \frac{\sin \omega}{\omega}$$

so that ω is to be sought as a solution of:

$$f(\omega) = A < 1$$

The function $f(\omega)$, which does not involve the " structural " constants a and b, can be graphed from the trigonometric functions.   Its form (for $\omega > 0$) is given in Fig. 32, as obtained in Frisch and Holme (1935).   It

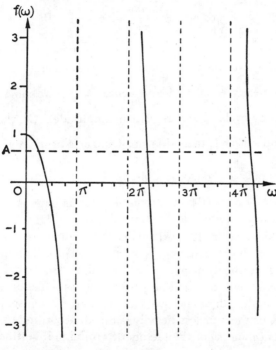

FIG. 32.

appears that there is one small value of ω $(0 < \omega < \pi)$ together with a series of higher values of ω in the ranges $(2\pi, 3\pi)$ $(4\pi, 5\pi)$ ......

The smallest value of ω is of major interest, since it corresponds to an oscillation in K of small frequency and long period.   The period is $\dfrac{2\pi}{\omega} > 2$, i.e. more than twice as long as the delay $(\theta = 1)$ in investment.   The other values of ω are all greater than 2π and correspond to oscillations of increasing frequency, i.e. of diminishing periods (all less than 1).   The high frequency oscillations in K all complete their cycles within the period of the investment delay, and they are of limited interest.

Once the unique long cycle (of period > 2) is determined for $0 < \omega < \pi$, the damping factor (α) of the oscillation is given by (6). It is possible, according to the values assumed by a and $b=a+k$, that $\alpha>0$ and hence that the oscillation is explosive. For quite likely values of a and k, however, it is found that $\alpha<0$ and hence that the oscillation is damped. One typical case occurs when $k=1-a(0<a<1)$ so that $b=\mathbf{1}.$ Then :

$$A=a-\log b=a<1$$

and
$$\alpha=\log b+\log\frac{\sin\omega}{\omega}=\log\frac{\sin\omega}{\omega}<0$$

The oscillation is always (more or less mildly) damped in this case. If a is near 1 and k small, then A is near 1 and ω is small (Fig. 32) ; with ω small, $\dfrac{\sin\omega}{\omega}$ is nearly equal to 1 and hence $\alpha=0$ approximately. This is the case of a long cycle, nearly regular in amplitude. On the other hand, if a is small and k near 1, then A is small and ω is near $\dfrac{\pi}{2}$; for such ω, the value of $\dfrac{\sin\omega}{\omega}$ falls a good deal short of 1, and α is definitely negative. This is the case of a short cycle (about 4 times as long as the investment delay) which can be quite heavily damped.

The conclusion on the Kalecki model of 8.4 above is that, again apart from a range of high frequency (short period) oscillations within the period of the investment delay, there is a unique sinusoidal oscillation in capital stock $K(t)$ over time. The period of the oscillation is likely to be several times the length of the investment delay. The oscillation may be nearly regular, or more or less heavily damped, according to the values of the coefficients (a and k) of the factors determining investment.

EXERCISES 8.5

1. If a and k are both small, show that it is possible to have $A=a-\log b>1$. Deduce that $K(t)$ thus includes a term which is a steady (damped) movement towards zero.

2. In the case of the previous exercise, show that no major oscillation in $K(t)$ is possible, but that there is still a range of high frequency oscillations.

3. Take $a=0.5$, $k=0.6$ and check $A<1$. Show that $\omega=\dfrac{\pi}{3}$ satisfies $f(\omega)=A$ approximately and that the major oscillation in $K(t)$ has a period of about 6 times the investment delay. Show that, for this oscillation, $\alpha=-0.1$, and hence that the oscillation is damped.

4. Compare the result of the previous exercise with that when $a=0.5$, $k=0.2$. Show that the major oscillation is now of longer period and more heavily damped.

8.6 Kalecki Model : Later Version

The model of 8.4 above has been developed in a number of ways by Kalecki (1943, 1954). Apart from refinements, some of which are indicated in Ex. 2 below, the latest version of Kalecki's theory can be expressed as follows.

The simple multiplier relation is taken as before :

$$Y = \frac{I + A}{1 - c} \quad \dots\dots\dots\dots\dots\dots(1)$$

but the factors influencing the decision to invest, and the subsequent investment outlays and deliveries of capital equipment, are elaborated and changed. It is assumed that investment is both in fixed capital assets and in stocks of materials, work in progress and finished products. Let I_k be investment outlays on fixed capital and I_s on stocks, so that $I = I_k + I_s$. The outlays on stocks are taken as dependent on changes in output with a fixed-time delay :

$$I_s(t) = v_1 \frac{d}{dt} Y(t - \tau') \quad \dots\dots\dots\dots\dots(2)$$

where v_1 is an investment coefficient and τ' the delay. The outlays on fixed capital are assumed to be made simultaneously with the installation of the equipment (i.e. payment on delivery) and to lag behind the corresponding investment decisions by a fixed time τ :

$$I_k(t) = \frac{dK(t)}{dt} = B(t - \tau) \quad \dots\dots\dots\dots\dots(3)$$

where $K(t)$ is the stock of capital assets and $B(t)$ the decision to invest in fixed capital at time t.

The factors influencing $B(t)$, taken net of depreciation of the fixed assets, are now assumed to be the rate of saving, *changes* in the rate of output (both affecting B directly), and *changes* in the stock of capital assets (influencing B inversely). Hence, with no time lags and a trend term (taken as constant) :

$$B = aS + v_2 \frac{dY}{dt} - k \frac{dK}{dt} + \epsilon$$

i.e.
$$B = a(1 - c) Y + v_2 \frac{dY}{dt} - k \frac{dK}{dt} + \epsilon \quad \dots\dots\dots\dots(4)$$

The relations (1), (2), (3), (4) together with $I = I_k + I_s$ describe the system.

Kalecki then proposes the following simplification. From (3) and (4):

$$I_k(t + \tau) = a(1 - c) Y(t) + v_2 \frac{d}{dt} Y(t) - k I_k(t) + \epsilon$$

Let θ be some average lag (weighted by k) such that

$$\frac{I_k(t+\tau)+kI_k(t)}{1+k}=I_k(t+\theta) \quad (0<\theta<\tau)$$

and assume θ is fixed. Then

$$I_k(t+\theta)=\frac{1}{1+k}\left\{a(1-c)\,Y(t)+v_2\frac{d}{dt}Y(t)+\epsilon\right\}$$

Next assume that the delay in stock building is equal to the average lag in investment in capital equipment ($\tau'=\theta$). Hence, from (2):

$$I_s(t+\theta)=v_1\frac{d}{dt}\,Y(t)$$

and
$$I(t+\theta)=I_k(t+\theta)+I_s(t+\theta)$$
$$=\frac{a(1-c)}{1+k}Y(t)+\left(v_1+\frac{v_2}{1+k}\right)\frac{d}{dt}Y(t)+\frac{\epsilon}{1+k}$$

Finally, using (1), the equation can be written throughout in terms either of investment $I(t)$ or of income $Y(t)$. Kalecki chooses the former case and gets:

$$I(t+\theta)=\frac{a(1-c)}{1+k}\frac{I(t)+A}{1-c}+\left(v_1+\frac{v_2}{1+k}\right)\frac{1}{1-c}\frac{dI(t)}{dt}+\frac{\epsilon}{1+k}$$
$$=\frac{a}{1+k}I(t)+\frac{1}{1-c}\left(v_1+\frac{v_2}{1+k}\right)\frac{dI(t)}{dt}+\frac{aA+\epsilon}{1+k}$$

There is a constant equilibrium level $I=\dfrac{aA+\epsilon}{1+k}$ consistent with this equation and, if $I(t)$ is now measured from this level, the relation is:

$$I(t+\theta)=\frac{a}{1+k}I(t)+\frac{1}{1-c}\left(v_1+\frac{v_2}{1+k}\right)\frac{dI(t)}{dt}$$

Choose the time unit so that $\theta=1$, i.e. the unit is the average delay in investment in capital equipment. The equation of the system is then the mixed difference-differential form:

$$\frac{dI(t)}{dt}=\alpha I(t+1)-\beta I(t) \quad\ldots\ldots\ldots\ldots\ldots\ldots\ldots\ldots\ldots(5)$$

where
$$\alpha=\frac{1-c}{v_1+\dfrac{v_2}{1+k}} \quad\text{and}\quad \beta=\frac{\dfrac{a(1-c)}{1+k}}{v_1+\dfrac{v_2}{1+k}}$$

Both constants, α and β, are positive. Further, $\dfrac{\beta}{\alpha} = \dfrac{a}{1+k}$ which can be assumed to be a positive fraction, since $\dfrac{a}{1+k} < a < 1$ on the same assumption as in 8.4 above. Hence, take $\alpha > \beta > 0$ in (5).

The equation (5) is of the same type as in 8.4 above, and the solution of 8.5 above applies, except that the lag is in the reverse direction. The right-hand side of (5) involves $(t+1)$ and t, instead of t and $(t-1)$ as in the equation solved in 8.5 above. The solution (see Ex. 1 below) is of the same general nature, i.e. there is one major oscillation in $I(t)$, together with a range of high frequency oscillations which are complete within the average delay in investment.

The later versions of Kalecki's model were designed to generalise the early version in various ways. Kalecki (1954) shows that the early version is a special case of the latest model, which also includes (as other special cases) multiplier-accelerator models of the usual linear types.

However, the early Kalecki model is still of interest, as in Chapter 9 below. It has some very characteristic features and a convenient simplicity ; yet its solution is of the same general nature as those of later versions. One point is to be noticed : the time dimensions of the constants in all Kalecki models are to be specified with care. In the early version, k (but not a) depends on the time unit chosen and its reciprocal is, in effect, the time-constant of the accelerator lag. In the solution of 8.5 above ($\theta = 1$), the reciprocal of k is the length of the accelerator lag relative to the fixed interval between orders and deliveries of equipment. So $k > 1$ implies a short accelerator lag in the sense that the lag is less than this fixed investment interval.

EXERCISES 8.6

1. Try $I = I_0 e^{\rho t}$ in the equation (5) above and show that ρ must be a root of $\rho = \alpha e^{\rho} - \beta$. Show by a diagram similar to Fig. 31 that it can be usually assumed that there is no real value of ρ (given $\alpha > \beta$). Then show that the possibilities of conjugate complex roots are much the same as in 8.5 above.

2. Assume (with Kalecki) that all saving and investment is related only to the income of " capitalists ", i.e. $P =$ profits after tax ; and replace Y in (1) and in the first term of (4) by P. However, keep total income Y (include the income of " workers " which is all spent) in the " accelerator " terms in $\dfrac{dY}{dt}$ in (2) and (4).

   Show that the model is effectively unchanged, provided that profits before tax and wages make up Y in a fixed proportion and provided the tax system is such that P is related linearly to profits before tax.

3. Take a fixed-time delay ψ in the multiplier and show that (1) above is replaced by :
$$Y(t) - cY(t - \psi) = I + A$$

Then take the left-hand side as equal to $(1-c)\,Y(t-\phi)$, interpret the lag ϕ and obtain the corresponding equation of the model in the form of (5) above. What difference does the introduction of the lagged multiplier make?

8.7 Phillips Model : Economic Regulation

The specification of Phillips' model is given in 3.4 and 3.5 above; it is summarised here, with the aid of the operator $D=\dfrac{d}{dt}$, and it is then used to throw light on the problem of economic regulation. The characteristic of the model is that demand Z and output Y are separately treated, one being lagged behind the other. Autonomous expenditure A, on investment and consumption goods together, is taken as given, either as a constant or as varying in a specified way over time.

The *multiplier model* is :

$$\text{Demand} \quad Z=C+A \quad \text{where} \quad C=(1-s)\,Y$$
$$\text{Supply} \quad Y=\frac{\lambda}{D+\lambda}\,Z$$

The lagged response of supply to demand is of the continuous exponential type, with speed of response λ or time constant $T=\dfrac{1}{\lambda}$. On substitution :

$$Y=\frac{\lambda}{D+\lambda}\{(1-s)\,Y+A\}$$

i.e.
$$DY+\lambda sY=\lambda A \quad \dots\dots\dots\dots\dots\dots\dots\dots\dots(1)$$

The solution, given $Y=Y_0$ at $t=0$, and $A=$ constant, is

$$Y=\frac{A}{s}(1-e^{-\lambda st})+Y_0 e^{-\lambda st} \quad \dots\dots\dots\dots\dots\dots(2)$$

which shows the path of Y from the initial value Y_0 towards the static multiplier level $Y=\dfrac{A}{s}$.

Ex. (a). $s=0\cdot25, \lambda=4, Y=0$ at $t=0$, $A=$ constant.
Equation (1) : $DY+Y=4A$ subject to $Y=0$ at $t=0$
Solution (2) : $Y=4A(1-e^{-t})$
which is shown as curve (i) of Fig. 33 (case $A=-1$).

The *multiplier-accelerator model* is :

$$\text{Demand} \quad Z=C+I+A \quad \text{where} \quad C=(1-s)\,Y$$
$$\text{and} \quad I=\frac{\kappa}{D+\kappa}\,vDY$$
$$\text{Supply} \quad Y=\frac{\lambda}{D+\lambda}\,Z$$

The accelerator has power v and a lagged response (speed κ) of the continuous exponential form. On substitution :

$$Y = \frac{\lambda}{(D+\kappa)(D+\lambda)}\{(1-s)(D+\kappa)Y + \kappa v DY + (D+\kappa)A\}$$

i.e. $\quad (D+\kappa)(D+\lambda)Y = \lambda\{(\kappa v + 1 - s)DY + \kappa(1-s)Y + (D+\kappa)A\}$

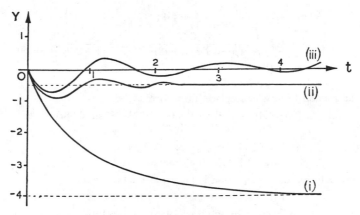

FIG. 33.

Collection of terms gives the differential equation :

$$D^2 Y + aDY + bY = \lambda(D+\kappa)A$$

where $\quad a = \lambda s + \kappa(1-\lambda v), \quad b = \kappa\lambda s \quad\Big\} \quad\text{...................}(3)$

If $A=$ constant, the right-hand side becomes $\kappa\lambda A$ since $DA = 0$. The static multiplier level $Y = \dfrac{A}{s}$ is then consistent with the equation. The solution (5.4 above) is :

$$Y = \frac{A}{s} + B_1 e^{p_1 t} + B_2 e^{p_2 t} \quad\text{...........................}(4)$$

where p_1 and p_2 are the roots of the quadratic $p^2 + ap + b = 0$ and where B_1 and B_2 are arbitrary constants. The constants are to be found from two initial values, e.g. $Y = Y_0$ and $DY = Y_0'$ at $t=0$.

In numerical cases, the solution of (3) in the form (4) can be obtained by this " classical " method. It can also be found by the method of Laplace Transforms (5.7 above), including the particular integral and specified initial values in one process. Since the Laplace Transform method is particularly useful later on, when numerical equations of order higher than the second have to be solved, it is illustrated now in a particular case of (3).

Ex. (*b*) $s = 0.25$, $v = 0.6$, $\kappa = 1$, $\lambda = 4$,
$Y = 0$ and $DY = 4A$ at $t = 0$, $A = $ constant.

Equation (3) : $D^2Y - 0.4DY + Y = 4A$ subject to $Y = 0$ and $DY = 4A$ at $t = 0$.
The subsidiary equation is

$$(p^2 - 0.4p + 1)\,\overline{Y}(p) = \frac{4A}{p} + 4A$$

Hence $$\overline{Y}(p) = 4A\,\frac{p+1}{p(p^2 - 0.4p + 1)} = 4A\left(\frac{1}{p} - \frac{p - 1.4}{p^2 - 0.4p + 1}\right)$$

$$= 4A\left\{\frac{1}{p} - \frac{(p - 0.2)}{(p - 0.2)^2 + (0.98)^2} + 1.225\,\frac{0.98}{(p - 0.2)^2 + (0.98)^2}\right\}$$

since $p^2 - 0.4p + 1 = (p - 0.2)^2 + 0.96 = (p - 0.2)^2 + (0.98)^2$
so that $p^2 - 0.4p + 1 = 0$ has roots $p = 0.2 \pm i\,0.98$.

Using the standard forms of Laplace Transforms :

$$Y(t) = 4A(1 - e^{0.2t}\cos 0.98t + 1.225e^{0.2t}\sin 0.98t)$$
$$= 4A\{1 - re^{0.2t}\cos(0.98t + \epsilon)\}$$

where $r = \sqrt{1 + (1.225)^2} = 1.58$
and $\epsilon = \tan^{-1} 1.225 = 0.89$ radians (51°)

Hence the solution of the equation is an explosive oscillation :

$$Y(t) = 4A\{1 - 1.58e^{0.2t}\cos(0.98t + 0.89)\}$$

This is one of the cases taken by Phillips (1954) ; the solution is shown graphically
as curve (*a*) of his Fig. 9.   It is reproduced as curve (i) of Fig. 34 for $A = -1$.

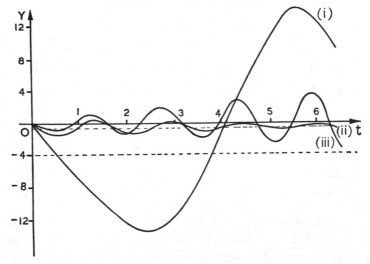

Fig. 34.

To return to the solution (4) of the general multiplier-accelerator model.
The path of $Y(t)$ depends on the nature of the roots (p_1 and p_2) of the
auxiliary equation.   It is steady or oscillating according as p_1 and p_2 are

real or complex; it is explosive or damped according as p_1 and p_2 (or their real part) are positive or negative. All the cases are possible, according to the values assumed by the structural constants s, v, κ and λ. In the following analysis, s and v are taken as given, and κ is put equal to unity. Attention is concentrated on the way in which the path of $Y(t)$ depends on the speed of response λ $\left(\text{or the time-constant } T=\frac{1}{\lambda}\right)$ of the lag on the supply side.

Though s and v may be given any values, subject only to $0<s<1$ and $v>0$, it is convenient to limit discussion to values which are likely to arise in practice, e.g. a small value of s up to about 0.25 and a value of v around unity. The analysis of Chapter 7 suggests that the power of the accelerator (v) can be taken as falling within the range from $(1-\sqrt{s})^2$ to $(1+\sqrt{s})^2$. This will be assumed here:

$$1-\sqrt{s}<\sqrt{v}<1+\sqrt{s} \quad\text{............................}(5)$$

The path of $Y(t)$ given by (4) is oscillatory if the roots (p_1 and p_2) of the auxiliary equation are conjugate complex. The equation is:

$$p^2+\{1-\lambda(v-s)\}p+\lambda s=0$$

i.e. $$p^2+\frac{1}{T}(T-v+s)p+\frac{s}{T}=0 \quad \left(T=\frac{1}{\lambda}\right) \quad\text{...................}(6)$$

For conjugate complex roots:

$$\frac{1}{T^2}(T-v+s)^2-\frac{4s}{T}<0$$

i.e. $$T^2-2(v+s)T+(v-s)^2<0$$

By the method of 4.6 above, this quadratic expression in T takes negative values for all T in the range $T_1<T<T_2$ where:

$$T_1,\ T_2=(v+s)\mp\sqrt{(v+s)^2-(v-s)^2}=(\sqrt{v}\mp\sqrt{s})^2$$

Hence $Y(t)$ is oscillatory for T in the range:

$$(\sqrt{v}-\sqrt{s})^2<T<(\sqrt{v}+\sqrt{s})^2$$

Notice that, by (5), the lower limit is less than 1 and the upper limit greater than 1. The oscillatory term in $Y(t)$, obtained by combining the two exponentials in (4), is of the form $re^{\alpha t}\cos(\omega t+\epsilon)$ where $p=\alpha\pm i\omega$ are the roots of (6). To distinguish an explosive $(\alpha>0)$ from a damped oscillation $(\alpha<0)$:

$$\alpha=-\frac{1}{2T}(T-v+s) \quad\text{from (6)}$$

Hence, the oscillation is explosive if $T < v - s$ and damped if $T > v - s$. The conditions for a steady variation of $Y(t)$, i.e. p_1 and p_2 real roots of (6), are easily added (see Ex. 5 below). The complete analysis of the possibilities is :

Values of T	Roots, p_1 and p_2	Path of $Y(t)$
$T < (\sqrt{v} - \sqrt{s})^2$	Real and positive	Non-oscillatory, explosive
	Complex $(\alpha \pm i\omega)$	
$(\sqrt{v} - \sqrt{s})^2 < T < v - s$	with $\alpha > 0$	Oscillatory, explosive
$v - s < T < (\sqrt{v} + \sqrt{s})^2$	with $\alpha < 0$	Oscillatory, damped
$(\sqrt{v} + \sqrt{s})^2 < T$	Real and negative	Non-oscillatory, damped

This table gives the values of the time-constant $\left(T = \dfrac{1}{\lambda} \right)$ of the supply lag for various paths of $Y(t)$. In its interpretation, it is to be remembered that the unit of time is the time-constant of the lag in the accelerator ($\kappa = 1$). Hence $T < 1$ means that the supply lag is shorter (speedier response) than the accelerator lag, and conversely for $T > 1$. The three critical values of T are :

$$(\sqrt{v} - \sqrt{s})^2 ; \quad v - s ; \quad (\sqrt{v} + \sqrt{s})^2$$

The first and last, by (5), are respectively less than and greater than 1 ; the middle value may well be less than 1. For example, if $s = 0.04$ and $v = 1$, the values of T are :

$$0.64 ; \quad 0.96 ; \quad 1.44$$

If $s = 0.25$ and $v = 0.6$, they are :

$$0.08 ; \quad 0.35 ; \quad 1.62$$

The conclusion is that an oscillatory path of $Y(t)$ is to be expected unless the supply lag is very much shorter (or longer) than the accelerator lag. The path is likely to be explosive if the supply lag is the shorter ; a damped path is only to be expected if the supply lag is at least as long (i.e. response at least as slow) as for the accelerator. An explosive oscillatory path of $Y(t)$ is, on balance, the most likely feature of this multiplier-accelerator model.

One limitation of the Phillips model, as set out here, is that it specifies a *single* exponential lag on the supply side and in the accelerator. In relaxing this condition, it is an easy matter, in the formulation of the model, to insert *multiple* exponential lags of more " realistic " kinds. The equations like (1) and (3) then become of higher order and their solutions more complicated. Certainly, the possibilities of an oscillatory path of $Y(t)$ are greater when the lags are of multiple form.

The multiplier model, equation (1), or the multiplier-accelerator model, equation (3), can be used to show the adjustment in output Y to a sudden shift in demand of amount A, occurring at time $t=0$. Suppose that the system is in equilibrium up to time $t=0$. Take $A=0$ and $Y=0$ as the equilibrium level ($t<0$). At $t=0$, demand shifts suddenly by the constant amount A, i.e. an increase (or decrease) in autonomous expenditure. On the multiplier model, the subsequent ($t>0$) path of Y is given by (1) subject to $Y=0$ at $t=0$. The path by (2) is:

$$Y=\frac{A}{s}(1-e^{-\lambda s t})$$

which represents a steady approach to the new equilibrium level $Y=\dfrac{A}{s}$.

On the multiplier-accelerator model, the path of Y for $t>0$ is given by (3) with $A=$ constant. Two initial values are required in solving (3). One of them is $Y=0$ at $t=0$. The other is derived from the fact that, at $t=0$ when the demand shift occurs, the system is adjusting itself according to the multiplier alone, the accelerator not having come into operation. Hence, as in 3.5 above, $DY=\lambda A$ according to the multiplier. The path of Y from the original equilibrium $Y=0$ is to be found from (3), subject to $Y=0$ and $DY=\lambda A$ at $t=0$. The most likely solution is an explosive oscillation about a value $Y=\dfrac{A}{s}$, representing the static multiplier level after the shift in demand.

Hence, the shift in demand introduces a new equilibrium level $Y=\dfrac{A}{s}$; the actual path of Y is a steady approach to this level if the multiplier alone is considered, but more probably an explosive oscillation about the new level when the accelerator comes into play. This raises two problems of *economic regulation*. First, if the shift in demand is downwards ($A<0$), the path of Y is towards, or oscillatory about, a lower level $\left(Y=\dfrac{A}{s}\right)$ than the original equilibrium ($Y=0$). The previous level may be the desired one and the question is: how to offset the shift in demand and to get back to or near the old level of output? Second, if the path of Y is an oscillation—and particularly if it is an explosive oscillation—the question is: how to counter-balance the unstable influence of the accelerator and to damp down oscillations in output? These are problems investigated, in the present context, by Phillips (1954); they are considered in the following sections.

EXERCISES 8.7

1. Examine the multiplier-accelerator model of (3) above in the case $\lambda \to \infty$ (no lag in supply) and $A =$ constant. Show that $Y = \dfrac{A}{s}(1 - e^{\rho t})$ where $\rho = \dfrac{\kappa s}{\kappa v - s}$ in this case. Compare with the Harrod-Domar theory (3.3 above) when $\kappa \to \infty$ also (no lag in accelerator).

2. Show that the path $Y(t)$ obtained in the particular case of Ex. (b) above is identical with the solution $Y = -4 - 6 \cdot 32 e^{0 \cdot 2t} \sin(56°t - 39°)$ given by Phillips (1954) where $A = -1$.

3. Show the equivalence of the particular path $Y(t)$ of Ex. (b) above with the form (4) obtained by " classical " methods.

4. Apply the method of Laplace Transforms to the differential equation (3) of the general model with $A =$ constant and $Y = 0$, $DY = \lambda A$ at $t = 0$. Show that the Laplace Transform of the solution is

$$\overline{Y}(p) = \lambda A \frac{1+p}{p(p^2 + ap + b)} = \frac{\lambda A}{b}\left(\frac{1}{p} + \frac{b+p_2}{p_1 - p_2}\frac{1}{p - p_1} - \frac{b+p_1}{p_1 - p_2}\frac{1}{p - p_2}\right)$$

where $p^2 + ap + b = (p - p_1)(p - p_2)$.
Hence derive $Y(t)$ by use of the standard forms of Laplace Transforms.

5. Show that the values p_1 and p_2 used in the solution (4) for Y are real if $T = \dfrac{1}{\lambda}$ is either less than $(\sqrt{v} - \sqrt{s})^2$ or greater than $(\sqrt{v} + \sqrt{s})^2$. Use the relations

$$p_1 + p_2 = -a \quad \text{and} \quad p_1 p_2 = b$$

to show that both p_1 and p_2 are positive in the first case, and both negative in the second. Interpret in terms of Y.

6. In the multiplier model, take a double exponential lag $Y = \left(\dfrac{2\lambda}{D + 2\lambda}\right)^2 Z$ on the supply side and show that the equation (1) is replaced by

$$D^2 Y + 4\lambda DY + 4\lambda^2 s Y = 4\lambda^2 A$$

with a steady and damped solution. Show further that the equation (3) of the multiplier-accelerator model becomes of third or fourth order if double exponential lags are introduced either on the supply side, or in the accelerator, or both.

8.8 Stabilisation Policy

There are various types of stabilisation policies which can be operated by the government with the object of offsetting a downward shift in demand and of damping down oscillations in output. The types analysed by Phillips (1954) involve the addition of an official demand for goods and services, created and planned by government, to the normal consumption and investment demands of the economy. Phillips distinguishes the following types :

(i) *Proportional Stabilisation Policy* : official demand $\overline{G} = -f_p Y$, so that, as output Y falls below the desired level ($Y = 0$), the demand created by government is in proportion to the deficit.

(ii) *Integral Stabilisation Policy*: official demand $\bar{G} = -f_i \int_0^t Y \, dt$, so that the demand added by government is proportional to the cumulative deficit in output Y below the desired level.

(iii) *Derivative Stabilisation Policy*: official demand $\bar{G} = -f_d DY$, so that governmental demand is geared, not to the deficit in output Y, but to the rate of decline $(-DY)$.

Here $\bar{G}$ is *planned demand* of government. *Actual demand* effective at any time is denoted by G and assumed to be lagged behind plans, according to a continuous exponential lag with speed of response β. Hence:

$$\bar{G} = -\left(f_p Y + f_i \int_0^t Y \, dt + f_d DY \right)$$

and

$$G = \frac{\beta}{D + \beta} \bar{G}$$

if all three types of stabilisation policy are applied together.

The *multiplier model* with official stabilisation policy incorporated is:

Demand $\qquad Z = (1 - s) Y + G + A$

Supply $\qquad Y = \dfrac{\lambda}{D + \lambda} Z$

which leads to the differential equation:

$$Y = \frac{\lambda}{D + \lambda} \left\{ (1 - s) Y + \frac{\beta}{D + \beta} \bar{G} + A \right\}$$

i.e. $(D + \beta)(D + \lambda) Y$

$$= \lambda \left\{ (1 - s)(D + \beta) Y - \beta \left(f_p Y + f_i \int_0^t Y \, dt + f_d DY \right) + (D + \beta) A \right\}$$

which on collection of terms becomes:

$$\left. \begin{array}{c} D^2 Y + a \, DY + b Y + c \int_0^t Y \, dt = \lambda (D + \beta) A \\[2mm] a = \beta + \lambda s + \beta \lambda f_d \\[1mm] b = \beta \lambda (s + f_p), \quad c = \beta \lambda f_i \end{array} \right\} \quad \dots\dots\dots\dots(1)$$

where

If $f_i = 0$, this is a differential equation of the second order in Y. However, if $f_i \neq 0$, (1) must be differentiated throughout to get rid of the integral. It is then a differential equation of the third order. It takes the place of the first-order differential equation, (1) of 8.7 above, which is found in the multiplier model in the absence of stabilisation policy.

The *multiplier-accelerator model* with official (stabilisation) demand is :

Demand $\qquad Z=(1-s)\,Y+\dfrac{\kappa}{D+\kappa}\,v\,DY+G+A$

Supply $\qquad Y=\dfrac{\lambda}{D+\lambda}\,Z$

giving :

$$Y=\frac{\lambda}{D+\lambda}\left\{(1-s)\,Y+\frac{\kappa}{D+\kappa}\,v\,DY+\frac{\beta}{D+\beta}\,\bar{G}+A\right\}$$

i.e. $\quad (D+\beta)(D+\kappa)(D+\lambda)Y=\lambda\Big\{(1-s)(D+\beta)(D+\kappa)\,Y+\kappa v(D+\beta)DY$

$$-\beta(D+\kappa)\left(f_p Y+f_i\int_0^t Y\,dt+f_d DY\right)+(D+\beta)(D+\kappa)A\Big\}$$

On collection of terms :

$$D^3Y+aD^2Y+bDY+cY+d\int_0^t Y\,dt=\lambda(D+\beta)(D+\kappa)A \left.\vphantom{\begin{array}{c}1\\1\\1\\1\end{array}}\right]$$

where
$$\begin{aligned}
a&=\beta+\lambda s+\kappa(1-\lambda v)+\beta\lambda f_d\\
b&=\kappa(\beta+\lambda s)+\beta\lambda(s+f_p)+\beta\kappa\lambda(f_d-v)\\
c&=\beta\kappa\lambda(s+f_p)+\beta\lambda f_i\\
d&=\beta\kappa\lambda f_i
\end{aligned}\right\}\quad\dots\dots(2)$$

This differential equation is of the third order if $f_i=0$ and, on differentiating through, of the fourth order if $f_i\neq0$. It replaces the second-order differential equation, (3) of 8.7 above, in the absence of stabilisation policy.

Suppose that $Y=0$ is an equilibrium (and desired) level of output ruling up to $t=0$ and that demand then falls suddenly by a given amount. To determine the effect of stabilisation policy, equation (1) or (2) can be solved with A a negative constant (the amount of the fall in demand) and with appropriate initial conditions at $t=0$. There are two practical difficulties in carrying out this process. One is that the equation to be solved is generally of the third or fourth order, involving a considerable number of parameters—the structural constants s and v, the speeds of response β, κ and λ in various lags and the parameters f_p, f_i and f_d of the stabilisation policy adopted. General solutions are, therefore, not to be expected. Rather it is a matter of solving numerical equations in a series of particular cases, and the solution is best done by the method of Laplace Transforms.

The other difficulty arises because autonomous expenditure is taken as constant, following the shift in demand. In fact, at $t=0$, A is subject to a sudden shift in value ; $A=$ constant only for $t>0$. Hence, the initial conditions for $Y, DY, D^2Y, \dots$ appropriate to the problem are values *just after* $t=0$. In 8.7 above, two such initial values are specified, i.e. $Y=0$ and $DY=\lambda A$, as required for a second-order differential equation. In addition, for an equation of the third order, the initial value of $D^2 Y$ is required; an equation of the fourth order needs initial values of $D^2 Y$ and $D^3 Y$. These initial values, just after $t=0$, are difficult to determine since they depend on the nature of the system and its response to the disturbance at $t=0$; see Phillips (1954), p. 319, footnote.

Tizard (1956) has proposed an alternative procedure, i.e. to carry the analysis back to the time *just before* $t=0$. The initial values are then quite simple :

$$Y=DY=D^2Y=\ldots=0$$

since $Y=0$ is a steady equilibrium level up to $t=0$. Against this simplification, there is the complication that autonomous expenditure A is no longer a constant, but rather a step-function $A(t)$ defined :

$$A(t)=0 \quad (t<0); \quad A(t)=\tfrac{1}{2}A \quad (t=0); \quad A(t)=A \quad (t>0) \quad \ldots\ldots(3)$$

The right-hand sides of the equations (1) and (2) to be solved involve derivatives of A which cannot be ignored when A is not constant. Further, to apply derivatives to the step-function (3), the function must first be approximated by a continuous function tending to the step-function in the limit.

To generalise the problem, the differential equation to be solved is :

$$\left.\begin{aligned} f(D)\,Y(t)&=\phi(D)A(t)\\ f(D)&=a_0 D^n + a_1 D^{n-1} + \ldots + a_{n-1}D + a_n\\ \phi(D)&=b_0 D^m + b_1 D^{m-1} + \ldots + b_{m-1}D + b_m \end{aligned}\right\} \ldots\ldots\ldots\ldots\ldots(4)$$

where and

Both (1) and (2) above are of this form, once the integral is eliminated by differentiating the equations as they stand. Appropriate initial conditions, i.e. the initial values Y_0, Y_0', Y_0'', ... of Y and its successive derivatives, are to be added to (4) and the solution obtained by Laplace Transforms. The alternatives are as follows.

First, take $A(t)=A=$ constant for $t>0$, so that the right-hand side of the equation (4) becomes $b_m A=$ constant. The required initial values are those just after $t=0$:

$$Y_0=Y(0+)=\operatorname*{Lim}_{\epsilon\to0} Y(\epsilon); \quad Y_0'=Y'(0+)=\operatorname*{Lim}_{\epsilon\to0} Y'(\epsilon); \ldots$$

The subsidiary equation (5.6 above) is :

$$f(p)\,\overline{Y}(p)=\frac{b_m A}{p}+(\text{expression in } Y_0,\ Y_0',\ Y_0'', \ldots) \quad \ldots\ldots\ldots(5)$$

which gives $\overline{Y}(p)$, the Laplace Transform of the solution $Y(t)$ of (4).

The exclusion of $t=0$ in (5) requires that the Laplace Transform should be interpreted:

$$\overline{Y}(p)=\underset{\epsilon\to0}{\mathrm{Lim}}\int_{\epsilon}^{\infty}e^{-pt}Y(t)\,dt$$

There is no difficulty with $\overline{Y}(p)$, as long as $Y(t)$ is continuous. The trouble with this solution is to find appropriate values of Y_0, $Y_0{}'$, $Y_0{}''$, ...

Second, take $A(t)$ as the step-function (3) and initial values just before $t=0$:

$$Y_0=Y(0-)=\underset{\epsilon\to0}{\mathrm{Lim}}\;Y(-\epsilon);\quad Y_0{}'=Y'(0-)=\underset{\epsilon\to0}{\mathrm{Lim}}\;Y'(-\epsilon);\;...$$

so that $Y_0=Y_0{}'=...=0$ since $Y=0$ is the steady position up to $t=0$. Then Tizard (1956) shows that the subsidiary equation for (4) is:

$$f(p)\,\overline{Y}(p)=\frac{\phi(p)}{p}\,A \quad\dots\dots\dots\dots\dots\dots\dots\dots(6)$$

which again gives $\overline{Y}(p)$, the Laplace Transform of the solution $Y(t)$ The Laplace Transform is here to be re-interpreted:

$$\overline{Y}(p)=\underset{\epsilon\to0}{\mathrm{Lim}}\int_{-\epsilon}^{\infty}e^{-pt}Y(t)\,dt$$

so that $t=0$ is included and not excluded. As long as $Y(t)$ is continuous, no difficulty arises.

The alternative applications of the method of Laplace Transforms can be compared and checked in a very simple case. Take the multiplier-accelerator model, with no stabilisation policy, and with the following parameters: $s=0.25$, $v=0.6$, $\kappa=1$, $\lambda=4$. Then, by (3) of 8.7 above, the equation to be solved for Y is:

$$D^2Y-0.4DY+Y=4(D+1)A$$

First, write $A=$ constant $(t>0)$ and take initial values:

$$Y=0 \quad\text{and}\quad DY=4A \quad\text{at }t=0+$$

so that the subsidiary equation (5) above gives:

$$(p^2-0.4p+1)\,\overline{Y}(p)=\frac{4A}{p}+4A$$

Second, take A as a step-function at $t=0$ and initial values:

$$Y=DY=0 \qquad\text{at }t=0-$$

so that the subsidiary equation (6) above gives:

$$(p^2-0.4p+1)\,\overline{Y}(p)=\frac{4(p+1)A}{p}=\frac{4A}{p}+4A$$

which is the same as before. Either method gives the solution, as in Ex. (*b*) of 8.7 above:

$$Y(t) = 4A\{1 - 1 \cdot 58e^{0 \cdot 2t} \cos (0 \cdot 98t + 0 \cdot 89)\}$$

In the following illustrations of the effects of stabilisation policies, various numerical equations are put up for solution. Either application of the Laplace Transform method can be used, but the second is generally to be preferred.

8.9 Some Illustrations of Stabilisation Policies

The simplest case arises in the *multiplier model* when only the *proportional stabilisation policy* is followed. Write $f_i = f_d = 0$ in (1) of 8.8. above :

$$D^2 Y + (\beta + \lambda s)DY + \beta\lambda(s + f_v) Y = \lambda(D + \beta)A$$

is the differential equation to be solved for the path of $Y(t)$ from $Y = 0$ at $t = 0$. This can be done, by the first alternative method of 8.8, writing $A = $ constant $(t > 0)$ and taking initial values $Y = 0$ and $DY = \lambda A$ at $t = 0 +$. The solution is :

$$Y = \frac{A}{s + f_v} + B_1 e^{p_1 t} + B_2 e^{p_2 t}$$

where p_1 and p_2 are the roots of the quadratic :

$$p^2 + (\beta + \lambda s)p + \beta\lambda(s + f_v) = 0$$

and where B_1 and B_2 are to be found from initial conditions. The equation and solution are similar to the case examined in 8.7 above. The values of the parameters which are likely to arise suggest that Y oscillates about the level $Y = \frac{A}{s + f_v}$. Further, if p_1 and p_2 are conjugate complex $(\alpha \pm i\omega)$ for the oscillatory case, then :

$$\alpha = \tfrac{1}{2}(p_1 + p_2) = -\tfrac{1}{2}(\beta + \lambda s) < 0$$

from the quadratic. The oscillation must be damped ($\alpha < 0$) ; it cannot be explosive.

In the multiplier model, without regulation, Y moves steadily towards the level $Y = \frac{A}{s}$. With proportional stabilisation, Y is likely to oscillate about the level $Y = \frac{A}{s + f_v}$. The object of stabilisation policy is to get Y back to its previous level ($Y = 0$) and without oscillations. The policy now considered is only partially successful. In the first place, since

$0 < \dfrac{A}{s+f_p} < \dfrac{A}{s}$, the new level of Y is intermediate between what is desired

$(Y=0)$ and the level before correction $\left(Y=\dfrac{A}{s}\right)$. Secondly, the correction achieved is at the expense (usually) of the introduction of a (damped) oscillatory path for Y. The coefficient f_p, the strength of the stabilisation policy, appears as an addition to the marginal propensity to save, s; it supplements s and serves to " pull back " the equilibrium level of output towards the desired level. But it also introduces an element of instability, i.e. an oscillation in output Y which was not there before.

Ex. (a) $s=0.25$, $\beta=2$, $\lambda=4$, $f_p=2$.

Equation : $D^2Y + 3DY + 18Y = 4(D+2)A$

Solve by Laplace Transforms, on the second alternative method of 8.8, and the subsidiary equation is :

$$(p^2+3p+18)\,\bar{Y}(p) = \frac{4\,(p+2)A}{p}$$

Since $p^2+3p+18 = 0$ has roots $-1.5 \pm i\,3.97$:

$$\bar{Y}(p) = 4A\,\frac{p+2}{p\,(p^2+3p+18)}$$
$$= \frac{4A}{9}\left\{\frac{1}{p} - \frac{p+1.5}{(p+1.5)^2+(3.97)^2} + 1.89\,\frac{3.97}{(p+1.5)^2+(3.97)^2}\right\}$$

So : $Y(t) = \dfrac{4A}{9}\,(1 - e^{-1.5t}\cos 3.97t + 1.89e^{-1.5t}\sin 3.97t)$

i.e. $Y(t) = \dfrac{4A}{9}\,\{1 - 2.14e^{-1.5t}\cos(3.97t+1.08)\}$

This is shown (for $A=-1$) as curve (ii) of Fig. 33 in comparison with the un-regulated multiplier case of curve (i).

Here the speed of response of the correction ($\beta=2$) is only half of that of the supply lag ($\lambda=4$). The time unit is such that the policy demand lag has a time-constant of $\frac{1}{2}$ unit, and the supply lag a time-constant of $\frac{1}{4}$ unit ; the time unit may be (e.g.) one year. The corrected path of Y is oscillatory but quite heavily damped, and it varies about a level $\left(Y=\dfrac{4A}{9}\right)$ which is not far from the desired level ($Y=0$).

The next case to consider in the *multiplier model* is that when a *mixed stabilisation policy* is pursued. The differential equation is (1) of 8.8 above. When differentiated to get rid of the integral :

$$D^3Y + aD^2Y + bDY + cY = \lambda D(D+\beta)A$$

where $a = \beta + \lambda s + \beta\lambda f_d$, $b = \beta\lambda(s+f_p)$, $c = \beta\lambda f_i$

Write $A=$ constant $(t>0)$ and the equation is homogeneous, with solution of the form :

$$Y = B_1 e^{p_1 t} + B_2 e^{p_2 t} + B_3 e^{p_3 t}$$

where p_1, p_2 and p_3 are the roots of $p^3 + ap^2 + bp + c = 0$, and where B_1, B_2 and B_3 are to be found from initial conditions.

Two general points can be made. The first is that, as long as the integral stabilisation policy is used ($f_i \neq 0$), the differential equation with A constant is homogeneous, so that $Y = 0$ is the steady (equilibrium) level, as desired. The effect of the integral stabilisation policy is to effect complete correction of the steady level of output. The second is that oscillations in Y are still possible, indeed probable. The roots p_1, p_2 and p_3 of the cubic are *either* all real, *or* one real and two conjugate complex. If they are all real :

$$p_1 + p_2 + p_3 = -a = -(\beta + \lambda s + \beta \lambda f_d) < 0$$

They have a negative sum and may well be all negative (steadily damped path of Y). If they are p_1 and p_2, $p_3 = \alpha \pm i\omega$:

$$p_1 + 2\alpha = -a = -(\beta + \lambda s + \beta \lambda f_d) < 0$$

and again p_1 and α may well both be negative. This means that, if there is an oscillation in Y, it is quite possibly damped. The likelihood is greater, the larger the coefficient f_d of the derivative stabilisation policy. It is never possible quite to rule out an explosive variation in Y. But a strong derivative stabilisation policy makes for heavy damping in the movement of output over time.

The conclusion, in broad terms, is that the proportional stabilisation policy affects only a partial correction of the level of output and that the addition of an integral stabilisation policy completes the correction. This may well be, however, at the expense of an oscillatory movement in output over time. If so, the use of a derivative stabilisation policy tends to damp out the oscillation.

Ex. (b). $s = 0.25$, $\beta = 2$, $\lambda = 4$, $f_p = f_i = 2$, $f_d = 0$.

Equation : $$D^3 Y + 3D^2 Y + 18DY + 16 Y = 4D(D+2)A$$

The subsidiary equation by the second alternative method of 8.8 is :

$$(p^3 + 3p^2 + 18p + 16)\,\overline{Y}(p) = \frac{4p\,(p+2)\,A}{p} = 4A\,(p+2)$$

Since $p^3 + 3p^2 + 18p + 16 = 0$ has roots -1, $-1 \pm i\,3.87$:

$$\overline{Y}(p) = 4A\,\frac{p+2}{p^3 + 3p^2 + 18p + 16}$$

$$= \frac{4A}{15}\left\{ \frac{1}{p+1} - \frac{p+1}{(p+1)^2 + (3.87)^2} + 3.87\,\frac{3.87}{(p+1)^2 + (3.87)^2} \right\}$$

So $$Y(t) = \frac{4A}{15}\,(e^{-t} - e^{-t}\cos 3.87t + 3.87e^{-t}\sin 3.87t)$$

i.e. $$Y(t) = \frac{4A}{15}\,e^{-t}\{1 - 4\cos(3.87t + 1.32)\}$$

This is shown (for $A = -1$) as curve (iii) of Fig. 33, in comparison with the effect of the proportional stabilisation policy of curve (ii).

The speed of response of the policy correction is the same as before and so is the strength of the proportional stabilisation. What is new is the addition of the integral stabilisation policy. The effect is to complete the correction to the desired level ($Y=0$) and at the same time to introduce an oscillation which is *less* damped than it was. The integral stabilisation policy gets rid of the first defect in the proportional stabilisation policy (the partial correction of level of output). It also makes the second defect (oscillations in output over time) worse rather than better.

The integral stabilisation policy need not be accompanied by an oscillatory path in output. The roots of the cubic equation in p may be all real, as illustrated by Ex. 2 below. Even so, there is generally a tendency for output Y to vary a good deal, without actually oscillating, before settling down at or near $Y=0$. The fact that the addition of the third type of policy (the derivative correction) can damp down any oscillation in output created by the other two policy types is illustrated in Ex. 3 below.

Finally, in the *multiplier-accelerator* model with *mixed stabilisation policy*, the differential equation for Y is given generally by (2) of 8.8 above. Little can be done in exploring the nature of the solution when the equation is in such general terms. One point can easily be made. If $f_i \neq 0$, and the integral stabilisation policy is used, the equation (2) needs to be differentiated to get rid of the integral. It becomes homogeneous of fourth order. Hence $Y=0$ is the equilibrium level and full correction is achieved. Let p_1, p_2, p_3 and p_4 be the roots of the quartic auxiliary equation, so that the solution is of the form:

$$Y = B_1 e^{p_1} + B_2 e^{p_2 t} + B_3 e^{p_3 t} + B_4 e^{p_4 t}$$

From the first coefficient of the equation:

$$p_1 + p_2 + p_3 + p_4 = -\{\beta + \lambda s + \kappa(1-v) + \beta\lambda f_d\}$$

This holds whether the roots are real or conjugate complex. The path of Y is *certain* to be explosive if the expression on the right-hand side is positive. A path with an explosive element is still quite possible when the expression is negative. It is only when the expression is both large and negative that a damped path of Y can be expected. It is seen that v, the power of the accelerator, tends to make the sum positive, whereas f_d tends to produce negative values. The coefficient f_d, the strength of the derivative stabilisation policy, is again found to have a damping influence, now needed to offset the explosive effect of the accelerator.

Further light is thrown on the model by considering various numerical cases and by solving the corresponding equations by the method of Laplace Transforms. Two such cases are taken here and the solutions represented graphically in Fig. 34 as curves (ii) and (iii). These are to be compared with curve (i) as the explosive oscillation arising in the corresponding multiplier-accelerator model without regulation, see 8.7, Ex. (b), above.

Ex. (c). $s = 0.25, v = 0.6, \beta = 2, \kappa = 1, \lambda = 4, f_p = 2, f_i = f_d = 0.$

Equation : $D^3 Y + 1.6 D^2 Y + 16.2 DY + 18 Y = 4 (D+1)(D+2)A$

Solving as before by the second alternative method of 8.8 :

$$(p^3 + 1.6p^2 + 16.2p + 18) \, \overline{Y}(p) = \frac{4(p+1)(p+2)A}{p}$$

Since $p^3 + 1.6p^2 + 16.2p + 18 = 0$ has roots $-1.15, -0.225 \pm i\,3.89$:

$$\overline{Y}(p) = 4A \frac{p^2 + 3p + 2}{p(p^3 + 1.6p^2 + 16.2p + 18)}$$

$$= \frac{4A}{9} \left\{ \frac{1}{p} + \frac{0.056}{p+1.15} - 1.056 \frac{p + 0.225}{(p+0.225)^2 + (3.89)^2} \right.$$

$$\left. + 2.266 \frac{3.89}{(p+0.225)^2 + (3.89)^2} \right\}$$

So : $Y(t) = \frac{4A}{9} (1 + 0.056e^{-1.15t} - 1.056e^{-0.225t} \cos 3.89t$

$$+ 2.266e^{-0.225t} \sin 3.89t)$$

i.e. $Y(t) = \frac{4A}{9} \{ 1 + 0.056e^{-1.15t} - 2.5e^{-0.225t} \cos(3.89t + 1.13) \}$

This is shown (for $A = -1$) as curve (ii) of Fig. 34.

The only policy correction here is of the proportional type. The time-constant of the policy demand lag is $\frac{1}{2}$ unit, as compared with 1 unit for the accelerator lag and $\frac{1}{4}$ unit for the supply lag. The policy correction operates with greater speed than the accelerator but more slowly than the supply response.

The steady level of output, after correction, is $Y = \frac{4A}{9}$. This represents a partial correction from the unregulated level ($Y = 4A$) towards the desired level ($Y = 0$). The main constituent in the path of output over time is a damped oscillation of period $\frac{2\pi}{3.89} = 1\frac{1}{2}$ units approximately, but the damping is quite mild. The policy correction is only partially successful, both in correcting the level of output and in damping down the explosive oscillations in output present in the original (unregulated) model.

Ex. (d). $s = 0.25, v = 0.6, \beta = 2, \kappa = 1, \lambda = 4, f_p = f_i = 2, f_d = 0.$

Equation : $D^4 Y + 1.6 D^3 Y + 16.2 D^2 Y + 34 DY + 16 Y = 4D(D+1)(D+2)A$

obtained from (2) of 8.8 above by differentiating through to eliminate the integral. The subsidiary equation is now :

$$(p^4 + 1.6p^3 + 16.2p^2 + 34p + 16) \, \overline{Y}(p) = \frac{4p(p+1)(p+2)A}{p}$$

Hence : $\overline{Y}(p) = 4A \dfrac{p^2 + 3p + 2}{p^4 + 1.6p^3 + 16.2p^2 + 34p + 16}$

$$= A \left\{ \dfrac{0.13}{p + 0.69} + \dfrac{0.07}{p + 1.43} - 0.21 \dfrac{p - 0.26}{(p - 0.26)^2 + (4.03)^2} \right.$$

$$\left. + 1.06 \dfrac{4.03}{(p - 0.26)^2 + (4.03)^2} \right\}$$

since -0.69, -1.43, $0.26 \pm i\, 4.03$ are the roots of the quartic equation in p :

$$p^4 + 1.6p^3 + 16.2p^2 + 34p + 16 = 0$$

So : $Y(t) = A\,(0.13e^{-0.69t} + 0.07e^{-1.43t} - 0.21e^{0.26t} \cos 4.03t + 1.06e^{0.26t} \sin 4.03t)$

i.e. $Y(t) = A\,\{0.13e^{-0.69t} + 0.07e^{-1.43t} - 1.08e^{0.26t} \cos (4.03t + 1.38)\}$

This is shown (for $A = -1$) as curve (iii) of Fig. 34.

The result here is to be compared with that of Ex. (c). The only difference is that an integral stabilisation policy is added to the proportional policy of the previous case. The correction of output level, to the desired value $Y = 0$, is now complete. The path of Y about $Y = 0$, apart from two damped and non-oscillatory components, comprises an oscillation which is more serious than before. The period is $\dfrac{2\pi}{4.03} =$ about $1\frac{1}{2}$ units, much as before ; but the oscillation is explosive, if only mildly so. The integral policy does serve to correct completely for level of output but at the cost of re-introducing the explosive feature.

The effects of economic regulation have been worked out fairly completely on the basis of Phillips' model of the multiplier-accelerator with single exponential lags. If demand falls off by amount A then the equilibrium level of output falls by $\dfrac{A}{s}$. The unregulated model with the accelerator in operation shows a path of income from the old equilibrium position which is likely to be oscillatory and explosive, as shown by curve (i) of Fig. 34. Economic regulation has the double purpose of offsetting the fall in the level of output and of damping down the oscillations in the path of output over time. A *proportional stabilisation policy* is no more than partially successful on both counts. The addition of an *integral stabilisation policy* does succeed in completing the correction of the fall in output, but only at the expense of amplifying the oscillations to an extent where they may again become explosive. This points up the importance of the third type of economic regulation, the *derivative stabilisation policy*. Such a policy tends to have a damping influence on the path of output over time, and its use can be quite effective for this purpose. It is particularly needed when there is a strong (and hence explosive) accelerator at work. A derivative stabilisation policy is needed, not only to offset the oscillations created by the proportional and (particularly) the integral policies, but also to counteract the inherent oscillations arising in the operation of the accelerator.

These results have been obtained in a multiplier-accelerator system with lags of the single (exponential) type.   They need to be modified quite considerably when the lags are of more complicated and " realistic " kinds, e.g. double, triple or higher multiple forms of the exponential lags. This is seen even in the very simplified cases of Ex. 4, 5 and 6 below, and the point is examined further in the next chapter.   It can be said, broadly, that the presence of multiple lags makes the oscillations introduced by the proportional and integral stabilisation policies more pronounced ; they may well be explosive.   At the same time, regulation by means of the derivative stabilisation policy becomes less effective.   Indeed, if strong proportional and integral policies are followed, it can happen that no derivative policy, no matter how strong, can iron out the resulting oscillations in output.   All this serves, at least, to bring out the fact that the *form* of the lags in a multiplier-accelerator system, and not only their existence, is a vital factor in determining the dynamic movements in the system, see Phillips (1957).

EXERCISES 8.9

1. Find the differential equation for the case : $s=0.25$, $\beta=8$, $\lambda=4$, $f_p=2$ (with $f_i=f_d=0$) in the multiplier model.   Show that the solution is :

$$Y(t) = \frac{4A}{9}\{1 - 1.17e^{-4.5t}\cos(7.19t + 0.56)\}$$

Compare with the case of Ex. (*a*) above and deduce that the effect of a faster response (smaller lag) in official policy is to damp down oscillations in Y. (This is the case of Phillips (1954), curve (*c*) of Fig. 4).

2. Examine the case : $s=0.25$, $\beta=8$, $\lambda=4$, $f_p=f_i=0.5$, $f_d=0$ in the multiplier model, and show that

$$Y(t) = \frac{28A}{9}\{e^{-t} - (1 + 1.71t)e^{-4t}\}$$

Trace the (non-oscillatory) path of Y towards the corrected value $Y=0$. (This is the case of a weak policy, proportional and integral, but operating with shorter lag ; it is given by Phillips (1954), curve (*b*) of Fig. 8).

3. Illustrate the effect of a derivative policy in the multiplier model by taking the case : $s=0.25$, $\beta=2$, $\lambda=4$, $f_p=f_i=8$, $f_d=1$.   Show that :

$$Y(t) = 0.08A\{e^{-1.18t} - 8.5e^{-4.91t}\cos(5.50t + 1.47)\}$$

and that the oscillation in Y is now heavily damped.

4. Consider the regulated multiplier model with differential equation (1) of 8.8 above.   Replace the single exponential lag on the supply side by the double lag :

$$Y = \left(\frac{2\lambda}{D+2\lambda}\right)^2 Z$$

Show that the differential equation becomes :

$$D^3Y + aD^2Y + bDY + cY + d\int_0^t Y\,dt = 4\lambda^2(D+\beta)A$$

MATHEMATICAL ECONOMICS

where
$$a = \beta + 4\lambda, \qquad b = 4\beta\lambda + 4\lambda^2(s + \beta f_d),$$
$$c = 4\beta\lambda^2(s + f_v), \qquad d = 4\beta\lambda^2 f_i$$

5. Examine the model of the previous exercise in the case :
$$s = 0 \cdot 25, \ \beta = 2, \ \lambda = 4, f_v = 2, f_i = f_d = 0$$
Find the solution for $Y(t)$ and compare with that of Ex. (a) above.

6. Extend the case of the previous exercise by replacing $f_i = 0$ by $f_i = 2$. Compare the solution for $Y(t)$ here with that of Ex. (b) above.

REFERENCES

Frisch (R.) and Holme (H.) (1935) : " The Characteristic Solutions of Mixed Difference and Differential Equations ", *Econometrica*, **3**, 225–39.

Goodwin (R. M.) (1951) : " The Non-linear Accelerator and the Persistence of Business Cycles ", *Econometrica*, **19**, 1–17.

Kalecki (M.) (1935) : " A Macrodynamic Theory of Business Cycles ", *Econometrica*, **3**, 327–44.

Kalecki (M.) (1943) : *Studies in Economic Dynamics* (Allen and Unwin, 1943).

Kalecki (M.) (1954) : *Theory of Economic Dynamics* (Allen and Unwin, 1954).

Le Corbeiller (Ph.) (1936) : " The Non-linear Theory of the Maintenance of Oscillations ", *Journal of the Institution of Electrical Engineers*, **79**, 361–78.

Phillips (A. W.) (1954) : " Stabilisation Policy in a Closed Economy ", *Economic Journal*, **64**, 290–323.

Phillips, (A. W.) (1957): " Stabilisation Policy and the Time-Form of Lagged Responses ", *Economic Journal*, **67**, 265–77.

Strotz (R. H.), McAnulty (J. C.) and Naines (J. B.) (1953) : " Goodwin's Non-linear Theory of the Business Cycle : An Electro-Analog Solution ", *Econometrica*, **21**, 390–411.

Tizard (R. H.) (1956) : " Note on Initial Conditions in the Solution of Linear Differential Equations with Constant Coefficients ", *Econometrica*, **24**, 192–7.

Tustin (A.) (1953) : *The Mechanism of Economic Systems* (Heinemann, 1953).

CHAPTER 9

ECONOMIC REGULATION : CLOSED-LOOP CONTROL SYSTEMS

9.1 A Schematic Representation

IN electric circuit theory and in other applications of closed-loop control systems, engineers deal with models similar to those discussed above in the economic field. They find it convenient to represent their systems in schematic form, a visual representation of the equations of the system. The models are characterised by inter-dependence of the variables, by equations both numerous and complex. The schematic diagram, at least, helps to disentangle the relationships.

The essential idea of a closed-loop system and its schematic diagram is easily expressed. Consider a system in which three variables (Q_1, Q_2, Q_3) are related by constant multiples. Suppose that Q_2 depends on Q_1: $Q_2 = k_{12}Q_1$ when the third variable is disregarded. Now suppose that Q_3 comes in, being influenced by Q_2 (multiple k_{23}) and in its turn influencing Q_2 (multiple k_{32}). Then the system is :

$$Q_2 = k_{12}Q_1 + k_{32}Q_3 \quad \text{and} \quad Q_3 = k_{23}Q_2$$

giving
$$Q_2 = \frac{k_{12}}{1 - k_{23}k_{32}} Q_1$$

as compared with $Q_2 = k_{12}Q_1$ in the absence of Q_3. This system is recognised by economists as the " multiplier " effect ; to engineers it is a " feed-back ".

The schematic form is shown in Fig. 35. The variables are enclosed in circles joined by lines on which arrows indicate the direction of dependence. The constant multiple of each dependence is shown in a box on the corresponding line. The diagram shows what any variable is influenced by (arrows coming into the circle) and what influence it has on other variables (arrows going out of the circle). When two arrows come in, the dependencies are added : as

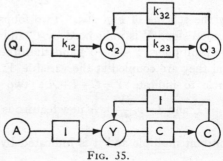

FIG. 35.

$Q_2 = k_{12}Q_1 + k_{32}Q_3$. When two dependencies are taken in sequence following the arrows, the multiples cumulate: as $Q_3 = k_{23}Q_2 = k_{12}k_{23}Q_1$ (in the absence of k_{32}). This scheme is complicated because of the feed-back or closed-loop $(Q_2 \rightarrow Q_3 \rightarrow Q_2)$; Q_2 is influenced by itself through Q_3. If the system represents current flows in electric circuit theory, the feed-back at Q_2 leads to a possible self-excitation in the circuit, an unstable element.

In economic terms the multiplier effect is a feed-back. The *static multiplier* without lags is:

$$Y = C + A \quad \text{and} \quad C = cY$$

giving
$$Y = \frac{A}{1 - c}$$

This is of the simple feed-back form of Fig. 35. It is only necessary to interpret the variables as $A =$ autonomous expenditure, $Y =$ income and $C =$ consumption. The particular values of the multiples are shown in the lower part of Fig. 35. The multiplier or feed-back arises because Y is influenced by itself through C.

More complicated systems, in engineering and economics alike, can be represented by schematic diagrams. Such a diagram provides a check on the consistency of the model and shows up visually the nature of the relations in it. Take the *multiplier-accelerator model* of Harrod-Domar type without lags:

$$Y = C + I + A \ ; \quad C = cY \quad \text{and} \quad I = v\frac{dY}{dt}$$

where the additional variable is induced investment (I) related to change in income $\left(\dfrac{dY}{dt}\right)$ by the coefficient v of the accelerator. This system gives rise to a differential equation: $v\dfrac{dY}{dt} = (1 - c)\,Y - A$. It can be represented by the scheme of Fig. 36a. Two loops, or feed-back relations, are now needed since Y is influenced by C and I as well as A. One loop is for the multiplier $(Y \rightarrow C \rightarrow Y)$ and the other for the accelerator $(Y \rightarrow I \rightarrow Y)$, and they are coupled at the variable Y. Three arrows come into the Y circle to indicate $Y = C + I + A$; two arrows go out for the relations $C = cY$ and $I = v\dfrac{dY}{dt}$. A new feature is that one of the relations is not a constant multiple and it is indicated by " $v\dfrac{d}{dt}$ " in its box. The use of operators, however permits the relation to be handled as though it were a constant multiple :

$$I = v\frac{dY}{dt} = \left(v\,\frac{d}{dt}\right)Y = (vD)\,Y$$

where the operator $\frac{d}{dt}$ or D is separated off for algebraic treatment.

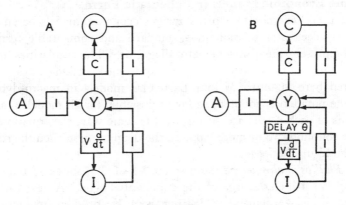

FIG. 36.

A characteristic of dynamic models is that they include, not only rates of change, but also lags of various kinds. These can be included in the schematic form ; it is found convenient to show a lag in a separate box in which is written the kind of lag, e.g. " Delay θ " for a fixed-time delay or " L_λ " for an exponential lag of speed of response λ. The simple multiplier-accelerator model with a delay in the accelerator is shown in Fig. 36b. It corresponds to the equations :

$$Y = C + I + A ; \quad C = cY \quad \text{and} \quad I = v\frac{d}{dt}Y(t-\theta)$$

where all variables are at time t unless otherwise specified. The scheme of Fig. 36b can clearly be varied by including lags in both the multiplier and the accelerator and by taking them of various forms.

The schematic diagrams are a help in visualising the nature of a model. More positive use of them is made in the following development in taking over into economic systems the methods of analysis found appropriate by engineers in the corresponding engineering problems. The parallel between an economic and an engineering model does not imply that their mechanisms are the same ; a decision to invest cannot be taken as equivalent, for example, to a voltage difference. All that is needed is a formal similarity, and hence the expectation that the techniques adopted by engineers will apply to economic models. Some economists, e.g. Goodwin

(1951), have designed economic models with an eye on what the engineers have done.   More recently, more explicit statements of the link between economic and engineering models have been made by Tustin (1953) as an engineer looking at economic problems, and by Phillips (1954) as an economist with engineering experience.

9.2 Some Economic Models in Schematic Form

It is a useful exercise to express various economic models based on the multiplier-accelerator relation in a standard and comparable form, and then to represent them in schematic diagrams.   The similarities and differences between the models are shown up in most striking ways.   This is illustrated here in terms of four particular models in macro-dynamics. The same notation is adopted, as far as possible, for all models ; and the equations of each model are written in the same way, the equations for a variable coupling two or more loops in the diagram first, then the relations which build up the loops.

The *Phillips multiplier-accelerator* model of 3.5 above is one of the simplest and it includes lags of the exponential type.   A new variable is introduced, i.e. $Z=$ demand as distinct from $Y=$ product (income).   The equations are :

$$Z=C+I+A$$

where $\qquad C=cY; \quad I=\dfrac{\kappa}{D+\kappa}vDY \quad$ and $\quad Y=\dfrac{\lambda}{D+\lambda}Z$

The operator $D=\dfrac{d}{dt}$ is used in this formulation ; κ and λ are the speeds of response of the two exponential lags.   The equations give rise to a differential equation of the second order in Y (3.5 above).   The schematic diagram is that of Fig. 37 I ; where " L_λ " stands for the lag of Y on Z, to be read as the multiple $\dfrac{\lambda}{D+\lambda}$, and similarly for " L_κ ".   The lags can be varied by changing the speed of response, and two limiting cases are of particular interest.   If $\kappa=0$ (infinite time constant of lag), then the accelerator is a complete blockage ; it goes out of action and the loop can be eliminated.   If $\lambda\to\infty$ (infinite speed of response), then there is effectively no lag at all ; Y and Z can be taken as equal and the two points in the diagram brought together.

The *Samuelson-Hicks multiplier-accelerator model* in Hicks' " elementary case " (3.7 above) is in period terms and the equations are :

$$Y_t=C_t+I_t+A_t$$

where $\qquad\qquad C_t=cY_{t-1} \quad$ and $\quad I_t=v(Y_{t-1}-Y_{t-2})$

The equations give a difference equation of second order. To obtain a schematic representation, the scheme so far used for continuous models needs to be adjusted. The operators for lags and derivatives (L and D) are replaced by various combinations of the shift operator E and its

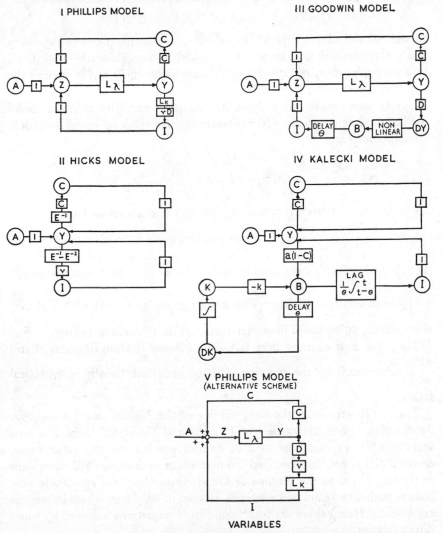

VARIABLES

A = AUTONOMOUS EXPENDITURES

B = INVESTMENT DECISIONS   K = CAPITAL STOCK   Y = OUTPUT

C = CONSUMPTION OUTLAYS   I = INVESTMENT OUTLAYS   Z = DEMAND

FIG. 37.

inverse E^{-1}. A lag of one period is E^{-1} since $Y_{t-1}=E^{-1}Y_t$. A difference is $(1-E^{-1})$ since $Y_t-Y_{t-1}=(1-E^{-1})\,Y_t$. A lagged difference is

$$(E^{-1}-E^{-2}),$$

i.e. $Y_{t-1}-Y_{t-2}=(E^{-1}-E^{-2})\,Y_t$. Hence the relations of the system are :

$$C_t=cE^{-1}Y, \quad \text{and} \quad I_t=v(E^{-1}-E^{-2})\,Y_t$$

All the variables have current-period values, multiplied where necessary by appropriate shift operators. The model is then shown by Fig. 37 II. As a particular case, put $v=0$ and the accelerator goes out of action, the accelerator loop being dropped.

The *Goodwin model* of 8.3 above has the same variables as in the model of Phillips, but a variable (B) representing decisions to invest is added. The equations are :

$$Z=C+I+A$$

where $\quad C=cY; \quad I=B(t-\theta); \quad B=\phi\left(\dfrac{dY}{dt}\right) \quad$ and $\quad Y=\dfrac{\lambda}{D+\lambda}Z$

All variables are currently timed except for the one case of a delay. The last relation $\left(Y=\dfrac{\lambda}{D+\lambda}Z\right)$ is written in the usual form for an exponential lag; but Goodwin's own version is $Y=Z-\epsilon\dfrac{dY}{dt}$, which is equivalent if $\epsilon=\dfrac{1}{\lambda}=$ time-constant of lag. The resulting equation, (4) of 8.3 above, is of mixed difference-differential form. The schematic diagram is Fig. 37 III ; the new element here is the non-linear relation between B and $\dfrac{dY}{dt}$, represented by the function ϕ to be specified, usually in empirical form.

The last illustration is the early version of the *Kalecki model*, 8.4 above. As compared with the models of Phillips and Goodwin, there is a new variable (K) representing stock of capital goods ; on the other hand, demand (Z) is not distinguished from product or income (Y), equivalent to putting $\lambda\to\infty$ in the Phillips or Goodwin model. An essentially new feature is that there are two relations, instead of only one, where influences are added. Hence there are two " coupling " equations followed by some direct relations :

$$Y=C+I+A \quad \text{and} \quad B=a(1-c)\,Y-kK$$

where $\qquad C=cY; \quad I=\dfrac{1}{\theta}\displaystyle\int_{t-\theta}^{t}B(t)dt \quad$ and $\quad \dfrac{dK}{dt}=B(t-\theta)$

These lead again to a mixed difference-differential equation, (7) of 8.4 above. The scheme is Fig. 37 IV where it is seen that three loops are required, a pair coupled at Y on much the same lines as before, and a new kind of loop coupled at B.

The schematic diagrams of Fig. 37 I–IV are drawn according to a method suggested by Tustin (1953). There is an alternative form which has been developed by engineers for the representation of electric circuits and other closed-loop systems in engineering problems. It is shown in Fig. 37 V in a representation of the Phillips model of Fig. 37 I. The variables now appear on the lines of the diagram. They can be thought of as flowing along the lines (like an electric current). The diagram shows a point where lines meet in an open circle (◯) ; here the variables are added (+ signs) or subtracted (– signs). The diagram also shows a point where a line goes into a solid circle (●) and then fans out into a number of separate lines ; here one and the same variable flows along all of the out-going lines in unchanged form. To show where and how one variable is changed into another—or to represent a functional dependence of one variable on another—a box is inserted on a line and the relation concerned is indicated by the entry in the box. So one variable goes into each box and one comes out, the second variable depending on the first according to the relation shown in the box.

A diagram of this alternative form is perhaps rather less intelligible to an economist at first sight. The first kind of schematic diagram is there-fore used in this chapter. The other form, however, has the double advantage that it is in common use in engineering problems, and is employed by Phillips (1954) in an economic model, and that it is more readily adapted in representing models of greater complexity than those considered here.

There are many points of interest in a comparison of the models of Fig. 37. There is, for example, the non-linear element in the Goodwin model, but otherwise its similarity with the Phillips model. The schematic form of the Kalecki model is particularly illuminating. The distinguishing features of this model are that investment is related first to the level of out-put (and not its rate of change), and second to the existing stock of capital goods. The first difference appears in the scheme as a modification of the " accelerator " loop. The second is more important since it requires a third loop to be added. The place of the new factor (the influence of capital stock on new investment) in the scheme is seen by the coupling of a new circuit at the point B (decisions to invest) in the main investment loop. The significance of this feature is perhaps more clear to the engineer used to designing closed-circuit systems than to an economist. Indeed, Kalecki himself eliminates just this feature in his later versions of the model (8.6 above).

The models considered are all highly aggregative and narrowly based on the multiplier-accelerator relation, with some closely related considerations of the distinction between decisions to invest, investment outlays and deliveries of capital goods. Even within these limits, the model can become quite complex and lead to differential, difference or mixed equations which are not easily solved. Kalecki's idea, that deliveries of capital goods, through the stock of capital goods and its influences on investment decisions, constitute a subsidiary loop of the system, can be taken over and applied equally well to consumption. If this is accepted, then a generalised model, built on the narrow basis considered here, would take on the form shown in Fig. 38. There are two main loops, one for

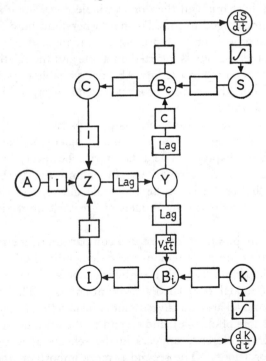

Fig. 38.

the multiplier and one for the accelerator. At the point in each where decisions to spend are taken (B_c and B_i), a subsidiary loop is coupled on, to represent the influence of the level of stocks (S and K). The decision to invest depends on the stock of capital assets (K) as in Kalecki's model ; equally, the decision of consumers to spend can depend on such factors as the amount of hire purchase outstanding (S). Some of the boxes of Fig. 38 are filled in, when the multiple is evident or usual ; others are left empty, to be filled in at choice, e.g. from the " standard " list of multiples, derivatives, integrals and lags. Indeed, some of the empty boxes may need to be filled in with empirical and non-linear relations.

What is clear is that a schematic model based on the multiplier and accelerator is sufficiently complex before the addition of the further factors (such as government operations, external trade, fiscal policy, prices and the rate of interest) which must be considered if the model is to be applied to the real world. The schematic diagram can grow at an alarming rate. It is, therefore, always necessary to compensate for additional factors in one part of the system by drastic simplification elsewhere, at least in the first instance and to experiment with the consequences of new influences on well-known systems. The models of Goodwin and Kalecki, for example, direct attention to the investment loop and its features by cutting down the multiplier loop to its simplest form.

EXERCISES 9.2

1. Show that the Goodwin model is less closely related to that of Hicks than to that of Phillips. In what sense is the Phillips model a simplified version of it?

2. Compare and contrast the Hicks model with those of Fig. 36b and of Fig. 37 I $(\lambda \to \infty)$.

3. Draw a schematic diagram for the Harrod-Domar model in period form (3.6 above).

9.3 Response to Sinusoidal Input in a Linear Model

Attention is now directed to properties of linear models in relation to possible variations of sinusoidal form. This is not as restrictive as might appear at first sight. A sinusoidal variation in a linear model is determined as to frequency and damping by the structure of the model, but as to amplitude and phase by extraneous conditions (see Appendix A, Section 9). If one variable has a sinusoidal variation, then all variables oscillate with the same frequency and damping ($p = \alpha + i\omega$ the same for all) but with different amplitudes and phasing. Moreover, the relations of a linear model are not confined to constant multiples. By the results of 4.9 above, derivatives, integrals, delays and exponential lags all leave the frequency and damping of an oscillation unchanged, and they can be included among linear relations (as indeed they are in operator terms).

It is true that a sinusoidal variation, which runs through a linear system with unchanged $p = \alpha + i\omega$, is a very special form of oscillation with a symmetrical upswing and downswing. On the other hand, it does include the case of a steady exponential variation, damped or explosive, by putting $\omega = 0$. Further, an oscillation not of sinusoidal form but with fixed period $\dfrac{2\pi}{\omega}$ can be analysed " harmonically " by means of the Fourier Series (4.7 above) into a sinusoidal oscillation of frequency ω (the fundamental) plus " harmonics " of successively higher frequency (2ω, 3ω, ...).

Consider any one relation of a linear model, one " leg " of the closed-loop scheme which represents it. One variable Y is then related as an output to a second variable Z as a given input. Examples of simple relations are :

(i) $Y = v \dfrac{dZ}{dt}$ an accelerator relation

(ii) $Y = \displaystyle\int_0^t Z \, dt$ a process of cumulation

(iii) $Y = Z(t - \theta)$ a fixed-time delay of θ

(iv) $Y = \dfrac{\lambda}{D + \lambda} Z$ a single exponential lag of time-constant $\dfrac{1}{\lambda}$

(v) $Y = \left(\dfrac{2\lambda}{D + 2\lambda}\right)^2 Z$ two equal exponential lags in sequence, with total time-constant $\dfrac{1}{\lambda}$

Notice that the last two are particular cases of a relation which consists of a differential equation in Y with Z as the " input " on the right-hand side :

$$a \frac{dY}{dt} + bY = Z, \quad a \frac{d^2 Y}{dt^2} + b \frac{dY}{dt} + cY = Z, \dots$$

The input is taken of sinusoidal form, a variation represented by the vector product $Z = A e^{i\epsilon} e^{pt} (p = \alpha + i\omega)$. The actual time-path of the variable is obtained as $A e^{\alpha t} \cos(\omega t + \epsilon)$ by taking the " real " part of Z. Since the system is linear, Y will have a sinusoidal variation with the same time vector e^{pt} but a different vector for amplitude and phase. Write $Y = B e^{i\eta} e^{pt}$. The problem is to find B and η from A and ϵ, given any value of $p = \alpha + i\omega$. What is sought is the vector ratio :

$$\frac{Y}{Z} = \frac{B e^{i\eta}}{A e^{i\epsilon}} = F(p) \quad \dots\dots\dots\dots\dots\dots\dots\dots(1)$$

which is not dependent on time but which is influenced by the particular p (frequency and damping) of the oscillation assumed. The ratio (1) is a complex number, which varies in value with the complex variable $p = \alpha + i\omega$; hence it is written as a function $F(p)$ of the complex variable. Suppose that it is found, for a given p, as the complex number

$$F(p) = \rho (\cos \phi + i \sin \phi) = \rho e^{i\phi} \quad \ldots\ldots\ldots\ldots\ldots\ldots(2)$$

Substitute (2) in (1) :

$$Be^{i\eta} = (\rho e^{i\phi})(Ae^{i\epsilon}) = \rho Ae^{i(\epsilon + \phi)}$$

Hence the output variable Y has :

Amplitude $\qquad B = \rho A$

Phase $\qquad\qquad \eta = \epsilon + \phi$

In other words, the complex number $F(p) = \rho e^{i\phi}$ represents the amplitude ratio (by the length of the vector, ρ) and the phase shift (by the angle of the vector, ϕ) as the sinusoidal variation passes from Z to Y. For this reason, the function $F(p)$ is called the *transfer function* of the relation of Y to Z :

For sinusoidal variation with given $p = \alpha + i\omega$ in a linear system, the relation of one variable Y to a second variable Z is :

$$Y = F(p)Z$$

where the transfer function $F(p)$ is a complex number $\rho e^{i\phi}$ which indicates by ρ the amplitude ratio and by ϕ the phase shift from Z to Y.

If the relation of Y to Z is given analytically in terms of the usual forms, such as the examples (i)–(v) above, the transfer function $F(p)$ can be written down at once from the results of 4.9 above. It is only necessary to write $D = p$ (for derivatives), $D^{-1} = \dfrac{1}{p}$ (for integrals) and a multiple of $e^{-p\theta}$ for a delay of θ. In the examples, the transfer functions are written down :

Relation	Transfer function : $Y = F(p)Z$
(i) $\ Y = v\dfrac{dZ}{dt}$	$Y = vpZ$
(ii) $\ Y = \displaystyle\int_0^t Z\,dt$	$Y = \dfrac{1}{p} Z$
(iii) $\ Y = Z(t - \theta)$	$Y = e^{-p\theta}Z$
(iv) $\ Y = \dfrac{\lambda}{D + \lambda} Z$	$Y = \dfrac{\lambda}{p + \lambda} Z$
(v) $\ Y = \left(\dfrac{2\lambda}{D + 2\lambda}\right)^2 Z$	$Y = \left(\dfrac{2\lambda}{p + 2\lambda}\right)^2 Z$

Any one of these can be checked from first principles. For example, the transfer function (iv) is :

$$Y = \frac{\lambda}{p+\lambda} Z = \frac{\lambda}{(\lambda+\alpha)+i\omega} Z = \frac{\lambda}{(\lambda+\alpha)^2+\omega^2}(\lambda+\alpha-i\omega)Z$$
$$= \rho e^{-i\phi} Z$$

where
$$\rho = \frac{\lambda}{\sqrt{(\lambda+\alpha)^2+\omega^2}} \quad \text{and} \quad \tan\phi = \frac{\omega}{\lambda+\alpha}$$

Hence the transfer function implies that the input variation $Z = e^{\alpha t}\cos\omega t$ is turned into the output variation $Y = (\rho e^{\alpha t})\cos(\omega t - \phi)$. But this is the result obtained directly in 5.8 above for the exponential lag $Y = \dfrac{\lambda}{D+\lambda} Z$.

One further example of a transfer function can be given to illustrate how it can be worked out from first principles.

Ex. Take Y as the average (smoothed) value of Z over an interval of length $2T$ centred at t :

$$Y = \frac{1}{2T}\int_{t-T}^{t+T} Z\, dt$$

This is not the same as the cumulation $\int_0^t Z\, dt$ and the operator result (for indefinite integrals) does not apply. In fact, $F(p)$ cannot be written down at all easily for this relation, except in the undamped case $\alpha = 0$. When $\alpha = 0$, the input variation is $A\cos(\omega t + \epsilon)$ and the corresponding variation in Y is :

$$\frac{A}{2T}\int_{t-T}^{t+T}\cos(\omega t + \epsilon)\,dt = \frac{A}{2\omega T}\{\sin(\omega t + \epsilon + \omega T) - \sin(\omega t + \epsilon - \omega T)\}$$
$$= \frac{A}{\omega T}\cos(\omega t + \epsilon)\sin\omega T$$
$$= \rho A\cos(\omega t + \epsilon) \quad \text{where } \rho = \frac{\sin\omega T}{\omega T}$$

Hence the transfer function for $p = i\omega$ is:

$$Y = \rho Z \quad \text{where } \rho = \frac{\sin\omega T}{\omega T}$$

In smoothing Z by a central moving average of length $2T$, there is no change in phase and the amplitude is reduced in the ratio $\rho = \dfrac{\sin\omega T}{\omega T}$. If ω is at all large, ρ is small. An oscillation of high frequency (short period) is easily smoothed out.

The transfer function $F(p)$ can be represented, for each $p = \alpha + i\omega$, as a point shown by (2) on an Argand Diagram. In cartesian co-ordinates, the point P is $(\rho\cos\phi, \rho\sin\phi)$; in polars it is (ρ, ϕ). As α and ω vary, the point P moves over the Oxy plane. The variation of P can be shown in the form of a network of curves or loci (very much like indifference curves in the theory of consumer choice). One set of loci is given by varying ω (α fixed), one curve corresponding to each fixed α. They are called *response-vector loci.* On one such locus (α fixed), the values of $F(p)$ and hence ρ and ϕ are given for varying ω. Hence, given α, one response-vector locus is picked out ; then given ω, one point P on it is located and hence the amplitude ratio (ρ = length of OP) and the phase shift (ϕ = angle POx) for the relation of Y to Z.

For example, the transfer function for a single exponential lag (with $\lambda = 1$) is :

$$F(p) = \frac{1}{p+1} = \frac{1}{(\alpha+1)+i\omega} = \frac{(\alpha+1)-i\omega}{(\alpha+1)^2+\omega^2}$$

and the corresponding point P on the Argand Diagram has co-ordinates :

$$P\left(\frac{\alpha+1}{(\alpha+1)^2+\omega^2}, \ -\frac{\omega}{(\alpha+1)^2+\omega^2}\right)$$

The response-vector locus for $\alpha = 0$ is the curve described by the point $P\left(\frac{1}{1+\omega^2}, -\frac{\omega}{1+\omega^2}\right)$ as ω varies from 0 to infinity. This is a semi-circle as shown by the curve (i) of Fig. 39 ; the values of ω for various points on

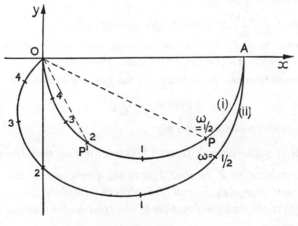

FIG. 39.

it are marked on the graph ($\omega = \frac{1}{2}$, 1, 2, 3, 4). The locus gives a visual impression of the amplitude ratio and the phase shift as a regular oscillation ($\alpha = 0$) of various frequencies passes through the exponential lag of Y on Z. The input $A \cos(\omega t + \epsilon)$ is changed as an output to

$$\rho A \cos(\omega t + \epsilon - \phi),$$

where ρ is the length of OP and ϕ is angle POx. For a low frequency (long period oscillation) such as $\omega = \frac{1}{2}$, there is little damping of amplitude and little change in phase. For a higher frequency (short period oscilla-tion) such as $\omega = 2$, the amplitude is more severely damped and there is a larger lag in phase. See OP and OP' of Fig. 39. Curve (ii) of Fig. 39 is the similar response-vector locus $(\alpha = 0)$ for a double exponential lag of the same total time constant $\left(\frac{1}{\lambda} = 1 \right)$, see Ex. 4 below.

Finally, the transfer function $F(p)$ can be interpreted as a Laplace Transform (5.6 above). Two particular cases suffice to illustrate :

Ex. (*a*). $Y = \frac{\lambda}{D + \lambda} Z$, a single exponential lag.

Take a unit change in Z and work out (as in 5.8 above) the response of Y

$$Y(t) = 1 - e^{-\lambda t} \quad \text{in cumulative form}$$
$$Y'(t) = \lambda e^{-\lambda t} \quad \text{as a time-distribution of response}$$

Let $f(t)$ be the time-form of response and $F(p)$ its Laplace Transform. Here :

$$f(t) = \lambda e^{-\lambda t} \quad \text{and} \quad F(p) = \frac{\lambda}{p + \lambda}$$

from the standard forms of 5.6 above. Hence, the Laplace Transform of $f(t)$ is the transfer function of the lag.

Ex. (*b*). $Y = \left(\frac{2\lambda}{D + 2\lambda} \right)^2 Z$, a double exponential lag.

For a unit change in Z, the cumulative and distributive responses are

$$Y(t) = 1 - (1 + 2\lambda t) e^{-2\lambda t} \quad \text{and} \quad Y'(t) = 4\lambda^2 t \, e^{-2\lambda t}$$

The time-form of response, $f(t) = 4\lambda^2 t \, e^{-2\lambda t}$, has Laplace Transform

$$F(p) = \frac{4\lambda^2}{(p + 2\lambda)^2}$$

which is the transfer function of the lag.

The result is quite general, from 5.8 above (noting that $D = p$) :

> *If Y is related to Z so that $f(t)$ is the time-form of the response of Y to a unit change in Z, and if $F(p)$ is the Laplace Transform of $f(t)$, then $F(p)$ is the transfer function of the relation for sinusoidal variation $(p = \alpha + i\omega)$.*

the result is not useful if the relation of Y to Z is a simple one, since $F(p)$ can be written down at once by putting (e.g.) $D = p$. For more complicated relations, it may be possible to get $f(t)$ in analytical form and then to write $F(p)$ as its Laplace Transform. The use of the result, how-ever, is primarily to deal with cases, which can be expected in practice, when the response of a lag $f(t)$ is empirical. As shown by Tustin (1953), it is then possible to derive $F(p)$ from $f(t)$ by numerical or graphical methods, i.e. to find the transfer function for an empirical relation.

EXERCISES 9.3

1. Check that $Y = \dfrac{1}{p} Z$ is the transfer function for $Y = \displaystyle\int_0^t Z \, dt$ by direct integration of $A e^{\alpha t} \cos (\omega t + \epsilon)$.

2. Consider the relation $\dfrac{d^2 Y}{dt^2} + a \dfrac{dY}{dt} + bY = Z$. Show that the solution of

$$\frac{d^2 Y}{dt^2} + a \frac{dY}{dt} + bY = 1 \quad \text{subject to } Y = \frac{dY}{dt} = 0 \text{ at } t = 0$$

is
$$Y(t) = \frac{1}{p_1 p_2} + \frac{1}{p_1 - p_2} \left(\frac{1}{p_1} e^{p_1 t} - \frac{1}{p_2} e^{p_2 t} \right)$$

where p_1 and p_2 are the roots of $p^2 + ap + b = 0$. Hence obtain the distribution of response $f(t)$ and show that $F(p) = \dfrac{1}{p^2 + ap + b}$. Derive this transfer function directly from the relation.

3. In the relation of the previous exercise, what can be said of the transfer function $F(p)$ when p is a root of $p^2 + ap + b = 0$?

4. Draw the response-vector locus ($\alpha = 0$) for the double exponential lag
$$Y = \frac{1}{(D+1)^2} Z$$

5. Show that another set of response-vector loci can be defined for α varying (ω fixed). How do these relate to the loci of the text? Why do you expect the two sets of loci to be orthogonal (intersecting at right angles)?

6. Obtain the transfer function $F(p)$ for $p = i\omega$ ($\alpha = 0$) when Y is a moving average of length $2T$ of Z, not centred but taken over the past period. Show that the amplitude ratio is $\rho = \dfrac{\sin \omega T}{\omega T}$ and that the phase lag is ωT.

7. Show that, if Z_t is a sinusoidal variation in period analysis, then
$$Y_t = Z_{t-\theta} = e^{-p\theta} Z_t$$

for a delay θ. Deduce that the analysis of the text applies to relations in period times by writing the shift operator $E = e^p$. Indicate the application to a model such as that of Samuelson-Hicks.

9.4 The Feed-back Transfer Function

The transfer function $F(p)$ for the relation of two variables (Y depending on Z) in a linear model is the basic construction. It is an *algebraic* version of the relation which may include derivatives, integrals, delays and lags of all kinds. It expresses the modification of a sinusoidal variation as it passes from variable Z to variable Y with unchanged frequency and damping ($p = \alpha + i\omega$). When it is extended to cover the whole closed-loop system, as is now to be done, it provides a means of handling sinusoidal variations in a linear model by methods of ordinary algebra and complex numbers.

Consider now a complete closed-loop system and any variable Y in it.

The feed-back of Y, after a sinusoidal variation has passed through the system is to be related to the input of Y at the same point and time. What is required is the feed-back transfer function:

$$\text{Feed-back} = F(p) \quad \text{Input}$$

$F(p)$ can be obtained, as in 9.3 above, if the equations of the system are used to eliminate other variables and so to relate the feed-back of Y to the input of Y. If Y is a point at which different loops of the system are coupled, there is a complication. It is necessary to specify which of the

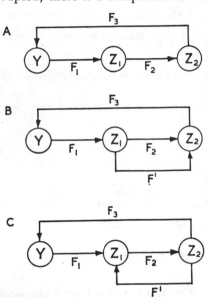

two (or more) feed-backs is considered, and to allow for the effect of the other loop (or loops) on Y. A different $F(p)$ is obtained for one feed-back than for another; this turns out to be immaterial in the application of the function (9.5 below).

It is also possible, either as a derivation or as a check, to obtain the feed-back transfer function from the separate transfer functions for all the " legs " of the closed-loop scheme. It is both useful and illuminating to have this method for application in particular cases. Fig. 40a shows a schematic diagram for a simple case of a system of one complete loop; Y is the selected point and Z_1 and Z_2 are two other points of the loop. The relations of each " leg " are replaced by their algebraic versions, the transfer functions $F_1(p)$, $F_2(p)$ and $F_3(p)$ as obtained in 9.3 above. The feed-back Y for any sinusoidal variation in the system is then:

$$\text{Feed-back } Y = F_3 Z_2 = F_3(F_2 Z_1) = F_3 F_2(F_1 Y)$$
$$= (F_1 F_2 F_3) \text{ Input } Y$$

Hence the feed-back transfer function for this whole system is :

$$F = F_1 F_2 F_3$$

The relations cumulate following the arrows of the diagram.

Next, add a second loop (which may proceed through other variables not shown) and take it as operating from Z_1 to Z_2 with transfer function F', i.e. in the same direction as the main loop, as Fig. 40b. Then:

$$\text{Feed-back } Y = F_3 Z_2 = F_3(F_2 Z_1 + F' Z_1) = F_3(F_2 + F')(F_1 Y)$$
$$= F_1(F_2 + F') F_3 \text{ Input } Y$$

The feed-back transfer function is:

$$F = F_1(F_2 + F') F_3$$

which is again as expected.

Finally, add the second loop in the opposite direction, so that it acts as a feed-back from Z_2 to Z_1, with transfer function F, as Fig. 40c. Then:

$$\text{Feed-back } Y = F_3 Z_2$$

where $Z_2 = F_2 Z_1$ and $Z_1 = F_1 Y + F' Z_2$

i.e. where $Z_2 = F_1 F_2 Y + F' F_2 Z_2$

i.e. where $Z_2 = \dfrac{F_1 F_2}{1 - F' F_2} Y$

and the feed-back transfer function is:

$$F = \frac{F_1 F_2 F_3}{1 - F' F_2}$$

which includes a " multiplier " effect for the supplementary feed-back F'.

The last result can be put in a more general form, when it is noticed that $F' F_2$ is the transfer function round the whole added loop ($Z_1 \rightarrow Z_2 \rightarrow Z_1$). The result is:

If the feed-back transfer function in a system is $F_1(p)$, and if a supplementary feed-back is added with transfer function $F_2(p)$ round the whole loop, then the feed-back transfer function of the new system is:

$$F(p) = \frac{F_1(p)}{1 - F_2(p)}$$

As an application of this result, consider the Phillips model of Fig. 37 I or V, omitting autonomous expenditure. Take the feed-back at Z in the accelerator loop. If the multiplier loop is ignored altogether, the transfer function is:

$$F_1(p) = v \frac{\kappa \lambda p}{(p + \kappa)(p + \lambda)}$$

Now add the multiplier loop as an extra feed-back; the transfer function round the whole loop is:

$$F_2(p) = c \frac{\lambda}{p + \lambda}$$

Hence, the feed-back transfer function (at Z in the accelerator loop) is:

$$F(p) = v \frac{\kappa \lambda p}{(p+\kappa)(p+\lambda)} \times \frac{1}{1 - \dfrac{c\lambda}{p+\lambda}}$$

i.e.
$$F(p) = v \frac{\kappa \lambda p}{(p+\kappa)(p+\lambda s)}$$

EXERCISES 9.4

1. Show that, if $F_1(p)$ is the feed-back transfer function at Y in an accelerator loop, then the addition of an unlagged multiplier loop changes the function to

$$F(p) = \frac{F_1(p)}{1-c}$$

2. Use the results of the previous exercise to show that, in the simple multiplier-accelerator model of Fig. 36, the feed-back transfer function at Y in the accelerator loop is (a) $F(p) = \dfrac{vp}{1-c}$ with no lags, (b) $F(p) = \dfrac{vpe^{-p\theta}}{1-c}$ with an accelerator delay of θ, and (c) $F(p) = \dfrac{v}{1-c}\dfrac{\kappa p}{p+\kappa}$ with an exponential lag in the accelerator.

3. For Phillips model of Fig. 37 I, show that the feed-back transfer function at Z *in the multiplier loop* is $F(p) = \dfrac{F_2(p)}{1 - F_1(p)}$, where F_1 and F_2 are as given in the text above. Why is this different from the $F(p)$ of the text?

9.5 Free Variations in a Linear Closed-loop System

The main application of transfer functions is to determine the frequency and damping ($p = \alpha + i\omega$) of the free or inherent sinusoidal variation, i.e. the variation which is self-sustaining in a linear system. For an early analysis of free oscillations, see Frisch (1933).

In 9.3 and 9.4 above, the assumed sinusoidal variation is completely at choice ; $p = \alpha + i\omega$ can be given any value. No distinction is made between forced and free or inherent oscillations ; this is quite immaterial. In particular, the feed-back transfer function $F(p)$, at a point Y in the complete system, takes various values as p is varied. For any p giving $F(p) \neq 1$, the amplitude and phase of Y on feed-back are different from those of the input Y. The oscillation with this particular p is not self-sustaining. Only those p giving $F(p) = 1$ correspond to self-sustaining oscillations, i.e. to free variation in the system.

The condition for free variation is simple : $F(p) = 1$. Algebraically, this is an equation in the complex variable $p = \alpha + i\omega$. From it can be determined one or more values of p, each of which corresponds to a free variation in the system. The variation may be steady ($\omega = 0$) or oscillatory ($\omega \neq 0$) ; it may be damped ($\alpha < 0$), explosive ($\alpha > 0$) or regular

($\alpha=0$). Ordinary algebraic methods can be used to solve the equation; alternatively, the real part of $F(p)$ can be equated to unity and the imaginary part to zero.

In diagrammatic terms, the response-vector loci can be drawn for $F(p)$, showing the effect of changing ω for various fixed α. Whenever a curve of this network passes through the point A $(1, 0)$, then $F(p)=1$ and the values of α and ω for free variation can be read off the curve.

To illustrate the method, and at the same time to obtain results which have some familiarity, the simplest kind of multiplier-accelerator model is taken, that of Fig. 36a. This basic model has no lags, and autonomous expenditures are ignored ($A=0$). The system, consisting of two closed loops coupled at Y (income), is:

$$Y=C+I \quad \text{where} \quad C=cY \text{ and } I=v\frac{dY}{dt}$$

Hence the input and feed-back are equated:

$$Y=\frac{v}{1-c}\frac{dY}{dt}$$

The model is then developed by introducing delays or lags of various kinds in the accelerator (but not the multiplier) loop. It is still very simple, as in Fig. 36b; but it does serve to show up the nature of the accelerator and the importance of the type of lag introduced.

The basic model is case (i) below. Three particular types of lag are then introduced: case (ii), a simple exponential lag; case (iii), two equal exponential lags in sequence; and case (iv), a fixed-time delay. The following table shows, first, the relation of input and feed-back, and then the corresponding transfer function $F(p)$ obtained by the ordinary rules (see also 9.4, Ex. 2, above). The operator notation $D=\frac{d}{dt}$ is used to facilitate the writing of $F(p)$. The scalar multiple of the feed-back is denoted by $k=\frac{v}{1-c}=\frac{v}{s}$, i.e. the ratio of the power of the accelerator to the marginal propensity to save. Hence, $k>0$ and the value can be quite large.

Case	Input/Feed-back	$F(p)$
(i) No lag	$Y=kDY$	kp
(ii) Single exponential lag	$Y=k\dfrac{\kappa}{D+\kappa}DY$	$k\dfrac{\kappa p}{p+\kappa}$
(iii) Two equal exponential lags	$Y=k\left(\dfrac{2\kappa}{D+2\kappa}\right)^{2}DY$	$k\left(\dfrac{2\kappa}{p+2\kappa}\right)^{2}p$
(iv) Fixed-time delay	$Y=k\,DY(t-\theta)$	$kpe^{-p\theta}$

In the analysis of the continuous lags, the unit of time can be chosen so that $\kappa = 1$, i.e. the time-constant of lag $T = \dfrac{1}{\kappa} = 1$. The time-unit is that of the lag in the accelerator. Similarly, in analysing the fixed-time delay, take $\theta = 1$ so that the time-unit is the fixed delay of the accelerator.

Case (i): No lag.

The free variation $(p = \alpha + i\omega)$ is given by $F(p) = kp = 1$, i.e. $p = \dfrac{1}{k}$. Hence,

$$\alpha = \frac{1}{k} = \frac{s}{v} \quad \text{and} \quad \omega = 0$$

The free variation is non-oscillatory ($\omega = 0$), and shown by the steady movement $e^{\alpha t}$ where $\alpha = \dfrac{s}{v} > 0$. The variation is steady and explosive, as in the Harrod-Domar growth theory.

Case (ii): Single exponential lag ($\kappa = 1$).

Free variation is given by $F(p) = k\,\dfrac{p}{p+1} = 1$, i.e. $p = \dfrac{1}{k-1}$

Hence $\qquad\qquad\qquad\qquad \alpha = \dfrac{1}{k-1} \quad \text{and} \quad \omega = 0$

Again the free variation is non-oscillatory of form $e^{\alpha t}$, where $\alpha = \dfrac{1}{k-1}$. The variation is usually explosive $\left(k = \dfrac{v}{s} > 1,\ \alpha > 0\right)$ but it is possible, when the accelerator is very weak, to have a damped movement

$$\left(k = \frac{v}{s} < 1,\ \alpha < 0\right).$$

Case (iii): Two equal exponential lags ($\kappa = 1$).

Free variation is given by $F(p) = k\,\dfrac{p}{(\frac{1}{2}p+1)^2} = 1$

i.e. $\qquad\qquad\qquad\qquad \frac{1}{4}p^2 - (k-1)p + 1 = 0$

giving $\qquad\qquad\qquad\qquad p = 2(k-1) \pm 2\sqrt{k(k-2)}$

When $k = \dfrac{v}{s} > 2$, which may be regarded as the more usual possibility, the two values of p are real and positive. Again $\omega = 0$ and $\alpha > 0$ for each of the two modes of free variation. Both variations are steady and explosive.

It is quite possible that $k=\dfrac{v}{s}<2$. In this case, the values of p are conjugate complex, i.e. $p=\alpha \pm i\omega$ where :

$$\alpha=2(k-1) \quad \text{and} \quad \omega=2\sqrt{k(2-k)}$$

The free variation is an oscillation of frequency ω $\left(\text{period } \dfrac{2\pi}{\omega}\right)$. It is explosive if $1<k=\dfrac{v}{s}<2$ and damped if $k=\dfrac{v}{s}<1$.

The introduction of the double lag makes for the possibility of an oscillatory free variation, usually explosive but just possibly damped. From the analysis of 5.8 above, it can be said that lags arising in practice are not likely to be of the simple (exponential) form ; a double lag is more realistic and more than two lags in sequence may be a still better fit to the distribution $f(t)$ actually found. Triple and higher-order lags can be examined on the same lines (see Ex. 1 and 2 below) and they make it more likely that the free variation of the multiplier-accelerator system is oscillatory (though perhaps explosive).

Case (iv): *Fixed-time delay* $(\theta=1)$.
The equation in p for free variation, $F(p)=1$, is now more complicated :

$$kpe^{-p}=1 \quad \dotfill (1)$$

Write $p=\alpha+i\omega$, $e^{-i\omega}=\cos \omega -i \sin \omega$, and equate " real " and imaginary parts of (1) :

$$(\alpha \cos \omega +\omega \sin \omega)e^{-\alpha}=\frac{1}{k} \quad \text{and} \quad \alpha \sin \omega -\omega \cos \omega=0 \quad \dots\dots(2)$$

From the second equation of (2), $\alpha=\dfrac{\omega}{\tan \omega}$. Substitute in the first equation :

$$-\frac{\omega}{\tan \omega}=\log \left(\frac{1}{k}\frac{\sin \omega}{\omega}\right)$$

Hence ω is given in terms of k, and then α in terms of ω and so in terms of k, by the pair of relations :

$$\frac{\omega}{\tan \omega}+\log \frac{\sin \omega}{\omega}=\log k \quad \text{and} \quad \alpha=\frac{\omega}{\tan \omega} \quad \dots\dots\dots(3)$$

Notice that $\omega=0$ is a possible solution, so that, of the equations (2), the second is automatically satisfied and the first gives $k\alpha e^{-\alpha}=1$, which is (1) with real root $p=\alpha$ substituted. Hence, real solutions of (1) are sought first (non-oscillatory free variation), and then values of α and ω satisfying (3) are to be found for free oscillations.

The solution proceeds in graphical terms, on exactly the same lines as in 8.5 above for the Kalecki model. It is also shown in Tustin (1953), Fig. 24. For smaller values of $k=\dfrac{v}{s}<2\cdot7$, there is no real root of (1); the main solution is a low frequency oscillation $(0<\omega<\pi)$ which is mildly damped or explosive according to the magnitude of k. The period of the oscillation is $\dfrac{2\pi}{\omega}>2$, i.e. more than twice the length of the delay. For large values of $k=\dfrac{v}{s}>2\cdot7$, there are two real and positive roots of (1) and the main solution is a steady and explosive free variation. This range of possibilities, for increasing power of the accelerator (and smaller propensities to save), is in line with expectation. However, to the main solution in each case is added a range of subsidiary solutions, given as oscillations of increasing frequency, i.e. a series of values of ω, the first in the range $2\pi<\omega<3\pi$ and the others at intervals of about 2π. The oscillations are increasingly explosive, as the frequency increases and also as k takes larger values. These subsidiary oscillations $\left(\text{with period } \dfrac{2\pi}{\omega}<1\right)$ all take place within the time-interval of the delay in the accelerator.

The range of increasingly explosive oscillations, of high frequency and small period, is characteristic of the solution of an economic model which has one or more fixed-time delays. What is now evident is that the high frequency solutions are essentially spurious, arising because of the rigid and unrealistic assumption of a fixed-time delay. Once a distributed lag is introduced, e.g. one approximated by a few exponential lags in sequence, the basic free variation (oscillatory or steady, damped or explosive) remains but the " overtones " of high frequency oscillations disappear.

EXERCISES 9.5

1. Show that for a triple exponential lag, with total time constant $=\dfrac{1}{\kappa}=1$, in the accelerator of the model of the text, the transfer function is $F(p)=k\,\dfrac{p}{(\frac{1}{3}p+1)^3}$. Hence show that the free variation is given by a cubic equation in p and that there cannot be more than one free oscillation.

2. Generalise the result of the previous exercise to the case of a multiple exponential lag of any order. Deduce that alternative free oscillations can arise when four (or more) exponential lags are taken in sequence.

9.6 The Engineer's Approach : Linear and Non-linear Systems

The method outlined above, using the engineer's concept of a transfer function, is designed to provide a quick solution of an economic (or engineering) model as represented by a *linear* closed-loop scheme. The frequency and damping of all free variations in the system are found, *provided* only that the transfer function $F(p)$ can be written and some means devised for the algebraic solution of $F(p) = 1$. All kinds of relations (derivatives, integrals, delays and lags, analytical or empirical) can appear in a linear model ; the operational approach of the method translates them all into algebraic equivalents and the solution depends only on algebraic manipulation (see Appendix A).

The limitations of the method are to be noticed. If the model is at all complex, the equation $F(p) = 1$ is not readily solved algebraically and in general terms. The method is better adapted to the solution of models in particular cases than in general form with unspecified parameters $\Big($like $k = \dfrac{v}{s}\Big)$. Even in numerical cases, the solution of $F(p) = 1$ may need to proceed graphically and empirically. Further, only the frequency and damping of the free variation is found, common to all variables in the linear system. To get the amplitude and phase of a particular variable, a separate calculation with initial conditions is needed.

It is instructive to compare the method with the " classical " approach, i.e. the reduction of the equations of the model to a single equation in a selected variable. This may be a differential, difference or some form of mixed equation. If the equation is a differential one, the transfer function method has no advantage ; the equation $F(p) = 1$ is exactly the same as the auxiliary equation of the differential equation. They are, therefore, solved in the same way, whether readily or not. Indeed, the use of the Laplace Transform method—also developed by engineers and related to the present approach to the problem—is required to complete the solution in particular cases, i.e. to give the full solution subject to specified initial conditions. Much the same is true if a difference equation results, except that the final solution in particular cases may need a step-by-step computation from the equation itself.

The advantage of the transfer function method, and of the engineer's approach, lies in other directions. The method works even if the single equation obtained is of mixed form, as in case (iv) of the example of 9.5 above. There is no need actually to get the mixed equation ; the schematic diagram and the algebraic conversion of relations (via Laplace

M.E.

Transforms) into $F(p)=1$ give the basis for computing solutions by numerical or graphical methods. Moreover, from what has been said at the end of 9.3 above, the relations of the model (e.g. the lags) do not need to be analytical ; they can be empirical and adjusted to each particular case.

Two points can be made which are obvious to an engineer, less so to an economist. The engineer does not introduce any kind of lag (or other relation) into a system ; he knows that the type and form of the lag, whether analytical or empirical, makes all the difference to the solution. The economist often takes a more casual line, noting the existence but paying little attention to the form of lags ; this is partly because his data are often time series, suitable only for handling with simple lags of one or more periods.

The other point is that the engineer does not often attempt general solutions ; he aims at computing (by numerical or graphical methods) particular solutions, usually a whole string of them. The job is a computational one, to be facilitated by all the practical devices to hand. This is an approach not readily adopted by the economist, brought up in the tradition of general solution of problems. The questions he puts tend to be of the kind : what ranges of values of v and s give rise to explosive oscillations in income? As economic models become more complex, and have a greater empirical content, to make them applicable to the real world, the answers to general questions become less possible. The economist may need, therefore, to shift his ground from the general to the particular, and to follow the methods and the experience of the engineer.

The computational job can only be done with the kind of tools used by the engineer—the draughtsman's board for graphical work and (particularly) the various types of mechanical or electronic analogue computors available. Analogue solutions have been obtained for such economic models as those of Goodwin and Kalecki, see Smith and Erdley (1952) and Tustin (1953). Analogue computors or simulators, moreover, have the advantage that they can be used in exposition and for trying out quickly many alternative hypotheses, see Phillips (1950, 1956).

There remains a basic limitation of the method of transfer functions developed above. Its application is, as yet, confined to sinusoidal variation (including steady exponential growth) in a linear system. Linear models may be generally appropriate in engineering problems where everything is more under control. They are certainly not so for economic models. A characteristic of economic variation, to be " explained " by a model, is that oscillations are not symmetric (and so not even approximately sinusoidal) and that their amplitude is not fixed by extraneous factors. A linear model leaves the amplitude of an oscillation to be determined either by the accidents of more or less remote historical (initial) conditions, or by extraneous factors. These should be brought into the model if it is to be fully explanatory.

Non-linear elements must appear in economic models ; the question is how and where to include them. One possible method is to design a basic model in linear form—and so easily handled—and then to use it in a wider context where non-linear elements (e.g. assumed and empirical " floors ", " ceilings " or mean values) can be introduced. The Samuelson-Hicks model, and also that of Phillips, are of this kind. The alternative is to " build in " a non-linear element in designing a model to be reasonably self-sufficient, as done by Goodwin in his model illustrated by Fig. 37 III.

The second method may be preferable but it makes solution very difficult, as is seen in the methods adapted by Goodwin (1951) in his own solution of his model. The shape of a self-sustaining oscillation in a non-linear model is not sinusoidal (or even approximately so). This would not matter, since any fixed-period oscillation can be analysed into sinusoidal components (by Fourier Series, 4.7 above), except for the fact that the sinusoidal components cannot be followed *separately* through a non-linear system because of their changing amplitudes and coefficients. It is only in certain circumstances that non-linear closed-loop systems can be analysed, e.g. by methods developed by Tustin (1947) and applied to the Goodwin model by Bothwell (1952). There is much room for development here, both in engineering and in economic problems.

9.7 Regulation in Closed-loop Systems

An economic model needs to be explanatory, but it must also provide an indication of what may go wrong and of how to put it right. For example, because of a shift in demand, the variation of national income may be about a level regarded as " too low " and showing " undesirable " fluctuations—whatever the criteria may be. The situation is to be " corrected " by bringing national income up to an appropriate level and by ironing out fluctuations. The same kind of problem arises in engineering when electric circuit systems, for example, are designed for automatic adjustment to certain standards. There is the question of regulation in economic and engineering problems alike.

Suppose that a certain system has free variation with a damping factor which is not sufficiently strong, e.g. $\alpha < 0$ and small (mild damping) or

$\alpha > 0$ (explosive). It may be required to regulate the system to achieve a damping of a certain standard (e.g. $\alpha = -0.5$). At the same time, it may be required that the period of any oscillations should not become short. One possibility is to alter the relations of the system, e.g. to change the lags ; this is scarcely practical in economics, whatever may be the case in engineering. An alternative is to introduce an additional feed-back loop in the system, a device adopted (e.g.) in electric circuit systems. Then, if $F_1(p)$ is the feed-back transfer function of the original system, and if $F_2(p)$ is the transfer function around the complete loop added, the result of 9.4 above shows that the regulated system has a feed-back transfer function of the form $\dfrac{F_1(p)}{1 - F_2(p)}$. The choice of the additional loop, and so of $F_2(p)$, may make it possible for the new condition :

$$\frac{F_1(p)}{1 - F_2(p)} = 1$$

to give a free variation $p = \alpha + i\omega$ of the required form.

One economic case of a simple kind is given below for illustration. It is deliberately chosen in a form which has an alternative and more straight-forward solution (see Ex. 2 below), so that the method, which is quite general, can be checked in its operation.

The multiplier-accelerator model of 9.5 above in case (iii) has a double exponential lag in the accelerator and its free variation is given by :

$$F_1(p) = k \frac{p}{(\tfrac{1}{2}p + 1)^2} = 1 \quad \dots\dots\dots\dots\dots\dots(1)$$

If $1 < k = \dfrac{v}{s} < 2$, the free variation is an explosive oscillation :

$$\alpha = 2(k - 1) \quad \text{and} \quad \omega = 2\sqrt{k(2 - k)} \quad \dots\dots\dots\dots(2)$$

The regulation proposed is the addition of an official demand (G) to income (Y) and official policy makes G depend on the rate of change of income with a negative multiple $(-g)$. Suppose further that the official response to changing income has the same (double exponential) lag as private investment demand. Then :

$$G = -g \frac{1}{(\tfrac{1}{2}D + 1)^2} DY$$

and the transfer function around the added loop (from Y to G back to Y, with allowance for the multiplier) is :

$$F_2(p) = -k' \frac{p}{(\tfrac{1}{2}p + 1)^2} \quad \left(k' = \frac{g}{s} \right) \quad \dots\dots\dots\dots(3)$$

Free variation in the regulated system, from (1) and (3), is given by :

$$k\frac{p}{(\tfrac{1}{2}p+1)^2}\frac{1}{1+k'\dfrac{p}{(\tfrac{1}{2}p+1)^2}}=1$$

i.e.

$$k\frac{p}{(\tfrac{1}{2}p+1)^2+k'p}=1$$

which gives p as the root of :

$$\tfrac{1}{4}p^2+(1-k+k')p+1=0$$

i.e.

$$p=-2(1-k+k')\pm 2i\sqrt{1-(1-k+k')^2}$$

Choose $k'=\dfrac{g}{s}$ in the range $k-1<k'<k$ and p is complex with :

$$\alpha=-2(1-k+k')\quad\text{and}\quad\omega=2\sqrt{1-(1-k+k')^2}\ \ldots\ldots\ldots\ldots(4)$$

The comparison of the regulated with the original system is between the oscillations of (4) and those of (2) above. Clearly, within limits, k' can be selected to make α equal the required level (say $\alpha=-0\cdot4$) without making ω unduly great, and the period of oscillation $\left(\dfrac{2\pi}{\omega}\right)$ too short.

As a numerical example, take $v=0\cdot4$, $s=0\cdot25$ and so $k=1\cdot6$. The unregulated (explosive) oscillation (2) has :

$$\alpha=1\cdot2\quad\text{and}\quad\omega=1\cdot6$$

If $\alpha=-0\cdot4$ is the criterion for regulation, then $k'=0\cdot8$ must be taken in (4), giving the regulated (damped) oscillation :

$$\alpha=-0\cdot4\quad\text{and}\quad\omega=1\cdot96$$

Hence $g=k's=0\cdot8\times0\cdot25=0\cdot2$ is the coefficient necessary in the official demand G, i.e. 20% of the change in income to be corrected.

The original period of oscillation $\left(\dfrac{2\pi}{1\cdot6}\right)$ is nearly four times the length of the accelerator lag ; the regulated period $\left(\dfrac{2\pi}{1\cdot96}\right)$ is still over three times.

When the regulating loop comes to be added in the schematic diagram (Fig. 41), it is seen that $G=-\dfrac{g}{v}I$ by the form of official

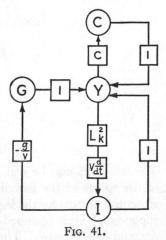

FIG. 41.

demand assumed and that the loop can be taken from I to Y with the multiple $\left(-\dfrac{g}{v}\right)$. In fact, this particular official demand is a regulation of induced private investment I; when income Y is falling, I is negative, replacement of assets are not being made and this is offset by a corresponding official demand (e.g. public works).

EXERCISES 9.7

1. Show that it is immaterial whether the feed-back transfer function of the regulated system is taken as $\dfrac{F_1(p)}{1-F_2(p)}$ (i.e. feed-back in the original loop), or as $\dfrac{F_2(p)}{1-F_1(p)}$ (i.e. feed-back in the added loop).

2. Show that the case of regulation in the multiplier-accelerator model of the text is equivalent to reducing the power of the accelerator from v to $(v-g)$. Change k to $(k-k')$ in (1) and hence obtain (4) directly from (2).

9.8 Economic Stabilisation Policy

The method of regulation, by the addition of one or more feed-back loops to the system, is the one used in 8.8 and 8.9 above in relation to the Phillips multiplier-accelerator model. The results of the regulation of this model can now be conveniently reviewed along the lines of the transfer function approach.

The basic multiplier-accelerator model is a very simple one; it has single exponential lags in the accelerator $\left(\text{time-constant}=\dfrac{1}{\kappa}\right)$ and in the production process $\left(\text{time-constant}=\dfrac{1}{\lambda}\right)$. The scheme is Fig. 37 I. The transfer function is obtained at once from the diagram (as in 9.4 above):

$$F_1(p)=v\,\frac{\kappa\lambda p}{(p+\kappa)(p+\lambda s)}$$

Hence free variation in the (unregulated) model is given by p satisfying:

$$v\,\frac{\kappa\lambda p}{(p+\kappa)(p+\lambda s)}=1$$

i.e. $$p^2+\{\kappa-\lambda(v\kappa-s)\}p+\kappa\lambda s=0$$

The two roots may be real, or they may be conjugate complex, according to the values of the parameters: v and s for the multiplier-accelerator structure, κ and λ for the lags. The free variation is either a pair of steady exponential terms (damped or explosive) or a sinusoidal oscillation (again damped or explosive). The possibilities are fully examined in 8.7 above, where it is indicated that an explosive oscillation is the likely result. For example :

if $\qquad\qquad s=0\cdot25,\ v=0\cdot6,\ \kappa=1,\ \lambda=4$

then $\qquad\qquad\qquad p^2-0\cdot4p+1=0$

giving $\qquad\qquad\qquad p=0\cdot2\pm0\cdot98i$

This is a mildly explosive oscillation ($\alpha=0\cdot2$) and the period is $\dfrac{2\pi}{0\cdot98}$, or a little over six times the accelerator lag.

The regulation of the system is taken as the addition of official demand G to the unregulated demand Z of the system. G can be related to income and its changes in various ways and it is taken with a single exponential lag $\left(\text{time-constant}=\dfrac{1}{\beta}\right)$. If three different policies (proportional, integral and derivative) are applied in combination, then

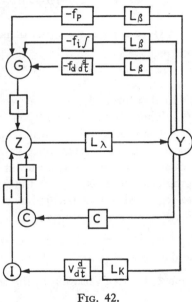

FIG. 42.

$$G=-\frac{\beta}{D+\beta}\Big(f_pY+f_i\int Y\,dt+f_dDY\Big)$$

and three feed-back loops are added to obtain the regulated system of Fig. 42. The feed-back transfer function (at Z in the model) taken round the additional loops together $\Big($and the multiplier loop with transfer function $\dfrac{c\lambda}{p+\lambda}\Big)$ is :

$$F_2(p)=-\frac{\beta}{p+\beta}\frac{\lambda}{p+\lambda}\,\bar{G}\,\frac{1}{1-\dfrac{c\lambda}{p+\lambda}}$$

$$=-\frac{\beta\lambda\bar{G}}{(p+\beta)(p+\lambda s)}$$

where $\bar{G}=f_p+\dfrac{1}{p}f_i+pf_d$, obtained by writing $D=p$ and $\int=\dfrac{1}{p}$ in the expression in G.

Hence the regulated system has a feed-back transfer function:

$$F(p) = \frac{F_1(p)}{1 - F_2(p)}$$

$$= \frac{\kappa\lambda v p}{(p+\kappa)(p+\lambda s)} \frac{1}{1 + \dfrac{\beta\lambda\bar{G}}{(p+\beta)(p+\lambda s)}}$$

$$= \frac{\kappa\lambda v p}{(p+\kappa)(p+\lambda s) + \beta\lambda\dfrac{p+\kappa}{p+\beta}\bar{G}}$$

The value of p for free variation is given by $F(p) = 1$, which is the equation:

$$p^2 + \{\kappa - \lambda(v\kappa - s)\}p + \kappa\lambda s + \beta\lambda\frac{p+\kappa}{p+\beta}\bar{G} = 0$$

In this form, the effect of regulation is seen in the additional term in $\bar{G}$. There is no easy and general way of solving this equation, for un-specified values of the additional parameters β, f_p, f_i and f_d of the regulating mechanism. However, once values of these parameters are specified, the equation can be solved by ordinary algebra (and usually by numerical or graphical methods) to give the values of p for free variation in the model as regulated in the specified way.

As a numerical case, take:

$$s = 0.25, \ v = 0.6, \ \beta = 2, \ \kappa = 1, \ \lambda = 4$$
and
$$f_p = 2, \ f_i = 2, \ f_d = 0.55$$

Hence, for free variation in the regulated system, p is given by:

$$p^2 - 0.4p + 1 + 16\frac{p+1}{p(p+2)}(0.275p^2 + p + 1) = 0$$

i.e. $$p^4 + 6p^3 + 20.6p^2 + 34p + 16 = 0$$

Solution by graphical methods gives four roots:

$$p = -0.74, \ -2.17 \text{ and } -1.55 \pm 2.76i$$

The first two roots correspond to steady exponential variations, both highly damped. The more important free variation in the regulated system is a sinusoidal oscillation given by the other roots; it is heavily damped ($\alpha = -1.55$) and the period is $\dfrac{2\pi}{2.76}$ or over twice the accelerator lag. The original explosive oscillation ($\alpha = 0.2$) has been regulated into a strongly damped one ($\alpha = -1.55$).

The model taken here has *single* exponential lags in the accelerator and on the supply side. The analysis is easily extended to apply to more " realistic " lags of *multiple* form, e.g. double or triple exponential lags. The equation in p, for free variation, becomes of higher order ; it has a larger number of roots and there is a greater range of possibilities of free variation to be considered. But the equation can be solved by algebraic and graphical processes ; the method of tackling the problem is the same.

The ease and power of the method based on transfer functions (and Laplace Transforms) is clear from the solution of this problem. The relations of the linear system and its regulating mechanism involve all kinds of *time variations* (derivatives, integrals, lags). The method replaces these by *algebraic expressions in the variable p* representing the frequency and damping of the free variations in the system. Functions of time are replaced by functions of frequency, the characteristic of the Laplace Transform. The result is that the whole problem is reduced to the algebraic solution of an ordinary equation in one variable. The equation itself is easily and quickly written ; its solution is a matter of algebra, aided by well-known numerical and graphical methods for particular cases. After the first and rapid transformation to a function of frequency, the solution is a job of computation of a familiar kind.

The method also has its limits. It is designed only to give the frequency and damping of the free variation in the system—usually the most important but not the only consideration. It still leaves open the problem of getting the amplitude and phase (and the ultimate level) of any of the variables in the system, e.g. income Y. In this *particular* case, the model and its forms of regulation are simple, and the whole system gives an equation in Y which is of linear differential form with constant coefficients. Hence, again in this *particular* case, the solution can proceed by tackling the differential equation by the Laplace Transform method in numerical cases with specified initial conditions. This is done by Phillips (1954), on the lines indicated in 8.9 above. The particular case of regulation considered above is one of Phillips' cases, shown in complete solution in curve (d) of his Fig. 9.

The type of economic model—the Phillips multiplier-accelerator—used here as an example of economic regulation also has its limits. First, it is highly simplified ; second, it is linear. On both scores it is not directly applicable to the real economic world. Consequently, the effects of regulation as analysed here are indicative, without being at all operative, of a policy of economic stabilisation to be applied in practice.

The model needs to be developed in two ways, and possibly in two stages. In the first development, the linear property of the model is retained while the relations can be extended to include other factors, e.g. external trade, factor prices and the rate of interest. At the same time, analytical (and simplified) expressions of some of the relations can be replaced by empirical forms, particularly in the lags of the model, see Phillips (1956, 1957). The result would be that the resulting equation in one variable (say, income) would cease to be of the simple differential type, and so no longer capable of complete solution by the method of Laplace Transforms. The important point, however, is that the transfer function $F(p)$ can still be written, so that the computation task of obtaining the frequency and damping of free variations is not essentially changed.

The other development is to introduce essential non-linear elements into the model, either by the device of assuming empirical " floors ", " ceilings " and so on, or in the relations of the model itself. Once a model has non-linear features, its free variation takes the more " realistic " form of non-sinusoidal oscillations of amplitude and phase fixed by the model itself. The method of transfer functions, as developed above, breaks down and needs to be replaced by other methods. Some appropriate methods have been developed more recently by engineers and it is here that there is greatest scope for further work.

The engineer does not have cut-and-dried techniques which the economist can take over. It remains true, however, that the methods of regulating closed-loop control systems in engineering need to be understood, and in part taken over, by the economist. Tustin (1953) observes that " one of the outstanding advances in engineering of modern times " has been " to combine precision of control with stability " which has " made possible new and effective control devices in almost every branch of industry from radio to oil refineries " (p. 72). The economist, if he is to develop models with practical applications, has much to learn from the engineer. Three things are at least clear : the importance of taking lags and other relations in particular and appropriate forms ; the need for non-linear elements, introduced with care and restraint ; the consequent shift in emphasis from the general to the particular—from broad analysis to a routine job of computation.

REFERENCES

Allen (R. G. D.) (1955) : " The Engineer's Approach to Economic Models ", *Economica*, **22,** 158–68.
Bothwell (F. E.) (1952) : " The Method of Equivalent Linearization ", *Econometrica*, **20,** 269–83.

Brown (G. S.) and Campbell (D. P.) (1948) : *Principles of Servomechanisms* (Wiley, 1948).

Carslaw (H. S.) and Jaeger (J. C.) (1941, 1948) : *Operational Methods in Applied Mathematics* (Oxford, First Ed. 1941, Second Ed. 1948).

Frisch (R.) (1933) : " Propagation Problems and Impulse Problems in Dynamic Economics ", in *Economic Essays in Honour of Gustav Cassel* (Allen and Unwin, 1933).

Gardner (M. F.) and Barnes (J. L.) (1942) : *Transients in Linear Systems* (Wiley, 1942).

Goodwin (R. M.) (1951) : " The Non-linear Accelerator and the Persistence of Business Cycles ", *Econometrica*, **19**, 1–17.

Phillips (A. W.) (1950) : " Mechanical Models in Economic Dynamics ", *Economica*, **17**, 283–305.

Phillips (A. W.) (1954) : " Stabilisation Policy in a Closed Economy ", *Economic Journal*, **64**, 290–323.

Phillips, (A. W.) (1956) : " Some notes on the Estimation of Time-Forms of Reactions in Interdependent Dynamic Systems ", *Economica*, **23**, 99–113.

Phillips (A. W.) (1957) : " Stabilisation Policy and the Time-Form of Lagged Responses ", *Economic Journal*, **67**, 265–77.

Smith (O. J. M.) and Erdley (H. F.) (1952) : " An Electronic Analogue for an Economic System ", *Electrical Engineering*, **71**, 362–66.

Tustin (A.) (1947) : " A Method of Analysing the Effect of Certain Kinds of Non-linearity in Closed Cycle Control Systems ", *Journal of the Institution of Electrical Engineers*, **94**, Part 2A, 152–60.

Tustin (A.) (1953) : *The Mechanism of Economic Systems* (Heinemann, 1953).

CHAPTER 10

GENERAL ECONOMIC EQUILIBRIUM

10.1 Equilibrium of Exchange

GENERAL equilibrium of production and exchange is developed here under static conditions of " pure competition ", in the sense that no individual (consumer or firm) is in a position to influence prices directly. Prices are parameters, given to consumers and firms, to be determined only by market conditions. Pure competition does not imply that there is " free entry " into any group of producers ; this is a separate concept and conditions for " free entry " may or may not be added to those of pure competition.

The analysis is based on the work of Walras and Pareto as developed by later writers such as Hicks (1939, 1946) and Samuelson (1947). It is of the most sweeping and all-embracing kind ; it is concerned with the multitude of individual consumers and producers in the economy and it restricts in no way the number of variables handled. The danger is that the analysis becomes so general as to be completely sterile. General equilibrium is closed in the sense that all variables are determined together from the given conditions. Equations may be counted against unknowns to determine that the system is consistent with equilibrium ; but little else may be known about the equilibrium, even whether there is one at all, or more than one. Nor is there any implication that an equilibrium is stable in a dynamic sense.

What is required is the derivation of " general laws for the working of a price-system with many markets " (Hicks (1946), p. 6), of " meaningful theorems . . . about empirical data which could conceivably be refuted if only under ideal conditions " (Samuelson (1947), p. 4). Something in the system is changed ; in what direction do the variables then move? To answer such questions it is generally necessary to consider an open system—a sector of the complete closed system in which some of the variables are parameters to which arbitrary values can be assigned. An open system may lead only to partial analysis, but it is flexible enough for " meaningful theorems " to be obtained.

The analysis of equilibrium of exchange was left by Walras in a form to which only minor glosses need be added. As a matter of notation, so important when large numbers of variables are handled, small letters like x are used for quantities bought or sold by individual consumers or producers, and capital letters like X for market aggregates. Subscripts are added to differentiate between commodities $(r=1, 2, \ldots m)$ or between individual consumers or producers $(i=1, 2, \ldots n \text{ or } j=1, 2, \ldots N)$. There are m commodities (subscript r), n individual consumers (subscript i) and later N firms (subscript j). So X_r may be the market aggregate for the rth commodity and x_{ri} the purchase of the rth commodity by the ith consumer.

In a general exchange economy, let $\bar{x}_{ri}$ be the given amount of the rth commodity initially held by the ith individual and x_{ri} the corresponding but unknown amount after exchange. The price at which the exchange of the rth commodity takes place is denoted by p_r. Only the price ratios are to be determined and it is convenient to take the mth commodity as *numéraire* and to write $p_m = 1$. The total number of variables is

$$m(n+1) - 1,$$

i.e. mn variables x_{ri} for $r=1, 2, \ldots m$ and $i=1, 2, \ldots n$ and $(m-1)$ prices p_r for $r=1, 2, \ldots (m-1)$.

There are two sets of conditions for equilibrium, one relating to the purchases or sales of individuals, the other to market factors.

(i) Each individual fixes his purchases or sales to maximise his " utility " subject to the balancing of his budget, given the market prices. An ordinal utility function is assumed for each individual :

$$u_i = u_i(x_{1i}, x_{2i}, \ldots x_{mi}) \qquad (i=1, 2, \ldots n)$$

with continuous partial derivatives :

$$u_{ri} = \frac{\partial u_i}{\partial x_{ri}} \qquad \begin{matrix} (r=1, 2, \ldots m) \\ (i=1, 2, \ldots n) \end{matrix}$$

The ratios of u_{ri}, for various r, are independent of the ordinal property of u_i. The condition $u_i = $ maximum subject to the budget balance :

$$\Sigma p_r(x_{ri} - \bar{x}_{ri}) = 0$$

is that the ratios of the " marginal utilities " u_{ri} (or the marginal rates of substitution) are equal to the given ratios of prices p_r. Since $p_m = 1$, the condition is

$$\frac{u_{ri}}{p_r} = u_{mi}$$

for each value of r from 1 to $(m-1)$ and for each i from 1 to n.

(ii) The market condition is that prices must be consistent with equality of demand and supply (purchases and sales) for each commodity in the aggregate. This is simply that $\sum_i (x_{ri} - \bar{x}_{ri}) = 0$ for each r. One of these relations, however, can be derived from the others. Suppose that

$$\sum_i (x_{ri} - \bar{x}_{ri}) = 0 \quad \text{for } r = 1, 2, \ldots (m-1).$$

Then, by summing the budget balance conditions for all individuals :

$$0 = \sum_i \sum_r p_r (x_{ri} - \bar{x}_{ri}) = \sum_r p_r \{ \sum_i (x_{ri} - \bar{x}_{ri}) \} = p_m \sum_i (x_{mi} - \bar{x}_{mi})$$

i.e. $\qquad\qquad \sum_i (x_{ri} - \bar{x}_{ri}) = 0 \qquad \text{also for } r = m.$

The last market condition, for $r = m$, can thus be eliminated.

The conditions for equilibrium are then :

(i) (a) $\dfrac{u_{ri}}{p_r} = u_{mi}$ $\qquad \begin{cases} r = 1, 2, \ldots (m-1) \\ i = 1, 2, \ldots n \end{cases}$

(b) $\sum_r p_r (x_{ri} - \bar{x}_{ri}) = 0 \qquad i = 1, 2, \ldots n$

(ii) $\sum_i (x_{ri} - \bar{x}_{ri}) = 0 \qquad r = 1, 2, \ldots (m-1)$

The number of equations is $(m-1)n$ in (i) (a), n in (i) (b) and $(m-1)$ in (ii), a total of $m(n+1) - 1$, equal to the number of variables. The system is closed and consistent with an equilibrium of exchange.

The complete system can be divided into open sectors and equilibrium reached in stages. For *individual demand*, there are $(m-1)$ equations in (i) (a) and one equation in (i) (b) for the ith individual. These m equations suffice to determine the variables x_{ri}, for $r = 1, 2, \ldots m$ and for given i, in terms of the prices. *Market equilibrium* is then concerned with the equation of aggregate demand and supply, i.e. the equations (ii). Write

$$X_r = \sum_i x_{ri} \quad \text{and} \quad \bar{X}_r = \sum_i \bar{x}_{ri}$$

so that X_r is the aggregate demand and $\bar{X}_r$ the aggregate supply of the rth commodity ($r = 1, 2, \ldots m$). $\bar{X}_r$ is a given datum and X_r is determined in terms of the prices p_r by individual demands. Hence conditions (ii) are simply :

$$X_r = \bar{X}_r \qquad r = 1, 2, \ldots (m-1)$$

or $(m-1)$ equations in terms of the $(m-1)$ prices p_r, with $p_m = 1$. On the market, individual demands (in relation to given initial supplies) come together to determine market prices consistent with equilibrium.

The market conditions (ii) imply that "prices must equate demand and supply". This does not rule out the possibility of negative prices. Can the conditions be strengthened to: "there must be non-negative prices equating demand and supply"? This is not so. In fact, as Zeuthen (1942, 1955) emphasizes, the conditions need to be recast: *either* demand equals supply (no unemployed resources) *or* the price of the commodity is zero. This is the kind of formulation most easily handled by the techniques of Chapters 16 and 17 below.

EXERCISES 10.1

1. Take the case of two individuals ($i = 1$, 2) and two commodities X and Y, and assume quadratic utility functions:

$$u_1 = a_1 x_1{}^2 + 2h_1 x_1 y_1 + b_1 y_1{}^2 \; ; \quad u_2 = a_2 x_2{}^2 + 2h_2 x_2 y_2 + b_2 y_2{}^2$$

Write the conditions for equilibrium of exchange and obtain the individual demands (x_1, y_1, x_2 and y_2) explicitly in terms of the price ratio p for the two commodities.

2. In the case of the previous exercise, show that the market conditions reduce to a single equation in p which is a cubic. Write the expression for the product of the three roots in p and indicate that, under plausible conditions on u_1 and u_2, the product is positive. Hence show that, under these conditions, there is at least one positive value of p consistent with equilibrium.

3. Show that, in obtaining the cubic in p of the previous exercise, it is necessary that $(a_1 - 2h_1 p + b_1 p^2)$ and $(a_2 - 2h_2 p + b_2 p^2)$ are not zero. Show that this is so if u_1 is positive for all values of x_1 and y_1 (not both zero) and similarly for u_2. Why can this be safely assumed?

10.2 Equilibrium with Fixed Production Coefficients

It is still assumed that there are n individuals ($i = 1, 2, \ldots n$) possessing initial amounts $\bar{x}_{ri}$ of m commodities ($r = 1, 2, \ldots m$) and demanding final amounts x_{ri} of the commodities at given price ratios $p_r(p_m = 1$ for *numéraire*). The conditions for individual demand are equations (i) (*a*) and (i) (*b*) of 10.1 above.

It is now assumed that, in addition to the exchange of commodities, there are new supplies coming on to the market from production, or transformation of the original resources $\bar{x}_{ri}$. For simplicity, commodities which are intermediate goods, and which are both consumer goods and factors of production, are ignored. The set of m commodities falls into two non-overlapping groups: k factors of production ($s = 1, 2, \ldots k$) and ($m - k$) consumer goods ($t = k + 1, k + 2, \ldots m$). The subscript r is used for the whole group of m commodities; when the division is considered the subscript s refers to k factors and t to ($m - k$) consumer goods.

In the aggregate on the market, write

$$X_r = \Sigma x_{ri} \quad \text{and} \quad \bar{X}_r = \Sigma \bar{x}_{ri}$$

for the demand at given prices and for the given supply of the rth commodity. Hence, $\bar{X}_r$ is either for exchange ($r=t$) or for use as a factor of production ($r=s$); X_r is either the amount demanded of a consumer good (exchanged or from new production) or the " reservation " demand of a factor service. For some commodities (subscript s) $X_s < \bar{X}_s$ and the balance is the supply of a factor. For others (subscript t) $X_t \geqslant \bar{X}_t$ and the additional demand is from new production. Hence :

Market supply (factors) $= -(X_s - \bar{X}_s)$ $s = 1, 2, \ldots k$
Market demand (goods)$=$ $X_t - \bar{X}_t$ $t = k+1, k+2, \ldots m$

All are given as functions of the prices p_r.

New production is assumed to take place under conditions of fixed technical coefficients (no joint products, constant returns to scale). Let a_{st} be the use of the sth factor in production of unit amount of the tth product (consumer good), where the a_{st} are given constants for $s = 1, 2, \ldots k$ and $t = k+1, k+2, \ldots m$. Write Y_r as the output of the rth commodity in new production so that $Y_s \leqslant 0$ for factors ($s = 1, 2, \ldots k$) and $Y_t \geqslant 0$ for consumer goods ($t = k+1, k+2, \ldots m$). The first technical condition is that $(-Y_s) = \Sigma a_{st} Y_t$, for the total use of the factor, given the technical coefficients. Hence :

$$\Sigma a_{st} Y_t + Y_s = 0 \qquad s = 1, 2, \ldots k$$

It is assumed, further, that there is " free entry " of firms into the production industries, so that receipts and costs are equal (zero profits) for new production at the given prices. For the tth consumer good, receipts are $p_t Y_t$ and costs are $(\Sigma_s p_s a_{st}) Y_t$. Hence, the second technical condition is :

$$\Sigma_s p_s a_{st} - p_t = 0 \qquad t = k+1, k+2, \ldots m$$

To complete the system, it remains to add the market conditions of equation of demand and supply. For factors, supply is $-(X_s - \bar{X}_s)$ and demand for new production is $(-Y_s)$. For consumer goods, demand by individuals from new production is $(X_t - \bar{X}_t)$ and supply is Y_t. Hence, for factors and consumer goods alike, market conditions are :

$$Y_r = X_r - \bar{X}_r \qquad r = 1, 2, \ldots m$$

As in 10.1 above, one of these conditions (say that for $r=m$) can be derived from the other conditions (see Ex. 1 below). The dependent condition is to be eliminated. The complete system is then:

(i) (a) $\dfrac{u_{ri}}{p_r} = u_{mi}$ $\begin{cases} r=1, 2, \ldots (m-1) \\ i=1, 2, \ldots n \end{cases}$

(b) $\sum\limits_r p_r(x_{ri} - \bar{x}_{ri}) = 0$ $i=1, 2, \ldots n$

(ii) (a) $\sum\limits_s a_{st} Y_t + Y_s = 0$ $s=1, 2, \ldots k$

(b) $\sum\limits_s p_s a_{st} - p_t = 0$ $t=k+1, k+2, \ldots m$

(iii) $Y_r = \sum\limits_i (x_{ri} - \bar{x}_{ri})$ $r=1, 2, \ldots (m-1)$

The variables are x_{ri}, Y_r and p_r; their number is

$$mn + m + (m-1) = m(n+2) - 1.$$

The equations are the same in number, made up of $(m-1)n$ in (i) (a). n in (i) (b), k in (ii) (a), $(m-k)$ in (ii) (b) and $(m-1)$ in (iii). The system is closed and consistent with equilibrium.

The following is one way of showing the derivation of equilibrium in stages. Conditions (i) (a) and (i) (b) serve to give *individual demands* x_{ri} in terms of the prices. Conditions (ii) (a), relating to *production techniques*, give the factor demand $(-Y_s)$ in terms of the outputs Y_t. Conditions (ii) (b), which express the fact that " *free entry* " implies " *competitive* " *prices*, serve to give the consumer goods prices p_t in terms of factor prices p_s. The *market conditions for consumer goods*, i.e. the equations (iii) for $t=k+1, k+2, \ldots (m-1)$, give the outputs Y_t first in terms of all prices and then in terms of the factor prices p_s alone (since p_t can now be eliminated in terms of p_s). All that remains is the set of *market conditions for factors*, or the equations (iii) for $s=1, 2, \ldots k$. By the previous relations, these conditions are simply k equations in the k factor prices p_s. It is on the market for factors that all other relations of the problem come together to determine market prices consistent with equilibrium.

EXERCISES 10.2

1. Write $\sum\limits_r p_r \{\sum\limits_i (x_{ri} - \bar{x}_{ri}) - Y_r\}$, summing for $r=1, 2, \ldots m$. Show that conditions (i) (b), (ii) (a) and (ii) (b) make this expression zero. Deduce that, if conditions (iii) hold for $r=1, 2, \ldots (m-1)$, then they hold also for $r=m$.

2. For some consumer good, suppose $X_t = \bar{X}_t$ so that demand is satisfied entirely by exchange. How are the equations (i)–(iii) affected? Are they still consistent with equilibrium?

3. Add another commodity (subscript u) to the system, an intermediate good in production (i.e. no initial holdings and no demand from individuals). It is produced from factors s with fixed coefficients a_{su}, and it is itself used in production of goods t with fixed coefficients a_{ut}. Show that (ii) (b) is augmented by a further equation $\sum_s p_s a_{su} - p_u = 0$ and (ii) (a) by $\sum_t a_{ut} Y_t + Y_u = 0$. Indicate that these simply fix the price and the amount produced (and used) of the extra commodity.

10.3 General Market Equilibrium

The equilibrium analysis of the previous section is one of production and exchange, but limited to the case of constant returns to scale in production. This condition can now be relaxed and the problem generalised to allow for production by individual firms with varying technical possibilities.

There are n individuals with initial resources $\bar{x}_{ri}$ and demands x_{ri} for m commodities ($r = 1, 2, \ldots m$ and $i = 1, 2, \ldots n$). Equilibrium conditions are again written in the form (i) (a) of the previous sections. It is now assumed further that the individuals include some who act as *entrepreneurs* in control of productive firms. The budget balance, previously written as equating expenditure $\sum_r p_r x_{ri}$ to income $\sum_r p_r \bar{x}_{ri}$ from initial resources then needs to be changed. It is true that, if " free entry " is taken as implying zero net profits for all firms and entrepreneurs, then the conditions (i) (b) of the previous sections still hold. But a rather more general case is taken here, in which the ith individual is assumed to have as entrepreneurial income a fixed and given proportionate share π_i of total profits R earned in all production. His income is increased by $\pi_i R$, fixed as far as the individual is concerned, but involving a parameter R to be determined. The budget balances of the individuals, replacing conditions (i) (b), are :

$$\sum_r p_r(x_{ri} - \bar{x}_{ri}) = \pi_i R \quad \text{(where } \sum \pi_i = 1) \quad (i = 1, 2, \ldots n)$$

Notice that, if $\pi_i = 0$ is given, then the ith individual is not an entrepreneur.

Production takes place through N firms, denoted by the subscript j, each working under technical conditions given by the production function :

$$f_j(y_{1j}, y_{2j}, \ldots y_{mj}) = 0 \quad (j = 1, 2, \ldots N)$$

where y_{rj} is (if positive) the amount of the rth commodity produced and (if negative) the amount of a factor used. There can also be commodities, either factors or products, for which $y_{rj} = 0$; the particular jth firm happens neither to use nor to produce them. It is assumed that f_j has continuous partial derivatives :

$$f_{rj} = \frac{\partial f_j}{\partial y_{rj}} \qquad \begin{cases} r = 1, 2, \dots m \\ j = 1, 2, \dots N \end{cases}$$

The ratios of f_{rj} represent the marginal rates of substitution in production.

Each firm organises its production to maximise net profits $R_j = \Sigma_r p_r y_{rj}$ subject to the limitations of its production function and given market prices. Some of the terms in R_j are positive (receipts, $y_{rj} > 0$) and others are negative (costs, $y_{rj} < 0$). The conditions for $R_j = $ maximum subject to $f_j = 0$ are :

$$\frac{f_{rj}}{p_r} = f_{mj} \qquad \begin{cases} r = 1, 2, \dots (m-1) \\ j = 1, 2, \dots N \end{cases}$$

The ratios $f_{1j} : f_{2j} : f_{3j} : \dots : f_{mj}$ (j given) represent the marginal rates of substitution between factors and/or products, for the production possibilities open to the jth firm.

As in 10.2, market conditions are that demand equals supply for all factors and consumer goods. Write $Y_r = \Sigma_j y_{rj}$. If Y_r is positive, it is the net amount of a good produced ; if Y_r is negative, its absolute value is the net use of a factor. The market conditions are $Y_r = X_r - \bar{X}_r$ in all cases, where $X_r = \Sigma_i x_{ri}$ and $\bar{X}_r = \Sigma \bar{x}_{ri}$. So :

$$\Sigma_j y_{rj} = \Sigma_i (x_{ri} - \bar{x}_{ri}) \qquad (r = 1, 2, \dots m)$$

In addition, the maximised net profits of all firms must be R :

$$\Sigma_r \Sigma_j p_r y_{rj} = \Sigma_j R_j = R$$

There is now one redundant equation to be eliminated. Since :

$$\Sigma_r \Sigma_j p_r y_{rj} = \Sigma_r p_r (\Sigma_j y_{rj}) = \Sigma_r p_r \Sigma_i (x_{ri} - \bar{x}_{ri})$$
$$= \Sigma_r \Sigma_i p_r (x_{ri} - \bar{x}_{ri}) = \Sigma_i \pi_i R = R$$

the last equation written follows from the others and can be dropped. The equation in R, however, is useful and it should be retained. It is better, therefore, to eliminate one of the other equations instead. The equation most conveniently dropped is one of the market conditions, say that for the last or mth commodity :

$$\Sigma y_{mj} = \Sigma_i (x_{mi} - \bar{x}_{mi})$$

The complete system is then :

(i) (a) $\dfrac{u_{ri}}{p_r}=u_{mi}$ $\begin{cases} r=1, 2, \dots (m-1) \\ i=1, 2, \dots n \end{cases}$

　(b) $\sum\limits_r p_r(x_{ri}-\bar{x}_{ri})=\pi_i R$ $i=1, 2, \dots n$

(ii) (a) $\dfrac{f_{ri}}{p_r}=f_{mj}$ $\begin{cases} r=1, 2, \dots (m-1) \\ j=1, 2, \dots N \end{cases}$

　(b) $f_j(y_{1j}, y_{2j}, \dots y_{mj})=0$ $j=1, 2, \dots N$

(iii) (a) $\sum\limits_j y_{rj}=\sum\limits_i (x_{ri}-\bar{x}_{ri})$ $r=1, 2, \dots (m-1)$

　(b) $\sum\limits_r \sum\limits_j p_r y_{rj}=R$

The variables are x_{ri}, y_{rj}, p_r and R, in number $mn+mN+(m-1)+1$ i.e. $m(n+N+1)$. The equations are of the same number, made up of mn in (i) (a) and (b), mN in (ii) (a) and (b), and m in (iii) (a) and (b). The system is closed and consistent with equilibrium.

The general market equilibrium of production and exchange, as developed here, is effectively that of Hicks (1939, 1946). It provides a complete and closed system of equations for determining the amounts of all commodities, factors and consumer goods alike, which are produced used up or exchanged, together with the amount of profits earned and all market prices (relative to *numéraire*).

The equilibrium position can be reached by stages, by dividing the complete closed system into various open sectors. The following is one way of proceeding. Conditions (i) give *individual demands* x_{ri} in terms of prices and of R. Hence, aggregate demand $(X_r-\bar{X}_r)$ follows in the same terms, for each commodity, whether a factor or a consumer good. Next, conditions (ii) give *production by firms* y_{rj} in terms of prices. Aggregate supply Y_r for each commodity follows in terms of prices. Next, on substitution in (iii) (b), R is found in terms of the prices. Finally, the *market conditions* of (iii) (a) are left; $(m-1)$ in number and expressed now in terms of the $(m-1)$ ratios of market prices. They express the equation of demand and supply on all the various markets for factors and consumer goods; they suffice to determine the ratios of market prices.

EXERCISES 10.3

1. Divide the list of commodities into factors ($s=1, 2, \dots k$) and consumer goods ($t=k+1, k+2, \dots m$). For any individual, it may be assumed that $x_i \geqslant 0$ ($s=1, 2, \dots k$) and that $x_{ti}=0$ ($t=k+1, k+2, \dots m$). Interpret and show that the system of equations (i)–(iii) above is not substantially affected by making such an assumption.

2. Examine the effect on the system (i)–(iii) of putting R (and R_j) zero and of assuming that entrepreneurial services are included among the given resources $\bar{x}_{ri}$ of individuals.

3. A single firm produces one consumer good Z by use of two factors X and Y. The production function is $f(x, y, z) = xy - az = 0$ where a is a positive constant, x and y are negative (factors used) and z is positive (output of product). Show that the conditions of production, equations (ii) (a) and (ii) (b), give :

$$-xp_x = -yp_y = z = ap_x p_y$$

where the prices are p_x, p_y ($p_z = 1$).

4. To the production conditions of the previous exercise, add equations (i) (a) and (i) (b) with two individuals and quadratic utility functions. The first individual supplies factor X and has no demand for factor Y ; the second supplies factor Y with no demand for factor X. The first individual also supplies the entrepreneurial services. Both demand the good Z but have no initial stocks. Derive the individual demands in terms of prices. Complete the system by adding market conditions (iii) and show how prices are determined.

5. In the problem of the previous exercise, assume that the services of the entrepreneur (the first individual) are freely variable and taken as the factor X. Replace the production function by $f(x, y, z) = xy - az^2 = 0$. Show that the conditions of production then give :

$$-xp_x = -yp_y = \tfrac{1}{2}z \quad \text{and} \quad p_x p_y = 1/4a$$

Check that $R = 0$.

6. Generalise the previous exercise (freely variable entrepreneurial services) to a production function $f(y_1, y_2, \ldots y_n) = 0$ and show that the form of the function is subject to the limitation

$$\Sigma_r f_r y_r = 0 \quad \left(f_r = \frac{\partial f}{\partial y_r} \right)$$

if profits are to be zero. Then show that, in the determination of equilibrium as given above, the scale of production is not determined at the stage of " production by firms ", i.e. that conditions (ii) only determine the ratios of y_{rj} for any firm j. Compare with Ex. 2 above, and with the particular equilibrium of 10.2 above.

10.4 Counting Equations

The essential feature of the systems of economic equilibrium described above is that the number of (independent) conditions is equal to the number of unknowns to be determined. This is a matter of counting equations and variables, of checking that they are equal in number. It is concluded that the system is consistent with equilibrium, that it is neither under-determined nor over-determined. In general, the conditions involve data which are given but unspecified in form. Only in particular cases can equations be taken, for example, as linear or quadratic in the variables. Consequently it is difficult to say more about a general economic system than the statement that it is consistent with equilibrium. In some particular instances, the system may have no (real) equilibrium position at all, i.e. the equations have no (real) solution. In other instances, there may be multiple solutions of the equations.

The point is illustrated by Fig. 43, which shows particular linear, quadratic and cubic equations between two variables X and Y. The system, in each case, has two equations represented by two curves in the plane OXY. It is consistent with equilibrium, i.e. equilibrium values of X and Y are given by the solution of the equations and the intersection of the curves. In a particular case such as Fig. 43a, there is a unique equilibrium shown by a single point P of intersection of the curves. In another particular case such as Fig. 43b, there is no (real) equilibrium at all; the system is consistent with equilibrium but no real solution happens to exist. Still further cases arise, as illustrated by Fig. 43c, where there are multiple equilibrium positions shown by a series of points $(P_1, P_2, ...)$ of intersection of the curves.

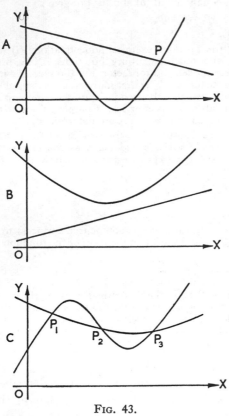

FIG. 43.

A good deal more can be said if the conditions of the problem imply that all the equations are linear, or if this can be assumed as an approximation for certain ranges of the variables. This case is examined generally in 14.2 below, with the following broad results. If there are fewer equations than variables, then there are " surplus " variables and their values cannot be determined from the equations. If there are more equations than variables, there are " surplus " equations which may or may not be consistent with the rest. If they are consistent, then they can be derived from other equations and they can be discarded, a process already considered above. If they are not consistent, something has gone wrong with the formulation of the problem; this is to be put right and the extra equations eliminated.

Generally, the system of linear equations has variables equal in number to the equations, or it is reducible to this form. The usual or " non-singular " case is that there is a solution for the variables and it is unique. However, there are still particular circumstances, in the " singular " case, when the situation is the same as if there were " surplus " equations or variables. This is so when a zero value is taken by the determinant formed from the coefficients in the equations. It is always necessary to guard against this possibility.

For example, the determination of market prices may be from a system of equations equal in number to the prices. If the equations are linear, then generally there is a unique set of prices for equilibrium. However, for certain configurations of the constants in the market relations, the " singular " case can arise and it is not then possible to determine all the prices or to determine them uniquely. In considering economic equilibrium, therefore, it is necessary to count equations. But this is not sufficient to determine that a unique solution—or indeed any solution—exists even when the equations are linear.

Finally, when an equilibrium position is known or assumed to exist, it is still necessary to go on to say something about its stability, and to determine (in various open systems) what will happen to one variable when some other variable is changed. These are problems in comparative statics—indeed stability can only be treated adequately in fully dynamic terms—and they remain to be considered.

10.5 Stability of Market Equilibrium

In the problem of general market equilibrium, the market prices, $(m-1)$ in number with $p_m = 1$ for *numéraire*, are determined by $(m-1)$ equations of form :

$$Y_r = X_r - \bar{X}_r \qquad r = 1, 2, \ldots (m-1) \quad\ldots\ldots\ldots\ldots\ldots\ldots(1)$$

Here, for the rth commodity, $Y_r = \Sigma y_{rj} =$ net production (or net use) aggregated over all firms, and $X_r - \bar{X}_r = \Sigma(x_{ri} - \bar{x}_{ri}) =$ net consumer demand (or net factor supply) aggregated over all individuals. These are equations (iii) of 10.3 above. Each condition represents the equality of market demand and supply for a commodity, i.e. a factor or a consumer good.

Let S_r and D_r be the supply and demand for the rth commodity on the rth market, so that :

$$\text{Consumer good :} \quad S_r = Y_r \qquad D_r = X_r - \bar{X}_r$$
$$\text{Factor :} \quad S_r = \bar{X}_r - X_r \qquad D_r = -Y_r$$

In each case, the excess of supply over demand is the same :

$$S_r - D_r = Y_r - (X_r - \bar{X}_r) \quad\ldots\ldots\ldots\ldots\ldots\ldots\ldots\ldots(2)$$

The market equations (1) simply state that $S_r - D_r = 0$ for each consumer good and factor.

The equations (1) are equations in the $(m-1)$ prices since it is assumed that the choices of individual consumers (equations (i) of 10.3) and the decisions of individual firms (equations (ii) of 10.3) give the aggregates X_r and Y_r as functions of the prices. Questions concerned with these choices and decisions, e.g. their stability, are here simply left on one side. Further, the mth equation of supply and demand, that for the mth good taken as *numéraire*, is ignored ; this equation is automatically satisfied if all the others hold. Equally, if any one of the equations (1) is not satisfied, so that a market is out of equilibrium at the prices taken, then the equation of the supply and demand for *numéraire* also ceases to hold. Any lack of equilibrium on one market is offset by a lack of " equilibrium " on the " market " for *numéraire*. This provides the flexibility needed for problems in comparative statics.

Any consideration of the stability of market equilibrium raises problems of economic dynamics. An equilibrium position in prices is stable if an initial variation in any one price is followed by a return of the price to the equilibrium level. All depends on the dynamic conditions assumed, as in 1.8 above for a single market, where varying results are obtained from different dynamic models. The Walrasian model is the one now taken, the dynamic assumption being that a price increases over time when demand exceeds supply at the ruling price. The result (1.8 above) is that price equilibrium on a single market is stable if the supply curve cuts the demand curve from below (see Fig. 2). If $S(p)$ and $D(p)$ are the supply and demand functions, the stability condition is :

$$\frac{d}{dp}(S-D) > 0 \qquad \text{for } p \text{ such that } S-D=0.$$

The excess of supply over demand $(S-D)$ is zero at the equilibrium price and becomes positive as the price is raised.

Hicks (1939, 1946) uses an extension of this Walrasian condition to *define* the stability of market equilibrium on inter-related markets. If S_r and D_r are the supply and demand for the rth commodity, functions of all the prices, there is market stability in the Hicksian sense if :

$$\frac{d}{dp_r}(S_r - D_r) > 0$$

for variation from equilibrium on each market ($r = 1, 2, \ldots m-1$). However, with many prices, this condition can be variously interpreted. At one extreme, the variation in the price p_r may occur while all other prices are held constant. This means, not only that the rth market gets out of equilibrium (because of the variation in p_r), but that all other markets are also out of equilibrium. At the other extreme, the variation in p_r is compensated by appropriate variations in all other prices so as to keep all markets (except the rth and that for *numéraire*) in equilibrium. In between there are cases where some prices are held constant (and the corresponding markets are out of equilibrium) and others are adjusted to keep equilibrium on the markets concerned. According to Hicks, there is *perfect stability* of price equilibrium if the condition $\dfrac{d}{dp_r}(S_r - D_r) > 0$ holds in all circumstances, whether prices other than p_r are held constant or adjusted to maintain equilibrium on other markets, or some held constant and others adjusted. By (2), since $\bar{X}_r$ is given, the condition for Hicksian perfect stability is :

$$\left. \begin{array}{l} Y_r - X_r = -\bar{X}_r \\[2mm] \dfrac{d}{dp_r}(Y_r - X_r) > 0 \end{array} \right\} r = 1, 2, \ldots m-1 \ldots\ldots\ldots\ldots\ldots(3)$$

and

in all cases whether other prices are adjusted or not.

Here $\dfrac{d}{dp_r}(Y_r - X_r)$ is a total derivative, for variation in p_r *and* in such other prices as are adjusted. It is to be obtained in terms of partial derivatives like $\dfrac{\partial}{\partial p_s}(Y_r - X_r)$, each valued *at the equilibrium position*, and so *constant* in value. Write these constants as :

$$a_{rs} = \frac{\partial}{\partial p_s}(Y_r - X_r) = \frac{\partial Y_r}{\partial p_s} - \frac{\partial X_r}{\partial p_s} \text{ at equilibrium prices.}$$

The conditions (3) can then be expressed in terms of the constants a_{rs}.

Let p_1 be the price which is varied, the first market then being out of equilibrium. Assume that all other prices are held constant, their markets being also out of equilibrium. By (3) :

$$\frac{d}{dp_1}(Y_1 - X_1) = \frac{\partial}{\partial p_1}(Y_1 - X_1) = a_{11} > 0$$

In the same way, $a_{22}, a_{33}, \ldots$ must all be positive since the price to be varied is at choice. Next, assume that as p_1 is varied there are adjustments in p_2 to keep the second market in equilibrium. Other prices are again constant and their markets out of equilibrium. Hence, by (3) :

$$\frac{d}{dp_1}(Y_1 - X_1) > 0 \quad \text{when} \quad \frac{d}{dp_1}(Y_2 - X_2) = 0$$

Now $\dfrac{d}{dp_1}(Y_1-X_1)=\dfrac{\partial}{\partial p_1}(Y_1-X_1)+\dfrac{\partial}{\partial p_2}(Y_1-X_1)\dfrac{dp_2}{dp_1}=a_{11}+a_{12}\dfrac{dp_2}{dp_1}$

and similarly $\qquad\qquad \dfrac{d}{dp_1}(Y_2-X_2)=a_{21}+a_{22}\dfrac{dp_2}{dp_1}$

The equation of the second of these to zero gives $\dfrac{dp_2}{dp_1}=-\dfrac{a_{21}}{a_{22}}$ and :

$$\dfrac{d}{dp_1}(Y_1-X_1)=a_{11}+a_{12}\left(-\dfrac{a_{21}}{a_{22}}\right)=\dfrac{a_{11}a_{22}-a_{12}a_{21}}{a_{22}}>0$$

Since a_{22} is positive :

$$a_{11}a_{22}-a_{12}a_{21}=\begin{vmatrix} a_{11} & a_{12} \\ a_{21} & a_{22} \end{vmatrix}>0$$

in the determinant notation (12.9 below). The same condition holds for any pair of prices and markets, i.e. all such determinants of the second order are positive. Further, if it is assumed that, as p_1 is varied, adjustments are made in p_2 and p_3 to keep two markets in equilibrium, the same procedure shows (Ex 1 below) that :

$$\begin{vmatrix} a_{11} & a_{12} & a_{13} \\ a_{21} & a_{22} & a_{23} \\ a_{31} & a_{32} & a_{33} \end{vmatrix}>0$$

and similarly for other third-order determinants. The results are clearly general, for adjustments in any number of the prices. Hence the conditions for Hicksian perfect stability of market equilibrium are :

$$a_{11}>0;\quad \begin{vmatrix} a_{11} & a_{12} \\ a_{21} & a_{22} \end{vmatrix}>0;\quad \begin{vmatrix} a_{11} & a_{12} & a_{13} \\ a_{21} & a_{22} & a_{23} \\ a_{31} & a_{32} & a_{33} \end{vmatrix}>0;\quad \ldots\ldots$$

and similarly for any group of commodities taken 1, 2, 3, ... at a time.

The Hicksian notion of perfect stability can be criticised, as by Samuelson (1944, 1947), on the ground that it is defined by analogy with the case of a single market. Only in this simple case is a particular dynamic model constructed as a criterion for stability. The general case of many markets is not considered, at least explicitly, in the light of a dynamic model showing the movements of the inter-related prices over time. The analysis is clearly incomplete and it is taken up again in 14.6 below. An unsuspected difficulty will then emerge from the fact that a_{rs} and a_{sr} are generally different, since it cannot be assumed either that $\dfrac{\partial X_r}{\partial p_s}=\dfrac{\partial X_s}{\partial p_r}$ or that

$\dfrac{\partial Y_r}{\partial p_s} = \dfrac{\partial Y_s}{\partial p_r}$. This lack of symmetry is troublesome and Hicks (1939, 1946) is well aware of it. He assumes it away, e.g. in consumer demand, by taking the " income terms " as negligible in comparison with the " substitution terms ".

EXERCISES 10.5

1. Consider the markets for the first three goods ; let p_1 be varied with adjustments in p_2 and p_3 to keep their markets in equilibrium. Show that, for perfect stability,

$$\begin{vmatrix} a_{11} & a_{12} & a_{13} \\ a_{21} & a_{22} & a_{23} \\ a_{31} & a_{32} & a_{33} \end{vmatrix} > 0$$

2. Hicks defines *imperfect stability* by conditions (3) above when p_r is varied and all the other prices adjusted. The conditions may also hold for some, but not for all, partial adjustments. What difference does this make to the stability conditions in terms of the a's?

3. Examine the conditions for imperfect stability when there are two goods in addition to *numéraire*. Show that :

$$\frac{1}{a_{22}} \begin{vmatrix} a_{11} & a_{12} \\ a_{21} & a_{22} \end{vmatrix} > 0$$

so that a_{22} and the determinant are of the same sign (which need not be positive). Extend to the case of three goods in addition to *numéraire*.

10.6 Some Problems of Comparative Statics

General market equilibrium, as analysed in 10.3 above, is a static and closed system. The equations can be counted and shown consistent with equilibrium, an essential but not very fruitful procedure. The interesting problems are in the field of comparative statics and dynamics. The typical question is : if specified shifts are made in the given elements (e.g. in consumers' tastes or in production techniques), how do the equilibrium values of the variables (e.g. prices or amounts purchased) then move? The aim in comparative statics is to get " meaningful theorems " ; but they are not easily derived nor are they straight-forward in interpretation. There is much more to comparative statics than bald statements like : " purchases rise when prices fall ".

Part of the difficulty is that the system is closed, so that, for example, all prices are determined together on the markets. It is *not* permissible to allow one price to shift and to trace the effect on other variables. The prices are a determined set and one of them can only be varied if some market or other is allowed to get out of equilibrium. One or more conditions of equilibrium are dropped ; the system becomes open rather than closed. This has already been illustrated in considering stability in 10.5 above.

A further point of importance is that useful results in comparative statics can be obtained by invoking the essentially dynamic conditions of stability, which is what Samuelson (1947) describes as the " correspondence principle ". This can be illustrated in the case of a single market (1.8 above). The price P and amount bought and sold X are given in equilibrium :

$$X = D(P) = S(P)$$

Let the supply curve shift, e.g. because of some change in production techniques. Take $S(P, \alpha)$ as the supply schedule, where the parameter α represents the shift, with $\dfrac{\partial S}{\partial \alpha} > 0$; an increase in α is an upward shift in supply. The equilibrium values of P and X are then given in terms of α :

$$X = D(P) = S(P, \alpha) \quad \dotfill (1)$$

Differentiate (1) with respect to α :

$$\frac{dX}{d\alpha} = \frac{dD}{dP}\frac{dP}{d\alpha} = \frac{\partial S}{\partial P}\frac{dP}{d\alpha} + \frac{\partial S}{\partial \alpha}$$

i.e. $\qquad \dfrac{dP}{d\alpha} = -\dfrac{\partial S}{\partial \alpha}\dfrac{1}{\dfrac{\partial}{\partial P}(S-D)} \quad$ and $\quad \dfrac{dX}{d\alpha} = -\dfrac{\partial S}{\partial \alpha}\dfrac{\dfrac{dD}{dP}}{\dfrac{\partial}{\partial P}(S-D)}$

Here $\dfrac{\partial S}{\partial \alpha} > 0$ and it can be taken that $\dfrac{dD}{dP} < 0$. The sign of $\dfrac{\partial}{\partial P}(S-D)$ is then critical. Stability conditions now come in and, on the Walrasian model, $\dfrac{\partial}{\partial P}(S-D) > 0$ for stable equilibrium. Hence, in a stable situation :

$$\frac{dP}{d\alpha} < 0 \quad \text{and} \quad \frac{dX}{d\alpha} > 0$$

An upward shift in supply reduces price and increases the amount bought and sold. In this sense, purchases rise when price falls. A similar result follows a shift in demand (see Ex. 1 below).

The same approach can be made to equilibrium on inter-related markets with the aid of the Hicksian conditions for stability. If there are two commodities (in addition to *numéraire*), two conditions of market equilibrium are written :

$$Y_1 - X_1 = -\bar{X}_1 \quad \text{and} \quad Y_2 - X_2 = -\bar{X}_2 \quad \dotfill (2)$$

where $\bar{X}_1$ and $\bar{X}_2$ are given. Here $(Y_1 - X_1)$ and $(Y_2 - X_2)$ represent excess of supply over demand, whether the commodities are factors or consumer goods. Let $(Y_1 - X_1)$ depend on a parameter α as well as on the two prices p_1 and p_2, and take $\dfrac{\partial(Y_1 - X_1)}{\partial\alpha} > 0$ so that an increase in α corresponds to an upward shift in supply or a downward shift in demand. The equilibrium prices fixed by (2) are then dependent on α, i.e. on the shifts in supply or demand of the first commodity. Write, as before, for $r, s = 1, 2$:

$$a_{rs} = \frac{\partial}{\partial p_s}(Y_r - X_r) \quad \text{at equilibrium prices}$$

Differentiate (2) with respect to α :

$$a_{11}\frac{dp_1}{d\alpha} + a_{12}\frac{dp_2}{d\alpha} = -\frac{\partial}{\partial\alpha}(Y_1 - X_1)$$

and
$$a_{21}\frac{dp_1}{d\alpha} + a_{22}\frac{dp_2}{d\alpha} = 0$$

Hence
$$\frac{dp_2}{d\alpha} = -\frac{a_{21}}{a_{22}}\frac{dp_1}{d\alpha}$$

and
$$\frac{dp_1}{d\alpha} = -a_{22}\frac{\partial(Y_1 - X_1)}{\partial\alpha}\bigg/\begin{vmatrix} a_{11} & a_{12} \\ a_{21} & a_{22} \end{vmatrix}$$

If the equilibrium has Hicksian stability, a_{22} and the determinant above are both positive. It follows that, when α increases (upward shift in supply or downward shift in demand) :

$$\frac{dp_1}{d\alpha} < 0 \quad \text{and} \quad \frac{dp_2}{d\alpha} \text{ has sign of } a_{21}$$

The price of the commodity falls when its supply is shifted upwards (or its demand shifted downwards). The effect on the price of the second commodity depends on the relation between the two commodities as given by :

$$a_{21} = \frac{\partial}{\partial p_1}(Y_2 - X_2)$$

If the " income effect " can be neglected, then for two commodities which are substitutes $a_{21} < 0$, and for complementary commodities $a_{21} > 0$. Hence, an upward shift in the supply of one commodity causes the price of a substitute commodity to fall, the price of a complementary commodity to rise. The same result follows a downward shift in the demand for the first commodity.

The analysis can be extended to cases where there are several commodities, all prices being affected by a shift in the demand or supply of one of them.   It is still true that $\dfrac{dp_1}{d\alpha}<0$ but the " cross effects " $\dfrac{dp_2}{d\alpha},\dfrac{dp_3}{d\alpha}, \ldots$

can be complicated.   This is pursued in Ex. 2 and 3 below.

EXERCISES 10.6

1. For a single commodity, let increasing α represent an upward shift in demand :
$D(P,\ \alpha)$ with $\dfrac{\partial D}{\partial \alpha}>0$.   Show that the variations in equilibrium price and purchases are :

$$\frac{dP}{d\alpha}=\frac{\partial D}{\partial \alpha}\,\frac{1}{\dfrac{\partial}{\partial P}(S-D)}\quad\text{and}\quad\frac{dX}{d\alpha}=\frac{\partial D}{\partial \alpha}\,\frac{\dfrac{dS}{dP}}{\dfrac{\partial}{\partial P}(S-D)}$$

Deduce that the upward shift in demand, if equilibrium is stable, raises prices, but that it only raises purchases if S is upward sloping.

2. There are three markets for commodities (apart from *numéraire*) and there is an upward shift in the supply on the first : $\dfrac{\partial}{\partial \alpha}(Y_1-X_1)>0$.   Show that :

$$a_{11}\frac{dp_1}{d\alpha}+a_{12}\frac{dp_2}{d\alpha}+a_{13}\frac{dp_3}{d\alpha}=-\frac{\partial}{\partial \alpha}(Y_1-X_1)$$

$$a_{21}\frac{dp_1}{d\alpha}+a_{22}\frac{dp_2}{d\alpha}+a_{23}\frac{dp_3}{d\alpha}=0$$

$$a_{31}\frac{dp_1}{d\alpha}+a_{32}\frac{dp_2}{d\alpha}+a_{33}\frac{dp_3}{d\alpha}=0$$

Solve for the three price variations.   Deduce that $\dfrac{dp_1}{d\alpha}<0$, that $\dfrac{dp_2}{d\alpha}$ has the sign of $\begin{vmatrix} a_{21} & a_{23} \\ a_{31} & a_{33} \end{vmatrix}$ and similarly for $\dfrac{dp_3}{d\alpha}$ if the equilibrium has Hicksian stability.

3. In the case of the previous exercise, ignore " income effects " and assume that the third commodity is not closely related to the others (a_{23} and a_{31} small). Deduce that $\dfrac{dp_2}{d\alpha}$ has the sign of a_{21} and interpret.   Examine the " substitute of substitute " effect which arises when a_{23} and a_{31} are significant.   See Hicks (1946), pp. 74 and 318.

10.7 Production Functions

The analysis of general economic equilibrium turns on the way in which it is decided to formulate the technical conditions of production or transformation of commodities.   In 10.3 above, production is in the hands of a number of individual firms and for each of them the technical possibilities are summarised and represented by a production function of the form $f(x_1, x_2, \ldots x_m)=0$, where the x's are inputs (negative values) and outputs (positive values).   In 10.2 on the other hand, production in the economy as a whole is assumed to take place under constant returns to scale with fixed technical coefficients, i.e. a_{rs} as the amount of rth factor used in producing a unit of the sth product (for various r and s). No formulations of the same general problem of techniques of production could differ more than these two ; they can be used to illustrate the range of possibilities.

As a matter of convenient notation, let x's denote amounts of inputs or factors used, and y's amounts of outputs or goods produced. All variables are positive, or at least non-negative. Then the two extreme formulations of the production techniques in an economy are *first* to take for each firm a production function :

$$f(x_1, x_2, \ldots x_m, y_1, y_2 \ldots y_n) = 0 \ldots\ldots\ldots\ldots\ldots\ldots\ldots(1)$$

and *second* to assume fixed technical coefficients for production as a whole :

$$\left.\begin{array}{l} x_{11} = a_{11}y_1 \quad x_{12} = a_{12}y_2 \ldots \quad x_{1n} = a_{1n}y_n \\ x_{21} = a_{21}y_1 \quad x_{22} = a_{22}y_2 \ldots \quad x_{2n} = a_{2n}y_n \\ \quad\quad\ldots\ldots\ldots\ldots\ldots\ldots \\ x_{m1} = a_{m1}y_1 \quad x_{m2} = a_{m2}y_2 \ldots \quad x_{mn} = a_{mn}y_n \end{array}\right\} \ldots\ldots\ldots\ldots(2)$$

where a_{rs} is the amount of the rth input (factor) used in the production of a unit of the sth output (good produced), so that the total usages are :

$$x_1 = \sum_{s=1}^{n} x_{1s} \quad x_2 = \sum_{s=1}^{n} x_{2s} \ldots x_m = \sum_{s=1}^{n} x_{ms}$$

The differences between the formulations are that (1) relates to a firm and (2) to the whole production economy ; (1) assumes continuous substitution between both inputs and outputs whereas (2) takes a rigid and fixed connection between inputs and outputs ; (1) can allow for varying returns to scale while (2) assumes that production varies with constant returns.

The choice between the two formulations, or any variations of them, is not a question of choosing between right and wrong, nor can it be made solely by reference to the facts of life. Technical conditions in the real world are so complex that any formulation of them for analysis involves simplification. Which simplified " production function " is to be adopted is a matter of economic convenience and of mathematical approximation. Production techniques, and the corresponding taking of decisions by producers, have various features in real life, and they can be looked at from various points of view according to which features are regarded as essential and which as incidental. It is convenient, economically speaking, to base any analysis on one or other particular view of production ; sometimes it may be appropriate to stress the possibilities of substitution between inputs and outputs and in other contexts to emphasise the rigidities of production processes. The mathematical formulation is then an approximation, based on explicit simplifying assumptions, e.g. that inputs and outputs are continuously variable and continuously substitutable one for another.

In order to pursue the question of formulation of production functions, take the simple case where there is one product y and two factors x_1 and x_2. This permits substitution between factors, and between a factor and a product, but not between products. However, the extension is easily made to the case of any numbers of factors and products, with joint production on the output as well as on the input side.

The first formulation starts from the firm as the decision-making unit. In practice this may be, not a " firm " in the ordinary sense, but an establishment, or a group of establishments, or even a department in an establishment. Inputs and outputs are taken as continuously variable and substitutable and the production function (1) can be written :

$$y = f(x_1, x_2)$$

with continuous partial derivatives :

$$\frac{\partial y}{\partial x_1} = f_1(x_1, x_2) \quad \text{and} \quad \frac{\partial y}{\partial x_2} = f_2(x_1, x_2)$$

which are the marginal products. To determine the returns to scale, take the factors in the fixed proportion $a_1 : a_2$ so that

$$y = f(\lambda a_1, \lambda a_2) = \phi(\lambda)$$

where the variable λ fixes the scale of production. If $\frac{dy}{d\lambda}$ is constant, then output y increases in proportion to the use of the factors ; there are constant returns to scale. Varying returns are shown by $\frac{dy}{d\lambda}$ increasing (or decreasing) as λ increases.

In a diagrammatic representation, the production function $y = f(x_1, x_2)$ is a surface in three dimensions which can be shown most conveniently as a system of contours, or constant product curves, in the factor plane $Ox_1 x_2$:

$$f(x_1, x_2) = y_1 ; \quad f(x_1, x_2) = y_2 ; \dots$$

for various fixed outputs $y_1, y_2, \dots$. Fig. 44a illustrates, three particular constant product curves being shown. At any point P_1 on one of the curves (product y_1), the slope of the tangent is negative and numerically equal to $\left(-\frac{dx_2}{dx_1} = \frac{f_1}{f_2} \right)$, the ratio of the marginal products or the *marginal rate of substitution* between x_1 and x_2. Returns to scale are shown by the rate at which output y increases as inputs are increased in proportion along some radius OP through O.

A particular case of great interest arises when *the production function is homogeneous of degree r*, so that an increase in the use of factors in the same ratio λ results in an increase in product in the ratio λ^r :

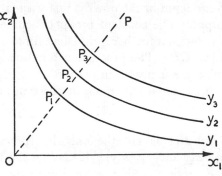

$$f(\lambda x_1, \lambda x_2) = \lambda^r f(x_1, x_2)$$

The dependence of the product y on the scale of operations λ, given by $\phi(\lambda)$ above, is then quite simple and independent of the fixed proportions chosen for the factors :

$$y = \phi(\lambda) = \lambda^r y_1$$

where y_1 is the output corresponding to $\lambda = 1$ and the original use of the factors (a_1 and a_2). There are constant returns to scale when $r = 1$, i.e. when the production function is linear homogeneous. Returns are increasing for $r > 1$ and decreasing for $r < 1$. In terms of the constant product curves of Fig. 44a, a homogeneous production func-

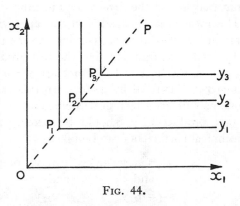

Fig. 44.

tion gives a system of curves each of which is an enlargement (or reduction) of any other by means of radii through O. If the constant product curve y_1 is enlarged in the ratio λ, then another constant product curve is obtained for which $y_2 = \lambda^r y_1$. In the particular case of linear homogeneity ($r = 1$), the fixed product is also enlarged in the same ratio ($y_2 = \lambda y_1$), i.e. constant returns to scale.

All this assumes continuous substitution of factors in the production of a single product, whether at constant or at variable returns to scale in the given firm. The alternative is to take fixed technical coefficients, i.e. the form (2) of " production function ", again for a given firm ; with two factors and one product only, the " production function " is :

$$x_1 \geqslant a_1 y \quad \text{and} \quad x_2 \geqslant a_2 y$$

where a_1 and a_2 are the constant coefficients, the amounts of the two

M

factors per unit of product. This can be viewed as a very special form of the production function $y = f(x_1, x_2)$ when it is assumed that the inputs must be used in the ratio $x_1 : x_2 = a_1 : a_2$ and in no other way. Any excess of one input or the other is just wasted, no increase being obtained in the output. The constant product " curves " then take the special form of Fig. 44b, output being in effect limited to combinations of inputs on the radius OP. The production function is also linear homogeneous ; if x_1 and x_2 are increased in proportion λ, output y also increases in proportion λ. In Fig. 44b, the ratios of constant products

$$y_1 : y_2 : y_3 : \ldots = OP_1 : OP_2 : OP_3 : \ldots$$

But this is not the only interpretation of the technical conditions ($x_1 = a_1 y$ and $x_2 = a_2 y$). It may be that x_1 and x_2 *could* be substituted, to give varying product according to the production function of Fig. 44a, but that in fact the firm *chooses* to limit the inputs to a given ratio $a_1 : a_2$. This means that, instead of x_1 and x_2 varying in any way over the constant product curves, they are confined to the particular radius OP. Then, on the further assumption that the full production function is linear homogeneous, the technical relations are $x_1 = a_1 y$ and $x_2 = a_2 y$ where the direction of OP is fixed by $a_1 : a_2$. In this case, there is no reason why only one pair of fixed technical coefficients, or one radius OP across the constant product map, should be taken. A finite number of alternative technical coefficients can be taken :

$$\left. \begin{array}{ccc} x_{11} = a_{11}y \; ; & \text{or} \; x_{12} = a_{12}y \; ; & \text{or} \; x_{13} = a_{13}y \; ; \; \ldots \\ \text{and} & \text{and} & \text{and} \\ x_{21} = a_{21}y & x_{22} = a_{22}y & x_{23} = a_{23}y \end{array} \right\} \ldots\ldots\ldots\ldots\ldots(3)$$

Each of these technical alternatives can be called a *production process*, a way of getting the product y from a particular fixed combination of factors x_1 and x_2. Then $x_{rs} = a_{rs}y$, with a_{rs} a fixed technical coefficient, indicates the use of the rth input (here $r = 1, 2$) in the production of y in the sth process. In Fig. 44a, each process corresponds to a single radius like OP across the constant product curves of a linear homogeneous production function. The assumption of technical conditions (3) for a firm implies the linear homogeneous case (constant returns to scale) and a choice etween a finite number of processes. Indeed, a further step can be taken by assuming that production can proceed by two or more processes simultaneously and the results added. The production function (3) is not as rigid as it may appear at first sight. Flexibility is obtained by combining (by addition) different processes. When extended, in an obvious way, to include many factors and products, this concept of a set of different processes, to be used singly or in combination, is the basis of " linear programming " (or " activity analysis ") of the firm, to be developed later on. It is a real alternative to a continuous production function of the type (1) above.

For example, in the one product-two factor case, the product may be obtained by use of four different types of machine, each with its corresponding labour requirements. There are then four processes, with fixed technical coefficients (labour per machine ratios), between which the firm chooses or which can be used in combination. The production function is of form (3), with four pairs of coefficients, and the decisions of the firm are an exercise in " linear programming ".

10.8 The Production Function as a Matrix

A firm has one output (y) and two inputs (x_1 and x_2). Assume that its technical decisions are limited to four processes, or that it chooses to confine its decisions to these four processes. Each process is described by a pair of fixed coefficients, the proportions in which the inputs are combined. In the linear homogeneous case (constant returns to scale), the effective production function is of type (3) of 10.7 above, or in this particular case :

$$x_{11}=a_{11}y \quad x_{12}=a_{12}y \quad x_{13}=a_{13}y \quad x_{14}=a_{14}y$$
$$x_{21}=a_{21}y \quad x_{22}=a_{22}y \quad x_{23}=a_{23}y \quad x_{24}=a_{24}y$$

There are eight fixed coefficients a_{rs} ($r=1, 2$; $s=1, 2, 3, 4$) which represent the amount of the rth input in unit production of the output on the sth process.

Each process is fully but simply expressed by a vector of three elements, i.e. $(1, -a_{1s}, -a_{2s})$ for the sth process, where 1 indicates unit output, $-a_{1s}$ and $-a_{2s}$ the corresponding inputs. The convention is that $+$ means an output and $-$ an input. The whole set of technical conditions of the firm is then shown by the " matrix " :

$$\begin{bmatrix} 1 & 1 & 1 & 1 \\ -a_{11} & -a_{12} & -a_{13} & -a_{14} \\ -a_{21} & -a_{22} & -a_{23} & -a_{24} \end{bmatrix}$$

as an ordered set of given elements, in rows for the commodities (one output and two inputs) and in columns for the processes. Such a matrix can be called the *technology* of the firm. Here the choice is between four processes, used singly or in combination, under constant returns to scale.

The technology is shown in a diagram in Fig. 45. Unit output can be obtained, on the four processes, by the combination (a_{1s}, a_{2s}) of inputs

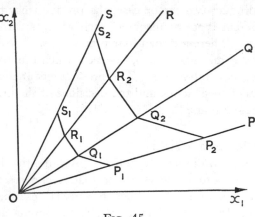

for $s = 1$, 2, 3 and 4, represented by the four points P_1 Q_1 R_1 and S_1 in the Ox_1x_2 plane. Output of two units is obtained from any one of the combinations $(2a_{1s}, 2a_{2s})$, the four points P_2 Q_2 R_2 and S_2. By the property of constant returns to scale, P_1 and P_2 lie on a radius OP such that $OP_2 = 2OP_1$, and similarly for the other processes. There are four radii one for each process,

Fig. 45.

showing the fixed ratio of inputs concerned. Across the radii a particular set of points P_1 Q_1 R_1 S_1 can be picked out for unit product ; to obtain any other product it is only necessary to enlarge (or reduce) proportionately. P_1 Q_1 R_1 S_1 is the constant product " curve " for unit product, and others can be obtained by enlargement (or reduction) with constant returns to scale. Instead of the " curve " being continuous, it comprises four points, joined by straight lines to indicate that processes can be combined.

If the four processes are both independent and " efficient "—in the sense that they could be chosen for use alone—then the four points P_1 Q_1 R_1 S_1 are convex to O as shown in Fig. 45. For example, if Q_1 happened to lie above and to the right of P_1 R_1, then a combination of the first and third processes (on P_1 R_1) would be more " efficient " than Q_1, smaller inputs being needed for unit output. It also follows that combinations of processes, to be " efficient ", are confined to those adjacent in the diagram ; P_1 and Q_1 can be combined, but not P_1 R_1 or P_1 S_1 which give points above and to the right of P_1 Q_1. Further, any combination of inputs represented by points within the cone defined by the radii OP, OQ, OR and OS is a possible combination on the processes—but not a combination outside this cone.

A very great range of possibilities arises in specifying the technology of a firm, varying according to the number of factors and products, the number of processes to be distinguished and the extent and nature of the relations between inputs and outputs. The following are a few simple and illustrative examples of the kinds of matrices which can express a firm's technology when there are no more than two factors and two products :

$$
(a) \begin{bmatrix} 1 & 1 & 0 & 0 \\ 0 & 0 & 1 & 1 \\ -a_{11} & -a_{12} & -a_{13} & -a_{14} \\ -a_{21} & -a_{22} & -a_{23} & -a_{24} \end{bmatrix}
\quad
(b) \begin{bmatrix} 1 & 1 & 1 & 0 \\ 0 & x_1 & x_2 & 1 \\ -a_{11} & -a_{12} & -a_{13} & -a_{14} \\ -a_{21} & -a_{22} & -a_{23} & -a_{24} \end{bmatrix}
$$

$$
(c) \begin{bmatrix} 1 & 1 & 1 & 0 \\ 0 & x_1 & -x_2 & 1 \\ -a_{11} & -a_{12} & -a_{13} & -a_{14} \\ -a_{21} & -a_{22} & -a_{23} & -a_{24} \end{bmatrix}
$$

In case (a), there is no joint production, two products being produced in two processes each. In case (b), there are two processes in which the products are produced jointly, x_1 and x_2 units of the second being produced respectively per unit of the first. The remaining case is still another variant, the second commodity being an output in two processes (in one process as a joint product) and an input in another process. The two commodities may be, for example, refrigerators and motors for them ; the motors may be produced jointly with refrigerators or separately (e.g. as spares), or they may be an input (e.g. from stock or another firm) in a third process.

A perfectly general form of the technology of a firm can be written easily :

$$
\mathbf{A} = \begin{bmatrix} a_{11} & a_{12} & a_{13} & \cdots \\ a_{21} & a_{22} & a_{23} & \cdots \\ a_{31} & a_{32} & a_{33} & \cdots \\ \cdots\cdots\cdots\cdots \end{bmatrix}
$$

The a's are given constants, some positive when the commodity is an output of the process concerned, and some negative when it is an input. Many of the a's can be zero, the item not appearing at all in the process concerned. If the coefficients are read across a row, one and the same commodity can appear sometimes as an input, sometimes as an output and sometimes not at all. Similarly, down the columns, there can be joint production of two or more commodities and joint use of factors.

For a firm, therefore, it may be convenient and useful to assume a continuous production function relating inputs and outputs and to analyse in marginal terms. This may be particularly appropriate in a long-run analysis. On the other hand, it may be argued that the theory of the firm is inevitably short-run, that the entrepreneur has a limited time-horizon and always takes something as fixed. There is indeed little evidence that an entrepreneur wishes to think, still less that he does think, in marginal terms. He can scarcely be expected to get together all the necessary data in time to take decisions ; he is more likely to operate in terms of straight alternatives between simple and rather rigid processes ; see Hall and Hitch (1939) and Gordon (1948). In this case, the appropriate formulation may be a technology of the form **A** above, and the analysis is in the large and not in marginal terms.

It may be objected that the assumption of a limited number of processes and of fixed technical coefficients is too rigid and restricted. There can be no serious objections to taking perfect divisibility (of inputs and outputs) or constant returns to scale in one process. The first is a convenient simplification and the other can be overcome by distinguishing two or more processes when there appear to be varying returns to scale. More serious are the objections that the different processes cannot be kept down to a small number and that they cannot be combined by addition of inputs and outputs. But some simplifications are necessary and it is well to appreciate which of those assumed are the more severe.

One further development remains for brief consideration. Analysis in terms of individual firms (as in 10.3 above) may be far too detailed for the purposes in hand. The alternative (as in 10.2 above) is to treat large sectors of the economy, or the productive processes as a whole. Again the formulation of the technology of one industry, a complex of industries, or " industry " as a whole, is largely a matter of economic or mathematical convenience. In the long-run and for a large sector of the economy, the assumption of perfectly continuous variation and substitutability may seem reasonable, leading to marginal analysis with a continuous production function. On the other hand, the range of a single production function, a single relation between all inputs and outputs, may be too sweeping to throw up the kind of results required.

Hence, even for production as a whole, it may be preferable to assume a technology of the form **A** above, i.e. to take a limited number of " activities " or " processes " connecting all the various commodities as inputs and outputs, and to limit the effective decision-taking to these alternatives. The actual form of **A** can be further restricted as appropriate. One particularly simple and useful form is :

$$A = \begin{bmatrix} 1 & -a_{12} & -a_{13} & \cdots \\ -a_{21} & 1 & -a_{23} & \cdots \\ -a_{31} & -a_{32} & 1 & \cdots \\ \cdots\cdots\cdots\cdots\cdots\cdots\cdots \end{bmatrix}$$

Here, each " activity " represented by a column in **A** is an industry producing one and only one characteristic output. Further, even when allowance is made for many zero entries, the output of an industry can appear as the input of several other industries as well as a " final " product. This is the formulation developed in the following chapter. It has obvious limitations—the grouping of miscellaneous products into a single and characteristic industry output, the assumption of constant returns and of fixed technical coefficients, the apparent lack of all substitution possibilities. How serious these are, and whether they are more than balanced by the advantages of a clear and simple formulation, can only be determined when some experience is gained in the technique in its applications. Later on more elaborate or detailed formulations will be examined, both for the firm and for large sectors of the economy.

In concluding this methodological survey, the importance of economic convenience and mathematical approximation can again be stressed. It is not necessary that any theoretical construction should be " realistic " in the sense that it is based narrowly on the way in which entrepreneurs are thought to act in practice. Marginal analysis may be perfectly appropriate as a matter of exposition ; it may certainly lead to a statement of the main results in the most illuminating form. On the other hand, a construction designed to be used with statistical data, in aiding firms to reach their decisions in full knowledge of the position, would clearly be based appropriately on the alternative analysis in terms of a technology matrix. It is well to have both methods of approach—one in marginal terms and one in the large—and to keep an open mind on which to adopt.

EXERCISES 10.8

1. A firm produces an output (y) with the use of two factors (x_1 and x_2). The production function is $x_1 x_2 - ay = 0$. Show that y is a function of x_1 and x_2 which is homogeneous of the second degree.

2. Take the production function of the previous exercise in the form $x_1 x_2 - ay^2 = 0$ and show that y is a linear homogeneous function of the factor usage. Further show that a process which uses the factors in the proportion $a : 1$ is possible and that it is described by fixed technical coefficients given by the vector $(1, a, 1)$. Define other processes which are consistent with this production function and hence build up a possible technology matrix for the firm.

3. A technology matrix is based on a production function of the form

$$f(x_1, x_2, \ldots x_m, y_1, y_2, \ldots y_n) = 0$$

Show that f must be homogeneous but of any degree.

REFERENCES

Bowley (A. L.) (1924) : *Mathematical Groundwork of Economics* (Oxford, 1924), Chapters II and V.

Gordon (R. A.) (1948) : " Short Period Price Determination in Theory and Practice ", *American Economic Review*, **38**, 265–88.

Hall (R. L.) and Hitch (C. J.) (1939) : " Price Theory and Business Behaviour " *Oxford Economic Papers*, **2**, 12–45.

Hicks (J. R.) (1934) : " Léon Walras ", *Econometrica*, **2**, 338–48.

Hicks (J. R.) (1937) : *Théorie mathématique de la Valeur* (Hermann, 1937).

Hicks (J. R.) (1939, 1946) : *Value and Capital* (Oxford, First Ed. 1939, Second Ed. 1946), Chapter IV–VIII and Appendix.

Metzler (L. A.) (1945) : " Stability of Multiple Markets : the Hicks Conditions ", *Econometrica*, **13**, 277–92.

Pareto (V.) (1909) : *Manuel d'économie politique* (Giard et Brière, Paris, 1909), Appendix.

Pareto (V.) (1911) : " Économie mathématique ", *Encyclopédie des Sciences mathématiques* (Librarie Gauthier-Villars, Paris, 1911).

Samuelson (P. A.) (1944) : " The Relation between Hicksian Stability and True Dynamic Stability ", *Econometrica*, **12**, 256–57.

Samuelson (P. A.) (1947) : *Foundations of Economic Analysis* (Harvard, 1947), Chapter IX.

Walras (L.) (1874) : *Éléments d'économie politique pure* (Lausanne, 1874).

Zeuthen (F.) (1942, 1955) : *Economic Theory and Method* (Longmans, 1955), Chapters 10–13 ; English translation of an earlier (1942) text in Danish.

CHAPTER 11

INTER-INDUSTRY RELATIONS

11.1 The Analysis of Industries by Inputs and Outputs

SYSTEMS of general market equilibrium are too detailed to serve as a basis for empirical application. In this chapter they are given up in favour of an analysis with a much broader sweep, in terms of industries rather than firms. Many difficulties are then avoided; for example, when no attention is paid to the way in which an industry is composed of decision-taking units, it is quite appropriate to assume both pure competition (given prices) and free entry (zero profits). This is at the cost of introducing a concept—that of an industry—which is both imprecise and a rough approximation. Industries are essentially empirical aggregates based on some statistical classification; the output of an industry, for example, is not a single product, as may be assumed for convenience, but rather a complex of main and subsidiary products.

The formulation of general economic equilibrium in terms of industries —with an essential empirical content and suitable for immediate empirical application—is due to Leontief (1941, 1951). It is an analysis of inter-industry relations, of the network of intermediate products passing from one industry to another, as well as of final products to consumers. Its central feature is the technology of the economy, assumed given and expressed in the form of a production function on the lines indicated at the end of 10.8 above. The analysis, however, is made under certain simplifying assumptions. In a general formulation, each industry would use several primary factors and produce a number of intermediate or final goods jointly; there would also be a considerable amount of overlapping between the outputs of different industries. All this is assumed away by taking, as a simplification, only one primary input (labour), only one output in any industry and a different output for each industry. There are n industries and n commodities, each of which is produced by just one industry but used as an intermediate product by any number of industries. In addition, there are the primary input (labour) and the final demand (of consumers), both of which run " across the board ", over all industries.

The main interest of the analysis is focused on the technology, represented by a matrix of coefficients of the kind written at the end of 10.8

above. The additional simplifications implied in this representation are that production takes place through " processes " with fixed technical coefficients (not in itself very unrealistic) and that there is only one " process " and no apparent substitution in each industry (something which does need further examination, as in 17.4 below). The input-output relations are thus of the simplest form—linear relations of direct proportionality. The Leontief input-output technique, in fact, is a very special case of the more general method of linear programming or activity analysis, developed in Chapters 16 and 17 below ; the " activities " which are " programmed " are a given set of industrial processes.

As an exercise in general economic equilibrium, the analysis of inter-industry relations is static. It is, however, easily extended to comparative statics, e.g. by varying the final " bill of goods ", and by introducing dynamic elements in various forms, as outlined in Leontief (1953a).

Much of the analysis is framed in terms of money values ; in practice, money is the only common unit for aggregating inputs and outputs of industries. But it falls naturally into a quantitative or real constituent and the corresponding system of prices. As a matter of notation, quantity aggregates are written as capital letters with suitable subscripts, and the corresponding small letters denote components of the aggregates and may carry two subscripts. Commodity prices and the wage rate for the single primary factor (labour) are denoted by small letters, p's for prices and w for the wage rate.

11.2 The Transactions Matrix

The basic construction of the input-output approach is a double table or matrix of transactions, either in quantitative or money value terms, covering the whole economy. Since the method is essentially empirical in content, and designed for practical application, it is instructive to begin with examples of actual transactions matrices in value terms.

Table 1 shows the transactions matrix for the U.K. in 1935 as constructed by Barna (1952) and a similar matrix for the U.S. in 1947 based on detailed computations made in the Bureau of Labor Statistics and given in Evans and Hoffenberg (1952). Each matrix is a condensed form for only ten industry groups, the original matrix having more rows and columns and a finer industrial classification.

The U.K. table is used for illustration. Total gross output of the agricultural and food industries in 1935 was £858 mn. at current market values. The first row of the table shows where the output went. £23 mn. was the value of that part which went as intermediate products to other industries, i.e. £2 mn. to building, £4 mn. to chemicals, £8 mn. to textiles, £3 mn. to services and £6 mn. not allocated in the statistical estimation from the data available. The rest of the output comprised end products satisfying final demand : £29 mn. as exports, £3 mn. in capital formation (here increases in stocks), £7 mn. for government consumption and the bulk (£796 mn.) to consumers. The first row therefore accounts entirely for the distribution of output ; in this case, it is mainly for consumption but the other destinations, though small, are significant. The other industry rows are similarly interpreted and the seventh can be taken as an example. Total output in metal making (iron, steel and non-ferrous metals) was £188 mn. in 1935, distributed mainly as intermediate products to the engineering, metal goods and building industries, with some exports and a little for direct consumption or capital formation.

The same figures of total gross output can be read down the columns of the table. The first column shows the inputs of the agriculture and food industries, with £170 mn. coming in the form of materials and services from other industries, and £130 mn. from imported materials. Indirect taxes (net of subsidies) amount to £176 mn. There remains the " value added " to the industries, estimated at £385 mn., and this represents the primary input or payments to the primary factors (wages, salaries, profits). In this particular construction, depreciation is also included in the primary input. The total of the first column is equal (apart from rounding errors) to the total of the first row, since by definition total gross input equals total gross output at £858 mn. The same is true of the rows and columns for the other industries ; in each case the row gives the distribution of output and the column shows the inputs of the industry group concerned.

The table is completed by the addition of entries in the bottom right-hand corner. These entries arise since there are imports which are either re-exported or entered directly into consumption, and since there are corresponding indirect taxes at the stage of final demand.

The table adds to the aggregate value of all transactions at current market prices. It is more comprehensive than gross national product or expenditure, but these national income aggregates can be derived, and their relation to the totality of transactions defined, from the table. It is, only necessary to read up and back from the bottom right-hand corner. If the table is read up the last column, gross national product at factor prices is the bottom figure, i.e. payments to primary factors, £4,225 mn. Total resources available (gross national product plus imports) at market

TABLE 1. TRANSACTIONS MATRICES U.K., 1935 AND U.S., 1947

Industries :
1. Agriculture and food
2. Coal and power
3. Building, building materials and timber
4. Chemicals and rubber
5. Textiles and clothing
6. Paper, printing and miscellaneous
7. Metal making
8. Engineering
9. Metal Goods.
10. Services

£ millions

U.K., 1935

Input from Industries:	Output to industries: 1	2	3	4	5	6	7	8	9	10	Not alloc.	Total	Exports	Capital formation	Gov't	Personal consumption	Total gross output
1	—	*	2	4	8	*	*	*	*	3	6	23	29	3	7	796	858
2	14	—	12	8	9	4	16	8	3	39	8	121	31	39	15	129	334
3	10	3	—	5	1	1	7	19	2	129	12	180	9	280	56	53	577
4	25	2	8	—	13	6	2	8	3	16	6	97	38	2	6	73	217
5	4	*	4	5	—	4	*	5	*	48	5	50	125	2	2	298	476
6	18	1	28	13	6	—	1	*	1	*	14	111	15	6	6	69	208
7	2	5	21	3	*	1	—	62	30	1	7	138	38	173	*	5	188
8	5	16	16	5	4	1	2	—	1	39	17	106	79	9	40	79	477
9	7	1	46	16	3	1	18	22	—	*	17	74	45	26	2	32	162
10	72	20	7	5	41	13	20	28	7	—	35	296	332	-3	304	1907	2865
Not allocated	13	8	14	—	18	5	—	—	6	30	—	122	15	-3	3	-5	132
Total	170	56	158	64	104	36	67	172	54	311	127	1318	756	544	441	3436	6494
Imports	130	5	41	48	102	23	30	16	37	19	9	460	52	18	8	266	804
Government	176	5	10	7	13	4	30	7	2	256	13	495	—	7	2	85	587
Primary input	385	268	369	98	258	147	86	282	70	2280	-18	4225	—	—	—	—	4225
Total gross input	858	334	577	217	476	208	188	477	162	2865	132	6494	808	569	450	3788	12108

* Less than £0·5 million.

U.S., 1947

$100 millions

Input from Industries :	Output to industries :												Final demand				Total gross output
	1	2	3	4	5	6	7	8	9	10	Not alloc.	Total	Exports	Capital formation	Gov't	Personal consumption	
1	—	*	3	19	27	1	*	*	*	49	4	103	30	-13	13	334	467
2	3	—	3	8	2	2	3	*	*	49	*	72	4	*	2	1	79
3	9	3	—	4	1	5	4	2	1	67	14	121	5	169	56	24	375
4	30	5	17	—	12	6	11	10	3	28	20	142	17	3	4	51	217
5	3	*	4	5	—	2	*	4	2	11	11	31	13	1	3	135	183
6	6	*	4	5	4	—	*	3	1	41	26	92	4	4	3	38	141
7	*	1	22	2	*	2	—	47	18	2	14	108	8	1	*	*	117
8	2	1	15	*	1	1	1	—	5	19	44	89	34	125	17	51	316
9	6	*	10	2	1	1	1	20	—	4	15	60	6	8	2	18	94
10	80	4	67	23	14	12	13	16	5	—	70	304	35	40	63	915	1358
Not allocated	22	4	22	30	21	21	15	39	14	82	—	269	*	-8	*	*	261
Total	160	17	168	98	82	52	48	154	51	343	219	1393	156	329	162	1569	3609
Imports	28	11	3	9	12	8	6	6	1	5	1	66	—	*	13	13	93
Government	21	11	15	17	12	10	8	18	5	139	22	278	8	3	35	313	637
Primary input	258	51	189	94	84	72	55	143	38	871	18	1872	8	2	301	21	2205
Total gross input	467	79	75	217	183	141	117	316	94	1358	261	3609	173	334	511	1916	6543

* Less than $50 millions.

Notes

U.K. Table taken with minor changes from Barna (1952).
Government: row   net indirect taxes only.
          column   consumption only, excluding capital formation.
Capital formation: fixed capital plus net inventory changes, including capital formation by government. Inventory changes estimated approximately and separated from column for " not allocated " in source table.

U.S. Table condensed from Evans and Hoffenberg (1952).
Government: row   all taxes and some miscellaneous payments
          column   consumption and capital formation.
Capital formation: fixed capital plus net inventory changes, excluding capital formation by government.
There are many other differences in scope and definition between the two tables ; reference should be made to the two sources.
Rows and columns do not necessarily add to totals because of rounding.

prices is the sum of the three bottom figures, i.e. £12,108 mn. – £6,494 mn. = £5,614 mn. If the table is read back along the last row, the same aggregate of £5,614 mn. is obtained as the sum of four items, representing the disposal of resources or national expenditure and exports. This aggregate of £5,614 mn. is *both* the sum of payments to primary factors and imports *and* the sum of consumption, capital formation and exports, all at market prices. This is the familiar identity of the product and expenditure sides in national income accounting.

The whole table falls into four sectors. The top left-hand sector comprises inter-industry transactions : the production and disposal of intermediate goods and services to the value of £1,318 mn. The bottom right-hand sector shows final demand met directly from imports, with the corresponding indirect taxes, valued at £438 mn. The other two sectors, in the top right-hand and the bottom left-hand positions, are the same aggregate of £6,494 mn. – £1,318 mn. = £5,176 mn. included twice, once for the transactions involved in meeting final demand from the output of domestic industries (top right-hand sector) and once for those arising in the payment of factors and for imports for use in industry (bottom left-hand sector). Hence, the total of £12,108 mn. of transactions is made up :

(i) inter-industry transactions which do not enter
　　into national income accounting :　　　　　　£1,318 mn.
(ii) transactions involved in the re-export and direct
　　consumption of imports :　　　　　　　　　£438 mn.
(iii) the rest of national product and imports (total
　　resources) counted twice, i.e. twice £5,176 mn.　£10,352 mn.

In a closed economy, with no external trade, the total value of transactions in the table would be twice the gross national product plus the value of inter-industry transactions. The last aggregate will depend on the industrial grouping adopted, being larger the finer the classification of industries.

11.3 Leontief's Open System

It is assumed that there are n industries or activities so defined that each produces a single and different commodity or product and that there is no government activity or external trade. The system is a static one and problems connected with capital investment are ignored.

There are two sets of conditions for equilibrium, one in terms of quantitative inputs and outputs, the other involving prices, receipts and costs. The quantitative or technical conditions of production are taken first.

The physical product of the rth industry is denoted by X_r ($r = 1, 2, \ldots n$), distributed in part as intermediate products to other industries and in part as final product to consumers. Denote by x_{rs} the amount X_r passed to the sth industry, and by x_r the amount X_r distributed to final consumers. The amounts x_{rs} for $s = 1, 2, \ldots n$ $(s \neq r)$ and x_r make up the rth row of a transactions matrix like those of Table 1, but in quantitative rather than value form ; the total of the row is X_r, gross output.

Equally, the sth industry draws its inputs of intermediate products from the other industries, in amounts x_{rs} for $r = 1, 2, \ldots n$ $(r \neq s)$. The remaining input is the primary factor, i.e. labour of all kinds, from unskilled to entrepreneurial services, lumped together for convenience as one factor. The total employment of labour is denoted by Y and employment in the sth industry by ξ_s. The amounts of inputs x_{rs} for $r = 1, 2, \ldots n$ $(r \neq s)$ and ξ_s make up the sth column of the transactions matrix.

The quantities x_{rs} for various r and s serve a double purpose ; they are entries in a matrix or double table. The order of the subscripts is essential : x_{rs} is the product of the rth industry going to the sth, and so the input of the sth industry coming from the rth. It is not true that $x_{rs} = x_{sr}$; the elements in the matrix are not symmetrical. There is no reason why x_{rs} and x_{sr} should be equal ; one is the output of the rth industry (going to the sth) and the other is the output of the sth industry (going to the rth), i.e. two different commodities.

In terms of the transactions matrix, as in Table 1, the amounts x_{rs} for $r, s = 1, 2, \ldots n$ make up the top left-hand sector. The rows are then completed by the final demands x_r for $r = 1, 2, \ldots n$. The columns are completed by the primary inputs ξ_s for $s = 1, 2, \ldots n$. Zero entries are inserted down the main diagonal, i.e. by convention take $x_{rr} = 0$ $(r = 1, 2, \ldots n)$ and take a zero in the bottom right-hand corner. So the *transactions matrix* is :

$$
\begin{array}{c}
n \text{ rows} \\
1 \text{ row}
\end{array}
\left[
\begin{array}{c|c|c}
x_{rs} & x_r & X_r \\
\hline
\xi_s & 0 & Y
\end{array}
\right]
$$
$$
\begin{array}{ccc}
n & 1 & \text{total} \\
\text{columns} & \text{column} & \text{column}
\end{array}
$$

There is no total row since the columns consist of entries in different units. It follows immediately that the rows must add to the totals :

$$
\left.
\begin{aligned}
X_r &= x_r + \sum_s x_{rs} \quad (r = 1, 2, \ldots n) \\
Y &= \sum_s \xi_s
\end{aligned}
\right\} \quad \ldots\ldots\ldots\ldots\ldots\ldots(1)
$$

where $\sum_s$ indicates a sum for all s $(s = 1, 2, \ldots n)$.

Something must now be said about the technical conditions of production, about the relations between inputs and outputs. It is assumed that there are fixed ratios between each input and the corresponding output :

$$x_{rs} = a_{rs}X_s \quad \text{and} \quad \xi_s = b_s X_s \quad\quad\quad\quad\quad\quad\quad(2)$$

for r and $s = 1, 2, \ldots n$. Since $x_{rr} = 0$ by convention, so $a_{rr} = 0$ also.

The constant a's and b's are *input coefficients*. The assumption that they are fixed may be interpreted in various ways. The sth industry has output X_s and this may be produced according to a " production function " which comprises a limited number of alternative processes, each with fixed technical coefficients. The particular process selected or in use would then give the relations (2). Or, there may be a continuous production function, of linear homogeneous form. Then, if input prices are given and inputs combined to minimise cost at each level of output, then the input combinations used again vary in proportion to output (see Ex. 1 and 2 below). In this case, the a's and b's in (2) are constants only for given input prices.

The relations (1), on substitution of (2), become :

$$X_r = x_r + \Sigma\, a_{rs}X_s \quad (r = 1, 2, \ldots n)$$

$$Y = \Sigma_s\, b_s X_s$$

which summarise the technical conditions of production.

For the second set of conditions for equilibrium, prices, receipts and costs are to be considered. With pure competition and free entry, profits in each industry are zero, i.e. receipts equal costs. If the product prices are p_r $(r = 1, 2, \ldots n)$ and if w is the wage rate, then the equality of receipts and costs in the sth industry gives :

$$p_s X_s = \Sigma_r\, p_r x_{rs} + w\,\xi_s = (\Sigma_r\, p_r a_{rs})X_s + wb_s X_s$$

i.e.
$$p_s = \Sigma_r\, p_r a_{rs} + wb_s \quad (s = 1, 2, \ldots n)$$

which summarise the price conditions of production.

The complete set of conditions for equilibrium are :

(i) (a)
$$X_r - \Sigma_s\, a_{rs}X_s \;\; = x_r \quad r = 1, 2, \ldots n$$

(b)
$$Y = \Sigma_s\, b_s X_s$$

(ii)
$$p_s - \Sigma_r\, p_r a_{rs} = wb_s \quad s = 1, 2, \ldots n$$

The input coefficients (the a's and b's) are all given data. Further, the system is open and certain parameters must be given and specified. For example, all the product prices p_r and the wage rate w may be taken as given (see Ex. 3 below). It is more convenient, however, to specify :

(a) the final demand or " bill of goods " x_r $(r=1, 2, \ldots n)$ and

(b) the wage rate w on the market for labour (primary input).

The system (i) and (ii) comprises $(2n+1)$ equations and there are $(2n+1)$ unknowns, i.e. n outputs X_r, employment Y and n prices p_r. The system is consistent with equilibrium.

There is one difference of some significance between this open system and the more general systems of closed type discussed in the previous chapter. None of the equations (i) and (ii) is derivable from the others, nor is there a price to be taken as *numéraire* and put equal to unity. In fact, the system gives the actual level of prices and not only the price ratios —given the wage rate w. The clue to the difference is that the wage rate has to be specified and this sets the level of all prices. If anything has to be taken as *numéraire*, then it is the wage rate.

The two sets of conditions are quite separate and distinct, (i) in quantities, (ii) in money values and each can be used without reference to the other. Given the wage rate w, equations (ii) are n in number and suffice for determination of the n equilibrium prices p_r. These are the supply prices which, together with the given " bill of goods ", can be set against the demand functions when the open system is closed.

Then, quite separately, equations (i) can be considered, given only the final demand or " bill of goods ". Equations (i) (a) are n in number and serve to determine the equilibrium outputs X_r. The single equation (i) (b) then gives total employment Y of the primary factor.

EXERCISES 11.3

1. A product y is produced by the use of two factors x_1 and x_2 according to the linear homogeneous production function $y = k\sqrt{x_1 x_2}$ where k is a constant. Given the factor prices (p_1 and p_2), find the optimum usage of the factors for minimum cost for given product y. Show that, at this optimum :

$$x_1 = c_1 y \quad \text{and} \quad x_2 = c_2 y$$

i.e. the factors are always combined in fixed proportions (depending on p_1 and p_2).

2. Generalise the result of the previous exercise for any production function which is linear homogeneous and illustrate diagrammatically (in the two factor case) with constant product curves.

3. Examine the conditions of equilibrium (i) (a) and (ii) from the point of view of the assumption that all the p's and w are given to the industries. Show why this is not a convenient assumption.

11.4 Transactions in Money Value

The transactions matrix of 11.3 is in quantities, and the units vary from one row to another. The matrix can be summed across a row, only one unit being involved, and the conditions (i) are obtained ; it cannot be summed down a column and there is no direct way of bringing in conditions (ii), i.e. the equality of receipts and costs. Such a system is not readily related to actual data. The transactions matrix in practice is in money values, as in Table 1 ; in particular, the given final demands are expenditures and not a quantitative " bill of goods ". The system of 11.3 needs to be adjusted to handle money values, to become more applicable and perhaps more intelligible.

The money values of all the quantities of 11.3 can be written once prices are determined by conditions (ii) for equilibrium. For the rth industry, total output is $V_r = p_r X_r$ in value, distributed :

$$v_{rs} = p_r x_{rs} \quad \text{and} \quad v_r = p_r x_r \quad (r, s = 1, 2, \dots n)$$

At the wage rate w, total labour payments (values added) are $W = wY$, again the sum of the values added in separate industries ($w\xi_s$). With these money values the *value transactions matrix* is :

$$
\begin{array}{c}
n \text{ rows} \\
1 \text{ row}
\end{array}
\left[
\begin{array}{c|c|c}
v_{rs} & v_r & V_r \\
\hline
w\xi_s & 0 & W
\end{array}
\right]
$$
$$
\begin{array}{ccc}
n & 1 & \text{total} \\
\text{columns} & \text{column} & \text{column}
\end{array}
$$

exactly as in Table 1.

The input coefficients need a corresponding adjustment :

$$\alpha_{rs} = \frac{v_{rs}}{V_s} = \frac{p_r x_{rs}}{p_s X_s} = \frac{p_r}{p_s} a_{rs}$$

and

$$\beta_s = \frac{w\xi_s}{V_s} = \frac{w\xi_s}{p_s X_s} = \frac{w}{p_s} b_s$$

The interpretation is still straightforward : α_{rs} is the value of the rth product used, and β_s is the payment to primary factors, each per unit value of product in the sth industry. The coefficients are no longer constants ; they depend on the prices as well as on the fixed technical coefficients, a_{rs} and b_s.

The conditions (i), obtained by summing across rows of the transactions matrix, are the same in values as in quantities :

(i) (a)
$$V_r - \sum_s \alpha_{rs} V_s = v_r$$

(b)
$$W = \sum_s \beta_s V_s$$

There is a difference ; what is now given is the set of values of final demands, not the quantitative " bill of goods " The conditions (i) then determine the values V_r of outputs and the total payment W to primary factors (value added).

Conditions (ii), which set total receipts equal to total costs for each industry, are now related to the sums of columns of the value transactions matrix. The sum of the sth column is total costs of the sth industry $\sum_r v_{rs} + w \, \xi_s = \sum_r \alpha_{rs} V_s + \beta_s \, V_s$, and this must equal V_s, the sum of the corresponding row. Hence the conditions are:

$$\text{(ii)} \qquad \sum_r \alpha_{rs} + \beta_s = 1 \quad (s = 1, 2, \ldots n)$$

The coefficients in (ii) involve the prices p_r and the wage rate w. The conditions determine the prices given the wage rate, exactly as before. Since the prices are the same, it doesn't matter that the values of final demands rather than the quantities are given for (i) ; the quantities follow from the values or conversely.

11.5 The Matrix of Input Coefficients

From the matrix of transactions, a matrix of input coefficients is derived. In quantities, it is :

$$\begin{bmatrix} 0 & a_{12} & a_{13} & \ldots & a_{1n} \\ a_{21} & 0 & a_{23} & \ldots & a_{2n} \\ \cdots & \cdots & \cdots & \cdots & \cdots \\ a_{n1} & a_{n2} & a_{n3} & \ldots & 0 \\ b_1 & b_2 & b_3 & \ldots & b_n \end{bmatrix}$$

The conventional zero figures are inserted for a_{rr} $(r = 1, 2, \ldots n)$. Since $a_{rs} = \dfrac{x_{rs}}{X_s}$, the new matrix is obtained from the transactions matrix by dividing by X_s down the sth column. The column for final demands is ignored.

The units or dimensions of the various a's and b's are different. The coefficient a_{rs} involves the quantity units both of the rth and of the sth product. It follows that neither rows nor columns of the input coefficient matrix can be summed as they stand. However, conditions (i) and (ii) of 11.3 can be read off the matrix. Multiply the entries in successive columns by $X_1, X_2, \ldots X_n$ and add across rows. The result by conditions (i) is $X_r - x_r$ for the rth row and Y for the last row. Multiply the entries in successive rows by $p_1, p_2, \ldots p_n$ and w and add down columns. The result for the sth column is p_s by conditions (ii).

A similar matrix, involving α_{rs} and β_s, is obtained from the transactions matrix in values. Here :

$$\alpha_{rs} = \frac{v_{rs}}{V_s} \quad \text{and} \quad \beta_s = \frac{w\xi_s}{V_s}$$

and V_s is the sum of both the sth row and the sth column in the transactions matrix. Matrices of input coefficients in value form are shown in Table 2, obtained directly from the transactions matrices of Table 1. The entries in the input coefficient matrix are now independent of units. Each entry (apart from the conventional zero figures) is a fraction, i.e. the fraction of the total value of product taken by the purchases of a commodity or primary input.

Summation across rows of the matrix in α_{rs} and β_s is to be done as before, i.e. by multiplication of columns by V_s. This gives conditions (i) of 11.4. The corresponding conditions (ii) are :

$$\Sigma \alpha_{rs} + \beta_s = 1 \quad (s = 1, 2, \ldots n)$$

which implies that summation down the columns of the input coefficient matrix is very simple : the sum of each column is unity. This can be checked in the empirical cases of Table 2.

A variant of the input coefficient matrix can be written :

$$\mathbf{A} = \begin{bmatrix} 1 & -a_{12} & -a_{13} & \cdots & -a_{1n} \\ -a_{21} & 1 & -a_{23} & \cdots & -a_{2n} \\ \cdots\cdots\cdots\cdots\cdots\cdots\cdots\cdots\cdots\cdots \\ -a_{n1} & -a_{n2} & -a_{n3} & \cdots & 1 \\ -b_1 & -b_2 & -b_3 & \cdots & -b_n \end{bmatrix}$$

Here all the input coefficients are entered with a $-$ sign and entries $+1$ are included along the main diagonal. The matrix is now of the form which represents the " technology " in the sense of 10.8 above. Each industry, or activity, is shown by a column in $\mathbf{A}$ with $+$ entries for output and $-$ entries for input ; and each column is " scaled " so that output appears as $+1$, inputs as amounts per unit of output. In short, $\mathbf{A}$ is the *technology matrix* of the production conditions assumed in the problem.

EXERCISES 11.5

1. In the input coefficient matrix, with α_{rs} and β_s, show that the formula for summing across rows is : $\Sigma_s \alpha_{rs} V_s = V_r - v_r$. What is the right-hand side here?

2. Test the matrices of Table 2 for summation across rows by the formula of the previous exercise.

3. Write the technology matrix $\mathbf{A}$ in terms of α_{rs} and β_s, obtained from the value transactions matrix. What is the rule for summation of $\mathbf{A}$ by columns?

TABLE 2. MATRICES OF INPUT COEFFICIENTS, U.K. 1935 AND U.S., 1947

(α_{rs} in value terms)

Industries : 1. Agriculture and food   6. Paper, printing and miscellaneous
2. Coal and power   7. Metal making
3. Building, building materials   8. Engineering
and timber   9. Metal goods
4. Chemicals and rubber   10. Services
5. Textiles and clothing

U.K., 1935   Purchases per £ of output of purchasing industry.

	Purchases by industries									
	1	2	3	4	5	6	7	8	9	10
From industries :										
1	0	·000	·003	·018	·017	·000	·000	·000	·000	·001
2	·016	0	·020	·037	·019	·019	·085	·017	·019	·014
3	·012	·009	0	·023	·002	·005	·037	·021	·012	·045
4	·029	·006	·024	0	·027	·029	·011	·040	·019	·002
5	·005	·000	·014	·023	0	·019	·000	·017	·000	·005
6	·021	·003	·007	·060	·013	0	·000	·010	·012	·017
7	·002	·015	·049	·014	·000	·005	0	·130	·185	·000
8	·006	·048	·036	·000	·008	·005	·011	0	·006	·014
9	·008	·003	·028	·023	·006	·005	·011	·046	0	·000
10	·084	·060	·080	·074	·086	·063	·096	·039	·043	0
Not allocated	·015	·024	·012	·023	·038	·024	·106	·021	·037	·010
Primary input*	·805	·832	·728	·705	·784	·837	·628	·639	·673	·892

U.S., 1947   Purchases per $ of output of purchasing industry

	Purchases by industries :									
	1	2	3	4	5	6	7	8	9	10
From industries :										
1	0	·000	·008	·087	•145	·005	·001	·000	·001	·036
2	·006	0	·008	·036	·009	·013	·030	·008	·007	·036
3	·019	·043	0	·020	·007	·035	·034	·032	·032	·049
4	·063	·066	·046	0	·065	·040	·092	·037	·019	·021
5	·007	·001	·010	·023	0	·013	·000	·011	·003	·001
6	·012	·001	·012	·023	·024	0	·001	·010	·027	·030
7	·000	·006	·060	·010	·000	·015	0	·150	·186	·002
8	·004	·008	·041	·000	·003	·005	·011	0	·053	·014
9	·014	·001	·028	·011	·001	·003	·002	·064	0	·003
10	·171	·046	·178	·106	·079	·082	·111	·052	·055	0
Not allocated	·047	·045	·058	·137	·114	·149	·128	·123	·152	·060
Primary input*	·657	·783	·552	·547	·553	·635	·590	·513	·459	·748

* Including imports and government (taxes).

Figures derived from Table 1 ; greater detail than shown in Table 1 used in calculating U.S. figures.

Columns do not necessarily add to unity because of rounding.

11.6 Solution for Three Industries

The nature of the solution of Leontief's open system is sufficiently illustrated in the case $n=3$. The equations for output, 11.3 above, are:

$$X_1 - a_{12}X_2 - a_{13}X_3 = x_1$$
$$-a_{21}X_1 + X_2 - a_{23}X_3 = x_2$$
$$-a_{31}X_1 - a_{32}X_2 + X_3 = x_3$$

to be solved for outputs (X_1, X_2, X_3) in terms of given final demands (x_1, x_2, x_3). The solution can be obtained by elementary algebra, but it is expressed most concisely in terms of determinants (see 12.9 and 14.2 below).

The technology matrix is:

$$\mathbf{A} = \begin{bmatrix} 1 & -a_{12} & -a_{13} \\ -a_{21} & 1 & -a_{23} \\ -a_{31} & -a_{32} & 1 \end{bmatrix}$$

Write A for the determinant value obtained from $\mathbf{A}$. The co-factors of A are:

$$A_{11} = \begin{vmatrix} 1 & -a_{23} \\ -a_{32} & 1 \end{vmatrix}, \quad A_{12} = - \begin{vmatrix} -a_{21} & -a_{23} \\ -a_{31} & 1 \end{vmatrix}, \quad \ldots$$

The solution is:

$$\left. \begin{aligned} X_1 &= \frac{1}{A}(A_{11}x_1 + A_{21}x_2 + A_{31}x_3) \\ X_2 &= \frac{1}{A}(A_{12}x_1 + A_{22}x_2 + A_{32}x_3) \\ X_3 &= \frac{1}{A}(A_{13}x_1 + A_{23}x_2 + A_{33}x_3) \end{aligned} \right\} \quad \ldots\ldots\ldots\ldots\ldots\ldots(1)$$

Total employment (primary input) follows from equation (i) (b) of 11.3:

$$Y = b_1X_1 + b_2X_2 + b_3X_3 \ldots\ldots\ldots\ldots\ldots\ldots\ldots\ldots(2)$$

These are the equilibrium values of outputs and employment, given the final " bill of goods ". Various results in comparative statics follow by varying the " bill of goods ", for example the effect of an increase in the demand for motor vehicles (directly and indirectly) on the output of steel. If x_1 increases, other final demands unchanged, then:

$$\frac{\partial X_1}{\partial x_1} = \frac{A_{11}}{A}; \quad \frac{\partial X_2}{\partial x_1} = \frac{A_{12}}{A}; \quad \frac{\partial X_3}{\partial x_1} = \frac{A_{13}}{A}$$

and

$$\frac{\partial Y}{\partial x_1} = b_1\frac{\partial X_1}{\partial x_1} + b_2\frac{\partial X_2}{\partial x_1} + b_3\frac{\partial X_3}{\partial x_1}$$

$$= \frac{1}{A}(b_1A_{11} + b_2A_{12} + b_3A_{13})$$

The solution in value terms is exactly similar. The results (1) and (2) hold with the x's, X's and Y replaced by the corresponding values. The matrix of input coefficients now gives the determinant

$$\begin{vmatrix} 1 & -\alpha_{12} & -\alpha_{13} \\ -\alpha_{21} & 1 & -\alpha_{23} \\ -\alpha_{31} & -\alpha_{32} & 1 \end{vmatrix} \quad \text{where } \alpha_{rs} = \frac{p_r}{p_s} a_{rs}$$

This involves the prices as well as the fixed technical coefficients.

The determination of equilibrium prices is the same whether the outputs and employment are found in quantity or value terms. The set of equations to be solved are the conditions (ii) of 11.3 :

$$p_1 - a_{21}p_2 - a_{31}p_3 = wb_1$$
$$-a_{12}p_1 + p_2 - a_{32}p_3 = wb_2$$
$$-a_{13}p_1 - a_{23}p_2 + p_3 = wb_3$$

Notice that the coefficients are here transposed, i.e. the rows and columns are interchanged. The solution is

$$\left. \begin{aligned} p_1 &= \frac{1}{A}(A_{11}b_1 + A_{12}b_2 + A_{13}b_3)w \\ p_2 &= \frac{1}{A}(A_{21}b_1 + A_{22}b_2 + A_{23}b_3)w \\ p_3 &= \frac{1}{A}(A_{31}b_1 + A_{32}b_2 + A_{33}b_3)w \end{aligned} \right\} \quad \dots\dots\dots\dots\dots(3)$$

The equilibrium prices are proportional to the given wage rate w, the proportion varying from one price to another according to the input coefficients.

In the solution (3) for prices, the labour input coefficients (the b's) only appear in conjunction with the wage rate. Write

$$w_1 = wb_1 ; \quad w_2 = wb_2 ; \quad w_3 = wb_3$$

as the wage costs per unit of output. Then

$$p_1 = \frac{1}{A}(A_{11}w_1 + A_{12}w_2 + A_{13}w_3) \dots\dots\dots\dots\dots(4)$$

and similar results for p_2 and p_3. There is considerable similarity in form between the results (1) and (4), but the constants are transposed in the two results.

It is also important to see the similarity in form between the original condition (i) (a) and the solution (1), when written as follows.

Conditions : $x_1 = X_1 - a_{12}X_2 - a_{13}X_3$ and two similar equations

Solution : $X_1 = \dfrac{A_{11}}{A}x_1 + \dfrac{A_{21}}{A}x_2 + \dfrac{A_{31}}{A}x_3$ and two similar equations.

The coefficients on the right-hand side of the conditions make up the determinant A. The coefficients in the solution are arranged as in the determinant

$$\begin{vmatrix} \dfrac{A_{11}}{A} & \dfrac{A_{21}}{A} & \dfrac{A_{31}}{A} \\[2mm] \dfrac{A_{12}}{A} & \dfrac{A_{22}}{A} & \dfrac{A_{32}}{A} \\[2mm] \dfrac{A_{13}}{A} & \dfrac{A_{23}}{A} & \dfrac{A_{33}}{A} \end{vmatrix}$$

This is a well-known determinant, the inverse or reciprocal of A (see 13.7 below). Hence, in writing the general form of the solution (1), it is convenient to have, not only the matrix of input coefficients (the a's), but also the inverse matrix involving the determinant A and its co-factors. An example of an inverse matrix is provided by Evans and Hoffenberg (1952), Table 6. The interpretation of the entries in the inverse matrix follow from the nature of the solution (1). The (r, s)th entry represents the total output of the rth industry required per unit of final demand for the sth product; this can be either in quantitative or value terms.

The results obtained, though written in the case of three industries, are quite general. A systematic development of the general case, in terms of the matrix notation, is given in 14.7 below.

EXERCISES 11.6

1. Set out the conditions of equilibrium in the case of two industries ($n = 2$) and find the solution.

2. The input coefficient matrix in the two industries case is $\mathbf{A} = \begin{bmatrix} 1 & -a_{12} \\ -a_{21} & 1 \end{bmatrix}$.

Show that the inverse is

$$\begin{bmatrix} \dfrac{1}{1 - a_{12}a_{21}} & \dfrac{a_{12}}{1 - a_{12}a_{21}} \\[2mm] \dfrac{a_{21}}{1 - a_{12}a_{21}} & \dfrac{1}{1 - a_{12}a_{21}} \end{bmatrix}$$

3. Show that, though the entries of the determinant in α's above depend on prices, its value is A.

4. For the three industries case, show that $p_1 = \dfrac{w\,\partial Y}{\partial x_1}$ and interpret this result.

11.7 The Walras-Leontief Closed System

In the open system, considered so far, two things are given : the final demands and the unit wage costs (including the wage rate). The first are the demands of " households ", who also determine their labour supply to industry at the given wage-rate. To close the system it is only necessary to add another " industry " (households), purchasing the products of other industries and supplying the labour input of other industries. When the new " industry " is added, all commodities become intermediate products ; there is neither a final demand nor a primary input, separately distinguished. It is assumed that there is pure competition and free entry, that there is no government activity or external trade, and that all problems connected with capital investment and other dynamic elements are ignored.

There are $(n+1)$ industries, each producing a single and distinct product in amount X_r $(r=1, 2, \dots n+1)$. The last industry is households with product X_{n+1}, the labour services supplied to the other industries. The transactions matrix is made up of the quantities x_{rs}, the output of the rth industry passed to the sth industry, with $x_{rr}=0$ by convention. In particular, x_{rn+1} is the amount of the rth commodity going to consumption by households (previously final demand), and x_{n+1s} is the amount of labour used by the sth industry (previously primary input).

The first set of conditions for equilibrium in the closed system is the same as before, the exact distribution of each total output :

$$X_r = \Sigma \, x_{rs} \quad (r=1, 2, \dots n+1)$$

and the rows in the transactions matrix add to total outputs. It is now convenient to insert $(-X_r)$, instead of zero, in the principal diagonal of the transactions matrix, i.e. to take $x_{rr} = -X_r$. With the transactions matrix so adjusted, the conditions are :

$$\Sigma_s x_{rs}=0 \quad (r=1, 2, \dots n+1) \quad \dots\dots\dots\dots\dots\dots(1)$$

and the transactions matrix adds across to zero. The matrix does not add down because the units in rows are different.

It is again assumed that there are constant input coefficients a_{rs} given by technical conditions :

$$x_{rs}=a_{rs}X_s \quad (r, s=1, 2, \dots n+1) \quad \dots\dots\dots\dots\dots(2)$$

Under the present convention that $x_{rr} = -X_r$, this holds for $r=s$ by writing $a_{rr} = -1$.

The new feature is the assumption that $x_{rn+1}=a_{rn+1}X_{n+1}$, i.e. that the consumption of the rth commodity by households is a fixed proportion of the labour they supply. Expenditure on each commodity is a fixed proportion of income (all in real terms). This is a very restrictive assumption, and it will be examined later in more detail.

Substitute (2) into (1) and the first set of equilibrium conditions becomes:

$$\sum_s a_{rs}X_s = 0 \quad (r=1, 2, \ldots n+1)$$

The second set of conditions introduces the prices p_r $(r=1, 2, \ldots n+1)$, where p_{n+1} is the wage rate (or the price of labour services). The conditions are that receipts equal costs in each industry. For the sth industry, receipts are p_sX_s and costs are $\sum_r p_r x_{rs}$ with $s=r$ excluded. Hence, with $x_{rr} = -X_r$ and $a_{rr} = -1$, the second set of equilibrium conditions is $\sum_r p_r x_{rs} = 0$, or by use of (2):

$$\sum_r p_r a_{rs} = 0 \quad (s=1, 2, \ldots n+1)$$

The conditions for general equilibrium, with fixed technical coefficients a_{rs}, are of the very simple form :

$$\text{(i)} \quad \sum_s a_{rs}X_s = 0 \quad (r=1, 2, \ldots n+1)$$

$$\text{(ii)} \quad \sum_r p_r a_{rs} = 0 \quad (s=1, 2, \ldots n+1)$$

The variables are the $n+1$ outputs X_r, which appear only in (i), and the $n+1$ prices p_r, which appear only in (ii). These conditions, however, are deceptively simple, and they raise peculiar difficulties not met when the system is open.

The nature of the problem can be seen in the case of two commodities (one industrial product and labour). The conditions are :

(i) $\quad -X_1 + a_{12}X_2 = 0$ $\qquad$ (ii) $\quad -p_1 + a_{21}p_2 = 0$

$\quad\ \ a_{21}X_1 - X_2 = 0$ $\qquad\qquad\qquad a_{12}p_1 - p_2 = 0$

From (i) : $\qquad\qquad\qquad \dfrac{X_1}{X_2} = a_{12} = \dfrac{1}{a_{21}}$

From (ii) : $\qquad\qquad\qquad \dfrac{p_1}{p_2} = a_{21} = \dfrac{1}{a_{12}}$

It follows that only the *ratios* of outputs or prices are given by the equilibrium system, and that the system is only *consistent* even with this limited result if the input coefficients satisfy a relation :

$$a_{12}a_{21} = 1 \quad \text{i.e.} \quad \begin{vmatrix} 1 & -a_{12} \\ -a_{21} & 1 \end{vmatrix} = 0.$$

This result can be generalised. The conditions (i) and (ii) are linear equations but they are homogeneous in the variables. Though the number of equations is equal to the number of variables, they can do no more than to give ratios of the variables, i.e. to provide a solution for n variables given an arbitrary value for the last variable. Even for this, one of the equations must be derivable from the others, which implies a restriction on the values of the input coefficients—the determinant formed from the technology matrix (made up of input coefficients) must be zero. It is also to be noticed that the two sets of equations, though quite separate (one for outputs, the other for prices), do hang together. If the input coefficients are such as to produce ratios of outputs, then they also provide ratios of prices. Hence, the closed system determines (at most) the *structure* of the economy, not its *scale*. There is no such limitation in the open system, where the production sector is determined as to scale as well as structure. It is, in fact, the assumption of given final demands which sets the scale for outputs, and the fixed wage rate sets the scale for prices. These questions are further examined in Ex. 1, and generally in 14.7 below.

The closed system examined here can be associated with the name Leontief; his assumption of fixed input coefficients is adopted. It is evident, however, that the system is of Walrasian form. It is the simplest particular version of the general economic equilibrium, as examined in Chapter 10 above; see Goodwin (1953). As noted by Cameron (1951), the system is one of general Walrasian equilibrium with all opportunities of " economising " eliminated.

EXERCISES 11.7

1. Write the equilibrium conditions in the case of three industries ($n = 3$). Show that ratios $X_1 : X_2 : X_3$ and $p_1 : p_2 : p_3$ are determined only if the input coefficients are such that the technology matrix

$$\begin{bmatrix} 1 & -a_{12} & -a_{13} \\ -a_{21} & 1 & -a_{23} \\ -a_{31} & -a_{32} & 1 \end{bmatrix}$$

has a zero determinant value. Show also that there are still difficulties if co-factors such as

$$\begin{bmatrix} 1 & -a_{12} \\ -a_{21} & 1 \end{bmatrix}$$

are zero.

2. In the analysis above in terms of quantities, the transactions matrix x_{rs} adds across to zero, but does not add down. Adjust the system so as to be based on a value transactions matrix, i.e. the matrix of $v_{rs} = p_r x_{rs}$. Show that, by the two sets of equilibrium conditions, this matrix adds across and down to zero.

3. Extend the adjustments of the previous exercise to the technology (input coefficient) matrix. Show that the matrix has entries $\alpha_{rs} = \dfrac{p_r}{p_s} a_{rs}$ and that, by equilibrium conditions (ii), the matrix adds down to zero. What can be said of summation across the matrix?

11.8 Leontief's Dynamic System

In the above treatment of inter-industry relations, capital formation is ignored in theory, and included in given final demands in practice. The system is both static and short-run. An extension is now made, introducing dynamic processes by the obvious device of taking the acceleration principle to relate capital stock to output, or investment to changes in output. Time lags are ignored (but see Ex. 3 below) and the assumption is made that plans on stocks are fulfilled. The system, in fact, is essentially one of moving equilibrium.

The *input coefficients* a_{rs} are defined as before: $x_{rs} = a_{rs} X_s$ for r, $s = 1$, 2, ... n. They relate to *current flows* of products; x_{rs} is the flow of the rth product to the sth industry in a period (such as a year) and it is taken as a fixed proportion of the corresponding flow of output X_s of the sth industry. It is generally assumed that the sth industry does not use its own product as an input, so that a_{ss} is not defined and set by convention as $a_{ss} = -1$. In parallel with these coefficients, a new set of *capital coefficients* b_{rs} is defined: $S_{rs} = b_{rs} X_s$ for r, $s = 1, 2, ... n$. These relate to *stocks* of commodities, i.e. S_{rs} is the stock of the rth commodity held by the sth industry, covering all kinds of capital formation from inventories of materials and products to plant and equipment, according to the nature of the rth commodity. In particular, S_{rr} and b_{rr} are defined since they show the stock of the rth commodity held by the industry which produces it.

There are two matrices of given and constant coefficients:

$$\mathbf{A} = \begin{bmatrix} 1 & -a_{12} & ... & -a_1 \\ -a_{21} & 1 & ... & -a_{2n} \\ .... \\ -a_{n1} & -a_{n2} & ... & 1 \end{bmatrix} \quad \text{and} \quad \mathbf{B} = \begin{bmatrix} b_{11} & b_{12} & ... & b_{1n} \\ b_{21} & b_{22} & ... & b_{2n} \\ .... \\ b_{n1} & b_{n2} & ... & b_{nn} \end{bmatrix}$$

Between them they describe the structure of the economy, $\mathbf{A}$ representing the *flow structure*, $\mathbf{B}$ the *capital structure*. The dimensions of the a's are as before, a_{rs} being in units of the rth product per unit of the sth product (both in a given period). The dimensions of the b's are different. The stock S_{rs} is in units of the rth commodity, held at a point of time; X_s is in units of the sth commodity, a flow in a period. Hence b_{rs} is so many units of the rth product held per unit flow of the sth product. For example, if steel is the rth product and if the sth product is motor vehicles, then b_{rs} is in terms of tons of steel held per motor vehicle produced in a period.

Each capital coefficient is to be interpreted as the constant of an accelerator. All quantities are varying over time and differentiation of $S_{rs} = b_{rs} X_s$ gives :

$$\frac{dS_{rs}}{dt} = b_{rs} \frac{dX_s}{dt}$$

for continuous changes. This is :

Investment in the rth product $= b_{rs}$ times change in output

for the sth industry. The accelerator here is in continuous form without lags (see Ex. 1–3 below).

Only the first set of equations in Leontief's system is now considered, i.e. the equations for exact distribution of outputs. The other set, in the prices, can be added very much as before. The open system of 11.3 and the closed system of 11.7 are both extended to dynamic forms.

Open system. There are n industries for each of which the final demand x_r ($r = 1, 2, \dots n$) is given. This now implies that x_r is a given flow over time, a *given function of time*. What is given is a " bill of goods " changing in a specified way. The conditions for the exact distribution of product is now :

$$X_r = x_r + \sum_s x_{rs} + \sum_s \frac{dS_{rs}}{dt} \quad (r = 1, 2, \dots n)$$

The product goes in part to final consumers (first term), in part as current input for other industries (second term) and in part as inputs on capital account for other industries (third term). The last term can be positive or negative according as (e.g.) inventories are being built up or run down ; there are some difficulties about negative terms, mentioned briefly below. If the two sets of structural coefficients are inserted with $(a_{rr} = -1)$, then :

$$\sum \left(a_{rs} X_s + b_{rs} \frac{dX_s}{dt} \right) + x_r = 0 \quad (r = 1, 2, \dots n) \dots\dots\dots\dots(1)$$

is the extended version of the conditions (i) (a) of 11.3 above.

Closed system. The nth industry is taken as households, transforming consumers' goods as inputs into labour services as output. The conditions for the exact distribution of products are (1) with x_r omitted :

$$\sum \left(a_{rs} X_s + b_{rs} \frac{dX_s}{dt} \right) = 0 \quad (r = 1, 2, \dots n) \dots\dots\dots\dots\dots(2)$$

This extends conditions (i) of 11.7 above.

Equations (1) or (2) are in the n outputs X_r ($r = 1, 2, \dots n$) but they apply to outputs varying over time and involve rates of change as well as levels. They are sets of differential equations, linear with constant coefficients. Their solution comprises each output as an explicit function of time—the path of output over time—and it must involve arbitrary constants to be fixed by initial conditions. Since the equations are of first order, there is one arbitrary constant for each product and the initial output of each industry is required.

The methods of Chapter 5 above, extended in obvious ways, apply to the solution of (1) or (2). The equations for the closed system are the simpler; they are of homogeneous form. However, once they are solved, the solution of the non-homogeneous equations for the open system is obtained by the addition of a particular integral which takes account of the term x_r (given as a function of time). The solution in the simplest case of two industries is given in the following section; more general solutions are indicated in 14.9 below.

It will be seen that the path of X_r (for each $r = 1, 2, \ldots n$) may or may not show oscillations, and may or may not be damped as times goes on. Being based on the same acceleration principle, the present dynamic system displays the same range of possibilities as in the trade cycle theory already examined. The system is also subject to familiar limitations, and needs corresponding extensions. It is assumed, in writing $\dfrac{dS_{rs}}{dt} = b_{rs} \dfrac{dX_s}{dt}$, that the accelerator is reversible, that stocks decline when output falls in the same way that they increase when output rises. In fact, at least for plant and equipment, if not for inventories, the accelerator needs to be taken as non-linear and not symmetrical. These difficulties are discussed in Chapter 7 above and they are examined by Leontief (1953a) in the present context.

EXERCISES 11.8

1. Modify the system of the text to period analysis by assuming an accelerator of the form : investment in rth product by sth industry equals b_{rs} times the current change in output $\{X_s(t) - X_s(t-1)\}$. Show that, for the closed system, the conditions of the system are a set of first-order difference equations :

$$\sum_s (a_{rs} + b_{rs}) X_s(t) - \Sigma b_{rs} X_s(t-1) = 0 \quad (r = 1, 2, \ldots n)$$

2. Introduce a time lag into the system of the previous exercise by taking investment as dependent on a past change in output $\{X_s(t-1) - X_s(t-2)\}$ and show that the difference equations are of second order :

$$\Sigma a_{rs} X_s(t) + \Sigma b_{rs} X_s(t-1) - \Sigma b_{rs} X_s(t-2) = 0$$

3. In the (continuous) system of the text, take purchases of the rth commodity on capital account by the sth industry at time t as :

$$\frac{d}{dt} S_{rs}(t) = b_{rs} \text{ times anticipated rate of change in } X_s.$$

Assume further that there is delay between delivery of capital equipment and the change in output, the delay being uniform and taken as the unit for time. Show that the conditions of the closed system are a set of mixed difference-differential equations :

$$\Sigma a_{rs} X_s(t) + \Sigma b_{rs} \frac{d}{dt} X_s(t+1) = 0$$

11.9 Dynamic Solution for Two Industries

In the simplest case of two industries, the conditions (1) of the previous section are :

$$\left.\begin{array}{l} X_1 - a_{12}X_2 - b_{11}\dfrac{dX_1}{dt} - b_{12}\dfrac{dX_2}{dt} = x_1 \\[2ex] - a_{21}X_1 + X_2 - b_{21}\dfrac{dX_1}{dt} - b_{22}\dfrac{dX_2}{dt} = x_2 \end{array}\right\} \quad\dots\dots\dots\dots\dots(1)$$

These are for the open system. The closed system is obtained when $x_1 = x_2 = 0$ (and households are one of the two industries). The equations (1) are then homogeneous and more easily solved, and they are taken first.

Closed system. On the method which worked in Chapter 5 above, try :

$$X_1 = e^{-\lambda t} \quad \text{and} \quad X_2 = ke^{-\lambda t}$$

so that

$$\frac{dX_1}{dt} = -\lambda e^{-\lambda t} \quad \text{and} \quad \frac{dX_2}{dt} = -\lambda ke^{-\lambda t}$$

where λ and k are some constants to be found in terms of the structural constants (the a's and b's). Substitute in (1) and cancel $e^{-\lambda t} \neq 0$ to get two equations for λ and k :

$$1 - ka_{12} + \lambda(b_{11} + kb_{12}) = 0 \quad \text{and} \quad -a_{21} + k + \lambda(b_{21} + kb_{22}) = 0$$

giving

$$k = \frac{1 + \lambda b_{11}}{a_{12} - \lambda b_{12}} = \frac{a_{21} - \lambda b_{21}}{1 + \lambda b_{22}} \quad\dots\dots\dots\dots\dots\dots(2)$$

Hence k follows once λ is found, and λ is given by the right-hand members of (2) arranged in the form of the quadratic :

$$(1 + \lambda b_{11})(1 + \lambda b_{22}) = (a_{12} - \lambda b_{12})(a_{21} - \lambda b_{21})$$

i.e.

$$\alpha\lambda^2 + \beta\lambda + \gamma = 0$$

where

and

$$\left.\begin{array}{l} \alpha = b_{11}b_{22} - b_{12}b_{21}; \quad \gamma = 1 - a_{12}a_{21} \\[1ex] \beta = b_{11} + b_{22} + a_{12}b_{21} + a_{21}b_{12} \end{array}\right\} \quad\dots\dots\dots\dots\dots(3)$$

There are two roots $\lambda = \lambda_1$, λ_2 which are real and distinct, since $\beta^2 > 4\alpha\gamma$, as can be shown :

$$\beta^2 = \{(b_{11} + a_{12}b_{21}) + (b_{22} + a_{21}b_{12})\}^2 = \{(b_{11} + a_{12}b_{21}) - (b_{22} + a_{21}b_{12})\}^2$$
$$+ 4(b_{11} + a_{12}b_{21})(b_{22} + a_{21}b_{12})$$

$$\therefore \ \beta^2 - 4\alpha\gamma = \{(b_{11} + a_{12}b_{21}) - (b_{22} + a_{21}b_{12})\}^2$$
$$+ 4(b_{11} + a_{12}b_{21})(b_{22} + a_{21}b_{12}) - 4(1 - a_{12}a_{21})(b_{11}b_{22} - b_{12}b_{21})$$
$$= \{(b_{11} + a_{12}b_{21}) - (b_{22} + a_{21}b_{12})\}^2$$
$$+ 4(b_{12}b_{21} + a_{12}b_{21}b_{22} + a_{21}b_{11}b_{12} + b_{11}b_{22}a_{12}a_{21})$$

which is positive since all the a's and b's are positive.

Two pairs of the constants λ and k are found. There are two real and distinct values λ_1 and λ_2 from (3) and two corresponding values of k from (2):

$$k_1 = \frac{1 + \lambda_1 b_{11}}{a_{12} - \lambda_1 b_{12}} \quad \text{and} \quad k_2 = \frac{1 + \lambda_2 b_{11}}{a_{12} - \lambda_2 b_{12}}$$

Hence $\qquad X_1 = e^{-\lambda_1 t} \quad \text{and} \quad X_2 = k_1 e^{-\lambda_1 t}$

and $\qquad X_1 = e^{-\lambda_2 t} \quad \text{and} \quad X_2 = k_2 e^{-\lambda_2 t}$

are both solutions of (1). Multiplying by arbitrary constants A_1 and A_2 and adding:

$$\left. \begin{array}{l} X_1 = A_1 e^{-\lambda_1 t} + A_2 e^{-\lambda_2 t} \\ X_2 = A_1 k_1 e^{-\lambda_1 t} + A_2 k_2 e^{-\lambda_2 t} \end{array} \right\} \quad \dots\dots\dots\dots\dots(4)$$

is also a solution. It is the general solution since it contains the requisite number of arbitrary constants, A_1 and A_2, to be found from initial outputs (see Ex. 2 below).

The solution (4) is easily interpreted but it does not appear immediately helpful. As time goes on, outputs X_1 and X_2 tend to zero if λ_1 and λ_2 are both positive, and grow indefinitely if either of λ_1 and λ_2 is negative. Production tends either to cease or to " explode ". This awkward result is simply another manifestation of the peculiar properties of the simplified closed system. The clue is that there is the possibility of one of λ_1 and λ_2 being zero. In the static closed system of 11.7 above, which can be reproduced by putting all the b's zero in (1), it is found that only the ratio $X_1 : X_2$ can be determined, and this only if the a's satisfy a particular condition :

$$\begin{vmatrix} 1 & -a_{12} \\ -a_{21} & 1 \end{vmatrix} = 1 - a_{12}a_{21} = 0 \quad \dots\dots\dots\dots\dots(5)$$

Assume now that the condition (5) still holds in the dynamic model. Then in the equation (3) for λ, the coefficient $\gamma = 0$ and one value of λ is zero with a corresponding $k = \dfrac{1}{a_{12}} = a_{21}$ from (2). The other λ and k are

$$\lambda = -\frac{\beta}{\alpha} = \frac{b_{11} + b_{22} + a_{12}b_{21} + a_{21}b_{12}}{b_{12}b_{21} - b_{11}b_{22}} \quad \text{and} \quad k = \frac{1 + \lambda b_{11}}{a_{12} - \lambda b_{12}} \quad \dots\dots(6)$$

The solution (4) then becomes :

$$X_1 = A_1 + A_2 e^{-\lambda t}$$
$$X_2 = \frac{A_1}{a_{12}} + A_2 k e^{-\lambda t}$$ ....(7)

where λ and k are structural constants given by (6).   If $\lambda > 0$, each output in (7) consists of a constant plus a term which peters out over time.   This is a more sensible result.   The ultimate levels of output are $X_1 = A_1$ and $X_2 = \frac{A_1}{a_{12}}$ and these are set by the initial outputs (through the arbitrary constant A_1).   However, the ratio of ultimate outputs $X_1 : X_2 = a_{12}$, given by the structure of the system.   The dynamic system is damped and stable ; the ultimate levels of output are fixed in ratio by the structure of the system and in scale by the initial outputs.

This result depends on a positive value of λ in (6).   This is so either if *one* of b_{11} and b_{22} is zero, or if *both* b_{11} and b_{22} are small.   Since the second of the two commodities is labour (provided by households), stocks of X_2 can be taken as zero and so $b_{22} = 0$.   Hence $\lambda > 0$ is the usual case.

Open system.   Here x_1 and x_2 in (1) are given functions of time.   The solution of the non-homogeneous equations (1) is the general homogeneous solution (4) with a particular integral, depending on x_1 and x_2, added to each variable.   The particular integrals can only be obtained when x_1 and x_2 are not only given, but also specified.   Two cases illustrate :

(i) *Final demands fixed and constant over time :* $x_1 = c_1$ and $x_2 = c_2$. Particular solutions are sought for

$$X_1 - a_{12}X_2 - b_{11}\frac{dX_1}{dt} - b_{12}\frac{dX_2}{dt} = c_1$$
$$- a_{21}X_1 + X_2 - b_{21}\frac{dX_1}{dt} - b_{22}\frac{dX_2}{dt} = c_2$$ ....(8)

Try $X_1 = B_1$ and $X_2 = B_2$, two constants to be found.   Then :

$$B_1 - a_{12}B_2 = c_1 \quad \text{and} \quad - a_{21}B_1 + B_2 = c_2$$

giving $\quad B_1 = \frac{c_1 + c_2 a_{12}}{1 - a_{12}a_{21}} \quad$ and $\quad B_2 = \frac{c_1 a_{21} + c_2}{1 - a_{12}a_{21}}$

Hence the general solution of (8) is :

$$X_1 = \frac{c_1 + c_2 a_{12}}{1 - a_{12}a_{21}} + A_1 e^{-\lambda_1 t} + A_2 e^{-\lambda_2 t}$$
$$X_2 = \frac{c_1 a_{21} + c_2}{1 - a_{12}a_{21}} + A_1 k_1 e^{-\lambda_1 t} + A_2 k_2 e^{-\lambda_2 t}$$

M.E.

where A_1 and A_2 are arbitrary (given by initial outputs) and where the λ's and k's are given by (2) and (3) as structural constants.

In the interpretation of this solution, the signs of λ_1 and λ_2, and of the two constant terms B_1 and B_2, are critical. From (3)

$$\lambda_1 + \lambda_2 = -\frac{\beta}{\alpha} \quad \text{and} \quad \lambda_1 \lambda_2 = \frac{\gamma}{\alpha}$$

Further : $\quad B_1$ and $B_2 =$ positive multiples of $\dfrac{1}{\gamma}$

Usually, $\alpha < 0$, e.g. when an industry has no (or small) stocks of its own product. In all cases, $\beta > 0$. However, $\gamma = 1 - a_{12}a_{21}$ can be positive or negative. There are then two possibilities :

Sign of :	$(a)\ 1 - a_{12}a_{21} > 0$	$(b)\ 1 - a_{12}a_{21} < 0$
$\lambda_1 + \lambda_2$	+	+
$\lambda_1 \lambda_2$	−	+
B_1 and B_2	+	−

In case (a), the larger of the λ's is positive and the smaller negative. The negative λ gives one term in X_1 and X_2 which increases indefinitely over time, while the other λ term dies away. The system is " explosive " in this case. On the other hand, in case (b), both λ's are positive and the corresponding terms in X_1 and X_2 die away ; but the levels (B_1 and B_2) to which outputs tend are negative and so inadmissible.

Hence, in what is the only practical case ($1 - a_{12}a_{21} > 0$), the dynamic system is explosive and outputs increase indefinitely over time. The reversible and linear accelerator, assumed in the model, leads again to the kind of problem discussed in Chapter 7 above. The model is not directly applicable to the real world ; a non-linear and non-symmetrical accelerator needs to be introduced.

(ii) *Final demands increasing at a given relative rate μ over time :*

$$x_1 = c_1 e^{\mu t} \quad \text{and} \quad x_2 = c_2 e^{\mu t}$$

The particular solutions sought are for :

$$\left. \begin{array}{l} X_1 - a_{12}X_2 - b_{11}\dfrac{dX_1}{dt} - b_{12}\dfrac{dX_2}{dt} = c_1 e^{\mu t} \\[2mm] -a_{21}X_1 + X_2 - b_{21}\dfrac{dX_1}{dt} - b_{22}\dfrac{dX_2}{dt} = c_2 e^{\mu t} \end{array} \right\} \quad \cdots\cdots\cdots\cdots(9)$$

Try $X_1 = B_1 e^{\mu t}$ and $X_2 = B_2 e^{\mu t}$, where B_1 and B_2 are constants to be found, i.e. each output increasing at the same relative rate as final demands. Substitute in (9) and cancel $e^{\mu t} \neq 0$:

$$B_1 - a_{12}B_2 - \mu b_{11}B_1 - \mu b_{12}B_2 = c_1$$
$$- a_{21}B_1 + B_2 - \mu b_{21}B_1 - \mu b_{22}B_2 = c_2$$

giving

$$B_1 = \frac{c_1(1 - \mu b_{22}) + c_2(a_{12} + \mu b_{12})}{(1 - \mu b_{11})(1 - \mu b_{22}) - (a_{12} + \mu b_{12})(a_{21} + \mu b_{21})}$$

and

$$B_2 = \frac{c_1(a_{21} + \mu b_{21}) + c_2(1 - \mu b_{11})}{(1 - \mu b_{11})(1 - \mu b_{22}) - (a_{12} + \mu b_{12})(a_{21} + \mu b_{21})}$$

The general solution of (9) is :

$$X_1 = B_1 e^{\mu t} + A_1 e^{-\lambda_1 t} + A_2 e^{-\lambda_2 t}$$
$$X_2 = B_2 e^{\mu t} + A_1 k_1 e^{-\lambda_1 t} + A_2 k_2 e^{-\lambda_2 t}$$

The situation is much the same as in the case of fixed final demands (see Ex. 5 below). There is usually only one possibility ; the dynamic system is then explosive around an exponential trend (or growth in output) which matches the given growth in final demand.

EXERCISES 11.9

1. Show that the quadratic equation for λ, obtained from (2) above, can be written

$$\begin{vmatrix} (-1 - \lambda b_{11}) & (a_{12} - \lambda b_{12}) \\ (a_{21} - \lambda b_{21}) & (-1 - \lambda b_{22}) \end{vmatrix} = 0$$

the determinant being formed in an obvious way from the structural constants.

2. If the initial conditions are $X_1 = X_{10}$ and $X_2 = X_{20}$ at $t = 0$, express the arbitrary constants in the solution (4) in terms of X_{10} and X_{20}. Repeat the process for the solution (7).

3. In the open system with constant final demands, why is it not necessary to put $1 - a_{12}a_{21} = 0$ as in the closed system? Add this case as an intermediate one to the two in the text above and examine its properties. What becomes of B_1 and B_2?

4. In the open system, let $x_1 = c_1 + d_1 t$ and $x_2 = c_2 + d_2 t$. Find particular integrals and examine the general solution.

5. Consider the solution of the open system, case (ii) above. Take $\alpha < 0$ and $\beta > 0$ as before, and $b_{11} = b_{22} = 0$ (no stocks of final products). Show that there are three cases :

Sign of :	(a)	(b)	(c)
$1 - (a_{12} + b_{12})(a_{21} + b_{21})$	+	−	+
$1 - a_{12}a_{21}$	+	+	−

Deduce that λ_1 and λ_2 are opposite in sign in cases (a) and (b), both positive in case (c) ; that B_1 and B_2 are only positive in case (a). Hence show that the only possibility is an explosive system, arising in case (a).

6. In the open system, let $x_1 = c_{11}e^{\mu_1 t} + c_{12}e^{\mu_2 t}$ and $x_2 = c_{21}e^{\mu_1 t} + c_{22}e^{\mu_2 t}$. Find

particular integrals and show that they evolve from constants of the form of B_1 and B_2 in case (ii) above.

7. Set up the equations for the closed system in the case of three industries and examine the nature of the solution, with particular reference to the possibilities of oscillations in outputs (see 14.9 below).

8. Consider the lagged system of 11.8, Ex. 3, involving mixed difference-differential equations, in the case of two industries. Put $a_{12} = a_{21} = 0$ and $b_{11} = b_{22} = 0$ and interpret these particular cases. Show that $X_1(t)$ and $X_2(t)$ each satisfy an equation of the form $b_{12}b_{21} \dfrac{d^2}{dt^2} X(t+2) = X(t)$, or $b_{12}b_{21} \dfrac{d^2}{dt^2} X(t) = X(t-2)$.

(For a method of solution, see Leontief (1953a), p. 84).

REFERENCES

Barna (T.) (1952): "The Interdependence of the British Economy", *Journal Royal Statistical Society*, Series A, 115, 29–77.

Cameron (B.) (1951): "The Construction of the Leontief System", *Review of Economic Studies*, 19, 19–27.

Evans (W. D.) and Hoffenberg (M.) (1952): "The Inter-Industry Relations Study for 1947", *Review of Economics and Statistics*, 34, 97–142.

Goodwin (R. M.) (1953): "Static and Dynamic Linear General Equilibrium Models", in *Input-Output Relations*: Proceedings of a Conference on Inter-Industrial Relations held at Driebergen, Holland (Stenfert Kroese, Leiden, 1953).

Leontief (W. W.) (1941, 1951): *The Structure of American Economy*, 1919–39 (Oxford, First Ed. 1941, Second Ed. 1951).

Leontief (W. W.) (Editor) (1953a): *Studies in the Structure of the American Economy* (Oxford, 1953), Chapters 1–3.

Leontief (W. W.) (1953b): "Domestic Production and Foreign Trade", *Proceedings American Philosophical Society*, 97, 332–49.

Stone (J. R. N.) and Utting (J. E. G.) (1953): "The Relationship between Input-Output Analysis and National Accounting", in *Input-Output Relations*: Proceedings of a Conference on Inter-Industrial Relations held at Driebergen, Holland (Stenfert Kroese, Leiden, 1953).

CHAPTER 12

MATHEMATICAL ANALYSIS: VECTORS AND MATRICES

12.1 Introduction

THE present and the following chapter deal with what can be called, rather broadly, the algebra of matrices. The nature of matrix algebra and the kind of problems in which it is useful need to be made clear at the outset. Some of the mystery which seems to surround the subject, and some of its complexity, will then disappear. An excellent introduction, simple and clear, is to be found in Kemeny, Snell and Thompson (1957).

Elementary algebra concerns itself with expressions which take real numerical values. The expressions are composed of constants and variables, all taking values from the system of real numbers. The constants may be specified numerically, e.g. 3 or $\sqrt{2}$, or they may be unspecified and written $a, b, c, \dots$. The variables, generally denoted by such letters as x, y and z, range over numerical values, either the whole system of real numbers, or some more limited system such as the set of integers or of rational numbers (ratios of integers). Examples of expressions appearing in elementary algebra are $\sqrt{a^2+b^2}$ and $(ax+by)$. If the constants a and b are specified, e.g. $a=1$, $b=2$, then the expressions become $\sqrt{a^2+b^2}=\sqrt{5}$ and $ax+by=x+2y$. The second expression takes different numerical values for different values of the variables x and y. So :

| x | 0 | 0 | 1 | 1 | .... |
y	0	1	0	1	....
$x+2y$	1	2	1	3	....

More advanced algebra breaks out of these narrow confines. It deals with other systems than that of real numbers, e.g. complex numbers (Chapter 4 above). It handles, not only " magnitudes " like mass or volume in physics, but also more general " vectors " like force or velocity which have " magnitude " and " direction ". Much of higher algebra, and matrix algebra in particular, is concerned with sets or groups of elements, ordered or arranged in some way, rather than with single values. The elements themselves can be real numerical values, as is assumed here ; but this is by no means necessary and they can be complex numbers, or indeed any kind of entities, abstract or otherwise.

As illustrations, consider groupings of elements which are constants taking real numerical values. A set of three constants, a, b and c, can be arranged in a definite order : a first, b second and c third. It can then be written (a, b, c) and associated with a point in space of three dimensions. A " vector " of three dimensions is one such grouping ; it may also be regarded as a particular case of a " matrix " in which there is only one row (or one column) of three elements.

Rather more generally, a set of four constants, a_1, a_2, b_1 and b_2, can be arranged in a block of two rows and two columns and written :

$$\begin{bmatrix} a_1 & b_1 \\ a_2 & b_2 \end{bmatrix}$$

The ordering is again essential. The first row, indicated by the subscript 1, comprises a_1 and b_1 in that order, and the second row is similarly ordered. This is a simple example of a " square matrix ".

It is important to distinguish carefully between a vector or matrix as an ordered set of elements and any single value (or expression) derived from the elements. From the vector (a, b, c) can be derived several expressions, e.g. the sum of the elements $(a+b+c)$, which take single values of the same kind as the elements themselves. Similarly, from the square matrix written above can be derived such expressions as the product of the elements in the principal (or leading) diagonal (a_1b_2), or the " cross product " of the four elements $(a_1b_2 - a_2b_1)$. These expressions are of a kind with the elements themselves (e.g. real numbers), and the laws of elementary algebra apply to them as to the elements. It does not follow that the vector or matrix itself obeys these, or any other, algebraic laws.

The test of matrix algebra in practice is whether it is convenient and helpful in handling problems which arise in various fields. It is one thing to design algebraic notations and to develop laws of operation which are consistent in themselves. It is quite another matter to find uses for the algebra which repay the effort in becoming familiar with new notations and laws of operation. Complex numbers provide one example of a new and useful development of algebra ; matrix algebra is to be developed as another example. Certain algebraic expressions are constantly appearing in practice, e.g. $(a_1b_2 - a_2b_1)$, $(a_1x_1 + a_2x_2 + a_3x_3)$ and $(ax^2 + 2hxy + by^2)$. Matrix notations and matrix algebra are the result of striving to handle these and many other such expressions in a general, uniform and convenient way. The success of the notations lies largely in the fact that, with their aid, extension becomes possible from simple cases of two or three dimensions to the general case of " n dimensions ".

For example, the expression $(a_1b_2 - a_2b_1)$ is simple in itself but, in generalising, it is convenient to regard it as the " cross product " of a square block of elements :

$$a_1 \nearrow\kern-1.2em\diagdown b_1$$
$$a_2 \longleftarrow b_2$$

and hence as arising from the square matrix :

$$\begin{bmatrix} a_1 & b_1 \\ a_2 & b_2 \end{bmatrix}$$

Similarly, the expression $(a_1x_1 + a_2x_2 + a_3x_3)$ is best viewed as derived from two sets of elements, the vectors (a_1, a_2, a_3) and (x_1, x_2, x_r) ; and

$$(ax^2 + 2hxy + by^2)$$

is conveniently thought of as arising from a square matrix

$$\begin{bmatrix} a & h \\ h & b \end{bmatrix}$$

and a vector (x, y).

Matrix algebra, then, introduces a notation which is *compact* and capable of dealing with rather cumbersome expressions and operations. Moreover, the notation is *general* and applies not only when there is a large number of elements to handle, but also to a number of elements which is unspecified. The matrix notation permits extension from the case of two or three dimensions to cases where the number of dimensions is large and unspecified.

12.2 Linear Equations and Transformations

The type of problems to which matrix algebra is usefully applied is well illustrated by the analysis of systems of linear equations or transformations. Systems of equations have been mentioned in passing in Chapter 10 above. When they are linear, they can be formulated in terms of a general notation on the following lines.

A single linear equation in one variable x is :

$$ax = y \qquad \dots\dots\dots\dots\dots\dots\dots\dots\dots\dots\dots(1)$$

where a and y are given. The solution is $x = \dfrac{y}{a}$ provided that $a \neq 0$. Two linear equations in two variables x_1 and x_2 are :

$$\left.\begin{array}{l} a_{11}x_1 + a_{12}x_2 = y_1 \\ a_{21}x_1 + a_{22}x_2 = y_2 \end{array}\right\} \qquad \dots\dots\dots\dots\dots\dots\dots\dots(2)$$

where the a's and the y's are given. Of the constants, the a's are arranged in a square block of elements (two rows and two columns), while the y's form an ordered column of two elements :

$$\begin{bmatrix} a_{11} & a_{12} \\ a_{21} & a_{22} \end{bmatrix} \quad \text{and} \quad \begin{bmatrix} y_1 \\ y_2 \end{bmatrix}$$

The solution is :

$$x_1 = \frac{a_{22}y_1 - a_{12}y_2}{a_{11}a_{22} - a_{12}a_{21}} \qquad x_2 = \frac{a_{11}y_2 - a_{21}y_1}{a_{11}a_{22} - a_{12}a_{21}}$$

provided that $a_{11}a_{22} - a_{12}a_{21} \neq 0$.

The form in which (2) is written, and the notation used for the block and column of given values, suggest the general case of a *system of linear equations*. There are m equations in n variables, $x_1, x_2, \ldots x_n$:

$$\left. \begin{aligned} a_{11}x_1 + a_{12}x_2 + \ldots + a_{1n}x_n &= y_1 \\ a_{21}x_1 + a_{22}x_2 + \ldots + a_{2n}x_n &= y_2 \\ \cdots\cdots\cdots\cdots\cdots\cdots\cdots\cdots \\ a_{m1}x_1 + a_{m2}x_2 + \ldots + a_{mn}x_n &= y_m \end{aligned} \right\} \quad \ldots\ldots\ldots\ldots\ldots(3)$$

What is given is, firstly, a block of a's, $m \times n$ in number, written in m rows and n columns and, secondly, a column of m y's :

$$\begin{bmatrix} a_{11} & a_{12} & \ldots & a_{1n} \\ a_{21} & a_{22} & \ldots & a_{2n} \\ \cdots & \cdots & \cdots & \cdots \\ a_{m1} & a_{m2} & \ldots & a_{mn} \end{bmatrix} \quad \text{and} \quad \begin{bmatrix} y_1 \\ y_2 \\ \\ y_m \end{bmatrix}$$

The exercise is to find the value of the x's, or as many of them as possible, in terms of the given a's and y's, and this will be carried through in 14.2 below. As long as the y's are not all zero, the system (3) is *non-homogeneous*. In the special case where all the y's are zero, (3) becomes a *system of homogeneous equations*. The word " homogeneous " is here used in the familiar sense that, if all the x's are multiplied by the same constant, the equations (and any solution) are not changed. One solution is then automatically provided, i.e. $x_1 = x_2 = \ldots = x_n = 0$, and interest is concentrated on a rather different kind of solution, that giving ratios or relative values of the x's.

Clearly, in the generalisation of (2) with $m = n = 2$ into (3) with unspecified m and n, the notation becomes cumbersome and the algebra tedious. A good deal depends on the design of a convenient notation and the development of a matching algebra. The algebra of vectors and matrices (to be developed) permits the system of equations to be written in alternative forms, both more compact than (3). The *first form* is in terms of vectors only.   Write :

$$\mathbf{a}_s = (a_{1s}, a_{2s}, \ldots a_{ms}) \qquad (s = 1, 2, \ldots n)$$

and
$$\mathbf{y} = (y_1, y_2, \ldots y_m)$$

as vectors of m dimensions.   Then (3) can be shown (12.8 below) as :

$$\sum_{s=1}^{n} \mathbf{a}_s x_s = \mathbf{y}$$

This means that, when the first element in each vector is taken, the first equation of (3) is obtained ; the second equation comes by taking the second elements in the vectors, and so on.   In the *second form*, write a matrix of dimensions $m \times n$:

$$\mathbf{A} = \begin{bmatrix} a_{11} & a_{12} & \ldots & a_{1n} \\ a_{21} & a_{22} & \ldots & a_{2n} \\ \cdots & \cdots & \cdots & \cdots \\ a_{m1} & a_{m2} & \ldots & a_{mn} \end{bmatrix}$$

a vector of n dimensions :

$$\mathbf{x} = (x_1, x_2, \ldots x_n)$$

and another vector of m dimensions :

$$\mathbf{y} = (y_1, y_2, \ldots y_m)$$

As will be shown, the system (3) can then be written in very compact form :

$$\mathbf{A}\mathbf{x} = \mathbf{y}$$

Once such a general and compact notation is designed, particular cases can always be derived ; for example, the pair of equations (2) is obtained when the matrix $\mathbf{A}$ takes the particular square (2×2) form :

$$\mathbf{A} = \begin{bmatrix} a_{11} & a_{12} \\ a_{21} & a_{22} \end{bmatrix}$$

and $\mathbf{x}$ and $\mathbf{y}$ are similarly vectors of two elements.

The same system of equations, in general form (3) or particular forms (1) and (2), can be viewed in another way. Suppose that the y's represent, not given values, but new variables to replace all or some of the original variables, the x's.   Then the system of equations is a *linear transformation* from the x variables to the y variables.   In the form in which the system is given in (3), the values of the y's are specified in terms of the x's.   The problem, corresponding to the " solution " of the system of linear equations, is now to "invert" the linear transformation to give the x's in terms of the y's. It will be written most compactly in the following form : the linear transformation $\mathbf{y} = \mathbf{Ax}$ shows what $\mathbf{y}$ is when $\mathbf{x}$ is given ; the inverse transformation $\mathbf{x} = \mathbf{A}^{-1}\mathbf{y}$ shows $\mathbf{x}$ for given $\mathbf{y}$.

A very simple example will illustrate. Imports of rubber are given as x_1 tons valued at £x_2, from which the average price in £ per ton is derived. It is required to transform into units of lbs. and pence respectively, so that the price is obtained in d. per lb.. If the new variables are y_1 lbs. and y_2 pence :

$$y_1 = 2240\, x_1 \quad \text{and} \quad y_2 = 240\, x_2$$

These are a pair of equations like (2), with $a_{12} = a_{21} = 0$. The average price is $\dfrac{x_2}{x_1}$ in £ per ton and $\dfrac{y_2}{y_1} = \dfrac{240}{2240}\dfrac{x_2}{x_1} = \dfrac{3}{28}\dfrac{x_2}{x_1}$ in d. per lb.

12.3 Vectors

The algebra of vectors and matrices considered here is based on real numbers. The totality of real numbers is a set F of the type known as a *field* (see Appendix B). They serve two purposes, providing the *components* of the vectors and matrices dealt with, and appearing as *scalars* in operations on these entities. In particular, a scalar is often used as a multiple ; vectors and matrices can be multipled by scalars. Scalars can also be real values arising from certain operations such as products of vectors and matrices

The concept of a *vector* has already been used profitably in the geometrical representation of a complex number (Chapter 4). This is in two dimensions and many of the properties obtained are specific to this case. But it is not difficult to extend the idea of a two-dimensional vector as an ordered pair of components (x, y), corresponding to a point P with these co-ordinates, or to the line OP with length and direction, in the plane Oxy. In three dimensions there is an ordered triple (x, y, z) with a corresponding point P in space $Oxyz$. Generally, in n dimensions, there are ordered n-tuples of components and these can be imagined if not visually represented by points in n-dimensional space.

A general and formal definition of a vector is in terms of a set of entities of any kind which meet certain specifications or rules on addition and multiplication by scalars (see Appendix B). What is done here is to limit consideration to one special type of vector, the generalised form of the concept of an ordering of components taken from the field F of real numbers. Briefly, a vector is then an n-tuple of real-number components. It is true that this is a particular case, but it is the one almost invariably used in practice. Unlike a scalar, a vector is *not* itself a real number ; it is an ordering of real numbers. The symbol selected to denote a vector must be such that it cannot be confused with a scalar. The notation adopted here shows a scalar as a letter in ordinary type and a vector as a letter in bold type.

DEFINITION : A vector of order n is an n-tuple of components from the field F of real numbers ; it is denoted :

$$\mathbf{a} = (a_1, a_2, \ldots a_n).$$

Consider a vector **a** of fixed order n. It can be interpreted as a point P. or as a line OP from the origin to P, in a geometrical space of n dimensions, P has co-ordinates $(a_1, a_2, \ldots a_n)$ referred to fixed axes mutually at right angles. The n-dimensional space is called *Cartesian space* if distances between points are not defined or considered ; it is *Euclidean space* if distances are needed and appropriately defined. When $n=2$, and the vector consists of two elements only, the representation as a point P or line OP in two dimensions follows the development of Chapter 4 above ; in this particular case, the vector can also be interpreted as a complex number. When $n=3$, the vector consists of three elements and it is represented by a point P (or a line OP) in three-dimensional space. Diagrams can actually be drawn ; for example, Fig. 46 shows three vectors OP_1, OP_2 and OP_3 of order 3 and the co-ordinates of the points P_1, P_2 and P_3, referred to the axes $Ox_1x_2x_3$, give the components of the vectors. When $n>3$, though no diagrams can be drawn, the geometrical interpretation of vectors as points or lines can still be used.

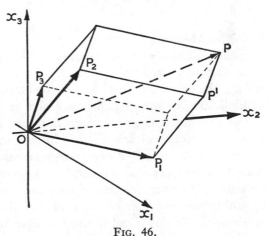

FIG. 46.

It must always be remembered, however, that a vector (as defined here) is an algebraic concept and that it is the algebra of vectors which is to be developed. If the algebra can be assisted by imagining a geometry of n dimensions, so much the better ; but the interpretation or analogy must not be pushed too far. It will work well enough for $n=2, 3$, when actual diagrams can be drawn ; but in general there is the risk of drawing misleading conclusions from geometrical considerations.

As a particular case, there is the *zero vector* $\mathbf{0}=(0, 0, \ldots 0)$ which performs the duties of the number zero in the algebra of real numbers. The geometrical interpretation of $\mathbf{0}$ is the origin O of co-ordinates in Cartesian or Euclidean space of n dimensions.

There are n particular vectors which can be called *unit vectors* :

$$\boldsymbol{\epsilon}_1=(1, 0, \ldots 0) \quad \boldsymbol{\epsilon}_2=(0, 1, \ldots 0) \ldots \boldsymbol{\epsilon}_n=(0, 0, \ldots 1)$$

It is found that these vectors form a " basis " of the whole system of vectors, in the sense that any vector whatever can be expressed in terms of the unit vectors. Geometrically, in Euclidean space of n dimensions, the unit vectors are represented by points unit distances along the n co-ordinate axes. The rth unit vector $\boldsymbol{\epsilon}_r$ has 1 in the rth place and zero components elsewhere. To denote this, it is convenient to use the *Kronecker delta* δ_{rs} defined as zero except for $r=s$ when it is unity :

$$\delta_{rs}=0 \ (r \neq s) \quad \text{and} \quad \delta_{rs}=1 \ (r=s)$$

So :

$$\boldsymbol{\epsilon}_r=(\delta_{r1}, \delta_{r2}, \ldots \delta_{rn}) \quad (r=1, 2, \ldots n)$$

12.4 The Algebra of Vectors

In the algebra of complex numbers, or vectors in two dimensions, there is no difficulty in defining equality, addition and multiplication by a scalar ; the only uncertainty is in the definition of an appropriate rule for multiplication of vectors (Chapter 4 above). If multiplication is left on one side for the moment, the algebra of two-dimensional vectors extends at once to vectors of any order. In its simplest terms, the algebra of vectors is built up so that two vectors are equal if the elements are separately equated and so that they add to a sum vector by adding the elements separately. Further, the multiplication of a vector by a scalar is achieved by multiplying each element separately by the scalar. These simple conventions can be elaborated in the following way, taking $\mathbf{a}=(a_1, a_2, \ldots a_n)$ and $\mathbf{b}=(b_1, b_2, \ldots b_n)$ as two given vectors.

Equality and inequality. The definition of equality is :

$$\mathbf{a}=\mathbf{b} \qquad \text{if } a_r=b_r \qquad (r=1, 2, \ldots n)$$

and of inequality :

$$\mathbf{a}>\mathbf{b} \qquad \text{if } a_r>b_r \quad (r=1, 2, \ldots n)$$

There is a complication arising from the fact that two vectors may not be equal, but neither are they unequal on this definition. Consider the concept of " greater than or equal to ". For scalars, there is a simple alternative : $a \geq b$ means either $a = b$ or $a > b$. For vectors there are other possibilities. If $\mathbf{a} = \mathbf{b}$ then *every* element of $\mathbf{a}$ equals the corresponding element of $\mathbf{b}$; if $\mathbf{a} > \mathbf{b}$ then *every* element of $\mathbf{a}$ is greater than the corresponding element of $\mathbf{b}$. Now define $\mathbf{a}$ greater than or equal to $\mathbf{b}$ as *every* element of $\mathbf{a}$ greater than or equal to the corresponding element of $\mathbf{b}$. Write in two notations according as equality $(\mathbf{a} = \mathbf{b})$ is included or not :

$$\mathbf{a} \geqq \mathbf{b} \qquad \text{if } a_r \geqq b_r, \text{ allowing all } a_r = b_r$$
$$\mathbf{a} \geqslant \mathbf{b} \qquad \text{if } a_r \geqq b_r, \text{ not allowing all } a_r = b_r$$

where $r = 1, 2, \dots n$. These differ only in that $\mathbf{a} = \mathbf{b}$ is included in the first but not in the second. What is to be noticed is that $\mathbf{a} \geqq \mathbf{b}$ is not just the two cases $\mathbf{a} = \mathbf{b}$ and $\mathbf{a} > \mathbf{b}$ taken together. Other possibilities are included, those where some elements of $\mathbf{a}$ are greater than and others equal to their opposite numbers in $\mathbf{b}$. Further, even with this wider scope for $\mathbf{a} \geqq \mathbf{b}$, it is still not correct to say that $\mathbf{a} \geqq \mathbf{b}$ and $\mathbf{a} < \mathbf{b}$ cover all cases. There are more cases where $\mathbf{a}$ and $\mathbf{b}$ are neither equal nor unequal, cases where some elements of $\mathbf{a}$ are greater and others less than their opposite numbers in $\mathbf{b}$.

The distinctions are important when $\mathbf{a}$ is compared with the zero vector :

$$\mathbf{a} > 0 \qquad \text{if } a_r > 0$$
$$\mathbf{a} \geqq 0 \qquad \text{if } a_r \geqq 0, \text{ allowing all } a_r = 0$$
$$\mathbf{a} \geqslant 0 \qquad \text{if } a_r \geqq 0, \text{ not allowing all } a_r = 0$$

where $r = 1, 2, \dots n$. A *positive* vector $\mathbf{a} > 0$ is clear enough. But $\mathbf{a} \geqq 0$ and $\mathbf{a} \geqslant 0$, both of which may be called *non-negative* vectors, are somewhat more involved. They include vectors of positive elements together with cases where some elements are positive and some zero. Such non-negative vectors are important in economic applications particularly in dealing with prices (see Ex. 2 below).

Addition. The definition is free of complications :

$$\mathbf{a} + \mathbf{b} = (a_1 + b_1, a_2 + b_2, \dots a_n + b_n)$$

When $n = 2$, let $\mathbf{a}$, $\mathbf{b}$ and $\mathbf{a} + \mathbf{b}$ be represented by the vectors OP_1, OP_2 and OP respectively, in a two-dimensional diagram. Then OP is derived from OP_1 and OP_2 by the parallelogram rule (Fig. 12a). The position is similar in three dimensions and it can be imagined in n dimensions.

The definition extends to the addition of three vectors (or indeed of any number of vectors). For :

$$\mathbf{a}+\mathbf{b}+\mathbf{c}=(\mathbf{a}+\mathbf{b})+\mathbf{c}=\mathbf{a}+(\mathbf{b}+\mathbf{c})=(a_1+b_1+c_1,\ a_2+b_2+c_2,\ ...\ a_n+b_n+c_n)$$

This is illustrated in three dimensions $(n=3)$ in Fig. 46. The three vectors are OP_1, OP_2 and OP_3. The sum of them is OP, obtained by completing the parallelogram-type figure from OP_1, OP_2 and $OP_{3\overline{\cdot}}$ Or, OP_1 and OP_2 can be first " compounded " to give OP' as representing $\mathbf{a}+\mathbf{b}$, and then OP' and OP_3 can be " compounded " to give OP for $(\mathbf{a}+\mathbf{b})+\mathbf{c}=\mathbf{a}+\mathbf{b}+\mathbf{c}$.

Multiplication by a scalar. There is again no difficulty :

$$\lambda\mathbf{a}=(\lambda a_1,\ \lambda a_2,\ ...\ \lambda a_n)$$

for any scalar λ. In a diagram, if OP_1 represents the vector $\mathbf{a}$, then the vector $\lambda\mathbf{a}$ is shown by OP in the same direction as OP_1 but of λ times the length. If $\lambda>1$, OP is longer than OP_1 ; and, if $0<\lambda<1$, OP is shorter than OP_1. Even if $\lambda<0$, the vector $\lambda\mathbf{a}$ or OP is still defined ; the elements of $\lambda\mathbf{a}$ are all of opposite sign to those of $\mathbf{a}$ and P is on the other side of O from P_1.

The negative $(-\mathbf{a})$ of a given vector $\mathbf{a}$ fits into the definitions of addition and multiplication by scalars :

$$\mathbf{a}+(-\mathbf{a})=\mathbf{0}\quad\text{and}\quad-\mathbf{a}=(-1)\mathbf{a}$$

In full :

$$-\mathbf{a}=(-a_1,\ -a_2,\ ...\ -a_n)$$

Note that the order in which vectors are written is not material : $\mathbf{a}+\mathbf{b}=\mathbf{b}+\mathbf{a}$, and that the zero vector finds its place in the process of addition : $\mathbf{a}+\mathbf{0}=\mathbf{0}+\mathbf{a}=\mathbf{a}$.

Inner products. The rule for multiplying two vectors (complex numbers) as defined in 4.3, and illustrated in Fig. 12b above, is specific to the case $n=2$. It is not generally profitable to attempt to define a product of two vectors to give another vector of the system. There is however a completely different type of product of two vectors ; this produces, not a vector, but a scalar. It is related to the concept of the " length " of a vector and it is appropriate when the vectors are interpreted in Euclidean space in which " distance " is defined.

In two dimensions, let $\mathbf{a}=(a_1, a_2)$ and $\mathbf{b}=(b_1, b_2)$ be two vectors OP_1 and OP_2 respectively. Define :

$$\mathbf{a} \cdot \mathbf{b} = a_1 b_1 + a_2 b_2$$

as the inner product of $\mathbf{a}$ and $\mathbf{b}$. In particular :

$$\mathbf{a} \cdot \mathbf{a} = a_1{}^2 + a_2{}^2 = |\mathbf{a}|^2$$

where $|\mathbf{a}| = \sqrt{a_1{}^2 + a_2{}^2}$ is the *absolute value* of $\mathbf{a}$ or the length of OP_1. Now take θ as the angle between OP_1 and OP_2 ; elementary trigonometry shows that :

$$\cos \theta = \frac{a_1 b_1 + a_2 b_2}{\sqrt{(a_1{}^2 + a_2{}^2)(b_1{}^2 + b_2{}^2)}}$$

Hence $$\cos \theta = \frac{\mathbf{a} \cdot \mathbf{b}}{|\mathbf{a}|\,|\mathbf{b}|}$$

For vectors of unit length, the inner product $\mathbf{a} \cdot \mathbf{b}$ is the cosine of the angle between the vectors. As a most important case, if the two vectors are at right angles (orthogonal), $\cos \theta = 0$ and so the scalar product

$$\mathbf{a} \cdot \mathbf{b} = a_1 b_1 + a_2 b_2 = 0$$

The algebra and geometry extend easily to 3 dimensions. In n dimensions, the algebra is a matter of definition, as follows.

DEFINITION. The inner product of two vectors $\mathbf{a}=(a_1, a_2, \ldots a_n)$ and $\mathbf{b}=(b_1, b_2, \ldots b_n)$ is :

$$\mathbf{a} \cdot \mathbf{b} = a_1 b_1 + a_2 b_2 + \ldots + a_n b_n$$

and the absolute value or length $|\mathbf{a}|$ of the vector $\mathbf{a}$ is given by :

$$|\mathbf{a}|^2 = \mathbf{a} \cdot \mathbf{a} = a_1{}^2 + a_2{}^2 + \ldots + a_n{}^2$$

The geometry is a matter of convenient interpretation ; or, more strictly, the algebraic concepts can be used to define the properties of Euclidean space. Two vectors $\mathbf{a}$ and $\mathbf{b}$ are represented by OP_1 and OP_2 in n dimensions. The length OP_1 is defined as $|\mathbf{a}| = \sqrt{a_1{}^2 + a_2{}^2 + \ldots + a_n{}^2}$ and the angle θ between OP_1 and OP_2 is defined by :

$$\cos \theta = \frac{\mathbf{a} \cdot \mathbf{b}}{|\mathbf{a}|\,|\mathbf{b}|} = \frac{a_1 b_1 + a_2 b_2 + \ldots + a_n b_n}{\sqrt{a_1{}^2 + a_2{}^2 + \ldots + a_n{}^2}\,\sqrt{b_1{}^2 + b_2{}^2 + \ldots + b_n{}^2}}$$

The two vectors $\mathbf{a}$ and $\mathbf{b}$ are orthogonal, and OP_1 and OP_2 are perpendicular, if

$$\mathbf{a} \cdot \mathbf{b} = a_1 b_1 + a_2 b_2 + \ldots + a_n b_n = 0$$

It is on this basis that the algebra and geometry of spaces of n dimensions can be built. Wide fields are opened up and it is possible to proceed in several directions. In one line of development, the concepts of lengths, angles and so on are taken as the starting point. In another direction, these concepts are completely abandoned and the notion of inter-connected space becomes fundamental. This leads to the subject of *topology* (or " analysis situs " in an older terminology) which is described in the following terms :

> " This branch of mathematics concerns itself with properties of spaces which are independent of their shape and size. Thus not distance, angle or straightness but the property of being one connected piece, of being bounded, of being a boundary, forms its subject matter."
>
> (*Chambers' Encyclopaedia*, 1950.)

This particular development is of use in such economic problems as linear programming and simple aspects of it are considered in the following section. These will not be pursued far, however, since it is more important here to take the purely algebraic properties of vectors and to extend them into matrix algebra. It is then found that the inner product of vectors falls into its place in the wider algebra of matrices.

EXERCISES 12.4

1. Represent the vectors $(2, 2, 2)$, $(2, 2, 1)$, $(2, 1, 1)$ and $(1, 1, 1)$ on a diagram in three dimensions. Is the first " greater than " the others?

2. If $\mathbf{p}$ is a price vector $(p_1, p_2, \dots p_n)$, distinguish between the two cases : $\mathbf{p} \geq 0$ and $\mathbf{p} \geqslant 0$. Either can be loosely described as a set of non-negative prices ; which would usually be adopted in a precise definition of an economic problem?

3. How does the parallelogram rule apply to $\mathbf{a} + (-\mathbf{a}) = 0$?

4. Assemble and prove the following rules for addition of vectors :
   (1) if $\mathbf{a}$ and $\mathbf{b}$ are vectors, so is $\mathbf{a} + \mathbf{b}$; (2) $\mathbf{a} + (\mathbf{b} + \mathbf{c}) = (\mathbf{a} + \mathbf{b}) + \mathbf{c}$;
   (3) $\mathbf{a} + \mathbf{b} = \mathbf{b} + \mathbf{a}$; (4) if $\mathbf{a} + \mathbf{b} = \mathbf{a} + \mathbf{c}$, then $\mathbf{b} = \mathbf{c}$;
   (5) there is a zero vector $\mathbf{0}$ so that $\mathbf{a} + \mathbf{0} = \mathbf{0} + \mathbf{a} = \mathbf{a}$;
   (6) there is a negative $(-\mathbf{a})$ so that $\mathbf{a} + (-\mathbf{a}) = (-\mathbf{a}) + \mathbf{a} = \mathbf{0}$.

5. Similarly for the following rules for scalar products :
   (1) If $\mathbf{a}$ is a vector, so is $\lambda \mathbf{a}$ for any scalar λ ;
   (2) $0\mathbf{a} = 0$ and $1\mathbf{a} = \mathbf{a}$; (3) $\lambda(\mu \mathbf{a}) = (\lambda \mu)\mathbf{a}$;
   (4) $\lambda(\mathbf{a} + \mathbf{b}) = \lambda \mathbf{a} + \lambda \mathbf{b}$; (5) $(\lambda + \mu)\mathbf{a} = \lambda \mathbf{a} + \mu \mathbf{a}$.

6. Similarly for the following rules for inner products :
   (1) if $\mathbf{a}$ and $\mathbf{b}$ are vectors, then $\mathbf{a} \cdot \mathbf{b}$ is a scalar ;
   (2) $\mathbf{a} \cdot \mathbf{b} = \mathbf{b} \cdot \mathbf{a}$; (3) $\mathbf{a} \cdot (\mathbf{b} + \mathbf{c}) = \mathbf{a} \cdot \mathbf{b} + \mathbf{a} \cdot \mathbf{c}$.

7. The *normalised* form of a vector $\mathbf{a}$ is defined as $\lambda \mathbf{a}$ such that the absolute value $|\lambda \mathbf{a}| = 1$. Show that $\left(\dfrac{a_1}{|\mathbf{a}|}, \dfrac{a_2}{|\mathbf{a}|}, \dots \dfrac{a_n}{|\mathbf{a}|}\right)$ is the normalised form, diagrammatically the vector of unit length in the same direction as the vector $\mathbf{a}$.

12.5 Linear Combinations of Vectors ; Convex Sets

There are two unit vectors, $\epsilon_1 = (1, 0)$ and $\epsilon_2 = (0, 1)$, in Cartesian space of two dimensions, represented by points A_1 and A_2 on the axes in the plane Ox_1x_2. By the rules of vector algebra, any vector $\mathbf{x} = (x_1, x_2)$ can be expressed :

$$\mathbf{x} = x_1\epsilon_1 + x_2\epsilon_2$$

where x_1 and x_2 are here scalars, both the components of $\mathbf{x}$ and the scalar multiples of ϵ_1 and ϵ_2. The vector $\mathbf{x}$ is said to be a *linear combination* of the two vectors ϵ_1 and ϵ_2. Here *every* $\mathbf{x}$ is such a linear combination ; ϵ_1 and ϵ_2 are said to *span* and to provide a *basis* for the Cartesian space. This is in the sense that the two particular vectors ϵ_1 and ϵ_2 are all that is needed to generate the whole system of vectors in the space of two dimensions.

In geometrical terms, $\mathbf{x}$ as a linear combination of the basis ϵ_1 and ϵ_2 is simply an expression of the following facts. The vectors of the basis are shown by OA_1 and OA_2 which serve to define both the axes of co-ordinates and the units of measurement. Then any vector OP is the sum of two vectors ; one is the vector which is a multiple x_1 of OA_1 and the other is a multiple x_2 of OA_2. In other words, P is reached by going x_1 units in the OA_1 direction and then x_2 units in the OA_2 direction. All this can be extended easily to Cartesian space of three dimensions.

In general, Cartesian space of n dimensions is *spanned* by the n unit vectors $\epsilon_1, \epsilon_2, \ldots \epsilon_n$, which serve as a *basis* of the space. This means that any vector $\mathbf{x} = (x_1, x_2, \ldots x_n)$ is a *linear combination* of the basis :

$$\mathbf{x} = \sum_{r=1}^{n} x_r\epsilon_r = x_1\epsilon_1 + x_2\epsilon_2 + \ldots + x_n\epsilon_n$$

In full :

$$x_1\epsilon_1 = x_1(1, 0, \ldots 0) = (x_1, 0, \ldots 0)$$
$$x_2\epsilon_2 = x_2(0, 1, \ldots 0) = (0, x_2, \ldots 0)$$
$$\cdots\cdots\cdots\cdots\cdots\cdots\cdots\cdots\cdots\cdots$$
$$x_n\epsilon_n = x_n(0, 0, \ldots 1) = (0, 0, \ldots x_n)$$

and so :

$$\sum_{r=1}^{n} x_r\epsilon_r = (x_1, 0, \ldots) + (0, x_2, \ldots 0) + \ldots + (0, 0, \ldots x_n)$$
$$= (x_1, x_2, \ldots x_n) = \mathbf{x}$$

Now take two vectors in Cartesian space of n dimensions :

$$\mathbf{x}^{(1)} = (x_1^{(1)}, x_2^{(1)}, \ldots x_n^{(1)}) ; \quad \mathbf{x}^{(2)} = (x_1^{(2)}, x_2^{(2)}, \ldots x_n^{(2)})$$

A *linear combination* of $\mathbf{x}^{(1)}$ and $\mathbf{x}^{(2)}$ is the vector :

$$\lambda_1 \mathbf{x}^{(1)} + \lambda_2 \mathbf{x}^{(2)} \quad \text{for any } \lambda_1, \lambda_2$$

The rth element of the linear combination is $\lambda_1 x_r^{(1)} + \lambda_2 x_r^{(2)}$, obtained as the addition of multiples of the rth elements of $\mathbf{x}^{(1)}$ and $\mathbf{x}^{(2)}$. As two particular cases, a *positive linear combination* of $\mathbf{x}^{(1)}$ and $\mathbf{x}^{(2)}$ is :

$$\lambda_1 \mathbf{x}^{(1)} + \lambda_2 \mathbf{x}^{(2)} \quad \text{for } \lambda_1, \lambda_2 \geqslant 0$$

and a *convex linear combination* of $\mathbf{x}^{(1)}$ and $\mathbf{x}^{(2)}$ is

$$\mu \mathbf{x}^{(1)} + (1 - \mu) \mathbf{x}^{(2)} \quad \text{for } 0 \leqslant \mu \leqslant 1$$

The way in which these combinations are formed is seen in Fig. 47. The given vectors $\mathbf{x}^{(1)}$ and $\mathbf{x}^{(2)}$ are shown by OP_1 and OP_2, defining the plane OP_1P_2 in space of n dimensions. The figure shows only the two-dimensional plane and it must be imagined as " embedded " in space of n dimensions, referred to axes $Ox_1 x_2 \ldots x_n$ which are omitted (and indeed cannot be drawn). Let OP be the convex linear combination

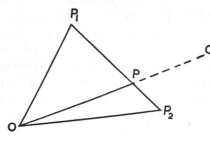

FIG. 47.

$$\mu \mathbf{x}^{(1)} + (1 - \mu) \mathbf{x}^{(2)}$$

for μ ranging from 0 to 1. It is easily shown by analytical geometry (see Ex. 2 below) that P lies on the line segment from P_2 to P_1 and divides it in the ratio $\mu : 1 - \mu$. Hence, as μ increases from 0 to 1, P moves from P_2 to P_1 and OP swings from OP_2 to OP_1. Let OQ be the positive linear combination :

$$\lambda_1 \mathbf{x}^{(1)} + \lambda_2 \mathbf{x}^{(2)} = (\lambda_1 + \lambda_2)\{\mu \mathbf{x}^{(1)} + (1 - \mu)\mathbf{x}^{(2)}\} \quad \text{for } \mu = \frac{\lambda_1}{\lambda_1 + \lambda_2} ; \; \lambda_1, \lambda_2 \geqslant 0$$

Hence OQ is a positive multiple of the corresponding OP. If the multiple is $\lambda_1 + \lambda_2 > 1$, then Q lies on OP but beyond P as illustrated ; if

$$0 \leqslant \lambda_1 + \lambda_2 \leqslant 1,$$

then Q lies between O and P. Hence, to obtain OQ given λ_1 and λ_2, first locate OP for $\mu = \dfrac{\lambda_1}{\lambda_1 + \lambda_2}$ and then derive OQ by expansion (or contraction) in the ratio $\lambda_1 + \lambda_2 : 1$. For various values of λ_1 and λ_2, OQ lies in the angle between the vectors OP_1 and OP_2 and is of various lengths. Finally, any linear combination is represented by a vector OR anywhere in the plane defined by OP_1 and OP_2.

The definitions and properties extend easily to the general case of any number of vectors in n dimensions:

DEFINITION. Given the vectors $\mathbf{x}^k = (x_1^{(k)}, x_2^{(k)}, \ldots x_n^{(k)})$ for $k = 1, 2,$ $\ldots m$, a linear combination is $\lambda_1 \mathbf{x}^{(1)} + \lambda_2 \mathbf{x}^{(2)} + \ldots + \lambda_m \mathbf{x}^{(m)}$ for any scalars λ_k. The linear combination is positive if $\lambda_k \geqslant 0$; it is convex if $\lambda_k \geqslant 0$ and $\lambda_1 + \lambda_2 + \ldots + \lambda_m = 1$.

The geometrical representation is to be shown in terms of the points $P_1, P_2, \ldots P_m$ corresponding to the given vectors in n dimensions. A convex linear combination is some point P on or within the figure defined by $P_1, P_2, \ldots P_m$ in a hyper-plane (if $m \leqslant n$). A positive linear combination is a point Q lying on the line from O to such a point P and continued beyond P, i.e. OQ lies on or within the hyper-cone defined by $OP_1, OP_2,$ $\ldots OP_m$. A linear combination is any point R in the sub-space (of at most m dimensions) defined by $O, P_1, P_2, \ldots P_m$.

Attention is now directed to the properties of a set of points

$$P_k \quad (k = 1, 2, 3, \ldots)$$

in space of n dimensions. The set, denoted by S, may comprise a finite number of points; it may be made up, for example, of the points at the corners of a solid figure bounded by planes in three dimensions. Or S may be an infinite set, e.g. comprising all points on the surface of a sphere in three dimensions. There is a trivial case, ruled out in the following account, where S consists of a single point only.

When axes $Ox_1 x_2 \ldots x_n$ and units of measurement are specified, the point P_k can be written as a vector which gives its co-ordinates:

$$\mathbf{x}^{(k)} = (x_1^{(k)}, x_2^{(k)}, \ldots x_n^{(k)})$$

In the present context, however, this is incidental. Indeed, the properties investigated do not depend on any particular measurement of the space, and they will not be affected even when the space is expanded and contracted in certain ways.

Take two points P_1 and P_2 of S, with vectors $\mathbf{x}^{(1)}$ and $\mathbf{x}^{(2)}$. The convex linear combination $\mathbf{x} = \mu \mathbf{x}^{(1)} + (1 - \mu) \mathbf{x}^{(2)}$ is shown by a point P which is on the line from P_1 to P_2 and divides it in the ratio $P_2 P : PP_1 = \mu : 1 - \mu$. As μ increases ($0 \leqslant \mu \leqslant 1$) P moves without break from P_2 to P_1. This property does not depend on the measurement of the space, or on how space may be distorted. The ratio $\mu : 1 - \mu$ and the straightness of the line from P_2 to P_1 can be abandoned. But P always moves, on some course or other, from P_2 to P_1 as μ goes from zero to unity. Hence the point P can be written:

$$P = \mu P_1 + (1 - \mu) P_2 \quad (0 \leqslant \mu \leqslant 1)$$

and P can be said to be " between " P_1 and P_2 on some line in space.

A point P so defined from P_1 and P_2 of S may or may not itself belong to S. The set S is a *convex set* if all points between any two points of S also belong to S. A convex set must be infinite and its feature, expressed loosely but in simple terms, is that it is " solid " and not " re-entrant ". Given S as a convex set, it is important to distinguish its " limits " from its " interior ". An *extreme point* of S is one which does not lie between any two other points of S; P is extreme if it cannot be expressed as a convex linear combination $\mu P_1 + (1 - \mu)P_2$ of any two points of S. It is the extreme points of S which make up its " limits ".

In two dimensions, all points on or inside a quadrilateral like that of Fig. 48*a*, or a circle as in Fig. 48*b*, make a convex set. The extreme

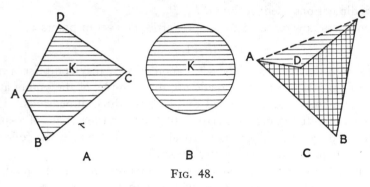

FIG. 48.

points in the first case are the four points A, B, C and D; in the other case they are all points on the circumference of the circle. On the other hand, the points of the area of a re-entrant quadrilateral, as cross-hatched in Fig. 48*c*, do not comprise a convex set; the points between A and C, for example, are not included.

Start now from any set S whatever, whether finite or infinite. Add to the set all points lying between any two members of S. This " fills out " the set to a certain extent; but not completely, since there may be points in the set as extended such that all points between them do not belong to the extended set. The process of adding to the set by inclusion of all intermediate points can be continued until S is filled out into a convex set. It will then include, not only the original points P_k, but all points P which are obtained as convex linear combinations of P_k:

$$P = \lambda_1 P_1 + \lambda_2 P_2 + \ldots + \lambda_k P_k + \ldots \quad (\lambda_k \geqslant 0, \ \lambda_1 + \lambda_2 + \ldots + \lambda_k + \ldots = 1)$$

i.e. $$\mathbf{x} = \lambda_1 \mathbf{x}^{(1)} + \lambda_2 \mathbf{x}^{(2)} + \ldots + \lambda_k \mathbf{x}^{(k)} + \ldots$$

in terms of any particular measurement. The extended set so obtained is called the " convex hull " of the original set.

The *convex hull K* of a given set *S* comprises all points which are convex linear combinations of the points of *S*, including *S* itself. In broad terms, *K* is the infinite and convex set of all points " within " the configuration $P_1, P_2, \ldots$ of *S*. It is the " solid " and non- " re-entrant " set which can be built up from *S*. The *extremal E* of the convex hull *K* is then the set of extreme points of *K*. The extremal is the " limits " of *K*.

Hence, from *S* is obtained another set *E*, as the extremal of the convex hull of *S*. The relation between *S* and *E* is a close one. It is clear that every point of *E* must also be in *S*. Let *P* be a point of *E*. If it is *not* a member of *S*, it still belongs to the convex hull of *S*, a linear combination of points of *S*. This is ruled out, however, by the definition of extreme points. Hence *P* must be a member of *S*. It is equally clear that all points of *S* need not be in *E* as well ; this is because of the " re-entrant " possibilities which permit points of *S* to be inside rather than a " limit " of the convex hull.

Fig. 48 illustrates in two dimensions. The shaded areas are the convex hulls. In Fig. 48*a*, the set *S* of four points *A*, *B*, *C* and *D* is also the extremal *E*. Similarly, in Fig. 48*b*, the set *S* of all points on the circumference of the circle is also the extremal *E*, an infinite set in this case. However, in Fig. 48*c*, the original set *S* of four points *A*, *B*, *C* and *D* gives rise to a convex hull which is effectively obtained from three of the points, the other lying within the hull ; the extremal *E* comprises only the three points *A*, *B* and *C*.

The process is to start with a given set *S*, to include all the convex linear combinations of points of *S* to get the convex hull *K*, and then to take the extremal *E*. This serves to eliminate from *S* all the " unnecessary " members, those points which are convex linear combinations of other points of the set. If *S* has no such points in the first place, then it is itself the extremal of its convex hull. But *S* usually contains other points, eliminated in reducing *S* to the extremal *E* of its convex hull.

It is sometimes convenient to use, not the points P_k of a set *S*, but rather the lines OP_k joining them to the origin. The convex hull of *S* is viewed as the " solid " bunch of lines *OP*, where *P* is any convex linear combination of the P_k. It is then called the *convex polyhedral cone* obtained from the given set *S*. The extremal set *E*, when its points are joined to *O*, gives a set of lines which form the " limits " of the cone.

EXERCISES 12.5

1. In two dimensions, the unit vectors are $\epsilon_1 = OA_1$ along Ox_1 and $\epsilon_2 = OA_2$ along Ox_2. Show that the equation of the line A_1A_2 is $x_1 + x_2 = 1$ and deduce that the general point $\mathbf{x} = x_1 \boldsymbol{\epsilon}_1 + x_2 \boldsymbol{\epsilon}_2$ lies on $A_1 A_2$ and between A_1 and A_2 if it can be written $\mathbf{x} = \mu \boldsymbol{\epsilon}_1 + (1 - \mu) \boldsymbol{\epsilon}_2$ for any μ $(0 \leqslant \mu \leqslant 1)$.

2. Extend the result of the previous exercise to show that the point P given by $\mathbf{x} = \mu \mathbf{x}^{(1)} + (1 - \mu) \mathbf{x}^{(2)}$ lies on the line between P_1 and P_2. From the co-ordinates of the points check that $P_2 P : P P_1 = \mu : 1 - \mu$. Interpret P as a " weighted average " of P_1 and P_2.

3. Given a set S of a finite number of points $P_k (k = 1, 2, 3, \ldots n)$, show that the convex polyhedral cone is obtained by taking all *positive* linear combinations of the P_k, as opposed to *convex* linear combinations which give the convex hull.

4. The set S consists of four points, which may or may not be re-entrant, in three dimensions. What is the convex hull and the extremal? If S is the set of all points on the surface of a sphere, what is then the convex hull and extremal?

12.6 Matrices

The most general concept to introduce in the new algebra is that of a *matrix* of any dimensions. The basic idea is already evident in the general account given (12.2 above) of one of the applications of matrices, and in the use (10.8 and Chapter 11 above) of the " technology matrix " as a representation of production possibilities. It is important, however, to give a precise definition and to devise an appropriate and convenient notation, before passing on to the main problem, that of developing the algebra of matrices. A systematic treatment of matrix algebra is given in the following chapter ; what is done here is to lay the foundations and to give examples of matrices of kinds which will be used later.

On the following definition, a matrix is an ordered arrangement (*not* a single value) of a set of elements. It is denoted by a single letter, a capital in bold type ; this is convenient because the bold type indicates that it is a complex of values and not one value, and because the use of a capital letter enables it to be distinguished from a vector.

DEFINITION. A matrix of order $m \times n$ is a set of $m \times n$ elements from the field F of real numbers, arranged in rectangular form in m rows and n columns ; it is denoted

$$\mathbf{A} = [a_{rs}] = \begin{bmatrix} a_{11} & a_{12} & \ldots & a_{1n} \\ a_{21} & a_{22} & \ldots & a_{2n} \\ \cdots\cdots\cdots\cdots\cdots\cdots \\ a_{m1} & a_{m2} & \ldots & a_{mn} \end{bmatrix}$$

where $r = 1, 2, \ldots m$ denotes the rows and $s = 1, 2, \ldots n$ the columns.

The order of the matrix, if not obvious, must always be specified, and this can be done by giving the range of values taken by r and s. The matrix is *square* when $m=n$ and *rectangular* when $m \neq n$; in the latter case, m may be greater or less than n. There is no particular geometrical or diagrammatic interpretation of a matrix (like that for vectors) and the terms "square" and "rectangular" are simply convenient expressions of the "shape" of the block of elements concerned. Other such terms can be used; for example, if a set of elements like $(a_{21}, a_{32}, \dots a_{m\,m-1})$ is selected by coming down (or up) the block of elements at an angle of 45°, the elements can be described as a "diagonal". In particular, if $\mathbf{A}$ is square, the set of elements $(a_{11}, a_{22}, \dots a_{nn})$ is called the *principal or leading diagonal*.

Among the numerous kinds of matrices, the following cases are of particular importance in practice :

(i) *Zero Matrix :* $\mathbf{0}=[0]=\begin{bmatrix} 0 & 0 & \dots & 0 \\ 0 & 0 & \dots & 0 \\ \dotfill \\ 0 & 0 & \dots & 0 \end{bmatrix}$ of order $m \times n$.

All the elements are zero and, if their number is not obvious, it is necessary to specify, e.g. $\mathbf{0}=[0]_{m \times n}$. If an equation in matrices is written with "zero" on the right-hand side, like $\mathbf{A} - \lambda \mathbf{B}=\mathbf{0}$, then the "zero" is *the zero matrix of appropriate order*. In an ordinary equation, there is no trouble about the right-hand side, the value zero. In an equation in matrices, the "zero" has dimensions and must be specified; it may be of any order $m \times n$.

(ii) *Unit Matrix :* this is a *square* matrix of any order $n \times n$:

$$\mathbf{I}=[\delta_{rs}]=\begin{bmatrix} 1 & 0 & \dots & 0 \\ 0 & 1 & \dots & 0 \\ \dotfill \\ 0 & 0 & \dots & 1 \end{bmatrix} \quad (r, s=1, 2, \dots n)$$

where δ_{rs} is the Kronecker delta defined in 12.3 above. The principal diagonal of $\mathbf{I}$ has entries 1; all other elements are 0. There is not just one unit matrix $\mathbf{I}$; there is such a matrix for each order $n \times n$ and the order must be understood or specified.

(iii) *Diagonal Matrix :* this is a *square* matrix, an extension of $\mathbf{I}$, of any order $n \times n$:

$$\boldsymbol{\lambda}=[\lambda_r \, \delta_{rs}]=\begin{bmatrix} \lambda_1 & 0 & \dots & 0 \\ 0 & \lambda_2 & \dots & 0 \\ \dotfill \\ 0 & 0 & \dots & \lambda_n \end{bmatrix} \quad (r, s=1, 2, \dots n)$$

The use of the small letter in $\bar{\lambda}$ can be justified here, since the matrix is composed of zero elements except for the principal diagonal which is the vector $\lambda = (\lambda_1, \lambda_2, \dots \lambda_n)$.

(iv) *Symmetric and Skew-symmetric Matrices.* A *square* matrix $\mathbf{A} = [a_{rs}]$ of order $n \times n$ is symmetric if:

$$a_{rs} = a_{sr} \qquad \text{(all } r \text{ and } s)$$

and it is skew-symmetric if:

$$a_{rs} = -a_{sr} \qquad \text{(all } r \text{ and } s)$$

Hence the elements on one side of the principal diagonal are the same as those on the other side, with the same sign (symmetric) or with the opposite sign (skew-symmetric). The elements (a_{rr}) of the principal diagonal of a symmetric matrix can take any values. For a skew-symmetric matrix, the principal diagonal must have all elements zero, since $a_{rr} = -a_{rr}$ by the definition and hence $a_{rr} = 0$. Examples are:

$$\begin{bmatrix} 0 & 1 & 2 \\ 1 & 0 & 3 \\ 2 & 3 & 0 \end{bmatrix} ; \quad \begin{bmatrix} 1 & -1 & 0 \\ -1 & 2 & 1 \\ 0 & 1 & 3 \end{bmatrix} ; \quad \begin{bmatrix} 0 & 0 & 1 \\ 0 & 0 & 0 \\ -1 & 0 & 0 \end{bmatrix} \text{ and } \begin{bmatrix} 0 & 1 & 2 \\ -1 & 0 & 3 \\ -2 & -3 & 0 \end{bmatrix}$$

the first two being symmetric and the other two skew-symmetric.

(v) *Triangular Matrix :* a *square* matrix of order $n \times n$ of the form:

$$\mathbf{T} = \begin{bmatrix} a_1 & * & * & \dots & * \\ 0 & a_2 & * & \dots & * \\ 0 & 0 & a_3 & \dots & * \\ \multicolumn{5}{c}{\dotfill} \\ 0 & 0 & 0 & \dots & a_n \end{bmatrix}$$

where * indicates an element which can take any value whatever. This is similar to the diagonal matrix, having the vector $\mathbf{a} = (a_1, a_2, \dots a_n)$ for principal diagonal, but the zero elements appear on one side only of the diagonal. This and the previous cases indicate the importance of the pattern of zero elements and non-zero elements in a matrix.

(vi) *Jacobian Matrix.* This is an example of the formation of a matrix from a set of functions of several variables and their derivatives. Let :

$$u_r = u_r(x_1, x_2, \dots x_n) \quad (r = 1, 2, \dots m)$$

be m functions in n variables, each having derivatives of the first order The matrix of order $m \times n$ is formed :

$$J = \left[\frac{\partial u_r}{\partial x_s} \right] = \begin{bmatrix} \dfrac{\partial u_1}{\partial x_1} & \dfrac{\partial u_1}{\partial x_2} & \cdots & \dfrac{\partial u_1}{\partial x_n} \\[2ex] \dfrac{\partial u_2}{\partial x_1} & \dfrac{\partial u_2}{\partial x_2} & \cdots & \dfrac{\partial u_2}{\partial x_n} \\[1ex] \cdots\cdots\cdots\cdots\cdots \\[1ex] \dfrac{\partial u_m}{\partial x_1} & \dfrac{\partial u_m}{\partial x_2} & \cdots & \dfrac{\partial u_m}{\partial x_n} \end{bmatrix}$$

As a particular case, let $u = u(x_1, x_2, \ldots x_n)$ be a function with derivatives of first and second order. Take J of order $n \times n$ with :

$$u_r = \frac{\partial}{\partial x_r} u(x_1, x_2, \ldots x_n) \quad (r = 1, 2, \ldots n)$$

It can then be written as H where :

$$H = \left[\frac{\partial^2 u}{\partial x_r \partial x_s} \right] = \begin{bmatrix} \dfrac{\partial^2 u}{\partial x_1{}^2} & \dfrac{\partial^2 u}{\partial x_1 \partial x_2} & \cdots & \dfrac{\partial^2 u}{\partial x_1 \partial x_n} \\[2ex] \dfrac{\partial^2 u}{\partial x_1 \partial x_2} & \dfrac{\partial^2 u}{\partial x_2{}^2} & \cdots & \dfrac{\partial^2 u}{\partial x_2 \partial x_n} \\[1ex] \cdots\cdots\cdots\cdots\cdots \\[1ex] \dfrac{\partial^2 u}{\partial x_1 \partial x_n} & \dfrac{\partial^2 u}{\partial x_2 \partial x_n} & \cdots & \dfrac{\partial^2 u}{\partial x_n{}^2} \end{bmatrix}$$

which is a square and symmetric matrix sometimes called a *Hessian*.

(vii) *Orthogonal Matrix :* the definition is given later (13.9 below), but an example of such a matrix of second order is :

$$\begin{bmatrix} \cos\theta & \sin\theta \\ -\sin\theta & \cos\theta \end{bmatrix}$$

which has the properties that the " cross product " is unity :

$$\cos\theta \cos\theta - (-\sin\theta)\sin\theta = \cos^2\theta + \sin^2\theta = 1$$

and that the sum of squares of elements in any row or column is unity :

$$\cos^2\theta + \sin^2\theta = 1$$

The use of the term " orthogonal " arises from properties such as these, and from the fact that the matrix applies to the rotation of co-ordinate axes which are at right angles (orthogonal). If (x_1, x_2) are the co-ordinates of a point P referred to axes Ox_1x_2, and if the axes are rotated through an angle θ giving (y_1, y_2) as the new co-ordinates of P, then from Fig. 49 :

$$y_1 = x_1 \cos\theta + x_2 \sin\theta$$
$$y_2 = -x_1 \sin\theta + x_2 \cos\theta$$

The orthogonal matrix above is the matrix of this transformation.

(viii) *Partitioned Matrix :* the elements of some matrices fall naturally into sub-blocks of various kinds, and it is then convenient to partition them and to use a compact notation for the matrix as partitioned ; for example :

$$
\begin{bmatrix}
a_{11} & a_{12} & a_{13} & 1 & 0 \\
a_{21} & a_{22} & a_{23} & 0 & 1 \\
0 & 0 & 0 & b_{11} & b_{12} \\
0 & 0 & 0 & b_{21} & b_{22} \\
0 & 0 & 0 & b_{31} & b_{32}
\end{bmatrix}
=
\left[
\begin{array}{ccc|cc}
a_{11} & a_{12} & a_{13} & 1 & 0 \\
a_{21} & a_{22} & a_{23} & 0 & 1 \\
\hline
0 & 0 & 0 & b_{11} & b_{12} \\
0 & 0 & 0 & b_{21} & b_{22} \\
0 & 0 & 0 & b_{31} & b_{32}
\end{array}
\right]
=
\left[
\begin{array}{c|c}
\mathbf{A} & \mathbf{I} \\
\hline
\mathbf{0} & \mathbf{B}
\end{array}
\right]
$$

where $\mathbf{A}=[a_{rs}]$ $(r=1, 2 ;\ s=1, 2, 3)$, $\mathbf{B}=[b_{rs}]$ $(r=1, 2, 3 ;\ s=1, 2)$ and $\mathbf{0}$ and $\mathbf{I}$ are appropriate zero and unit matrices, both square ($\mathbf{0}$ of order 3, $\mathbf{I}$ of order 2). The original matrix, square of order 5×5, is thus partitioned into two simpler matrices, $\mathbf{A}$ of order 2×3 and $\mathbf{B}$ of order 3×2, together with a zero and a unit matrix. This kind of partitioning often facilitates analysis.

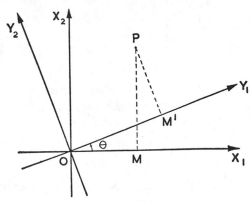

FIG. 49.

EXERCISES 12.6

1. What kind of matrices are the following :

(a) $\begin{bmatrix} 2 & 0 & 0 \\ 0 & 2 & 0 \\ 0 & 0 & 2 \end{bmatrix}$ (b) $\begin{bmatrix} 1 & 0 & 0 \\ 0 & 0 & 1 \\ 0 & 1 & 0 \end{bmatrix}$ (c) $\begin{bmatrix} 0 & -1 & 1 \\ 1 & 0 & 0 \\ -1 & 0 & 0 \end{bmatrix}$ (d) $\begin{bmatrix} \dfrac{1}{\sqrt{2}} & \dfrac{1}{\sqrt{2}} \\ -\dfrac{1}{\sqrt{2}} & \dfrac{1}{\sqrt{2}} \end{bmatrix}$

Show the relation of (d) to the rotation of co-ordinate axes through 45° in two dimensions.

2. A *scalar matrix* is a diagonal matrix with all elements (in the principal diagonal) equal. Show that (a) of the previous exercise is scalar and devise a notation for any scalar matrix.

3. I is the unit matrix of order n. The matrix $E_{(rs)}$ is defined from I by interchange of rth and sth rows. Show that the same matrix is obtained by interchange of columns and that $E_{(rs)}$ is symmetric. Illustrate when $n=3$ and show that (b) of Ex. 1 is $E_{(23)}$.

4. From the unit matrix I of order n, obtain (a) $H_{(rs)}$ by replacing the zero at the intersection of rth row and sth column by h, and (b) $K_{(r)}$ by replacing the element 1 in the rth row and column by k. Illustrate with actual cases when $n=3$.

5. Write out in full the partitional matrix

$$\begin{bmatrix} a & : & b \\ \cdots\cdots \\ I & : & 0 \end{bmatrix}$$

where a is the vector (a_1, a_2) and b the vector (b_1, b_2, b_3). What order are I and 0? What is the order of the full matrix?

12.7 Vectors and Matrices

There is evidently a connection between matrices and vectors, and it is two-fold: a matrix is built up from vectors and a vector is a particular case of a matrix. The first point needs little examination. The matrix of order $m \times n$

$$A = [a_{rs}] \quad (r = 1, 2, \ldots m;\ s = 1, 2, \ldots n)$$

is built up from the m vectors each of order n:

$$a_r = (a_{r1}, a_{r2}, \ldots a_{rn}) \quad (r = 1, 2, \ldots m)$$

The elements in the vectors make the rows of A. Equally, the matrix can be constructed from n vectors of order m, the columns of the matrix:

$$a_s = (a_{1s}, a_{2s}, \ldots a_{ms}) \quad (s = 1, 2, \ldots n)$$

There are further types of analysis of a matrix into vectors by splitting up the set of elements in various ways. Some are useful in particular cases, as when the diagonal matrix $\bar{a} = (a_r \delta_{rs})$ $(r = 1, 2, \ldots n)$ is derived solely from one vector $a = (a_1, a_2, \ldots a_n)$, the principal diagonal of the matrix $\bar{a}$.

For example, the unit matrix I of order $n \times n$ gives the set of unit vectors:

$$\epsilon_1 = (1, 0, 0, \ldots 0);\quad \epsilon_2 = (0, 1, 0, \ldots 0);\quad \ldots \epsilon_n = (0, 0, 0, \ldots 1)$$

either as its rows or as its columns. The Kronecker delta notation is particularly helpful here. I is $[\delta_{rs}]$ and it is made up from the vectors $\epsilon_r = (\delta_{r1}, \delta_{r2}, \ldots \delta_{rn}) = (\delta_{1r}, \delta_{2r}, \ldots \delta_{nr})$; ϵ_r consists of zero elements, except for an element 1 in the rth place.

The other connection, however, leads to a slight extension of the concept of vector and to a new notation. The matrix $A = [a_{rs}]$ has m rows and n columns; m and n can be any positive integers. If $m = n = 1$, A reduces to a single element a_{11}, i.e. $\mathbf{A}$ is a scalar. If $m=1$ but $n>1$, then $\mathbf{A}$ consists of a single row and the elements make up the vector

$$(a_{11}, a_{12}, \ldots a_{1n})$$

Such a relation can arise in another way ; if $m>1$ and $n=1$, $\mathbf{A}$ consists of a single column obtained from the vector $(a_{11}, a_{21}, \ldots a_{m1})$. When the procedure is reversed, it appears that any vector whatever :

$$\mathbf{a}=(a_1, a_2, \ldots a_n) \quad \text{(order } n\text{)}$$

can be regarded as a particular case of a matrix, but arising in two ways. The vector $\mathbf{a}$ is a matrix of one row, i.e. a matrix of order $1 \times n$. Equally, it is a matrix of order $n \times 1$, consisting of one column.

There must, therefore, be a distinction between a *row vector* and a *column vector*. Moreover, if the elements are the same, the two are close relations. A new notation is required to bring this out. The more important of the two, on balance, is the column vector. The notation for the *column vector* made up of the elements a_r $(r=1, 2, \ldots m)$ is :

$$\mathbf{a}=\{a_r\}= \begin{bmatrix} a_1 \\ a_2 \\ \ldots \\ a_m \end{bmatrix}$$

This is a matrix of one column, of order $m \times 1$. Then, a *row vector* made up of the elements a_s $(s=1, 2, \ldots n)$ is denoted :

$$\mathbf{a}'=[a_s]=[a_1 \, a_2 \, \ldots \, a_n]$$

a matrix of one row, of order $1 \times n$. The two can be quite different, comprising elements differing in number and values. However, if $m=n$ and the a's are the same, then $\mathbf{a}$ and $\mathbf{a}'$ are alternative arrangements of the same vector.

The use of the notation $\mathbf{a}$ and $\mathbf{a}'$ arises because of the relation when $m=n$ and the a's are one given set of n values. It requires an anticipatory word of explanation. Take the matrix $\mathbf{A}=[a_{rs}]$ of any order $m \times n$. Transpose the rows and the columns by interchanging them. A different matrix is then obtained, the elements are the same but the ordering is different; the new matrix is of order $n \times m$ and it will be denoted (13.5 below) by $\mathbf{A}'$, the prime being added to indicate transposition. It is clear that, when $m=n$, the row vector $\mathbf{a}'$ is the transpose of the column vector $\mathbf{a}$ and conversely. Interchange of rows and columns in a matrix $\mathbf{a}$, of one column, gives a matrix $\mathbf{a}'$ of one row. The order of the matrix changes from $n \times 1$ to $1 \times n$. Hence it is convenient from the outset to use the notation $\mathbf{a}$ and $\mathbf{a}'$ which fit in with one operation in matrix algebra.

12.8 The Σ Notation ; Inner Products

Compactness and generality is obtainable, at least up to a certain level, by use of the summation (Σ) notation in expressions which are sums of terms in the given elements of vectors and matrices. The Σ notation is both useful in itself and needed in the handling of the even more compact matrix notation. The notation depends on the specification of different elements by a subscript or subscripts. Consider the sum of n elements $(a+b+c+\ldots+k)$. Nothing can be done in this particular notation. Replace the elements by $a_1, a_2. \ldots a_n$, and the specification is far simpler. The elements are a_s where $s=1, 2, \ldots n$. The sum can be written :

$$\sum_{s=1}^{n} a_s = a_1 + a_2 + \ldots + a_n$$

When there is no ambiguity, the sum is written as Σa_s, or even as $\underset{s}{\Sigma} a_s$.

The notation is convenient and flexible, but experience is needed in its use. For example, since a common and constant multiple comes outside the bracket :

$$\underset{s}{\Sigma} (\lambda a_s) = \lambda \Sigma a_s \quad (\lambda \text{ constant})$$

However, care must be taken not to " bring outside " something which in fact varies from one term to another, e.g.

$$\underset{s}{\Sigma} a_s b_s = a_1 b_1 + a_2 b_2 + \ldots a_n b_n$$

is not reducible ; in particular $\Sigma a_s b_s$ is *not* equal to any of the following : $a_s \underset{s}{\Sigma} b_s$; $b_s \underset{s}{\Sigma} a_s$; $(\underset{s}{\Sigma} a_s)(\underset{s}{\Sigma} b_s)$.

The advantages of the notation become apparent in passing from a simple series of elements to a double series, i.e. an ordered block of elements. In the block of $m \times n$ elements of a matrix :

$$\begin{bmatrix} a_{11} & a_{12} & \ldots & a_{1n} \\ a_{21} & a_{22} & \ldots & a_{2n} \\ \ldots\ldots\ldots\ldots\ldots \\ a_{m1} & a_{m2} & \ldots & a_{mn} \end{bmatrix} \quad \ldots\ldots\ldots\ldots\ldots\ldots(1)$$

the general term is a_{rs} $(r=1, 2, \ldots m ; s=1, 2, \ldots n)$. The sum of elements in the first column is then

$$\sum_{r=1}^{m} a_{r1} = a_{11} + a_{21} + \ldots + a_{m1}$$

More generally $\overset{m}{\underset{r=1}{\Sigma}} a_{rs}$ is the sum of elements in the sth column and $\overset{n}{\underset{s=1}{\Sigma}} a_{rs}$ the sum of elements in the rth row.

Now consider equations (3) of 12.2 above, a system of linear equations or transformations. The m equations can be written compactly as :

$$\sum_{s=1}^{n} a_{rs}x_s = y_r \quad (r=1, 2, \dots m) \quad \dots\dots\dots\dots\dots(2)$$

These can be further shortened in the vector notation :

$$\sum_{s=1}^{n} x_s\mathbf{a}_s = \mathbf{y} \quad \dots\dots\dots\dots\dots\dots\dots(3)$$

where $\mathbf{a}_s = (a_{1s}, a_{2s}, \dots a_{ms})$ and $\mathbf{y} = (y_1, y_2, \dots y_m)$ are both of order m. The expression on the left-hand side of (3) is a vector sum ; by the rules of addition and scalar products of 12.4 above, it is itself a vector of order m. The equation in vectors (3) is then the separate equation of m elements in two vectors. The equation for the rth element is $\sum_{s=1}^{n} a_{rs}x_s = y_r$, true for any r, which is (2).

The use of the two subscripts r and s in (2) is particularly to be noticed. For one equation of the system, r is given, e.g. $r=2$ for the second equation ; the left-hand side of the equation is a sum of n terms with s ranging from 1 to n. The coefficients a_{rs} run across one particular row of the block (1). The different equations are indicated by r ranging from 1 to m and the coefficients a_{rs} are in different rows of the block (1).

The characteristic of equations (2), which is a very common one in matrix algebra, is that one subscript (r) appears *once* on the left-hand side and the other subscript (s) appears *twice*. The subscript (r) which appears once is a *free subscript* ; it can be assigned any value, here from the range $r=1, 2, \dots m$. The subscript (s) appearing twice is " knocked out " by the summation Σ ; for this reason it is called a *dummy subscript*.

The use of dummy subscripts in various sums of products of elements is both general and of basic importance in matrix algebra. In particular, there are sums of products called *inner products*. These have been met already (12.4 above) in the form of the inner product of two vectors :

$$\mathbf{a} \cdot \mathbf{b} = a_1b_1 + a_2b_2 + \dots + a_nb_n$$

Any two vectors of the *same number of elements* can be multiplied to an inner product in this way. It only remains to define a greater range of them, using elements of matrices as well as vectors. The various cases can be arranged :

DEFINITION : (i) Two vectors $(a_1, a_2, \dots a_n)$ and $(x_1, x_2, \dots x_n)$ each containing n elements give rise to the *inner product* :

$$\sum_{s=1}^{n} a_s x_s = a_1x_1 + a_2x_2 + \dots + a_nx_n$$

(ii) (a) A matrix of $m \times n$ elements :

$$\begin{bmatrix} a_{11} & a_{12} & \dots & a_{1n} \\ a_{21} & a_{22} & \dots & a_{2n} \\ \dotfill \\ a_{m1} & a_{m2} & \dots & a_{mn} \end{bmatrix}$$

and a vector $(x_1, x_2, \dots x_n)$ of n elements give rise to m *inner products* :

$$\sum_{s=1}^{m} a_{rs}x_s = a_{r1}x_1 + a_{r2}x_2 + \dots + a_{rn}x_n \quad (r = 1, 2, \dots m)$$

(ii) (b) The same matrix together with the vector $(y_1, y_2, \dots y_m)$ of m elements give rise to n *inner products* :

$$\sum_{s=1}^{n} a_{rs}x_s = a_{r1}x_1 + a_{r2}x_2 + \dots + a_{rn}x_n \quad (r = 1, 2, \dots m)$$

(iii) Two matrices respectively of $m \times k$ and of $k \times n$ elements :

$$\begin{bmatrix} a_{11} & a_{12} & \dots & a_{1k} \\ a_{21} & a_{22} & \dots & a_{2k} \\ \dotfill \\ a_{m1} & a_{m2} & \dots & a_{mk} \end{bmatrix} \text{ and } \begin{bmatrix} b_{11} & b_{12} & \dots & b_{1n} \\ b_{21} & b_{22} & \dots & b_{2n} \\ \dotfill \\ b_{k1} & b_{k2} & \dots & b_{kn} \end{bmatrix}$$

give rise to $m \times n$ *inner products*, in which *rows* of the first matrix are matched with *columns* of the second :

$$\sum_{p=1}^{k} a_{rp}b_{ps} = a_{r1}b_{1s} + a_{r2}b_{2s} + \dots + a_{rk}b_{ks} \quad (r = 1, 2, \dots m \text{ and } s = 1, 2, \dots n)$$

In (i) and (ii) (a) the dummy subscript is s, in (ii) (b) it is r, and in (iii) it is p. There is no free subscript in (i) ; there is one free subscript in each of (ii) (a) and (b) ; there are two free subscripts in (iii). A free subscript can be specified, taking any value from the appropriate range.

In obtaining experience in the use of the Σ notation, and of inner products in particular, some simple and obvious points need to be borne in mind. Since the a's, b's, x's and so on are real numbers, the order in which their products are written is quite immaterial. So :

$$\sum_s a_{rs}x_s = \sum_s x_s a_{rs} ; \quad \sum_r y_r a_{rs} = \sum_r a_{rs}y_r ; \quad \sum_p a_{rp}b_{ps} = \sum_p b_{ps}a_{rp}$$

Again, the subscript which appears twice and so generates the sum can be denoted by any convenient letter, as long as the range of its values remains unchanged. So :

$$\sum_s a_{rs}x_s = \sum_t a_{rt}x_t$$

as long as s and t are taken as ranging from 1 to n. It is for this reason that the subscript is called a dummy one. On the other hand, a free subscript cannot be changed without altering the value of the inner product. For example, $\Sigma_s a_{rs}x_s$ is different from $\Sigma_s a_{ts}x_s$ (unless $r=t$) ; the first is the sth and the second the tth inner product in a whole set of m different inner products. Equally, $\Sigma_s a_{rs}x_s$ and $\Sigma_r a_{rs}x_r$ are quite different ; the first is a sum of n terms specified for m values of r, the second a sum of m terms specified for n values of s. In full :

$$\sum_{s=1}^{n} a_{rs}x_s = a_{r1}x_1 + a_{r2}x_2 + \ldots + a_{rn}x_n \quad (r=1, 2, \ldots m)$$

$$\sum_{r=1}^{m} a_{rs}x_r = a_{1s}x_1 + a_{2s}x_2 + \ldots + a_{ms}x_m \quad (s=1, 2, \ldots n)$$

It is conventional, and clearly convenient as a matter of tidiness in notation, to write products in such a way that the two appearances of a dummy subscript are next to each other. Though the order of the terms in a product of real numbers is immaterial, it is convenient to write $a_{rs}x_s$ rather than $x_s a_{rs}$, $y_r a_{rs}$ rather than $a_{rs}y_r$ and $a_{rp}b_{ps}$ rather than $b_{ps}a_{rp}$. This rule is followed in setting out the definitions of inner products above.

EXERCISES 12.8

1. Show that the inner product (iii) above when $n=1$ corresponds to a matrix of order $m \times k$ taken with a column vector of order $k \times 1$ and gives the inner product (ii) (a), i.e.

$$\sum_{p=1}^{k} a_{rp}b_p = a_{r1}b_1 + a_{r2}b_2 + \ldots + a_{rk}b_k$$

2. Similarly show that the inner product (iii) when $m=1$ involves a row vector and gives the inner product (ii) (b).

3. Complete the study of these special cases by taking $m=n=1$, and show that inner product (iii) then reduces to inner product (i). Conclude that inner products (i) and (ii) are particular cases of the more general inner product (iii) and that it is essential to distinguish between row and column vectors.

4. Illustrate the use of two dummy subscripts in double sums by showing :

$$\sum_{s=1}^{n} \sum_{t=1}^{n} a_{rs}b_{st}x_t = \sum_{s=1}^{n} a_{rs} \left(\sum_{t=1}^{n} b_{st}x_t \right) = \sum_{t=1}^{n} x_t \left(\sum_{s=1}^{n} a_{rs}b_{st} \right)$$

5. $\sum_{s=1}^{n} a_{rs}x_s$ consists of m linear forms ($r=1, 2, \ldots m$) in the n variables x_s ($s=1, 2,$ $\ldots n$). Apply the linear transformation $x_s = \sum_{t=1}^{n} b_{st}y_t$, and show that the linear forms become $\sum_{t=1}^{n} c_{rt}y_t$, where $c_{rt} = \sum_{s=1}^{n} a_{rs}b_{st}$. Show also that, when transformed, the linear forms are still m in number and include n variables.

12.9 Determinants

A matrix $\mathbf{A} = [a_{rs}]$ is an ordered set of elements, a complex of values, and *not* a single value itself. As indicated in 12.1 above, from $\mathbf{A}$ may be obtained all kinds of expressions which *are* single values, i.e. scalars. It is essential always to distinguish between a matrix $\mathbf{A}$ and any scalar obtained from it. This is true particularly of determinants as the most important scalars derived from (square) matrices. Determinants are well-known expressions appearing in ordinary algebra ; they are defined and their properties obtained in any moderately advanced text book on algebra, e.g. Ferrar (1941), and also Allen (1938). It is not necessary to do more than summarise the theory of determinants here. Indeed, it would be positively harmful. The emphasis now is on a new concept (a matrix) and on a new algebra to match ; any major diversion back to ordinary algebra would only confuse the issue. The risk would be of slipping unconsciously into thinking that a matrix is " something like " a deter-minant, into looking for " the value " of a matrix. A matrix is *not* like a determinant and it does *not* have a value. The simple fact is that, once matrices are handled (as new concepts), various scalar values can be derived from them ; amongst these scalar values, determinant values are the most important.

A determinant is defined only for a square matrix $\mathbf{A} = [a_{rs}]$ (r and $s = 1, 2, \ldots n$), and its order (n) is the same as that of the square matrix ($n \times n$). There are several possible ways of defining a determinant, perhaps the best being by induction as given below ; the value of a determinant of the nth order is then defined in terms of determinants of order $(n-1)$ and so on, back to determinants of the first order. Before the definition is set out, however, the notation and some related terms can be given. The determinant from $\mathbf{A}$, being an ordinary value (real number), can be denoted by a letter in ordinary type, to distinguish it from matrices in bold type. Hence A (in ordinary type) can indicate the determinant value obtained from the matrix $\mathbf{A}$ (in bold type) ; there is no risk of con-fusion. It is also an established notation that the square brackets $[a_{rs}]$ for a matrix are replaced by parallel lines $| a_{rs} |$ for the determinant value. Hence :

$$A = | \mathbf{A} | = | a_{rs} | = \begin{vmatrix} a_{11} & a_{12} & \ldots & a_{1n} \\ a_{21} & a_{22} & \ldots & a_{2n} \\ \cdots\cdots\cdots\cdots\cdots \\ a_{n1} & a_{n2} & \ldots & a_{nn} \end{vmatrix}$$

all denote the determinant value (scalar) obtained from $\mathbf{A}$.

Now consider the matrix $\mathbf{A}_{rs}$ obtained from $\mathbf{A}$ by dropping the rth row and sth column, where $\mathbf{A}_{rs}$ is of order $(n-1) \times (n-1)$. The determinant obtained from $\mathbf{A}_{rs}$ is called the *minor* of a_{rs} in A. As a closely related (and alternative) concept, the minor can be given the sign $(-1)^{r+s}$ and called the *co-factor* of a_{rs} in A. Hence :

$$\text{Minor} \quad M_{rs} = |\mathbf{A}_{rs}|$$
$$\text{Co-factor} \quad A_{rs} = (-1)^{r+s}|\mathbf{A}_{rs}|$$

For example, for a_{11} the element in the leading position in $\mathbf{A}$, the minor and co-factor are the same, i.e. the determinant obtained from the matrix which is $\mathbf{A}$ without the first row and column. But, for a_{12} the second element in the first row of $\mathbf{A}$, the minor and co-factor are opposite in sign ; the minor here is the determinant obtained from the matrix which is $\mathbf{A}$ without the first row and second column.

DEFINITION : The determinant A obtained from $\mathbf{A}$ of order n is defined in terms of the determinants (co-factors) of order $(n-1)$:

$$A = \sum_{s=1}^{n} a_{rs} A_{rs}$$

The definition is completed by taking a determinant of the first order as the value of the single element (a_{11}) which appears.

One point still needs attention to make the definition self-consistent. A is defined as the sum obtained for elements in the rth row of A, each multiplied by its appropriate co-factor. This sum is in fact independent of which row is taken, and indeed it is the same for a column instead of a row. A proof is, strictly speaking, needed ; the result is included among the following properties of determinants, all of which are proved in text-books on algebra but omitted here.

PROPERTY (i).   The algebraic value A, written out in full, consists of the sum of all possible terms, which are products of n elements one from each row and one from each column of A, together with an appropriate sign ; see Ferrar (1941), pp. 8–11.

PROPERTY (ii). $A = \sum_{s=1}^{n} a_{rs} A_{rs} = \sum_{r=1}^{n} a_{rs} A_{rs}$ for any r and $s = 1, 2, \ldots n$.

PROPERTY (iii).   Transposition of rows and columns leaves the determinant value unchanged :

$$|\mathbf{A}| = |\mathbf{A}'| \quad \text{or} \quad |a_{rs}| = |a_{sr}|$$

PROPERTY (iv).   Interchange of two rows (or two columns) in A changes only the sign of the determinant value, e.g.

$$\begin{vmatrix} a_{21} & a_{22} & \cdots & a_{2n} \\ a_{11} & a_{12} & \cdots & a_{1n} \\ \cdots\cdots\cdots\cdots\cdots\cdots \\ a_{n1} & a_{n2} & \cdots & a_{nn} \end{vmatrix} = - \begin{vmatrix} a_{11} & a_{12} & \cdots & a_{1n} \\ a_{21} & a_{22} & \cdots & a_{2n} \\ \cdots\cdots\cdots\cdots\cdots\cdots \\ a_{n1} & a_{n2} & \cdots & a_{nn} \end{vmatrix}$$

PROPERTY (v). A determinant with two identical rows (or two identical columns) is zero, e.g.

$$\begin{vmatrix} a_{11} & a_{12} & \cdots & a_{1n} \\ a_{11} & a_{12} & \cdots & a_{1n} \\ a_{31} & a_{32} & \cdots & a_{3n} \\ \cdots\cdots\cdots\cdots\cdots\cdots \\ a_{n1} & a_{n2} & \cdots & a_{nn} \end{vmatrix} = 0$$

PROPERTY (vi). Multiplication of each element in a row (or a column) by a scalar λ changes the determinant value in the ratio λ, e.g.

$$\lambda \begin{vmatrix} a_{11} & a_{12} & \cdots & a_{1n} \\ a_{21} & a_{22} & \cdots & a_{2n} \\ \cdots\cdots\cdots\cdots\cdots \\ a_{n1} & a_{n2} & \cdots & a_{nn} \end{vmatrix} = \begin{vmatrix} \lambda a_{11} & \lambda a_{12} & \cdots & \lambda a_{1n} \\ a_{21} & a_{22} & \cdots & a_{2n} \\ \cdots\cdots\cdots\cdots\cdots \\ a_{n1} & a_{n2} & \cdots & a_{nn} \end{vmatrix} = \begin{vmatrix} \lambda a_{11} & a_{12} & \cdots & a_{1n} \\ \lambda a_{21} & a_{22} & \cdots & a_{2n} \\ \cdots\cdots\cdots\cdots\cdots \\ \lambda a_{n1} & a_{n2} & \cdots & a_{nn} \end{vmatrix}$$

PROPERTY (vii). Addition of λ times each element of one row (or column) to the corresponding elements of another row (or column), where λ is a scalar, leaves the determinant value unchanged, e.g.

$$\begin{vmatrix} (a_{11}+\lambda a_{21}) & (a_{12}+\lambda a_{22}) & \cdots & (a_{1n}+\lambda a_{2n}) \\ a_{21} & a_{22} & & a_{2n} \\ \cdots\cdots\cdots\cdots\cdots\cdots\cdots\cdots\cdots \\ a_{n1} & a_{n2} & & a_{nn} \end{vmatrix} = \begin{vmatrix} a_{11} & a_{12} & \cdots & a_{1n} \\ a_{21} & a_{22} & \cdots & a_{2n} \\ \cdots\cdots\cdots\cdots\cdots \\ a_{n1} & a_{n2} & \cdots & a_{nn} \end{vmatrix}$$

Finally an application of the definition, together with Properties (ii) and (v), leads to the most generally used of all the properties of determinants. This is the *rule for expansion in terms of co-factors* :

$$\sum_{k=1}^{n} a_{rk}A_{rk} = \sum_{k=1}^{n} a_{ks}A_{ks} = A$$

and

$$\sum_{k=1}^{n} a_{rk}A_{tk} = \sum_{k=1}^{n} a_{ks}A_{kt} = 0$$

for any value of r, s and t $(t \neq r, s)$ in the range $1, 2, \ldots n$. The rule, in effect, says two things ; if the elements of a row (or column) of **A** are each multiplied by their proper co-factors, the sum is the determinant $A = |\mathbf{A}|$; but, if the elements are each multiplied by the wrong co-factors (those of the elements in another row or column), the sum is zero.

EXERCISES 12.9

1. Find the determinant values for each of the matrices of 12.6, Ex. 1.

2. If $\mathbf{I}$ is a unit matrix and $\bar{\mathbf{a}}$ the diagonal matrix formed from the vector $(a_1, a_2, \ldots a_n)$, show that $|\mathbf{I}| = 1$ and $|\bar{\mathbf{a}}| = a_1 a_2 \ldots a_n$.

3. Show that $\begin{vmatrix} 1 & -\frac{1}{2} & -\frac{1}{2} \\ -\frac{1}{2} & 1 & -\frac{1}{2} \\ -\frac{1}{2} & -\frac{1}{2} & 1 \end{vmatrix} = 0$. Is the value of $\begin{vmatrix} 1 & a & a \\ a & 1 & a \\ a & a & 1 \end{vmatrix} = 0$ for any other value than $a = -\frac{1}{2}$.

4. By property (v) show that $\begin{vmatrix} 1 & a & a^2 \\ 1 & b & b^2 \\ 1 & c & c^2 \end{vmatrix} = (a-b)(b-c)(c-a)$ and check by direct expansion and evaluation.

5. Show that the orthogonal matrix of 12.6 (vii) above has determinant $= 1$.

6. Show that $\begin{vmatrix} a_1 & x & y \\ 0 & a_2 & z \\ 0 & 0 & a_3 \end{vmatrix} = a_1 a_2 a_3$ and deduce that, in a diagonal matrix, the replacement of the zero elements on *one* side of the diagonal by any other values does not change the value of the determinant. See triangular matrix of 12.6 (v) above.

7 Use the result of the previous exercise to show that $|\mathbf{H}_{(rs)}| = 1$, where $\mathbf{H}_{(rs)}$ is the matrix defined in 12.6, Ex. 4, above.

8. For the matrices given in 12.6, Ex. 3 and 4, above, show that
$$|\mathbf{E}_{(rs)}| = -1 \quad \text{and} \quad |\mathbf{K}_{(r)}| = k$$

9. $\mathbf{A} = \begin{bmatrix} 0 & 1 & 1 \\ 1 & 0 & x \\ 1 & x & 1 \end{bmatrix}$ is a symmetric matrix. Show that $A = |\mathbf{A}| = (2x - 1)$.

Evaluate all nine co-factors and show that the matrix made up of elements A_{rs} is also symmetric. Show also that the determinant of this second matrix (elements A_{rs}) has value A^2. Which of these results do you think will be true of any symmetric matrix?

10. $\mathbf{A} = [a_{rs}]$ is skew symmetric of order $n \times n$. $\mathbf{A}'$ is the matrix obtained by transposing rows and columns in $\mathbf{A}$ and $(-\mathbf{A})$ is the matrix with elements opposite in sign to those of $\mathbf{A}$. Show that $\mathbf{A}' = (-\mathbf{A})$ and that (n odd) :
$$|-\mathbf{A}| = -|\mathbf{A}| \quad \text{and so} \quad |\mathbf{A}| = 0.$$

REFERENCES

Allen (R. G. D.) (1938) : *Mathematical Analysis for Economists* (Macmillan, 1938), Chapter XVIII.

Birkhoff (G.) and MacLane (S.) (1941) : *A Survey of Modern Algebra* (Macmillan, 1941), Chapter VII.

Durell (C. V.) and Robson (A.) (1937) : *Advanced Algebra* (Bell, 1937), Chapter XVI.

Ferrar (W. L.) (1941) : *Algebra* (Oxford, 1941), Chapters I, II and VI.

Kemeny (J. G.), Snell (J. L.) and Thompson (G. L.) (1957) : *Introduction to Finite Mathematics* (Prentice-Hall, 1957), Chapter V.

Murdoch (D. C.) (1957) : *Linear Algebra for Undergraduates* (Wiley, 1957) Chapters 1 and 2.

Thrall (R. M.) and Tornheim (L.) (1957) : *Vector Spaces and Matrices* (Wiley, 1957), Chapter 1.

CHAPTER 13

MATHEMATICAL ANALYSIS : MATRIX ALGEBRA

13.1 Introduction ; the Basic Rules of Algebra

The algebra of matrices is to be developed—from scratch. It is from scratch since the familiar rules of the arithmetic and algebra of numbers, learnt in the schoolroom, cannot be translated as they are to new entities called matrices. Where can we seek guidance in constructing the new algebra? Determinants are no help ; they are real numbers and obey the familiar rules. Complex numbers (4.5 above) may be better—with appropriate conventions, they can be manipulated by familiar algebraic processes. The question is : can the same trick be turned for matrix algebra? The answer is broadly : despite attempts to define operations with matrices so that matrix algebra is as similar to elementary algebra as possible, there still remain vital differences.

Hence it is important to avoid taking anything over from elementary to matrix algebra without full justification. Consider multiplication ; to " multiply " two matrices is not the same as, not even " something like ", multiplying two numbers or two determinants. The product of two matrices is yet to be defined and the definition is at choice. In choosing a definition, we hope that familiar rules will be obeyed, but we cannot take it for granted. In fact, it turns out that matrix products are not completely well-behaved. For example, $\mathbf{a'Aa}$ stands for the product of the vector $\mathbf{a}$ first by the matrix $\mathbf{A}$ and then by the vector $\mathbf{a'}$. Products of numbers have the commutative property that the numbers can be multiplied in any order. This is not so for matrices. Reverse the order in $\mathbf{a'Aa}$ and a *different* result $\mathbf{aAa'}$ is obtained. Products of matrices are not commutative.

There is something of a dilemma here. If the terms " product " and " multiplication " are used for the newly-defined operations on matrices, it is only too easy to slip into the error of taking the products as commutative. It might be better to call the operations, not multiplication, but some less-question-begging term such as " conformation ". This is not practicable since multiplication of matrices is an established term ; nor would it be very helpful in view of the advantage of keeping to recognised terminology. It may be easier to remember that some rules are not obeyed by matrix products than to try to get used to an entirely new label.

Exactly what are the rules of elementary algebra? It is certainly worth while to attempt to set them out, to see how conventional they are, and then to put them into a more general setting. Algebra is concerned with sets of elements, which may be numbers as in elementary algebra, but which can be well-defined entities of almost any kind, abstract or concrete ; for example : polynomials, matrices, transformations. Hence, algebra has to do with some set of elements $S = \{a, b, c, \ldots\}$; what it deals with are operations performed on the elements $a, b, c, \ldots$ of S.

Some of the operations are of the *unary* type ; there is a *rule of translation* from any *one* element of S to give another element of S. Examples : taking the square root of a real number, transposing a matrix. But *binary operations* are more important, each defining a *rule of combination* of any *two* elements of S to give another element of S. The prototypes are addition and multiplication ; if a and b belong to S, then a sum $a + b$ is defined to belong to S, and similarly for a product $a \times b$. Indeed, as found for complex numbers, most binary operations are so defined that they can be identified as addition or multiplication. The definition of binary operations can be illustrated first in a familiar case, for the set $N = \{1, 2, 3, \ldots\}$ of positive integers. The definition of sums and products is then a matter of specifying the cases, of forming the addition and multiplication tables learnt so painfully at school :

+	1	2	3	...
1	2	3	4	...
2	3	4	5	...
3	4	5	6	...
...				

×	1	2	3	...
1	1	2	3	...
2	2	4	6	...
3	3	6	9	...
...				

For sets generally, a binary operation can be defined by a listing of the cases, by writing appropriate addition or multiplication tables, which may be of quite odd form. Or, it may be done by providing a specification of the operation in terms of other operations and so (usually, in the end) in terms of other addition or multiplication tables. Consider the set of three integers $S \{0, 1, 2\}$ and define addition and multiplication as taking the ordinary sum and product, except that only the remainder on division by three is retained in each case. The tables are then short and concise :

+	0	1	2
0	0	1	2
1	1	2	0
2	2	0	1

×	0	1	2
0	0	0	0
1	0	1	2
2	0	2	1

since, for example, $1 + 2 = 3$ written 0 ; $2 \times 2 = 4$ written 1.

Table 1A sets out the operational rules for addition and multiplication of numbers, but classified and expressed rather precisely and put in terms of the elements of any set $S = \{a, b, c, \ldots \}$. The system of rules applies *completely* to the set of rational numbers (ratios of integers); it continues to hold for the wider sets of real numbers and of complex numbers. The point about the set of rationals (and equally about real or complex numbers) is that it is self-contained or closed under the operations of addition, multiplication and their inverses. From the inverse rules (A5 and M5) we can write $a - b = a + (-b)$ and $a/b = a \times b^{-1} (b \neq 0)$ and we can call these subtraction and division. Any one of the four operations applied to rationals gives a rational; it does not take us outside the set.

The rules are *not* all satisfied for other sets of numbers, as two cases illustrate. The set of positive integers has no zero and hence no nega-

TABLE 1. *The Operational Rules of Algebra*

A. Addition and Multiplication in $S = \{a, b, c, \ldots \}$

Rule	Addition (+)	Multiplication (×)
Closure	(A1) $a + b$ belongs to S	(M1) $a \times b$ belongs to S
Associative	(A2) $a + (b + c) = (a + b) + c$	(M2) $a \times (b \times c) = (a \times b) \times c$
Commutative	(A3) $a + b = b + a$	(M3) $a \times b = b \times a$
Identity	(A4) S has zero 0 so that $a + 0 = 0 + a = a$	(M4) S has unity 1 so that $a \times 1 = 1 \times a = a$
Inverse	(A5) S has negative $(-a)$ so that $a + (-a) = (-a) + a = 0$	(M5) S has reciprocal a^{-1} so that $a \times a^{-1} = a^{-1} \times a = 1$ $(a \neq 0)$
Cancellation	(A5′) if $a + b = a + c$ then $b = c$	(M5′) if $a \times b = a \times c$ $(a \neq 0)$ then $b = c$
Distributive	(D) $a \times (b + c) = a \times b + a \times c$ and $(a + b) \times c = a \times c + b \times c$	

B. Scalar Multiplication in $S = \{a, b, c, \ldots \}$ by Scalars from $F = \{\lambda, \mu, \nu, \ldots \}$

Closure	(S1) $\lambda \,.\, a$ belongs to S	(S2) $0 \,.\, a = 0$ and $1 \,.\, a = a$
Associative	(S3) $\lambda \,.\, (\mu \,.\, a) = (\lambda \mu) \,.\, a$	
Distributive	(S4) $\lambda \,.\, (a + b) = \lambda \,.\, a + \lambda \,.\, b$	(S5) $(\lambda + \mu) \,.\, a = \lambda \,.\, a + \mu \,.\, a$

tive; though it has a unity, it has no reciprocals apart from 1 itself. The set of odd integers is even less obedient. Addition is defined but the very first rule (closure) fails; the sum of two odd integers is not another odd integer but an even integer. In passing to other sets of entities (such as matrices) in which sums and products are defined, we can only say that the operational rules (A1–5), (M1–5) and (D) are desirable but not inevitable. We would like them all to hold; failing this, we try to define the operations so that as many as possible do hold.

The two rules which often fail in practice are (M3) and (M5), the commutative and inverse rules for products. This is so for matrices. Not all matrices can be multiplied; when they can, it is only in special cases that reciprocals exist, and in even rarer cases that the products commute. Commutative multiplication is so engrained in our experience that we find it painful to cut across the grain and write $A \times B \neq B \times A$ for matrices.

Particular attention needs to be paid to the inverse rules (A5) and (M5). The table also shows cancellation rules, denoted (A5′) and (M5′) since they are alternatives to the inverse rules in a specific sense. Consider multiplication as the more important operation in this connection. If (M5) holds, then a non-zero element a has a reciprocal a^{-1} and division by a is possible (i.e. multiplication by the reciprocal). Then (M5′) also holds, on dividing through by a. The converse is not true. It is possible to have cancellation (M5′) without reciprocals or division (M5 not true). This is so for the set of positive integers. Hence we can :

   either take (M5) and have division *and* cancellation ;
   or   take (M5′) and have cancellation *without* division.

TABLE 2. *The Main Algebraic Systems*

System	Operations	Rules valid	Examples
Group	Product	M1, 2, 4, 5	Non-singular linear transforms Non-singular matrices
Integral Domain*	Sum and Product	A1–5, D, M1–4, M5′	Integers Polynomials, integral coefficients
Field*	Sum and Product	A1–5, D, M1–5	Rational numbers Real numbers Complex numbers
Vector Space	Sum and Scalar Product	A1–5, S1–5	Vectors in m dimensions Matrices of order $m \times n$
Linear Algebra*	Sum, Product and Scalar Product	A1–5, D, S1–5 M1, 2 and perhaps others	Rational fractions (ratios of polynomials) Matrices of order $n \times n$

* These have the structure of a Ring, i.e. rules (A1–5), (D) and (M1–2) as a minimum.

Rule (M5′) is a weaker alternative to (M5). Rational or real numbers satisfy (M5) ; only the weaker (M5′) holds for integers. Matrices generally satisfy neither (M5) nor the weaker (M5′).

Other operations can be defined in a set of elements more complicated in nature than numbers. One example of great use is the operation of *scalar multiplication*, as for vectors in 12.4 above. There is now a set $S = \{a, b, c, \ldots\}$ of elements of any kind and, in addition, another set $F = \{\lambda, \mu, \nu, \ldots\}$ of elements called scalars (typically real numbers). The operation takes a scalar from F, say λ, as a multiple of an element a of S to give the scalar product $\lambda . a$ as another element of S. The desirable rules to be satisfied are the five (S1–5) shown in Table 1B.

Modern algebra has developed to deal with the algebras of all kinds of systems, with sets of entities of various kinds, in which specific operations are defined to satisfy, more or less completely, the operational rules set out in Table 1. The range of algebraic systems is extraordinarily wide and varied. Appendix B attempts to provide an introduction to such algebraic systems and some impression of their range can be got from Table 2, given here as a summary. The table lists briefly the more important types of algebraic systems and it gives a few examples of each.

Two of the systems of Table 2 have already been used. In the definition of vectors and matrices in 12.3 and 12.6, the field F of real numbers is introduced, both for components of vectors and matrices, and for use as scalars. A field of rational numbers, or of complex numbers, would do equally well. Then, the algebra of vectors is so developed that the rules required for a vector space are in fact satisfied (see particularly Exs. 4 and 5 of 12.4 above). The system of vectors, as defined here, is just one instance of a vector space.

EXERCISES 13.1

1. The set of rational numbers comprises all numbers $\frac{p}{q}$, where p and q are integers (positive, negative and zero). Show that the set is self-contained with respect to addition, subtraction, multiplication and division.

2. Show that the property of the set of the previous exercise does not hold for the sets of (*a*) all integers, (*b*) even integers and (*c*) odd integers. Which operations break out of the set in each case?

3. As long as the commutative law holds, then the distributive law $a(b + c) = ab + ac$ implies equally that $(b + c)a = ab + ac$. Is this so if the commutative law does not hold?

4. The set of numbers $x + y\sqrt{2}$ (x and y rational) is wider than the field of rationals, narrower than the field of real numbers. Show that the set is also a field.

13.2 Illustrations of Operations with Matrices

The following illustrations serve to indicate a field of application of matrices and to show that the definitions adopted for addition and multiplication of matrices are of practical significance. The illustrations are confined to the simplest cases, when the vectors are of the second order and the matrices of 2×2 type. In such cases the algebra can be set out in full.

A linear transformation in two variables is :

$$\left.\begin{aligned} y_1 &= a_{11}x_1 + a_{12}x_2 \\ y_2 &= a_{21}x_1 + a_{22}x_2 \end{aligned}\right\} \quad \dots\dots\dots\dots\dots\dots\dots(1)$$

This involves a square matrix $\mathbf{A} = \begin{bmatrix} a_{11} & a_{12} \\ a_{21} & a_{22} \end{bmatrix}$ in addition to the vectors

which represent the original variables (x_1, x_2) and the new variables (y_1, y_2). A compact notation for (1), which can be extended (12.2 above), is provided by the matrix notation, combined with the concept of inner products (12.8 above). Taking the matrix $\mathbf{A}$ in conjunction with the variable x's arranged as a column vector $\mathbf{x} = \begin{bmatrix} x_1 \\ x_2 \end{bmatrix}$ and form the two inner

products $(a_{11}x_1 + a_{12}x_2)$ and $(a_{21}x_1 + a_{22}x_2)$. These are, by (1), the elements of the column vector $\mathbf{y} = \begin{bmatrix} y_1 \\ y_2 \end{bmatrix}$. This process can be used as the definition

of the product of a vector and a matrix and it can be written :

$$\begin{bmatrix} a_{11} & a_{12} \\ a_{21} & a_{22} \end{bmatrix} \times \begin{bmatrix} x_1 \\ x_2 \end{bmatrix} = \begin{bmatrix} (a_{11}x_1 + a_{12}x_2) \\ (a_{21}x_1 + a_{22}x_2) \end{bmatrix} = \begin{bmatrix} y_1 \\ y_2 \end{bmatrix}$$

or concisely : $\mathbf{Ax} = \mathbf{y}$

Once this definition is framed, the linear transformation (1) becomes :

$$\mathbf{y} = \mathbf{Ax} \dots\dots\dots\dots\dots\dots\dots\dots\dots(2)$$

Next, consider two linear transformations, one from the original variables (x's) to new variables (y's) and the other from the same original variables to a second set of new variables (z's). In the full forms as in (1) they are :

$$\begin{aligned} y_1 &= a_{11}x_1 + a_{12}x_2 \\ y_2 &= a_{21}x_1 + a_{22}x_2 \end{aligned} \quad \text{and} \quad \begin{aligned} z_1 &= b_{11}x_1 + b_{12}x_2 \\ z_2 &= b_{21}x_1 + b_{22}x_2 \end{aligned}$$

Take variable u's as the sums of corresponding y's and z's, i.e.

$$u_1 = y_1 + z_1 \quad \text{and} \quad u_2 = y_2 + z_2$$

The problem is to get the u's in terms of the x's, i.e. to get the " additive " transformation from the x's to the u's. The solution is simple :

$$u_1 = (a_{11} + b_{11})x_1 + (a_{12} + b_{12})x_2$$
$$u_2 = (a_{21} + b_{21})x_1 + (a_{22} + b_{22})x_2$$

The matrix which now appears consists of 2×2 elements, each being the sum of an element from the matrix of a's and the corresponding element from the matrix of b's. It is natural to define the sum of two matrices in this way :

$$\begin{bmatrix} a_{11} & a_{12} \\ a_{21} & a_{22} \end{bmatrix} + \begin{bmatrix} b_{11} & b_{12} \\ b_{21} & b_{22} \end{bmatrix} = \begin{bmatrix} (a_{11}+b_{11})(a_{12}+b_{12}) \\ (a_{21}+b_{21})(a_{22}+b_{22}) \end{bmatrix} = \begin{bmatrix} c_{11} & c_{12} \\ c_{21} & c_{22} \end{bmatrix}$$

i.e. $\mathbf{A} + \mathbf{B} = \mathbf{C}$ where $c_{rs} = a_{rs} + b_{rs}$ $(r, s = 1, 2)$ ....(3)

The whole process of " adding " transformations, in matrix notation as in (3), reduces to :

Given two linear transformations $\mathbf{y} = \mathbf{A}\mathbf{x}$ *and* $\mathbf{z} = \mathbf{B}\mathbf{x}$, *then the transformation to* $\mathbf{u} = \mathbf{y} + \mathbf{z}$ *is* $\mathbf{u} = (\mathbf{A} + \mathbf{B})\mathbf{x}$.

Further, consider two linear transformations applied in succession from variable x's to variable y's and to variable z's. In the full forms as in (1)

$$y_1 = a_{11}x_1 + a_{12}x_2 \quad \text{and} \quad z_1 = b_{11}y_1 + b_{12}y_2$$
$$y_2 = a_{21}x_1 + a_{22}x_2 \qquad\qquad z_2 = b_{21}y_1 + b_{22}y_2$$

The problem is to get the z's expressed in terms of the x's, i.e. the transformation from the x's to the z's which can be regarded as the " multiplication " of the two original transformations. The solution is only a matter of straight-forward substitution :

$$z_1 = b_{11}(a_{11}x_1 + a_{12}x_2) + b_{12}(a_{21}x_1 + a_{22}x_2)$$
$$z_2 = b_{21}(a_{11}x_1 + a_{12}x_2) + b_{22}(a_{21}x_1 + a_{22}x_2)$$

i.e.
$$z_1 = (b_{11}a_{11} + b_{12}a_{21})x_1 + (b_{11}a_{12} + b_{12}a_{22})x_2$$
$$z_2 = (b_{21}a_{11} + b_{22}a_{21})x_1 + (b_{21}a_{12} + b_{22}a_{22})x_2$$

The matrix which is now obtained consists of inner products of the elements of the matrices of a's and of b's. This suggests a definition of the product of two matrices :

$$\begin{bmatrix} b_{11} & b_{12} \\ b_{21} & b_{22} \end{bmatrix} \times \begin{bmatrix} a_{11} & a_{12} \\ a_{21} & a_{22} \end{bmatrix} = \begin{bmatrix} (b_{11}a_{11}+b_{12}a_{21})(b_{11}a_{12}+b_{12}a_{22}) \\ (b_{21}a_{11}+b_{22}a_{21})(b_{21}a_{12}+b_{22}a_{22}) \end{bmatrix} = \begin{bmatrix} c_{11} & c_{12} \\ c_{21} & c_{22} \end{bmatrix}$$

i.e. $\mathbf{BA} = \mathbf{C}$ where $c_{rs} = \sum_{p=1}^{2} b_{rp}a_{ps}$ $(r, s = 1, 2)$ ....(4)

The process of applying transformations successively, or of "multiplying" them, is now much more concisely expressed in the matrix notation :

Given the linear transformations $y = Ax$ *and* $z = By$, *then the transformation from* x *to* z *is* $z = (BA)x$.

Finally, consider successive transformations of the same type but applied in the other direction, not from the x's to the y's to the z's, but taking the y's in terms of the x's and then in terms of the z's. In full :

$$y_1 = a_{11}x_1 + a_{12}x_2 \quad \text{and} \quad x_1 = b_{11}z_1 + b_{12}z_2$$
$$y_2 = a_{21}x_1 + a_{22}x_2 \qquad\qquad x_2 = b_{21}z_1 + b_{22}z_2$$

gives
$$y_1 = (a_{11}b_{11} + a_{12}b_{21})z_1 + (a_{11}b_{12} + a_{12}b_{22})z_2$$
$$y_2 = (a_{21}b_{11} + a_{22}b_{21})z_1 + (a_{21}b_{12} + a_{22}b_{22})z_2$$

Hence, a second product is to be defined :

$$\begin{bmatrix} a_{11} & a_{12} \\ a_{21} & a_{22} \end{bmatrix} \times \begin{bmatrix} b_{11} & b_{12} \\ b_{21} & b_{22} \end{bmatrix} = \begin{bmatrix} (a_{11}b_{11} + a_{12}b_{21})(a_{11}b_{12} + a_{12}b_{22}) \\ (a_{21}b_{11} + a_{22}b_{21})(a_{21}b_{12} + a_{22}b_{22}) \end{bmatrix} = \begin{bmatrix} d_{11} & d_{12} \\ d_{21} & d_{22} \end{bmatrix}$$

i.e. $\quad AB = D \qquad$ where $d_{rs} = \sum\limits_{p=1}^{2} a_{rp}b_{ps}$ $(r, s = 1, 2)$ ....(5)

The successive transformations appear in matrix notation :

Given the linear transformations $y = Ax$ *and* $x = Bz$, *then the transformation from* z *to* y *is* $y = (AB)z$.

The addition of matrices, matching the addition of linear transformations, is defined by (3). There is no difficulty here ; in particular the order in which the matrices A and B are written is quite immaterial so that $A + B = B + A$ for matrices as for real numbers. The multiplication of matrices, matching the successive application of linear transformations, is defined as in (4) and (5). Here there is an essential difference. In one direction, $BA = C$ where the elements of C are given by (4) ; in the other direction $AB = D$ where the elements of D are given by (5). The two sets of inner products (4) and (5) are quite different, and hence the two matrices $C = BA$ and $D = AB$ are different. In $C = BA$, elements in *rows* of B are matched with elements in *columns* of A. In $D = AB$, elements in *rows* of A are matched with elements in *columns* of B. Multiplication of these matrices is not commutative.

In the present chapter, the algebra of matrices is developed in the general case of matrices of order $m \times n$. It is based on a simple rule of addition of form (3) and on a less simple (and non-commutative) rule of multiplication of form (4) or (5). There is also the special case of the multiplication of a matrix and a vector, of which form (2) is representative.

The rules are here seen as arising (in the simple example of second order matrices) in application to linear transformations. Such applications of matrix algebra are considered more generally in the following chapter.

EXERCISES 13.2

1. Use the definition of inner products to show why the right-hand sides of the transformation (1) above are expressed $\mathbf{Ax}$ but not $\mathbf{xA}$. Can $\mathbf{xA}$ be defined?

2. A linear transformation $y_1 = a_{11}x_1 + a_{12}x_2 + a_{13}x_3$, $y_2 = a_{21}x_1 + a_{22}x_2 + a_{23}x_3$ is from 3 variables (x's) to 2 variables (y's). Define the appropriate $\mathbf{A}$, $\mathbf{x}$ and $\mathbf{y}$ and specify their orders. Express the transformation as $\mathbf{y} = \mathbf{Ax}$.

3. The transformation $\mathbf{y} = \mathbf{Ax}$ of the previous exercise is combined with $\mathbf{z} = \mathbf{By}$ where $\mathbf{B}$ is a matrix of order 2×2. Show that $\mathbf{z} = (\mathbf{BA})\mathbf{x}$ where $\mathbf{BA}$ is of order 2×3. Can $\mathbf{AB}$ be defined?

4. The same transformation $\mathbf{y} = \mathbf{Ax}$ (of the previous exercises) is combined with $\mathbf{x} = \mathbf{Bz}$ where $\mathbf{B}$ is a matrix of order 3×3. Show that $\mathbf{y} = (\mathbf{AB})\mathbf{z}$ where $\mathbf{AB}$ is of order 2×3. Can $\mathbf{BA}$ be defined?

13.3 Equalities, Inequalities, Addition and Scalar Products

The algebra of matrices is a set of rules for operating with matrices of general form. The rules are conventional and at choice. Those actually adopted, however, are far from arbitrary; they are taken with one eye on the laws of elementary algebra and with the other on the applications of matrices, as briefly sketched in 13.2 above.

The simplest part of the task, as with vectors (12.4 above), is to define equality, addition and multiplication by scalars. These rules are obvious extensions of those adopted for vectors. In the following account of them, $\mathbf{A} = [a_{rs}]$, $\mathbf{B} = [b_{rs}]$ and $\mathbf{C} = [c_{rs}]$ are matrices of order $m \times n$.

Equality and inequality. The definitions are :

$$\mathbf{A} = \mathbf{B} \quad \text{if} \quad a_{rs} = b_{rs}$$

and

$$\mathbf{A} > \mathbf{B} \quad \text{if} \quad a_{rs} > b_{rs}$$

for all r and s ($r = 1, 2, \ldots m$, $s = 1, 2, \ldots n$). As for vectors (12.4 above), there is a little difficulty in handling the relation of " greater than or equal to " for matrices. There are two notations :

$$\mathbf{A} \geqq \mathbf{B} \quad \text{if} \quad a_{rs} \geqq b_{rs}, \quad \text{allowing all} \quad a_{rs} = b_{rs}$$
$$\mathbf{A} \geqslant \mathbf{B} \quad \text{if} \quad a_{rs} \geqslant b_{rs}, \quad \text{not allowing all} \quad a_{rs} = b_{rs}$$

for all r and s ($r = 1, 2, \ldots m$, $s = 1, 2, \ldots n$). In $\mathbf{A} \geqq \mathbf{B}$, the cases included are $\mathbf{A} = \mathbf{B}$, $\mathbf{A} > \mathbf{B}$ and those instances where $a_{rs} > b_{rs}$ for some r and s and $a_{rs} = b_{rs}$ for others. $\mathbf{A} \geqslant \mathbf{B}$ is the same except that the possibility $\mathbf{A} = \mathbf{B}$ is omitted.

As a particular application, consider the relation of $\mathbf{A}$ to the zero matrix of the same order. $\mathbf{A}=0$ means that every element of $\mathbf{A}$ is zero, i.e. $\mathbf{A}$ is itself a zero matrix. $\mathbf{A}>0$ indicates a *positive* matrix in which *all* elements are positive. Both $\mathbf{A}\geqq 0$ and $\mathbf{A}\geqslant 0$ can be called *non-negative* matrices in which *no* element is negative—though some can be positive and others zero. In general, e.g. in economic applications, the non-negative matrix is more appropriate than the rather limited positive matrix. Zero elements usually appear in matrices and the question is whether all the other elements in $\mathbf{A}$ are positive so that $\mathbf{A}$ is non-negative.

Addition. The definition is :

$$\mathbf{C}=\mathbf{A}+\mathbf{B} \quad \text{if} \quad c_{rs}=a_{rs}+b_{rs}$$

for all r and s ($r=1, 2, \ldots m$, $s=1, 2, \ldots n$). This is straight-forward and fits in with (3) of 13.2 above. To add two matrices, each of the pairs of corresponding elements are added separately. The definition extends in an obvious way to the sum of more than two matrices. It is, however, to be noticed that $\mathbf{A}$ and $\mathbf{B}$ must be of the same order if they are to be added. The " addition " of matrices of different orders, such as

$$\begin{bmatrix} a_{11} & a_{12} \\ a_{21} & a_{22} \end{bmatrix} + \begin{bmatrix} b_{11} & b_{12} & b_{13} \\ b_{21} & b_{22} & b_{23} \end{bmatrix}$$

has no meaning whatever.

Some simple examples of addition of matrices are :

Ex. (a). $\begin{bmatrix} 1 & 0 \\ 0 & 1 \end{bmatrix} + \begin{bmatrix} 0 & 1 \\ 1 & 0 \end{bmatrix} = \begin{bmatrix} 1 & 1 \\ 1 & 1 \end{bmatrix}$

Ex. (b). $\begin{bmatrix} 1 & 0 \\ 0 & 1 \end{bmatrix} + \begin{bmatrix} 1 & 0 \\ 0 & 1 \end{bmatrix} = \begin{bmatrix} 2 & 0 \\ 0 & 2 \end{bmatrix} = 2\begin{bmatrix} 1 & 0 \\ 0 & 1 \end{bmatrix}$

Ex. (c). $\begin{bmatrix} 1 & -2 \\ -2 & 1 \end{bmatrix} + \begin{bmatrix} -1 & 2 \\ 2 & -1 \end{bmatrix} = \begin{bmatrix} 0 & 0 \\ 0 & 0 \end{bmatrix} = \mathbf{0}$ of order 2×2.

Ex. (d). $\begin{bmatrix} 1 & 2 & 3 \\ 4 & 5 & 6 \end{bmatrix} + \begin{bmatrix} 4 & 5 & 6 \\ 7 & 8 & 9 \end{bmatrix} = \begin{bmatrix} 5 & 7 & 9 \\ 11 & 13 & 15 \end{bmatrix}$

Multiplication by scalars. The definition is again straight-forward :

$$\lambda\mathbf{A}=[\lambda a_{rs}]$$

for any scalar λ. Every element in $\mathbf{A}$, and not just those in one row or column, is to be multiplied by λ. The value of λ is not restricted ; it may be positive or negative, e.g.

$$2\begin{bmatrix} 1 & -\frac{1}{2} \\ -\frac{1}{2} & 1 \end{bmatrix} = \begin{bmatrix} 2 & -1 \\ -1 & 2 \end{bmatrix} ; \quad (-1)\begin{bmatrix} 1 & -\frac{1}{2} \\ -\frac{1}{2} & 1 \end{bmatrix} = \begin{bmatrix} -1 & \frac{1}{2} \\ \frac{1}{2} & -1 \end{bmatrix} ;$$

$$k\begin{bmatrix} 1 & 0 \\ 0 & 1 \end{bmatrix} = \begin{bmatrix} k & 0 \\ 0 & k \end{bmatrix}$$

A series of *properties* and a number of special cases can now be developed. Some of these are associated with the rules of algebra, numbered as in 13.1 above. The proofs are quite straight-forward. In the following $A = [a_{rs}]$, $B = [b_{rs}]$, $C = [c_{rs}]$, ... are all matrices of order $m \times n$.

(i) *Addition of matrices is commutative.* Rule (A3) of 13.1.

$$A + B = B + A$$

each being equal to C where $c_{rs} = a_{rs} + b_{rs} = b_{rs} + a_{rs}$

(ii) *Addition of more than two matrices.* The sum of A, B, C, ... is obtained by repeated application of the addition rule:

$$A + B + C... = [(a_{rs} + b_{rs} + c_{rs} + ...)]$$

(iii) *Addition of matrices is associative.* Rule (A2) of 13.1.

$$A + (B + C) = (A + B) + C$$

each being equal to D where $d_{rs} = a_{rs} + b_{rs} + c_{rs}$.

(iv) *Repeated addition* of the matrix A gives a result which agrees with multiplication of A by an integral $\lambda = N$ ($N = 1, 2, 3, ...$):

$$A + A = [2a_{rs}] = 2A$$
$$A + A + A = [3a_{rs}] = 3A$$

and so on.

(v) *Scalar multiplication* obeys rules (S2–5) of 13.1:

$$0 . A = 0 ; \quad 1 . A = A ; \quad \lambda(\mu A) = \lambda\mu A ;$$
$$\lambda(A + B) = \lambda A + \lambda B \quad \text{and} \quad (\lambda + \mu)A = \lambda A + \mu A.$$

In general, $\lambda A + \mu B + \nu C + ...$ is a matrix of order $m \times n$ with general element $(\lambda a_{rs} + \mu b_{rs} + \nu c_{rs} + ...)$.

(vi) *Addition of a zero matrix* leaves the original matrix unchanged:

$$A + 0 = 0 + A = A$$

Hence the zero matrix (of appropriate order) behaves as a zero element, rule (A4) of 13.1.

(vii) *Subtraction of two matrices.* Rule (A5) of 13.1. First the negative matrix is defined as scalar multiplication by (-1), i.e. $-A$ is A with the sign of all elements changed:

$$-A = [(-a_{rs})]$$

Then, subtraction is the addition of one matrix to the negative of the other:

$$A - B = A + (-B)$$

i.e. $$[a_{rs}] - [b_{rs}] = [(a_{rs} - b_{rs})]$$

In particular : $\quad \mathbf{A} - \mathbf{A} = \mathbf{A} + (-\mathbf{A}) = \mathbf{0}$

where $\mathbf{0}$ is the zero matrix of order $m \times n$.

These results agree with the definition of equality of matrices, since

$$\mathbf{A} - \mathbf{B} = \mathbf{0} \quad \text{implies} \quad \mathbf{A} = \mathbf{B}$$

EXERCISES 13.3

1. Prove the properties (i)–(vii) above, with particular reference to property (v).

2. Check that the definition of $(-\mathbf{A})$ in (vii) above is equivalent to $\mathbf{A} + (-\mathbf{A}) = \mathbf{0}$ (cf. rule (A5) of 13.1 above).

3. Show that $2\begin{bmatrix} 1 & 0 \\ 0 & 1 \end{bmatrix} - \begin{bmatrix} 1 & 0 \\ 0 & 1 \end{bmatrix} = \begin{bmatrix} 2 & 0 \\ 0 & 2 \end{bmatrix} - \begin{bmatrix} 1 & 0 \\ 0 & 1 \end{bmatrix} = \begin{bmatrix} 1 & 0 \\ 0 & 1 \end{bmatrix}$ Generalise.

4. Write $\mathbf{A} + \mathbf{B}$ and $\mathbf{A} - \mathbf{B}$ for $\mathbf{A} = \begin{bmatrix} 1 & 2 & 3 \\ 4 & 5 & 6 \\ 7 & 8 & 9 \end{bmatrix}$, $\mathbf{B} = \begin{bmatrix} 9 & 8 & 7 \\ 6 & 5 & 4 \\ 3 & 2 & 1 \end{bmatrix}$

5. Show that the rule for scalar multiplication $\lambda \mathbf{A}$ reduces to repeated addition of matrices as long as λ is rational of form $\frac{p}{q}$ (p and q integers).

13.4 Multiplication of Matrices

The next stage is to define a process of multiplication of matrices. This should include a unit element so that a matrix is unchanged when multiplied by unity. If it can be arranged that a matrix has a reciprocal, then division may be derived as the inverse of multiplication. The rules of algebra involved here are those denoted (M1–5) in 13.1 above, and rule (D) is relevant to addition and multiplication together. Some of the rules are found to be not satisfied by matrices and the inverse process (reciprocals and division) is postponed to a later section (13.7 below).

The results (4) and (5) of 13.2 above provide the necessary guidance in framing a definition of multiplication. The essential feature is the formation of inner products from the elements of the two matrices concerned (as defined in 12.8 above).

The *inner products* $\sum\limits_{p=1}^{k} a_{rp} b_{ps}$ ($r = 1, 2, \dots m$; $s = 1, 2, \dots n$) are $m \times n$ in number (one of each r and s) and each involves the sum of k products (one for each p) of an a and a b. The subscript p is a *dummy* and the subscripts r and s are *free*, serving to generate the different inner products in the whole set. The a's make up one matrix and the b's a second matrix :

$$\mathbf{A} = [a_{rp}] \quad \text{and} \quad \mathbf{B} = [b_{ps}]$$

They are to be taken **A** first and **B** second, not in the opposite sequence.

There are two things to consider in turn in writing inner products, and equally in writing products of matrices. The first is whether the matrices **A** and **B** are of appropriate order for writing the inner product at all. The inner product above can only be written if **A** is of order $m \times k$ and **B** of order $k \times n$, where the k is common to the two, while m and n can have any values. The k corresponds to the dummy subscript p and must be the same in **A** and **B** ; m and n correspond to the free subscripts. Hence the condition is that the number of columns in **A** must be the same as the number of rows in **B**. If this condition is satisfied then **A** can be said to be *conformable* with **B**. Conformable matrices of orders $(m \times k)$ and $(k \times n)$ give $(m \times n)$ inner products.

The second consideration is the formation of the inner product. The value $\sum\limits_{p=1}^{k} a_{rp} b_{ps}$ is formed by taking a *row* (rth) of **A** and a *column* (sth) of **B**, by matching the elements, and by adding their products. The essential thing is that a row of the first matrix **A** is taken with a column of the second matrix **B**—not the other way round. The inner product is written by going *across* **A** and *down* **B**, which can be described as the rule of " across and down " or " row into column ".

DEFINITION : $\mathbf{A} = [a_{rp}]$ is *conformable* with $\mathbf{B} = [b_{ps}]$ if **A** has as many columns as **B** has rows :

A of order $m \times k$ and **B** of order $k \times n$

for any m and n. The *product* **AB** is then the matrix $\mathbf{C} = [c_{rs}]$ of order $m \times n$, where c_{rs} is the inner product $\sum\limits_{p=1}^{k} a_{rp} b_{ps}$,

i.e. $\mathbf{C} = \mathbf{AB}$ implies $c_{rs} = \sum\limits_{p=1}^{k} a_{rp} b_{ps}$

An alternative expression of the definition is in terms of inner products of vectors. If **A** is of order $m \times k$ and **B** of order $k \times n$, then the (r, s)th element in the product **AB** is the inner product of the rth row of **A**, $_r = (a_{r1}, a_{r2}, \dots a_{rk})$, with the sth column of **B**, $\mathbf{b}_s = (b_{1s}, b_{2s}, \dots b_{ks})$. The essential thing is that these vectors have the same number of elements, i.e. **A** has as many columns as **B** has rows. Then the rule of " across and down ", or of " row by column ", implies that vectors across **A** are taken with vectors down **B**.

In applications of the definition, the first step is to check that the matrices to be multiplied are indeed conformable. For example, matrices **A** and **B** of (3×2) and (2×2) respectively are conformable and give a product **AB** of order (3×2). Put briefly : order (3×2) with order (2×2) gives order (3×2). The second step is to apply the rule of " across and down ". The product **AB** is obtained most easily by writing the definition in the form :

$$[a_{rp}] \times [b_{ps}] = [(\sum_{p=1}^{k} a_{rp} b_{ps})]$$

Any one element of the product comes from a *row* of **A** matched off with a *column* of **B** ; if the element is the (r, s)th, then it comes from the rth row of **A** and the sth column of **B**. For example :

$$\begin{bmatrix} 2 & 1 \\ 1 & 0 \\ 0 & 1 \end{bmatrix} \times \begin{bmatrix} 0 & 1 \\ -2 & 0 \end{bmatrix} = \begin{bmatrix} -2 & 2 \\ 0 & 1 \\ -2 & 0 \end{bmatrix}$$

The leading element in the product is the inner product formed from the first row $(2, 1)$ of **A** and the first column $(0, -2)$ of **B** :

$$2 \times 0 + 1 \times (-2) = -2$$

and similarly for the other elements. Other examples are :

Ex. (a). $\begin{bmatrix} 1 & 0 \\ 0 & 1 \end{bmatrix} \times \begin{bmatrix} 1 & 0 \\ 0 & 1 \end{bmatrix} = \begin{bmatrix} 1 & 0 \\ 0 & 1 \end{bmatrix}$; (2×2) with (2×2) gives (2×2).

Further : $\begin{bmatrix} a & b \\ c & d \end{bmatrix} \times \begin{bmatrix} 1 & 0 \\ 0 & 1 \end{bmatrix} = \begin{bmatrix} a & b \\ c & d \end{bmatrix}$

Ex. (b). $\begin{bmatrix} 1 & 2 \\ 3 & 4 \\ 5 & 6 \end{bmatrix} \times \begin{bmatrix} 0 \\ 1 \end{bmatrix} = \begin{bmatrix} 2 \\ 4 \\ 6 \end{bmatrix}$; (3×2) with (2×1) gives (3×1).

But $\begin{bmatrix} 0 \\ 1 \end{bmatrix} \times \begin{bmatrix} 1 & 2 \\ 3 & 4 \\ 5 & 5 \end{bmatrix}$ has no meaning, since (2×1) does not go with (3×2)

Ex. (c). $\begin{bmatrix} 1 & 2 \\ 3 & 4 \\ 5 & 6 \end{bmatrix} \times \begin{bmatrix} 0 & 1 & -1 \\ 1 & 0 & 1 \end{bmatrix} = \begin{bmatrix} 2 & 1 & 1 \\ 4 & 3 & 1 \\ 6 & 5 & 1 \end{bmatrix}$; (3×2) with (2×3) gives (3×3)

And $\begin{bmatrix} 0 & 1 & -1 \\ 1 & 0 & 1 \end{bmatrix} \times \begin{bmatrix} 1 & 2 \\ 3 & 4 \\ 5 & 6 \end{bmatrix} = \begin{bmatrix} -2 & -2 \\ 6 & 8 \end{bmatrix}$; (2×3) with (3×2) gives (2×2)

The *unit matrices* $\mathbf{I} = [\delta_{rs}]$ of various orders $n \times n$ do serve, in a sense, the purposes of an identity element (unity) in products of matrices. But there is a complication. If **A** is of order $m \times n$, let $\mathbf{I}_m$ and $\mathbf{I}_n$ denote unit matrices of order $m \times m$ and $n \times n$ respectively :

$$I_m A = A \quad \text{and} \quad A I_n = A$$

Hence it can be said that A is unchanged on multiplication by a unit matrix I—but I varies in its order according as the product is on the left or the right. Rule (M4) of 13.1 is not strictly valid ; there is not a *single* unity. The difficulty disappears in the case where A is square ; then $AI = IA = A$ for I of the same order as A.

The following *properties* of multiplication of matrices serve to make some essential points and to develop the rules of matrix algebra on the lines of 13.1 above. The proofs (where not given) are quite straightforward. The matrices used are $A = [a_{rs}]$, $B = [b_{rs}]$ and $C = [c_{rs}]$, of orders stated in the context.

(i) *Matrix products are not generally commutative*, i.e. $AB \neq BA$ except in special cases. See rule (M3) of 13.1.

The difference between AB and BA may arise because one of them is not defined at all (not conformable), or because they are of different orders, or because though of the same order, they have different elements. Suppose A is of order $(m \times k)$ and B of order $(k \times n)$, so that AB exists, of order $m \times n$. There are various possibilities.

(1) $m \neq n$. Here BA does not exist since $(k \times n)$ with $(m \times k)$ gives nothing as long as m and n are different ; see Ex. (*b*) above.

(2) $m = n \neq k$. Here BA does exist, since $(k \times n)$ with $(n \times k)$ gives $(k \times k)$. But AB is of order $n \times n$ and BA is of order $k \times k$; they are of different orders and cannot be equal, see Ex. (*c*) above.

(3) $m = n = k$. Here BA exists and is of the same order $(n \times n)$ as AB. Hence AB and BA *could* be equal in this case when both A and B are square of the same order. In general, however, they are not equal since their elements are not formed in the same way and so are different :

$$AB = [\sum_{p=1}^{n} a_{rp} b_{ps}] \quad \text{and} \quad BA = [\sum_{p=1}^{n} b_{rp} a_{ps}]$$

It is still only in *special cases of square matrices* A and B that $AB = BA$. For example, if A and the unit matrix I are taken of order $n \times n$, then $AI = IA$, both being A. (It is not true that $AI = IA$ for A of order $m \times n$, for then I would need to be of order $n \times n$ on its first appearance, and of order $m \times m$ on its second.)

(ii) *Products of several matrices* can be sufficiently illustrated by three matrices A, B and C. To get the product ABC (with matrices in this sequence, and this sequence only), it is not enough that the three matrices are conformable in pairs. It is necessary that $\mathbf{A}$ is conformable with $\mathbf{B}$ and then $\mathbf{AB}$ with $\mathbf{C}$. The condition, however, is very simple : $\mathbf{ABC}$ exists if the orders are :

$$\mathbf{A}\ (m \times k) \qquad \mathbf{B}\ (k \times j) \qquad \mathbf{C}\ (j \times n)$$

and $\mathbf{ABC}$ is then of order $(m \times n)$. Here there are two free subscripts (m and n giving the order of $\mathbf{ABC}$) and two dummy subscripts (k and j), the elements of $\mathbf{ABC}$ involving double summation. If $\mathbf{ABC}$ is taken from $(\mathbf{AB})\mathbf{C}$, the double summation arises as follows. $\mathbf{AB}$ is of order $(m \times j)$ with general element $\sum\limits_{p=1}^{k} a_{rp}b_{pq}$ ($r = 1, 2, \dots m$; $q = 1, 2, \dots j$); $\mathbf{C}$ is of order $(j \times n)$ with general element c_{qs} ($q = 1, 2, \dots j$; $s = 1, 2, \dots n$). Hence, $\mathbf{ABC}$ is of order $(m \times n)$ with general element

$$\sum_{q=1}^{j} \sum_{p=1}^{k} a_{rp}b_{pq}c_{qs} \quad\dots\dots\dots\dots\dots\dots\dots\dots\dots\dots\dots(1)$$

This double sum must be carefully interpreted (see Ex. 5 below). It is made up from $\sum\limits_{q=1} c_{qs}(\sum\limits_{p=1}^{k} a_{rp}b_{pq})$. Here, r and s are free subscripts. The sum of k terms $\sum\limits_{p=1}^{k} a_{rp}b_{pq}$ has j different values according to the q taken ($q = 1, 2, \dots j$) while r is free ; each of these is matched with the corresponding c_{qs} for $q = 1, 2, \dots j$ (s being free) and the products summed over $q = 1, 2, \dots j$. Hence, in (1), there are j terms each consisting of a single c multiplied by a sum of k terms ; all told, there are $k \times j$ terms in (1), generated by p ranging from 1 to k and q ranging from 1 to j.

(iii) *Matrix products are associative.* See rule (M2) of 13.1. As long as $\mathbf{A}$, $\mathbf{B}$ and $\mathbf{C}$ are matrices which conform, then :

$$\mathbf{A}(\mathbf{BC}) = (\mathbf{AB})\mathbf{C}$$

$(\mathbf{AB})\mathbf{C}$ is already obtained, (1) above, with general term :

$$\sum_{q=1}^{j} (\sum_{p=1}^{k} a_{rp}b_{pq})c_{qs} = \sum_{q=1}^{j} \sum_{p=1}^{k} a_{rp}b_{pq}c_{qs}$$

$\mathbf{A}(\mathbf{BC})$ is obtained similarly, with general term

$$\sum_{p=1}^{k} a_{rp}(\sum_{q=1}^{j} b_{pq}c_{qs}) = \sum_{q=1}^{j} \sum_{p=1}^{k} a_{rp}b_{pq}c_{qs}$$

(iv) *Matrices are distributive* with respect to addition and multiplication. See rule (D) of 13.1. If **A** is conformable with **B** and with **C** (so that **AB** and **AC** exist) and if **B** and **C** are of the same order (so that **B** + **C** exists), then :

$$A(B+C) = AB + AC$$

For this result, if **A** is of order $m \times k$, then **B** and **C** must each be of order $k \times n$. The result $A(B+C)$ or $AB + AC$ is of order $m \times n$.

(v) *Cancellation* with matrices is not generally possible. See rule (M5′) of 13.1. If **AB** = **0**, the zero matrix of appropriate order, it does *not* follow that either **A** = **0** or **B** = **0**.

It is sufficient to quote a case :

$$\begin{bmatrix} 1 & 1 \\ 0 & 0 \end{bmatrix} \times \begin{bmatrix} 1 & 1 \\ -1 & -1 \end{bmatrix} = \begin{bmatrix} 0 & 0 \\ 0 & 0 \end{bmatrix} = 0$$

but neither of the matrices on the left is a zero matrix.

In the same way, but more generally, if **A** is conformable with **B** and with **C** so that **AB** = **AC**, it does *not* follow that **B** = **C**.

(vi) *Multiplication by zero matrices.* The difficulty just met does not arise when the question is put in reverse. The product of any matrix and a conformable zero matrix is another zero matrix :

$$A0_{nn} = 0_{mn} = 0_{mm}A$$

where the subscripts indicate the orders of the zero matrices. In particular, when **A** is square of order $n \times n$, then only one zero matrix (order $n \times n$) is needed : $A0 = 0A = 0$.

The use of the unit matrix **I** can be extended by employing various mutations of **I** of the kind described in 12.6, Ex. 3 and 4, above. Define $E_{(rs)}$ as the matrix obtained from **I** by interchange of the rth and sth rows, $H_{(rs)}$ as the matrix obtained by substituting h for the zero in the (r, s)th place in **I**, and $K_{(r)}$ as the matrix obtained by substituting k for the element 1 in the rth row and column of **I**. All these matrices are square but they can be of any order, as appropriate to the operations involved. They can be applied, by multiplication, to a given matrix **A** of order $m \times n$ with the results as tabulated at top of page 420.

The important feature of these results is that the matrix product is of the form **PAQ**, when **P** is a square matrix of order $m \times m$ and **Q** is a square matrix of order $n \times n$. Various " crosses " of the above results can be

Matrix	Result : **A** with
$\mathbf{E}_{(rs)}\mathbf{AI}$ $\mathbf{IAE}_{(uv)}$ $\mathbf{E}_{(rs)}\mathbf{AE}_{(uv)}$	rth and sth rows interchanged uth and vth columns interchanged rth and sth rows *and* uth and vth columns interchanged
$\mathbf{H}_{(rs)}\mathbf{AI}$ $\mathbf{IAH}_{(uv)}$ $\mathbf{H}_{(rs)}\mathbf{AH}_{(uv)}$	multiple h of sth row added to rth row multiple h of uth column added to vth column multiple h of sth row added to rth row *and* multiple h of uth column added to vth column
$\mathbf{K}_{(r)}\mathbf{AI}$ $\mathbf{IAK}_{(u)}$ $\mathbf{K}_{(r)}\mathbf{AK}_{(u)}$	rth row multiplied by k uth column multiplied by k rth row and uth column multiplied by k

made, e.g. $\mathbf{E}_{(rs)}\mathbf{AK}_{(u)}$, with obvious interpretations. They can also be extended to such results as $(\mathbf{K}_{(r)}\mathbf{E}_{(rs)})\mathbf{AH}_{(uv)}$, again with clear interpretations. They are still of the form **PAQ**, which can therefore represent the result of performing all the three types of operation, singly or together, on the matrix **A**. This is a result which will be used later on (13.8 below).

The position now reached can be surveyed. Let S_{mn} be the set of all matrices of *given* order $m \times n$. It appears from 13.3 above that S_{mn} is perfectly well-behaved under the operations of addition and scalar multiplication. All the relevant rules given in 13.1 are obeyed. In short, like vectors, matrices of fixed order form a set which is a *vector space*. As for products, the position is equally simple—*no* matrices can be multiplied in $S_{mn}(m \neq n)$ and *all* matrices can be multiplied in $S_{mn}(m=n)$. Hence, $S_{mn}(m \neq n)$ is a vector space—with sums and scalar products but no products—and this is the end of the story for such matrices.

Multiplication of matrices can be pursued in two ways. First, consider the particular set S_{nn} of square matrices of *given* order $n \times n$. These matrices are better-behaved than rectangular matrices generally and three points can be made at once. S_{nn} is still a vector space under addition and scalar multiplication. All matrices can be multiplied in S_{nn} which is closed under multiplication. Finally, S_{nn} has an identity **I** of order $n \times n$; for any **A** of S : $\mathbf{AI}=\mathbf{IA}=\mathbf{A}$. Much of the rest of the chapter is concerned with following up the properties of square matrices.

Secondly, consider the comprehensive set S of all matrices of all orders. This S is *not* a vector space since two matrices of S cannot generally be added. Neither is S closed under multiplication since not all matrices are conformable. It can be said that *some* matrices of S can be multiplied to give another matrix and it is of interest to see whether the rules (M2–5) hold for these. The associative rule (M2) is true but not generally the commutative rule (M3). The identity rule (M4) holds only in the loose form already described. But this is generally enough in practice, since a unit matrix **I** of *appropriate* order can always be slipped into any product of matrices without changing it. For example:

$$\mathbf{AB} = \mathbf{IAB} = \mathbf{AIB} = \mathbf{ABI}$$

as long as **I** is allowed to change its order from one appearance to the next. Finally, the inverse rule (M5) does not generally hold.

EXERCISES 13.4

1. Prove the properties (iv) and (vi) above.

2. In the product **AB**, **A** is square of order $m \times m$ and **B** is of order $m \times n$. Can **BA** now be defined?

3. Show that the distribution law $\mathbf{A(B+C)} = \mathbf{AB} + \mathbf{AC}$ can be applied also to $\mathbf{(B+C)A}$ but with a different result.

4. Form as many products as you can from pairs of

$$\mathbf{A} = \begin{bmatrix} 0 & 1 & -1 \\ 1 & 0 & 1 \end{bmatrix} \quad \mathbf{B} = \begin{bmatrix} 1 & 2 \\ 3 & 4 \\ 5 & 6 \\ 7 & 8 \end{bmatrix} \quad \mathbf{C} = \begin{bmatrix} 1 & 2 & 3 \\ 4 & 5 & 6 \\ 7 & 8 & 9 \end{bmatrix} \quad \mathbf{D} = \begin{bmatrix} 0 & 1 & 2 & 3 \\ 4 & 0 & 5 & 6 \\ 7 & 8 & 0 & 9 \end{bmatrix}$$

5. With the matrices of the previous exercise, write the product **CDB** as a matrix of order 3×2, and show each element as a double sum $\Sigma\Sigma_{pq} c_{rp} d_{pq} b_{qs}$. Express the double sum in full to check the number of terms and to verify that

$$\mathbf{(CD)B} = \mathbf{C(DB)}$$

6. With the same matrices, write **ACDB** as a matrix. Can you also write **CDBA**, **CDAB** and **DBAC**?

7. If $\mathbf{AB} = \mathbf{BA}$, show that the two matrices must be square and of the same order but that the converse is not at all necessarily true. Examine the product of
$$\mathbf{A} = \begin{bmatrix} 2 & 1 \\ -1 & 1 \end{bmatrix} \text{ and } \mathbf{B} = \begin{bmatrix} 1 & -1 \\ 1 & 2 \end{bmatrix} \text{ showing that } \mathbf{AB} = \mathbf{BA} = 3\mathbf{I}. \text{ Check that}$$
$|\mathbf{A}| = |\mathbf{B}| = 3$, $|\mathbf{AB}| = 9$.

8. If **A**, **B**, **C**, ... are all square matrices of the same order, show that the product of any number of them in any sequence always exists as a matrix of the same order.

9. Define $\mathbf{A}^2 = \mathbf{AA}$, $\mathbf{A}^3 = \mathbf{AAA}$, ... when **A** is square; check that $\mathbf{AA}^2 = \mathbf{A}^2\mathbf{A} = \mathbf{A}^3$ and prove that $\mathbf{A}^m\mathbf{A}^n = \mathbf{A}^{m+n}$ (m, n integers). Illustrate with $\mathbf{A} = \begin{bmatrix} 1 & 2 \\ 3 & 4 \end{bmatrix}$

If $\mathbf{B} = \begin{bmatrix} 0 & 1 & 0 \\ 0 & 0 & 1 \\ 0 & 0 & 0 \end{bmatrix}$ show that $\mathbf{B}^n = 0$ for $n \geqslant 3$.

10. If $\mathbf{A} = \begin{bmatrix} a^2 & 1 \\ 0 & a^2 \end{bmatrix}$ and $\mathbf{B} = \begin{bmatrix} b & 1 \\ 0 & b \end{bmatrix}$, find $\mathbf{C} = \mathbf{AB}$. Hence write $\mathbf{C}^2$ and $\mathbf{C}^3$ and deduce a general expression for $\mathbf{C}^n$ (n integer).

11. If $\mathbf{A}$ and $\mathbf{B}$ are square matrices of the same order, show that :

$$(\mathbf{A}+\mathbf{B})^2 \neq \mathbf{A}^2 + 2\mathbf{AB} + \mathbf{B}^2 \; ; \; (\mathbf{A}+\mathbf{B})(\mathbf{A}-\mathbf{B}) \neq (\mathbf{A}-\mathbf{B})(\mathbf{A}+\mathbf{B}) \neq \mathbf{A}^2 - \mathbf{B}^2$$

What are the correct expressions for $(\mathbf{A}+\mathbf{B})^2$, $(\mathbf{A}+\mathbf{B})(\mathbf{A}-\mathbf{B})$ and $(\mathbf{A}-\mathbf{B})(\mathbf{A}+\mathbf{B})$?

12. The diagonal matrix $\bar{\lambda}$ is made up from the vector $\lambda = (\lambda_1 \lambda_2 \; \dots \; \lambda_n)$. If $\mathbf{A} = [a_{rs}]$ is a square matrix of order $n \times n$, show that :

$$\bar{\lambda}\mathbf{A} = \begin{bmatrix} \lambda_1 a_{11} & \lambda_1 a_{12} & \dots & \lambda_1 a_{1n} \\ \lambda_2 a_{21} & \lambda_2 a_{22} & \dots & \lambda_2 a_{2n} \\ \dots\dots\dots\dots\dots \\ \lambda_n a_{n1} & \lambda_n a_{n2} & \dots & \lambda_n a_{nn} \end{bmatrix} \; ; \; \mathbf{A}\bar{\lambda} = \begin{bmatrix} \lambda_1 a_{11} & \lambda_2 a_{12} & \dots & \lambda_n a_{1n} \\ \lambda_1 a_{21} & \lambda_2 a_{22} & \dots & \lambda_n a_{2n} \\ \dots\dots\dots\dots\dots \\ \lambda_1 a_{n1} & \lambda_2 a_{n2} & \dots & \lambda_n a_{nn} \end{bmatrix}$$

If $\bar{\lambda}$ is also scalar $(\lambda_1 = \lambda_2 = \dots = \lambda_n = \lambda)$, show that $\bar{\lambda} = \lambda\mathbf{I}$; what is the product $\bar{\lambda}\mathbf{A}$ in this case? Use these results to show that, if $\mathbf{A}$ and $\mathbf{B}$ are square matrices of the same order, then (a) $\mathbf{AB} \neq \mathbf{BA}$ for $\mathbf{B}$ a diagonal matrix unless it is also scalar, and (b) $\mathbf{AB} = \mathbf{BA}$ for $\mathbf{A}$ and $\mathbf{B}$ both diagonal matrices.

13. If $\mathbf{A} = \begin{bmatrix} a & x_1 & x_2 \\ \alpha_1 & a_{11} & a_{12} \\ \alpha_2 & a_{21} & a_{22} \end{bmatrix}$ and $\mathbf{B} = \begin{bmatrix} b & y_1 & y_2 \\ \beta_1 & b_{11} & b_{12} \\ \beta_2 & b_{21} & b_{22} \end{bmatrix}$, show that :

$$\mathbf{AB} = \left[\begin{array}{c|c} (ab + \mathbf{x}'\boldsymbol{\beta}) & (a\mathbf{y}' + \mathbf{x}'\mathbf{B}^*) \\ \hline (\alpha b + \mathbf{A}^*\boldsymbol{\beta}) & (\alpha\mathbf{y}' + \mathbf{A}^*\mathbf{B}^*) \end{array} \right]$$

where $\mathbf{x}' = [x_1 x_2]$, $\boldsymbol{\alpha} = \begin{bmatrix} \alpha_1 \\ \alpha_2 \end{bmatrix}$, $\mathbf{A}^* = \begin{bmatrix} a_{11} & a_{12} \\ a_{21} & a_{22} \end{bmatrix}$ and similarly for $\mathbf{y}'$, $\boldsymbol{\beta}$ and $\mathbf{B}^*$.

14. *Multiplication of partitioned matrices.* Show that the result of the previous exercise is a particular case of :

$$\mathbf{AB} = \left[\begin{array}{c|c} \mathbf{A}_{11} & \mathbf{A}_{12} \\ \hline \mathbf{A}_{21} & \mathbf{A}_{22} \end{array} \right] \left[\begin{array}{c|c} \mathbf{B}_{11} & \mathbf{B}_{12} \\ \hline \mathbf{B}_{21} & \mathbf{B}_{22} \end{array} \right] = \left[\begin{array}{c|c} \mathbf{A}_{11}\mathbf{B}_{11} + \mathbf{A}_{12}\mathbf{B}_{21} & \mathbf{A}_{11}\mathbf{B}_{12} + \mathbf{A}_{12}\mathbf{B}_{22} \\ \hline \mathbf{A}_{21}\mathbf{B}_{11} + \mathbf{A}_{22}\mathbf{B}_{21} & \mathbf{A}_{21}\mathbf{B}_{12} + \mathbf{A}_{22}\mathbf{B}_{22} \end{array} \right]$$

provided that the sub-matrices like $\mathbf{A}_{11}$ and $\mathbf{B}_{11}$ are appropriately comformable. This result is true generally ; interpret the multiplication of matrices by blocks as an extension of the ordinary multiplication rule. Illustrate by showing that :

$$[\mathbf{A}_1 \mid \mathbf{A}_2] \left[\begin{array}{c} \mathbf{B}_1 \\ \hline \mathbf{B}_2 \end{array} \right] = \mathbf{A}_1\mathbf{B}_1 + \mathbf{A}_2\mathbf{B}_2$$

and indicate what orders $\mathbf{A}_1$, $\mathbf{A}_2$, $\mathbf{B}_1$ and $\mathbf{B}_2$ must have for this to be possible. Express $\mathbf{A}[\mathbf{B}_1 \mid \mathbf{B}_2]$ similarly.

13.5 Transpose of a Matrix

A new process, not to be found in elementary algebra, can now be introduced into matrix algebra. A given matrix of order $m \times n$ consists of $m \times n$ elements arranged in m rows and n columns. The same $m \times n$ elements can be arranged differently, in n rows and m columns, by simply interchanging the rows and columns. The result is a different matrix of order $n \times m$. It is called the transpose of the original matrix.

DEFINITION : The *transpose* of a matrix $\mathbf{A} = [a_{rs}]$ of order $m \times n$ is the matrix $\mathbf{A}' = [a_{sr}]$ of order $n \times m$.

The notation is simple ; the addition of a prime to any matrix indicates transposition of rows and columns, e.g. $(\mathbf{AB})'$ is the product matrix $\mathbf{AB}$ with rows and columns transposed. The following *examples* illustrate :

Ex. (*a*) $\mathbf{A} = \begin{bmatrix} 1 & 2 \\ 3 & 4 \\ 5 & 6 \end{bmatrix}, \mathbf{A}' = \begin{bmatrix} 1 & 3 & 5 \\ 2 & 4 & 6 \end{bmatrix}$

Ex. (*b*). $\mathbf{a} = \begin{bmatrix} 1 \\ 2 \\ 3 \end{bmatrix}, \mathbf{a}' = \begin{bmatrix} 1 & 2 & 3 \end{bmatrix}$ (as in 12.7 above).

Ex. (*c*) $\mathbf{I} = \begin{bmatrix} 1 & 0 \\ 0 & 1 \end{bmatrix}, \mathbf{I}' = \begin{bmatrix} 1 & 0 \\ 0 & 1 \end{bmatrix} = \mathbf{I}$

A number of *properties* and particular cases of transposed matrices can be derived :

(i) *Transpose of a transpose* is the original matrix, i.e. $(\mathbf{A}')' = \mathbf{A}$. This is easily extended ; an even number of transposes of $\mathbf{A}$ gives $\mathbf{A}$, an odd number of transposes gives $\mathbf{A}'$.

(ii) *Transpose of a sum.* $(\mathbf{A} + \mathbf{B})' = \mathbf{A}' + \mathbf{B}'$
where $\mathbf{A}$ and $\mathbf{B}$ are matrices of the same order.

(iii) *Transpose of a product.* $(\mathbf{AB})' = \mathbf{B}'\mathbf{A}'$
where $\mathbf{A}$ of order $m \times k$ is conformable with $\mathbf{B}$ of order $k \times n$. It is to be noted that transposition of a product inverts the sequence of the matrices. This is checked by observing that $\mathbf{B}'$ of order $n \times k$ is conformable with $\mathbf{A}'$ of order $k \times m$, and not the other way round. The product matrix $\mathbf{AB}$ of order $m \times n$ is obtained from $\mathbf{A}$ conformable with $\mathbf{B}$; the transpose $(\mathbf{AB})'$ is of order $n \times m$ and obtained from $\mathbf{B}'$ conformable with $\mathbf{A}'$.

(iv) *Transpose of a unit matrix.* If $\mathbf{I}$ is the unit matrix of order n, then $\mathbf{I}' = \mathbf{I}$. This is illustrated by Ex. (*c*) above.

Symmetric and skew-symmetric matrices are particular cases of square matrices, as defined in 12.6 (iv) above, and they can be handled easily in terms of transposes. The property of a *symmetric matrix* $\mathbf{A}$ is that $\mathbf{A} = \mathbf{A}'$; the corresponding property of a *skew-symmetric matrix* is that $\mathbf{A} = -\mathbf{A}'$.

Among many results for symmetric and skew-symmetric matrices, which are of interest, the following can be given as examples. $\mathbf{A}$ is *any* square matrix with transpose $\mathbf{A}'$. Let $\mathbf{B} = \mathbf{AA}', \mathbf{C} = \mathbf{A} + \mathbf{A}'$ and $\mathbf{D} = \mathbf{A} - \mathbf{A}'$. Then :

$$\mathbf{B}' = (\mathbf{AA}')' = (\mathbf{A}')'\mathbf{A}' = \mathbf{AA}' = \mathbf{B}$$
$$\mathbf{C}' = (\mathbf{A} + \mathbf{A}')' = \mathbf{A}' + (\mathbf{A}')' = \mathbf{A}' + \mathbf{A} = \mathbf{A} + \mathbf{A}' = \mathbf{C}$$
$$\mathbf{D}' = (\mathbf{A} - \mathbf{A}')' = \mathbf{A}' - (\mathbf{A}')' = \mathbf{A}' - \mathbf{A} = -(\mathbf{A} - \mathbf{A}') = -\mathbf{D}$$

Hence, both $\mathbf{AA'}$ and $\mathbf{A+A'}$ are always symmetric, and $\mathbf{A-A'}$ is always skew-symmetric, for any square matrix $\mathbf{A}$.

EXERCISES 13.5

1. Prove the properties (ii) and (iii) above.

2. Extend property (iii) to show that $(\mathbf{ABC})' = \mathbf{C'B'A'}$ and generalise.

3. If $\mathbf{A} = \begin{bmatrix} 1 & 2 & 3 \\ 4 & 5 & 6 \\ 7 & 8 & 9 \end{bmatrix}$, write the matrix $\mathbf{AA'}$ and check that it is symmetric.

4. Show that $\mathbf{A}^2 = \mathbf{AA}$ is symmetric when $\mathbf{A}$ is either symmetric or skew-symmetric.

5. With the definitions given at the end of 13.4 above, show that $\mathbf{E'}_{(rs)} = \mathbf{E}_{(rs)}$ ($\mathbf{E}_{(rs)}$ symmetric) and that $\mathbf{H'}_{(rs)} = \mathbf{H}_{(sr)}$.

13.6 Multiplication of Vectors and Matrices

When vectors are written as matrices of one row or of one column (12.7 above), the rules of matrix algebra apply to them as to any other matrices. In particular, the multiplication rule gives the product of two vectors or of a vector and a matrix of any order, provided only that the vectors and matrices are conformable. Some of the results are so useful, however, that they merit separate treatment.

Several general cases can be examined :

(i) *Product of two vectors.* The vectors must be of the same order n. Let them be $\mathbf{x} = \{x_s\}$ and $\mathbf{y} = \{y_s\}$ as column vectors and $\mathbf{x'} = [x_s]$ and $\mathbf{y'} = [y_s]$ as row vectors ($s = 1, 2, \dots n$).

The pair $\mathbf{x'}$ and $\mathbf{y}$ are conformable, of order $1 \times n$ and $n \times 1$ respectively. Their product is a matrix of order 1×1; this consists of one element only, i.e. it is a scalar. Equally, the pair $\mathbf{y'}$ and $\mathbf{x}$ are conformable and the product is again a scalar. On application of the multiplication rule, it is found that the two products have the same value :

$$\mathbf{x'y} = \mathbf{y'x} = \sum_{s=1}^{n} x_s y_s$$

The scalar $(x_1 y_1 + x_2 y_2 + \dots + x_n y_n)$ is either the product $\mathbf{x'y}$ or the product $\mathbf{y'x}$; this is the inner product already considered (12.4 above) but in a new notation. As a particular case : $\mathbf{x'x} = \sum_{s=1}^{n} x_s^2$. A sum of squares is the product of a vector and its transpose.

(ii) *Product of a matrix and column vector.* Write the matrix $\mathbf{A} = [a_{rs}]$ of order $m \times n$ and let the column vector be $\mathbf{x} = \{x_s\}$ of order n. Here $= 1, 2, \dots m$ and $s = 1, 2, \dots n$.

The pair $\mathbf{A}$ and $\mathbf{x}$ are conformable, of order $m \times n$ and $n \times 1$ respectively. Their product is a matrix of order $m \times 1$, i.e. a column vector of order m :

$$\mathbf{Ax} = \sum_{s=1}^{n} a_{rs} x_s \quad (r=1, 2, \dots m)$$

If the product is denoted by the vector $\mathbf{y} = \{y_r\}$ of order m $(r=1, 2, \dots m)$ then

$$\mathbf{y} = \mathbf{Ax}$$

which means
$$\begin{bmatrix} y_1 \\ y_2 \\ \dots \\ y_m \end{bmatrix} = \begin{bmatrix} a_{11} & a_{12} & \dots & a_{1n} \\ a_{21} & a_{22} & \dots & a_{2n} \\ \dots & & & \\ a_{m1} & a_{m2} & \dots & a_{mn} \end{bmatrix} \begin{bmatrix} x_1 \\ x_2 \\ \dots \\ x_n \end{bmatrix}$$

and this in its turn stands for the linear transformation :

$$y_r = \sum_{s=1}^{n} a_{rs} x_s \quad (r=1, 2, \dots m)$$

from the n variables x_s to the m variables y_r.

The same pair in reverse order, $\mathbf{x}$ and $\mathbf{A}$, are not conformable. Matrices of order $(n \times 1)$ with $(m \times n)$ produce nothing. Hence $\mathbf{xA}$ is a product which does not exist.

(iii) *Product of a matrix and row vector.* Take the same matrix $\mathbf{A} = [a_{rs}]$ of order $m \times n$ with a row vector $\mathbf{y}' = [y_r]$ of order m.

The pair $\mathbf{y}'$ and $\mathbf{A}$ are now conformable (but not the pair $\mathbf{A}$ and $\mathbf{y}'$). For matrices of order $(1 \times m)$ with $(m \times n)$ produce a matrix of order $(1 \times n)$. The product is a row vector of order n :

$$\mathbf{y}'\mathbf{A} = \sum_{r=1}^{m} y_r a_{rs} \quad (s=1, 2, \dots n)$$

If the product vector is denoted by $\mathbf{x}' = [x_s]$, then :

$$\mathbf{x}' = \mathbf{y}'\mathbf{A}$$

i.e.
$$\begin{bmatrix} x_1 x_2 \dots x_n \end{bmatrix} = \begin{bmatrix} y_1 y_2 \dots y_m \end{bmatrix} \begin{bmatrix} a_{11} a_{12} & \dots & a_{1n} \\ a_{21} a_{22} & \dots & a_{2n} \\ \dots & & \\ a_{m1} a_{m2} & \dots & a_{mn} \end{bmatrix}$$

and this in its turn stands for $x_s = \sum_{r=1}^{m} y_r a_{rs} \ (s=1, 2, \dots n)$.

(iv) *Product of a matrix with row and column vectors.* With the same matrix $\mathbf{A} = [a_{rs}]$, of order $m \times n$, let the column vector be $\mathbf{x} = \{x_s\}$ of order n and the row vector $\mathbf{y}' = [y_r]$, of order m $(r=1, 2, \dots m, s=1, 2, \dots n)$.

The product $\mathbf{y}'\mathbf{A}$ is obtained, as in (iii), as a row vector of order n and this can be multiplied, as in (i), by $\mathbf{x}$ as a column vector of order n. Hence the product $\mathbf{y'Ax}$ can be written as a scalar. This fact can be checked by noting the orders of the matrices in $\mathbf{y'Ax}$; this involves matrices of orders $(1 \times m)$ with $(m \times n)$ with $(n \times 1)$ and the result is of order 1×1, or a scalar.

It remains to obtain the value of the scalar $\mathbf{y'Ax}$. The general element in the row vector $\mathbf{z'} = \mathbf{y'A}$ is $z_s = \sum_{r=1}^{m} y_r a_{rs}$ $(s = 1, 2, \dots n)$. This is matched with the general element in the column vector $\mathbf{x}$, i.e. x_s $(s = 1, 2, \dots n)$. The product $\mathbf{y'Ax} = \mathbf{z'x}$ and so :

$$\mathbf{y'Ax} = \sum_{s=1}^{n} x_s \left(\sum_{r=1}^{m} y_r a_{rs} \right)$$

i.e.
$$\mathbf{y'Ax} = \sum_{s=1}^{n} \sum_{r=1}^{m} a_{rs} x_s y_r$$
$$= a_{11}x_1y_1 + a_{12}x_2y_1 + \dots + a_{1n}x_ny_1$$
$$+ a_{21}x_1y_2 + a_{22}x_2y_2 + \dots + a_{2n}x_ny_2$$
$$\dots\dots\dots\dots\dots\dots\dots\dots\dots\dots\dots\dots$$
$$+ a_{m1}x_1y_m + a_{m2}x_2y_m + \dots + a_{mn}x_ny_m$$

This is a bilinear form (see 14.5 below). An innovation introduced by products of matrices and vectors is that they can represent bilinear and quadratic forms (see Ex. 4 below).

There are also some particular cases involving vectors of special forms :

(v) *Unit vectors.* The unit vectors of order n are

$$(\delta_{r1}, \delta_{r2}, \dots \delta_{rn}) \quad (r = 1, 2, \dots n)$$

where δ_{rs} is the Kronecker delta. All the elements are 0 except that 1 appears in one place (12.3 above). These can now be written as column and row vectors :

$$\boldsymbol{\epsilon}_s = \{\delta_{rs}\} = \begin{bmatrix} \delta_{1s} \\ \delta_{2s} \\ \dots \\ \delta_{ns} \end{bmatrix} \quad \text{and} \quad \boldsymbol{\epsilon}_r' = [\delta_{rs}] = [\delta_{r1}, \delta_{r2}, \dots \delta_{rn}]$$

In terms of the unit matrix $\mathbf{I} = [\delta_{rs}]$, $\boldsymbol{\epsilon}_s$ is the sth column and $\boldsymbol{\epsilon}_r'$ is the rth row.

Let $x_1, x_2, \dots x_n$ be any given set of n values, making up a column vector $\mathbf{x} = \{x_s\}$ and a row vector $\mathbf{x'} = [x_r]$. Then each of these vectors can be shown as a sum :

$$\mathbf{x} = \sum_{s=1}^{n} x_s \boldsymbol{\epsilon}_s$$

and
$$\mathbf{x'} = \sum_{r=1}^{n} x_r \boldsymbol{\epsilon}_r'$$

Any vector in space of n dimensions can be expressed in terms of the unit vectors which " span " the space. This is a result given already, as a linear combination of vectors, in 12.5 above.

(vi) *The sum of elements of a vector.* The vectors comprising n elements each of value 1 are :

$$\{1\} = \begin{bmatrix} 1 \\ 1 \\ \cdots \\ 1 \end{bmatrix} \quad \text{and} \quad [1] = [1 \quad 1 \quad \ldots \quad 1]$$

Multiplication by such a vector performs the process of adding the elements of any given vector $\mathbf{x} = \{x_s\}$ or $\mathbf{x}' = [x_r]$ of order n. The results are :

$$\mathbf{x}'\{1\} = [1]\,\mathbf{x} = \sum_{r=1}^{n} x_r$$

(vii) *The sum of elements in rows or columns of a matrix.* The same vectors $\{1\}$ and $[1]$ serve to add the elements in a given matrix $\mathbf{A} = [a_{rs}]$ of order $m \times n$, either by rows or by columns. The results are :

$$\mathbf{A}\{1\} = \{\sum_s a_{rs}\} \quad \text{and} \quad [1]\mathbf{A} = [\sum_r a_{rs}]$$

where $\{1\}$ is of order n and $[1]$ of order m. Hence :

The sums of the rows of the matrix $\mathbf{A} = [a_{rs}]$ *of order* $m \times n$ *make up a column vector of order* m :

$$\{\sum a_{rs}\} = \mathbf{A}\{1\}$$

and the sums of the columns of $\mathbf{A}$ *make up a row vector of order* n :

$$[\sum a_{rs}] = [1]\mathbf{A}$$

For example, if the entries in a double table of the ordinary statistical form are taken as the elements of $\mathbf{A} = [a_{rs}]$, then the marginal (total) column of the table is $\mathbf{A}\{1\}$ and the marginal (total) row of the table is $[1]\mathbf{A}$.

(viii) *Diagonal matrices.* When a vector $\lambda = (\lambda_1, \lambda_2, \ldots \lambda_n)$ of order n is written as the principal diagonal of a matrix, other elements being zero, the result is a diagonal matrix of order $n \times n$:

$$\bar{\lambda} = \begin{bmatrix} \lambda_1 & 0 & \ldots & 0 \\ 0 & \lambda_2 & \ldots & 0 \\ \cdots & \cdots & \cdots & \cdots \\ 0 & 0 & \ldots & \lambda_n \end{bmatrix}$$

as given in 12.6 (iii) above. The product of such a diagonal matrix and any square matrix $\mathbf{A} = [a_{rs}]$ of order $n \times n$ gives :

$$\bar{\lambda}\mathbf{A} = \begin{bmatrix} \lambda_1 a_{11} & \lambda_1 a_{12} & \ldots & \lambda_1 a_{1n} \\ \lambda_2 a_{21} & \lambda_2 a_{22} & \ldots & \lambda_2 a_{2n} \\ \ldots\ldots\ldots\ldots\ldots\ldots\ldots \\ \lambda_n a_{n1} & \lambda_n a_{n2} & \ldots & \lambda_n a_{nn} \end{bmatrix}$$

i.e. the matrix $\mathbf{A}$ with rows multiplied successively by $\lambda_1, \lambda_2, \ldots \lambda_n$. Again :

$$\mathbf{A}\bar{\lambda} = \begin{bmatrix} \lambda_1 a_{11} & \lambda_2 a_{12} & \ldots & \lambda_n a_{1n} \\ \lambda_1 a_{21} & \lambda_2 a_{22} & \ldots & \lambda_n a_{2n} \\ \ldots\ldots\ldots\ldots\ldots\ldots\ldots \\ \lambda_1 a_{n1} & \lambda_2 a_{n2} & \ldots & \lambda_n a_{nn} \end{bmatrix}$$

i.e. $\mathbf{A}$ with columns multiplied successively by $\lambda_1, \lambda_2, \ldots \lambda_n$.

EXERCISES 13.6

1. The column vectors $\mathbf{x}$ and $\mathbf{y}$ are of order n so that $\mathbf{x'y} = \mathbf{y'x}$ is a scalar. What are $\mathbf{xy'}$ and $\mathbf{yx'}$? Can any of the four products be written if $\mathbf{x}$ and $\mathbf{y}$ are of *different* orders?

2. If $\mathbf{x}$ is a column vector of order n, obtain $\mathbf{xx'}$ and check that it is a symmetric matrix.

3. Form as many products as possible from pairs of :

$$\mathbf{x'} = \begin{bmatrix} 1 & -2 & 3 \end{bmatrix} ; \quad \mathbf{y} = \begin{bmatrix} 3 \\ -2 \\ 1 \end{bmatrix} ; \quad \mathbf{A} = \begin{bmatrix} 0 & 1 & -1 \\ 1 & 0 & 1 \end{bmatrix} ; \quad \mathbf{C} = \begin{bmatrix} 1 & 2 & 3 \\ 4 & 5 & 6 \\ 7 & 8 & 9 \end{bmatrix}$$

Write the product $\mathbf{x'Cy}$ as a scalar.

4. $\mathbf{A}$ is a square matrix of order $n \times n$; explain why $\mathbf{Ax}$ and $\mathbf{x'A}$ can be written only for a vector $\mathbf{x}$ of order n. Then write $\mathbf{x'Ax}$ and interpret as a scalar (quadratic form) in the variables $\mathbf{x}$. What is $\mathbf{x'Ix}$, where $\mathbf{I}$ is the unit matrix of order n?

5. If $\mathbf{x}$ is a column vector of order n, show that :

$$\{1\}\mathbf{x'} = \begin{bmatrix} x_1 & x_2 & \ldots & x_n \\ x_1 & x_2 & \ldots & x_n \\ \ldots\ldots\ldots\ldots \\ x_1 & x_2 & \ldots & x_n \end{bmatrix} \quad \text{and} \quad \mathbf{x}[1] = \begin{bmatrix} x_1 & x_1 & \ldots & x_1 \\ x_2 & x_2 & \ldots & x_2 \\ \ldots\ldots\ldots\ldots \\ x_n & x_n & \ldots & x_n \end{bmatrix}$$

What are $\{1\}[1]$ and $[1]\{1\}$? Also obtain and interpret $[1]\mathbf{I}\{1\}$.

6. The diagonal matrix $\bar{\lambda}$ is of order $n \times n$ and $\mathbf{x}$ is a column vector of order n. Form the products $\bar{\lambda}\mathbf{x}$ and $\mathbf{x'}\bar{\lambda}$. If λ is the vector (in column form) which is used in $\bar{\lambda}$, find $\lambda'\mathbf{x}$ and $\mathbf{x'}\lambda$; how are these related to $\bar{\lambda}\mathbf{x}$ and $\mathbf{x'}\bar{\lambda}$?

7. In (viii) above, $\bar{\lambda}\mathbf{A}$ and $\mathbf{A}\bar{\lambda}$ are given for $\mathbf{A}$ square of order $n \times n$. Show that the products can be defined, with similar results, when $\mathbf{A}$ is of any order $m \times n$. What orders must the diagonal matrix $\bar{\lambda}$ then take?

8. Illustrate the uses of a unit matrix $\mathbf{I}$ by showing that :

$$\mathbf{x'x} = \mathbf{Ix'x} = \mathbf{x'Ix} = \mathbf{x'xI}$$

the common value being the scalar $\sum_{s=1}^{n} x_s^2$, the sum of squares of the elements of **x**. Of what orders is **I** in these various appearances?

13.7 Inverse of a Square Matrix ; Determinant Values

The general form of a matrix, as considered so far, is rectangular ; its order is $m \times n$ where m is generally not equal to n. In the present section, particular attention is paid to the case $m = n$, to a square matrix of order $n \times n$. The lack of reference to determinants in the present chapter is also due to the generality of treatment. A rectangular matrix $(m \neq n)$ has no corresponding determinant, at least if all the elements are used. A determinant is essentially one particular value (scalar) derived from the elements of a square matrix. Other scalars can be obtained from rectangular as well as from square matrices. e.g. the scalar $\mathbf{y}'\mathbf{Ax}$ derived from a matrix **A** of any order, as in 13.6 (iv) above. A determinant, however, implies a square matrix and it will take its place in the present section.

There is an important distinction for matrices $\mathbf{A} = [a_{rs}]$ of order $n \times n$.

DEFINITION : If $A = |\mathbf{A}| = |a_{rs}|$ is the determinant obtained from **A**, then **A** is singular when $A = 0$ and non-singular when $A \neq 0$.

In the following development, it is assumed that **A** is non-singular ($A \neq 0$). The *co-factor* of a_{rs} in A is denoted by A_{rs}, a determinant of order $(n-1)$ obtained from A of order n by dropping the rth row and the sth column and by attaching the sign $(-1)^{r+s}$ (see 12.9 above). There are as many co-factors as there are elements and they can be arranged in a matrix $[A_{rs}]$ of order $n \times n$. Write the transpose of this matrix, called the *adjoint matrix* of **A** :

$$[A_{rs}]' = \begin{bmatrix} A_{11} & A_{21} & \dots & A_{n1} \\ A_{12} & A_{22} & \dots & A_{n2} \\ \multicolumn{4}{c}{\dotfill} \\ A_{1n} & A_{2n} & \dots & A_{nn} \end{bmatrix}$$

A third matrix is formed by dividing each element in $[A_{rs}]'$ by the deter-minant value A, given that $A \neq 0$. This matrix is denoted by $\mathbf{A}^{-1}$.

DEFINITION : $\mathbf{A}^{-1} = \left[\dfrac{A_{rs}}{A} \right]' = \dfrac{1}{A} \begin{bmatrix} A_{11} & A_{21} & \dots & A_{n1} \\ A_{12} & A_{22} & \dots & A_{n2} \\ \multicolumn{4}{c}{\dotfill} \\ A_{1n} & A_{2n} & \dots & A_{nn} \end{bmatrix}$ $(A \neq 0)$

So far, this is just an arbitrary definition; A^{-1} is a particular matrix derived from a given square matrix A. The co-factors of the determinant A are written as a matrix; each element is then divided by A and the whole matrix transposed to give A^{-1}. It remains to interpret A^{-1} and, in fact, to justify the use of the power (-1). In elementary algebra a^{-1} is the inverse (reciprocal) of a and satisfies $a \times a^{-1} = a^{-1} \times a = 1$ so that $a^{-1} = \dfrac{1}{a}$ $(a \neq 0)$. This is rule (M5) of 13.1 above. A^{-1} will turn out to serve the same purpose in the algebra of matrices.

Matrix algebra contains unit elements, the unit matrices I of appropriate (square) order. If A is square of order $n \times n$ and I the corresponding unit matrix, then A^{-1} should satisfy $AA^{-1} = A^{-1}A = I$. It can be shown that A^{-1} does this and that it is the only matrix to do so. The proof proceeds:

$$AA^{-1} = \frac{1}{A} [a_{rs}] [A_{rs}]'$$

$$= \frac{1}{A} \left[\sum_{p=1}^{n} a_{rp} A_{sp} \right] \text{ by the multiplication rule (13.4)}$$

$$= \frac{1}{A} \begin{bmatrix} A & 0 & \dots & 0 \\ 0 & A & \dots & 0 \\ & \dots & & \\ 0 & 0 & \dots & A \end{bmatrix} \quad \text{by the expansion rules (12.9)}$$

$$= \begin{bmatrix} 1 & 0 & \dots & 0 \\ 0 & 1 & \dots & 0 \\ & \dots & & \\ 0 & 0 & \dots & 1 \end{bmatrix} = I \quad \begin{array}{l} \text{by the rule for multiplication by} \\ \text{scalars (13.3)} \end{array}$$

Similarly $A^{-1}A = I$, and A^{-1} satisfies $AA^{-1} = A^{-1}A = I$.

To show that no other matrix does this, suppose B exists so that $AB = I$. Then:

$$A^{-1} = A^{-1}I = A^{-1}(AB) = (A^{-1}A)B = IB = B.$$

Hence $B = A^{-1}$ for $AB = I$. Similarly, $B = A^{-1}$ for $BA = I$.

Hence, A^{-1} is the inverse (reciprocal) of A, the only matrix to satisfy $AA^{-1} = A^{-1}A = I$. It is necessary that A is square and that $A \neq 0$. The process of division then follows as the inverse of multiplication. Just as there are two products AB and BA, so there are two ways of dividing A into B. One of them is BA^{-1} and the other is $A^{-1}B$. A^{-1} is uniquely defined (if A is square and $A \neq 0$), but it can be pre- or post-multiplied by

B, i.e. **A** can be post- or pre-divided into **B**. Hence, for square matrix, rule (M5) takes the form :

$\mathbf{A}^{-1}$ inverse of **A** : $\mathbf{AA}^{-1}=\mathbf{A}^{-1}\mathbf{A}=\mathbf{I}$

Division : $\mathbf{A}^{-1}\mathbf{B} \neq \mathbf{BA}^{-1}$

The matrices **A** and **B** must be square and $A \neq 0$.

The following *properties* of inverse matrices are useful and illustrative of the handling of matrices and determinants :

(i) *The basic property is* $\mathbf{AA}^{-1}=\mathbf{A}^{-1}\mathbf{A}=\mathbf{I}$

i.e. the product $\mathbf{AA}^{-1}$ is commutative.

(ii) *Inverse of an inverse.* $(\mathbf{A}^{-1})^{-1}=\mathbf{A}$.

By (i) $\mathbf{AA}^{-1}=\mathbf{I}$ and $(\mathbf{A}^{-1})(\mathbf{A}^{-1})^{-1}=\mathbf{I}$

Now $\mathbf{A}=\mathbf{AI}=\mathbf{AA}^{-1}(\mathbf{A}^{-1})^{-1}=\mathbf{I}(\mathbf{A}^{-1})^{-1}=(\mathbf{A}^{-1})^{-1}$

(iii) *Inverse of a product.* $(\mathbf{AB})^{-1}=\mathbf{B}^{-1}\mathbf{A}^{-1}$, inverting the order of the matrices.

By (i) $\mathbf{A}^{-1}\mathbf{A}=\mathbf{B}^{-1}\mathbf{B}=\mathbf{I}$ and $(\mathbf{AB})(\mathbf{AB})^{-1}=\mathbf{I}$

Now $\mathbf{B}^{-1}\mathbf{A}^{-1}=\mathbf{B}^{-1}\mathbf{A}^{-1}\mathbf{I}=\mathbf{B}^{-1}\mathbf{A}^{-1}\mathbf{AB}(\mathbf{AB})^{-1}=\mathbf{B}^{-1}\mathbf{IB}(\mathbf{AB})^{-1}$
$=\mathbf{B}^{-1}\mathbf{B}(\mathbf{AB})^{-1}=\mathbf{I}(\mathbf{AB})^{-1}=(\mathbf{AB})^{-1}$

(iv) *Inverse of a transpose.* $(\mathbf{A}')^{-1}=(\mathbf{A}^{-1})'$

By (i) $\mathbf{A}^{-1}\mathbf{A}=\mathbf{I}$. By 13.5 (iii) $(\mathbf{A}^{-1}\mathbf{A})'=\mathbf{A}'(\mathbf{A}^{-1})'$

Combining these two results : $\mathbf{A}'(\mathbf{A}^{-1})'=(\mathbf{A}^{-1}\mathbf{A})'=\mathbf{I}'=\mathbf{I}$

Hence **A**′ and $(\mathbf{A}^{-1})'$ are inverse, i.e. $(\mathbf{A}')^{-1}=(\mathbf{A}^{-1})'$

(v) *Determinants of an inverse.* The reciprocal $\mathbf{A}^{-1}$ and both the quotients $\mathbf{BA}^{-1}$ and $\mathbf{A}^{-1}\mathbf{B}$ are square matrices of the same order as **A**. Their determinants can be written and it is to be expected that they obey the ordinary algebraic rules, i.e. that

$$|\mathbf{A}^{-1}|=\frac{1}{|\mathbf{A}|} \quad \text{and} \quad |\mathbf{BA}^{-1}|=|\mathbf{A}^{-1}\mathbf{B}|=\frac{|\mathbf{B}|}{|\mathbf{A}|}$$

This is, in fact, the case. The proof is an exercise in writing the determinant values of square matrices. First, the determinant of the unit matrix **I** is unity :

$$|\mathbf{I}|=\begin{vmatrix} 1 & 0 & ... & 0 \\ 0 & 1 & ... & 0 \\ \multicolumn{4}{c}{............} \\ 0 & 0 & ... & 1 \end{vmatrix}=1$$

Next, the determinant of $\mathbf{A}^{-1}$ is obtained from the relation $\mathbf{AA}^{-1}=\mathbf{I}$. A general result is required, i.e. if **AB** is the product of two square matrices, then $|\mathbf{AB}|=|\mathbf{A}||\mathbf{B}|$. This appears to be so since the rule for multiplication of determinants follows the same inner-product form as that for multiplication of matrices (cf. Ex. 1 below). The result, however, is somewhat difficult to prove in a formal way, see Wade (1951), Appendix. It is assumed here. Hence :

$$|\mathbf{AA^{-1}}|=|\mathbf{I}|$$

gives $\quad\quad |\mathbf{A}||\mathbf{A^{-1}}|=1 \quad$ i.e. $\quad |\mathbf{A^{-1}}|=\dfrac{1}{|\mathbf{A}|}$

Finally, there are two different quotient matrices $\mathbf{BA^{-1}}$ and $\mathbf{A^{-1}B}$ from the same pair of square matrices $\mathbf{A}$ and $\mathbf{B}$. Writing determinants :

$$|\mathbf{BA^{-1}}|=|\mathbf{A^{-1}B}|=|\mathbf{B}||\mathbf{A^{-1}}|=\dfrac{|\mathbf{B}|}{|\mathbf{A}|}$$

Though different as matrices, the determinant values of $\mathbf{BA^{-1}}$ and $\mathbf{A^{-1}B}$ are the same, each being $|\mathbf{B}|$ divided by $|\mathbf{A}|$.

The computation of inverse matrices in numerical cases can be carried out from the definition by evaluating co-factors. This has already been done in effect in 11.6 above. Two *examples* illustrate :

Ex. (a). $\mathbf{A}=\begin{bmatrix} 1 & 2 \\ 0 & 2 \end{bmatrix}$ with $\begin{matrix} A_{11}=2 & A_{12}=0 \\ A_{21}=-2 & A_{22}=1 \end{matrix}$ and $A=2$.

Hence : $\mathbf{A^{-1}}=\begin{bmatrix} 1 & -1 \\ 0 & \frac{1}{2} \end{bmatrix}$ from the definition.

Ex. (b). $\mathbf{A}=\begin{bmatrix} 1 & 2 & 3 \\ 0 & 1 & 2 \\ 0 & 0 & 1 \end{bmatrix}$ with $\begin{matrix} A_{11}=1 & A_{12}=0 & A_{13}=0 \\ A_{21}=-2 & A_{22}=1 & A_{23}=0 \\ A_{31}=1 & A_{32}=-2 & A_{33}=1 \end{matrix}$ and $A=1$.

Hence : $\mathbf{A^{-1}}=\begin{bmatrix} 1 & -2 & 1 \\ 0 & 1 & -2 \\ 0 & 0 & 1 \end{bmatrix}$ from the definition.

These examples suggest that the inverse of a *triangular matrix*, as defined in 12.6 (v) above, is also a triangular matrix ; see Ex. 9 below.

The evaluation of $\mathbf{A^{-1}}$ is laborious when $\mathbf{A}$ is of large order. Instead of using the co-factors of A, it is possible in some cases to find a matrix $\mathbf{B}$ for which $\mathbf{AB}=\mathbf{I}$ and then to associate $\mathbf{B}$ with $\mathbf{A^{-1}}$. Another practical method is indicated later (13.9 below).

It remains to find the inverse of the unit matrix $\mathbf{I}$, and of various matrices obtained from $\mathbf{I}$, where $\mathbf{I}$ is of any square order $n \times n$. Since $\mathbf{II}=\mathbf{I}$, it follows that $\mathbf{I^{-1}}=\mathbf{I}$, which can be checked in terms of co-factors. The result, as expected, is :

The inverse of $\mathbf{I}$ *is* $\mathbf{I}$ *itself.*

The matrix obtained from $\mathbf{I}$ by interchange of rth and sth rows is written $\mathbf{E_{(rs)}}$, see end of 13.4 above. The transpose of $\mathbf{E_{(rs)}}$ is the same matrix, i.e. $\mathbf{E}_{(rs)}{}' = \mathbf{E}_{(rs)}$, indicating that the interchange of columns in $\mathbf{I}$ is the same as the interchange of the corresponding rows. It is also easily checked from the definition (see Ex. 7 below) that $\mathbf{E}_{(rs)}{}^{-1} = \mathbf{E}_{(rs)}$. Hence, like $\mathbf{I}$ itself, the matrix $\mathbf{E}_{(rs)}$ is its own transpose and inverse. For example:

$$\mathbf{E}_{(rs)}\mathbf{A}\mathbf{E}_{(rs)}{}^{-1} = \mathbf{E}_{(rs)}\mathbf{A}\mathbf{E}_{(rs)}{}' = \mathbf{E}_{(rs)}\mathbf{A}\mathbf{E}_{(rs)}$$

for any square matrix $\mathbf{A}$ of order $n \times n$. The common value of these products is the matrix obtained from $\mathbf{A}$ by interchange of rth and sth rows and of rth and sth columns.

These processes can be generalised. A *permutation matrix* $\mathbf{P}^*$ is defined as a matrix of order $n \times n$ which has exactly one entry 1 in each row and exactly one in each column, all other entries being zero. It follows that $\mathbf{P}^*$ is obtained from $\mathbf{I}$ of order $n \times n$ by permuting or shuffling the rows in some specified way. Further, $(\mathbf{P}^*)'$ is obtained from $\mathbf{I}$ by the same permutation of columns. There are many such permutations; $\mathbf{P}^*$ is a convenient notation for a whole set of matrices related to $\mathbf{I}$. See Kemeny, Snell and Thompson (1957), p. 237.

An example of order 3×3 illustrates. Permute rows and columns of $\mathbf{I}$ from the sequence $(1, 2, 3)$ to the sequence $(3, 1, 2)$:

$$\mathbf{P}^* = \begin{bmatrix} 0 & 0 & 1 \\ 1 & 0 & 0 \\ 0 & 1 & 0 \end{bmatrix} \quad \text{and} \quad (\mathbf{P}^*)' = \begin{bmatrix} 0 & 1 & 0 \\ 0 & 0 & 1 \\ 1 & 0 & 0 \end{bmatrix}$$

Generally, $\mathbf{P}^*$ and $(\mathbf{P}^*)'$ are different. But from the definition:

$$(\mathbf{P}^*)^{-1} = \begin{bmatrix} 0 & 1 & 0 \\ 0 & 0 & 1 \\ 1 & 0 & 0 \end{bmatrix} = (\mathbf{P}^*)'$$

The transpose and inverse of $\mathbf{P}^*$ are the same, not generally equal to $\mathbf{P}^*$ itself. This is unlike the particular permutation matrix $\mathbf{E}_{(rs)}$ (see Ex. 8 below). So $\mathbf{P}^*(\mathbf{P}^*)' = \mathbf{I}$ and $(\mathbf{P}^*)'$ reverses the permutation given by $\mathbf{P}^*$.

With the same $\mathbf{P}^*$, take $\mathbf{x} = \{x_1, x_2, x_3\}$ as a column vector:

$$\mathbf{P}^*\mathbf{x} = \{x_3, x_1, x_2\}$$

and $\mathbf{P}^*$ serves to permute the elements of the vector $\mathbf{x}$. For any 3×3 $\mathbf{A}$:

$$\mathbf{P}^*\mathbf{A} = \begin{bmatrix} a_{31} & a_{32} & a_{33} \\ a_{11} & a_{12} & a_{13} \\ a_{21} & a_{22} & a_{23} \end{bmatrix}; \quad \mathbf{A}(\mathbf{P}^*)' = \begin{bmatrix} a_{13} & a_{11} & a_{12} \\ a_{23} & a_{21} & a_{22} \\ a_{33} & a_{31} & a_{32} \end{bmatrix}; \quad \mathbf{P}^*\mathbf{A}(\mathbf{P}^*)' = \begin{bmatrix} a_{33} & a_{31} & a_{32} \\ a_{13} & a_{11} & a_{12} \\ a_{23} & a_{21} & a_{22} \end{bmatrix}$$

These processes give respectively the matrix $\mathbf{A}$ with rows permuted in the given way, with columns so permuted, with rows *and* columns so permuted. In general, the results extending those of 13.4 above are:

$$\mathbf{P^*A}=\mathbf{A} \quad \text{with rows permuted}$$
$$\mathbf{A(P^*)}'=\mathbf{A} \quad \text{with columns permuted}$$
$$\mathbf{P^*A(P^*)}'=\mathbf{A} \quad \text{with rows and columns permuted}$$

This is for any $n \times n$ matrix $\mathbf{A}$ and for a permutation defined by $\mathbf{P^*}$. As a particular case, take $\mathbf{A}=\mathbf{I}$. Then $\mathbf{P^*(P^*)}'=\mathbf{P^*I(P^*)}'$ is $\mathbf{I}$ with rows and columns permuted, giving $\mathbf{I}$ back again. Hence:

$$\mathbf{P^*(P^*)}'=\mathbf{I} \quad \text{or} \quad (\mathbf{P^*})^{-1}=(\mathbf{P^*})'$$

The inverse and transpose of $\mathbf{P^*}$ are the same. If the rows *and* the columns of $\mathbf{A}$ are permuted in the same way, the result is a matrix :

$$\mathbf{P^*A(P^*)}'=\mathbf{P^*A(P^*)}^{-1}$$

EXERCISES 13.7

1. Show that the following three matrices all have determinant value equal to 3 :

$$\mathbf{A}=\begin{bmatrix} 2 & 1 \\ -1 & 1 \end{bmatrix}, \quad \mathbf{B}=\begin{bmatrix} 2 & 1 \\ 1 & 2 \end{bmatrix}, \quad \mathbf{C}=\begin{bmatrix} 1 & -1 \\ 1 & 2 \end{bmatrix}$$

Show that $\mathbf{AB} \neq \mathbf{BA}$ but that $|\mathbf{AB}|=|\mathbf{BA}|=|\mathbf{A}| \times |\mathbf{B}|=9$. Do the products $\mathbf{AC}$ and $\mathbf{CA}$ differ?

2. If $\mathbf{A}=\begin{bmatrix} 2 & 1 \\ 1 & 3 \end{bmatrix}$ show that $A=5$. Write the four co-factors in A and hence obtain
$$\mathbf{A}^{-1}=\begin{bmatrix} \frac{3}{5} & -\frac{1}{5} \\ -\frac{1}{5} & \frac{2}{5} \end{bmatrix} \quad \text{from the definition.}$$

Check the properties that $\mathbf{AA}^{-1}=\mathbf{A}^{-1}\mathbf{A}=\mathbf{I}$ and that $|\mathbf{A}^{-1}|=\dfrac{1}{A}$

3. If $\mathbf{A}=\begin{bmatrix} 1 & 1 & 1 \\ 0 & 1 & 0 \\ 0 & 0 & 1 \end{bmatrix}$ show that $\mathbf{A}^{-1}=\begin{bmatrix} 1 & -1 & -1 \\ 0 & 1 & 0 \\ 0 & 0 & 1 \end{bmatrix}$. If $\mathbf{B}=\begin{bmatrix} 1 & a & b \\ 0 & 1 & 0 \\ 0 & 0 & 1 \end{bmatrix}$ what is $\mathbf{B}^{-1}$?

4. It is given only that $\mathbf{A}^{-1}$ satisfies $\mathbf{AA}^{-1}=\mathbf{I}$. Assume $\mathbf{B}$ exists for $\mathbf{BA}=\mathbf{I}$ and show that $\mathbf{B}=\mathbf{A}^{-1}$, i.e. proving $\mathbf{A}^{-1}\mathbf{A}=\mathbf{I}$ also.

5. If $\mathbf{A}$ is a square matrix, define $(\mathbf{A}^{-1})^2=\mathbf{A}^{-1}\mathbf{A}^{-1}$. Show that $\mathbf{A}^2(\mathbf{A}^{-1})^2=\mathbf{I}$ and interpret. Hence develop the concept of a negative integral power $\mathbf{A}^{-n}$, the reciprocal of $\mathbf{A}^n$. Finally show that $\mathbf{A}^m\mathbf{A}^n=\mathbf{A}^{m+n}$ for any values of m and n (positive or negative integers). Does $\mathbf{A}^0=\mathbf{I}$ complete the set of integral powers of $\mathbf{A}$?

6. Illustrate the algebra of powers of $\mathbf{A}$, given in the previous exercise, by taking $\mathbf{A}$ as the diagonal matrix $\mathbf{\bar{a}}$. Show that :

$$(\mathbf{\bar{a}})^2=\begin{bmatrix} a_1{}^2 & 0 & \ldots \\ 0 & a_2{}^2 & \ldots \\ \multicolumn{3}{c}{\ldots} \end{bmatrix}, \quad (\mathbf{\bar{a}})^{-1}=\begin{bmatrix} a_1{}^{-1} & 0 & \ldots \\ 0 & a_2{}^{-1} & \ldots \\ \multicolumn{3}{c}{\ldots} \end{bmatrix}, \quad \text{etc.}$$

7. If **I** is of order 3×3, derive $\mathbf{E}_{(23)}$ and from the definitions write $\mathbf{E}'_{(23)}$ and $\mathbf{E}_{(23)}{}^{-1}$. Generalise.

8. Write the six permutation matrices $\mathbf{P}^*$ obtained from **I** of order 3×3. Show that three of them are of the form $\mathbf{E}_{(rs)}$ for which $\mathbf{P}^* = (\mathbf{P}^*)' = (\mathbf{P}^*)^{-1}$, but that the other three are such that $\mathbf{P}^* \neq (\mathbf{P}^*)' = (\mathbf{P}^*)^{-1}$.

9. A triangular matrix is $\mathbf{T} = \begin{bmatrix} a_1 & a_{12} & a_{13} \\ 0 & a_2 & a_{23} \\ 0 & 0 & a_3 \end{bmatrix}$. Try $\mathbf{T}^{-1} = \begin{bmatrix} b_1 & b_{12} & b_{13} \\ 0 & b_2 & b_{23} \\ 0 & 0 & b_3 \end{bmatrix}$.

Write $\mathbf{T}\mathbf{T}^{-1}$ by multiplication and equate to **I**. Show that $b_r = \dfrac{1}{a_r}$ and that b_{12}, b_{13} and b_{23} can be found in terms of the a's. Hence deduce that the inverse of a triangular matrix is also triangular.

13.8 Equivalence and Rank of Matrices

Results which hold for any matrix $\mathbf{A} = [a_{rs}]$ of order $m \times n$ will first be derived. For convenience of exposition it is taken that $m \leqslant n$, i.e. that the columns are not less in number than the rows. When **A** has more rows than columns, the transpose $\mathbf{A}'$ can be written and the result for $m \leqslant n$ applied to $\mathbf{A}'$.

An *elementary operation* on rows of a matrix is defined as any one of the following :

  (*a*) interchange of two rows
  (*b*) addition of multiple h of one row to another row
  (*c*) multiplication of one row by k

for any non-zero values of the scalars h and k. There are similar elementary operations applied to the columns of the matrix.

The *elementary matrices* are the result of applying elementary operations to the unit matrix **I** of any order $n \times n$. For operations on rows of **I**, the elementary matrices are:

$$(a)\ \mathbf{E}_{(rs)} ; \quad (b)\ \mathbf{H}_{(rs)} ; \quad (c)\ \mathbf{K}_{(r)}$$

as defined in 13.4 above. Here r and s are the two rows concerned and they can take any values : r and $s = 1, 2, \ldots n$, $r \neq s$. It can be noted that elementary operation (*a*) is a particular case of any specific shuffling or permutating of rows, and hence that $\mathbf{E}_{(rs)}$ is a particular case of the permutation matrix $\mathbf{P}^*$. However, the interchange of two rows and the matrix $\mathbf{E}_{(rs)}$ are the basic concepts ; any other shuffling of rows is a sequence of interchanges and $\mathbf{P}^*$ is a product of **E**'s. For example, if $n = 3$ and the permutation of rows is in the sequence $(3, 1, 2)$, then $\mathbf{P}^* = \mathbf{E}_{(12)}\mathbf{E}_{(23)}$ implying an interchange of 2nd and 3rd rows, followed by an interchange of 1st and 2nd rows. The results obtained at the end of 13.4 above, as exercises in multiplying matrices, are collected and reduced to one simple theorem, as a result of the following analysis.

The concept of *equivalent matrices* is first defined :

DEFINITION : If **A** is obtained from **B** by a sequence of elementary operations, then **A** is equivalent to **B**.

The following important properties are a consequence of the nature of elementary operations, e.g. that they are applicable in any order and can be inverted :

(i) **A** is equivalent to itself ;

(ii) If **A** is equivalent to **B**, then **B** is equivalent to **A** ;

(iii) If **A** is equivalent to **B** and **B** to **C**, then **A** is equivalent to **C**.

These are in fact general properties of equivalence (see Appendix B).

The idea of going from **A** to an equivalent **B** is to obtain a *simpler* matrix. Indeed the simplification can be very drastic. Given **A** of order $m \times n$, then **A** is equivalent to the matrix :

$$\mathbf{D} = \left[\begin{array}{c|c} \mathbf{I}_r & \mathbf{0} \\ \hline \mathbf{0} & \mathbf{0} \end{array} \right] \qquad (\mathbf{I}_r \text{ unit matrix of order } r \times r)$$

for some fixed r. And all matrices equivalent to **A** have the same $\mathbf{D}_r$. Proof : A zero matrix is already of the required form. Any other matrix has a non-zero element which can be brought into the leading position (first row and column) by interchanging rows and/or columns, and then reduced to 1 by an appropriate multiple of the first row. Subtract multiples of the first row from other rows, and similarly for columns, until the first row and column contain only zero values, apart from 1 in the leading position. Hence **A** is equivalent to :

$$\left[\begin{array}{c|c} 1 & \mathbf{0} \\ \hline \mathbf{0} & \mathbf{C} \end{array} \right] \qquad \text{for } \mathbf{C} \text{ of order } (m-1) \times (n-1)$$

The process continues with **C** until finally **A** becomes equivalent to $\mathbf{D}_r$.

Some examples illustrate :

Ex. (*a*). $\mathbf{A} = \begin{bmatrix} 1 & 2 & 3 \\ 2 & 4 & 6 \\ 3 & 6 & 9 \end{bmatrix}$ equiv. to $\begin{bmatrix} 1 & 2 & 3 \\ 0 & 0 & 0 \\ 0 & 0 & 0 \end{bmatrix}$ equiv. to $\begin{bmatrix} 1 & 0 & 0 \\ 0 & 0 & 0 \\ 0 & 0 & 0 \end{bmatrix} = \mathbf{D}_1$

In the first step, $2 \times$ first row is subtracted from the second, and $3 \times$ first row is subtracted from the third. In the second step, similar subtractions are done on columns.

Ex. (*b*). $\mathbf{A} = \begin{bmatrix} 0 & 1 & 0 & 0 \\ -3 & -6 & 3 & -\frac{3}{2} \\ 4 & 8 & -4 & 2 \end{bmatrix}$ equiv. to $\begin{bmatrix} 4 & 8 & -4 & 2 \\ 0 & 1 & 0 & 0 \\ -3 & -6 & 3 & -\frac{3}{2} \end{bmatrix}$

equiv. to $\begin{bmatrix} 4 & 8 & -4 & 2 \\ 0 & 1 & 0 & 0 \\ 0 & 0 & 0 & 0 \end{bmatrix}$ equiv. to $\begin{bmatrix} 1 & 2 & -2 & \frac{1}{2} \\ 0 & 1 & 0 & 0 \\ 0 & 0 & 0 & 0 \end{bmatrix}$

equiv. to $\begin{bmatrix} 1 & 0 & 0 & 0 \\ 0 & 1 & 0 & 0 \\ 0 & 0 & 0 & 0 \end{bmatrix} = \mathbf{D_2}$

Notice that the second step is the addition of $\frac{3}{4}$ × first row to the third row, and that the third step is the multiplication of the first row by $\frac{1}{4}$. The first step is an interchange of rows and the last the subtraction of multiples of the first column from other columns.

Ex. (*c*). $\mathbf{A} = \begin{bmatrix} 3 & 2 & 1 \\ 2 & 1 & 0 \\ 1 & 0 & 0 \end{bmatrix}$ equiv. to $\begin{bmatrix} 1 & 2 & 3 \\ 0 & 1 & 2 \\ 0 & 0 & 1 \end{bmatrix}$

equiv. to $\begin{bmatrix} 1 & 0 & 0 \\ 0 & 1 & 2 \\ 0 & 0 & 1 \end{bmatrix}$ equiv. to $\begin{bmatrix} 1 & 0 & 0 \\ 0 & 1 & 0 \\ 0 & 0 & 1 \end{bmatrix} = \mathbf{D_3} = \mathbf{I}$

The steps should now be obvious. As a matter of interest, it can be noticed that here (as in the other examples and generally) $\mathbf{A}$ is made equivalent at some intermediate stage to a triangular matrix with zero elements below the principal diagonal.

The concept of equivalent matrices leads to that of the *rank* of a matrix. By omitting rows and/or columns, a matrix $\mathbf{A}$ of order $m \times n$ (say with $m \leqslant n$) gives a variety of *sub-matrices* of order $r \times s$ for $r \leqslant m$ and $s \leqslant n$. Consider *square sub-matrices* of various orders up to $m \times m$, some with zero and some with non-zero determinants. Pick out the biggest of those with non-zero determinants. Then :

DEFINITION : The matrix $\mathbf{A}$ of order $m \times n$ has rank r if at least one of the sub-matrices of order $r \times r$ has a non-zero determinant and if all square sub-matrices of higher order have zero determinants. The rank $r \leqslant m$ or n, whichever is the smaller.

In particular : if $\mathbf{A}$ is square of order $n \times n$, then $r = n$ if $\mathbf{A}$ is *non-singular* and $r < n$ if $\mathbf{A}$ is *singular*.

Ex. (*d*). It is laborious to determine the rank from the definition :

$$\mathbf{A} = \begin{bmatrix} 0 & 1 & 0 & 0 \\ -3 & -6 & 3 & -\frac{3}{2} \\ 4 & 8 & -4 & 2 \end{bmatrix} \text{ of order } 3 \times 4 \text{ and of rank } 2.$$

$\mathbf{A}$ has four sub-matrices of order 3×3, each with zero determinant :

$$\begin{vmatrix} 1 & 0 & 0 \\ -6 & 3 & -\frac{3}{2} \\ 8 & -4 & 2 \end{vmatrix} = \begin{vmatrix} 0 & 0 & 0 \\ -3 & 3 & -\frac{3}{2} \\ 4 & -4 & 2 \end{vmatrix} = \begin{vmatrix} 0 & 1 & 0 \\ -3 & -6 & -\frac{3}{2} \\ 4 & 8 & 2 \end{vmatrix} = \begin{vmatrix} 0 & 1 & 0 \\ -3 & -6 & 3 \\ 4 & 8 & -4 \end{vmatrix} = 0$$

It has eighteen sub-matrices of order 2×2, including $\begin{bmatrix} 0 & 1 \\ -3 & -6 \end{bmatrix}$ which has deter-

minant$=3 \neq 0$. Hence $\mathbf{A}$ is proved to have rank 2.

Some simpler way of handling rank is required and the concept of equivalent matrices provides one. The necessary result is :

All equivalent matrices have the same rank, and conversely all matrices of a given rank are equivalent.

Proof : if $\mathbf{A}$ and $\mathbf{B}$ are equivalent, then $\mathbf{B}$ is obtained from $\mathbf{A}$ by a sequence of elementary operations, none of which can turn a sub-matrix with a non-zero determinant into one with a zero determinant. Hence the sub-matrices of $\mathbf{A}$ and $\mathbf{B}$ are alike in their determinant values (zero or non-zero) and $\mathbf{A}$ and $\mathbf{B}$ have the same rank. Further, if $\mathbf{A}$, $\mathbf{B}$, ... are all equivalent to the matrix $\mathbf{D}_r$ of rank r, then they all have rank r. Conversely, if $\mathbf{A}$ and $\mathbf{B}$ are of the same rank r, then each separately must reduce to the equivalent $\mathbf{D}_r$. By property (iii) of equivalent matrices (above), $\mathbf{A}$ and $\mathbf{B}$ are themselves equivalent.

Hence, if $\mathbf{A}$ is given and reduced to its equivalent matrix $\mathbf{D}_r$, then its rank is determined to be r. In the case of a non-singular matrix of order $n \times n$, the rank is known to be n. So it must be equivalent to $\mathbf{D}_n$ which is $\mathbf{I}$ of order $n \times n$. Hence :

All non-singular matrices of given order $n \times n$ are equivalent and each is obtained from $\mathbf{I}$ of the same order by elementary operations.

Finally, an important condition for equivalent matrices is obtained. Let $\mathbf{A}$ be of order $m \times n$. By 13.4 above, one elementary operation on rows gives an equivalent matrix : $\mathbf{E}_{(rs)}\mathbf{A}$; $\mathbf{H}_{(rs)}\mathbf{A}$; or $\mathbf{K}_{(r)}\mathbf{A}$. A sequence of such operations turns $\mathbf{A}$ into equivalent $\mathbf{PA}$, for some $\mathbf{P}$ of order $m \times m$, a product of elementary matrices. Similarly, a sequence of elementary operations on the columns of $\mathbf{A}$ gives the equivalent $\mathbf{AQ}$ for some $\mathbf{Q}$ of order $n \times n$. For a mixed sequence of operations on rows and columns, $\mathbf{A}$ is turned into an equivalent form $\mathbf{PAQ}$. Here $\mathbf{P}$ and $\mathbf{Q}$ are products of elementary matrices, $\mathbf{P}$ of order $m \times m$ and $\mathbf{Q}$ of order $n \times n$. Since all non-singular matrices are of this type, by the above result, $\mathbf{P}$ and $\mathbf{Q}$ are simply any non-singular matrices of appropriate order. So :

$\mathbf{A}$ *and* $\mathbf{B}$ *are equivalent matrices of order $m \times n$ if and only if* $\mathbf{B}=\mathbf{PAQ}$ *for non-singular matrices* $\mathbf{P}$ *of order $m \times m$ and* $\mathbf{Q}$ *of order $n \times n$.*

Consider the set S_{mn} of all matrices of given order $m \times n$, a vector space in which no products are defined (unless $m=n$). The equivalence relation for matrices $\mathbf{A}$ and $\mathbf{B}$, i.e. $\mathbf{B}=\mathbf{PAQ}$ for non-singular $\mathbf{P}$ and $\mathbf{Q}$, serves to partition S_{mn} into subsets. This is a general property of equivalence relations (see Appendix B) and the way in which partitioning is achieved is easily described in this case. Take any matrix $\mathbf{A}$ of S_{mn} and find *all* equivalent matrices $\mathbf{B} = \mathbf{PAQ}$ for various non-singular $\mathbf{P}$ and $\mathbf{Q}$. Put these into one subset. Now take another matrix of S_{mn} not in this first subset, find all its equivalents and assemble into a second subset. The process continues until S_{mn} is exhausted. The subsets are called *equivalence classes*, in this case of $m \times n$ matrices. Since equivalent matrices have the same rank, all the matrices in one equivalence class have a common rank ; the equivalence classes can be denoted $S_0, S_1, S_2, \ldots$ comprising matrices of rank 0, 1, 2, ... respectively. It is often useful to pick out of each equivalence class one convenient representative or *canonical form*. The best candidate here is the matrix $\mathbf{D}_r$ of rank r, the canonical form. of the equivalence class S_r of rank r.

In summary, the results obtained are :

All matrices of order $m \times n$ make up a vector space S_{mn} in which no products are defined (unless $m = n$). Two of the matrices $\mathbf{A}$ and $\mathbf{B}$ are equivalent if and only if $\mathbf{B} = \mathbf{PAQ}$ for non-singular $\mathbf{P}$ and $\mathbf{Q}$, and they have the same rank. S_{mn} can be partitioned into equivalence classes $S_0, S_1, S_2, \ldots$ where S_r comprises all equivalent matrices of common rank r and is represented by the canonical form :

$$\mathbf{D}_r = \left[\begin{array}{c|c} \mathbf{I}_r & \mathbf{0} \\ \hline \mathbf{0} & \mathbf{0} \end{array} \right] \qquad \text{where } \mathbf{I}_r \text{ is the } r \times r \text{ unit matrix.}$$

This is about as far as the analysis can go in general terms. However, when the given matrix $\mathbf{A}$ is square, there are several specific developments and a number of particular cases to be considered. These are explored in the next section.

EXERCISES 13.8

1. Given any matrix $\mathbf{A}$ of order 3×3, evaluate $\mathbf{PA}$, where $\mathbf{P} = \mathbf{K}_{(1)}\mathbf{E}_{(23)} = \begin{bmatrix} k & 0 & 0 \\ 0 & 0 & 1 \\ 0 & 1 & 0 \end{bmatrix}$,

and check that it is $\mathbf{A}$ with first row multiplied by k and the other two rows interchanged.

2. Show that $\begin{bmatrix} 4 & 4 & 2 \\ 4 & 1 & 2 \\ 6 & 6 & 3 \end{bmatrix}$ equiv. to $\begin{bmatrix} 4 & 4 & 2 \\ 0 & -3 & 0 \\ 0 & 0 & 0 \end{bmatrix}$ equiv. to $\begin{bmatrix} 1 & 1 & \frac{1}{2} \\ 0 & 1 & 0 \\ 0 & 0 & 0 \end{bmatrix}$ by operations on rows only, indicating which operations are used at each stage. What is the rank of the matrix?

3. Reduce $\begin{bmatrix} 1 & 1 & 1 \\ 1 & 1 & 1 \\ 1 & 1 & 1 \end{bmatrix}$ and $\begin{bmatrix} 1 & 2 & -3 \\ 2 & 4 & -6 \\ -3 & -6 & 9 \end{bmatrix}$ to equivalent form **D** and show that
each is of rank 1.

4. Show that **0** is the only matrix of rank 0.

5. If $\mathbf{A} \neq \mathbf{0}$ is a skew-symmetric matrix, show that some of the 2×2 sub-matrices have non-zero determinants and hence that the rank of **A** is $r \geqslant 2$.

6. Given $\mathbf{A} = \begin{bmatrix} 1 & a & b \\ 0 & 1 & c \\ 0 & 0 & 1 \end{bmatrix}$, show alternative operations in which **A** can be made

equivalent to **I**. Express **A** in the form **PI**, or **IQ**, or **PIQ** for the operations selected.

7. Show that $\mathbf{A} = \begin{bmatrix} 2 & 1 & 3 & -5 \\ 1 & -3 & 5 & 2 \\ 0 & -7 & 7 & 9 \end{bmatrix}$ equiv. to $\begin{bmatrix} 1 & -3 & 5 & 2 \\ 0 & 7 & -7 & 9 \\ 0 & 0 & 0 & 0 \end{bmatrix}$ and hence of rank

2. Check by writing the determinant values of all 3×3 sub-matrices in **A**, showing that the rank of **A** is less than 3.

13.9 Square Matrices

It has been clear throughout the development of matrix algebra that *square matrices* are more easily handled than rectangular, that they satisfy more of the system of algebraic rules. Further, it appears that the simplest matrices are those which are *non-singular*—matrices with determinants which are not zero.

All the results on rank and equivalence, obtained in the last section for matrices of any given order $m \times n$, also hold for the particular case of matrices of given square order $n \times n$. So, any matrix **A** of order $n \times n$ and rank r is equivalent to the square *diagonal matrix* $\mathbf{D}_r$ which has r elements 1 followed by $(n-r)$ elements 0 in the diagonal. In particular if **A** is non-singular, of rank n, then it is equivalent to **I** of order $n \times n$. In the present section, further properties of square matrices are examined, in general and in particular.

(i) *Square matrices generally*. Consider the set S_{nn} of all square matrices of order $n \times n$. This is a vector space, closed under addition and scalar multiplication, in which products of matrices are also defined for all matrices. The rules satisfied by products are the following: closure (M1), associative (M2), existence of identity **I** (M4), and distribution of multiplication over addition (D). This is above the operational minimum, certainly enough for the set S_{nn} to be classified as a *linear algebra*. It is sometimes denoted by $M_n(F)$ where n indicates the order of the square matrices and F the field (of real numbers here) from which scalars are drawn. The only deficiencies in the set are that, in general, it is not commutative and that it lacks reciprocals or inverses for all its members.

The equivalence relation between square matrices $\mathbf{A}$ and $\mathbf{B}$ is $\mathbf{B} = \mathbf{PAQ}$ for some non-singular $\mathbf{P}$ and $\mathbf{Q}$ of the same order as $\mathbf{A}$ and $\mathbf{B}$. This serves to partition S_{nn} into subsets $S_0, S_1, S_2, \ldots S_n$ of equivalence classes. The class S_r comprises matrices of the same rank r and its canonical (or representative) form is the diagonal matrix $\mathbf{D}_r$. The last class S_n consists of all the non-singular matrices of order $n \times n$, including the unit matrix $\mathbf{I}$ as canonical form.

One particular case of the equivalence relation is obtained when $\mathbf{Q}$ is taken as $\mathbf{P}^{-1}$, always possible since $\mathbf{P}$ is non-singular. This gives the concept of *similar matrices* :

DEFINITION : Square matrices $\mathbf{A}$ and $\mathbf{B}$ are similar if $\mathbf{B} = \mathbf{PAP}^{-1}$ for some non-singular matrix $\mathbf{P}$ of the same order as $\mathbf{A}$ and $\mathbf{B}$.

If the non-singular matrix $\mathbf{P}$ is given, then $\mathbf{B} = \mathbf{PAP}^{-1}$ specifies a one-one relation between any square matrix $\mathbf{A}$ and its similar " image " $\mathbf{B}$. From this point of view, $\mathbf{B}$ is called the *transform* of $\mathbf{A}$ by the given $\mathbf{P}$; each $\mathbf{A}$ has just one transform by $\mathbf{P}$. On the other hand, if $\mathbf{A}$ is given, then all matrices $\mathbf{B}$ similar to $\mathbf{A}$ are obtained by allowing $\mathbf{P}$ to vary. Since similarity is a particular case of equivalence, all similar matrices have the same rank. The converse is not true ; not all matrices of the same rank are similar to each other. The similarity relation, in fact, provides a further subdivision of the equivalence classes $S_0, S_1, S_2, \ldots S_n$ into which S_{nn} is partitioned.

Notice that, *if* matrix products were commutative, then $\mathbf{P}$ would cancel $\mathbf{P}^{-1}$ in $\mathbf{B} = \mathbf{PAP}^{-1}$ and $\mathbf{A}$ and $\mathbf{B}$ would be equal. But matrices are *not* generally commutative under multiplication. Because of the non-commutative nature of matrix algebra, $\mathbf{A}$ and $\mathbf{B}$ can only be described as similar, and not as equal. However, there is not the same trouble with determinants, which are scalar values, and similar matrices $\mathbf{A}$ and $\mathbf{B}$ have the *same determinant values A and B*. This is since :

$$B = |\mathbf{PAP}^{-1}| = |\mathbf{P}||\mathbf{A}||\mathbf{P}^{-1}| = |\mathbf{P}||\mathbf{A}|/|\mathbf{P}| = A$$

Hence, if non-singular matrices are similar, then they are of the same " size " in that their determinants are equal. For singular matrices, whether similar or not, the determinants are zero,

Similar matrices have a great variety of uses. One of them is in connection with the " diagonalisation " of any given square matrix and this will be pursued later (14.4 below).

(ii) *Non-singular matrices.* Let $\mathbf{A}$ be a non-singular matrix of order $n \times n$. From the results obtained so far, $\mathbf{A}$ has a non-zero determinant A, it is of rank n, and it is equivalent to the unit matrix $\mathbf{I}$ of the same order. Further, $\mathbf{A}$ always has a reciprocal $\mathbf{A}^{-1}$, i.e. products of non-singular matrices satisfy the rule (M5) and division is possible.

It might be thought that the set of all non-singular matrices of given order is an even better linear algebra than the set of all square matrices. This is not so ; the gain on the side of products is offset by a loss for addition. In fact, addition ceases to be closed in the set of non-singular matrices : two non-singular matrices do not necessarily add to another non-singular matrix. They frequently add to a matrix which is singular, as in the following simple case :

$$\begin{bmatrix} 1 & 1 \\ 0 & 1 \end{bmatrix} + \begin{bmatrix} -1 & 0 \\ 0 & -1 \end{bmatrix} = \begin{bmatrix} 0 & 1 \\ 0 & 0 \end{bmatrix}$$

Each of the matrices on the left has a determinant value 1 but the matrix on the right has a zero determinant.

Hence, the set of non-singular matrices no longer has the structure of a vector space. It is most easily regarded from the point of view of one binary operation only, that of multiplication of matrices. The set then appears as a non-commutative *group* under multiplication ; it satisfies all the rules for products with the sole exception of the commutative rule (see Appendix B). The set is sometimes described as a *full linear group* and denoted by $L_n(F)$ for a field F from which scalars are drawn (here real numbers).

A good deal of the interest in non-singular matrices is concentrated on the inverse $\mathbf{A}^{-1}$ of a given $\mathbf{A}$. In many practical problems it is necessary to invert a matrix of quite large size, a difficult computational job. All that can be remarked here is that there is a method of deriving $\mathbf{A}^{-1}$ from $\mathbf{A}$ without laborious resort to the definition. Suppose that the elementary operations by which $\mathbf{A}$ is reduced to $\mathbf{I}$ are known. Then the same operations applied to $\mathbf{I}$ serve to give $\mathbf{A}^{-1}$.

Ex. (*a*). $\mathbf{A} = \begin{bmatrix} 1 & 2 & 3 \\ 0 & 1 & 2 \\ 0 & 0 & 1 \end{bmatrix}$ equiv. to $\begin{bmatrix} 1 & 0 & 0 \\ 0 & 1 & 2 \\ 0 & 0 & 1 \end{bmatrix}$ equiv. to $\begin{bmatrix} 1 & 0 & 0 \\ 0 & 1 & 0 \\ 0 & 0 & 1 \end{bmatrix} = \mathbf{I}$

by *first* subtracting twice the first column from the second and three times the first column from the third ; and *secondly* subtracting twice the second column from the third. Apply the operations to $\mathbf{I}$:

$\mathbf{I} = \begin{bmatrix} 1 & 0 & 0 \\ 0 & 1 & 0 \\ 0 & 0 & 1 \end{bmatrix}$ equiv. to $\begin{bmatrix} 1 & -2 & -3 \\ 0 & 1 & 0 \\ 0 & 0 & 1 \end{bmatrix}$ equiv. to $\begin{bmatrix} 1 & -2 & 1 \\ 0 & 1 & -2 \\ 0 & 0 & 1 \end{bmatrix} = \mathbf{A}^{-1}$

which is the result obtained in Ex. (b) of 13.7 above.

(iii) *Orthogonal matrices.* In 12.6 (vii) above, an example is given of a linear transformation :

$$y_1 = x_1 \cos \theta + x_2 \sin \theta \quad \text{and} \quad y_2 = -x_1 \sin \theta + x_2 \cos \theta$$

from the vector (x_1, x_2) to the vector (y_1, y_2) in two dimensions. The feature of this transformation is that the two vectors represent the same point in space, provided that the co-ordinate axes are rotated through an angle θ, i.e. the transformation gives the change in co-ordinates of any point when the axes are rotated. Hence the transformation leaves all distances and angles in space quite unaffected. These properties are invariant under the linear transformation. This is an instance of what is known as an *orthogonal transformation.* The matrix :

$$\begin{bmatrix} \cos \theta & \sin \theta \\ -\sin \theta & \cos \theta \end{bmatrix}$$

of the transformation is an example of an *orthogonal matrix,* a special type of non-singular matrix. It remains to generalise these ideas.

DEFINITION : A non-singular matrix $\mathbf{A}$ is orthogonal if its inverse and transpose are the same, i.e. $\mathbf{A}^{-1} = \mathbf{A}'$.

An equivalent form of the condition is that $\mathbf{AA}' = \mathbf{A}'\mathbf{A} = \mathbf{I}$.

The following are the main properties of an orthogonal matrix $\mathbf{A} = [a_{rs}]$ of order $n \times n$:

(a) The value of the determinant $A = \pm 1$.

(b) The sum of squares of elements in any row of $\mathbf{A}$ is unity :

$$\sum_{t=1}^{n} a_{rt}^2 = 1 \quad \text{for any } r = 1, 2, \ldots n.$$

(c) The sum of elements in any one row of $\mathbf{A}$, each multiplied by the corresponding element in a second row, is zero :

$$\sum_{t=1}^{n} a_{rt}a_{st} = 0 \quad \text{for any } r, s = 1, 2, \ldots n \quad \text{and} \quad r \neq s.$$

The last two properties are equally true of columns. The proofs are : For (a)—$|\mathbf{A}| \, |\mathbf{A}'| = |\mathbf{I}| = 1$, since $\mathbf{AA}' = \mathbf{I}$. But both $|\mathbf{A}|$ and $|\mathbf{A}'|$ equal A. So $A^2 = 1$ and $A = \pm 1$.

For (b) and (c)—write $\mathbf{a}_r = (a_1, a_2, \ldots a_n)$ for the rth row of $\mathbf{A}$. Consider the product $\mathbf{AA}'$. The (r, r) th element is the inner product of the rth row of $\mathbf{A}$ and the rth column of $\mathbf{A}'$, each being $\mathbf{a}_r$. Similarly the (r, s)th element is the inner product of $\mathbf{a}_r$ and $\mathbf{a}_s$. Since $\mathbf{AA}' = \mathbf{I}$, the (r, r)th element is 1 and the (r, s)th element is 0. So :

$$\mathbf{a}_r \cdot \mathbf{a}_r = \sum_{t=1}^{n} a_{rt}^2 = 1$$

and
$$\mathbf{a}_r \cdot \mathbf{a}_s = \sum_{t=1}^{n} a_{rt} a_{st} = 0.$$

The latter means that any two distinct rows of $\mathbf{A}$, considered as vectors, are at right angles (orthogonal).

Now consider the linear transformation $\mathbf{y} = \mathbf{Ax}$, from the n-tuple $\mathbf{x}$ to the n-tuple $\mathbf{y}$, in the case where $\mathbf{A}$ is an orthogonal matrix. The transformation, like the matrix, is then called orthogonal. Let $\mathbf{x}_1, \mathbf{x}_2, \ldots$ be represented by points $P_1, P_2, \ldots$ in Euclidean space of n dimensions, in which distances and angles are defined :

Distance OP_1 : $\qquad\qquad OP_1^2 = \mathbf{x}_1 \cdot \mathbf{x}_1$

Angle θ between OP_1 and OP_2 : $\quad \cos \theta = \dfrac{\mathbf{x}_1 \cdot \mathbf{x}_2}{|\mathbf{x}_1|\,|\mathbf{x}_2|}$

where $|\mathbf{x}_1|^2 = OP_1^2 = \mathbf{x}_1 \cdot \mathbf{x}_1$ and $|\mathbf{x}_2|^2$ similarly (see 12.4 above). Now suppose that $\mathbf{y}_1, \mathbf{y}_2, \ldots$ are points $Q_1, Q_2, \ldots$ in another Euclidean space of n dimensions, as obtained from the orthogonal transformation $\mathbf{y} = \mathbf{Ax}$. Write the product of two vectors (13.6 above) :

$$\mathbf{y}_1'\mathbf{y}_2 = (\mathbf{Ax}_1)'(\mathbf{Ax}_2) = \mathbf{x}_1'\mathbf{A}'\mathbf{Ax}_2 = \mathbf{x}_1'\mathbf{Ix}_2 = \mathbf{x}_1'\mathbf{x}_2$$

since $\mathbf{A}$ is orthogonal and so $\mathbf{A}'\mathbf{A} = \mathbf{I}$. But $\mathbf{x}_1'\mathbf{x}_2$ is equal to the inner product $\mathbf{x}_1 \cdot \mathbf{x}_2$, and similarly $\mathbf{y}_1'\mathbf{y}_2 = \mathbf{y}_1 \cdot \mathbf{y}_2$. Hence, under the linear transformation, inner products are invariant : $\mathbf{x}_1 \cdot \mathbf{x}_2 = \mathbf{y}_1 \cdot \mathbf{y}_2$. It follows at once that distances and angles are invariant under the orthogonal transformation :

$$OP_1 = OQ_1 \qquad \text{and} \qquad \text{Angle}\,P_1OP_2 = \text{Angle}\,Q_1OQ_2$$

Ex. (b). The matrix $\mathbf{P} = \begin{bmatrix} \dfrac{1}{\sqrt{2}} & \dfrac{1}{\sqrt{6}} & \dfrac{1}{\sqrt{3}} \\[2mm] -\dfrac{1}{\sqrt{2}} & \dfrac{1}{\sqrt{6}} & \dfrac{1}{\sqrt{3}} \\[2mm] 0 & -\dfrac{2}{\sqrt{6}} & \dfrac{1}{\sqrt{3}} \end{bmatrix}$ is orthogonal, since $\mathbf{PP}'$ is found,

on multiplying out, to be the unit matrix $\mathbf{I}$. The properties of orthogonal matrices are also easily checked, as follows.

For (a) : $\quad |\mathbf{P}| = \dfrac{1}{\sqrt{2}}\left(\dfrac{1}{\sqrt{6}}\dfrac{1}{\sqrt{3}} + \dfrac{2}{\sqrt{6}}\dfrac{1}{\sqrt{3}}\right) + \dfrac{1}{\sqrt{2}}\left(\dfrac{1}{\sqrt{6}}\dfrac{1}{\sqrt{3}} + \dfrac{2}{\sqrt{6}}\dfrac{1}{\sqrt{3}}\right)$

$\qquad\qquad = \dfrac{2}{\sqrt{2}}\dfrac{3}{\sqrt{18}} = 1$

For (b), take the first row of $\mathbf{P}$ as an example :

$$\left(\dfrac{1}{\sqrt{2}}\right)^2 + \left(\dfrac{1}{\sqrt{6}}\right)^2 + \left(\dfrac{1}{\sqrt{3}}\right)^2 = \dfrac{1}{2} + \dfrac{1}{6} + \dfrac{1}{3} = 1$$

and, for (c), take the first two rows :

$$\left(\frac{1}{\sqrt{2}}\right)\left(-\frac{1}{\sqrt{2}}\right)+\left(\frac{1}{\sqrt{6}}\right)\left(\frac{1}{\sqrt{6}}\right)+\left(\frac{1}{\sqrt{3}}\right)\left(\frac{1}{\sqrt{3}}\right)=-\frac{1}{2}+\frac{1}{6}+\frac{1}{3}=0$$

(iv) *Indecomposable matrices*. If $\mathbf{A}$ is a given matrix of order $n \times n$, and if $\mathbf{P}^*$ is a given permutation matrix (and so orthogonal), suppose that the transform of $\mathbf{A}$ by $\mathbf{P}^*$ is of the form :

$$\mathbf{A}_\pi = \mathbf{P}^*\mathbf{A}(\mathbf{P}^*)^{-1} = \left[\begin{array}{c|c} \mathbf{A}_1 & * \\ \hline \mathbf{0} & \mathbf{A}_2 \end{array}\right]$$

where $\mathbf{A}_1$ is a matrix of order $r \times r$ $(r < n)$ and hence $\mathbf{A}_2$ is a matrix of order $(n-r) \times (n-r)$. In the lower left-hand corner of $\mathbf{A}_\pi$ is a block of zero elements, of order $(n-r) \times r$. In the upper right-hand corner is a block of any elements, shown by *, of order $r \times (n-r)$. In this case, $\mathbf{A}$ is said to be *decomposable*. If no such permutation matrix $\mathbf{P}^*$ can be found, then $\mathbf{A}$ is *indecomposable*.

Hence, an indecomposable matrix is such that no shuffling of rows, matched by the same shuffle of columns, produces a block of zero elements in the lower left-hand corner. Any other (and so decomposable) matrix $\mathbf{A}$ can always be arranged, by shuffling rows and columns, in a partitioned form with indecomposable matrices placed along the principal diagonal. The first stage is to get $\mathbf{A}$ transformed into $\mathbf{A}_\pi$ as above. If $\mathbf{A}_1$ and $\mathbf{A}_2$ are indecomposable, then the arrangement is as required. If either is decomposable, then in its turn it can be split up according to the same process. This continues until $\mathbf{A}$ is finally transformed into :

$$\left[\begin{array}{ccc|c|ccc} \mathbf{A}_1 & & * & & & * & \\ \mathbf{0} & & \mathbf{A}_2 & & & * & \\ & & & & & & \\ \hline & & & & & & \\ \mathbf{0} & & \mathbf{0} & & & \mathbf{A}_k & \end{array}\right]$$

where $\mathbf{A}_1$, $\mathbf{A}_2$, ... $\mathbf{A}_k$ are indecomposable matrices (including single elements as particular cases) grouped along the diagonal, with zero elements to one side and any elements to the other.

As an example of a 4×4 matrix which is decomposable :

$$\mathbf{A} = \begin{bmatrix} 0 & 3 & 2 & 1 \\ 0 & 1 & 2 & 0 \\ 0 & 0 & 1 & 0 \\ 1 & 4 & 3 & 2 \end{bmatrix} \quad \text{transforms to} \quad \left[\begin{array}{cc|cc} 0 & 1 & 2 & 3 \\ 1 & 2 & 3 & 4 \\ \hline 0 & 0 & 1 & 0 \\ 0 & 0 & 2 & 1 \end{array}\right]$$

by interchange of second and fourth rows and columns. The block $\begin{bmatrix} 0 & 1 \\ 1 & 2 \end{bmatrix}$ is indecomposable but $\begin{bmatrix} 1 & 0 \\ 2 & 1 \end{bmatrix}$ is decomposable by a further interchange of rows and columns. With this done, the original matrix $\mathbf{A}$ is transformed into the equivalent :

$$\mathbf{A}_n = \left[\begin{array}{cc|c|c} 0 & 1 & 2 & 3 \\ 1 & 2 & 3 & 4 \\ \hline 0 & 0 & 1 & 2 \\ \hline 0 & 0 & 0 & 1 \end{array}\right]$$

where $\begin{bmatrix} 0 & 1 \\ 1 & 2 \end{bmatrix}$, 1 and 1 are indecomposable blocks along the diagonal.

EXERCISES 13.9

1. Show how the non-singular matrix $\mathbf{A} = \begin{bmatrix} 1 & 1 & 1 \\ 0 & 1 & 0 \\ 0 & 0 & 1 \end{bmatrix}$ can be derived from $\mathbf{I}$ by elementary operations, and hence deduce that $\mathbf{A}^{-1} = \begin{bmatrix} 1 & -1 & -1 \\ 0 & 1 & 0 \\ 0 & 0 & 1 \end{bmatrix}$.

2. Two matrices $\mathbf{A}$ and $\mathbf{B}$ of the same square order are such that $\mathbf{AB} = 0$. Show that $\mathbf{B} = 0$ if $|\mathbf{A}| \neq 0$. What are the other possibilities? Hence show that the cancellation rule is :

    If $\mathbf{A}$ and $\mathbf{B}$ are square and such that $\mathbf{AB} = 0$, then *either* $\mathbf{A} = 0$ *or* $\mathbf{B} = 0$ *or* both $\mathbf{A}$ and $\mathbf{B}$ are singular.

3. Show that $\begin{bmatrix} \cos\theta & \sin\theta \\ -\sin\theta & \cos\theta \end{bmatrix}$ is orthogonal and check the properties of (iii) above.

4. If $\mathbf{A}$ and $\mathbf{B}$ are orthogonal, show that $\mathbf{A}'$, $\mathbf{A}^{-1}$ and $\mathbf{AB}$ are all orthogonal.

5. Show that the sequence in which $\mathbf{PAP}^{-1}$ is written can be reversed in the definition of similar matrices.

6. If $\mathbf{B} = \mathbf{PAP}'$ where $\mathbf{A}$ is square and $\mathbf{P}$ non-singular, show that the same set of elementary operations (represented by $\mathbf{P}$) applied to rows and to columns turns $\mathbf{A}$ into $\mathbf{B}$.

7. Check by multiplication that $\begin{bmatrix} \dfrac{1}{\sqrt{2}} & \dfrac{1}{\sqrt{2}} \\ \dfrac{-1}{\sqrt{2}} & \dfrac{1}{\sqrt{2}} \end{bmatrix} \begin{bmatrix} 0 & 1 \\ 1 & 0 \end{bmatrix} \begin{bmatrix} \dfrac{1}{\sqrt{2}} & \dfrac{-1}{\sqrt{2}} \\ \dfrac{1}{\sqrt{2}} & \dfrac{1}{\sqrt{2}} \end{bmatrix} = \begin{bmatrix} 1 & 0 \\ 0 & -1 \end{bmatrix}$

    and hence deduce that the symmetric matrix $\begin{bmatrix} 0 & 1 \\ 1 & 0 \end{bmatrix}$ is similar to the diagonal matrix $\begin{bmatrix} 1 & 0 \\ 0 & -1 \end{bmatrix}$.

8. **A** of order $n \times n$ has one of its columns with h on the principal diagonal and zero elements elsewhere. Show that **A** can be transformed by a permutation matrix **P*** into :

$$\mathbf{A}_\pi = \begin{bmatrix} h & * \\ \hline 0 & \mathbf{A}_1 \end{bmatrix}$$

where $\mathbf{A}_1$ is of order $(n-1) \times (n-1)$. Why cannot this be done if the element h is not on the principal diagonal? Interpret in terms of decomposable matrices.

9. Show that **A** of the previous exercise is equivalent to $\mathbf{B} = \begin{bmatrix} h & 0 \\ \hline 0 & \mathbf{A}_1 \end{bmatrix}$ and that

the matrix with h not on the principal diagonal can be also expressed as equivalent to a matrix of the same form. Hence examine the limitations of transformation by a permutation matrix.

REFERENCES

Aitken (A. C.) (1939, 1949) : *Determinants and Matrices* (Oliver and Boyd, First Ed. 1939, Sixth Ed. 1949), Chapters I and III.

Birkhoff (G.) and MacLane (S.) (1941) : *A Survey of Modern Algebra* (Macmillan, 1941), Chapters VIII and X.

Debreu (G.) and Herstein (I. N.) (1953) : " Non-negative Square Matrices ", *Econometrica*, **21**, 597–606.

Ferrar (W. L.) (1941) : *Algebra* (Oxford, 1941), Chapters VI–IX.

Ferrar (W. L.) (1951) : *Finite Matrices* (Oxford, 1951), Chapters I–IX.

Frazer (R. A.), Duncan (W. J.) and Collar (A. R.) (1947) : *Elementary Matrices* (Cambridge, 1947), Chapters I and III.

Kemeny (J. G.), Snell (J. L.) and Thompson (G. L.) (1957) : *Introduction to Finite Mathematics* (Prentice-Hall, 1957), Chapter V.

Littlewood (D. E.) (1950) : *University Algebra* (Heinemann, 1950), Chapters I and II.

Murdoch (D. C.) (1957) : *Linear Algebra for Undergraduates* (Wiley, 1957), Chapters 2 and 3.

Thrall (R. M.) and Tornheim (L.) (1957) : *Vector Spaces and Matrices* (Wiley, 1957), Chapters 2 and 3.

Tintner (G.) (1952) : *Econometrics* (Wiley, 1952), Appendices.

Wade (T. L.) (1951) : *Algebra of Vectors and Matrices* (Addison-Wesley Press, 1951), Chapters 1, 5, 6, and 9.

CHAPTER 14

APPLICATIONS OF VECTOR AND MATRIX ALGEBRA

14.1 Linear Combination and Dependence

These concepts apply to all kinds of entities in a set $\{x_1, x_2, x_3, \ldots\}$ as long as the entities can be multiplied by scalars and added. A *linear combination* of $x_1, x_2, x_3, \ldots$ is:

$$x = \sum_r \lambda_r x_r \quad \text{for some scalars } \lambda_1, \lambda_2, \lambda_3, \ldots$$

A set $\{x_1, x_2, x_3, \ldots\}$ is *linearly dependent* if at least one member is a linear combination of other members. The concepts are particularly important, indeed quite fundamental, for sets of vectors and matrices.

Vectors are taken, as in Chapter 12, as m-tuples of real numbers represented by points in Cartesian or Euclidean space of m dimensions with reference to fixed co-ordinate axes. Consider a set of n such vectors $\mathbf{x}^{(k)} = (x_1^{(k)}, x_2^{(k)}, \ldots x_m^{(k)})$ represented by points P_k for $k = 1, 2, \ldots n$. The vectors are *linearly dependent* if scalar multiples λ_k, not all zero, can be found so that:

$$\sum_{k=1}^{n} \lambda_k \mathbf{x}^{(k)} = 0 \quad \ldots\ldots\ldots\ldots\ldots\ldots\ldots(1)$$

Then, if λ_t is the last non-zero value among the λ's, the vector $\mathbf{x}^{(t)}$ is a *linear combination* of the previous vectors:

$$\mathbf{x}^{(t)} = -\frac{1}{\lambda_t} \sum_{k=1}^{t-1} \lambda_k \mathbf{x}^{(k)} \quad \ldots\ldots\ldots\ldots\ldots\ldots(2)$$

Here (1) and (2) are alternative expressions of the same thing. Moreover, (2) can be written for *any* vector $\mathbf{x}^{(k)}$ provided only that the corresponding $\lambda_k \neq 0$. On the other hand, if no multiples λ_k (except for the trivial case where all $\lambda_k = 0$) can be found so that (1) holds, then the vectors are *linearly independent* and no one of them is a linear combination of the others.

To see the meaning of linear dependence, write out (1) in full:

$$\lambda_1 x_1^{(1)} + \lambda_2 x_1^{(2)} + \ldots + \lambda_n x_1^{(n)} = 0$$
$$\lambda_1 x_2^{(1)} + \lambda_2 x_2^{(2)} + \ldots + \lambda_n x_2^{(n)} = 0$$
$$\ldots\ldots\ldots\ldots\ldots\ldots\ldots\ldots\ldots\ldots\ldots\ldots\ldots\ldots$$
$$\lambda_1 x_m^{(1)} + \lambda_2 x_m^{(2)} + \ldots + \lambda_n x_m^{(n)} = 0$$

Then, if $\lambda_n \neq 0$, the fact that $\mathbf{x}^{(n)}$ is a linear combination of the other vectors, by (2), is represented by m relations :

$$x_1^{(n)} = -\frac{1}{\lambda_n}(\lambda_1 x_1^{(1)} + \lambda_2 x_1^{(2)} + \ldots\ldots)$$

$$x_2^{(n)} = -\frac{1}{\lambda_n}(\lambda_1 x_2^{(1)} + \lambda_2 x_2^{(2)} + \ldots\ldots)$$

$$\ldots\ldots\ldots\ldots\ldots\ldots\ldots\ldots\ldots\ldots\ldots\ldots$$

$$x_m^{(n)} = -\frac{1}{\lambda_n}(\lambda_1 x_m^{(1)} + \lambda_2 x_m^{(2)} + \ldots\ldots)$$

The relations (1) and (2) are to be taken as holding for each component separately.

Fig. 50 illustrates in the case of two-dimensional vectors. The three points P_1, P_2 and P_3 represent the given vectors $\mathbf{x}^{(1)} = (x_1^{(1)}, x_2^{(1)})$, $\mathbf{x}^{(2)} = (x_1^{(2)}, x_2^{(2)})$ and $\mathbf{x}^{(3)} = (x_1^{(3)}, x_2^{(3)})$, referred to axes Ox_1x_2 on which can be marked off by A_1 and A_2 the unit vectors $\boldsymbol{\epsilon}_1 = (1, 0)$ and $\boldsymbol{\epsilon}_2 = (0, 1)$. As illustrated, P_3 is a linear combination of P_1 and P_2. By the parallelogram rule, OP_3 is the sum of OQ_1 and OQ_2, where Q_1 and Q_2 lie on OP_1 and OP_2 respectively. Let λ_1 be the ratio of OQ_1 to OP_1 and λ_2 the ratio of OQ_2 to OP_2. Then :

$$OP_3 = OQ_1 + OQ_2$$

i.e.
$$OP_3 = \lambda_1 OP_1 + \lambda_2 OP_2$$

This is the geometrical equivalent of the linear combination :

$$\mathbf{x}^{(3)} = \lambda_1 \mathbf{x}^{(1)} + \lambda_2 \mathbf{x}^{(2)}$$

and so of the relation of linear dependence

$$\lambda_1 \mathbf{x}^{(1)} + \lambda_2 \mathbf{x}^{(2)} - \mathbf{x}^{(3)} = \mathbf{0}$$

This particular expression of linear dependence of three vectors depends on OP_1, OP_2 and OP_3 being distinct and different directions. There is linear dependence, however, even when any two or all three of the points are co-linear with O. For example, if OP_1 and OP_2 are on the same radius from O, then $OP_2 = \lambda OP_1$, where λ is the ratio of lengths along the radius. The relation

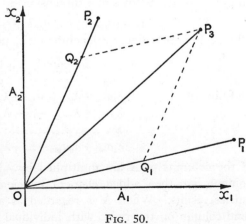

FIG. 50.

of linear dependence is then $\lambda\mathbf{x}^{(1)} - \mathbf{x}^{(2)} = 0$. It does not matter that the third vector fails to appear; one of the multiples is zero, but the other two are not.

The conclusion is that any *three* vectors are linearly dependent in two dimensions. It also appears that *two* vectors may or may not be linearly dependent. If OP_1 and OP_2 are co-linear, the vectors are linearly dependent; otherwise they are linearly independent. Indeed, it is always possible to find two vectors which are linearly independent in two dimensions, specifically the unit vectors OA_1 and OA_2 which " span " the two-dimensional space.

The results can be generalised to vectors in three or more dimensions as shown in Appendix B. First, as a definition, a particular set of n vectors *spans* a system of vectors V if every vector of V is a linear combination of the particular n vectors. Then :

> V *is a system of vectors in m dimensions. There exist sets of m vectors which are linearly independent and which span V. A set of fewer than m vectors may be linearly independent but cannot span V. A set of more than m vectors may span V but cannot be linearly independent.*

That there *is* such a set of m vectors is shown by the fact that the unit vectors $\boldsymbol{\epsilon}_1, \boldsymbol{\epsilon}_2, \dots \boldsymbol{\epsilon}_m$ are linearly independent and span V. Such a set of m vectors is called a *basis* of V. The unit vectors make one basis; there are generally many others.

The application to a matrix $\mathbf{A} = [a_{rs}]$ of order $m \times n$ is to be made in two ways, first in terms of the n columns in m dimensions :

$$\mathbf{a}_s = (a_{1s}, a_{2s}, \dots a_{ms}) \quad (s = 1, 2, \dots n)$$

and then for the m rows in n dimensions :

$$\mathbf{a}_r' = (a_{r1}, a_{r2}, \dots a_{rn}) \quad (r = 1, 2, \dots m)$$

The n columns are linearly dependent if λ_s, not all zero, can be found so that

$$\sum_{s=1}^{n} \lambda_s \mathbf{a}_s = \mathbf{0} \dots\dots\dots\dots\dots\dots\dots\dots\dots\dots\dots\dots(3)$$

In full :
$$\lambda_1 a_{11} + \lambda_2 a_{12} + \dots + \lambda_n a_{1n} = 0$$
$$\lambda_1 a_{21} + \lambda_2 a_{22} + \dots + \lambda_n a_{2n} = 0$$
$$\dots\dots\dots\dots\dots\dots\dots\dots\dots\dots$$
$$\lambda_1 a_{m1} + \lambda_2 a_{m2} + \dots + \lambda_n a_{mn} = 0$$

If the columns of $\mathbf{A}$ are multiplied by $\lambda_1, \lambda_2, \dots \lambda_n$ in turn, and if the columns are then added element by element, then a column of zero entries results. When $\mathbf{A}$ is regarded as a double table of entries, the total column on the right, with individual columns multiplied by $\lambda_1, \lambda_2,$

... λ_n, consists of zero entries ; for appropriate multiples the table adds across to zero.

The relation (3) can be expressed more concisely in matrix notation. Write λ for the column vector of order $n \times 1$, made up of $\lambda_1, \lambda_2, \dots \lambda_n$. Then :

$$A\lambda = 0 \quad \text{or} \quad \lambda'A' = 0 \quad (\lambda \neq 0) \quad \dots\dots\dots\dots\dots\dots(4)$$

is the expression of linear dependence of the columns of A.

The corresponding concept of linear dependence of rows of A is that a column vector μ of order $m \times 1$, composed of $\mu_1, \mu_2, \dots \mu_m$, not all zero, can be found so that

$$\sum_{r=1}^{m} \mu_r a_r' = 0, \quad \text{i.e.} \quad A'\mu = 0 \quad \text{or} \quad \mu'A = 0 \quad (\mu \neq 0)$$

which correspond to (3) and (4) for columns.

DEFINITION : The $m \times n$ matrix A has linearly dependent columns if an $n \times 1$ column vector $\lambda \neq 0$ exists so that :

$$A\lambda = 0 \quad \text{or} \quad \lambda'A' = 0$$

and it has linearly dependent rows if an $m \times 1$ column vector $\mu \neq 0$ exists so that :

$$A'\mu = 0 \quad \text{or} \quad \mu'A = 0$$

Several properties follow from the results for linear dependence of vectors. If A contains more columns than rows, then the column vectors are greater in number (n) than their dimensions (m). Hence there must be at least one relation of linear dependence between columns when $n > m$. Now suppose that the n columns of A are linearly dependent. Then one column of A is a linear combination of the other columns, i.e. it is the sum of fixed multiples of the other columns. By the elementary operation of subtracting multiples (13.8 above), A can be shown equivalent to a matrix B with a column of zero elements. The rank of B is less than n and, since equivalent matrices are of the same rank, so is the rank of A. Similar results hold for the rows of A. Two examples illustrate.

Ex. (a). $A = \begin{bmatrix} 1 & 2 & 2 \\ 2 & 4 & 4 \\ 2 & 1 & 4 \end{bmatrix}$ equiv. to $\begin{bmatrix} 1 & 2 & 0 \\ 2 & 4 & 0 \\ 2 & 1 & 0 \end{bmatrix}$ of rank 2. Here twice the first

column is subtracted from the third. The three column vectors are :

$$a_1 = (1, 2, 2) \quad a_2 = (2, 4, 1) \quad a_3 = (2, 4, 4)$$

and there is one relation of linear dependence :

$$2a_1 - a_3 = 0$$

with multiples $\lambda_1 = 2$, $\lambda_2 = 0$ and $\lambda_3 = -1$. This simply expresses the fact that the third column is twice the first. The matrix A of order 3×3 and rank 2 has two linearly independent columns (first and second) and one column (third) linearly dependent on the others.

Ex. (b). $\mathbf{A} = \begin{bmatrix} 1 & 2 & 2 & -1 \\ 2 & 4 & 4 & -2 \\ 2 & 1 & 4 & 1 \end{bmatrix}$ equiv. to $\begin{bmatrix} 1 & 2 & 0 & 0 \\ 2 & 4 & 0 & 0 \\ 2 & 1 & 0 & 0 \end{bmatrix}$ of rank 2. The four column vectors :

$$\mathbf{a}_1 = (1, 2, 2) \quad \mathbf{a}_2 = (2, 4, 1) \quad \mathbf{a}_3 = (2, 4, 4) \quad \mathbf{a}_4 = (-1, -2, 1)$$

are connected by two relations of linear dependence :

$$2\mathbf{a}_1 - \mathbf{a}_3 \quad = 0 \quad (\lambda_1 = 2, \lambda_2 = 0, \quad \lambda_3 = -1, \lambda_4 = 0)$$
$$\mathbf{a}_1 - \mathbf{a}_2 - \mathbf{a}_4 = 0 \quad (\lambda_1 = 1, \lambda_2 = -1, \quad \lambda_3 = 0, \quad \lambda_4 = -1)$$

These express the facts that the third column is twice the first, and that the fourth column is the difference of the first and second. The matrix $\mathbf{A}$ is of order 3×4 and must have columns linearly dependent ; in fact it is of rank 2 and has only two linearly independent columns and two columns linearly dependent on them.

There is clearly a relation between linear dependence and rank. This needs to be pursued. Let $\mathbf{A}$ be square of order $n \times n$ and rank $r \leqslant n$. First, if the columns are linearly dependent, then $\mathbf{A}$ is equivalent to $\mathbf{B}$ with a column of zero elements. The rank of $\mathbf{A}$ is $r < n$. Conversely, if the rank $r < n$, then the columns of $\mathbf{A}$ are linearly dependent. $\mathbf{A}$ contains an $r \times r$ sub-matrix $\mathbf{A}_1$ with $| \mathbf{A}_1 | \neq 0$. Add another row and column (from $\mathbf{A}$) to $\mathbf{A}_1$ to give the $(r+1) \times (r+1)$ sub-matrix $\mathbf{A}_2$, where $| \mathbf{A}_2 | = 0$ since the rank of $\mathbf{A}$ is only r. Take λ of order n to comprise the $(r+1)$ co-factors of the added row in $\mathbf{A}_2$ plus $(n - r - 1)$ zero elements to complete. Then the expansion rule for $| \mathbf{A}_2 | = 0$ gives $\mathbf{A}\lambda = 0$. Not all the elements of λ are zero since one of the co-factors involves $| \mathbf{A}_1 | \neq 0$. Hence the columns of $\mathbf{A}$ are linearly dependent, as is to be proved.

Further, in the above proof, it is clear that it is the column added in $\mathbf{A}_2$ which is linearly dependent on the r columns of $\mathbf{A}_1$. The added column can be selected from $\mathbf{A}$ in $(n - r)$ different ways. Hence, $\mathbf{A}$ contains $(n - r)$ columns each linearly dependent on the other r columns, which are themselves linearly independent.

Though these results are expressed for square $\mathbf{A}$, they are easily extended to incorporate the case of a rectangular matrix of $m \times n$ order $(m \neq n)$. There is either an excess of columns or an excess of rows. These additional columns (or rows) must be linearly dependent on the others. The results for the square case are simply augmented by further linear dependencies of columns (or rows). Hence :

Linear Dependence of Columns of a Matrix

A matrix is of order $m \times n$ and rank r. It is always possible to select r columns which are linearly independent, but any set of $(r+1)$ column must be linearly dependent. If $r < n$ there is at least one set of linearly *dependent columns ; if $r=n$ the whole set of columns is linearly independent.*

An exactly similar result holds for rows.

The non-singular matrix now stands out as of great simplicity and convenience. If a matrix is non-singular of order $n \times n$, its rank $r=n$ and there are no " spare " rows or columns. More precisely, the columns and the rows must be linearly independent in a non-singular matrix and, conversely, a non-singular matrix is the only case where there are no relations of linear dependence between columns or rows.

For any other kind of matrix—whether it is square but singular, or rectangular with different numbers of columns and rows—there must be some linear dependence of columns or rows or both. Broadly, whenever there is an excess of columns (rows) above the rank of a matrix, then these extra columns (rows) are linearly dependent on the others. A matrix of rank r " boils down " to a sub-matrix of order $r \times r$ with linearly independent rows and columns ; all other rows and columns are linearly dependent.

EXERCISES 14.1

1. Four vectors are given in three dimensions. Represent them as points in space and assume that they are the corners of a pyramid-like solid figure. Show that one of the vectors can be expressed as a linear combination of the other three. Examine the special case where the four points lie on one plane and where two or more of them are co-linear with 0.

2. Examine for linear dependence the rows and columns in $\begin{bmatrix} 3 & -4 & 2 \\ 5 & -6 & -1 \\ 0 & 2 & -1 \end{bmatrix}$

3. Show that $A = \begin{bmatrix} 2 & 1 & 3 & -5 \\ 1 & -3 & 5 & 2 \\ 0 & -7 & 7 & 9 \end{bmatrix}$ has one dependent row and two dependent columns. What can be said of the transpose A'?

4. The matrix A of order $m \times n$ has linearly dependent rows, the multiples being $\lambda_1, \lambda_2, \ldots \lambda_m$ $(\lambda_m \neq 0)$. If A is transformed into equivalent form B with a last row of zero elements, then $B = PAQ$ for suitable P and Q, non-singular square matrices. Show that $Q = I$ and indicate a form for P.

5. A is of order $m \times n$ with $m < n$. A matrix B of order $n \times n$ is defined by adding $(n-m)$ rows of zero elements to A. Show that $|B| = 0$, that the columns of B are linearly dependent and hence that the columns of A are linearly dependent.

14.2 Linear Equations and their Solution

The general system of linear equations can be written (as in 12.2 above)

$$a_{11}x_1 + a_{12}x_2 + \ldots + a_{1n}x_n = y_1$$
$$a_{21}x_1 + a_{22}x_2 + \ldots + a_{2n}x_n = y_2$$
$$\ldots\ldots\ldots\ldots\ldots\ldots\ldots\ldots\ldots\ldots$$
$$a_{m1}x_1 + a_{m2}x_2 + \ldots + a_{mn}x_n = y_m$$

In matrix notation :

$$\mathbf{Ax=y}$$

where $\mathbf{A}=[a_{rs}]$ is a matrix of $m \times n$ coefficients, $\mathbf{x}=(x_1, x_2, \ldots x_n)$ is a column vector of n variables and $\mathbf{y}=(y_1, y_2, \ldots y_m)$ is a column vector of the given constants in the m equations.

The problem is to find the vector $\mathbf{x}$ given $\mathbf{A}$ and $\mathbf{y}$, i.e. to find the x's (or as many as possible) in terms of the given a's and y's. It is illustrated in the simplest case of two equations in two variables :

$$a_{11}x_1 + a_{12}x_2 = y_1 \quad \text{and} \quad a_{21}x_1 + a_{22}x_2 = y_2$$

giving :
$$x_1 = \frac{y_1 a_{22} - y_2 a_{12}}{a_{11}a_{22} - a_{21}a_{12}} \qquad x_2 = \frac{y_2 a_{11} - y_1 a_{21}}{a_{11}a_{22} - a_{21}a_{12}}$$

i.e.
$$\frac{x_1}{\begin{vmatrix} y_1 & a_{12} \\ y_2 & a_{22} \end{vmatrix}} = \frac{x_2}{\begin{vmatrix} a_{11} & y_1 \\ a_{21} & y_2 \end{vmatrix}} = \frac{1}{\begin{vmatrix} a_{11} & a_{12} \\ a_{21} & a_{22} \end{vmatrix}}$$

in the determinant notation. Difficulties arise only when one (or more) of the three determinants written takes a zero value. It is thus clear that the cases of difficulty are those in which the vector $\mathbf{y}=0$, the matrix $\mathbf{A}$ (if square) is singular, or both. If $\mathbf{y}=0$, the first two determinants vanish and the variable x's, take zero values. If $|\mathbf{A}|=0$, the third determinant is zero and the variable x's take infinite values. If $\mathbf{y}=0$ and $|\mathbf{A}|=0$, all determinants are zero and the x's are indeterminate, as the ratios of zero values. There are further complications when $\mathbf{A}$ is not square and the number of equations differs from that of the variables.

When there are several numerical equations in several variables, the practical approach of elementary algebra is to eliminate variables one by one in a process of partial solution and substitution. Sometimes this works out to a unique solution, i.e. values for all variables. Sometimes, when all equations are used, variables are left over as surplus, and the solution gives only some variables in terms of others. This may be because there is a shortage of equations, or because some of the equations are not independent of others. Sometimes, when all variables are found, equations are left over as surplus, and the question is whether these are consistent or not with the others. From this angle, the difficulties arise because some equations may not be consistent with, or independent of other equations in the system.

It will, therefore, appear that the solution of $\mathbf{Ax=y}$ depends on the rank of $\mathbf{A}$ (e.g. whether a square $\mathbf{A}$ is singular) and on the relations of dependence and consistency between equations. The concept of linear dependence in 14.1 above is likely to be very relevant.

(i) *Homogeneous linear equations :* $\mathbf{Ax} = 0$

This is the case where $\mathbf{y} = 0$, one of those expected to lead to difficulties. Two preliminary points can be made at once. There is always one solution $\mathbf{x} = 0$ in which all the variables are zero ; but this is so trivial that it can be ignored. On the other hand, if $\mathbf{x}$ is a non-zero solution, then so is $k\mathbf{x}$ for any value of k. Hence a unique (non-zero) solution is never possible ; the equations being homogeneous cannot determine the " scale " of the x's. What is sought is the ratios of the variables, or more generally some variables in terms of others.

In the equations $\mathbf{Ax} = 0$, let $\mathbf{A}$ be of order $m \times n$ and of rank r. If the columns of $\mathbf{A}$ are linearly dependent, then there are n multiples $\lambda_1, \lambda_2, \ldots \lambda_n$, not all zero, making up a vector λ such that $\mathbf{A}\lambda = 0$. Hence $\mathbf{x} = \lambda$ is a solution of the equations. This is seen in full in the conditions (3) of 14.1 above ; the multiples (λ's) for linear dependence of columns of $\mathbf{A}$ are substituted for the variables (x's) in the homogeneous equations and satisfy them. Hence, *any* linear dependence among columns of $\mathbf{A}$ implies a solution of $\mathbf{Ax} = 0$; the multiples of the dependence provide the values of the variables, both being determinate as to ratios but not as to scale. Hence, from 14.1 above, the condition for a non-trivial solution to exist at all is that $r < n$; the rank of the matrix $\mathbf{A}$ must be less than the number of variables (columns in $\mathbf{A}$). The implications of the condition are easily worked out. If there are fewer equations than variables ($m < n$), then $r \leqslant m$ and $r < n$ in all cases ; there are always solutions. If the numbers of equations and variables are equal ($m = n$), then $\mathbf{A}$ is square of order $n \times n$ and $r \leqslant n$. For a solution, $r < n$ and $|\mathbf{A}| = 0$, i.e. $\mathbf{A}$ must be singular. The case ruled out, as giving no solution, is $r = n$, $|\mathbf{A}| \neq 0$ and $\mathbf{A}$ non-singular. If there are more equations than variables, the position is similar ; here $r \leqslant n < m$ and the case $r = n$ where the rank of $\mathbf{A}$ is the largest possible (equal to the number of variables and columns in $\mathbf{A}$) must be ruled out.

The result is :

> *If* $\mathbf{Ax} = 0$ *is a system of m homogeneous equations in n variables, where* $\mathbf{A}$ *is a given matrix of order* $m \times n$ *and rank r, then the condition for a non-zero solution of* $\mathbf{x}$ *is that* $r < n$. *If* $m < n$, *there is always a solution ; if* $m = n$, *there is a solution if* $\mathbf{A}$ *is singular ; if* $m > n$, *there is a solution if* $\mathbf{A}$ *does not have the largest possible rank, i.e. if* $r < n$.

A practical method of finding the solution or solutions is to pick out of $\mathbf{A}$

a square sub-matrix of order $r \times r$ with non-zero determinant. This fixes r equations in r variables, the other $(n-r)$ variables being given assigned values. The equations are non-homogeneous and (as shown below) give unique expressions for r variables in terms of the other $(n-r)$. The remaining $(m-r)$ equations are then found to be consistent with the solution. One important case arises when there are n homogeneous equations in n variables and when the $n \times n$ matrix $\mathbf{A}$ is of rank $(n-1)$. In this case, one variable is given assigned values and the other $(n-1)$ variables found in terms of it ; the *ratios* of the variables are then fixed by the equations.

Two examples illustrate, using the matrices examined in Ex. (*a*) and Ex. (*b*) of 14.1 above.

Ex. (a).
$$\begin{array}{l} x_1 + 2x_2 + 2x_3 = 0 \\ 2x_1 + 4x_2 + 4x_3 = 0 \\ 2x_1 + x_2 + 4x_3 = 0 \end{array} \text{ with } \mathbf{A} = \begin{bmatrix} 1 & 2 & 2 \\ 2 & 4 & 4 \\ 2 & 1 & 4 \end{bmatrix} \text{ of rank 2.}$$

The third column of $\mathbf{A}$ is linearly dependent on the others. Hence, assign values to x_3 and use the first and third equations to find x_1 and x_2 :
$$x_1 + 2x_2 = -2x_3 \quad \text{and} \quad 2x_1 + x_2 = -4x_3$$
giving :
$$x_1 = -2x_3 \quad \text{and} \quad x_2 = 0$$
The second equation is consistent, being the same as the first. Hence there is a unique solution in the ratios :
$$x_1 : x_2 : x_3 = -2 : 0 : 1$$
This is an example of the case where $\mathbf{A}$ is of order $n \times n$ and rank $(n-1)$.

Ex. (b).
$$\begin{array}{l} x_1 + 2x_2 + 2x_3 - x_4 = 0 \\ 2x_1 + 4x_2 + 4x_3 - 2x_4 = 0 \\ 2x_1 + x_2 + 4x_3 + x_4 = 0 \end{array} \text{ with } \mathbf{A} = \begin{bmatrix} 1 & 2 & 2 & -1 \\ 2 & 4 & 4 & -2 \\ 2 & 1 & 4 & 1 \end{bmatrix} \text{ of rank 2.}$$

The last two columns of $\mathbf{A}$ are dependent on the others ; and the second equation can again be dropped as equivalent to the first. Hence, assign x_3 and x_4 and solve the first and third equations for x_1 and x_2 :
$$x_1 + 2x_2 = -2x_3 + x_4 \quad \text{and} \quad 2x_1 + x_2 = -4x_3 - x_4$$
giving :
$$x_1 = -2x_3 - x_4 \quad \text{and} \quad x_2 = x_4$$
Since there are four variables and the rank of $\mathbf{A}$ is 2, two of the variables must be given assigned values and the other two variables are then determined.

(ii) *Non-homogeneous linear equations :* $\mathbf{Ax = y}$ $(\mathbf{y} \neq \mathbf{0})$

In general, there are m equations in n variables. The column vector $\mathbf{y}$ of order m is given, the right-hand sides of the equations. The column vector $\mathbf{x}$ of order n comprises the variables to be found. The matrix $\mathbf{A}$ is of order $m \times n$ and its rank is taken as r, not greater than the smaller of m and n.

(iia) *Non-singular case.* The most important and convenient system of equations arises in the non-singular case where $\mathbf{A}$ is of order $n \times n$ and of rank n. There are as many equations as variables and $|A| \neq 0$. There are no complications and a unique solution can be found by one of several equivalent methods.

Elimination of variables : from the equations taken one by one, each variable can be found explicitly in terms of other variables and eliminated by substitution in other equations.   In the end a unique value of the last variable is determined and, by re-tracing steps, corresponding unique values of the other variables.   This method is straight-forward but laborious.

Cramer's rule : the general formula for the unique solution is :

$$x_s = \frac{|A_s|}{|A|} = \frac{\sum\limits_{r=1}^{n} y_r A_{rs}}{\sum\limits_{r=1}^{n} a_{rs} A_{rs}} \qquad (s = 1, 2, \dots n)$$

where A_s is the matrix formed from A by substituting the vector y for the sth column.   The expansion of the determinants $|A_s|$ and $|A|$ is done in terms of the sth column, the co-factors in $|A|$ being A_{rs} for $r = 1, 2, \dots n$.

To prove the formula, multiply the n equations $Ax = y$ by $A_{1s}, A_{2s}, \dots A_{ns}$ respectively and add to get :

$$\sum_{t=1}^{n} \left(\sum_{r=1}^{n} a_{rt} A_{rs} \right) x_t = \sum_{r=1}^{n} y_r A_{rs} \quad (s = 1, 2, \dots n)$$

Now
$$\sum_{r=1}^{n} a_{rt} A_{rs} = 0 \qquad (s \neq t)$$
$$= |A| \qquad (s = t)$$

and
$$\sum_{r=1}^{n} y_r A_{rs} = |A_s|$$

by the expansion rule for determinants.   Hence :

$$|A| \, x_s = |A_s|$$

which establishes the formula.

Inversion of A *:* from $Ax = y$, on pre-multiplication by A^{-1} which exists since $|A| \neq 0$, is obtained :

$$A^{-1}Ax = A^{-1}y$$

Since $A^{-1}A = I$ and since $Ix = x$, the solution is

$$x = A^{-1}y$$

The unique solution x is thus obtained by multiplying y by A^{-1}.

The practical technique for numerical equations is to use whichever method involves least computation. Elimination of variables is practicable only if the number of equations is small. Cramer's rule is a matter of evaluating determinants, straight-forward but laborious. The inversion of A to get A^{-1} is also a lengthy process. In some cases, as in the example below, elementary operations which turn A into I can be applied to I to give A^{-1}. More generally, matrix inversion can be done following computational procedures devised for use on high-speed computators. The following example illustrates :

Ex. (c).
$$-x_1 + x_2 + x_3 = 2a \quad \text{with} \quad A = \begin{bmatrix} -1 & 1 & 1 \\ 1 & -1 & 1 \\ 1 & 1 & -1 \end{bmatrix}$$
$$x_1 - x_2 + x_3 = 2b$$
$$x_1 + x_2 - x_3 = 2c$$

Here A equiv. to $\begin{bmatrix} -1 & 0 & 0 \\ 1 & 0 & 2 \\ 1 & 2 & 0 \end{bmatrix}$ equiv. to $\begin{bmatrix} -1 & 0 & 0 \\ 0 & 0 & 2 \\ 0 & 2 & 0 \end{bmatrix}$ equiv. to I.

The first step is to add the first column to the other two. The second step is to take half the second column and half the third from the first column. The last step is to multiply columns by $-1, \frac{1}{2}, \frac{1}{2}$ and to transpose the last two columns. Applying these processes to I, the successive matrices obtained are :

$$I = \begin{bmatrix} 1 & 0 & 0 \\ 0 & 1 & 0 \\ 0 & 0 & 1 \end{bmatrix} \cdots \begin{bmatrix} 1 & 1 & 1 \\ 0 & 1 & 0 \\ 0 & 0 & 1 \end{bmatrix} \cdots \begin{bmatrix} 0 & 1 & 1 \\ -\frac{1}{2} & 1 & 0 \\ -\frac{1}{2} & 0 & 1 \end{bmatrix} \cdots \begin{bmatrix} 0 & \frac{1}{2} & \frac{1}{2} \\ \frac{1}{2} & 0 & \frac{1}{2} \\ \frac{1}{2} & \frac{1}{2} & 0 \end{bmatrix} = A^{-1}$$

Hence : $$x = \begin{bmatrix} 0 & \frac{1}{2} & \frac{1}{2} \\ \frac{1}{2} & 0 & \frac{1}{2} \\ \frac{1}{2} & \frac{1}{2} & 0 \end{bmatrix} \begin{bmatrix} 2a \\ 2b \\ 2c \end{bmatrix} = \begin{bmatrix} b+c \\ c+a \\ a+b \end{bmatrix}$$

The solution is : $x_1 = b + c, \quad x_2 = c + a, \quad x_3 = a + b$.

(ii*b*) *Singular cases*. It remains to examine other cases in which either A is square but singular, or A is rectangular. Write the *augmented matrix*

$$B = [A \vdots y]$$

which consists of A with an additional column made up of the y's. The order of B is $m \times (n+1)$ and its rank is either r or $(r+1)$. If the last column (the y's) is linearly dependent on the columns of A, the rank of B is r, the same as A. If the column of y's is linearly independent of the columns of A, the rank of B is $(r+1)$.

The system of equations $Ax = y$ can be written with the y's shifted to the left-hand sides. It then appears :

$$Bz = 0$$

where z is the column vector $(x_1, x_2, \ldots x_n, -1)$ of order $(n+1)$. This is a set of homogeneous equations and, by the results of (i), the columns of

B must be linearly dependent for a solution. But this is not enough. The multiples $\lambda_1, \lambda_2, \ldots \lambda_n, \lambda_{n+1}$ of the linear dependence provide the solution for **z**. Only the ratios of the λ's are relevant, so that λ_{n+1} can be " scaled " to the required value (-1), *provided* that $\lambda_{n+1} \neq 0$. This is so only if the last column of **B** (the y's) is linearly dependent on the other columns, i.e. if **B** has rank r, the same as **A**. Hence the first result is that no solution exists if **B** has rank $(r+1)$. This is because the y's are linearly independent of the columns of **A**, i.e. because the equations are not consistent.

In all other cases, **A** and **B** having rank r, a solution can be found. The cases only differ in how many of the variables are determined in value, given assigned values to the other variables. There is a square sub-matrix in **A** or **B** of order $r \times r$ and with non-zero determinant. The non-singular solution gives unique values of the corresponding r variables in terms of the remaining $(n-r)$ variables. Only r equations are used, but the other $(m-r)$ equations are consistent. Notice that r is not greater than the smaller of m and n. Only in the non-singular case is $r=m=n$. In all the other cases, either $r<m$, or $r<n$, or both. When $r<m$, there are " surplus " equations which cause no trouble ; provided that **B** is of rank r, these equations are derivable from the others and consistent with them. When $r<n$, there are " surplus " variables which also cause no trouble, once they are assigned arbitrary values and the r selected variables found in terms of them.

The results in cases other than the non-singular case can be brought together :

> *The system of equations* $\mathbf{Ax}=\mathbf{y}$, *where* **A** *is of order* $m \times n$ *and of rank* r, *is inconsistent, without solution, if the augmented matrix* $\mathbf{B}=[\mathbf{A} \vdots \mathbf{y}]$ *is of rank* $(r+1)$. *In all cases where* **B** *is of rank* r, *there is a solution in which a set of appropriate variables* r *in number is given in terms of the remaining* $(n-r)$ *variables. The solution is obtained from* r *equations and the remaining* $(m-r)$ *equations are ignored as derivable from them.*

Two of the possibilities are indicated in the following example and others in Ex. 6, 7 and 8 below.

Ex. (*d*). The system of equations

$$x_1 + x_2 + x_3 = 3$$
$$x_1 - 2x_2 + 2x_3 = 1$$
$$2x_1 - x_2 + 3x_3 = 2$$

has $\mathbf{A} = \begin{bmatrix} 1 & 1 & 1 \\ 1 & -2 & 2 \\ 2 & -1 & 3 \end{bmatrix}$ of rank 2 and $\mathbf{B} = \begin{bmatrix} 1 & 1 & 1 & 3 \\ 1 & -2 & 2 & 1 \\ 2 & -1 & 3 & 2 \end{bmatrix}$ of rank 3. There is no solution ; the equations are inconsistent. The addition of the first two equations gives :

$$2x_1 - x_2 + 3x_3 = 4$$

which is inconsistent with the third equation.

If the system is modified by changing the constant of the third equation from 2 to 4, it becomes consistent and the third equation can be dropped as obtainable from the other two (by addition). The matrix $\mathbf{B}$, with 4 instead of 2 in the bottom right-hand corner, is of rank 2, the same as $\mathbf{A}$. The first two equations then give on solution :

$$x_1 = \tfrac{1}{3}(7 - 4x_3) \quad \text{and} \quad x_2 = \tfrac{1}{3}(2 + x_3)$$

Two variables (x_1 and x_2) are given in terms of the third (x_3) to which arbitrary values can be assigned. In this case, $\mathbf{A}$ of order 3×3 and rank 2, there is one " surplus " variable and one " surplus " equation.

EXERCISES 14.2

1. In Ex. (a) above, assign arbitrary values to x_2 and attempt to derive x_1 and x_3. Why cannot this be done?

2. See whether and what solutions of

$$\begin{aligned} x_1 + 2x_2 + 2x_3 + x_4 &= 0 \\ 2x_1 + 4x_2 + 4x_3 + x_4 &= 0 \\ 2x_1 + x_2 + 4x_3 + x_4 &= 0 \end{aligned} \quad \text{and of} \quad \begin{aligned} x_1 + 2x_2 + 2x_3 &= 0 \\ 2x_1 + 4x_2 + 4x_3 &= 0 \\ 2x_1 + x_2 + 4x_3 &= 0 \\ x_1 + x_2 + x_3 &= 0 \end{aligned}$$

exist. Compare with the solutions of Ex. (a) and Ex. (b) above.

3. Obtain the solution of Ex. (c) above by elimination of variables and by Cramer's rule.

4. Prove that $\mathbf{x} = \mathbf{A}^{-1}\mathbf{y}$ as the solution of $\mathbf{Ax} = \mathbf{y}$ is equivalent to Cramer's rule.

5. Show that

$$\begin{vmatrix} a-b-c & 2a & 2a \\ 2b & b-c-a & 2b \\ 2c & 2c & c-a-b \end{vmatrix} = (a+b+c)^3$$

and hence solve :

$$\begin{aligned} (a-b-c)x + 2ay + 2az &= 0 \\ 2bx + (b-c-a)y + 2bz &= 0 \\ 2cx + 2cy + (c-a-b)z &= 0 \end{aligned}$$

6. Examine the system

$$\begin{aligned} 2x_1 + 4x_2 + 4x_3 &= 2 \\ 2x_1 + 4x_2 + x_3 &= -1 \\ x_1 + 2x_2 + 2x_3 &= 1 \end{aligned}$$

Show that the matrix and augmented matrix both have rank 2. Find a solution for x_3 and show that x_1 can be obtained in terms of x_2 (or conversely). What happens when (a) the constant (-1) of the second equation is changed to some other value, and (b) the constant (1) of the third system is changed?

7. Show that the system

$$\begin{aligned} 2x_1 + 4x_2 + x_3 &= -1 \\ x_1 + 2x_2 + 2x_3 &= 1 \end{aligned}$$

has the same solution as the system of the previous exercise. Why?

8. Examine the system

$$2x_1 + 4x_2 + 4x_3 = 2$$
$$2x_1 + 4x_2 + x_3 = -1$$
$$x_1 + 2x_2 + 2x_3 = 1$$
$$x_1 + x_2 + x_3 = 1$$

and show that it is effectively equivalent to a non-singular (3×3) system with solution $x_1 = 1$, $x_2 = -1$, $x_3 = 1$. Compare with the system of Ex. 6. above.

14.3 Linear Transformations

A transformation is a mapping of one set of entities into another set. The general definition of a *linear transformation* is a mapping of one set of *vectors* into another set so that a linear combination of the first set maps into the same linear combination of the second set (see Appendix B). The discussion is here limited to vectors which are n-tuples of real numbers or points in Cartesian space of n dimensions. A particular basis (the unit vectors) is taken ; points are referred to fixed co-ordinate axes. A linear transformation then appears analytically in terms of a specific matrix : $y = Ax$ where $A = [a_{rs}]$ of order $m \times n$. This is a transformation from n-tuples $x = (x_1, x_2, \dots x_n)$ to m-tuples $y = (y_1, y_2, \dots y_m)$; it is the system of equations of 14.2 in reverse.

The problem for a system of equations is to find x given y. The *same* problem appears in the *inversion* of a linear transformation to give x in terms of y. The solution of the first problem only needs re-interpretation.

(i) *Non-singular case :* A is of order $n \times n$ and rank n, with an inverse A^{-1}. Here x and y are sets of variables equal in number. Then :

$$y = Ax \qquad \text{inverts to} \qquad x = A^{-1}y$$

In practice, the inverse transformation may be obtained by writing A^{-1}, or by eliminating variables, or by Cramer's rule (14.2 above).

Ex. (a).

$$y_1 = -x_1 + x_2 + x_3$$
$$y_2 = x_1 - x_2 + x_3$$
$$y_3 = x_1 + x_2 - x_3$$

Here $A = \begin{bmatrix} -1 & 1 & 1 \\ 1 & -1 & 1 \\ 1 & 1 & -1 \end{bmatrix}$ and $A^{-1} = \begin{bmatrix} 0 & \frac{1}{2} & \frac{1}{2} \\ \frac{1}{2} & 0 & \frac{1}{2} \\ \frac{1}{2} & \frac{1}{2} & 0 \end{bmatrix}$ as in Ex. (c) of 14.2.

Hence $\qquad x_1 = \frac{1}{2}(y_2 + y_3) \qquad x_2 = \frac{1}{2}(y_3 + y_1) \qquad x_3 = \frac{1}{2}(y_1 + y_2)$

as can also be found directly from the original equations.

The linear transformation can be given a geométrical interpretation and a corresponding application (e.g.) to the theory of convex sets. A set of points in n dimensions may be a finite set such as the corners of an n-dimensional figure ; or it may be an infinite set, e.g. the points on some curve or surface. Represent a point by an n-tuple $x = (x_1, x_2, \dots x_n)$ referred to axes $Ox_1x_2 \dots x_n$ and apply the linear transformation $y = Ax$.

The set of points is then mapped into a new set of points

$$\mathbf{y} = (y_1, y_2, \ldots y_n)$$

referred to axes $Oy_1y_2 \ldots y_n$ in another n-dimensional space. The mapping fixes a unique (one-one) relation between the set of points in one space and that in the other. The corners of a figure in $\mathbf{x}$ space transform into the corners of a different figure in $\mathbf{y}$ space; or the curve or surface in $\mathbf{x}$ space changes into a different curve or surface in $\mathbf{y}$ space. In the transformation, there can be all kinds of " stretching " of one space into the other, according to the nature of $\mathbf{A}$. This is illustrated easily in two dimensions, as in the following examples which use well-known matrices $\mathbf{A}$ of order 2×2.

Ex. (*b*). $\mathbf{y} = \begin{bmatrix} k & 0 \\ 0 & 1 \end{bmatrix} \mathbf{x}$, i.e. $y_1 = kx_1$ and $y_2 = x_2$.

The matrix is an example of the $\mathbf{K}$ matrix of 13.4 above. It can be used to transform a square in Ox_1x_2 space into a rectangle in Oy_1y_2 space, as illustrated in case $k = 2$ in Fig. 51. Similarly, a circle can be transformed into an ellipse. If $k > 1$

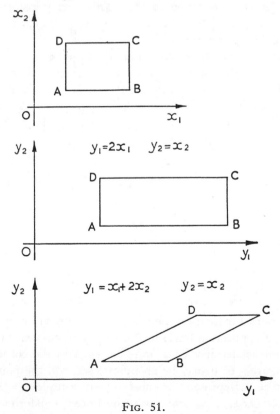

Fig. 51.

(and $x_1 > 0$) the transformation involves a shift to the right and a " stretching " in the horizontal direction.

The inverse transformation is

$$\mathbf{x} = \begin{bmatrix} \dfrac{1}{k} & 0 \\ 0 & 1 \end{bmatrix} \mathbf{y},$$

or $x_1 = \dfrac{1}{k} y_1$ and $x_2 = y_2$. When applied, in the case of $k = 2$, to the circle with centre $(2, 2)$ and radius 1 :

$$(x_1 - 2)^2 + (x_2 - 2)^2 = 1$$

the corresponding curve in y space is :

$$(\tfrac{1}{2} y_1 - 2)^2 + (y_2 - 2)^2 = 1$$

i.e.

$$(y_1 - 4)^2 + 4(y_2 - 2)^2 = 4$$

which is an ellipse.

Ex. (c). $\mathbf{y} = \begin{bmatrix} 1 & h \\ 0 & 1 \end{bmatrix} \mathbf{x}$, i.e. $y_1 = x_1 + h x_2$ and $y_2 = x_2$, which involves the **H** matrix of 13.4 above. When applied to a square in $Ox_1 x_2$ space, this transformation produces a rhombus in $Oy_1 y_2$ space, as illustrated in Fig. 51 in the case $h = 2$. Again, a circle is transformed into an ellipse, with its major axis now at an angle to the horizontal. If $h > 1$ (and $x_2 > 0$) the transformation is a shift to the right which is not constant but increases in proportion to the height above the horizontal.

Apply the transformation, in the inverse form :

$$\mathbf{x} = \begin{bmatrix} 1 & -h \\ 0 & 1 \end{bmatrix} \mathbf{y} \quad \text{or} \quad x_1 = y_1 - h y_2 \quad \text{and} \quad x_2 = y_2$$

to the same circle $(x_1 - 2)^2 + (x_2 - 2)^2 = 1$, and the curve in y space is (for $h = 2$) :

$$(y_1 - 2 y_2 - 2)^2 + (y_2 - 2)^2 = 1$$

i.e.

$$y_1^2 - 4 y_1 y_2 + 5 y_2^2 - 4 y_1 + 4 y_2 + 7 = 0$$

which can be shown to be an ellipse.

A very useful non-singular transformation is obtained from an orthogonal matrix (13.9 above). $\mathbf{y} = \mathbf{Ax}$ is *an orthogonal transformation* when **A** is orthogonal, so that $\mathbf{AA'} = \mathbf{I}$ and $\mathbf{A}^{-1} = \mathbf{A'}$. The inverse transformation is then :

$$\mathbf{x} = \mathbf{A}^{-1}\mathbf{y} = \mathbf{A'y}$$

which is also orthogonal, since $\mathbf{A'}$ is orthogonal if **A** is.

A particular orthogonal transformation in two dimensions is :

$$\begin{aligned} y_1 &= x_1 \cos \theta + x_2 \sin \theta \\ y_2 &= -x_1 \sin \theta + x_2 \cos \theta \end{aligned} \quad \text{with} \quad \mathbf{A} = \begin{bmatrix} \cos \theta & \sin \theta \\ -\sin \theta & \cos \theta \end{bmatrix}$$

It corresponds, geometrically, to a rotation of axes anti-clockwise through an angle θ, from $Ox_1 x_2$ to $Oy_1 y_2$, all figures being completely unchanged in shape and size (see Fig. 49 above). Corresponding sets of points, in **x** space and in **y** space, are of exactly the same orientation ; one set is simply rotated into the other. In particular, and in contrast to the transformations of Fig. 51, all distances between points are unaffected. Algebraically, the square of the distance from O to any point in **x** space is $Q = x_1^2 + x_2^2$. Invert the transformation to obtain :

$$x_1 = y_1 \cos \theta - y_2 \sin \theta \quad \text{and} \quad x_2 = y_1 \sin \theta + y_2 \cos \theta$$

and apply to Q :

$$Q = (y_1 \cos \theta - y_2 \sin \theta)^2 + (y_1 \sin \theta + y_2 \cos \theta)^2 = y_1^2 + y_2^2$$

Hence :
$$Q = x_1^2 + x_2^2 = y_1^2 + y_2^2$$

and distance from the origin is unchanged. This is easily generalised (see Ex. 7 below).

It can be established, conversely, that any orthogonal transformation in two dimensions has matrix $\mathbf{A} = \begin{bmatrix} \cos \theta & \sin \theta \\ -\sin \theta & \cos \theta \end{bmatrix}$ for a suitable angle θ, except for the incidental detail that either a row or a column (or both) in **A** can be multiplied by (-1). To prove, let $\mathbf{A} = \begin{bmatrix} a_{11} & a_{12} \\ a_{21} & a_{22} \end{bmatrix}$ be orthogonal so that (13.9 above) :

$$a_{11}^2 + a_{12}^2 = 1 \quad \dots\dots\dots\dots\dots\dots\dots\dots(1)$$
$$a_{21}^2 + a_{22}^2 = 1 \quad \dots\dots\dots\dots\dots\dots\dots\dots(2)$$
$$a_{11}a_{21} + a_{12}a_{22} = 0 \quad \dots\dots\dots\dots\dots\dots\dots\dots(3)$$

From (1), a_{11} must be numerically less than 1 so that a unique angle θ (in range $0, \pi$) can be found for $a_{11} = \cos \theta$, and hence $a_{12} = \sin \theta$ (or $a_{12} = -\sin \theta$, giving one of the variants mentioned above). Similarly, from (2), a unique angle ϕ can be found for $a_{21} = \sin \phi$, $a_{22} = \cos \phi$. Condition (3) gives :

$$\cos \theta \sin \phi + \sin \theta \cos \phi = 0$$
i.e. $$\sin (\theta + \phi) = 0$$
i.e. $$\phi = -\theta$$

again apart from the variants in sign of $\sin \phi$ and $\cos \phi$. Hence

$$\mathbf{A} = \begin{bmatrix} \cos \theta & \sin \theta \\ -\sin \theta & \cos \theta \end{bmatrix}$$

or one of the variants.

Consequently, in two dimensions, any orthogonal transformation is simply a rotation of axes, and all distances (and shapes of figures) are invariant under the transformation.

The invariance of distances and of shapes of figures is a property of orthogonal transformations in any number of dimensions. The general result was established in 13.9 (iii) above ; it can be expressed :

> If $y=Ax$ is an orthogonal transformation, so that $A^{-1}=A'$, then inner products are invariant : $x_1 . x_2 = y_1 . y_2$, and so distances and angles are invariant, under the transformation.

In particular, distances from the origin are invariant : $Q = \underset{r}{\Sigma} x_r^2 = \underset{r}{\Sigma} y_r^2$.

The algebra of linear transformations is simply the algebra of the corresponding matrices. It is straight-forward when the matrices are square and non-singular ; the determinant value and inverse of any such matrix can always be written. The results given in 13.2 above for two dimensions are easily extended. For example, if $x=Ay$ and $y=Bz$ are two non-singular linear transformations, then a direct relation between x and z is derived :

$$x = A(Bz) = (AB)z$$

a linear transformation with matrix AB. In terms of inverses :

$$y = A^{-1}x \text{ and } z = B^{-1}y \text{ give } z = B^{-1}A^{-1}x = (AB)^{-1}x$$

which is the inverse of $x = (AB)z$.

(ii) *Singular cases.* When the matrix of a linear transformation is either rectangular, or square and singular, the problem of obtaining the inverse is more complicated. The results of 14.2 (ii*b*) above apply but they need to be re-interpreted.

Take the case $y=Ax$ where A is square of order $n \times n$ and of rank $r < n$. The numbers of x and y variables are the same ; but the fact that A is singular $(r < n)$ prevents any direct inversion of the linear transformation. There is no difficulty in interpreting the transformation as it stands : given any arbitrary or assigned values of the x's, a unique set of values of the y's correspond. To a given point in x space there corresponds just one point in y space. To invert the transformation, assign any values to the y's and attempt to find the corresponding x's, i.e. given a point in y space, try to locate a corresponding point in x space. The answer is that it can't be done, at least in the full n dimensions.

A is of rank r and has a square sub-matrix of order $r \times r$ which is non-singular. There correspond r particular x's (say $x_1, x_2, \dots x_r$) and r particular equations and y's (say $y_1, y_2, \dots y_r$). Given any values for the r

y's, unique values of the r x's are found, very much as in the non-singular case, (i) above. Geometrically, a point in $\mathbf{x}$ space of r dimensions (within the full n dimensions) corresponds to a point in $\mathbf{y}$ space of r dimensions, and conversely. The question that remains is : what is to be done with the " surplus " $(n-r)$ variables, i.e. x_{r+1}, x_{r+2}, ... x_n and y_{r+1}, y_{r+2}, ... y_n, i.e. with the " surplus " dimensions of the $\mathbf{x}$ and $\mathbf{y}$ spaces?

The treatment of the " surplus " $(n-r)$ variables among the x's is to assign them arbitrary values, which are in fact used in determining x_1, x_2, ... x_r from the selected r equations of the linear transformation. The " surplus " $(n-r)$ variables among the y's can be ignored ; alternatively, they can be assigned certain values. If these extra assigned values are to be taken into account, then they must be such that the augmented matrix $\mathbf{B}=[\,\mathbf{A} \;\vdots\; \mathbf{y}\,]$ is of rank r. The extra equations in the transformation are consistent with the others. However, if the extra y's are assigned values such that $\mathbf{B}=[\,\mathbf{A} \;\vdots\; \mathbf{y}\,]$ is of rank $(r+1)$, then they are not consistent with the full inversion of the transformation. In short, to invert the transformation in the full n dimensions, there must be a limitation on the values assigned to the y's and some of the x's must be given arbitrary values as well. An example illustrates.

Ex. (d).
$$y_1 = x_1 + x_2 + x_3 \quad \text{with} \quad \mathbf{A} = \begin{bmatrix} 1 & 1 & 1 \\ 1 & -2 & 2 \\ 2 & -1 & 3 \end{bmatrix} \text{ of rank 2.}$$
$$y_2 = x_1 - 2x_2 + 2x_3$$
$$y_3 = 2x_1 - x_2 + 3x_3$$

The right-hand side of the last equation is derived by addition from the other two. Values are to be given to the y's in order to obtain the x's in terms of them. Any values can be assigned to y_1 and y_2, but then y_3 must be given the value $y_1 + y_2$ if the three equations are to be consistent ; in which case the third equation is simply dropped as adding nothing. If y_3 is assigned any other value, then the third equation is inconsistent ; it can still be dropped, not because it fits in, but because it is useless. Hence, to work with all three equations, there must be a relation between, or a limitation on, the values assigned to the y's : $y_3 = y_1 + y_2$. Even when this is done, only two of the x's can be found and the other must be given an arbitrary value. Solving the first two equations :
$$x_1 = \tfrac{1}{3}(2y_1 + y_2 - 4x_3) \quad \text{and} \quad x_2 = \tfrac{1}{3}(y_1 - y_2 + x_3)$$
is the only form which can be written for the inverse of the linear transformation. Here, x_3 is assigned any arbitrary value and the " surplus " y_3 is either ignored altogether, or it is assigned to be $y_3 = y_1 + y_2$, when it fits in with all the rest.

The case where $\mathbf{A}$ is rectangular of order $m \times n$ and of rank $r \leqslant$ smaller of m and n is much the same. If $m < n$, then there are additional " surplus " x's to be assigned arbitrary values in inverting the transformation. If $m > n$, then there are additional " surplus " y's to be ignored or related in particular ways to other y's. Geometrically, to a point in $\mathbf{x}$ space of n dimensions, there corresponds a unique point in $\mathbf{y}$ space of m dimensions. But, conversely, the correspondence between points in $\mathbf{x}$ space and given points in $\mathbf{y}$ space can only be achieved in a limited number (r) of dimensions or within certain limitations in the full set of dimensions.

The algebra of singular linear transformations must proceed with caution. The dimensions or orders involved need to be checked and the inverse transformations cannot generally be written. For example,

$$\mathbf{x}=\mathbf{Ay} \quad \text{and} \quad \mathbf{y}=\mathbf{Bz} \quad \text{give} \quad \mathbf{x}=(\mathbf{AB})\mathbf{z}$$

since $\mathbf{A}$ and $\mathbf{B}$ are conformable. If $\mathbf{A}$ is of order $m \times k$ and $\mathbf{B}$ of order $k \times n$, then $\mathbf{AB}$ can be written, of order $m \times n$. This means that m variables $\mathbf{x}$ can be related to n variables $\mathbf{z}$ through the intermediate k variables $\mathbf{y}$. This cannot, in general, be reversed.

EXERCISES 14.3

1. Show that the linear transformation $\mathbf{y}=\mathbf{E}_{(12)}\mathbf{x}$, where $\mathbf{E}_{(12)}$ is the matrix defined in 13.4 above, simply transposes axes, figures remaining unchanged.

2. Show that

$$\begin{aligned} y_1 &= x_1 \\ y_2 &= x_1 + x_2 \\ y_3 &= x_1 + x_2 + x_3 \end{aligned} \quad \text{inverts to} \quad \begin{aligned} x_1 &= y_1 \\ x_2 &= y_2 - y_1 \\ x_3 &= y_3 - y_2 \end{aligned}$$

Generalise and interpret in terms of difference of cumulative totals.

3. Examine the following linear transformation and find the limitations on the y's. Drop one y and obtain the inverse transformation. Check with the results of 14.2, Ex. 8, above.

$$\begin{aligned} y_1 &= 2x_1 + 4x_2 + 4x_3 \\ y_2 &= 2x_1 + 4x_2 + x_3 \\ y_3 &= x_1 + 2x_2 + 2x_3 \\ y_4 &= x_1 + x_2 + x_3 \end{aligned}$$

4. Find the z's in terms of the x's given :

$$\begin{aligned} y_1 &= -x_1 + x_2 + x_3 \\ y_2 &= x_1 - x_2 + x_3 \\ y_3 &= x_1 + x_2 - x_3 \end{aligned} \quad \text{and} \quad \begin{aligned} z_1 &= \tfrac{1}{2}(y_1 + y_2) \\ z_2 &= y_1 + y_2 + y_3 \end{aligned}$$

Check by multiplication of matrices.

5. If $\mathbf{y}=\mathbf{Ax}$, $\mathbf{z}=\mathbf{Bx}$, where $\mathbf{A}$ and $\mathbf{B}$ are square and non-singular, show that $\mathbf{y}=\mathbf{AB}^{-1}\mathbf{z}$ and $\mathbf{z}=\mathbf{BA}^{-1}\mathbf{y}$. What can be said if $\mathbf{A}$ or $\mathbf{B}$ is (a) singular and (b) rectangular?

6. Show that $\mathbf{A}=\tfrac{1}{3}\begin{bmatrix} -1 & 2 & -2 \\ 2 & -1 & -2 \\ 2 & 2 & 1 \end{bmatrix}$ is orthogonal, and check that the orthogonal transformation $\mathbf{y}=\mathbf{Ax}$ preserves distances in $\mathbf{x}$ and $\mathbf{y}$ spaces.

7. Show that the distance between any pair of points in two dimensions is unchanged under an orthogonal transformation.

14.4 Characteristic Equation of a Square Matrix

The characteristic equation obtained from a square matrix is a concept of considerable use in matrix algebra. Only the basic ideas are developed here, together with the particular application to symmetric matrices and quadratic forms ; see Thrall and Tornheim (1957), pp. 142–6.

The matrix $\mathbf{A} = [a_{rs}]$ is square of order $n \times n$ and $\mathbf{I}$ is the corresponding unit matrix. For any multiple or parameter λ, the *characteristic matrix* of $\mathbf{A}$ is :

$$\mathbf{A} - \lambda\mathbf{I} = \begin{bmatrix} a_{11} - \lambda & a_{12} & \dots & a_{1n} \\ a_{21} & a_{22} - \lambda & \dots & a_{2n} \\ \dots & & & \\ a_{n1} & a_{n2} & \dots & a_{nn} - \lambda \end{bmatrix}$$

The determinant value $|\mathbf{A} - \lambda\mathbf{I}|$ when expanded in full appears as a polynomial of degree n in λ, the coefficients being obtained from the a's. The first term in the polynomial is $(-1)^n \lambda^n$ and the last or constant term is $|\mathbf{A}|$. The other terms, in λ^{n-1}, λ^{n-2}, ., can be obtained with more difficulty in general form (see Ex. 3 below). When equated to zero, the polynomial gives an equation of degree n in λ, with roots λ_1, λ_2, ... λ_n which may be real or conjugate complex in pairs. This is the *character-istic equation* of the square matrix $\mathbf{A}$. The roots are the *characteristic or latent roots*, sometimes called *eigenvalues*, of $\mathbf{A}$.

DEFINITION : The characteristic equation of the $n \times n$ matrix $\mathbf{A}$ is

$$\mathbf{A} - \lambda\mathbf{I}| = 0$$

with characteristic or latent roots, or eigenvalues, λ_1, λ_2, ... λ_n. If λ_r is a characteristic root, so that $|\mathbf{A} - \lambda_r\mathbf{I}| = 0$, then the matrix $\mathbf{A} - \lambda_r\mathbf{I}$ is singular. Hence (14.1 above) its rows and columns are linearly dependent and a set of multiples, not all zero, can be found and arranged in a column vector :

$$\mathbf{k}_r = \{k_{1r}, k_{2r}, \dots k_{nr}\} \qquad (\mathbf{k}_r \neq \mathbf{0})$$

so that

$$(\mathbf{A} - \lambda_r\mathbf{I})\mathbf{k}_r = \mathbf{0}$$

The vector $\mathbf{k}_r$ is called the *eigenvector* corresponding to the *eigenvalue* λ_r.

The constant term in the characteristic equation is $|\mathbf{A}|$. If $\mathbf{A}$ is non-singular, $|\mathbf{A}| \neq 0$, and no root is zero. If $\mathbf{A}$ is singular, there is at least one zero root. The suggestion to be pursued is that there are r non-zero roots and $(n - r)$ zero roots if $\mathbf{A}$ has rank r.

Ex. (a). $\mathbf{A} = \begin{bmatrix} 2 & -1 & -1 \\ -1 & 2 & -1 \\ -1 & -1 & 2 \end{bmatrix}$ is singular, of rank 2.

The characteristic equation reduces to $\lambda^3 - 6\lambda^2 + 9\lambda = 0$ with roots $\lambda = 3, 3, 0$. The zero root indicates that $\mathbf{A}$ has rank one less than 3.

The concept of similar matrices is used in pursuing the matter. All matrices are taken as square, of order $n \times n$. **A** and **B** are similar if **B** = **PAP**$^{-1}$ for some non-singular **P**. The idea is to get **A** similar to some diagonal matrix $\bar{\lambda}$ and then to identify the diagonal elements of $\bar{\lambda}$ as the characteristic roots of **A**. This is a matter of considerable difficulty and, indeed, this " diagonalisation " of **A** cannot always be done. The following development is partial, see Murdoch (1957).

One thing is easy : *if* **A** *of rank r is* similar to $\bar{\lambda}$ with diagonal elements $(\lambda_1, \lambda_2, \dots \lambda_n)$, then **A** has the λ's as characteristic roots and exactly r of them are non-zero. This follows from two results; :

(i) *Similar matrices have the same rank and characteristic roots.*

Proof : For **A** and **B** similar (of same rank, see 13.9), **B** = **PAP**$^{-1}$ and

$$\mathbf{B} - \lambda\mathbf{I} = \mathbf{PAP}^{-1} - \lambda\,\mathbf{PIP}^{-1} = \mathbf{P}(\mathbf{A} - \lambda\mathbf{I})\mathbf{P}^{-1}$$

since **PIP**$^{-1}$ = **PP**$^{-1}$ = **I**. Now $|\mathbf{P}^{-1}| = 1/|\mathbf{P}|$ and so

$$|\mathbf{B} - \lambda\mathbf{I}| = |\mathbf{P}|\,|\mathbf{A} - \lambda\mathbf{I}|\,|\mathbf{P}^{-1}| = |\mathbf{A} - \lambda\mathbf{I}| \qquad \text{Q.E.D.}$$

(ii) *The diagonal matrix $\bar{\lambda}$ has characteristic roots* $\lambda_1, \lambda_2, \dots \lambda_n$.

Proof : The matrix $(\bar{\lambda} - \lambda\mathbf{I})$ is also diagonal with elements $(\lambda_1 - \lambda)$, $(\lambda_2 - \lambda)$ $\dots (\lambda_n - \lambda)$ in the diagonal. Hence the characteristic equation is

$$(\lambda_1 - \lambda)(\lambda_2 - \lambda) \dots (\lambda_n - \lambda) = 0 \qquad \text{Q.E.D.}$$

Hence, from (i) and (ii), if **A** is similar to $\bar{\lambda}$, both of rank r, then **A** has the characteristic roots of $\bar{\lambda}$, i.e. $(\lambda_1, \lambda_2, \dots \lambda_n)$. But $\bar{\lambda}$ is only of rank r if exactly r of the λ's are non-zero.

The problem is to " diagonalise " **A**. Only one case is taken here, where **A** is a *symmetric matrix* so that **A**$'$ = **A**. Then : **A** *has characteristic roots which are all real*. This is a great simplification ; there are no difficulties about complex elements in any matrices used. The proof of the result proceeds as follows. Suppose that symmetric **A** has a characteristic root $\lambda = \alpha + i\beta$ and write $\lambda' = \alpha - i\beta$ for its conjugate. Then $|\mathbf{A} - \lambda\mathbf{I}| = 0$. Write :

$$\mathbf{B} = (\mathbf{A} - \lambda\mathbf{I})(\mathbf{A} - \lambda'\mathbf{I}) = \mathbf{A}^2 - 2\alpha\mathbf{A} + (\alpha^2 + \beta^2)\mathbf{I} = (\mathbf{A} - \alpha\mathbf{I})^2 + \beta^2\mathbf{I}$$

which is a real square matrix. **B** is singular since $|\mathbf{B}| = 0$ from $|\mathbf{A} - \lambda\mathbf{I}| = 0$. Hence **Bx** = **0** for some non-zero vector **x** by case (i) of 14.2 above. So **x**$'$**Bx** = **x**$'$**0** = 0. But :

$$\mathbf{x}'\mathbf{Bx} = \mathbf{x}'(\mathbf{A} - \alpha\mathbf{I})^2\mathbf{x} + \mathbf{x}'\beta^2\mathbf{Ix}$$

The first term here is easily seen to be non-negative (as a quadratic form) and the second term is $\beta^2\mathbf{x}'\mathbf{Ix} = \beta^2\mathbf{x}'\mathbf{x} = \beta^2(x_1^2 + x_2^2 \dots + x_n^2)$, using the components of $\mathbf{x}$. Hence, $\mathbf{x}'\mathbf{Bx}=0$ for non-zero $\mathbf{x}$ only if the first term is zero, which means $|\mathbf{A}-\alpha\mathbf{I}|=0$, and if the second term is also zero, which means $\beta=0$. Hence $\lambda=\alpha$ and is real.   Q.E.D.

Write the real characteristic roots of the symmetric $\mathbf{A}$ as $\lambda_1, \lambda_2, \ldots \lambda_n$ and form the diagonal matrix from them. The main result is :

> *For any symmetric matrix $\mathbf{A}$ there is an orthogonal matrix $\mathbf{P}$ so that $\mathbf{P}^{-1}\mathbf{AP}$ is the diagonal matrix $\bar\lambda$ of the characteristic roots of $\mathbf{A}$.*

From $\mathbf{P}^{-1}\mathbf{AP}=\bar\lambda$, it follows that $\mathbf{A}=\mathbf{P}\bar\lambda\mathbf{P}^{-1}$ and $\mathbf{A}$ is similar to the diagonal matrix $\bar\lambda$ and our problem is solved. The proof of the result is :

Let non-zero $\mathbf{x}_r$ be the eigenvector corresponding to the characteristic root λ_r of $\mathbf{A}$, i.e. $(\mathbf{A}-\lambda_r\mathbf{I})\mathbf{x}_r=0$. Hence :

$$\mathbf{Ax}_r=\lambda_r\mathbf{x}_r \qquad (r=1, 2, \ldots n) \quad\ldots\ldots\ldots\ldots\ldots\ldots(1)$$

Write $\mathbf{P}$ for the matrix obtained from $\mathbf{x}_r(r=1, 2, \ldots n)$ as columns. Then the n equations (1) compound into :

$$\mathbf{AP}=\mathbf{P}\bar\lambda$$

i.e. $$\mathbf{P}'\mathbf{AP}=\mathbf{P}'\mathbf{P}\bar\lambda \quad\ldots\ldots\ldots\ldots\ldots\ldots\ldots\ldots\ldots\ldots(2)$$

Transpose each side of (2), noting that $\mathbf{A}'=\mathbf{A}$ and $\bar\lambda'=\bar\lambda$ since both matrices are symmetric :

$$\mathbf{P}'\mathbf{AP}=\bar\lambda\mathbf{P}'\mathbf{P} \quad\ldots\ldots\ldots\ldots\ldots\ldots\ldots\ldots\ldots\ldots(3)$$

The two matrices on the right in (2) and (3) are the same :

$$\mathbf{P}'\mathbf{P}\bar\lambda=\bar\lambda\mathbf{P}'\mathbf{P}$$

and this is only possible if $\mathbf{P}'\mathbf{P}=\mathbf{I}$, or $\mathbf{P}'=\mathbf{P}^{-1}$. Hence, the matrix $\mathbf{P}$ is orthogonal and (2) reduces to :

$$\mathbf{P}^{-1}\mathbf{AP}=\bar\lambda \qquad\qquad\text{Q.E.D.}$$

All the results obtained can now be summarised in one proposition :

> *A symmetric matrix $\mathbf{A}$ of order $n \times n$ and rank r has n real characteristic roots forming a diagonal matrix $\bar\lambda$ similar to $\mathbf{A}$:*
>
> $$\mathbf{A}=\mathbf{P}\bar\lambda\mathbf{P}^{-1} \quad \text{for some orthogonal matrix } \mathbf{P}.$$

The characteristic roots comprise r non-zero and $(n-r)$ zero values. An example illustrates.

Ex (b). $\mathbf{A}=\begin{bmatrix} 2 & -1 & -1 \\ -1 & 2 & -1 \\ -1 & -1 & 2 \end{bmatrix}$ symmetric and of rank 2, with characteristic roots, 3, 3, 0 (see Ex. (a) above). Consider the following matrix $\mathbf{P}$ which has been shown, in Ex. (b) of 13.9 above, to be orthogonal :

$$\mathbf{P} = \begin{bmatrix} \dfrac{1}{\sqrt{2}} & \dfrac{1}{\sqrt{6}} & \dfrac{1}{\sqrt{3}} \\[2mm] -\dfrac{1}{\sqrt{2}} & \dfrac{1}{\sqrt{6}} & \dfrac{1}{\sqrt{3}} \\[2mm] 0 & -\dfrac{2}{\sqrt{6}} & \dfrac{1}{\sqrt{3}} \end{bmatrix} \quad \text{so that} \quad \mathbf{P}' = \mathbf{P}^{-1} = \begin{bmatrix} \dfrac{1}{\sqrt{2}} & -\dfrac{1}{\sqrt{2}} & 0 \\[2mm] \dfrac{1}{\sqrt{6}} & \dfrac{1}{\sqrt{6}} & -\dfrac{2}{\sqrt{6}} \\[2mm] \dfrac{1}{\sqrt{3}} & \dfrac{1}{\sqrt{3}} & \dfrac{1}{\sqrt{3}} \end{bmatrix}$$

By the rule of matrix multiplication, applied twice in succession :

$$\mathbf{P}^{-1}\mathbf{A}\mathbf{P} = \begin{bmatrix} 3 & 0 & 0 \\ 0 & 3 & 0 \\ 0 & 0 & 0 \end{bmatrix} = \bar{\lambda} \quad \text{formed from the characteristic roots of } \mathbf{A}.$$

Hence the reduction of $\mathbf{A}$ to its similar diagonal form $\bar{\lambda}$ is achieved :

$$\mathbf{A} = \mathbf{P}\bar{\lambda}\mathbf{P}^{-1}$$

where $\mathbf{P}$ is the orthogonal matrix written above. Notice that the eigenvector corresponding to the characteristic root 3 is the vector $\mathbf{x} = (x_1, x_2, x_3)$ such that

$$(\mathbf{A} - 3\mathbf{I})\mathbf{x} = \begin{bmatrix} -1 & -1 & -1 \\ -1 & -1 & -1 \\ -1 & -1 & -1 \end{bmatrix} \mathbf{x} = 0$$

On multiplying out, each of the components here is found to be $-(x_1 + x_2 + x_3)$, which must therefore be zero. Hence, $\mathbf{x} = (1, -1, 0)$ and $\mathbf{x} = (1, 1, -2)$ are both possible eigenvectors. Two eigenvectors must be sought since there are two characteristic roots 3. These two particular vectors are taken—they are proportional to the first and second columns of $\mathbf{P}$. The other characteristic root 0 has an eigenvector $(1, 1, 1)$, proportional to the third column of $\mathbf{P}$.

Another type of square matrix $\mathbf{A}$ of considerable interest is that consisting of non-negative elements, i.e. $\mathbf{A} \geqslant 0$. These are matrices which frequently appear in economic applications. Suppose also that $\mathbf{A}$ is indecomposable in the sense of 13.9 (v) above. The matrix $(\lambda \mathbf{I} - \mathbf{A})$, which gives the characteristic equation of $\mathbf{A}$, has then a number of properties, established by Debreu and Herstein (1953). If λ_m is the largest of the characteristic roots of $\mathbf{A}$, it is the largest root of $|\lambda \mathbf{I} - \mathbf{A}| = 0$, an equation with first term λ^n. Then $|\lambda \mathbf{I} - \mathbf{A}| > 0$ if $\lambda > \lambda_m$. Debreu and Herstein first proceed to show that all the principal square sub-matrices of $(\lambda \mathbf{I} - \mathbf{A})$, i.e. those which omit the same set of rows and columns, have positive determinant values if and only if $\lambda > \lambda_m$. Further, the inverse matrix $(\lambda \mathbf{I} - \mathbf{A})^{-1}$ is positive if and only if $\lambda > \lambda_m$.

EXERCISES 14.4

1. Find the characteristic roots of $\begin{bmatrix} 1 & -1 \\ -1 & 1 \end{bmatrix}$ and of $\begin{vmatrix} 1 & 0 & -\frac{1}{2} \\ 0 & 1 & -\frac{1}{2} \\ -\frac{1}{2} & -\frac{1}{2} & 1 \end{vmatrix}$.

2. Show that $\mathbf{A} = \begin{bmatrix} 0 & 1 \\ 1 & 0 \end{bmatrix}$ is similar to $\bar{\lambda} = \begin{bmatrix} 1 & 0 \\ 0 & -1 \end{bmatrix}$ by finding that the characteristic roots of $\mathbf{A}$, which is non-singular and symmetric, are 1 and -1. Then show that the orthogonal matrix

$$\mathbf{P} = \begin{bmatrix} \dfrac{1}{\sqrt{2}} & -\dfrac{1}{\sqrt{2}} \\ \dfrac{1}{\sqrt{2}} & \dfrac{1}{\sqrt{2}} \end{bmatrix}$$

is appropriate to the relation $\mathbf{A} = \mathbf{P}\bar{\lambda}\mathbf{P}^{-1}$.

3. $\mathbf{A} = [a_{rs}]$ is any matrix of order 3×3. Show that :

$$| \mathbf{A} - \lambda \mathbf{I} | = -\lambda^3 + p_1\lambda^2 - p_2\lambda + p_3$$

where $p_1 = a_{11} + a_{22} + a_{33}$, $p_2 = \begin{vmatrix} a_{11} & a_{12} \\ a_{21} & a_{22} \end{vmatrix} + \begin{vmatrix} a_{22} & a_{23} \\ a_{32} & a_{33} \end{vmatrix} + \begin{vmatrix} a_{11} & a_{13} \\ a_{31} & a_{33} \end{vmatrix}$

and $p_3 = | \mathbf{A} |$. Indicate the general result for $\mathbf{A}$ of order $n \times n$.

4. $\mathbf{A}$ is an orthogonal matrix ($\mathbf{A}\mathbf{A}' = \mathbf{I}$). Show that :

$$-\frac{1}{\lambda} \mathbf{A}(\mathbf{A} - \lambda \mathbf{I})' = \mathbf{A} - \frac{1}{\lambda} \mathbf{I}$$

Deduce that, if $| \mathbf{A} - \lambda \mathbf{I} | = 0$, then $\left| \mathbf{A} - \dfrac{1}{\lambda} \mathbf{I} \right| = 0$; and hence that if λ is a characteristic root of an orthogonal matrix, so is $\dfrac{1}{\lambda}$.

14.5 Quadratic Forms

Much use has been made of linear forms in which variables x_1, x_2, ... x_n are each multiplied by a constant and added. The left-hand sides of a system of linear equations are all linear forms and the same forms appear in a linear transformation. In general, a *linear form* is :

$$L = \sum_{r=1}^{n} a_r x_r = a_1 x_1 + a_2 x_2 + \ldots + a_n x_n$$

where the a's are constants and the x's variables. Write $\mathbf{a}$ for the column vector of a's and $\mathbf{x}$ for that of x's. Then :

$$L = \mathbf{a}'\mathbf{x} = \mathbf{x}'\mathbf{a}$$

is the matrix expression for a linear form.

Now suppose that the a's are not constants but a second set of variables denoted as y's. Then a very simple case of a " bilinear form " :

$$x_1 y_1 + x_2 y_2 + \ldots + x_n y_n = \mathbf{x'y} = \mathbf{y'x}$$

is obtained. This is " bilinear " since two sets of variables are involved and each appears in a linear way. If the two sets of variables are the same $(x=y)$, then a particular case of the bilinear form results :

$$x_1{}^2 + x_2{}^2 + \ldots + x_n{}^2 = \mathbf{x'x}$$

This is a simple case of a " quadratic form " in the variable x's.

More general bilinear and quadratic forms involve cross products such as $x_1 y_2$ or $x_1 x_2$, and constant coefficients can be added to make the forms completely general. Given a matrix $\mathbf{A} = [a_{rs}]$ of order $m \times n$ consisting of constant elements, and two sets of variables written as column vectors $\mathbf{x} = \{x_r\}$ and $\mathbf{y} = \{y_s\}$ for $r = 1, 2, \ldots m$ and $s = 1, 2, \ldots n$, then the general *bilinear form* is :

$$B = \Sigma_r \Sigma_s a_{rs} x_r y_s = \left. \begin{array}{l} a_{11} x_1 y_1 + a_{12} x_1 y_2 + \ldots + a_{1n} x_1 y_n \\ + a_{21} x_2 y_1 + a_{22} x_2 y_2 + \ldots + a_{2n} x_2 y_n \\ \cdots\cdots\cdots\cdots\cdots\cdots\cdots\cdots\cdots \\ + a_{m1} x_m y_1 + a_{m2} x_m y_2 + \ldots + a_{mn} x_m y_n \end{array} \right\} \ldots\ldots(1)$$

In the particular case where $m = n$ and the two sets of variables are the same, the *quadratic form* of general type is obtained :

$$Q = \Sigma_r \Sigma_s a_{rs} x_r x_s = \left. \begin{array}{l} a_{11} x_1{}^2 + a_{12} x_1 x_2 + \ldots + a_{1n} x_1 x_n \\ + a_{21} x_1 x_2 + a_{22} x_2{}^2 + \ldots + a_{2n} x_2 x_n \\ \cdots\cdots\cdots\cdots\cdots\cdots\cdots\cdots\cdots \\ a_{n1} x_1 x_n + a_{n2} x_2 x_n + \ldots + a_{nn} x_n{}^2 \end{array} \right\} \ldots\ldots(2)$$

Here, the matrix $\mathbf{A} = [a_{rs}]$ is square of order $n \times n$ and the variables make up a column vector $\mathbf{x} = \{x_r\}$ of order n.

It is easily seen (Ex. 1 below) that there is no loss of generality in taking $a_{rs} = a_{sr}$ for all r and s. The matrix $\mathbf{A} = [a_{rs}]$ is then symmetric. Hence any quadratic form Q can be written with a *symmetric matrix* of coefficients $\mathbf{A} = [a_{rs}]$, and the determinant value $A = |\mathbf{A}|$ is called the *discriminant* of Q. Three very simple cases, of the second order (in a pair of variables x_1 and x_2), are :

Ex. (a). $Q = x_1{}^2 + x_2{}^2$ with $\mathbf{A} = \begin{bmatrix} 1 & 0 \\ 0 & 1 \end{bmatrix}$ and $A = \begin{vmatrix} 1 & 0 \\ 0 & 1 \end{vmatrix} = 1$

Ex. (b) $Q = x_1{}^2 - x_2{}^2$ with $\mathbf{A} = \begin{bmatrix} 1 & 0 \\ 0 & -1 \end{bmatrix}$ and $A = \begin{vmatrix} 1 & 0 \\ 0 & -1 \end{vmatrix} = -1$

Ex. (*c*) $Q = x_1^2 + x_2^2 - 2x_1x_2 = \begin{array}{l} x_1^2 - x_1x_2 \\ - x_1x_2 + x_2^2 \end{array}$

with $\mathbf{A} = \begin{bmatrix} 1 & -1 \\ -1 & 1 \end{bmatrix}$ and $A = \begin{vmatrix} 1 & -1 \\ -1 & 1 \end{vmatrix} = 0$

The three examples illustrate various possibilities on the sign of Q as x_1 and x_2 take different values. $Q = 0$ for $x_1 = x_2 = 0$ in all cases, and this trivial possibility is ruled out by taking the vector $\mathbf{x} = (x_1, x_2)$ as being not zero. It is assumed, therefore, that $\mathbf{x} \neq \mathbf{0}$, and x_1 and x_2 are not both zero. In Ex. (*a*), Q takes only positive values ; in Ex. (*b*), Q can take positive or negative values according to the values assigned to x_1 and x_2. The quadratic form Q of Ex. (*c*) is rather more awkward, as can be guessed from the fact that $\mathbf{A}$ is singular ($A = 0$) in this case. Since :

$$Q = (x_1 - x_2)^2$$

it follows that Q can take positive values ($x_1 \neq x_2$) or zero values ($x_1 = x_2$) but never negative values. In case Ex. (*c*), Q is non-negative, in contrast with case Ex. (*a*) where Q is positive.

Hence, in examining the sign of a quadratic form Q, it is a useful exercise to " complete the square " and to attempt a reduction of Q to the sum of squares. Consider other examples :

Ex. (*d*). $Q = x_1^2 + 2x_2^2 - 2x_1x_2$ with $\mathbf{A} = \begin{bmatrix} 1 & -1 \\ -1 & 2 \end{bmatrix}$ not singular.

Then : $Q = (x_1^2 - 2x_1x_2 + x_2^2) + x_2^2$

i.e. $Q = (x_1 - x_2)^2 + x_2^2$

which takes only positive values. The difference here is that Q is the sum of two squares (positive values), in contrast with Ex. (*c*) where Q is one square only (taking positive and zero values).

This suggests that, if $\mathbf{A}$ is non-singular, then Q can be expressed as the sum of two squares ; but if $\mathbf{A}$ is singular then there is one square missing. This is, in fact, the case.

However, the " sum " of two squares when $\mathbf{A}$ is non-singular must be interpreted as " sum or difference ". For example :

$$\begin{aligned} Q &= x_1^2 - x_2^2 - 2x_1x_2 \\ &= (x_1 - x_2)^2 - 2x_2^2 \end{aligned}$$

is a non-singular case where Q can take positive or negative values.

In pursuing these ideas, it is essential to have the general bilinear form (1), and the quadratic form (2), written in the matrix notation. The following results are obtained by direct application of the rule for the product of matrices. The general *bilinear form* is :

$$B = \mathbf{x}'\mathbf{A}\mathbf{y} \quad \dots\dots\dots\dots\dots\dots\dots\dots\dots\dots\dots (3)$$

where the column vectors $\mathbf{x}$ and $\mathbf{y}$ represent sets of variables of number m

and n respectively and where $\mathbf{A}=[a_{rs}]$ is a matrix of constant coefficients of order $m \times n$.   The general quadratic form is a particular case

$$Q=\mathbf{x}'\mathbf{A}\mathbf{x} \dotfill (4)$$

where $\mathbf{x}$ is a variable column vector of order n and $\mathbf{A}$ is square of order $n \times n$.   It can be checked that the matrices of (3) and (4) are conformable ; $\mathbf{x}'\mathbf{A}\mathbf{y}$ is the product of matrices of order $1 \times m$, $m \times n$ and $n \times 1$ respectively, giving a scalar (which is B).

The particular case where the matrix $\mathbf{A}$ is the unit matrix $\mathbf{I}$ of order $n \times n$ is of interest.   From (3),

$$B=\mathbf{x}'\mathbf{I}\mathbf{y}=\mathbf{x}'\mathbf{y}$$

stands for

$$B=x_1y_1+x_2y_2+\dots+x_ny_n$$

From (4)

$$Q=\mathbf{x}'\mathbf{I}\mathbf{x}=\mathbf{x}'\mathbf{x}$$

stands for

$$Q=x_1^2+x_2^2+\dots+x_n^2$$

These have already been written above.

The quadratic form Q is a scalar, a function of the variable x's.   If a linear transformation from x's to new variable y's, equal in number, is applied, then Q transforms into a function of the y's and it is also a quadratic form in the new variables.   The matrix of coefficients is easily obtained.   Let the linear transformation $\mathbf{x}=\mathbf{C}\mathbf{y}$ be applied to $Q=\mathbf{x}'\mathbf{A}\mathbf{x}$:

$$Q=(\mathbf{C}\mathbf{y})'\mathbf{A}(\mathbf{C}\mathbf{y})=\mathbf{y}'\mathbf{C}'\mathbf{A}\mathbf{C}\mathbf{y}$$

i.e.

$$Q=\mathbf{y}'\mathbf{B}\mathbf{y} \quad \text{where} \quad \mathbf{B}=\mathbf{C}'\mathbf{A}\mathbf{C} \dotfill (5)$$

is the transformed quadratic form.   The matrix $\mathbf{B}$ is equivalent to the original matrix $\mathbf{A}$ and hence the rank of $\mathbf{B}$ must be the same as that of $\mathbf{A}$.

The matrix $\mathbf{A}$ of the quadratic form Q is symmetric, so that its characteristic roots are all real.   This means that the result of 14.4 above applies : $\mathbf{A}$ is similar to the diagonal matrix $\bar{\lambda}$ with the characteristic roots of $\mathbf{A}$ in the diagonal.   For this purpose, an *orthogonal* matrix $\mathbf{P}$ is used :

$$\mathbf{A}=\mathbf{P}\bar{\lambda}\mathbf{P}^{-1}=\mathbf{P}\bar{\lambda}\mathbf{P}' \quad \text{since} \quad \mathbf{P}^{-1}=\mathbf{P}' \quad \text{for an orthogonal matrix.}$$

Now apply the transformation $\mathbf{x}=\mathbf{P}\mathbf{y}$, or its inverse $\mathbf{y}=\mathbf{P}^{-1}\mathbf{x}=\mathbf{P}'\mathbf{x}$, to the quadratic form Q.   By (5) :

$$Q=\mathbf{y}'\mathbf{B}\mathbf{y} \quad \text{where} \quad \mathbf{B}=\mathbf{P}'\mathbf{A}\mathbf{P}=\mathbf{P}^{-1}(\mathbf{P}\bar{\lambda}\mathbf{P}^{-1})\mathbf{P}=\bar{\lambda}$$

i.e.

$$Q=\mathbf{y}'\bar{\lambda}\mathbf{y}=\lambda_1y_1^2+\lambda_2y_2^2+\dots+\lambda_ny_n^2 \dotfill (6)$$

The n characteristic roots $(\lambda_1, \lambda_2, \dots \lambda_n)$ of $\mathbf{A}$, though all real, need not be all different and they can include zero values.   If the rank of $\mathbf{A}$ is $r \leqslant n$, then $(n-r)$ of the roots are zero and the other r have non-zero values (including multiple roots).

The transformation of any quadratic form (4) into a sum of squares (6) is the basic result for quadratic forms :

Any quadratic form $Q = x'Ax$ is written as the sum of squares

$$Q = y'\overline{\lambda}y = \lambda_1 y_1^2 + \lambda_2 y_2^2 + \ldots + \lambda_n y_n^2$$

by the application of some orthogonal transformation $x = Py$. The λ's are the characteristic roots of A and the y's are definite expressions in the x's (given by $y = P'x$). If A is of rank $r \leqslant n$, then Q consists of the sum of exactly r squares with non-zero coefficients.

An example of a quadratic form in three variables is :

Ex. (e). $Q = 2(x_1^2 + x_2^2 + x_3^2 - x_2 x_3 - x_3 x_1 - x_1 x_2)$

The results found in 14.4, Ex. (a), above apply. The matrix of Q is

$$A = \begin{bmatrix} 2 & -1 & -1 \\ -1 & 2 & -1 \\ -1 & -1 & 2 \end{bmatrix} \text{ orthogonally equivalent to } \begin{bmatrix} 3 & 0 & 0 \\ 0 & 3 & 0 \\ 0 & 0 & 0 \end{bmatrix}$$

The appropriate transformation is $x = Py$ or $y = P'x$ with P as in 14.4, Ex. (b) :

$$y_1 = \frac{1}{\sqrt{2}}(x_1 - x_2) \qquad \text{or} \qquad x_1 = \frac{1}{\sqrt{2}}y_1 + \frac{1}{\sqrt{6}}y_2 + \frac{1}{\sqrt{3}}y_3$$

$$y_2 = \frac{1}{\sqrt{6}}(x_1 + x_2 - 2x_3) \qquad x_2 = -\frac{1}{\sqrt{2}}y_1 + \frac{1}{\sqrt{6}}y_2 + \frac{1}{\sqrt{3}}y_3$$

$$y_3 = \frac{1}{\sqrt{3}}(x_1 + x_2 + x_3) \qquad x_3 = -\frac{2}{\sqrt{6}}y_2 + \frac{1}{\sqrt{3}}y_3$$

On substitution : $Q = 3(y_1^2 + y_2^2)$

i.e. $Q = \frac{3}{2}(x_1 - x_2)^2 + \frac{1}{2}(x_1 + x_2 - 2x_3)^2$

In this case, A is of rank 2 with characteristic roots 3, 3 and 0 ; the quadratic form Q is the sum of two squares.

The expression of Q as the sum of squares is not unique. Indeed, in a simple numerical case such as this, the process of " completing the square " gives an alternative sum of squares, and much more quickly :

$$\begin{aligned}\tfrac{1}{2}Q &= (x_1^2 - x_1 x_2 - x_1 x_3) + (x_2^2 + x_3^2 - x_2 x_3) \\ &= (x_1 - \tfrac{1}{2}x_2 - \tfrac{1}{2}x_3)^2 - \tfrac{1}{4}x_2^2 - \tfrac{1}{4}x_3^2 - \tfrac{1}{2}x_2 x_3 + (x_2^2 + x_3^2 - x_2 x_3) \\ &= (x_1 - \tfrac{1}{2}x_2 - \tfrac{1}{2}x_3)^2 + \tfrac{3}{4}(x_2^2 + x_3^2 - 2x_2 x_3) \\ &= (x_1 - \tfrac{1}{2}x_2 - \tfrac{1}{2}x_3)^2 + \tfrac{3}{4}(x_2 - x_3)^2 \end{aligned}$$

Hence : $Q = \tfrac{1}{2}(2x_1 - x_2 - x_3)^2 + \tfrac{3}{4}(x_2 - x_3)^2$

which is another version of the expression obtained above. The " completing the square " process works in practice in numerical cases ; the point of the orthogonal transformation result is that it is perfectly general.

The main application of the reduction of a quadratic form Q to a sum of squares is in the determination of the sign of the values taken by Q. Take $Q = x'Ax$ in n variables, where the discriminant $|A| \neq 0$, i.e. A non-singular. Then Q is the sum of exactly n squares :

$$\lambda_1 y_1^2 + \lambda_2 y_2^2 + \ldots + \lambda_n y_n^2$$

All the y's cannot be zero no matter what values (not all zero) are assigned to the x's. The x's are obtained from the y's by an orthogonal transformation $x = Py$ with inverse $y = P'x$; to each x there is one y and conversely. Since $y = 0$ corresponds to $x = 0$, it cannot also correspond to another $\mathbf{x} \neq 0$. Hence, the sign of Q depends on the signs of $\lambda_1, \lambda_2, \ldots \lambda_n$, the characteristic roots of $\mathbf{A}$. If all the roots are positive, then Q is always positive, and conversely.

A quadratic form Q is defined as *positive definite* if it takes only positive values no matter what values (not all zero) are assigned to the variables. As long as $\mathbf{A}$ is non-singular, the condition for a positive definite form is that all the characteristic roots of $\mathbf{A}$ are positive. The condition is necessary and sufficient.

It remains to examine the case where $\mathbf{A}$ is singular, of rank $r < n$. Of the characteristic roots of $\mathbf{A}$, $(n - r)$ are zero; Q is expressed as the sum of only r squares, involving only r of the variables $y_1, y_2, \ldots y_n$ obtained from the x's. It is always possible to select values of the x's (not all zero) to make these r y's zero, though the other y's will not all be zero. Hence, even if the r characteristic roots of $\mathbf{A}$ which do not vanish are positive, and Q is the sum of r positive squares, it is always possible to find values of the x's which make Q zero. It follows that the condition laid down for Q positive definite, i.e. *all* the characteristic roots of $\mathbf{A}$ positive, must be strictly applied. The singular case when $\mathbf{A}$ has some zero characteristic roots must be ruled out.

The distinction between Q which takes only positive values, and Q taking non-negative values, is important. $Q > 0$ always, if and only if $\mathbf{A}$ has n positive characteristic roots, ruling out $\mathbf{A}$ singular with some zero characteristic roots. The case which nearly, but not quite, serves is when $\mathbf{A}$ is singular with r characteristic roots positive and the other $(n - r)$ zero. Q is then *positive semi-definite*, taking zero as well as positive values.

For the characteristic roots of $\mathbf{A}$ to be all positive, the characteristic equation $| \mathbf{A} - \lambda\mathbf{I} | = 0$ must consist of successive terms which alternate in sign and this implies that sub-matrices of $\mathbf{A}$, read off down the principal diagonal and of increasing order from 1 to n, must all have positive determinant values (see Ex. 5 below). The result for a positive definite quadratic form is :

The quadratic form $Q = \mathbf{x'Ax}$ in n variables is positive definite when it takes a positive value for any values of the variables (not all zero). This is so if and only if the n characteristic roots of $\mathbf{A} = [a_{rs}]$, symmetric of order $n \times n$, are all positive, equivalent to :

$$a_{11} > 0 \; ; \quad \begin{vmatrix} a_{11} & a_{12} \\ a_{12} & a_{22} \end{vmatrix} > 0 \; ; \; \ldots \quad \begin{vmatrix} a_{11} & a_{12} & \ldots & a_{1n} \\ a_{12} & a_{22} & \ldots & a_{2n} \\ \ldots\ldots\ldots\ldots\ldots \\ a_{1n} & a_{2n} & \ldots & a_n \end{vmatrix} > 0$$

A *negative definite* quadratic form Q takes only negative values for any values of the variables (not all zero). The condition is that $(-Q)$ is positive definite ; in terms of determinant values, the expressions written above must be alternatively negative and positive.

Further results can be derived from the basic property now established. The most important is the condition for a quadratic form Q in n variables to be positive definite (or negative definite) subject to a linear relation between the variables :

$$\alpha'\mathbf{x} = \alpha_1 x_1 + \alpha_2 x_2 + \dots + \alpha_n x_n = 0$$

where α is a given vector of constants (not all zero). When the relation is used to give one variable in terms of the others, Q reduces to a quadratic form in $(n-1)$ variables. The required condition is that Q, as reduced, shall be positive (or negative) definite. As shown by Allen (1938), the condition can be expressed in terms of determinant values as follows :

The quadratic form $Q = \mathbf{x}'\mathbf{A}\mathbf{x}$ in n variables is positive definite subject to the linear relation $\alpha'\mathbf{x} = 0$ if

$$\begin{vmatrix} 0 & \alpha_1 & \alpha_2 \\ \alpha_1 & a_{11} & a_{12} \\ \alpha_2 & a_{12} & a_{22} \end{vmatrix} < 0 \,; \quad \begin{vmatrix} 0 & \alpha_1 & \alpha_2 & \alpha_3 \\ \alpha_1 & a_{11} & a_{12} & a_{13} \\ \alpha_2 & a_{12} & a_{22} & a_{23} \\ \alpha_3 & a_{13} & a_{23} & a_{33} \end{vmatrix} < 0 \,; \quad \dots \quad \begin{vmatrix} 0 & \alpha_1 & \alpha_2 & \dots & \alpha_n \\ \alpha_1 & a_{11} & a_{12} & \dots & a_{1n} \\ \alpha_2 & a_{12} & a_{22} & \dots & a_{2n} \\ \dots & \dots & \dots & \dots & \dots \\ \alpha_n & a_{1n} & a_{2n} & \dots & a_{nn} \end{vmatrix} < 0$$

Q is negative definite, subject to the same relation, if the expressions shown are alternatively positive and negative.

One further property of quadratic forms can be given here for use later (19.2 below). Let $Q = \mathbf{x}'\mathbf{A}\mathbf{x}$ be positive definite so that $\mathbf{A}$ is a non-singular and symmetric matrix (with positive characteristic roots). Apply the non-singular transformation $\mathbf{y} = \mathbf{A}\mathbf{x}$, or $\mathbf{x} = \mathbf{A}^{-1}\mathbf{y}$, so that one set of y's (not all zero) correspond to any given x's (not all zero). Then :

$$Q = (\mathbf{A}^{-1}\mathbf{y})'\mathbf{A}(\mathbf{A}^{-1}\mathbf{y}) = \mathbf{y}'(\mathbf{A}^{-1})'(\mathbf{A}\mathbf{A}^{-1})\mathbf{y} = \mathbf{y}'\mathbf{A}^{-1}\mathbf{y}$$

since $\mathbf{A}\mathbf{A}^{-1} = \mathbf{I}$ and $(\mathbf{A}^{-1})' = \mathbf{A}^{-1}$ by the symmetric property of $\mathbf{A}$. Hence :

If $\mathbf{x}'\mathbf{A}\mathbf{x}$ is positive definite, so is $\mathbf{y}'\mathbf{A}^{-1}\mathbf{y}$

Now suppose $Q = \underset{r}{\Sigma}\,\underset{s}{\Sigma}\, a_{rs}\, x_r x_s$ is positive definite subject to :

$$\Sigma\, \alpha_r x_r = \alpha_1 x_1 + \alpha_2 x_2 + \dots + \alpha_n x_n = 0$$

Write $R = \underset{r}{\Sigma}\,\underset{s}{\Sigma}\, a_{rs} x_r x_s + 2\lambda \underset{r}{\Sigma}\, \alpha_r x_r$ for any λ

i.e.
$$R = \mathbf{x}'\mathbf{B}\mathbf{x}$$

where $\mathbf{x}$ is the set of $(n+1)$ variables $(\lambda, x_1, x_2, \ldots x_n)$ and where $\mathbf{B}$ is $\mathbf{A}$ bordered by the α's as written above. The conditions for Q to be positive definite subject to the side relations are that R is positive definite for any x, except that $x_1, x_2, \ldots, x_n$ are all zero and subject to $\sum_r \alpha_r x_r = 0$. Apply the transformation $\mathbf{y} = \mathbf{Bx}$ or $\mathbf{x} = \mathbf{B}^{-1}\mathbf{y}$ and note that, if

$$\mathbf{y} = (y_0, y_1, y_2, \ldots y_n),$$

then
$$y_0 = \sum_r \alpha_r x_r = 0$$

Hence, as above, R transforms to

$$R = \mathbf{y}'\mathbf{B}^{-1}\mathbf{y}$$

where $\mathbf{y} = (0, y_1, y_2, \ldots y_n)$ and the y's can take any values (not all zero). R is positive definite and, since the first element in y is zero, it can be written as $\sum_r \sum_s \dfrac{B_{rs}}{B} y_r y_s$. Here B is $|\mathbf{B}|$ and B_{rs} is the co-factor of a_{rs} in $\mathbf{B}$; the summation applies over n values of the y's. Hence:

If $\sum_r \sum_s a_{rs} x_r x_s > 0$ subject to $\sum_r \alpha_r x_r = 0$, then

$$\sum_r \sum_s \frac{B_{rs}}{B} y_r y_s > 0$$

for any y's not all zero, where $\mathbf{B}$ is the determinant formed from $\mathbf{A} = [a_{rs}]$ bordered with the α's.

Similar results hold if the quadratic forms are negative definite.

EXERCISES 14.5

1. The quadratic form $Q = \sum_r \sum_s a_{rs} x_r x_s$ has $a_{rs} \neq a_{sr}$. Show that it can be written $Q = \sum_r \sum_s \alpha_{sr} x_r x_s$ where $\alpha_{rs} = \frac{1}{2}(a_{rs} + a_{sr}) = \alpha_{sr}$. Hence establish that Q can always be written with a symmetric matrix. Illustrate with

$$Q = \begin{array}{l} x_1{}^2 - 3x_1 x_2 = \\ + x_1 x_2 + \quad x_2{}^2 \end{array} \quad \begin{array}{l} x_1{}^2 - x_1 x_2 \\ - x_1 x_2 + \quad x_2{}^2 \end{array}$$

2. $Q = x_1{}^2 + x_2{}^2 - 2x_1 x_2$ has matrix $\mathbf{A} = \begin{bmatrix} 1 & -1 \\ -1 & 1 \end{bmatrix}$ of rank 1 with characteristic roots 0 and 2. Show that the orthogonal transformation:

$$y_1 = \frac{1}{\sqrt{2}}(x_1 - x_2) \quad \text{and} \quad y_2 = \frac{1}{\sqrt{2}}(x_1 + x_2)$$

transforms Q into a single square.

3. $Q = 2x_1 x_2$ is a quadratic form in two variables. Write its matrix, obtain the characteristic roots and show that the orthogonal transformation of the previous exercise puts Q into the form of the difference between two squares. Deduce that neither this, nor the previous quadratic form, is positive definite.

4. Show that $Q = x_1{}^2 + x_2{}^2 + x_3{}^2 - x_1x_3 - x_2x_3$ is positive definite, first by finding the characteristic roots of its matrix, and then by putting it into the form of the sum of three squares.

5. $Q = \mathbf{x'Ax}$ is a quadratic form in three variables. Write the characteristic equation of $\mathbf{A}$ in the form :

$$- \lambda^3 + p_1\lambda^2 - p_2\lambda + p_3 = 0$$

(14.4, Ex. 3, above) and show that the characteristic roots (λ_1, λ_2 and λ_3) are all positive if and only if p_1, p_2 and p_3 are all positive. Show that this is equivalent to :

$$a_{11} > 0, \quad \begin{vmatrix} a_{11} & a_{12} \\ a_{12} & a_{22} \end{vmatrix} > 0, \quad \begin{vmatrix} a_{11} & a_{12} & a_{13} \\ a_{12} & a_{22} & a_{23} \\ a_{13} & a_{23} & a_{33} \end{vmatrix} > 0.$$

Indicate how this result can be generalised.

6. $\mathbf{x'Ay}$ is a bilinear form. Transform to new variables u and v by $\mathbf{x = Cu}$ and $\mathbf{y = Dv}$ and show that $\mathbf{u'Bv}$ is the transformed bilinear form, where $\mathbf{B = C'AD}$. What must the orders of the matrices be? Under what conditions can $\mathbf{D}$ be taken as $\mathbf{C}$?

14.6 Stability of Market Equilibrium

It is now possible to tie together the loose ends left in the Hicksian conditions for stability of market equilibrium (10.5 above). There are m commodities, the last being *numéraire* with price $p_m = 1$; the other prices p_r ($r = 1, 2, \ldots m - 1$) are determined in market equilibrium by the equation of demand and supply :

$$S_r - D_r = Y_r - (X_r - \overline{X}_r) = 0 \quad r = 1, 2, \ldots (m - 1) \quad \ldots\ldots\ldots\ldots(1)$$

where Y_r and X_r are functions of the prices and $\overline{X}_r$ is given.

The equilibrium is stable if all prices, once disturbed, tend to return to their equilibrium values over time. Stability can only be expressed, therefore, in terms of a specified dynamic system. In the version of 10.5, which follows Hicks (1939, 1946), this was not done and a short cut was attempted. This must be supplemented by investigating the dynamics of prices on inter-related markets.

In the single-market case in Walrasian form (1.8 above), the dynamic model is :

$$\frac{dp}{dt} = - \mu(S - D) \quad \ldots\ldots\ldots\ldots\ldots\ldots\ldots\ldots\ldots(2)$$

and, with linear forms $D = \alpha + ap$ and $S = \beta + bp$, the solution is

$$p = p_0 e^{-\mu(b-a)t}$$

where p_0 is the initial disturbance from equilibrium and p is the subsequent path of price (measured from the equilibrium level). The same result holds whatever the form of the demand and supply curves, but only approximately for small variations ; a and b are then the slopes of the curves at equilibrium.   For stability

$$b - a = \frac{d}{dp}(S - D) > 0 \text{ at equilibrium}$$

The Walrasian model can be extended to inter-related markets, as by Samuelson (1947).   The equation (2) is replaced by :

$$\frac{dp_r}{dt} = -\mu_r(S_r - D_r) \quad r = 1, 2, \dots (m-1) \quad \dots\dots\dots\dots\dots(3)$$

where $S_r - D_r$ is given by (1) as dependent on all prices and is zero at equilibrium.   The constants μ_r represent the speeds of adjustment on the several markets.   Write S_r and D_r as linear in all prices, at least approximately for small variations from equilibrium, so that

$$S_r - D_r = \text{constant} + \sum_{s=1}^{m-1} a_{rs} p_s \quad r = 1, 2, \dots (m-1)$$

where a_{rs} is the equilibrium value of $\frac{\partial}{\partial p_s}(S_r - D_r) = \frac{\partial Y_r}{\partial p_s} - \frac{\partial X_r}{\partial p_s}$.

dynamic conditions (3) written in terms of p_r, a divergence from equilibrium, are then :

$$\frac{dp_r}{dt} = -\mu_r \sum_s a_{rs} p_s \quad r = 1, 2, \dots (m-1)$$

Assume the particular case (which is not a limitation) where all speeds of adjustment are taken as unity by the appropriate choice of the units in which time and the commodities are measured :

$$\frac{dp_r}{dt} + \sum_s a_{rs} p_s = 0 \quad r = 1, 2, \dots (m-1) \dots\dots\dots\dots\dots(4)$$

These are to be solved for the paths of p_r over time.

The solution in the single-market case suggests that :

$$p_r = A_r e^{-\lambda t} \quad r = 1, 2, \dots (m-1)$$

where λ is a constant to be found and where the A's are constants to be given by the initial disturbance.   Substitute in (4) :

$$\sum (a_{rs} - \lambda \delta_{rs}) A_s = 0 \quad r = 1, 2, \dots (m-1)$$

where δ_{rs} is the Kronecker delta.   This system of homogeneous equations must be satisfied by some non-zero set of A's so that (by 14.2 above) :

$$|a_{rs} - \lambda \delta_{rs}| = \begin{vmatrix} a_{11} - \lambda & a_{12} & \dots & a_{1\,m-1} \\ a_{21} & a_{22} - \lambda & \dots & a_{2\,m-1} \\ \dots\dots\dots\dots\dots\dots\dots\dots\dots\dots\dots\dots \\ a_{m-1\,1} & a_{m-1\,2} & \dots & a_{m-1\,m-1} - \lambda \end{vmatrix} = 0 \quad \dots\dots\dots\dots(5)$$

The appropriate values of λ are given by (5), the characteristic equation of the matrix $\mathbf{A} = [a_{rs}]$; there are $(m-1)$ roots $\lambda_1, \lambda_2, \dots \lambda_{m-1}$ which may be real or complex. Each root is a possible value of λ so that, on adding the various solutions with arbitrary constants, the general solution of (4) is :

$$p_r = \sum_{s=1}^{m-1} A_{rs} e^{-\lambda_s t} \quad r = 1, 2, \dots (m-1) \quad \dots\dots\dots\dots\dots(6)$$

Here, the λ's are the roots of (5) and the A's are arbitrary constants given by initial conditions.

Equilibrium on inter-related markets, given by (1), is stable on this dynamic model if the path of each price, given by (6), is such that $p_r \to 0$ as $t \to \infty$. This is so if all the real roots among λ_s are positive and if all the conjugate complex pairs of roots have positive real parts. A negative and real λ_s introduces a steadily explosive term in (6) ; a complex pair of roots with a negative real part introduces an explosive oscillation.

In general, the matrix $\mathbf{A}$ is not symmetric since $a_{rs} = \dfrac{\partial Y_r}{\partial p_s} - \dfrac{\partial X_r}{\partial p_s}$ is not equal to $a_{sr} = \dfrac{\partial Y_s}{\partial p_r} - \dfrac{\partial X_s}{\partial p_r}$. Little can then be said about the characteristic equation (5) and its roots. As a particular case, assume that $a_{rs} = a_{sr}$ and hence that $\mathbf{A}$ is symmetric. The stability conditions are then simplified since, by 14.4 above, the equation (5) has all its roots real ; for stability, the roots must also be positive. It follows (14.5 above) that the quadratic form $Q = \mathbf{x}'\mathbf{A}\mathbf{x}$, with the symmetric discriminant $A = |a_{rs}|$, is positive definite and hence that :

$$a_{11} > 0 ; \quad \begin{vmatrix} a_{11} & a_{12} \\ a_{12} & a_{22} \end{vmatrix} > 0 ; \quad \begin{vmatrix} a_{11} & a_{12} & a_{13} \\ a_{12} & a_{22} & a_{23} \\ a_{13} & a_{23} & a_{33} \end{vmatrix} > 0 ; \dots$$

These are the Hicksian conditions for perfect stability.

Hence, *if the matrix* $\mathbf{A} = [a_{rs}]$ *is symmetric*, the Hicksian conditions are necessary and sufficient for stability of this Walrasian model (equivalent to all λ's having positive real parts). Now :

$$a_{rs} = \frac{\partial Y_r}{\partial p_s} - \frac{\partial X_r}{\partial p_s} \quad \text{at equilibrium}$$

and Hicks (1939, 1946) assumes symmetry by neglecting the " income terms " in Y_r and X_r. This is no more than an approximation which can be appropriately made under certain circumstances. Whenever symmetry is lacking, e.g. because of income effects on the demand side, then the

Hicksian conditions can still be necessary and sufficient for stability if $\mathbf{A} = [a_{rs}]$ has the *Metzlesian property*: $a_{rr} > 0$, $a_{rs} < 0$ (all r and s, $r \neq s$), the commodities being gross substitutes : see Metzler (1945). Following Hicks, Samuelson and Metzler, the problem has been further explored by several writers ; see Newman (1958).

EXERCISES 14.6

1. Expand the characteristic equation (5) in the form :
$$(-1)^{m-1}(\lambda^{m-1} + p_1\lambda^{m-2} + p_2\lambda^{m-3} + \dots + p_{m-2}\lambda + p_{m-1})$$
and find the p's in terms of determinants formed from $\mathbf{A} = [a_{rs}]$.
2. Assume $\mathbf{A}$ is symmetric and equate the coefficients (the p's) in the previous exercise to sums and products of the $(m-1)$ real roots $\lambda_1, \lambda_2 \dots \lambda_{m-1}$. For stability, all λ's are positive ; translate this into properties of $\mathbf{A}$.

14.7 Leontief's Static System

The matrix notation provides a compact expression of Leontief's inter-industry systems (Chapter 11 above). In the *closed system* there are $(n+1)$ industries ; the last comprises households supplying labour services and using consumer goods as inputs. Let x_{rs} be the amount of the output X_r of the rth industry passed to the sth industry, giving a *transaction matrix* :
$$\mathbf{T} = [x_{rs}] \quad \text{of order } (n+1) \times (n+1)$$
By convention, write $x_{rr} = 0$ for $r = 1, 2, \dots (n+1)$, so that $\mathbf{T}$ has a principal diagonal of zero entries. Then $\mathbf{T}$ sums across rows to the vector $\mathbf{X} = \{X_r\}$ of total output. Alternatively, by convention, write $x_{rr} = -X_r$ so that $\mathbf{T}$ then sums by rows to zero.

Fixed input coefficients are assumed :
$$a_{rs} = \frac{x_{rs}}{X_s} \quad r, s = 1, 2, \dots (n+1)$$
with $\qquad\qquad a_{rr} = 0 \quad$ by convention

These make up an *input coefficient matrix* :
$$\mathbf{A}^* = [a_{rs}] \quad \text{of order } (n+1) \times (n+1)$$
and a *technology matrix* (in the sense of 10.8 above) :
$$\mathbf{A} = \mathbf{I} - \mathbf{A}^* = \begin{bmatrix} 1 & -a_{12} & \cdots & -a_{1\,n+1} \\ -a_{21} & 1 & \cdots & -a_{2\,n+1} \\ \cdots\cdots\cdots\cdots\cdots\cdots\cdots\cdots \\ -a_{n+1\,1} & -a_{n+1\,2} & \cdots & 1 \end{bmatrix}$$

The conditions for equilibrium, expressing the facts that each output is exactly distributed over uses, and that receipts equal costs in each industry, are then :
$$\text{(i) } \mathbf{AX} = 0 \quad \text{and} \quad \text{(ii) } \mathbf{p}'\mathbf{A} = 0 \quad \dots\dots\dots\dots\dots(1)$$

where $\mathbf{p}=\{p_r\}$ is the vector of prices. The two conditions are quite separate ; (i) gives outputs and (ii) prices. Each set is a system of homogeneous linear equations, with a non-zero solution only if $\mathbf{A}$ is singular, of rank $r<n+1$. In the usual case, the rank of $\mathbf{A}$ is $r=n$, in which case it is the *ratios* of outputs and prices which are determined by (1), see Ex. 3 below. The scale of outputs and prices is then only fixed if one output (e.g. labour supply) is given, and one price (e.g. the wage rate).

If assigned values are given to one (or more) row and column in $\mathbf{T}$, then the system becomes open. Typically, in Leontief's *open system*, the last row (labour inputs) and the last column (households) are fixed in the transactions matrix, which then becomes :

$$\mathbf{T}=\begin{bmatrix} x_{rs} & x_r \\ \hline \xi_s & 0 \end{bmatrix}$$

for $r,\ s=1,\ 2,\ \ldots n$. $\mathbf{T}$ is still of order $(n+1)\times(n+1)$ but the last row consists of given labour inputs (ξ_s) and the last column of given final demands (x_r). The input coefficient matrix is $\mathbf{A}^*=[a_{rs}]$ and the technology matrix $\mathbf{A}=\mathbf{I}-\mathbf{A}^*$, both of order $n\times n$. However, the latter can be extended to

$$\mathbf{B}=\begin{bmatrix} \mathbf{A} \\ \cdots \\ -\mathbf{b}' \end{bmatrix} \qquad \text{where} \quad \mathbf{b}'=[b_s]$$

by adding a row of labour input coefficients $(-b_s)=-\dfrac{\xi_s}{X_s}\ (s=1,\ 2,\ \ldots\ n)$

The conditions (1) for equilibrium are now :

$$\text{(i) } \mathbf{AX}=\mathbf{x} \quad \text{and} \quad \text{(ii) } \mathbf{p}'\mathbf{A}=\mathbf{w}' \quad \ldots\ldots\ldots\ldots\ldots\ldots(2)$$

Further :

$$\begin{aligned} \text{Employment} &\quad Y=\mathbf{b}'\mathbf{X} \\ \text{National income} &\quad Z=\mathbf{p}'\mathbf{x}=\mathbf{w}'\mathbf{X} \end{aligned}$$

These conditions are (i) and (ii) of 11.3 above in matrix form. Apart from the technology matrix $\mathbf{A}$ of order $n\times n$, the conditions (2) involve the following vectors (in column or row form), all of order n :

$$\begin{aligned} \mathbf{X}&=\{X_r\}=\text{total output} & \mathbf{x}&=\{x_r\}\ =\text{final demand} \\ \mathbf{p}&=\{p_r\}\ =\text{prices} & \mathbf{w}&=w\{b_s\}=\text{unit wage costs} \end{aligned}$$

In addition to the technology $\mathbf{A}$, the open system takes, as given data, both the final demand $\mathbf{x}$ and the unit wage costs $\mathbf{w}$. The latter involves the labour input coefficients (b_s) and the wage rate (w). The labour input coefficients, by themselves, are needed to get total employment Y.

The variables to be determined by (2) are total output $\mathbf{X}$ and prices $\mathbf{p}$. Employment Y and national income Z can also be determined. If $\mathbf{A}$ is non-singular, which is generally so if the $(n+1) \times (n+1)$ technology matrix of the closed system is of rank $r = n$, then (2) have a unique solution :

$$\mathbf{X} = \mathbf{A}^{-1}\mathbf{x} ; \quad \mathbf{p}' = \mathbf{w}'\mathbf{A}^{-1} ; \quad Y = \mathbf{b}'\mathbf{A}^{-1}\mathbf{x} \text{ and } Z = \mathbf{w}'\mathbf{A}^{-1}\mathbf{x} \quad \ldots\ldots\ldots(3)$$

The conditions (2) are quite separate, as appears in the solution (3). The outputs $\mathbf{X}$ are given in terms of the fixed final demand $\mathbf{x}$ (and so is employment Y). The prices $\mathbf{p}$ come from the fixed unit wage costs $\mathbf{w}$. As a matter of computation, the outputs, employment, prices and national income are obtained when the technology matrix $\mathbf{A}$ is inverted to $\mathbf{A}^{-1}$.

EXERCISES 14.7

1. In terms of the determinant $A = |\mathbf{A}|$ and its co-factors, show that the solution of Leontief's open system is (for $r = 1, 2, \ldots n$) :

$$X_r = \frac{1}{A} \sum_s x_s A_{sr} \quad \text{and} \quad p_r = \frac{w}{A} \sum_s A_{rs} b_s$$

2. Interpret $\mathbf{AX} = \mathbf{x}$ as a linear transformation (from total output to final demand) and $\mathbf{X} = \mathbf{A}^{-1}\mathbf{x}$ as its inverse. What is the corresponding transformation for prices?

3. In Leontief's closed system of $(n+1)$ industries, assume that $\mathbf{A}$ is of rank n and that the sub-matrix $\mathbf{A}_{nn}$ obtained by omitting the last row and column is non-singular. Write $\mathbf{c}$ for the last column of $\mathbf{A}$, omitting the last entry. Hence solve the first n equations of $\mathbf{AX} = \mathbf{0}$ to give the column vector of the first n outputs as $\mathbf{A}_{nn}^{-1}\mathbf{c}X_{n+1}$, where X_{n+1} is the last output. If the $(n+1)$th " industry " is households, show that this gives each output in terms of the wage rate.

4. In Leontief's open system, write $\bar{\mathbf{x}}$ and $\bar{\mathbf{w}}$ for the diagonal matrices formed from the final demands and unit wage costs. Show that the matrix $\mathbf{U} = \bar{\mathbf{w}}\mathbf{A}^{-1}\bar{\mathbf{x}}$ has (r, s)th element $w_r x_s \dfrac{A_{sr}}{A}$, where A_{sr} is a co-factor in $A = |\mathbf{A}|$. Show further that $\mathbf{U}$ has row sums $\{w_r X_r\}$ and column sums $[p_s x_s]$. Deduce that $\mathbf{U}$ can serve as a transactions matrix for national income accounts, where national income is the sum of values added in industries = sum of final expenditure by sectors ; see Barna (1952).

14.8 Transactions Matrices

The transactions matrix $\mathbf{T} = [x_{rs}]$, with $x_{rr} = -X_r$ by convention, is such that each row adds to zero. This expresses the first condition for equilibrium, i.e. the exact disposal of each output. The columns of $\mathbf{T}$ are, however, not additive, since $\mathbf{T}$ is in quantity form and the entries of a column are in different units. If the prices p_r are taken as given, or determined by the second equilibrium conditions, then the *value transactions matrix* is :

$$\mathbf{V} = [v_{rs}] = [(p_r x_{rs})]$$

with $\qquad v_{rr} = -p_r X_r = -V_r \qquad$ by convention.

The rows of V still add to zero, the equilibrium condition being that the value of each output (V_r) is exactly disposed over the values of the various usages. In addition, the columns of V add to zero ; this expresses the other equilibrium condition that the prices must be such that receipts equal costs in each industry. Hence, if equilibrium prices are used, V incorporates in itself, by the conditions of summing to zero by rows and columns, both the sets of equilibrium equations.

The technology can be re-defined to give $A = I - A^*$ in terms, not of the technical coefficients a_{rs}, but of the corresponding value coefficients :

$$\alpha_{rs} = \frac{v_{rs}}{V_s} = \frac{p_r}{p_s} a_{rs}$$

Then (see Ex. 1 below), if X is the vector of total outputs *in value*, the first conditions for equilibrium (V adding to zero by rows) is in exactly the same form as in quantity terms : $AX = 0$.

The same re-definition can be applied to Leontief's open system. If A, X and x are all expressed in value terms, then equilibrium conditions are :

$$AX = x \quad \text{giving} \quad X = A^{-1}x$$

and the total wage bill is $b'A^{-1}x$. Notice also that the extended technology matrix, when derived from values, is :

$$B = \begin{bmatrix} A \\ \cdots \\ -b' \end{bmatrix}$$

and such that the sum of each column is zero ; see equations (ii) of 11.4 above. This is the form of the analysis of the open system which is relevant to empirical applications.

The concept of a transactions matrix, as used in the Leontief system, has been developed and put in a wider setting by Stone (1951) and Goodwin (1953). A closed economy has n activities, which may or may not be interpreted as industries. Write x_{rs} for the sales of the rth to the sth activity in quantity terms, and $v_{rs} = p_r x_{rs}$ in value terms, p_r being the prices in the rth activity. By convention, write

$$x_{rr} = -X_r \quad \text{and} \quad v_{rr} = -p_r X_r = -V_r,$$

where X_r and V_r are the total sales of the rth activity in quantity and value. The transactions matrices are

$$T = [x_{rs}] \quad \text{and} \quad V = [v_{rs}] \quad r, s = 1, 2, \ldots n$$

in quantity and value respectively.

The technical coefficients of the economy are the relations between the *purchases* of one activity (from other activities) and its own total *sales*. These can be expressed in quantity terms (see Ex. 2 below) ; or they can be written, as here, entirely in terms of values. Assume that there are *fixed technical coefficients*, defined :

$$a_{rs} = \frac{v_{rs}}{V_s} \quad r, s = 1, 2, \dots n$$

i.e. the ratio of the value of purchases of the sth activity (from the rth activity) to its total sales by value. By convention $v_{rr} = -V_r$, i.e.

$$a_{rr} = \frac{v_{rr}}{V_r} = -1 \quad r = 1, 2, \dots n$$

Write
$$\mathbf{A} = [(-a_{rs})] = \begin{bmatrix} 1 & -a_{12} & \dots & -a_{1n} \\ -a_{21} & 1 & \dots & -a_{2n} \\ \dots\dots\dots\dots\dots\dots\dots\dots\dots \\ -a_{n1} & -a_{n2} & \dots & 1 \end{bmatrix}$$

as the matrix summarising the technical conditions of the economy.

The relation between the transactions matrix $\mathbf{V}$ and the technical matrix $\mathbf{A}$ is easily obtained. Denote by $\bar{\mathbf{v}}$ the diagonal matrix formed from the total value of sales (V_r) of the n activities.

Then :
$$\mathbf{V} = [v_{rs}] = [(a_{rs}V_s)] = -\mathbf{A}\bar{\mathbf{v}}$$

by the multiplication rule for matrices.

Two quite separate conditions can be laid down, for the economy as a whole : (i) that total sales of an activity are exactly distributed as purchases by other activities, and (ii) receipts balance costs (value of purchases) in each activity. Hence :

Conditions (i) : the matrix $\mathbf{V}$ adds by rows to zero,

i.e. $$\mathbf{V}\{1\} = 0$$
i.e. $$\mathbf{A}\bar{\mathbf{v}}\{1\} = 0$$
i.e. $$\mathbf{AX} = 0$$

since $\bar{\mathbf{v}}\{1\}$ is the vector made up of V_r, and this can be written as $\mathbf{X}$, or total sales by value. This is the familiar Leontief condition (closed system) in value terms.

Conditions (ii) : the matrix $\mathbf{V}$ adds by columns to zero,

i.e. $$[1]\mathbf{V} = 0$$
i.e. $$[1]\mathbf{A}\bar{\mathbf{v}} = 0$$
i.e. $$[1]\mathbf{A}\bar{\mathbf{v}}\bar{\mathbf{v}}^{-1} = 0 \quad (\bar{\mathbf{v}} \text{ being non-singular})$$
i.e. $$[1]\mathbf{A} = 0$$

This is simply a restraint on the technical matrix $\mathbf{A}$; the columns must add to zero.

From the closed transactions economy, an open system can be derived by taking one row and one column of the transactions matrix $\mathbf{T}$ or $\mathbf{V}$ as fixed. Suppose that it is the last row and column so that the purchases of the nth activity are given. The technical matrix $\mathbf{A}$ can be reduced to order $(n-1)$ and similarly the vector $\mathbf{X}$ of the total sales of $(n-1)$ activities. It is then found (see Ex. 3 below) that conditions (i) become :

$$\mathbf{AX} = \text{Vector of given purchases of } n\text{th activity.}$$

This is the familiar conditions of the Leontief open system, when the nth activity is interpreted as consumption of households.

EXERCISES 14.8

1. In Leontief's closed system, re-define $\mathbf{A^*} = [\alpha_{rs}]$ in terms of values by writing $\alpha_{rs} = \dfrac{v_{rs}}{V_s}$. Show that the conditions for equilibrium (exact distribution of each output) then give $\mathbf{AX} = 0$, where $\mathbf{A} = \mathbf{I} - \mathbf{A^*}$ and $\mathbf{X}$ is the vector of *values* of total outputs.

2. Consider the value transactions matrix $\mathbf{V} = [v_{rs}]$ in a closed transactions economy when fixed technical coefficients $a_{rs} = \dfrac{x_{rs}}{X_s}$ are defined in quantity terms. Show that $\mathbf{V} = \bar{\mathbf{p}}\mathbf{A}\bar{\mathbf{x}}$, where $\mathbf{A}$ is obtained as before from a_{rs}, $\bar{\mathbf{p}}$ is the diagonal matrix from the price vector $\mathbf{p}$ and $\bar{\mathbf{x}}$ is the diagonal matrix from the total sales vector $\mathbf{X}$. Deduce that the conditions of the economy are then : $\mathbf{AX} = 0$ and $\mathbf{p}'\mathbf{A} = 0$, as in Leontief's closed system.

3. Write

$$\mathbf{B} = \begin{bmatrix} 0 & 0 & \dots & 0 & a_{1n} \\ 0 & 0 & \dots & 0 & a_{2n} \\ \multicolumn{5}{c}{\dotfill} \\ 0 & 0 & & 0 & -1 \end{bmatrix} \quad \text{and show} \quad \mathbf{A} + \mathbf{B} = \left[\begin{array}{c|c} \mathbf{A^*} & 0 \\ \hline \mathbf{a}_n & 0 \end{array} \right]$$

where $\mathbf{A}$ is the technical matrix of order n, $\mathbf{A^*}$ the same matrix reduced to order $(n-1)$ by omission of nth activity and $\mathbf{a}_n$ is some vector of order $(n-1)$. Take the conditions $\mathbf{AX} = 0$ of a closed transactions system, as in the previous exercise, and show that they reduce to :

$$\mathbf{A^*X^*} = \text{purchases of } n\text{th activity}$$

where $\mathbf{X^*}$ is the vector of sales of the $(n-1)$ activities.

4. Pursue the analysis of the previous two exercises by showing that the condition $\mathbf{p}'\mathbf{A} = 0$ of the closed system becomes

$$\mathbf{p^*}'\mathbf{A^*} = \text{unit wage costs}$$

where the nth activity, which is omitted, is interpreted as households.

5. Interpret the transactions matrix $\mathbf{T} = [x_{rs}]$, not for n industries, but for n types of transactors such as households, enterprises, government ; and so indicate its applications to national income accounts. See Stone and Utting (1953).

14.9 Leontief's Dynamic System

The static conditions for equilibrium in Leontief's closed system are $\mathbf{AX}=0$, where $\mathbf{A}=\mathbf{I}-\mathbf{A}^*$ and $\mathbf{A}^*=[a_{rs}]$ is the flow structure of the economy. The a's are fixed input-output coefficients. In extending to a dynamic system (11.8 above), a second matrix $\mathbf{B}=[b_{rs}]$ is added for the capital structure of the economy, the b's being fixed capital (stock-output) coefficients. The dynamic conditions for exact distribution of product, equations (2) of 11.8, are:

$$\mathbf{AX}=\mathbf{B}\frac{d\mathbf{X}}{dt} \quad\dots\dots\dots\dots\dots\dots\dots\dots\dots\dots\dots(1)$$

where $\mathbf{X}=\{X_r\}$ is the column vector of total outputs as before and where

$$\frac{d\mathbf{X}}{dt}=\left\{\frac{dX_r}{dt}\right\}$$

is the column vector of rates of change of output $(r=1, 2, \dots n)$.

To solve (1) as a system of first order differential equations, try

$$\mathbf{X}=\mathbf{k}e^{-\lambda t}$$

where $\mathbf{k}=\{k_r\}$ is a column vector of constants and where λ is a scalar to be found. Then $\dfrac{d\mathbf{X}}{dt}=-\mathbf{k}\lambda e^{-\lambda t}$ and cancelling $e^{-\lambda t}\neq 0$, the system (1) becomes:

$$\mathbf{Ak}=-\lambda\mathbf{Bk}$$

i.e.
$$(\mathbf{A}+\lambda\mathbf{B})\mathbf{k}=0 \quad\dots\dots\dots\dots\dots\dots\dots\dots\dots\dots\dots(2)$$

The matrix $(\mathbf{A}+\lambda\mathbf{B})=\begin{bmatrix} 1+\lambda b_{11} & -a_{12}+\lambda b_{12} & \dots & -a_{1n}+\lambda b_{1n} \\ -a_{21}+\lambda b_{21} & 1+\lambda b_{22} & \dots & -a_{2n}+\lambda b_{2n} \\ \dots\dots\dots\dots\dots\dots\dots\dots\dots\dots\dots\dots\dots\dots \\ -a_{n1}+\lambda b_{n1} & -a_{n2}+\lambda b_{n2} & \dots & 1+\lambda b_{nn} \end{bmatrix}$

i.e. a generalised form of the characteristic matrix (14.4 above).

The conditions (2) consist of a column vector of order n equated to zero; there are n equations, sufficient to determine λ and the *ratios* of the elements k_r in $\mathbf{k}$. The values of k_r are not all zero in (2), so that:

$$|\mathbf{A}+\lambda\mathbf{B}|=0 \quad\dots\dots\dots\dots\dots\dots\dots\dots\dots\dots\dots(3)$$

which is an equation of the nth degree in λ, the coefficients depending on the structural constants (the a's and b's). Equation (3) has n roots, λ_1, $\lambda_2, \dots \lambda_n$. Since $\mathbf{A}$ and $\mathbf{B}$ are not symmetric matrices, it is not to be expected that all λ's are real. Some of the λ's may occur in pairs as conjugate complex roots, and they give rise to oscillatory time-paths for outputs.

Consider the root $\lambda = \lambda_s$ of (3). The matrix $(\mathbf{A} + \lambda_s \mathbf{B})$ is singular, since $|\mathbf{A} + \lambda_s \mathbf{B}| = 0$; assume it is of rank $(n-1)$. Then, by 14.2 above, the equations (2) determine the ratios of elements in $\mathbf{k} = k_r$. To the eigenvalue λ_s there corresponds an eigenvector $\mathbf{k}_s = \{k_{rs}\}$, i.e. a particular set of k's given in their ratios $k_{1s} : k_{2s} : \ldots : k_{ns}$ in terms of λ_s and of the structural constants (the a's and b's) of the system (see Ex. 2 below). Hence one solution of (1) is $\mathbf{X} = \mathbf{k}_s e^{-\lambda_s t}$. There are n such solutions for $s = 1, 2, \ldots n$ and they can be combined by addition, with multiplicative arbitrary constants, into the general solution :

$$\mathbf{X} = \sum_{s=1}^{n} A_s \mathbf{k}_s e^{-\lambda_s t}$$

i.e. $\quad X_r = A_1 k_{r1} e^{-\lambda_1 t} + A_2 k_{r2} e^{-\lambda_2 t} + \ldots + A_n k_{rn} e^{-\lambda_n t} \quad (r = 1, 2, \ldots n) \quad \ldots\ldots(4)$

In (4), the A's are arbitrary constants to be given by initial conditions. On the other hand, the λ's and k's are structural constants given by the a's and b's of the equations (1); the λ's are the roots of (3) and the corresponding k's then come from (2).

The successive terms in the solution for X_r may involve real or conjugate complex values of the λ's. If λ_1 is real, the first term dies away over time if $\lambda_1 > 0$ and increases indefinitely if $\lambda_1 < 0$. If λ_1 and λ_2 are conjugate complex $(\alpha \pm i\omega)$, then the first two terms combine into an expression of the form :

$$Ak_r e^{-\alpha t} \cos(\omega t - \epsilon)$$

where A and ϵ are the arbitrary constants. This introduces an oscillatory element in the path of X_r over time, the period being $\dfrac{2\pi}{\omega}$. The oscillations die down if $\alpha > 0$ and increase indefinitely if $\alpha < 0$.

Attention can be concentrated on the ultimate values of outputs as time goes on indefinitely, i.e. on the dominant term in (4). This term is given by the root λ_m which has the smallest " real " part. Each output dies away or increases indefinitely according as the " real " part of λ_m is positive or negative. The ultimate path of each output is an oscillation if λ_m is not real; it is a steady progression if λ_m is real. The ultimate path is :

$$X_r = A_m k_{rm} e^{-\lambda_m t} \quad (\lambda_m \text{ real})$$

or $\qquad X_r = A_m k_{rm} e^{-\alpha_m t} \cos(\omega_m t - \epsilon) \quad (\lambda_m \text{ complex} = \alpha_m + i\omega_m)$

approximately when t is large. It follows that $(\lambda_m \text{ real})$:

$$\frac{1}{X_r} \frac{dX_r}{dt} \to -\lambda_m \quad \text{and} \quad \frac{X_r}{X_s} \to \frac{k_{rm}}{k_{sm}} \quad \text{as } t \to \infty$$

Hence, ultimately, each output has the same relative rate of growth, and the different outputs vary in proportion, the rate and the proportions being fixed by the structure of the system.

In the static case (14.7 above), equilibrium outputs only exist (in ratio form) if the matrix $\mathbf{A}$ of the flow structure is singular, $|\mathbf{A}| = 0$. If this case also holds in the dynamic system, then (as in 14.4 above) the term independent of λ in the equation (3) is zero and $\lambda = 0$ is one root of (3). In the solution (4), write $\lambda_1 = 0$ so that the first term in X_r is a constant $A_1 k_{r1}$. The path of X_r is then a damped or explosive variation about a constant level. If damped (the smallest of the other λ's positive), then the ultimate output is the constant $A_1 k_{r1}$. Clearly, for this case to be possible, the k's must be positive.

The dynamic version of the open system has the same set of differential equations (1) except for the addition of the vector of final demands $\mathbf{x} = \{x_r\}$ on the right-hand side. Each x_r is a given function of time. The solution is again of form (4) with the addition of particular integrals to be obtained from the specific functions of time taken for $\mathbf{x}$. For example, let $\mathbf{x} = \mathbf{c} e^{\mu t}$, where $\mathbf{c} = \{c_r\}$ is a vector of given constants and where μ is a given scalar, so that all final demands increase over time at the same relative rate as in 11.9, case (ii), above. Then the differential equations are $\mathbf{A}\mathbf{X} = \mathbf{B}\dfrac{d\mathbf{X}}{dt} + \mathbf{c} e^{\mu t}$ and particular integrals are required. Try $\mathbf{X} = \mathbf{C} e^{\mu t}$, where $\mathbf{C} = \{C_r\}$ are constants to be found. Then, on substitution :

$$\mathbf{A}\mathbf{C} = \mu\mathbf{B}\mathbf{C} + \mathbf{c}$$

i.e.
$$\mathbf{C} = (\mathbf{A} - \mu\mathbf{B})^{-1}\mathbf{c}$$

where the given matrix $(\mathbf{A} - \mu\mathbf{B})$ is assumed to be non-singular. The general solution is then :

$$\mathbf{X} = \mathbf{C} e^{\mu t} + \sum_{s=1}^{n} A_s \mathbf{k}_s e^{-\lambda_s t}$$

and the path of each output is a variation (damped or explosive, oscillatory or progressive) about a trend term which increases at the same rate as the final demands.

EXERCISES 14.9

1. The matrix $[A_{sr}]$ formed from $\mathbf{A} = [a_{rs}]$ by writing co-factors and transposing is called the *adjoint* of $\mathbf{A}$. If $\mathbf{A}$ is singular ($|\mathbf{A}| = 0$), show that the product of $\mathbf{A}$ and any column of its adjoint is a zero column vector.

2. Consider the homogeneous linear equations $(\mathbf{A} + \lambda_s \mathbf{B})\mathbf{k} = 0$ for the variables $\mathbf{k} = \{k_r\}$ in the singular case $|\mathbf{A} + \lambda_s \mathbf{B}| = 0$. Use the result of the previous

exercise to show that the equations are satisfied if $\mathbf{k}$ is taken as proportional to any column of the adjoint of $(\mathbf{A} + \lambda_s \mathbf{B})$.

3. Use the results of the previous exercises to show that the adjoint of a singular matrix has rank 1 with only one independent column.

4. Consider the dynamic open system $\mathbf{AX} = \mathbf{B}\dfrac{d\mathbf{X}}{dt} + \mathbf{c}$ where $\mathbf{c} = \{c_r\}$ are final demands, constant over time. Find particular integrals and hence write the general solution.

5. Examine a dynamic model based on an unlagged accelerator in period analysis (see 11.8, Ex. 1, above). Show that the open system can be so formulated that the output vector $\mathbf{X}_t$ is given by a set of difference equations :

$$\mathbf{X}_t = \mathbf{CX}_{t-1} + \mathbf{K}$$

where $\mathbf{C}$ is a square matrix of constants given by the flow and capital structure of the system and where $\mathbf{K}$ is a vector depending on final demand. Examine the conditions under which the ultimate outputs are $\mathbf{X} = (\mathbf{I} - \mathbf{C})^{-1}\mathbf{K}$.

REFERENCES

Allen (R. G. D.) (1938) : *Mathematical Analysis for Economists* (Macmillan, 1938), Chapter XVIII.

Barna (T.) (1952) : " The Interdependence of the British Economy ", *Journal Royal Statistical Society*, Series A, **115**, 29–77.

Birkhoff (G.) and MacLane (S.) (1941) : *A Survey of Modern Algebra* (Macmillan, 1941), Chapter X.

Debreu (G.) and Herstein (I. N.) (1953) : " Non-negative Square Matrices ", *Econometrica*, **21**, 597–606.

Ferrar (W. L.) (1941) : *Algebra* (Oxford, 1941), Chapters X–XIII.

Goodwin (R. M.) (1953) : " Static and Dynamic Linear General Equilibrium Models ", in *Input-Output Relations* : Proceedings of a Conference on Inter-Industrial Relations held at Driebergen (Stenfort Kroese, Leiden, 1953).

Hicks (J. R.) (1939, 1946) : *Value and Capital* (Oxford, First Ed. 1939, Second Ed. 1946), Chapter VIII and Appendix.

Leontief (W. W.) (Editor) (1953) : *Studies in the Structure of the American Economy* (Oxford, 1953), Chapter 3.

Metzler (L. A.) (1945) : " Stability of Multiple Markets : the Hicksian Conditions ", *Econometrica*, **13**, 277–92.

Murdoch (D. C.) (1957) : *Linear Algebra for Undergraduates* (Wiley, 1957).

Newman (P. K.) (1958) : " Some Notes on Stability Conditions ", *Review of Economic Studies* (to appear).

Samuelson (P. A.) (1947) : *Foundations of Economic Analysis* (Harvard, 1947), Chapter IX.

Stone (J. R. N.) (1951) : " Simple Transaction Models, Information and Computing ", *Review of Economic Studies*, **19**, 67–84

Stone (J. R. N.) and Utting (J. E. G.) (1953) : " The Relationship between Input-Output Analysis and National Accounting ", in *Input-Output Relations* : Proceedings of a Conference on Inter-Industrial Relations held at Driebergen (Stenfert Kroese, Leiden, 1953).

Thrall (R. M.) and Tornheim (L.) (1957) : *Vector Spaces and Matrices* (Wiley, 1957), Chapters 2–3 and 5–7.

CHAPTER 15

ELEMENTARY THEORY OF GAMES

15.1 Economic Applications of the Theory of Games

IN many economic problems the solution appears as the determination of a maximum position, subject only to certain restraints imposed by the conditions of the problem. For example, an individual consumer maximises utility subject to the condition that his budget is balanced. Often the problem can be expressed alternatively as one of maximum or as one of minimum positions ; a firm may, for example, maximise output for a given cost or minimise cost for a given output. The point is that the solution is straightforward and involves either a maximum or a minimum. On a competitive market there can be a large number of buyers and a large number of sellers ; each individual attempts to obtain his own maximum return and he is not influenced by the actions of others. Equally, the problems of monopoly or monopsony—a single seller and a large number of buyers or conversely—are expressed simply in terms of maximum positions.

In other economic situations, however, quite different problems arise, as has been stressed by von Neumann and Morgenstern (1944, 1954). Situations arise where there is some conflict of interests to be resolved The best known of these situations are bilateral monopoly (monopoly-monopsony) where there is only one buyer and only one seller, and duopoly or oligopoly where two or a limited number of sellers deal with a large number of buyers. More complicated situations of the same kind involve combinations or coalitions, as when wage rates are determined by unions or federations of workers and employers. The solution of such a problem is not one of simple maximum or minimum. It raises more involved questions of the *strategies* adopted by the participants and the mathematical formulation is often (but not always) of a *minimax* type. If there are two sellers, A and B, on a market, for example, A must plan his actions on some expectation of what B will do and conversely. In considering any line of action or strategy, A may attempt to determine the worst that B can do ; A then decides on the best (maximum) strategy, allowing for the worst (minimum) reaction of B. At the same time, B is making his decisions with an eye similarly on what A may do. The action of each participant is then based on minimax considerations, a minimum and a maximum being jointly involved in the decision. Further, there is the question whether there is any consistent outcome of the several actions of the participants, i.e. whether the minimax position of A is in agreement with the minimax position of B.

Mathematical problems such as these are examined in the theory of games. If there are two players of a game, each has a number of strategies open to him according to the rules of the game. Each tries to maximise his own winnings (e.g. in money, not in " utility ") over many plays of the game, or his expectation of winnings in one play. Whether the game has any *optimum* or *stable* outcome depends on whether the minimax position aimed at by one player is consistent with that of the other.

The theory of games is thus of relevance to economic problems. However, the theory can only be formulated in mathematical terms which are far from simple, and it would not be necessary to make use of such a sledge-hammer merely to crack the nut of a duopoly problem. But it is found that a certain group of economic problems which involve a network of technical relations (e.g. of production) can be handled satisfactorily with the aid of the mathematical theory of games. The input-output relations of Chapter 11 above are of this kind. The more general economic problems known as linear programming, or activity analysis, provide one of the main fields of economic application of the theory of games. It is interesting to note that the same kind of technical-economic problem faces the statistician when he makes a decision in which accuracy of estimation is to be balanced against cost, or when he attempts to minimise the maximum risk involved in a decision. Like the economist, the statistician can get by with elementary considerations up to a point, but as more complicated problems are tackled he needs to make use of the mathematical theory of games. The developments of linear programming (activity analysis) by economists and of statistical decision functions by statisticians have proceeded simultaneously but almost independently, with the aid of much the same types of mathematical tools.

15.2 The Two-Person Zero-Sum Game and its Pay-off Matrix

The games considered in the theory of games may involve an element of chance, but they are essentially games of skill in which strategy (i.e. choice of action) plays its part. In actual practice such games vary from simple games like " noughts and crosses " to highly developed games like chess and bridge.

Some definitions or distinctions must be made. A *game* is the whole set of rules and procedures of play ; a *play* is one particular realisation of the game, a particular application of the rules leading to a definite result. A *move* is a point in the game where the players are faced with alternatives ; a *choice* is the actual alternative picked in a play of the game. Payments are made at the end of each play according to the outcome ; it is of no importance whether the " payments " are in money, or in terms of points or a score. If there are more than two players, the payments may be from any one of them to any other. A simple illustration is given in Ex. 1 below.

The only type of game considered here is that in which there are only two players, A and B, and in which the sum of the payments made is always zero. At the end of a play of such a two-person zero-sum game, player A receives a net amount a from player B, and equally player B receives a net amount $b = -a$ from player A, where a can be positive (A wins) or negative (B wins). There is only one actual transfer, but it can be from A to B or conversely. This type of game is more general than it might appear at first sight. For example, bridge is a two-person zero-sum game. There are four individuals playing but they work in pairs ; there are two " players " each being a team of two individuals.

Even so, two-person zero-sum games are of infinite variety. The number of moves can vary from one to any finite or infinite number, and so can the alternatives open at each move. The amount of information available to each player can vary, e.g. as regards knowledge at each move of choices made at earlier moves. Chance elements can enter to a greater or less extent, e.g. the deal of cards or the tossing of a coin to fix which player chooses at the first move. The only things common to two-person zero-sum games are that there is a conflict of interests between the two players and that, in the outcome, what one loses the other gains.

A game with several moves can be called an *extensive game*. It may be that there is a finite number of moves and a finite number of alternatives open at each move, i.e. that the game is *finite* and that the " strategies " open to the players can be enumerated. This is, however, not at all necessary ; there are games where the number of moves is indefinite and the number of " strategies " infinite. The present account is, in fact, confined to finite games ; although these are important, they are not the only games of interest and a definite limitation is imposed on the development.

The theory of games is a highly-developed exercise in the mathematics of convex sets (12.5 above). The situation is broadly as follows. If a certain number of solutions, on the minimax principle, is found for a game, it follows that the convex hull of the set of solutions represents an infinite set of solutions of the game. The problem is to get the complete convex set of solutions. Some of the more advanced theory of games is to be found in the references at the end of this chapter.

The object here is to give a simpler development, concentrating on the main results. The best introductions to game theory on these lines are by McKinsey (1952) and by Kemeny, Snell and Thompson (1957). A popular, and highly entertaining, account is given by Williams (1954). Luce and Raiffa (1957) pay attention, not only to two-person zero-sum games, but also to games of many other types. In these references, the stress is on concepts and methods rather than on mathematical detail.

Assume that the game is *finite*, comprising a finite number of moves and a finite number of alternatives open at each move. Then it is possible to say that A has a choice of m *strategies* for the whole play of the game and these can be numbered $r = 1, 2, \dots m$. Equally, B has a choice of n strategies, $s = 1, 2, \dots n$. Once A selects his strategy, and B selects his, the whole play of the game follows automatically from the rules. The strategies must each lay down the choice made by the player concerned at every move and under each possible set of circumstances. The number of different strategies, m and n, may be very large, and in practice it usually is very large, but it is finite. It is always possible to enumerate the strategies for each player.

When the game has only one move, the enumeration of strategies is simple enough. At the move, A has a finite number of alternatives to choose from ; number them $r = 1, 2, \dots m$. At the same time, B has a finite set of alternatives open, $s = 1, 2, \dots n$. The play of the game is fixed once A chooses a number r and B a number s. However, as is made clear in Ex. (g) below, the enumeration of strategies, m for A and n for B, can always be made no matter what (finite) number of moves there may be. In any game it may be difficult in practice to enumerate all the different strategies ; but this is purely a practical, and not a conceptual, difficulty.

Let the game be played by A choosing his rth strategy and B choosing his sth. The play is then determined and in the outcome a definite payment is made. Let a_{rs} be the amount received by A from B where a_{rs} is determined by r and s and can be positive, negative or zero. There are $m \times n$ different ways of playing the game and for each a definite pay-off a_{rs} ($r = 1, 2, \dots m$, $s = 1, 2, \dots n$). These amounts can be arranged in a *pay-off matrix* for A :

$$\mathbf{A} = [a_{rs}] = \begin{bmatrix} a_{11} & a_{12} & \cdots & a_{1n} \\ a_{21} & a_{22} & \cdots & a_{2n} \\ \cdots\cdots\cdots\cdots\cdots\cdots \\ a_{m1} & a_{m2} & \cdots & a_{mn} \end{bmatrix}$$

There is also a pay-off matrix for **B** :

$$\mathbf{B} = [b_{rs}] \text{ where } b_{rs} = -a_{rs}$$

Since $\mathbf{B} = -\mathbf{A}$, there is no need to consider it separately.

The interpretation of the pay-off matrix is very straight-forward. Each row of elements represents a choice of strategy by A ; there are m rows, one for each of A's strategies. Similarly, there are n columns, one for each of B's strategies. When A and B each select a strategy, one row and one column are determined in **A** and the element a_{rs} at the intersection is the amount received by A following the play on the strategies selected.

Ex. (*a*).   A game of one move at which A calls 1 or 2 and B calls 1 or 2. At the pay-off, A receives £1 from B if the numbers called are different, A pays £1 to B if they are the same.   The pay-off matrix for A is :

$$\mathbf{A} = \begin{bmatrix} -1 & 1 \\ 1 & -1 \end{bmatrix}$$

Ex. (*b*).   A game as in the previous example, except that the pay-off matrix is different :

$$\mathbf{A} = \begin{bmatrix} 2 & 1 \\ 3 & -2 \end{bmatrix}$$

e.g. if A and B both call 1, then A receives £2 from B.

Ex. (*c*).   A game of 1 move at which A calls 1, 2 or 3 and B draws a card selected from the Aces in an ordinary pack of cards.   Enumerate B's strategies according to the suit selected : 1 ... Spade, 2 ... Heart, 3 ... Diamond, 4 ... Club.   Define the pay-off matrix :

$$\mathbf{A} = \begin{bmatrix} 0 & -2 & -1 & 3 \\ 2 & 3 & 1 & 2 \\ 3 & 4 & 0 & -4 \end{bmatrix}$$

e.g. the play is a draw (no payment) if A calls 1 and B draws the Ace of Spades.

Ex. (*d*).   Two horses run in a race ; betting is at odds (2 to 1 on and 2 to 1 against for the two horses) which are set in advance of the race.   Player A bets £1 on one of the horses but knows nothing of " form ".   Player B is a combination of the forces determining the result of the race (e.g. the bookmaker, owners and jockeys).   The pay-off matrix for the " punter " A is

$$\mathbf{A} = \begin{bmatrix} \tfrac{1}{2} & -1 \\ -1 & 2 \end{bmatrix}$$

Ex. (*e*).   A fur coat valued at £100 can be insured against loss by fire for £1. Player A owns the coat and chooses between strategies :

1 ... To insure,   2 ... Not to insure

Player B is the forces of Nature, or the acts of God, which decide on whether there is a fire (strategy 1) or not (strategy 2). The pay-off matrix to A is :

$$\mathbf{A} = \begin{bmatrix} -1 & -1 \\ -100 & 0 \end{bmatrix}$$

Ex. (*f*). The game *Morra* is frequently played in Italy. In the *two-finger version*, player A shows one or two fingers and calls his guess of the number of fingers shown by his opponent ; player B does likewise and simultaneously. Each player has four strategies which can be enumerated :

$$1 \ldots (1, 1), \quad 2 \ldots (2, 1), \quad 3 \ldots (1, 2), \quad 4 \ldots (2, 2)$$

where the first number in the bracket is the number of fingers shown and the second is the number called. In the pay-off, if only one player guesses correctly, he receives an amount equal to the sum of number of fingers shown ; if neither or both guess correctly, there is no payment. The pay-off matrix is :

$$\mathbf{A} = \begin{bmatrix} 0 & -3 & 2 & 0 \\ 3 & 0 & 0 & -4 \\ -2 & 0 & 0 & 3 \\ 0 & 4 & -3 & 0 \end{bmatrix}$$

Ex. (*g*). A game of three moves I, II and III, at which :

I B chooses a number p from 1, 2
II   Without knowledge of p, A chooses a number q from 1, 2
III   Without knowledge of p or q, B chooses a number r from 1, 2

For the third move to be as stated, either B forgets what number he chose at the first move, or B comprises two individuals each choosing without knowledge of the other's choices. In the pay-off, the settlement is the amount $(p + q + r)$ which goes to A if q is the same as r and to B otherwise. There are two strategies for $\mathbf{A}$:

$$1 \ldots (q = 1), \quad 2 \ldots (q = 2)$$

and four strategies for B :

$$1 \ldots (p = 1, r = 1), \quad 2 \ldots (p = 2, r = 1), \quad 3 \ldots (p = 1, r = 2), \quad 4 \ldots (p = 2, r = 2)$$

The pay-off is then :

$$\mathbf{A} = \begin{bmatrix} 3 & 4 & -4 & -5 \\ -4 & -5 & 5 & 6 \end{bmatrix}$$

EXERCISES 15.2

1. Define the game and the moves of " noughts and crosses " and hence describe the play and choices. Show that there is an indefinite but finite number of moves. Indicate a scheme of pay-off.

2. How many " moves " in the game of bridge ; how many choices in a play of the game?

3. Write down the pay-off matrix for player B in Ex. (*a*) above.

4. Invent a description of a game of one move with pay-off matrix

$$\begin{bmatrix} 1 & 2 & 0 \\ 2 & -1 & 3 \end{bmatrix}$$

5. Extend Ex. (*d*) above to the case of three horses, the odds being fixed at evens, 2—1 against and 3—1 against. Show that

$$\begin{bmatrix} 1 & -1 & -1 \\ -1 & 2 & -1 \\ -1 & -1 & 3 \end{bmatrix}$$

is the pay-off matrix.

6. Extend Ex. (*f*) to the case of *three-finger Morra* and show that the pay-off matrix is now of order 9×9.

15.3 Expectation of the Game ; Pure and Mixed Strategies

If a game with pay-off matrix $\mathbf{A} = [a_{rs}]$ ($r = 1, 2, \dots m$, $s = 1, 2, \dots n$) is played once, a definite amount a_{rs} is paid to player A according to the strategies chosen by both players. If the game is played a large number N of times, let E be the average amount paid to A, the *expectation* of the game. Then E depends on the pattern of strategies played by both players over successive plays. The general object of A is to choose his strategies in repeated plays to make E as large as possible ; B's object is to choose his pattern of strategies to make E as small as possible. In choosing the pattern of strategies, each player must allow for his opponent's action as far as he can ; neither player, of course, can influence directly what the other player chooses to do.

Player A follows a *pure strategy* in repeated plays if he selects one and the same strategy, from all the alternatives open to him, at each and every play. If both players follow pure strategies, then one play of the game is the same as any other. At each play, A follows the rth of his strategies, B adopts the sth of his strategies and the pay-off to A is a_{rs}. Hence the expectation is also a_{rs} and this can be interpreted as a function of two variables each taking only integral values :

$$E(r, s) = a_{rs} \quad (r = 1, 2, \dots m, s = 1, 2, \dots n)$$

A chooses r with the object of making E as large as possible, after allowance for possible choices of s by B. Similarly, B chooses s and attempts to allow for the choice of r by A in making E as small as possible. The question is whether simultaneous choices of r and s are possible which are stable (optimal) and consistent. If so, the game has a solution with pure strategies. It will be seen that there is a solution only in special cases. Even if there is a solution, however, it is not particularly interesting, since it is a dull game which can be played with the same stable result play after play.

A more important question concerns the play of a game when each player adopts different strategies in successive plays. A player follows a *mixed strategy* if he varies his choice of strategy according to some pattern from one play of the game to another. The " pattern " is not a particular sequence of strategies to be played in order ; it is rather a randomised order of specified proportions of strategies. For example, if the pattern calls for the play of the first strategy once in ten times, this means that on the average over a run of plays the first strategy is chosen in one-tenth of them, *not* that every tenth play is the first strategy. The expectation E is then more complicated and its value depends on how the strategies of the two players are mixed. A formulation of E as a function of two variables is obtained only in the simplest case of a game with two strategies for each player. This case merits some attention in detail before the general case is considered (15.7 below).

The players each have two strategies, (r, $s=1$, 2) and the pay-off matrix is of 2×2 order :

$$A = \begin{bmatrix} a_{11} & a_{12} \\ a_{21} & a_{22} \end{bmatrix}$$

Player A mixes his strategies, playing the first in proportion x of the plays and the second in a proportion $(1-x)$. Similarly, B plays his strategies in proportions y and $(1-y)$. It is taken that there is no association between the choices of A and B so that the four combinations of pairs of strategies occur with the following frequencies in N plays :

$$\begin{bmatrix} xyN & x(1-y)N \\ (1-x)yN & (1-x)(1-y)N \end{bmatrix}$$

Hence in xyN plays out of N the pay-off to A is a_{11}, and so on. The *average amount* received by A per play is then :

$$E(x, y) = a_{11}xy + a_{12}x(1-y) + a_{21}(1-x)y + a_{22}(1-x)(1-y) \quad \text{......(1)}$$

This is a function of two variables x and y, each of which can be assigned any value from 0 to 1, i.e. $0 \leqslant x, y \leqslant 1$. Equation (1) is :

$$E(x, y) = (a_{11} - a_{12} - a_{21} + a_{22})xy - (a_{22} - a_{12})x - (a_{22} - a_{21})y + a_{22}$$

When $(a_{11} - a_{12} - a_{21} + a_{22}) \neq 0$, it can be written :

$$\left.\begin{aligned} & E(x, y) = a(x - \alpha)(y - \beta) + b \\ \text{where} \quad & a = a_{11} - a_{12} - a_{21} + a_{22} \neq 0 \\ & b = \frac{a_{11}a_{22} - a_{12}a_{21}}{a_{11} - a_{12} - a_{21} + a_{22}} \\ & \alpha = \frac{a_{22} - a_{21}}{a_{11} - a_{12} - a_{21} + a_{22}} \quad \text{and} \quad \beta = \frac{a_{22} - a_{12}}{a_{11} - a_{12} - a_{21} + a_{22}} \end{aligned}\right\} \quad \text{.........(2)}$$

This is a familiar quadratic (hyperbolic) function. When

$$(a_{11} - a_{12} - a_{21} + a_{22}) = 0,$$

the function $E(x, y)$ of (1) reduces to the even simpler linear form :

$$E(x, y) = a_{22} - (a_{22} - a_{12})x - (a_{22} - a_{21})y \dots\dots\dots \dots(3)$$

Ex. (a). Let $A = \begin{bmatrix} -1 & 1 \\ 1 & -1 \end{bmatrix}$ so that

$$\begin{aligned} E(x, y) &= -xy + x(1 - y) + (1 - x)y - (1 - x)(1 - y) \\ &= -4xy + 2x + 2y - 1 \\ &= -4(x - \tfrac{1}{2})(y - \tfrac{1}{2}) \end{aligned}$$

Ex. (b). Let $A = \begin{bmatrix} 2 & 1 \\ 3 & -2 \end{bmatrix}$ so that $E(x, y) = -4(x - \tfrac{5}{4})(y - \tfrac{3}{4}) + \tfrac{7}{4}$

Ex. (c). Let $A = \begin{bmatrix} -1 & 3 \\ -2 & 2 \end{bmatrix}$ so that $E(x, y) = x - 4y + 2$

Ex. (d). The value E is here defined as the average amount paid to A over a long run of plays of the game. This is also the *mathematical expectation* of A in any one play. As an illustration of this interpretation of E, consider the case of betting on a horse race as in 15.2, Ex. (d).

Here :

$$A = \begin{bmatrix} \tfrac{1}{2} & -1 \\ -1 & 2 \end{bmatrix}$$

If a player A places his £1 bet on the first horse in proportion x of a long run of races between the same horses and if the first horse wins the race in a proportion y of the races, then the average amount won by A is

$$\begin{aligned} E(x, y) &= \tfrac{1}{2}xy - x(1 - y) - y(1 - x) + 2(1 - x)(1 - y) \\ &= \tfrac{9}{2}(x - \tfrac{2}{3})(y - \tfrac{2}{3}) \end{aligned}$$

Alternatively, suppose that there is only one race and the chance that the first horse wins is y. Let player A split his £1 bet by placing £x on the first horse and £$(1 - x)$ on the second. His expectation of winnings is the same expression $E(x, y)$.

EXERCISES 15.3

1. Write $E(x, y)$ for the game with pay-off matrix $\begin{bmatrix} 1 & -1 \\ -1 & 1 \end{bmatrix}$. How does this game and expectation differ from those of Ex. (a) above?

2. Make up a 2×2 pay-off matrix for which $E(x, y) = a(x + \alpha)(y + \beta) + b$ with a, α and β positive. Show that a_{11} is necessarily larger than the other three elements in the matrix.

3. Show that the elements of the pay-off matrix (of order 2×2) are $E(1, 1)$, $E(1, 0)$, $E(0, 1)$ and $E(0, 0)$. In the case of the previous exercise, show that $b > 0$ implies a game in which player A always wins no matter what B does.

4. In the horse-betting case of Ex. (d) above, take the slightly different pay-off matrix $\begin{bmatrix} \tfrac{1}{2} & -1 \\ -1 & 1 \end{bmatrix}$. What are the fixed odds? Write the function $E(x, y)$ and explain in what sense it is true that here the " bookie " generally wins.

5. In the insurance example of 15.2, Ex. (*e*), above, suppose that the question of insuring the fur coat arises in a run of periods. *A* insures in a proportion *x* of the periods and the chance of a fire is *y* each period. Show that *A*'s average loss (£) is :

$$E = x + 100y - 100xy$$

What is the loss if *A* insures all the time and if *A* insures none of the time? What is the chance of a fire to make these two losses the same? Interpret the result.

6. A game has a pay-off matrix of order $2 \times n$. Show that the expectation, when player *A* mixes his strategies while *B* plays a pure strategy, can be written in the form $E(x, s)$, where $0 \leqslant x \leqslant 1$ and $s = 1, 2, \dots n$. Obtain *E* in terms of the elements of the matrix and illustrate with the case of 15.2, Ex. (*g*).

15.4 Minimax, Saddle Points and Solutions of Games

The expectation of a game, under certain circumstances, is a function of two variables, $E(x, y)$, where *x* is chosen by player *A* and *y* by player *B*. The function $E = E(x, y)$ may be represented diagrammatically by a surface in three dimensions, as in Fig. 52*a*. The varying height of the surface shows the changing expectation of the game to *A* as different choices of *x* and *y* are made. Such a representation applies to a game with a 2×2 pay-off matrix played with mixed strategies. The variables *x* and *y* are then continuous but limited to the range : $0 \leqslant x, y \leqslant 1$. Hence, as illustrated in Fig. 52*a*, only that part of the surface given for $0 \leqslant x, y \leqslant 1$ is relevant to the problem. The representation can also apply to a game with a $m \times n$ pay-off matrix played with pure strategies by both players. In this case the variables

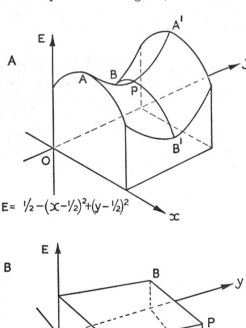

$$E = \tfrac{1}{2} - (x - \tfrac{1}{2})^2 + (y - \tfrac{1}{2})^2$$

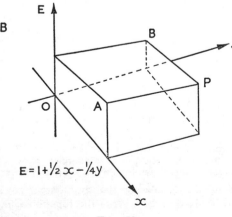

$$E = 1 + \tfrac{1}{2}x - \tfrac{1}{4}y$$

Fig. 52.

x and y take only certain discrete values, i.e. $x=r=1, 2, \ldots m$ and $y=s=1, 2, \ldots n$. All that is relevant is then the corresponding set of discrete points on the surface.

The object of player A is to choose x, allowing for possible reactions of player B, so as to climb as high on the surface as possible. The object of B is to keep as low on the surface as he can. The game has a solution if consistent and stable choices of x and y can be made simultaneously. This is easily seen to be a minimax problem, i.e. a matter of maximising a set of minimum values and conversely. The clue is that A must determine the worst (minimum) that B can do for each of A's own choices, and then to make his best (maximum) choice, or to pick out the least disadvantageous possibility.

Consider the surface of Fig. 52a, in the case where x and y are continuous variables. The relevant feature is that there is a ridge line AA' and a trough line BB' intersecting in a saddle point P. Any move away from P in the direction Ox is downhill ; any move in the direction Oy is uphill. The saddle point P is one of maximum for x and minimum for y. For a given x, $E(x, y)$ varies with y and $\min_y E(x, y)$ can be picked out ; this gives a point on the trough line BB'. Then, for moves along the trough line BB', the x which makes $\min_y E(x, y)$ as large as possible can be picked out ; this leads to the point P, where $\max_x \min_y E(x, y)$ occurs. Similarly, for a given y, $E(x, y)$ varies with x, $\max_x E(x, y)$ is on the ridge line AA', and the x which gives $\min_y \max_x E(x, y)$ corresponds again to the point P. If x^*, y^* are the values of the variables at P, then this saddle point has the property :

$$\max_x \min_y E(x, y) = \min_y \max_x E(x, y) = E(x^*, y^*) \quad \ldots\ldots\ldots\ldots (1)$$

The surface in Fig. 52a is drawn for $0 \leqslant x, y \leqslant 1$ and $x^* = y^* = \frac{1}{2}$.

This can be interpreted in terms of the game with expectation $E(x, y)$. Player A, fixing x (at choice for him), determines the worst (to him) choice of y which might be made by B, i.e. $\min_y E(x, y)$ on trough line BB'. He then chooses x which gives the highest value to $\min_y E(x, y)$ on BB', i.e. he chooses x for $\max_x \min_y E(x, y)$ at P on BB'. No matter how his opponent plays, A cannot get less than the amount shown by the height of the surface at P. In other words, whatever x is chosen by A, his opponent can keep him down to a payment shown by the height of a point

on the trough line BB'. It is up to A to get as high on the trough line as he can by choice of x; hence he chooses x to get to P where his winnings from the game are max min $E(x, y)$, the height of the surface at P. Player
$$\text{\small$x$ \qquad \small$y$}$$
B works in the same way but tries to keep E down and prevent his opponent pushing E up. Whatever y is chosen by B, his opponent can push up the payment made to the height of a point on the ridge line AA'. Then B keeps as low down on the ridge line as he can and chooses y to get to P where the payment is min max $E(x, y)$. The fact that P is a saddle point
$$\text{\small$y$ \qquad \small$x$}$$
means that both players arrive at the same point on the surface; there are consistent and stable choices, x^* and y^*. The game has a solution and the amount expected by A is

$$E(x^*, y^*) = \max_x \min_y E(x, y) = \min_y \max_x E(x, y).$$

It is important to be clear on the nature of the solution. On the surface $E = E(x, y)$, there is a saddle point (x^*, y^*) where (1) holds. Player A chooses x^* among all the alternatives x open to him because then he can be sure of getting $E(x^*, y^*)$ out of the game no matter what strategies his opponent adopts. He may get more if his opponent is wild in play, but he cannot get less. Player B in his part chooses y^* among the various y available to him because he can be sure of keeping his payment to his opponent down to $E(x^*, y^*)$ no matter what his opponent does. He may pay out less if his opponent is less astute, but he cannot pay more. According to the rules of rational behaviour assumed, the two players are well advised to settle on $E(x^*, y^*)$, A playing x^* and B playing y^*. It is in this sense that the game has a solution.

Now suppose that the surface has no saddle point P within the range of the variables considered. It might be thought that the game has no solution, since there is no single point on the surface to which both players will tend. This is in fact so if the variables have limitless ranges. It is not necessarily so if they take only limited sets of values, if only part of the surface is considered. There is no point *within* the sector of the surface at which both players will agree, but there may be such a point *on the boundary* of the sector. This is sufficiently indicated by Fig. 52b, where the surface $E = E(x, y)$ is a plane. The point P in one corner of the relevant sector of the surface is, in fact, a saddle point within the limited range of variation allowed for x and y. Any permissible move from P is downhill in the direction of Ox (along PB) and uphill in the direction of Oy (along PA). If (x^*, y^*) are the values at P, it is still true that the relations of minimax, (1) above, are satisfied. The minima and maxima simply have to be limited to least and greatest values obtained within the specified ranges of the variables.

As a special and preliminary problem, suppose that the players, of a game with pay-off matrix $A=[a_{rs}]$ of any order $m \times n$, play *only their pure strategies*. The expectation of player A then assumes the particular form :

$$E(r, s) = a_{rs} \qquad r=1, 2, \dots m \text{ and } s=1, 2, \dots n$$

Here E is a function of two variables, r and s, each of which take only a discrete range of integral values. It is a different kind of function altogether to the expectation $E(x, y)$ for mixed strategies in a 2×2 game ; in the simple game of order 2×2, pure strategies are played when $x=0, 1$ and $y=0, 1$. However, a result of form (1) above holds for pure strategies in a game of any dimensions. There is a solution or stable outcome among pure strategies if the matrix A has a *saddle point* such that :

$$\max_{r} \min_{s} E(r, s) = \min_{s} \max_{r} E(r, s) = E(r^*, s^*) \dots\dots\dots\dots(2)$$

for some integer r^* in the range $r=1, 2, \dots m$ and some integer s^* in the range $s=1, 2, \dots n$. The solution is that A plays the pure strategy r^* and B plays the pure strategy s^*. On the minimax principle, this is the best that they can do. The diagrammatic representation is as before, except that the surface is not continuous but consists only of a discrete set of points (for r from 1 to m and s from 1 to n). The heights of the points are given by the elements of A itself and a saddle is sought amongst them.

If there is such a solution, i.e. if A has a saddle point as it stands and for pure strategies only, then there is no need to look further. Mixed strategies are not required. But there is no necessity that such a saddle point exists at all ; on the contrary, there is generally no saddle point of A. It is in this sense that a search for a suitable point is a preliminary. It is quite possible that one exists and that is the end of the matter. Generally there is not a saddle point and the solution must be sought in mixed strategies.

That a game generally has no stability when pure strategies are played is seen in such a simple pay-off matrix as :

$$A = \begin{bmatrix} 4 & 1 \\ 2 & 3 \end{bmatrix}$$

If A starts with strategy 1, B selects strategy 2 in order to pay only 1 to A. But then A switches to strategy 2 in order to collect 3 from B. This leads B to change to strategy 1 and keep his payment down to 2. The process continues and there is no agreement to settle.

Ex. (*a*).   The game of 15.2, Ex. (*c*), with

$$A = \begin{bmatrix} 0 & -2 & -1 & 3 \\ 2 & 3 & 1 & 2 \\ 3 & 4 & 0 & -4 \end{bmatrix}$$

Player A chooses $r = 1$, 2 or 3. For each choice of pure strategy, the worst that can happen is shown by the entries in **A** in italics, the minima of the rows. If A chooses $r = 1$, the worst is that he pays out 2 ; if he chooses $r = 2$, he gets 1 at least ; if he chooses $r = 3$, he can pay out as much as 4. Hence A plans to choose $r = 2$ and expects his opponent to choose the third of his strategies to keep A's receipts down to 1. Player B chooses $s = 1$, 2, 3, or 4 and, for each of these choices, he determines the most that he would pay to his opponent, the maxima of the columns. These maxima are 3, 4, 1 and 3 in the four columns. Hence B plans to choose $s = 3$ to keep his payment down to 1 and expects his opponent to choose the second of his strategies to keep the payment up to 1. There is a consistency here which leads to a solution : $r^* = 2$, $s^* = 3$. The players can agree on these strategies and A receives amount 1 from B at each play.

In terms of the conditions (2), the same argument proceeds as follows. For player A and any selected r :

$$\min_{s} E(r, s) = -2, 1 \text{ or } -4 \quad \text{according as } r = 1, 2 \text{ or } 3$$

Hence $\max_{r} \min_{s} E(r, s) = E(2, 3) = 1$

Similarly $\max_{r} E(r, s) = 3, 4, 1 \text{ or } 3 \quad \text{according as } s = 1, 2, 3 \text{ or } 4$

and $\min_{s} \max_{r} E(r, s) = E(2, 3) = 1$

Conditions (2) are satisfied for $r^* = 2$, $s^* = 3$.

Ex. (*b*).   *Two-finger Morra*, 15.2, Ex. (*f*), with

$$A = \begin{bmatrix} 0 & -3 & 2 & 0 \\ 3 & 0 & 0 & -4 \\ -2 & 0 & 0 & 3 \\ 0 & 4 & -3 & 0 \end{bmatrix}$$

Here $\min_{s} E(r, s) = -3, -4, -2 \text{ or } -3 \quad \text{according as } r = 1, 2, 3 \text{ or } 4$

as shown by the entries in italics in **A**.

So $\max_{r} \min_{s} E(r, s) = E(3, 1) = -2$

But $\min_{s} \max_{r} E(r, s) = E(1, 3) = 2$

as found from the maxima of columns in **A**.

Conditions (2) are not satisfied. There is no solution of the game when pure strategies are played ; in fact, Morra is by no means a dull game. If A selects strategy 3, he may have to pay out as much as 2, B choosing strategy 1. For any other selection, he may have to pay out more. Conversely, if B selects strategy 3, he too may pay out 2 when A chooses strategy 1 ; he can pay out more if he chooses another strategy. There is plenty of room here for manoeuvre.

EXERCISES 15.4

1. If the games are played with pure strategies, show that the game with pay-off matrix $\begin{bmatrix} -1 & 1 \\ 1 & -1 \end{bmatrix}$ has no solution while that with $\begin{bmatrix} 2 & 1 \\ 3 & -2 \end{bmatrix}$ has a solution.
What is the solution in the second case?

2. Show that there is no solution with pure strategies in the horse-betting case of 15.2, Ex. (*d*). Interpret this result.

3. Show that the game of 15.2, Ex. 4, has no solution with pure strategies.

4. If $\begin{bmatrix} 1 & 2 \\ -1 & 0 \\ 1 & 3 \end{bmatrix}$ is the pay-off matrix, show that the game has two solutions with

pure strategies, player *A* having two optimal strategies. Consider what happens when *B* makes a wild (i.e. a non-optimal) play and show that one of *A*'s optimal strategies is a " better optimal " than the other.

5. For a pay-off matrix $A = [a_{rs}]$ and with pure strategies, show that there is a solution if a row minimum happens to be the maximum of the column in which it lies. Express the condition as : $r*$ and $s*$ is a solution if :

$$a_{r*s*} > a_{rs*} \ (r = 1, 2, \ldots m) \text{ and } a_{r*s*} < a_{r*s} \ (s = 1, 2, \ldots n)$$

6. If $E(x, y) = (x - \tfrac{1}{2})^2 - (y - \tfrac{1}{2})^2 + \tfrac{1}{2}$, show that the surface has a saddle point at $x = \tfrac{1}{2}, y = \tfrac{1}{2}$ in the geometrical sense, but not in the sense of the conditions (1) above. What form does (1) take in this case? Indicate that *E* could be the expectation for player *B* (instead of player *A*), in which case the saddle point is appropriate to the game.

15.5 Solution for a 2 × 2 Pay-off Matrix

A game has the pay-off matrix $\mathbf{A} = \begin{bmatrix} a_{11} & a_{12} \\ a_{21} & a_{22} \end{bmatrix}$ and is played with

mixed strategies. *A* plays the first of his two strategies in a proportion *x* of the plays and *B* plays the first of his strategies in a proportion *y*. The expectation of the game to *A* is given by equation (1) of 15.3 above.

The considerations of 15.4 now apply, with the great simplification that $E(x, y)$ takes a special form. Except in a particular case ($a = 0$) which can be ignored for the moment, the function can be written

$$E(x, y) = a(x - \alpha)(y - \beta) + b \ \ldots\ldots\ldots\ldots\ldots\ldots(1)$$

where the constants are given in (2) of 15.3 above. The surface representing (1) always has one saddle point *P*, at $x = \alpha$, $y = \beta$, and its shape is illustrated by Fig. 53. It is a particular example of a ruled surface, generated by straight lines. All sections of the surface by planes at right angles to *Ox* are straight lines and the particular section through *P* is a horizontal line ($E = b$). In Fig. 53, for example, as the given value of *x* increases, the straight line of the section is first a rising one (in the direction *Oy*), it becomes horizontal when $x = \alpha$ at *P* and finally it is a falling line for larger *x*. Hence if player *A* fixes α for his *x*, he gets $E = b$ whatever *B* does ; for any other *x* he can do worse. Similarly the straight line sections at right angles to *Oy* show that player *B* pays $E = b$ if he fixes β for his *y*, no matter what *A* does, but he can pay more on selecting any other y. The two players do well to settle on $x^*=\alpha$, $y^*=\beta$, which is the solution of the game, and A receives $E=b$ from B. All this assumes that there are no limitations on the values taken by x and y.

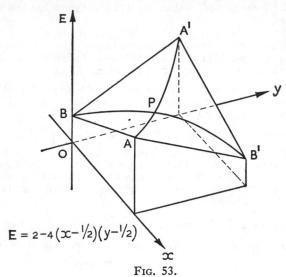

$$E = 2-4\left(x-\tfrac{1}{2}\right)\left(y-\tfrac{1}{2}\right)$$

FIG. 53.

However, there are limitations on x and y; they must each lie in the range from 0 to 1. If $0 \leqslant \alpha, \beta \leqslant 1$, then all is well; the saddle point of (1) is in the appropriate sector of the surface and the game has a solution. Otherwise, the saddle point falls outside the effective sector of the surface and the suggested solution is to be rejected. Attention must then be concentrated on the boundaries of the sector, where one or other player adopts a pure strategy ($x=0$ or 1 and $y=0$ or 1). It appears reasonable to expect that the situation of Fig. 52b then arises, i.e. a curved surface (or a plane when $a=0$) with a saddle point at a corner of the boundary. This is, in fact, the case. However, to allow properly for the limitation on the range of x and y, it is now necessary to abandon the geometrical approach and to re-frame definitions and conditions in algebraic terms. This will also facilitate extension to the general case (15.7 below).

At first, no reference need be made to the particular form (1) for the expectation of a game with a 2×2 pay-off matrix. Whatever form E takes, the following definition can be framed :

DEFINITION : If values x^* and y^* can be found so that for any x and y $(0 \leqslant x, y \leqslant 1)$

$$E(x, y^*) \leqslant E(x^*, y^*) \leqslant E(x^*, y) \quad \dots\dots\dots\dots\dots\dots(2)$$

then (x^*, y^*) is a *saddle point* of E, the game has a *stable outcome* or *solution* (x^*, y^*) with x^* and y^* as *optimal strategies* of players A and B respectively, and $E(x^*, y^*)$ is the *value* of the game to A.

The conditions (2) are a direct translation of the geometrical properties of a saddle point into algebraic form. The interpretation of these conditions in terms of the game is straightforward. Player A chooses x^* in mixing his strategies since he then gets at least $E(x^*, y^*)$ whatever y is played by his opponent, and since he may get less if he chooses some other x and y^* is played by his opponent. Player B chooses y^* for similar reasons.

The conditions (2) can be related to the minimax properties of $E(x, y)$:

$E(x, y)$ has a saddle point at (x^*, y^*) if and only if

$$\max_x \min_y E(x, y) = \min_y \max_x E(x, y) = E(x^*, y^*) \ \dots\dots\dots\dots(3)$$

provided that the minimax values exist in the range $0 \leqslant x, y \leqslant 1$.

The proof is in two parts:

First, suppose (3) holds. Hence $E(x^*, y^*) = \max_x \min_y E(x, y)$ is the maximum value (at $x = x^*$) of $\min_y E$ as a function of x; this value is $\min_y E(x^*, y)$. So, by the definition of a minimum:

$$E(x^*, y^*) = \min_y E(x^*, y) \leqslant E(x^*, y) \text{ for any } y \ (0 \leqslant y \leqslant 1).$$

Similarly, $E(x^*, y^*) = \max_x E(x, y^*) \geqslant E(x, y^*)$ for any x $(0 \leqslant x \leqslant 1)$.

Hence: $E(x^*, y) \leqslant E(x^*, y^*) \leqslant E(x, y^*)$ for any x and y $(0 \leqslant x, y \leqslant 1)$ which is condition (2) for (x^*, y^*) as a saddle point of E.

Second, suppose E has a saddle point at (x^*, y^*) so that (2) holds. In these conditions, select x which makes $E(x, y^*)$ a maximum and y which makes $E(x^*, y)$ a minimum:

$$\max_x E(x, y^*) \leqslant E(x^*, y^*) \leqslant \min_y E(x^*, y)$$

But, by definition of maxima and minima:

$$\min_y \max_x E(x, y) \leqslant \max_x E(x, y^*) \text{ and } \max_x \min_y E(x, y) \geqslant \min_y E(x^*, y)$$

Hence: $\min_y \max_x E(x, y) \leqslant E(x^*, y^*) \leqslant \max_x \min_y E(x, y) \ \dots\dots\dots\dots(4)$

On the other hand, from the definition of maxima and minima:

$$\max_x E(x, y) \geqslant E(x, y) \geqslant \min_y E(x, y) \quad \text{for any } x \text{ and } y \ (0 \leqslant x, y \leqslant 1)$$

Select x to make $\min\limits_{y} E(x, y)$ a maximum as a function of x, and y to make $\max\limits_{x} E(x, y)$ a minimum as a function of y :

$$\min_{y} \max_{x} E(x, y) \geqslant \max_{x} \min_{y} E(x, y) \quad\text{.....................(5)}$$

Both (4) and (5) hold only if all signs are equalities, i.e. if

$$\max_{x} \min_{y} E(x, y) = \min_{y} \max_{x} E(x, y) = E(x^*, y^*)$$

which is condition (3). This completes the proof.

The fact that $E(x, y)$ takes the particular form (1) is now used for the first time, to establish a particular case of a *Minimax Theorem* :

A game with a 2×2 pay-off matrix always has a solution. The value of the game is $E(x^*, y^*) = \max\limits_{x} \min\limits_{y} E(x, y) = \min\limits_{y} \max\limits_{x} E(x, y)$ and x^*, y^* are optimal strategies.

First, suppose $a \neq 0$ in $E(x, y) = a(x - \alpha)(y - \beta) + b$ and that α and β are in the range from 0 to 1. Then :

$$E(x, \beta) = E(\alpha, \beta) = E(\alpha, y) \quad \text{for all } x \text{ and } y \ (0 \leqslant x, y \leqslant 1)$$

By definition, $x^* = \alpha$ and $y^* = \beta$ are optimal strategies and the value of the game is $E(\alpha, \beta) = b$. This is the case of the saddle point illustrated by Fig. 53.

Second, in all other cases it is easily shown that both players follow pure strategies. For example, suppose $a > 0$; $\alpha, \beta > 1$. Then :

$$E(0, 1) = a\alpha(\beta - 1) + b$$
$$E(x, 1) = -a(x - \alpha)(\beta - 1) + b = a\alpha(\beta - 1) + b - a(\beta - 1)x \leqslant E(0, 1)$$
$$E(0, y) = a\alpha(\beta - y) + b = a\alpha(\beta - 1) + b + a\alpha(1 - y) \geqslant E(0, 1)$$
$$\text{for any } x \text{ and } y \quad (0 \leqslant x, y \leqslant 1)$$

So $\quad E(x, 1) \leqslant E(0, 1) \leqslant E(0, y) \quad$ for any x and $y \quad (0 \leqslant x, y \leqslant 1)$

By definition, $x^* = 0$, $y^* = 1$ are optimal strategies ; in this instance A plays his second and B his first strategy. The same kind of solution arises for all other α and β outside the range $(0 \leqslant \alpha, \beta \leqslant 1)$ and also in cases when $a = 0$ (see Ex. 1 below). This completes the proof.

One further point needs consideration. A game with a 2×2 pay-off matrix always has a solution, but this does not rule out the possibility of multiple solutions. In certain cases it is found that the game has more than one solution, and it then has an infinite number of solutions. This is illustrated in Ex. (*c*) and in Ex. 3 and 4 below ; it will be further explored in 15.6, Ex. (*b*).

Ex. (*a*). $\mathbf{A} = \begin{bmatrix} -1 & 1 \\ 1 & -1 \end{bmatrix}$. $E(x, y) = -4(x - \frac{1}{2})(y - \frac{1}{2})$ from 15.3, *Ex.* (*a*).

The solution of the game is $x^* = y^* = \frac{1}{2}$ and the value of the game is zero. Each player mixes his strategies, playing them equally often.

Ex. (*b*). $\mathbf{A} = \begin{bmatrix} 2 & 1 \\ 3 & -2 \end{bmatrix}$. $E(x, y) = -4(x - \frac{5}{4})(y - \frac{3}{4}) + \frac{7}{4}$ from 15.3, *Ex.* (*b*).

The solution of the game is $x^* = 1$, $y^* = 0$. For :

$$E(1, 0) = 1 \; ; \quad E(x, 0) = 3x - 2 = 1 - 3(1 - x) \leqslant 1 \; ; \quad E(1, y) = 1 + y \geqslant 1$$

i.e. $\qquad E(x, 0) \leqslant E(1, 0) \leqslant E(1, y) \quad \text{for } 0 \leqslant x, y \leqslant 1$

The value of the game is 1 and each player employs a pure strategy, A selecting his first and B his second strategy.

Ex. (*c*). $\mathbf{A} = \begin{bmatrix} 0 & -1 \\ 1 & 1 \end{bmatrix}$. $E(x, y) = xy - 2x + 1 = 1 - x(2 - y)$

On general grounds, it is seen that A must play his second strategy ($x^* = 0$) since this gives him more than his first strategy whatever B does. But what of B's choice? It is easily seen that he can play in any way whatever ($0 \leqslant y^* \leqslant 1$) since he pays out the same amount in all cases when A plays the second strategy. Formally, it can be shown at once that :

$$E(x, y^*) \leqslant E(0, y^*) = E(0, y) \quad \text{for any } y^* \quad (0 \leqslant y^* \leqslant 1)$$

There is an infinite number of solutions. The value of the game is 1 and this is unique. There is, however, a " best optimum " for B (the second strategy) since, if he plays this, he stands to gain more if A makes any mistake, i.e. if A plays his first strategy at all.

EXERCISES 15.5

1. Examine the case of a game, with a 2×2 pay-off matrix, in which $E(x, y)$ is of linear form. Show that $x^* = 0$, $y^* = 1$ is a solution when $a_{22} > a_{12}$ and a_{21}. Show that pure strategies are also solutions for other values of the a's.

2. Show that the game with pay-off matrix $\begin{bmatrix} 2 & 0 \\ -1 & 3 \end{bmatrix}$ has a solution with mixed strategies $x^* = \frac{2}{3}$ for A and $y^* = \frac{1}{2}$ for B.

3. If $\mathbf{A} = \begin{bmatrix} 0 & 2 \\ 1 & 1 \end{bmatrix}$, show that $E(x, y) = 1 - 2x(y - \frac{1}{2})$ and deduce that, in the solution of the game, the first player follows a pure strategy while the second has an infinite number of mixed strategies. Is there a " best optimum "?

4. Extend the results of *Ex.* (*c*) above, and of the previous exercise, by examining the case of a pay-off matrix $\mathbf{A} = \begin{bmatrix} a_1 & a_2 \\ a & a \end{bmatrix}$ with a row of equal elements. If $a > a_1$ and a_2, show that $x^* = 0$ and $0 \leqslant y^* \leqslant 1$. If a lies between a_1 and a_2 in value, show that the solution is the same except that the range of y^* is limited. Is there an infinity of solutions also when $a < a_1$ and a_2?

15.6 Graphical Solution for a $2 \times n$ Pay-off Matrix

A graphical method can be used to facilitate the process of solving a game with a particular 2×2 pay-off matrix. The same method can be employed more generally when the pay-off matrix is of order $2 \times n$, a case which is more difficult to handle in purely algebraic terms. As long as the matrix has only two rows the choice of player A can be represented by a variable x $(0 \leqslant x \leqslant 1)$ which is the proportion in which he plays the first of his two strategies. The method is to find the optimal mixture of strategies (x^*) for A first, and then to attend to the optimal play for B separately. A number of examples illustrate the graphical process sufficiently.

Ex. (a). $\mathbf{A} = \begin{bmatrix} -1 & 1 \\ 1 & -1 \end{bmatrix}$

A plays his two strategies in proportions x and $(1 - x)$. If B plays his first strategy, then (from the first column of the matrix) A's expectation is :

$$E = -x + (1 - x) = 1 - 2x$$

If B plays his second strategy, then from the second column

$$E = x - (1 - x) = 2x - 1$$

Each of these equations can be plotted as a line, over the range $0 \leqslant x \leqslant 1$, in the plane OxE. They are shown as A_1A_1' and A_2A_2' respectively in Fig. 54 ; in this case the lines intersect at P where $x = \frac{1}{2}$ and $E = 0$. A's object is to choose x to make E as large as possible. For given x, Fig. 54 shows the two values of E he can get if B plays pure strategies ; intermediate values of E are got when B mixes

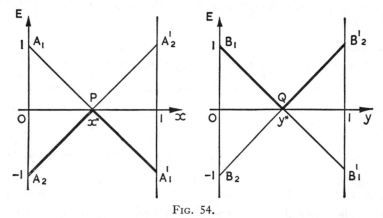

Fig. 54.

his strategies. The lower of the two values shows the least A can get playing x. Hence, for varying x $(0 \leqslant x \leqslant 1)$, the broken line A_2PA_1' shows what A is certain to get. He chooses x to achieve the highest point on A_2PA_1', i.e. $x^* = \frac{1}{2}$ with $E = 0$ at P.

The play of B can be similarly analysed in terms of the lines B_1B_1' and B_2B_2' (according to the strategy of A) in OyE of Fig. 54. B_1B_1' is $E = 1 - 2y$ when A plays his first strategy ; B_2B_2' is $E = 2y - 1$ when A plays his second strategy. The broken line B_1QB_2' represents the most B must pay for different choices of y. He chooses y to reach the lowest point on B_1QB_2', i.e. $y^* = \frac{1}{2}$ with $E = 0$ at Q. Hence, the solution of the game is $x^* = y^* = \frac{1}{2}$ and the value of the game is zero.

Ex. (b). $\mathbf{A} = \begin{bmatrix} 0 & -1 \\ 1 & 1 \end{bmatrix}$

The lines to be plotted for A and B are :

$$A_1A_1' \qquad E = 1 - x \qquad A_2A_2' \qquad E = 1 - 2x$$
$$B_1B_1' \qquad E = y - 1 \qquad B_2B_2' \qquad E = 1$$

where A_1A_1' is the expectation when A plays mixed strategies (x) and B plays his first strategy only, and so on. They are shown in Fig. 55. It is then evident that A plays his second strategy $(x^* = 0)$ and that B can play as he pleases (with

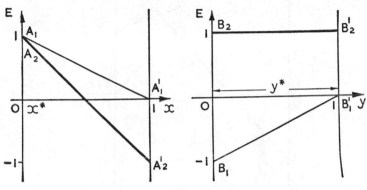

FIG. 55.

$0 \leqslant y^* \leqslant 1$), since x^* is the highest point on A_2A_2' and there is no lowest point on B_2B_2'. This is the case of an infinite number of solutions.

Ex. (c). $\mathbf{A} = \begin{bmatrix} 1 & 2 & 0 \\ 2 & -1 & 3 \end{bmatrix}$

Consider A with mixed strategies in proportions x and $1 - x$. Then :

B's strategy	Line	Expectation
1	A_1A_1'	$E = 2 - x$
2	A_2A_2'	$E = 3x - 1$
3	A_3A_3'	$E = 3(1 - x)$

These are plotted in Fig. 56. A chooses x^* for the highest point on the broken line A_2PA_3'. This is $x^* = \frac{2}{3}$ and $E = 1$, obtained graphically or by solving the last two equations above.

Next consider B. From Fig. 56, it is clear that he need never use his first strategy, since he can keep the payment E lower by following one or other of the other strategies (or a combination of them) whatever A does. Hence, effectively, B chooses between the two strategies of the columns of :

$$\begin{bmatrix} 2 & 0 \\ -1 & 3 \end{bmatrix}$$

and, solving graphically as in Ex. 2 below, he plays the strategies with equal frequencies giving $E = 1$.

In terms of the original matrix $\mathbf{A}$, the game has a solution in which A plays his two strategies in the proportions $\frac{2}{3}$ and $\frac{1}{3}$ (i.e. the first twice as often as the second) and in which B does not play his first strategy at all and the others with equal frequency. The value of the game is 1.

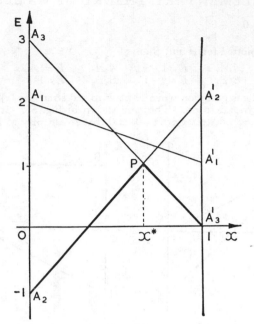

FIG. 56.

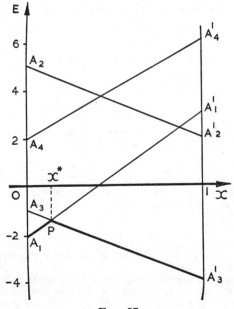

FIG. 57,

Ex. (*d*). $A = \begin{bmatrix} 3 & 2 & -4 & 6 \\ -2 & 5 & -1 & 2 \end{bmatrix}$

If A plays his strategies in proportions x and $1 - x$:

B's strategy	Line	Expectation
1	A_1A_1'	$E = 5x - 2$
2	A_2A_2'	$E = 5 - 3x$
3	A_3A_3'	$E = -3x - 1$
4	A_4A_4'	$E = 4x + 2$

From Fig. 57, A chooses $x^* = \frac{1}{8}$ for the highest point on the broken line A_1PA_3' where $E = -\frac{11}{8}$. These values can be obtained by solving the equations for A_1A_1' and A_3A_3'. Hence A plays his strategies in the proportions $\frac{1}{8}$ and $\frac{7}{8}$.

Of B's strategies, those numbered 2 and 4 are not effective. B's choice lies between the two strategies given by the columns in :

$$\begin{bmatrix} 3 & -4 \\ -2 & -1 \end{bmatrix}$$

Hence, solving graphically as in Ex. 3 below, B plays these two strategies in the proportions $\frac{3}{8}$ and $\frac{5}{8}$ and $E = -\frac{11}{8}$.

The game has a value $-\frac{11}{8}$ and the optimum strategies are for A to play his two strategies in the proportion 1 : 7 and for B to play his first and third strategies in the proportions 3 : 5.

The graphical method in application to a game with a pay-off matrix of order $2 \times n$ is illustrated rather generally in Fig. 58. This shows the variation of the expectation E of the player A as the value of x is varied, for any mixed strategy $(x, 1 - x)$ with $0 \leqslant x \leqslant 1$. There are n straight lines, one for each choice of a pure strategy by player B. The minimum expectation of A varies with x according to the locus $PQRS \dots$ made up of the lowest line segments as in Fig. 58. The highest point or points on the locus gives the optimal value or values of x on the min-max principle. The general situation is that there is *either* a range of such optimal x corresponding to a horizontal line segment (as RS of Fig. 58), *or* a single optimal x given by the apex of the set of line segments. A particular case

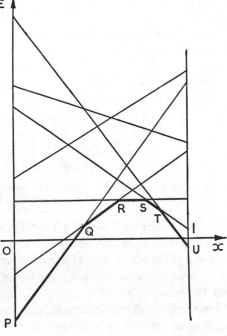

Fig. 58.

arises when the apex occurs at the beginning or end of the range of x, i.e. at $x=0$ or at $x=1$, in which case A plays a pure strategy in the stable outcome.

The same method applies to a game with pay-off matrix of order $m \times 2$. The graph then relates to the proportion $y:1-y$ in which player B mixes his strategies. It is possible, though not as a very practicable proposition, to use three dimensional diagrams in solving games with pay-off matrices of order $3 \times n$ or $m \times 3$. The lines of Fig. 58 then become planes in three dimensions. The optimal mixed strategies (for the player with three strategies) are given either by a horizontal plane segment, or a horizontal line segment, or an apex, all in three dimensions.

EXERCISES 15.6

1. If $\mathbf{A} = \begin{bmatrix} 2 & 1 \\ 3 & -2 \end{bmatrix}$, solve the game graphically and hence check the solution given in 15.5, Ex. (b).

2. Show graphically that the solution of the game with $\mathbf{A} = \begin{bmatrix} 2 & 0 \\ -1 & 3 \end{bmatrix}$ has $y^* = \frac{1}{2}$. What is x^* and the value of the game? See Ex. (c) above.

3. Show graphically that, if $\mathbf{A} = \begin{bmatrix} 3 & -4 \\ -2 & -1 \end{bmatrix}$, the solution is $x^* = \frac{1}{8}$, $y^* = \frac{3}{8}$ and the value of the game is $-\frac{11}{8}$. See Ex. (d) above.

4. Examine graphically the case $\mathbf{A} = \begin{bmatrix} 0 & 2 \\ 1 & 1 \end{bmatrix}$ where there is an infinite number of solutions. See 15.5, Ex. 3.

5. Show graphically that the game with
$$\mathbf{A} = \begin{bmatrix} 1 & 2 \\ -1 & 0 \\ 1 & 3 \end{bmatrix}$$
has an infinite number of solutions. See 15.4, Ex. 4.

6. Examine the game of 15.2, Ex. (g), in graphical terms. In what sense can it be said that B's choice of strategies does not matter much?

15.7 The General Case of a Two-Person Zero-Sum Game

The groundwork has now been laid for a consideration of the general case of a game with a pay-off matrix of order $m \times n$. This will be facilitated by a flexible use of the notation for matrices and vectors (Chapters 12 and 13 above).

Let the pay-off matrix be $\mathbf{A} = [a_{rs}]$ ($r=1, 2, \ldots m$, $s=1, 2, \ldots n$). Player A chooses between m strategies and he can mix them at will over successive plays. Let him play his strategies in the proportions $x_1, x_2, \ldots x_m$

where the x's are non-negative and add to unity. Broadly, the x's are positive fractions, but some of them (though not all) can be zero if there are strategies which he does not play at all. As a special case, all x's can be zero except one and that x must then be 1 ; this is the case of a pure strategy in which one of the strategies is played by itself and repeatedly. All the other cases are of mixed strategy.

A given *mixed strategy* for A is thus represented by the vector :

$$(x_1, x_2, \dots x_m)$$

subject to the essential limitations :

$$x_r \geqslant 0 \quad (r = 1, 2, \dots m) \quad \text{and} \quad \sum_{r=1}^{m} x_r = 1 \dots\dots\dots\dots\dots(1)$$

This includes the special case of a *pure strategy* :

$$x_r = 1 \text{ and } x_{r'} = 0 \quad (r' = 1, 2, \dots m, r' \neq r)$$

There are m pure strategies according to the choice of r. In the matrix notation the vector of x's can be denoted either as a column or as a row vector :

$$\mathbf{x} = \{x_r\} = \begin{bmatrix} x_1 \\ x_2 \\ \dots \\ x_m \end{bmatrix}; \quad \mathbf{x}' = [x_r] = [x_1 \, x_2 \dots x_m]$$

The prime in $\mathbf{x}'$ indicates, as usual, a transposition of rows and columns.

In the same way, player B chooses between n strategies according to a vector $(y_1, y_2, \dots y_n)$ subject to limitations similar to (1). The vector can be denoted $\mathbf{y} = \{y_s\}$ in column form and as $\mathbf{y}' = [y_s]$ in row form, where $s = 1, 2, \dots n$.

If A plays the mixed strategy $\mathbf{x} = \{x_r\}$ and B the mixed strategy $\mathbf{y} = \{y_s\}$, then the expectation of the game to A is :

$$E(\mathbf{x}, \mathbf{y}) = \sum_{r=1}^{m} \sum_{s=1}^{n} a_{rs} x_r y_s \dots\dots\dots\dots\dots\dots(2)$$

The notation $E(\mathbf{x}, \mathbf{y})$ now means that the single value E is a function of the two vectors $\mathbf{x}$ and $\mathbf{y}$, the function being expressed in terms of the double sum (2) involving the elements of $\mathbf{x}$ and $\mathbf{y}$. In matrix notation, (2) can be written (14.5 above) as the bilinear form :

$$E(\mathbf{x}, \mathbf{y}) = \mathbf{x}' \mathbf{A} \mathbf{y} \dots\dots\dots\dots\dots\dots\dots(3)$$

As a check the orders of the three matrices multiplied are respectively $1 \times m$, $m \times n$ and $n \times 1$, giving a scalar E (see 13.6 above).

It is important to consider the set of all vectors $\mathbf{x} = \{x_r\}$ which satisfy the conditions (1). Denote this set by X, so that "$\mathbf{x}$ in X" means one admissible vector $\mathbf{x}$, out of the complete set X. Similarly the set of all vectors $\mathbf{y} = \{y_s\}$ satisfying conditions like (1) is denoted by Y. When $m = 3$, the vectors $\mathbf{x} = \{x_r\}$ $(r = 1, 2, 3)$ can be shown as points (x_1, x_2, x_3) in a space of three dimensions. The set X then comprises all such points for which $x_1 \geqslant 0$ $x_2 \geqslant 0$, $x_3 \geqslant 0$ and $x_1 + x_2 + x_3 = 1$. These are the points

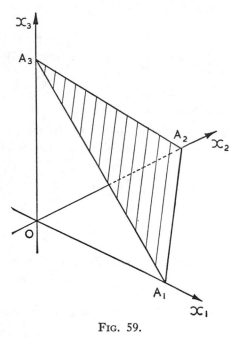

FIG. 59.

which lie on the segment of a plane cut off by the co-ordinate planes. The segment is $A_1 A_2 A_3$ of Fig. 59 where $OA_1 = OA_2 = OA_3 = 1$. Any point on the segment X represents a pattern of strategies for A; at A_1, A_2 or A_3, a pure strategy is followed; at the other points the strategy is mixed. For $m > 3$, the set X of vectors $\mathbf{x}$ can be thought of as a set of points lying on a segment of a "hyper-plane" in m dimensions.

The value of E given by (3) is defined for any one vector $\mathbf{x}$ in X and any one vector $\mathbf{y}$ in Y. The general object of player A is to make E as great as possible by choice of $\mathbf{x}$ in X, having regard to what his opponent may do on selecting $\mathbf{y}$ from Y. Player B similarly aims at making E as small as possible. The whole theory of such games turns on a definition taken over direct from 15.5 above:

DEFINITION : If vectors $\mathbf{x}^*$ and $\mathbf{y}^*$ can be found so that for any $\mathbf{x}$ in X and $\mathbf{y}$ in Y :

$$E(\mathbf{x}, \mathbf{y}^*) \leqslant E(\mathbf{x}^*, \mathbf{y}^*) \leqslant E(\mathbf{x}^*, \mathbf{y})$$

i.e. $$\mathbf{x}'\mathbf{A}\mathbf{y}^* \leqslant (\mathbf{x}^*)'\mathbf{A}\mathbf{y}^* \leqslant (\mathbf{x}^*)'\mathbf{A}\mathbf{y}$$

then $(\mathbf{x}^*, \mathbf{y}^*)$ is a saddle point of E, the game has a *stable outcome* or *solution* $(\mathbf{x}^*, \mathbf{y}^*)$ and $v = E(\mathbf{x}^*, \mathbf{y}^*)$ is the value of the game to A.

When x^* is described as an optimal strategy for A, what is implied is that the optimal way for A to play is to follow his m strategies in proportions $x_1^*, x_2^*, \dots x_m^*$, where $\mathbf{x}^*$ is the vector $(x_1^*, x_2^*, \dots x_m^*)$. The definition means that A chooses $\mathbf{x}^*$ because he can then receive at least $E(\mathbf{x}^*, \mathbf{y}^*)$ whatever his opponent does, while any other choice $\mathbf{x}$ makes it possible for his opponent to keep his gain below $E(\mathbf{x}^*, \mathbf{y}^*)$.

It follows, exactly as proved in 15.5 above :

$E(\mathbf{x}, \mathbf{y})$ has a saddle point at $(\mathbf{x}^*, \mathbf{y}^*)$ if and only if
$$\max_x \min_y E(\mathbf{x}, \mathbf{y}) = \min_y \max_x E(\mathbf{x}, \mathbf{y}) = E(\mathbf{x}^*, \mathbf{y}^*)$$

The basic theory is then completed by :

MINIMAX THEOREM : The bilinear form $E(\mathbf{x}, \mathbf{y}) = \mathbf{x}'\mathbf{A}\mathbf{y}$ is such that $\max_x \min_y E(\mathbf{x}, \mathbf{y})$ and $\min_y \max_x E(\mathbf{x}, \mathbf{y})$ exist and are equal.

A special case of this theorem is proved in 15.5 above, but no general proof is offered here. The proof given by von Neumann and Morgenstern (1944, 1954), pp. 153-5, and that of Wald (1950), pp. 52–4, are far from simple. There are several simpler proofs available. One of them is an application of the Brower Fixed Point Theorem in topology ; it is due to J. F. Nash and given in Luce and Raiffa (1957), Appendix 2. Another by Loomis (1946) is algebraic and self-contained.

The minimax theorem is part of the basic mathematics common to game theory and to minimax decision theories with a variety of applications. The consequence for game theory is :

A two-person zero-sum game with expectation $E(\mathbf{x}, \mathbf{y})$ *always* has a solution $\mathbf{x}^*$, $\mathbf{y}^*$, the saddle point of $E(\mathbf{x}, \mathbf{y})$. Player A has at least one optimal strategy ($\mathbf{x}^*$ in X) and player B at least one optimal strategy ($\mathbf{y}^*$ in Y). The value of the game is $v = E(\mathbf{x}^*, \mathbf{y}^*)$, the common value of $\max_x \min_y E(\mathbf{x}, \mathbf{y})$ and $\min_y \max_x E(\mathbf{x}, \mathbf{y})$.

In certain cases, there is more than one optimal strategy, and there are then an infinite number of them. The value of the game is, however, unique ; it is possible for the value to be achieved, in some instances, by any one of an infinite number of strategies by one player or the other. This additional point has already been illustrated in simple cases. It is not ruled out by the above basic results.

Some properties of the solution of a game are now derived. At first sight they may appear formal, if not arid ; they are in fact the basis of practical rules without which it is scarcely possible to solve particular games, with specified and numerical pay-off matrices, when the players each have more than two strategies. The task of solving a game, or even of finding and checking such properties as its value, is a formidable one in practice. Properties like the following are an essential part of the task.

The first of the properties relates to the pay-off matrix and shows how it can be adjusted, e.g. so that no element is negative, for ease of calculation. The second property provides an important check on optimal strategies, as derived or even guessed, against the value of the game. A third property is used in conjunction with the second and it relates to circumstances under which one strategy is not played at all in the optimal position. The properties are :

PROPERTY (i). If $\mathbf{x}^*$ and $\mathbf{y}^*$ are optimal strategies for the players of a game with pay-off matrix $\mathbf{A}$ of order $m \times n$, they are also optimal for a game with pay-off matrix $(c\mathbf{A} + \mathbf{B})$, where c is a positive scalar and $\mathbf{B}$ of order $m \times n$ has all elements equal to a scalar b. If v is the value of the first game, then the second game has value $(cv + b)$.

PROPERTY (ii). If a game has value v, then $\mathbf{x}^*$ and $\mathbf{y}^*$ are optimal strategies for the players if and only if :

(a) $E(\mathbf{x}^*, \mathbf{y}) \geqslant v$ for every $\mathbf{y}$ in Y
$E(\mathbf{x}, \mathbf{y}^*) \leqslant v$ for every $\mathbf{x}$ in X

and hence if and only if :

(b) $\displaystyle\sum_{s=1}^{n} a_{rs}y_s^* \leqslant v \leqslant \sum_{r=1}^{m} a_{rs}x_r^*$

for all $r = 1, 2, \ldots m$ and $s = 1, 2, \ldots n$.

PROPERTY (iii). If a game has value v and optimal strategies $\mathbf{x}^*$ and $\mathbf{y}^*$:

$$\sum_{s=1}^{n} a_{rs}y_s^* < v \text{ implies } x_r^* = 0$$

and $\displaystyle\sum_{r=1}^{m} a_{rs}x_r^* > v \text{ implies } y_s^* = 0$

for any r and s ($r = 1, 2, \ldots m$, $s = 1, 2, \ldots n$).

The conditions of Properties (ii) and (iii) can be expressed in matrix notation :

(ii) (a) $(\mathbf{x}^*)'\mathbf{A}\mathbf{y} \geqslant v$ for every $\mathbf{y}$ in Y
            $\mathbf{x}'\mathbf{A}\mathbf{y}^* \leqslant v$ for every $\mathbf{x}$ in X
    (b) $\mathbf{A}\mathbf{y}^* \leqslant v\{1\} \leqslant \mathbf{A}'\mathbf{x}^*$
         where $\{1\}$ consists of m or n elements each unity.

(iii) In $\mathbf{A}\mathbf{y}^* \leqslant v\{1\}$, the fact that $<$ rather than $=$ holds for one element implies that the corresponding element in $\mathbf{x}^*$ is zero, and similarly for $\mathbf{A}'\mathbf{x}^* \geqslant v\{1\}$.

The proofs of the properties are based on the definition of the solution of a game and, to illustrate, the proof of Property (ii) (a) is given here.

First, given $\mathbf{x}^*$ and $\mathbf{y}^*$ as optimal strategies. By definition :

$$E(\mathbf{x}, \mathbf{y}^*) \leqslant v = E(\mathbf{x}^*, \mathbf{y}^*) \leqslant E(\mathbf{x}^*, \mathbf{y})$$

for every $\mathbf{x}$ in X and $\mathbf{y}$ in Y.   Q.E.D.

Second, given $E(\mathbf{x}, \mathbf{y}^*) \leqslant v \leqslant E(\mathbf{x}^*, \mathbf{y})$ for every $\mathbf{x}$ in X and $\mathbf{y}$ in Y. Put $\mathbf{x} = \mathbf{x}^*$ and $\mathbf{y} = \mathbf{y}^*$: $E(\mathbf{x}^*, \mathbf{y}^*) \leqslant v \leqslant E(\mathbf{x}^*, \mathbf{y}^*)$

i.e. $$v = E(\mathbf{x}^*, \mathbf{y}^*).$$

The given relations are then :

$$E(\mathbf{x}, \mathbf{y}^*) \leqslant E(\mathbf{x}^*, \mathbf{y}^*) \leqslant E(\mathbf{x}^*, \mathbf{y})$$

for every $\mathbf{x}$ in X and $\mathbf{y}$ in Y, i.e. $(\mathbf{x}^*, \mathbf{y}^*)$ is a saddle point of E by definition and $\mathbf{x}^*$ and $\mathbf{y}^*$ are optimal strategies.   Q.E.D.

One particular case is important enough to be given alongside the more general properties :

PROPERTY (iv). If the pay-off matrix of a game is *square and skew-symmetric*, then the same strategy is optimal for each player and the value of the game is zero.

A skew-symmetric pay-off matrix $\mathbf{A}$ means that the game has *symmetry* as between the two players. If the players are interchanged and the pay-off to A reversed in sign to give the pay-off to B, then the pay-off matrix becomes $(-\mathbf{A}')$. This equals $\mathbf{A}$ by the definition of a skew-symmetric matrix. The pay-off matrix is the same for one player as for the other and so the optimal strategies are to be expected to be the same. Quite apart from this, a game may be called *fair* if its value is zero so that, when played at optimum, neither player wins from the other on balance. All kinds of games are fair in this sense, including most parlour games. In particular, however, a game which has symmetry is to be expected to be also fair. For example, in two-finger Morra, the game described in Ex. (f) of 15.2 above, the pay-off matrix is skew-symmetric :

$$\mathbf{A} = \begin{bmatrix} 0 & -3 & 2 & 0 \\ 3 & 0 & 0 & -4 \\ -2 & 0 & 0 & 3 \\ 0 & 4 & -3 & 0 \end{bmatrix}$$

The game is symmetric between the players ; it is natural to suppose that it is fair. This is what Property (iv) asserts.

The formal proof is an exercise in the use of Property (ii) (*b*). Let the game have optimal strategies $\mathbf{x}^*$ and $\mathbf{y}^*$ and value v so that :

$$\mathbf{A}\mathbf{y}^* \leqslant v\{1\} \leqslant \mathbf{A}'\mathbf{x}^* \dots\dots\dots\dots\dots\dots\dots\dots\dots\dots\dots\dots (7)$$

Hence : $\qquad (-\mathbf{A})\mathbf{y}^* \geqslant (-v)\{1\} \geqslant (-\mathbf{A}')\mathbf{x}^*$

Since $\qquad\quad \mathbf{A}' = -\mathbf{A}$ and $-\mathbf{A}' = \mathbf{A}$, it follows that :

$$\mathbf{A}'\mathbf{y}^* \geqslant (-v)\{1\} \geqslant \mathbf{A}\mathbf{x}^* \dots\dots\dots\dots\dots\dots\dots\dots\dots (8)$$

Add (7) and (8) to give :

$$\mathbf{A}(\mathbf{x}^* + \mathbf{y}^*) \leqslant 0 \leqslant \mathbf{A}'(\mathbf{x}^* + \mathbf{y}^*) \dots\dots\dots\dots\dots\dots (9)$$

since $v\{1\} + (-v)\{1\} = \mathbf{0}$. Now $\mathbf{x}^*$ and $\mathbf{y}^*$ belong to the same set of vectors since $\mathbf{A}$ is square and the vector $\mathbf{z}^* = \frac{1}{2}(\mathbf{x}^* + \mathbf{y}^*)$ also belongs to the same admissible set (see Ex. 3 below). Hence $\mathbf{z}^*$ is a possible strategy for each player. Since (9) is :

$$\mathbf{A}\mathbf{z}^* \leqslant 0 \leqslant \mathbf{A}'\mathbf{z}^*$$

then Property (ii) (*b*) shows that each player has the same optimal strategy $\mathbf{z}^*$ and that the value of the game is zero, as is to be proved.

Some consideration may also be given to games which are not fair and for which the value $v \neq 0$. Let $v > 0$ so that in a stable position B must pay something to A on balance. Why should B play at all? Indeed, if he knows the solution, there is no reason why he should. But there may be a compensatory arrangement, a *side payment* from A to B at each play of the game. The question is : what side payment makes the game fair? The answer is provided by Property (i) and it is obvious enough. If A pays an amount v to B at each play, then the pay-off matrix in effect becomes $(\mathbf{A} - \mathbf{B})$, where $\mathbf{B}$ has all its elements equal to v. The value of the game is then $v - v = 0$. A side payment of v from A to B makes the game fair ; B can play with good grace, and without loss if he is skilful.

EXERCISES 15.7

1. The vector $\mathbf{x}$ belongs to the set X of (1) above. When the order is 2, show that $\mathbf{x}$ is a point P in a plane Ox_1x_2 and that X comprises all points lying on the line between A_1 and A_2 on the axes and such that $OA_1 = OA_2 = 1$. Hence show that $\mathbf{x}$ is the vector $(x, 1 - x)$ for $0 \leqslant x \leqslant 1$ and interpret.

2. If the vector $\mathbf{x}$ is of order 3, show that X comprises all points of the triangle $A_1A_2A_3$ of Fig. 59. Interpret when the points lie on the sides of the triangle. In general, show that $\mathbf{x}$ is the vector $(x_1, x_2, 1 - x_1 - x_2)$ for two variables x_1 and x_2 such that (x_1, x_2) lies in the triangle OA_1A_2.

3. Let $\mathbf{x}^{(1)}$ and $\mathbf{x}^{(2)}$ be two vectors in X ; show that $\mathbf{x} = \frac{1}{2}(\mathbf{x}^{(1)} + \mathbf{x}^{(2)})$ is also in X and illustrate in terms of Fig. 59. Generalise for any number of vectors in X and in terms of convex linear combinations (12.5 above).

4. A game has a pay-off matrix of order $2 \times n$. If $(x^{(1)}, 1 - x^{(1)})$ and $(x^{(2)}, 1 - x^{(2)})$ are both optimal strategies for player A, show that $(x, 1 - x)$ is also optimal if x lies between $x^{(1)}$ and $x^{(2)}$. Deduce that, if there are two different optimal strategies, then there is an infinite number. Generalise for a matrix of order $m \times n$ in terms of convex linear combinations.

5. Prove Property (i) above.

6. Deduce Property (ii) (b) from (ii) (a) and then prove Property (iii).

7. Show that a game cannot have two different values, i.e. that the value of a game is unique even when there is an infinite number of optimal strategies.

15.8 Solutions of Particular Games

A game can always be solved on the lines of 15.5 and 15.6 above, when the matrix is of order $2 \times n$ or $m \times 2$, i.e. one player at least has only two strategies. By the Minimax Theorem, a game of order $m \times n$ always has a solution, either unique or (at worst) one of an infinite set. Hence there is something to find; the problem is how to find it.

The expectation $E(\mathbf{x}, \mathbf{y})$ is not likely to be helpful in practice, since it is a function of two vectors $\mathbf{x}$ and $\mathbf{y}$ and appears as a double sum not handled at all easily. The practical technique is to be devised in other ways and it has two stages. The pay-off matrix of a game is $\mathbf{A} = [a_{rs}]$ of order $m \times n$. In the *first stage*, the matrix $\mathbf{A}$ is reduced by the elimination of redundant rows and columns (strategies never used), it is adjusted by Property (i) of 15.7 above so that its elements are of a form (e.g. without negative and fractional values) which is easily handled, and it is finally tested for a saddle point in case the players use pure strategies in the stable outcome. If there is a saddle point, there is nothing further to be done; a solution is found. Otherwise, and generally, the *second stage* of the practical technique is needed. Here the idea is to winkle out what is thought to be an optimal strategy for each player, by some means or other, and to check it against the value of the game. This is where Properties (ii), (iii) and (iv) of 15.7 above come into the picture. No holds are barred; even sheer guessing will do. For, by Property (ii) (b), any suggested pair of optimal strategies can be tested, and so accepted or rejected, in a very simple way.

The first stage needs elaboration. The definition of, and the means of detecting, redundant rows and columns in $\mathbf{A}$ must be given. Consider the rows of $\mathbf{A}$. One row can be eliminated as redundant if it is *dominated* by another, in the sense that each element is less than or equal to the corresponding element in the other row. The player A never has reason to play the strategy of the first row, alone or in combination; he can do as well or better by substituting the other row. For example, if

$\mathbf{A} = \begin{bmatrix} 0 & -1 \\ 1 & 1 \end{bmatrix}$, the first row can be eliminated and the player A need con-

sider only the second, or dominating, strategy. An obvious extension is that one row can be eliminated as dominated by some combination of other rows, the combination being by means of multiples which are positive fractions adding to unity. For example, if :

$$\mathbf{A} = \begin{bmatrix} 0 & -1 & 1 \\ 1 & 1 & 0 \\ 1 & -2 & 2 \end{bmatrix}$$

a combination of half the second and half the third strategy gives the mixed strategy with pay-offs : 1, $-\frac{1}{2}$, 1. The first row of $\mathbf{A}$, being not greater than these, can be eliminated as dominated by the other two rows.

The columns of $\mathbf{A}$ can be considered in a similar way, with the difference that the player B is now concerned so that small values of the elements are sought. Hence a column of $\mathbf{A}$ can be eliminated as redundant if it *dominates* another column or any combination of other columns. The combination is again a convex linear one. The following examples illustrate.

Ex. (a). $\mathbf{A} = \begin{bmatrix} 3 & 2 & -4 & 6 \\ -2 & 5 & -1 & 2 \end{bmatrix}$

Strike out the second and fourth columns as dominating the third. The solution of the game comes from $\begin{bmatrix} 3 & -4 \\ -2 & -1 \end{bmatrix}$ with the addition of zero frequencies for the second and fourth strategies of player B. As in Ex. (d) and Fig. 57 of 15.6 above, the optimal strategies are :

$$\mathbf{x}^* = (\tfrac{1}{8}, \tfrac{7}{8}) \quad \text{and} \quad \mathbf{y}^* = (\tfrac{3}{8}, 0, \tfrac{5}{8}, 0)$$

and the value of the game is $v = -\frac{11}{8}$.

Ex. (b). $\mathbf{A} = \begin{bmatrix} 1 & 2 & 0 \\ 2 & -1 & 3 \end{bmatrix}$

Strike out the first column since it dominates the other two :

$$1 > \tfrac{1}{3}(2) + \tfrac{2}{3}(0) \quad \text{and} \quad 2 > \tfrac{1}{3}(-1) + \tfrac{2}{3}(3)$$

The solution comes from $\begin{bmatrix} 2 & 0 \\ -1 & 3 \end{bmatrix}$. The optimal strategies are :

$$x^* = (\tfrac{2}{3}, \tfrac{1}{3}) \quad \text{and} \quad y^* = (0, \tfrac{1}{2}, \tfrac{1}{2})$$

and the value of the game is $v = 1$, as in Ex. (c) of 15.6 above.

Ex. (c). $\mathbf{A} = \begin{bmatrix} 0 & 2 & -1 & 3 \\ 2 & 3 & 1 & 2 \\ 3 & 4 & 0 & -4 \end{bmatrix}$

Strike out the first two columns as dominating the third, and the third row of what is left as dominated by the second. Finally, in $\begin{bmatrix} -1 & 3 \\ 1 & 2 \end{bmatrix}$, the second column and then the first row are ruled out and all that is left is the single element 1. The value of the game is 1 and there is a saddle point, only pure strategies being used, i.e. A's second and B's third strategy in the original $\mathbf{A}$.

Ex. (d). $\mathbf{A} = \begin{bmatrix} \frac{1}{3} & -\frac{1}{3} & -\frac{1}{3} \\ -\frac{1}{3} & 0 & -\frac{1}{6} \\ -\frac{1}{3} & \frac{2}{3} & -\frac{1}{3} \\ -\frac{1}{3} & -\frac{1}{3} & 1 \end{bmatrix}$

Strike out the second row as dominated by a combination (equal frequencies) of the third and fourth rows. The residual matrix, of order 3×3, remains for solution.

The next point in the first stage is to simplify $\mathbf{A}$ by means of Property (i) of 15.7 above. To get rid of negative elements in $\mathbf{A}$, find the largest of them numerically and add this numerical amount to every element. The adjusted matrix has zero as its smallest element; the corresponding game has the same optimal strategies as that to be solved and its value is the original value increased by the added constant amount. In the same way, fractional values in $\mathbf{A}$ can be eliminated by multiplying through by an appropriate scalar c, without disturbing the optimal strategies and only changing the value by the multiple c. It is not always necessary to go to the extreme of eliminating all negative and fractional elements in $\mathbf{A}$, since the solution may be obtained without going so far. But it can be done whenever appropriate or required. The game of Ex. (d) above provides a good illustration. If $\mathbf{A}$ (without the second row) is multiplied through by 3 and if 1 is then added to each element, an adjusted matrix is formed:

$$\begin{bmatrix} 2 & 0 & 0 \\ 0 & 3 & 0 \\ 0 & 0 & 4 \end{bmatrix}$$

and this is the matrix of a game capable of easy solution. The original game has the same optimal strategies as the adjusted game. Further, if the value of the original game is v, this is to be found from the fact that the adjusted game has value $(3v + 1)$.

Finally, at a point in the first stage, the matrix of the game can be tested for a saddle point, i.e. it can be determined whether the game has pure strategies for its solution. This can be done for the matrix without any adjustment; or it can be tried for any partly or completely adjusted matrix. Consider Ex. (c) above as a case in point. The row minima of $\mathbf{A}$ are $-1, 1, -4$ respectively; the column maxima are $3, 4, 1, 3$. Hence, according to the method given at the end of 15.4 above, the value of the game is $v = 1$, and the player A uses only his second, and player B his third, strategy. The same result is obtained above by elimination of redundant rows and columns in $\mathbf{A}$.

Few games have pure strategies as outcome. But they must be tested for saddle points at the first stage of the practical technique, to save the labour of working through the second stage to what (for pure strategies) only turns out to be an inconclusive result. This is illustrated by an example :

Ex. (e). *The Coal Problem*, based on Example 15 of Williams (1954). You have the following data on the amount and price of coal needed to heat your house in the winter :

Type of winter	Coal needed (tons)	Average price (£ per ton)
Mild	4	7·0
Normal	5	7·5
Cold	6	8·0

These prices relate to purchases of coal made currently during the winter. However, in the summer, coal can be bought at £6 per ton and you have storage space for up to 6 tons. You contemplate three strategies, to stock 4, 5 and 6 tons respectively in summer and to buy the rest (if any needed) at winter prices. Any coal you have left over at the end of the winter is to be written off ; you are leaving your house and you cannot dispose of any coal. The pay-off matrix (in £ is :

$$
\begin{array}{c}
& \text{Winter :} \\
& \begin{array}{ccc} \textit{Mild} & \textit{Normal} & \textit{Cold} \end{array} \\
\text{Summer stock (tons)} \quad \begin{array}{c} 4 \\ 5 \\ 6 \end{array}
& \left[\begin{array}{ccc}
-24 & -31\frac{1}{2} & -40 \\
-30 & -30 & -38 \\
-36 & -36 & -36*
\end{array} \right]
\end{array}
$$

The " game " has a saddle point and solution, marked with an asterisk above.

Your optimal strategy is a 6-ton summer stock. In a " game " against nature like this, you are supposed to have no knowledge of what " strategy " nature plays. In effect, here, the solution of the " game " is an insurance against a cold winter, There is no implication that you " should " play it so. On the contrary, you may plump for a normal winter, buy a 5-ton stock and minimise cost. You would then lose as compared with the " game " solution, if the winter is cold.

At the *second stage* of the practical technique of solution, the general method is shown sufficiently well by the case of a game with a pay-off matrix of order 3×3. A larger game merely has more variables and more relations between them ; there is nothing new, just more of the same. The pay-off matrix is $\mathbf{A} = [a_{rs}]$ for r and $s = 1, 2, 3$. Let the value of the game be v and let (x_1, x_2, x_3) and (y_1, y_2, y_3) be optimal strategies for the two players. Then, by Property (ii) (b) of 15.7 above, the seven unknowns (the x's, the y's and v) are subject to eight relations :

$$
\begin{array}{ll}
x_1 + x_2 + x_3 = 1 & y_1 + y_2 + y_3 = 1 \\
a_{11}x_1 + a_{21}x_2 + a_{31}x_3 \geqslant v & a_{11}y_1 + a_{12}y_2 + a_{13}y_3 \leqslant v \\
a_{12}x_1 + a_{22}x_2 + a_{32}x_3 \geqslant v & a_{21}y_1 + a_{22}y_2 + a_{23}y_3 \leqslant v \\
a_{13}x_1 + a_{23}x_2 + a_{33}x_3 \geqslant v & a_{31}y_1 + a_{32}y_2 + a_{33}y_3 \leqslant v
\end{array}
$$

In addition, there is the limitation that none of the x's and y's is negative. The interpretation of the relations is clear. $(a_{11}x_1 + a_{21}x_2 + a_{31}x_3)$ is the pay-off to A when he plays his optimal strategy $(x_1,\ x_2,\ x_3)$, and B adopts a pure strategy, his first. Hence, as long as A plays his optimal strategy it does not matter which pure strategy B plays—the pay-off to A is at least v ; the same is true however B mixes his strategies. Similarly, if B plays his optimal strategy, A's play is immaterial to the extent that B never pays out more than v. This is automatically a check on any suggested optimal strategies and any suggested value of the game.

The situation is that there are more relations than variables—and that the relations involve inequalities. It is not just a matter of counting equations and then solving them. On the contrary, this serves no immediate purpose ; the relations are not all equations, and the count would show " too many " of them if they were equations. This is the kind of problem met in linear programming and there are procedures (e.g. the Simplex Method) for handling the computational job of solution, as explained in 16.8 below.

As an interim measure, at least, a more rough and ready method of solution is suggested here. When variables are related by inequalities, their values fall within certain overlapping ranges. In geometrical terms, when the variables are shown by points in space, the points do not lie inevitably on lines, planes, and so on ; they fall within (or outside) certain areas defined by lines, planes, etc. The solution sought is still one point, or a set of points, but not as the intersection of lines, planes, etc., but rather as the common overlap of definite areas. However, what can be hoped is that some (but not all) of the boundaries of the areas serve to provide the solution, i.e. that some (but not all) of the inequality relations can be turned into equations and solved to give the solution. The essential difference, between this idea and the ordinary solution of systems of equations, is that a *selection* of some relations from all possible ones has to be made for turning into equations ; the other relations remain as strict inequalities. The question is : *which* relations are to be written as equations?

With this in mind another look can be taken at the solution (optimal strategy for player A) in the case of a game with a matrix of order $2 \times n$, as illustrated in Fig. 58 above. If A's optimal strategy is (x_1, x_2) then there is one equation $(x_1 + x_2 = 1)$ and there are m inequalities between the two x's. Write $x_1 = x$ and $x_2 = 1 - x$, and the result is m inequalities in one variable x, together with the value v of the game. Any two of these, written as equations, serve to give values for x and v, but they may be quite inconsistent with others of the m relations, or x may turn out to be negative. The graphical method of Fig. 58 is to write *all* the relations as equations, to plot them as lines showing v varying with x ranging from 0 to 1, to pick out the smallest v for each x and then the x for the largest of the minimised v's. If there is a unique solution, x comes in the end by solving two of the equations, and the graph shows which two.

The method suggested by this line of thought is to fish around in the complete set of relations, solving some of them as equations and checking the result against the others as inequalities. The method can be systematised in terms of sub-matrices, and their determinant values, formed from the pay-off matrix. This is, in effect, a use of Cramer's rule in solving sub-groups of equations. A simple exposition of the method on these lines is given in the 3×3 case in Williams (1954), pp. 91–8. The method used here is a direct approach to the question of deciding on which relations to write as equations, and it brings in explicitly the important property (iii) of 15.7 above. The method can be explained in terms of the eight relations in seven variables obtained in the 3×3 case.

First write all eight relations as equations, solve any seven of them for the variables, check that the x's and y's are non-negative and see if the eighth equation is also satisfied. If so, well and good ; a solution is obtained. If not, abandon this line and try another. Write a selected relation as a strict inequality and the other seven as equations. If the strict inequality is one of the relations in the x's, then a corresponding y is zero, by Property (iii) of 15.7. There are now seven equations in six variables (the zero y being eliminated) and the process is repeated. Eventually, some set of equations provide a solution in the variables, other than those which are zero by Property (iii). The method is illustrated in actual cases in 15.9 below. Meanwhile, a further interpretation can be placed on the inequality relations of Property (ii) (*b*), backed by the conditions of Property (iii).

If a relation between the x's is in the form " $>v$ ", then the corresponding y is zero, i.e. if A's optimal strategy matched with a pure strategy of B gives a pay-off to A greater than v, then B does not use this strategy at his optimum. Similarly for relations between the y's in the form " $<v$ ". With these cases eliminated, there remain a set of relations in the x's equated to v and a set of relations in the y's equated to v. These correspond to optimal y's and x's which are not zero, i.e. to strategies which are used in the stable outcome. The result is that, if A uses his optimal mixed strategy, then *any* pure strategy played by B gives a pay-off to A of *exactly* v—provided only that the pure strategy is one which B would

use in his optimal mixture. In this sense, as long as A plays well, it doesn't matter how B plays. Similarly, when B plays his optimum strategy, it doesn't matter how A plays, selecting pure strategies from his optimum mixture in any way whatever. Here is the simplest check on any suggested optimal strategies for both players. Take A's optimal mixture and value it up at each one of the pure strategies (used by B in his optimal mixture); the result is the same pay-off (v) to A in every case. Similarly, the same pay-off (v) is found by valuing up B's optimal mixture at each and every pure strategy used by A.

EXERCISES 15.8

1. If $A = \begin{bmatrix} 1 & 2 \\ -1 & 0 \\ 1 & 3 \end{bmatrix}$, show that the second row is redundant. Hence solve the game and check Ex. 4 of 15.4 and Ex. 5 of 15.6.

2. By eliminating a redundant row and column, show that the game with

$$A = \begin{bmatrix} 0 & 3 & -3 \\ 3 & 9 & -6 \\ 3 & -1 & 2 \end{bmatrix}$$

has value $v = \frac{2}{3}$, the optimal strategies being $(0, \frac{1}{6}, \frac{5}{6})$ for A and $(0, \frac{4}{9}, \frac{5}{9})$ for B.

3. Adjust the matrix of the previous exercise to eliminate negative elements. Solve again to give $v = \frac{2}{3}$ for the original game.

4. Solve the game with $A = \begin{bmatrix} -1 & 1 & 1 \\ 1 & -1 & 1 \\ 1 & 1 & -1 \end{bmatrix}$ by first eliminating the *positive* elements. It is suggested that $v = \frac{1}{3}$ is the value of the game.

5. Take A in the form of the previous exercise but of order $n \times n$. Use Property (ii) (b) of 15.7 above to show that $\left(\dfrac{1}{n}, \dfrac{1}{n}, \dots \dfrac{1}{n}\right)$, i.e. equal frequencies, is an optimal strategy for each player. Why would you expect this? Deduce that the value of the game is $\dfrac{n-2}{n}$.

6. A game has $A = \begin{bmatrix} 3 & 0 & 0 \\ 1 & -\frac{1}{2} & 2 \\ 2 & \frac{3}{2} & -1 \end{bmatrix}$. Adjust A to eliminate negative and fractional elements and eliminate a redundant column. Hence solve graphically, as a game of order 3×2, to show that B's optimal strategy is $(0, \frac{3}{5}, \frac{2}{5})$. What is A's optimal strategy?

7. Show that $A = \begin{bmatrix} -3 & 3 & -1 & 0 \\ 1 & 2 & 0 & 1 \\ 3 & -2 & -4 & -1 \end{bmatrix}$ has a saddle point. Deduce that the stable outcome of the game has pure strategies played by both players and that the game is fair.

8. Use $\mathbf{A} = \begin{bmatrix} 1 & \frac{1}{2} & 1 & \frac{1}{2} \\ -2 & 0 & -\frac{1}{2} & -2 \\ 2 & \frac{1}{2} & 1 & \frac{1}{2} \\ -\frac{1}{2} & -1 & 1 & -1 \end{bmatrix}$ to show that multiple saddle points are

possible. What is the solution of the game and how is it to be interpreted? What side payment could A make to B at each play?

15.9 Illustrations

The following examples illustrate the practical technique described above for the solution of a given game. They are all games in which the stable outcome is a mixed strategy. They are also games which are interesting to play ; some are " fair " and others, though not fair, are still not without attractions to the players, e.g. the game which represents a typical case of betting on horse races.

Ex. (*a*). $\mathbf{A} = \begin{bmatrix} 1 & 2 & 3 \\ 2 & 3 & 1 \\ 3 & 1 & 2 \end{bmatrix}$ a matrix of the type known to statisticians and others

as a Latin Square, each digit (1, 2, 3) appearing once in each row and once in each column. The matrix is symmetric.

The matrix needs no adjustment, there is no saddle point and the variables are to be found from :

$$x_1 + x_2 + x_3 = 1$$
$$x_1 + 2x_2 + 3x_3 \geqslant v$$
$$2x_1 + 3x_2 + x_3 \geqslant v$$
$$3x_1 + x_2 + 2x_3 \geqslant v$$

and similar relations in the y's. The optimal strategies of the two players are the same. The relations, as four equations, give

$$x_1 = x_2 = x_3 = \tfrac{1}{3} \quad \text{and} \quad v = 2$$

Hence, in the stable outcome, the mixed strategy of each player is $(\tfrac{1}{3}, \tfrac{1}{3}, \tfrac{1}{3})$, i.e. equal frequencies, and the value of the game to A is 2.

Ex. (*b*). $\mathbf{A} = \begin{bmatrix} 3 & 0 & 0 \\ 1 & -\frac{1}{2} & 2 \\ 2 & \frac{3}{2} & -1 \end{bmatrix}$ which is neither symmetric nor skew-symmetric

It is, therefore, to be expected that the players adopt different strategies. Let the value of the game be v, which is likely to be positive.

Adjust $\mathbf{A}$ by multiplying through by 2 and then by adding 2 to each element. The game with matrix $\begin{bmatrix} 8 & 2 & 2 \\ 4 & 1 & 6 \\ 6 & 5 & 0 \end{bmatrix}$ has the same optimum strategies, and value

$v = 2(v + 1)$. There is no saddle point. The variables satisfy :

$$x_1 + x_2 + x_3 = 1 \qquad\qquad y_1 + y_2 + y_3 = 1$$
$$8x_1 + 4x_2 + 6x_3 \geqslant v \qquad\qquad 8y_1 + 2y_2 + 2y_3 \leqslant v$$
$$2x_1 + x_2 + 5x_3 \geqslant v \qquad\qquad 4y_1 + y_2 + 6y_3 \leqslant v$$
$$2x_1 + 6x_2 \qquad\ \geqslant v \qquad\qquad 6y_1 + 5y_2 \qquad\ \leqslant v$$

Take all relations as equations and solve the block on the left to give :

$$x_1 = -\tfrac{1}{2}, \quad x_2 = \tfrac{3}{4}, \quad x_3 = \tfrac{3}{4}, \quad v = \tfrac{7}{2}$$

which is not admissible since $x_1 < 0$. Next, take one of the relations as a strict inequality. Try $8x_1 + 4x_2 + 6x_3 > \nu$ with which is associated $y_1 = 0$. The equations are now:

$$
\begin{aligned}
x_1 + x_2 + x_3 &= 1 & y_2 + y_3 &= 1 \\
2x_1 + x_2 + 5x_3 &= \nu & 2y_2 + 2y_3 &= \nu \\
2x_1 + 6x_2 &= \nu & y_2 + 6y_3 &= \nu \\
& & 5y_2 &= \nu
\end{aligned}
$$

The last two give $y_2 = \dfrac{\nu}{5}$, $y_3 = \dfrac{2\nu}{15}$, which are not admissible—they do not satisfy the other equations. The equations are not consistent. Any other selection of one relation leads to the same negative result.

Next, take two relations as strict inequalities. The previous attempt suggests that it may be well to try one of the relations in the y's, e.g.

$$
\begin{aligned}
8x_1 + 4x_2 + 6x_3 &> \nu & \text{with} \quad y_1 &= 0 \\
8y_1 + 2y_2 + 2y_3 &< \nu & \text{with} \quad x_1 &= 0
\end{aligned}
$$

The remaining relations, as equations, are:

$$
\begin{aligned}
x_2 + x_3 &= 1 & y_2 + y_3 &= 1 \\
x_2 + 5x_3 &= \nu & y_2 + 6y_3 &= \nu \\
6x_2 &= \nu & 5y_2 &= \nu
\end{aligned}
$$

and these are all consistent with:

$$
x_2 = \tfrac{1}{2}, \quad x_3 = \tfrac{1}{2}, \quad y_2 = \tfrac{3}{5}, \quad y_3 = \tfrac{2}{5}, \quad \nu = 3
$$

Hence, for the original game, the solution is that A has an optimal strategy $(0, \tfrac{1}{2}, \tfrac{1}{2})$ and that B has an optimal strategy $(0, \tfrac{3}{5}, \tfrac{2}{5})$. The value of the game is v, where

$$
\nu = 2(v + 1) = 3
$$

i.e. the value is $v = \tfrac{1}{2}$. The game becomes " fair " if A pays $\tfrac{1}{2}$ to B at each play.

Ex. (c). Player A bets on three horses priced at evens, $2 : 1$ against and $3 : 1$ against. The pay-off matrix is $\begin{bmatrix} 1 & -1 & -1 \\ -1 & 2 & -1 \\ -1 & -1 & 3 \end{bmatrix}$ which can be adjusted by the addition of 1 to each element to:

$$
\mathbf{A} = \begin{bmatrix} 2 & 0 & 0 \\ 0 & 3 & 0 \\ 0 & 0 & 4 \end{bmatrix}
$$

If the value of the original game is v, then the game with matrix $\mathbf{A}$ has the same optimal strategies, and value $(v + 1)$. Writing the relations as equations:

$$
x_1 + x_2 + x_3 = 1, \quad 2x_1 = v + 1, \quad 3x_2 = v + 1, \quad 4x_3 = v + 1
$$

and exactly the same set in the y's. They provide a consistent solution:

$$
x_1 = y_1 = \tfrac{6}{13}, \quad x_2 = y_2 = \tfrac{4}{13}, \quad x_3 = y_3 = \tfrac{3}{13}, \quad v + 1 = \tfrac{12}{13}
$$

The horse-race game has value $v = -\tfrac{1}{13}$; the " punter " loses on balance and the " bookie " wins. To achieve this optimal result, the " punter " must back the horses according to the mixed strategy $(\tfrac{6}{13}, \tfrac{4}{13}, \tfrac{3}{13})$. His best bet is to divide his stake $6 : 4 : 3$ between the runners.

The " authorities " who decide the result of the race know that the chances of the horses winning are also $(\tfrac{6}{13}, \tfrac{4}{13}, \tfrac{3}{13})$. Knowing these $6 : 4 : 3$ chances, they would fix odds at $7 : 6$, $9 : 4$ and $10 : 3$ against if they were going to be perfectly " fair ". The actual odds fixed (evens, $2 : 1$ and $3 : 1$ against) are slightly less favourable, which is what gives the " bookie " his gain.

It is not inevitable that the odds are set in such a way that a negative v results and the " bookie " wins. For example, as Dr. G. Morton has remarked, the call-over prices on the eve of the 1954 Grand National were such that the optimal distribution of a bet would have won 4% of the money staked—and that the " bookies " stood to lose on balance to this extent.

Ex. (d). The pay-off matrix for *two-finger Morra* is
$$\begin{bmatrix} 0 & -3 & 2 & 0 \\ 3 & 0 & 0 & -4 \\ -2 & 0 & 0 & 3 \\ 0 & 4 & -3 & 0 \end{bmatrix}$$

This is skew-symmetric ; the game is fair (value zero) and the two players have the same optimal strategy. This simplifies the relations, which can be written :

$$\begin{aligned} x_1 + x_2 + x_3 + x_4 &= 1 \\ 3x_2 - 2x_3 &\geqslant 0 \\ -3x_1 \qquad\qquad +4x_4 &\geqslant 0 \\ 2x_1 \qquad\qquad -3x_4 &\geqslant 0 \\ -4x_2 + 3x_3 \qquad &\geqslant 0 \end{aligned}$$

The y's are exactly the same as the x's, once these are found from the above five relations in four variables.

The five relations, as equations, can be checked to be inconsistent with a solution for non-negative x's. Next, take one of the relations as a strict inequality. Try $3x_2 - 2x_3 > 0$, so that $y_1 = 0$ and hence (by the symmetry) $x_1 = 0$ also. The relations are then :

$$\begin{aligned} x_2 + x_3 + x_4 &= 1 \\ 4x_4 = -3x_4 &= 0 \\ -4x_2 + 3x_3 &= 0 \end{aligned}$$

which give $x_2 = \frac{3}{7}$, $x_3 = \frac{4}{7}$ and $x_4 = 0$. Hence an optimal strategy for either player is $(0, \frac{3}{7}, \frac{4}{7}, 0)$. It is not, however, a unique solution. Try $-4x_2 + 3x_3 > 0$, so that $y_4 = 0$ and hence $x_4 = 0$ also. The relations are then :

$$\begin{aligned} x_1 + x_2 + x_3 &= 1 \\ 3x_2 - 2x_3 &= 0 \\ -3x_1 = 2x_1 &= 0 \end{aligned}$$

which give $x_1 = 0$, $x_2 = \frac{2}{5}$ and $x_3 = \frac{3}{5}$. Hence. another optimal strategy for each player is $(0, \frac{2}{5}, \frac{3}{5}, 0)$. With two solutions found, it follows that there is an infinite set of solutions, i.e.

$(0, x, 1 - x, 0)$ *is an optimal strategy for any* x *in the range* $\frac{2}{5} \leqslant x \leqslant \frac{3}{7}$.

The result given at the end of 15.8 above can be checked and illustrated. Suppose player A uses the mixed strategy $(0, \frac{29}{70}, \frac{41}{70}, 0)$, which is one of his optimal mixtures. Then if B uses the second or third strategy alone, the game is a draw (the value of the game is zero) :

$$\begin{aligned} -3 \times 0 + 0 \times \tfrac{29}{70} + 0 \times \tfrac{41}{70} + 4 \times 0 &= 0 \\ 2 \times 0 + 0 \times \tfrac{29}{70} + 0 \times \tfrac{41}{70} - 3 \times 0 &= 0 \end{aligned}$$

But if B uses the first or fourth strategy alone, these not being among his optimal mixtures, then A wins :

$$\begin{aligned} 0 \times 0 + 3 \times \tfrac{29}{70} - 2 \times \tfrac{41}{70} + 0 \times 0 &= \tfrac{1}{14} \\ 0 \times 0 - 4 \times \tfrac{29}{70} + 3 \times \tfrac{41}{70} + 0 \times 0 &= \tfrac{1}{10} \end{aligned}$$

Hence, even if A announces what he is going to do (e.g. playing the second and third strategies in proportions 2 : 3), there is nothing B can do about it. If B sticks to the same two strategies, in any proportions whatever, he always forces a draw. Once B strays, and uses either the first or fourth strategies, he loses to A.

The solution of this game is by no means obvious to anyone playing it for the first time. The advice is then useful—that he should play only the second and third strategies (i.e. show two fingers and call one, or show one finger and call two) ; and that he should use the second 14 or 15 times, and the third 21 or 20 times, out of every 35 plays.

Ex. (e).   The Investment Problem, based on Example 16 of Williams (1954).

You have a debt to pay in a year's time and £1,000 to play with now. You consult your broker about investing the sum in three types of shares and he tells you that the year's returns (dividends and capital appreciation together) depend on the estimate made of the economic prospects during the year and are likely to be as set out (in £) in the pay-off matrix :

Prospects :

Shares :	Good	Fair	Bad
Gilt-edged	40	30	20
Armaments	0	100	250
Other industrials	150	50	-50

The question is : how do you play the market for greatest returns?

It is assumed that you work on the minimax principle and allow for the worst that can happen as regards the economic climate. You solve the " game " against the economic forces, given the pay-off matrix. There are eight relations between seven variables, the x's (your proportionate investment), the y's (the chances of the economic climate) and your return v. The solution proceeds according to the technique developed here (see Ex. 5 below). Alternatively, you can notice that the first row of the matrix is dominated by various combinations (e.g. 1 : 1) of the other two rows and can be eliminated to give the matrix :

$$\mathbf{A} = \begin{bmatrix} 0 & 100 & 250 \\ 150 & 50 & -50 \end{bmatrix}$$

The graphical method of solution given in 15.6 above now applies (see Ex. 6 below). By either method, you find that your optimal strategy is $(0, \frac{1}{2}, \frac{1}{2})$ and that the value of the game is £75. You decide, therefore, to invest your £1,000 equally in armament and other industrial shares, and to leave gilt-edged shares alone. If the year turns out to be fair or good, you sell out with a profit of £75. If the year is bad—a " strategy " the economic climate will not play on minimax principles—you gain more, i.e. £100. There are even larger returns possible, £150 gained from other industrials if the year is good and £250 from armament shares if it is bad ; for such returns, however, you need to know or guess what the year will turn out to be. Lacking this information, you invest 50 : 50 and ensure a safe £75 gain.

EXERCISES 15.9

1. Show that the game with the Latin Square $\mathbf{A} = \begin{bmatrix} 1 & 2 & 3 & 4 \\ 2 & 3 & 4 & 1 \\ 3 & 4 & 1 & 2 \\ 4 & 1 & 2 & 3 \end{bmatrix}$ has value $v = \frac{5}{2}$.

2. Extend the result of the previous exercise to show that $\frac{n+1}{2}$ is the value of a game with $\mathbf{A}$ as a Latin Square of order $n \times n$.

3. In two-finger Morra, player A knows that his opponent is using only the second and third strategies and then restricts his play to the same two strategies. Show that the result, a game which is a draw with pay-off matrix $\begin{bmatrix} 0 & 0 \\ 0 & 0 \end{bmatrix}$, is

not inconsistent with the statement that optimal strategies for the players are $(0, x, 1-x, 0)$ for $\frac{2}{5} \leqslant x \leqslant \frac{3}{7}$.

4. Three-finger Morra has a pay-off matrix of order 9×9. Show that an optimal strategy for each player is $(0, 0, \frac{5}{12}, 0, \frac{4}{12}, 0, \frac{3}{12}, 0, 0)$. Interpret and compare with the solution for two-finger Morra.

5. Solve Ex. (e) above from the eight relations between the seven variables.

6. Take the 2×3 matrix **A** of Ex. (e) above and solve the game graphically by the method of 15.6, to give $x : 1 - x = 1 : 1$ as the unique solution.

7. If $\mathbf{A} = \begin{bmatrix} 0 & -1 & -3 & 1 & 3 \\ 1 & 0 & 3 & -3 & -1 \\ -1 & -2 & 3 & 1 & -1 \\ 0 & 3 & -3 & 1 & -1 \end{bmatrix}$, show that for a stable outcome player A

must play his four strategies with equal frequency and that the game is fair. Show further that player B has more than one optimal strategy.

8. The following defines a game with a chance move. An unbiassed coin is tossed (H or T) at move I. Knowing the result, player A calls a number $p = 1, 2$ and B a number $q = 1, 2$ at move II. There is no payment if $p = q$; otherwise A gets $(p + q)$ if H at move I and B gets $(p + q)$ if T at move I. Show that each player has four strategies (r, s) for r and $s = 1, 2$, where r is the call if H, and s if T, at move I, and that the pay-off matrix is :

$$\begin{bmatrix} 0 & \frac{3}{2} & -\frac{3}{2} & 0 \\ \frac{3}{2} & 0 & 0 & -\frac{3}{2} \\ -\frac{3}{2} & 0 & 0 & \frac{3}{2} \\ 0 & -\frac{3}{2} & \frac{3}{2} & 0 \end{bmatrix}$$

Discuss the solution with reference to the similarity with two-finger Morra.

9. Illustrate the possibilities of a game with infinitely many strategies by considering a pay-off function $A(x, y) = 4(x - \frac{1}{2})(\frac{1}{2} - y)$, where A selects x and B selects y, both continuous variables in the range $(0, 1)$. On minimax principles, show that $x = \frac{1}{2}$, $y = \frac{1}{2}$ is an optimal play. Explain how the two-strategy game with pay-off matrix $\begin{bmatrix} -1 & 1 \\ 1 & -1 \end{bmatrix}$ can be regarded as a particular case.

REFERENCES

Kemeny (J. G.), Snell (J. L.) and Thompson (G. L.) (1957) : *Introduction to Finite Mathematics* (Prentice-Hall, 1957), Chapter VI.

Kuhn (H. W.) and Tucker (A. W.) (Editors) (1950, 1953) : *Contributions to the Theory of Games* (Princeton, Vol. I 1950, Vol. II 1953).

Loomis (L. H.) (1946) : " On a Theorem of von Neumann ", *Proceedings National Academy of Sciences, U.S.A.*, **32**, 213–15.

Luce (R. D.) and Raiffa (H.) (1957) : *Games and Decisions* (Wiley, 1957).

McDonald (J.) (1950) : *Strategy in Poker, Business, and War* (Norton, 1950).

McKinsey (J. C. C.) (1952) : *Introduction to the Theory of Games* (McGraw-Hill, 1952).

Neumann (J. von) (1928) : " Zur Theorie der Gesellschaftsspiele ", *Mathematische Annalen*, **100**, 295–320.

Neumann (J. von) and Morgenstern (O.) (1944, 1954) : *Theory of Games and Economic Behaviour* (Princeton, First Ed. 1944 ; Third Ed. 1954).

Vajda (S.) (1956) : *The Theory of Games and Linear Programming* (Methuen, 1956).

Wald (A.) (1950) : *Statistical Decision Functions* (Wiley, 1950).

Williams (J. D.) (1954) : *The Compleat Strategyst* (McGraw-Hill, 1954).

CHAPTER 16

LINEAR PROGRAMMING

16.1 A Simple Example of Linear Programming

CONSIDER the problem of nutrition in its economic aspects, as in Stigler (1945). A consumer buys a range of foods : bread, meat, milk and so on. In determining his purchases, e.g. given prices on the market and his income, his " preferences " for the various foods are taken into account, as in the usual theory of consumer behaviour. What are these "preferences "? In part, they are his tastes in food and his habits (and those of his neighbours) in consumption. But, in part, they may also be an expression of his nutritional needs in terms of calories, protein, vitamins, and so on.

Only the nutritional aspect is considered here ; there is no reference to the fact that the consumer may buy (e.g.) butter rather than margarine because he prefers the taste or because the Jones' buy butter. The problem is one of *transformation* : the foods bought at market prices are transformed into intake of nutrients. There are two sides to the problem : the consumers' diet is specified as to aggregate content of calories, grammes of protein, and so on ; foods are then bought at given market prices to minimise the cost of achieving the given nutritional content. The given technical data of the problem consist of the specification of the nutrients in one unit of each food ; this is a transformation function, here assumed to be a set of constant coefficients. With the given data, the standard diet can be achieved in all kinds of ways by buying foods in various quantities. A *feasible solution* of the problem is any such set of purchases. The problem is then resolved, and an *optimum feasible solution* obtained, if the set of purchases for smallest cost is found.

A simple example has two foods, X_1 (bread) and X_2 (cheese), each containing two nutrients, measured in calories and grammes of protein. The given data comprise the following. The nutrient contents of the foods are 1,000 calories and 25 gr. of protein per lb. of bread, 2,000 calories and 100 gr. of protein per lb. of cheese. The standard diet to be achieved (at least) is 3,000 calories and 100 gr. of protein per day. The market prices are 6d. per lb. of bread, 1s. 9d. per lb. of cheese. In convenient units (1,000 calories, 25 grammes of protein, 1 lb. of bread or cheese), the data can be tabled :

| | One unit of | | Requirements |
	X_1	X_2	
Price (d. per unit)	6	21	
Calories (1,000)	1	2	3
Protein (25 gr.)	1	4	4

The statement of the problem is then as follows :

To find purchases, x_1 and x_2 lb. per day, such that :

$$\left. \begin{array}{c} z = 6x_1 + 21x_2 = \text{min.} \\ x_1 + 2x_2 \geqslant 3 \\ x_1 + 4x_2 \geqslant 4 \\ x_1 \geqslant 0 \quad x_2 \geqslant 0 \end{array} \right\} \quad \text{................}(1)$$

subject to

The cost (d. per day) to be minimised is z, a linear function of the variables x_1 and x_2. The side relations are inequalities expressing the requirement that the given diet must be at least achieved. Only non-negative values of the variables are admissible.

This is a problem in linear programming. It is doubly linear : a *linear* function of non-negative variables is to be minimised subject to *linear* inequalities. Because of the inequalities, the solution is to be sought by means other than the calculus of restrained minima. Indeed, the calculus does not help even if the side relations of (1) are written as equations :

$$\left. \begin{array}{c} z = 6x_1 + 21x_2 = \text{min.} \\ x_1 + 2x_2 = 3 \text{ and } x_1 + 4x_2 = 4 \end{array} \right\} \quad \text{................}(2)$$

subject to

The difficulty is that (2) contains too much ; any two of the three conditions provides a " solution ". For example, the minimum of z can be found subject to one side relation : $x_1 + 2x_2 = 3$. Substitute $x_1 = 3 - 2x_2$:

$$z = 6x_1 + 21x_2 = 18 + 9x_2$$

which is a minimum (for non-negative x_2) when $x_2 = 0$ and so $x_1 = 3$. Hence, buying 3 lbs. of bread and no cheese gives a minimum cost of 18d. per day. This " solution " achieves the calories requirement of 3,000 calories (the side relation used), but not the protein requirement of 100 gr., as can be easily checked (only 75 gr. obtained). On the other hand, the two side relations themselves give a " solution ". From $x_1 + 2x_2 = 3$ and $x_1 + 4x_2 = 4$ is obtained $x_1 = 2$ and $x_2 = \frac{1}{2}$. This " solution " achieves both nutritional requirements but it ignores the cost of the diet altogether.

A graphical solution of the linear programme (1) is possible in this

simple case.   In the plane Ox_1x_2 of Fig. 60, AA' is the line $x_1 + 2x_2 = 3$
and BB' is the line $x_1 + 4x_2 = 4$.   The inequalities of (1) show that feasible

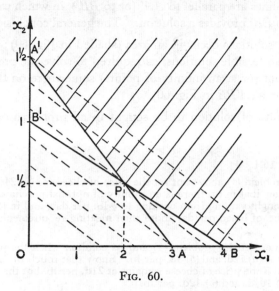

FIG. 60.

solutions are points (x_1, x_2) in the shaded area of Fig. 60.   It remains to
select the point of the shaded area with minimum cost.   Insert the constant cost lines, shown broken in Fig. 60 :

$$6x_1 + 21x_2 = \text{constant } (z)$$

These are parallel lines (slope $-\frac{2}{7}$ to Ox_1) and the cost diminishes as the
lines move nearer to O.   Hence the minimum cost occurs at P where AA'
and BB' intersect.   The solution (optimum feasible) is :

$$x_1 = 2 \qquad x_2 = \tfrac{1}{2} \qquad z = 22\tfrac{1}{2} \text{ (min.)}$$

If 2 lb. of bread and $\frac{1}{2}$ lb. of cheese are bought daily, the nutrient requirements are met and the cost is a minimum at $22\frac{1}{2}$d. per day.

It happens in this case that the solution meets the requirements of
nutrients exactly and that both foods are bought.   This coincidence
depends on the fact that the slope of the constant cost lines is intermediate
between those of AA' and BB'.   If the prices were changed, or if the
nutrient contents of the two foods were different, the constant cost lines
may no longer lie between AA' and BB' in slope.   Various cases are
explored in Ex. 1–3 below.

It is clear that the solution may occur at B in Fig. 60 (e.g. if cheese is
dear) or at A' (e.g. if bread is dear) and one requirement can be more

than met. It also appears that there are cases where an infinite number of solutions exist. Prices and nutrient contents may be such that the constant cost lines are parallel to AA' (or to BB'), in which case any point on $A'P$ (or on PB) provides a solution. The general conclusions are that :

   (i) feasible solutions occur in an area (shaded in Fig. 60) ;

  (ii) optimum feasible solutions, as required to solve the problem, occur at a point (or at an infinity of points) somewhere on the boundary of the area ($A'PB$ in Fig. 60).

This is the kind of solution to be sought in all problems of linear programming.

EXERCISES 16.1

1. Take the problem (1) above but set the price of cheese as (a) 24d. and (b) 30d. per lb. Show that in (a) there is an infinity of optimal purchases, the amount of cheese bought varying from nothing to $\frac{1}{2}$ lb. per day, and in (b) no cheese is bought, 4 lbs. of bread per day more than meeting requirements at minimum cost.

2. Similarly interpret the problem (1) and its solution when the price of cheese is set as low as (a) 12d. and (b) 9d. per lb. Show that much the same solutions are obtained if the price of cheese remains at 21d. per lb. but the price of bread is put at (a) $10\frac{1}{2}$d. and (b) 12d. per lb.

3. Express the problem (1) when the prices are p_1 and p_2 respectively, fixed but not specified. Show that, at the optimum, only bread is bought if $p_1 < \frac{1}{4}p_2$ and only cheese if $p_1 > \frac{1}{2}p_2$. Show that botn are bought if $\frac{1}{4}p_2 < p_1 < \frac{1}{2}p_2$ and that there are multiple solutions if $p_1 = \frac{1}{4}p_2$ or $\frac{1}{2}p_2$.

4. Show that the same range of possibilities arises, as in the previous exercise, if the nutrients contents of the foods are changed, instead of the food prices.

5. Take the nutrient problem of the text, with two foods (bread and cheese) but add carbohydrate as a third nutrient in the requirements. The carbohydrates requirement is 400 gr. per day. The content of bread is 250 gr. and of cheese 50 gr. of carbohydrate per lb. Write the new linear programme for minimum cost of diet and solve graphically. Compare with the two-nutrient solution of the text. Show that, in the graph, the boundary of feasible purchases of the foods may be defined by one line, by two or by all three according to the technical constants. If one line is not used in defining the boundary show that the corresponding nutrient requirement is automatically met by any feasible purchases.

6. Again take the nutrient problem of the text, keep the two nutrients but add a third food (say minced meat or macaroni) available to meet nutrient requirements. The food contains 2,000 calories, 75 gr. of protein and costs 18d. per lb. Write the linear programme for minimum cost of diet ; what form does the diagrammatic or graphical solution now take?

7. The following is a simple version of one type of shipping (transportation) problem, discussed in Koopmans (1951). The variables are the number of ships per month sailing between two ports P and Q : x_1 with cargo both ways, x_2 with cargo P to Q returning empty, x_3 empty P to Q returning with cargo, x_4 empty both ways. The times in months taken on the four types of round

trips are t_1, t_2, t_3, and t_4. The requirement is that the monthly cargo to be moved is b_1 from P to Q and b_2 from Q to P (measured in shiploads). The problem is to minimise the fleet z employed in the traffic between the ports. Show that non-negative x's are to be found such that :

$$z = t_1 x_1 + t_2 x_2 + t_3 x_3 + t_4 x_4 = \min$$

subject to
$$x_1 + x_2 \geqslant b_1$$
$$x_1 + x_3 \geqslant b_2$$

What is the significance of the " $\geqslant$ " in the side relations ; can they be replaced by " $=$ " without loss of generality? What is the use of x_4 ; can it be put zero?

8. A simple case of another shipping problem is to tranship a homogeneous product from two ports P_1 and P_2 to two other ports Q_1 and Q_2 at minimum cost. The total shipments available are a_1 at P_1 and a_2 at P_2 ; they are required to be delivered b_1 to Q_1 and b_2 to Q_2. The variable x's are the amounts shipped between ports :

	Shipped to		Total
	Q_1	Q_2	
Shipped from P_1	x_{11}	x_{12}	a_1
P_2	x_{21}	x_{22}	a_2
Total	b_1	b_2	$a_1 + a_2$ $= b_1 + b_2$

The costs of shipment are c_{rs} ($r, s = 1, 2$) per unit of product for the various routes. Show that non-negative x's are sought such that :

$$z = \sum_r \sum_s c_{rs} x_{rs} = \min$$

subject to
$$\sum_s x_{rs} = a_r \quad (r = 1, 2)$$
$$\sum_r x_{rs} = b_s \quad (s = 1, 2)$$

Show that one of the four side equations can be eliminated as dependent on the others.

16.2 Simple Example : Dual Problem

The nutrition problem of 16.1 is a minimum one. In the simple case :

$$\left. \begin{aligned} z = 6x_1 + 21x_2 = \min \\ x_1 + 2x_2 \geqslant 3 \\ x_1 + 4x_2 \geqslant 4 \\ x_1 \geqslant 0 \quad x_2 \geqslant 0 \end{aligned} \right\} \quad \dots\dots\dots\dots\dots(1)$$

subject to

In terms of formal algebra, a minimum problem of this kind always has a *dual*—a corresponding maximum problem. To write the dual is an important step ; certainly it is not obvious. The dual of (1) is written as follows. A diet comprising 3,000 calories and 100 gr. of protein per day is to be obtained by buying bread and cheese. Take units (1,000 calories, 25 gr. protein) as before and let ξ_1 and ξ_2 be the values (in d. per unit) of the two nutrients. The total (imputed) value of the diet is

$\zeta = 3\xi_1 + 4\xi_2$; attempt to maximise ζ. But the amount spent per lb. of each food cannot exceed its market price (6d. for bread, 21d. for cheese). For bread, with 1,000 calories and 25 gr. protein per lb., the expenditure per lb. is $\xi_1 + \xi_2$ which cannot exceed 6d. per lb. For cheese, similarly, expenditure is $2\xi_1 + 4\xi_2 \leqslant 21$d. per lb. The *dual problem* is:

To find values, ξ_1 and ξ_2, such that

subject to

$$\left.\begin{aligned} \zeta = 3\xi_1 + 4\xi_2 &= \text{max.} \\ \xi_1 + \xi_2 &\leqslant 6 \\ 2\xi_1 + 4\xi_2 &\leqslant 21 \\ \xi_1 \geqslant 0 \quad \xi_2 &\geqslant 0 \end{aligned}\right\} \quad \dots\dots\dots\dots\dots\dots(2)$$

The problem of nutrition has dual forms (1) and (2). The relation between them is both simple and easily generalised to linear programmes of all kinds. In (1), z is minimum and the side relations are " $\geqslant$ "; in (2), ζ is maximum and the side relations are " $\leqslant$ ". Both contain the matrix $\begin{bmatrix} 1 & 2 \\ 1 & 4 \end{bmatrix}$ of technical coefficients (nutrient content of foods), but in (2) it is transposed in the side relations as compared with (1). In (1), the prices (6, 21) appear in the minimised function and the requirements (3, 4) in the side relations ; in (2), they appear in opposite places.

It remains to show that the dual problems have the same solution in the sense that min. z of (1) equals max. ζ of (2). The solution of (1) is :

$$x_1 = 2 \quad x_2 = \tfrac{1}{2} \quad z = 22\tfrac{1}{2} \quad \text{(min. cost of diet)}$$

The solution of (2) can be obtained in the same way, graphically as in Ex. 1 below, and it is found to be :

$$\xi_1 = \tfrac{3}{2} \quad \xi_2 = \tfrac{9}{2} \quad \zeta = 22\tfrac{1}{2} \quad \text{(max. value of diet)}$$

The same expenditure of $22\tfrac{1}{2}$d. per day is obtained whether through optimal purchases of 2 lbs. of bread and $\tfrac{1}{2}$ lb. of cheese, or through optimal valuation of $1\tfrac{1}{2}$d. per 1,000 calories and $4\tfrac{1}{2}$d. per 25 gr. of protein.

All this is formal algebra. The problem and its dual must also have economic interpretations ; indeed, the fact of an economic duality is easily seen in general terms. In allocating limited resources in production, a cost function arises when a given output is produced at *minimum* cost in the prices of resources, or equally when a given amount is spent on *maximum* output. Allocation of resources and their pricing are dual aspects of the same problem. If the resources happen to have no market prices, it is necessary to invent them, to write imputed or accounting prices. This is the clue to follow up.

The problem (1) seeks the minimum cost of foods at given market prices—with restraints on given nutrient requirements. There is no pricing of nutrients, though these (rather than the foods) are basic. Now introduce imputed prices of nutrients : ξ_1 d. per 1,000 calories and ξ_2 d. per 25 gr. protein. The dual problem (2) then arises : the maximum imputed value of the given nutrient diet—with restraints that expenditures per unit on foods cannot exceed given market prices. The aim of the original problem is to get the goods with lowest cost, given nutrient requirements. The aim of the dual problem is to get the diet of highest value in nutrients, given market prices of foods.

EXERCISES 16.2

1. Solve the dual problem (2) by the graphical method Fig. 60 and indicate the main differences in the geometry of the method.

2. Vary the prices in the problem (2) and examine the changes in the solution in graphical terms, as in 16.1, Ex. 1–3.

3. Write and interpret the dual problem of 16.1, Ex. 6. Solve the dual graphically in two dimensions and show that the addition of the third food adds nothing to the problem of Ex. 1 above.

4. Explain why the dual problem of 16.1, Ex. 5, cannot be solved graphically in two dimensions. Show that it is similar to the original problem of 16.1, Ex. 6.

5. Show that the dual shipping problem to that of 16.1, Ex. 7, is : to find non-negative ξ_1 and ξ_2 such that
$$\zeta = b_1\xi_1 + b_2\xi_2 = \max.$$
subject to $\quad \xi_1 + \xi_2 \leqslant t_1 \quad \xi_1 \leqslant t_2 \quad \text{and} \quad \xi_2 \leqslant t_3$
Interpret this dual problem.

16.3 Reduction to the Solution of a Game

The nutrition problem of two foods and two nutrients can be written with arbitrary constants for the given elements of the problem. The dual problems are then based on the given data :

	One unit of		Requirements
	X_1	X_2	
Price (d. per unit)	p_1	p_2	
Calories (units)	a_{11}	a_{12}	b_1
Protein (units)	a_{21}	a_{22}	b_2

They can be expressed :

$$\begin{aligned} z = p_1 x_1 + p_2 x_2 = \min. \qquad && \zeta = b_1\xi_1 + b_2\xi_2 = \max. \\ \text{subject to} \quad a_{11}x_1 + a_{12}x_2 \geqslant b_1 \qquad && \text{subject to} \quad a_{11}\xi_1 + a_{21}\xi_2 \leqslant p_1 \\ a_{21}x_1 + a_{22}x_2 \geqslant b_2 \qquad && a_{12}\xi_1 + a_{22}\xi_2 \leqslant p_2 \\ x_1 \geqslant 0 \quad x_2 \geqslant 0 \qquad && \xi_1 \geqslant 0 \quad \xi_2 \geqslant 0 \end{aligned} \qquad \Bigg\} \dots(1)$$

Feasible solutions, for the x's and ξ's, satisfy the inequalities of (1); the optimum feasible solution also satisfies the maximum or minimum condition.

Consider a two-person zero-sum game with a 5×5 pay-off matrix:

$$\begin{bmatrix} 0 & 0 & a_{11} & a_{21} & -p_1 \\ 0 & 0 & a_{12} & a_{22} & -p_2 \\ -a_{11} & -a_{12} & 0 & 0 & b_1 \\ -a_{21} & -a_{22} & 0 & 0 & b_2 \\ p_1 & p_2 & -b_1 & -b_2 & 0 \end{bmatrix} \quad \dots\dots\dots\dots(2)$$

Since this is skew-symmetric, it follows from 15.7 above that the value of the game is zero and that the same mixed strategy $y = (y_1, y_2, y_3, y_4, y_5)$ is optimal for each player. Then by Property (ii) of 15.7:

$$\left. \begin{array}{ll} \text{(i)} & a_{11}y_3 + a_{21}y_4 - p_1 y_5 \leqslant 0 \\ \text{(ii)} & a_{12}y_3 + a_{22}y_4 - p_2 y_5 \leqslant 0 \\ \text{(iii)} \quad -a_{11}y_1 - a_{12}y_2 & + b_1 y_5 \leqslant 0 \\ \text{(iv)} \quad -a_{21}y_1 - a_{22}y_2 & + b_2 y_5 \leqslant 0 \\ \text{(v)} \quad p_1 y_1 + p_2 y_2 - b_1 y_3 - b_2 y_4 & \leqslant 0 \end{array} \right\} \quad \dots\dots\dots\dots(3)$$

The zero values on the right-hand side arise because the game has zero value.

Assume $y_5 \neq 0$. Then, by Property (iii) of 15.7, an inequality ($<$) in (v) of (3) would imply that $y_5 = 0$ for both players. Hence this relation is an equation

$$\text{(v)} \quad p_1 y_1 + p_2 y_2 - b_1 y_3 - b_2 y_4 = 0$$

Write $x_1 = \dfrac{y_1}{y_5}$, $x_2 = \dfrac{y_2}{y_5}$, $\xi_1 = \dfrac{y_3}{y_5}$, and $\xi_2 = \dfrac{y_4}{y_5}$ so that (3) becomes:

(i) $a_{11}\xi_1 + a_{21}\xi_2 \leqslant p_1$

(ii) $a_{12}\xi_1 + a_{22}\xi_2 \leqslant p_2$

(iii) $a_{11}x_1 + a_{12}x_2 \geqslant b_1$

(iv) $a_{21}x_1 + a_{22}x_2 \geqslant b_2$

(v) $p_1 x_1 + p_2 x_2 = b_1 \xi_1 + b_2 \xi_2$

Here, (i)–(iv) are the side relations of the linear programme and its dual as in (1) above. Since the y's of a mixed strategy are essentially non-negative, so are the x's and ξ's, as also required in (1) above. All that remains, to complete the relation between the linear programme (1) and the game (2), is to find the significance of (v).

Write $z = p_1 x_1 + p_2 x_2$ and $\zeta = b_1 \xi_1 + b_2 \xi_2$ for *any* strategies adopted by the two players, not necessarily optimal. Then (v) states that $z = \zeta$ when the strategies are optimal. It is reasonable to suppose that, when the strategies are *not* optimal, then z becomes greater than ζ, or that z becomes greater than (or at least equal to) its optimal (i.e. minimum) value and ζ becomes less than (or at least equal to) its optimal (i.e. maximum) value. This is, in fact, the case but it is not easily established formally (see 16.4 and 16.5 below). If it is accepted, then (v) is to be interpreted as follows. At the optimal strategy of the game, $z = p_1 x_1 + p_2 x_2$ attains a minimum value and $\zeta = b_1 \xi_1 + b_2 \xi_2$ attains a maximum value, the two being equal.

Hence, the game (2) has a solution which comprehends both the solution of the linear programme and that of its dual, as in (1). The result is:

The game with pay-off matrix (2) *has an optimum solution*

$$(y_1, y_2, y_3, y_4, y_5).$$

If $y_5 \neq 0$, *then* $x_1 = \dfrac{y_1}{y_5}$ *and* $x_2 = \dfrac{y_2}{y_5}$ *is the solution of the linear programme*

(1), *and* $\xi_1 = \dfrac{y_3}{y_5}$ *and* $\xi_2 = \dfrac{y_4}{y_5}$ *is the solution of the dual problem.*

In the problems (1) the minimum of z is the same as the maximum of ζ. Two things are here achieved. The linear programme and its dual are shown to have the same solution. Either is to be obtained from the solution of a game with a particular pay-off matrix.

For this result, y_5 must be non-zero. If $y_5 = 0$, the game (2) still has a solution, but the linear programme and its dual have no solution. The only difference this makes to the result obtained is to add the statement that the problems (1) either have the same solution or no solution at all.

Ex. In the nutrition case of 16.1 and 16.2, the linear programme and its dual take the following numerical form for non-negative x's and ξ's:

$$\left. \begin{array}{ll} z = 6x_1 + 21x_2 = \min. & \zeta = 3\xi_1 + 4\xi_2 = \max. \\ x_1 + 2x_2 \geqslant 3 & \xi_1 + \xi_2 \leqslant 6 \\ x_1 + 4x_2 \geqslant 4 & 2\xi_1 + 4\xi_2 \leqslant 21 \end{array} \right\} \quad \ldots\ldots\ldots\ldots\ldots(4)$$

The corresponding game has a pay-off matrix

$$\begin{bmatrix} 0 & 0 & 1 & 1 & -6 \\ 0 & 0 & 2 & 4 & -21 \\ -1 & -2 & 0 & 0 & 3 \\ -1 & -4 & 0 & 0 & 4 \\ 6 & 21 & -3 & -4 & 0 \end{bmatrix} \quad \ldots\ldots\ldots\ldots\ldots\ldots\ldots(5)$$

The solution of (4) is to be obtained from (5) or conversely. All that needs to be done is to associate the optimal strategy y_1, y_2, y_3, y_4, y_5 of (5) with the x's and the ξ's of (4):

$$x_1 = \frac{y_1}{y_5} \quad x_2 = \frac{y_2}{y_5} \quad \xi_1 = \frac{y_3}{y_5} \quad \xi_2 = \frac{y_4}{y_5}$$

Both ways of solving can be illustrated in this simple case.

First, as in 16.1 and 16.2, graphical methods solve (4) to give

$$x_1 = 2 \quad x_2 = \tfrac{1}{2} \quad \xi_1 = \tfrac{3}{2} \quad \xi_2 = \tfrac{9}{2}$$

and
$$\text{min. } z = \text{max. } \zeta = 22\tfrac{1}{2}$$

Hence the solution of the game (5) is such that

$$y_1 : y_2 : y_3 : y_4 : y_5 = 2 : \tfrac{1}{2} : \tfrac{3}{2} : \tfrac{9}{2} : 1$$

To get the actual y's, it is only necessary to " scale up " so that the y's add to 1 (an essential feature of strategies). It is easily found that multiplication by $\tfrac{2}{19}$ does this. Hence the solution of (5) is the mixed strategy $(\tfrac{4}{19}, \tfrac{1}{19}, \tfrac{3}{19}, \tfrac{9}{19}, \tfrac{2}{19})$; the value is zero.

Second, the method of 15.8 above solves (5). If $(y_1, y_2, y_3, y_4, y_5)$ is an optimal strategy (for each player), the value of the game being zero, then

$$
\begin{aligned}
y_1 + y_2 + y_3 + y_4 + y_5 &= 1 \\
y_3 + y_4 - 6y_5 &\leqslant 0 \\
2y_3 + 4y_4 - 21y_5 &\leqslant 0 \\
-y_1 - 2y_2 \qquad\quad + 3y_5 &\leqslant 0 \\
-y_1 - 4y_2 \qquad\quad + 4y_5 &\leqslant 0 \\
6y_1 + 21y_2 - 3y_3 - 4y_4 \quad &\leqslant 0
\end{aligned}
$$

Try all equals signs, all the y's being positive. In this instance, this turns the trick. Solving the second and third equations gives

$$y_3 : y_4 : y_5 = \tfrac{3}{2} : \tfrac{9}{2} : 1$$

Solving the fourth and fifth equation gives

$$y_1 : y_2 : y_5 = 2 : \tfrac{1}{2} : 1$$

Substitution in the first equation then gives the y's, i.e. $(\tfrac{4}{19}, \tfrac{1}{19}, \tfrac{3}{19}, \tfrac{9}{19}, \tfrac{2}{19})$. If this is the solution of (5) it must satisfy the last equation ; it is easily checked that it does so. Hence (5) is solved. The solutions of (1) then follow

$$x_1 = 2 \quad x_2 = \tfrac{1}{2} \quad \xi_1 = \tfrac{3}{2} \quad \xi_2 = \tfrac{9}{2}$$

The first two give min. $z = 22\tfrac{1}{2}$; the others give max. $\zeta = 22\tfrac{1}{2}$.

EXERCISES 16.3

1. Write the problem of 16.1, Ex. 5, with arbitrary constants

$$
\begin{aligned}
z = \quad & p_1 x_1 + p_2 x_2 = \text{min.} \\
& a_{11}x_1 + a_{12}x_2 \geqslant b_1 \\
& a_{21}x_1 + a_{22}x_2 \geqslant b_2 \\
& a_{31}x_1 + a_{32}x_2 \geqslant b_3
\end{aligned}
$$

Then write the dual problem with the same set of constants. In the example of the text the matrix of a's is square ; here it is rectangular. What difference does this make to the symmetry of problem and dual?

2. Write the pay-off matrix of the game which corresponds to the problem in linear programming of the previous exercise. Show that it is of order 6×6. Why is it still square even though the matrix of a's is rectangular?

3. Obtain the solution of the game of the previous exercise when the coefficients are numerical, as in 16.1, Ex. 5. Hence check the solution of the linear programme of 16.1, Ex. 5. Find also the solution of the dual problem and compare with 16.2, Ex. 4, where graphical methods were not possible.

4. Take the problem of 16.1, Ex. 6. Write it and its dual with arbitrary constants and then find the pay-off matrix of the corresponding game. Show that the latter is similar to the matrix of Ex. 2 above.

16.4 A General Linear Programme and its Dual

The nutrition problem of two nutrients and two foods, as in 16.3 above, can be generalised to the case of m nutrients and n foods. It is then in a general form covering a range of linear programmes of various economic and other interpretations. For simple accounts, see Dorfman, Samuelson and Solow (1958), and Kemeny, Snell and Thompson (1957).

A general linear programming problem and its dual are:

(i)
$$z = p_1 x_1 + p_2 x_2 + \ldots + p_n x_n = \min.$$

subject to
$$a_{11} x_1 + a_{12} x_2 + \ldots + a_{1n} x_n \geqslant b_1$$
$$a_{21} x_1 + a_{22} x_2 + \ldots + a_{2n} x_n \geqslant b_2$$
$$\ldots\ldots\ldots\ldots\ldots\ldots\ldots\ldots\ldots\ldots$$
$$a_{m1} x_1 + a_{m2} x_2 + \ldots + a_{mn} x_n \geqslant b_m$$
$$x_1 \geqslant 0 \quad x_2 \geqslant 0 \quad \ldots \quad x_n \geqslant 0$$

(ii)
$$\zeta = b_1 \xi_1 + b_2 \xi_2 + \ldots + b_m \xi_m = \max.$$

subject to
$$a_{11} \xi_1 + a_{21} \xi_2 + \ldots + a_{m1} \xi_m \leqslant p_1$$
$$a_{12} \xi_1 + a_{22} \xi_2 + \ldots + a_{m2} \xi_m \leqslant p_2$$
$$\ldots\ldots\ldots\ldots\ldots\ldots\ldots\ldots\ldots\ldots$$
$$a_{1n} \xi_1 + a_{2n} \xi_2 + \ldots + a_{mn} \xi_m \leqslant p_n$$
$$\xi_1 \geqslant 0 \quad \xi_2 \geqslant 0 \quad \ldots \quad \xi_m \geqslant 0$$

The nutritional problem is merely one application or example; the a's are then the technical relations between m nutrients and n foods, the b's are the m nutrient requirements, the p's are n food prices, the x's are the variable purchases and z is cost to be minimised. In different problems, these constants and variables have other interpretations.

The statement of the linear programme is shorter in terms of matrix algebra:

$$z = \mathbf{p}'\mathbf{x} = \min. \qquad\qquad \zeta = \mathbf{b}'\boldsymbol{\xi} = \max.$$

subject to $\quad \mathbf{Ax} \geqslant \mathbf{b} \qquad$ subject to $\quad \mathbf{A}'\boldsymbol{\xi} \leqslant \mathbf{p}$

and $\qquad \mathbf{x} \geqslant \mathbf{0} \qquad\qquad$ and $\qquad \boldsymbol{\xi} \geqslant \mathbf{0}$

In this formulation, the given elements are:

$\mathbf{A} = [a_{rs}]$ a matrix of technical coefficients of order $m \times n$

$\mathbf{b} = \{b_r\}$ a vector of order m

$\mathbf{p} = \{p_s\}$ a vector of order n

$\left(\begin{matrix} r = 1, 2, \ldots m \\ s = 1, 2, \ldots n \end{matrix} \right)$

The transposes of these are $\mathbf{A}'$, $\mathbf{b}'$ and $\mathbf{p}'$.

The solution is in the vector $\mathbf{x}$ of order n, or the vector $\boldsymbol{\xi}$ of order m, according as the problem or its dual is taken. Feasible solutions satisfy the inequalities ; an optimum feasible solution also satisfies the maximum (or minimum) condition. In the particular application to the nutrition problem, the solution is the vector $\mathbf{x}$ of purchases to minimise the cost of the foods, or the vector $\boldsymbol{\xi}$ of imputed nutrient prices to maximise the imputed value of the diet.

It is reasonable to expect, in the light of the analysis of the simple example in 16.3 above, that the problem and its dual have the same solution, i.e. that min. z and max. ζ are the same thing. This is so, provided that the possibility of no solution is ruled out. The basic result, the *Duality Theorem*, is :

> *The linear programme and its dual have either a common solution or no solution at all.*

A formal proof is by no means easy ; it has been no more than illustrated in a particularly simple case in 16.3 above. One proof is given by Gale, Kuhn and Tucker in Koopmans (1951), Chapter XIX ; this proof is developed in connection with the theory of games and it is framed in terms of linear programming problems of even wider scope than those considered here. Another proof is given by Charnes in Charnes, Cooper and Henderson (1953), Lecture VIII ; it makes use of the work of Dantzig and the Simplex Method (16.8 below). Perhaps the simplest of the available proofs is that given by Danø (1958).

16.5 Equivalence of General Linear Programmes and Two-Person Zero-Sum Games

The results of 16.3, where a simple linear programme was reduced to the solution of a particular game, can now be generalised. The development is based on that given by Dantzig in Koopmans (1951), Chapter XX, and it assumes the Duality Theorem stated above. The result is :

> *A given linear programme, $z = \mathbf{p}'\mathbf{x} = min$, subject to $\mathbf{Ax} \geqslant \mathbf{b}$ and $\mathbf{x} \geqslant 0$, and its dual problem, $\zeta = \mathbf{b}'\boldsymbol{\xi} = max$, subject to $\mathbf{A}'\boldsymbol{\xi} \leqslant \mathbf{p}$ and $\boldsymbol{\xi} \geqslant 0$, can be together reduced to a particular two-person zero-sum game. Conversely, a two-person zero-sum game can be expressed in the form of a particular linear programming problem.*

First, the direct result can be proved. Assume that a solution of the linear programme exists so that min. z and max. ξ have a common value M. Feasible values of the x's and ξ's satisfy the double set of inequalities :

$$\mathbf{Ax} \geqslant \mathbf{b} \quad \text{and} \quad \mathbf{A}'\boldsymbol{\xi} \leqslant \mathbf{p}$$

In full:

$$a_{11}\,x_1+a_{12}\,x_2+\ldots+a_{1n}\,x_n\geqslant b_1 \qquad a_{11}\xi_1+a_{21}\xi_2+\ldots+a_{m1}\xi_m\leqslant p_1$$
$$a_{21}\,x_1+a_{22}\,x_2+\ldots+a_{2n}x_n\geqslant b_2 \qquad a_{12}\xi_1+a_{22}\xi_2+\ldots+a_{m2}\xi_m\leqslant p_2 \Bigg\}\ \ldots(1)$$
$$a_{m1}x_1+a_{m2}x_2+\ldots+a_{mn}x_n\geqslant b_m \qquad a_{1n}\xi_1+a_{2n}\xi_2+\ldots+a_{mn}\xi_m\leqslant p_n$$

The optimum feasible values also make $z=\zeta=M$. Hence $z-\zeta=0$:

$$p_1x_1+p_2x_2+\ldots+p_nx_n-(b_1\xi_1+b_2\xi_2+\ldots+b_n\xi_n)=0 \ \ldots\ldots\ldots(2)$$

Arrange (1) with a " dummy " variable u (equal to unity) so that zero values appear on the right-hand sides and with the inequalities all " $\leqslant$ ". Then (1) and (2) together form the system :

$$a_{11}\xi_1+a_{21}\xi_2+\ldots+a_{m1}\xi_m-p_1u\leqslant 0$$
$$a_{12}\xi_1+a_{22}\xi_2+\ldots+a_{m2}\xi_m-p_2u\leqslant 0$$
$$a_{1n}\xi_1+a_{2n}\xi_2+\ldots+a_{mn}\xi_m-p_nu\leqslant 0$$
$$-a_{11}\,x_1-a_{12}\,x_2-\ldots-a_{1n}\,x_n \qquad\qquad +b_1u\leqslant 0$$
$$-a_{21}\,x_1-a_{22}\,x_2-\ldots-a_{2n}\,x_n \qquad\qquad +b_2u\leqslant 0 \Bigg\}\ \ldots(3)$$
$$-a_{m1}x_1-a_{m2}x_2-\ldots-a_{mn}x_n \qquad\qquad +b_mu\leqslant 0$$
$$p_1x_1+\ p_2x_2+\ldots+\ p_nx_n-\quad b_1\xi_1\ -b_2\xi_2\quad -\ldots-b_m\xi_m \qquad =0$$

By Property (ii) of 15.7 above, (3) implies that

$$(x_1,\,x_2,\,\ldots\,x_n,\,\xi_1,\,\xi_2,\,\ldots\,\xi_m,\,u) \ \ldots\ldots\ldots\ldots\ldots\ldots(4)$$

is proportional to an optimal strategy of the game with skew-symmetric pay-off matrix :

$$\begin{bmatrix} 0 & a_{sr} & -p_s \\ -a_{rs} & 0 & b_r \\ p_s & -b_r & 0 \end{bmatrix}$$

n rows $(s=1,2,\ldots n)$

m rows $(r=1,2,\ldots m)$

1 row

n cols m cols. 1
$(s=1,2,\ r=1,2,$ col.
$\ldots n)\quad \ldots m)$

This particular partitional matrix can be written more shortly :

$$\begin{bmatrix} 0 & \mathbf{A'} & -\mathbf{p} \\ -\mathbf{A} & 0 & \mathbf{b} \\ \mathbf{p'} & -\mathbf{b'} & 0 \end{bmatrix} \ \ldots\ldots\ldots\ldots\ldots\ldots\ldots(5)$$

The value of the game is zero, as shown by the skew-symmetric matrix (5) and the zero values on the right-hand sides of (3). Both players have the same optimal strategy, but (4) is only proportional to it since the elements need to be " scaled up " to add to 1. However, (3) is homogeneous in all variables and the scaling up does not matter. The last relation of (3) is an equality since a solution of (1) is assumed to exist and since $u \neq 0$. Hence, if the linear programme has a solution, then the game with matrix (5) has an optimal strategy with last element non-zero, and the linear programme and game correspond. The limitation can be removed by allowing the linear programme to have no solution and the game to have the last element zero in its optimal strategy. This completes the proof. To summarise : for a given linear programme, the associated game has pay-off matrix (5). The optimal strategy which must exist is given by (4). If $u = 0$, the linear programme has no solution. If $u \neq 0$, (4) can be scaled up to give $u = 1$ and the x's and ξ's are then the solution of the linear programme and its dual.

Second, the converse result can be proved. A given game has pay-off matrix $\mathbf{C} = [c_{rs}]$ of order $m \times n$. If the first (maximising) player adopts a mixed strategy $(z_1, z_2, \dots z_m)$, his expectation is $M = \min\limits_{s} \sum\limits_{r=1}^{m} c_{rs} z_r$ and he wishes to maximise M. Hence $\sum\limits_{r=1}^{m} c_{rs} z_r \geqslant M$ for each s.

So $$\mathbf{C}\mathbf{z} \geqslant M\{1\}$$ in matrix notation

i.e. $$\mathbf{C}\mathbf{x} \geqslant \{1\}$$ with $\mathbf{x} = \dfrac{\mathbf{z}}{M}$

It can always be arranged that $M > 0$ (e.g. by adding a fixed constant to each c_{rs}). The limitations are (i) that $\mathbf{z} \geqslant \mathbf{0}$ and so $\mathbf{x} \geqslant \mathbf{0}$, and (ii) that $\sum\limits_{r=1}^{m} z_r = 1$ and so $\sum\limits_{r=1}^{m} x_r = \dfrac{1}{M}$ or $[1]\mathbf{x} = \dfrac{1}{M}$. When the player maximises M, he plays his optimal strategy. Then $[1]\mathbf{x} = \dfrac{1}{M} = $ minimum. Hence the optimal strategy of the game is given by the vector $\mathbf{x}$ such that

$$\frac{1}{M} = [1]\mathbf{x} = \min.$$

subject to $$\mathbf{C}\mathbf{x} \geqslant \{1\}$$
and $$\mathbf{x} \geqslant \mathbf{0}$$

This is a linear programme with technical matrix $\mathbf{C}$ and with the two given vectors as unit vectors. The optimal strategy of the second (minimising) player leads to another linear programme of the dual type. This completes the proof.

The utility of this result is that a method of solving a game also solves a linear programme, and conversely a method of solving a linear programme also solves a game. Further, as pointed out by Dorfman, Samuelson and Solow (1958), a given game can be expressed as a linear programme which in its turn becomes a game with a skew-symmetric matrix. So any game can be translated into a game with a skew-symmetric matrix, i.e. with value zero and the same optimal strategies for both players. This is a considerable advantage.

It remains to devise a comprehensive method of solving linear programmes (and games). Such a process is the Simplex Method, essentially a method of practical computation by iteration and it is designed to be used with automatic computing machines. It is only one of several possible computational methods, see Koopmans (1951), but it is perhaps the best to be used so far.

The equivalence of problems in game theory and in linear programming is one of formal algebra, serving to widen the possibilities of solution of either problem. It is not necessarily an equivalence in interpretation. When two players engage in a game, they are *not* solving linear programming problems. When a linear programme, such as the nutrition problem, is set up, this does *not* imply that two players are playing a game. It is true that, in the nutrition problem, the consumer may be regarded as a " player " minimising the cost of his diet, against a hostile opponent " nature " which is niggardly in providing the necessary nutrients. But this stretches the concept of a " game " to the point of artificiality.

16.6 Linear Programmes arranged for Computation

The solution of a linear programming problem in practice is likely to involve very heavy computational work. It is important, therefore, to lay out the work in a careful and systematic way and to arrange it for high-speed computing machines. The general linear programme considered is that of 16.4 above ; a linear function of non-negative variables is to be maximised or minimised subject to a system of linear inequalities. The first step now is to put the programme in a rather different form in which a linear function of non-negative variables is *maximised* subject to a system of linear *equations*. A given programme can always be put in this form, first by turning a minimum (if this is specified) into a maximum and then by adding further variables to change inequalities into equations. The method involved is sufficiently illustrated by the simple example (16.3 above) of two variables and two inequalities ; the general case is considered in Ex. 2 and 3 below.

Take the linear programme :

$$p_1x_1 + p_2x_2 = \text{min.}$$

subject to
$$a_{11}x_1 + a_{12}x_2 \geqslant b_1$$
$$a_{21}x_1 + a_{22}x_2 \geqslant b_2$$
$$x_1 \geqslant 0 \quad x_2 \geqslant 0$$

First, write $c_1 = -p_1$ and $c_2 = -p_2$ so that :

$$z = c_1x_1 + c_2x_2 = \text{max.}$$

Next, put $x_1 = \lambda_1$ and $x_2 = \lambda_2$. Take λ_3 as the non-negative difference $(a_{11}\lambda_1 + a_{12}\lambda_2) - b_1$ and λ_4 similarly in the other side relation. So :

$$a_{11}\lambda_1 + a_{12}\lambda_2 - \lambda_3 = b_1 \quad \text{and} \quad a_{21}\lambda_1 + a_{22}\lambda_2 - \lambda_4 = b_2$$

Finally, extend $z = c_1\lambda_1 + c_2\lambda_2$ to $z = c_1\lambda_1 + c_2\lambda_2 + c_3\lambda_3 + c_4\lambda_4$ when $c_3 = c_4 = 0$. The linear programme is then :

$$z = c_1\lambda_1 + c_2\lambda_2 + c_3\lambda_3 + c_4\lambda_4 = \text{max.}$$

subject to
$$a_{11}\lambda_1 + a_{12}\lambda_2 - \lambda_3 \qquad = b_1$$
$$a_{21}\lambda_1 + a_{22}\lambda_2 \qquad - \lambda_4 = b_2$$
$$\lambda_1 \geqslant 0 \quad \lambda_2 \geqslant 0 \quad \lambda_3 \geqslant 0 \quad \lambda_4 \geqslant 0$$

A linear function of four non-negative variables (two having zero coefficients) is to be maximised subject to a system of two linear equations in the variables. Of the four variables, two are the original variables and the other two are additional and conventional variables introduced for convenience. The latter can be called *slack variables*. The matrix of technical coefficients is also extended from order 2×2 to order 2×4 :

$$\mathbf{A} = \begin{bmatrix} a_{11} & a_{12} & -1 & 0 \\ a_{21} & a_{22} & 0 & -1 \end{bmatrix}$$

The general linear programme of the type considered can be written :

$$\left. \begin{array}{c} z = \mathbf{c}'\boldsymbol{\lambda} = \text{max.} \\ \mathbf{A}\boldsymbol{\lambda} = \mathbf{b} \\ \boldsymbol{\lambda} \geqslant 0 \end{array} \right\} \quad \dots\dots\dots\dots\dots\dots\dots\dots(1)$$

subject to

and

where $\mathbf{A}$ is a matrix (order $m \times n$) of technical coefficients suitably extended, $\mathbf{b}$ is a vector (order m) of requirements and availabilities, $\mathbf{c}$ is a vector (order n) specifying the objective or maximum, and $\boldsymbol{\lambda}$ is the vector (order n) of variables to be found. By the way in which the list of variables has been extended, it can be taken that $m < n$, as indicated below. A basic result, due to Gale and proved simply by Danø (1958), states that the (optimum) solution of (1), if it exists, has positive values for *at most m* of the n variables λ.

The form (1) is better written in terms of vectors of order m and sets of coefficients n in number, at least for computational purposes. Extend the matrix $\mathbf{A}$ by the addition of b as a last column, making it of order $m \times (n+1)$. Denote by $\mathbf{p}^{(s)}$ $(s = 1, 2, \ldots n)$ and $\mathbf{p}$ the columns of this matrix of given coefficients, each being a vector of order m :

$$[\mathbf{p}^{(1)}\mathbf{p}^{(2)} \cdots \mathbf{p}^{(n)}\mathbf{p}] = \begin{bmatrix} a_{11} & a_{12} & \cdots & a_{1n} & b_1 \\ a_{21} & a_{22} & \cdots & a_{2n} & b_2 \\ \cdots\cdots\cdots\cdots\cdots\cdots\cdots \\ a_{m1} & a_{m2} & \cdots & a_{mn} & b_m \end{bmatrix} \quad \ldots\ldots\ldots\ldots(2)$$

Then the linear programme (1) can be expressed :
  To find non-negative $\lambda_s \geqslant 0$ $(s = 1, 2, \ldots n)$ such that :

$$z = c_1\lambda_1 + c_2\lambda_2 + \ldots + c_n\lambda_n = \max \quad \ldots\ldots\ldots\ldots\ldots(3)$$

subject to $\qquad \lambda_1\mathbf{p}^{(1)} + \lambda_2\mathbf{p}^{(2)} + \ldots + \lambda_n\mathbf{p}^{(n)} = \mathbf{p} \quad \ldots\ldots\ldots\ldots\ldots(4)$

The Σ notation can also be used for (3) and (4), i.e.

$$z = \sum_{s=1}^{n} c_s\lambda_s = \max \quad \text{subject to} \quad \sum_{s=1}^{n} \lambda_s\mathbf{p}^{(s)} = \mathbf{p}$$

The vectors used in this statement of the problem are of two orders, m and n where $m < n$. They are to be interpreted in terms of points in two spaces of m and n dimensions respectively. These " geometrical " terms will be used consistently in the development so that the theory of convex sets can be applied. The two spaces must be carefully distinguished :

(i) *Requirements space* of m dimensions is the lower order $(m < n)$. It contains points $\mathbf{p}^{(1)}$, $\mathbf{p}^{(2)}$, $\ldots \mathbf{p}^{(n)}$ and $\mathbf{p}$ defined by the technical coefficients of $\mathbf{A}$ and the requirements of $\mathbf{b}$ by (2). These are all given data of the problem ; they appear in the equations (4).

(ii) *Solutions space* of n dimensions is the higher order $(n > m)$. It contains, in addition to the point $\mathbf{c} = (c_1, c_2, \ldots c_n)$ for the linear function to be maximised (3), the points $\boldsymbol{\lambda} = (\lambda_1, \lambda_2, \ldots \lambda_n)$ with elements which are the variables to be found. The point appears as the variable in (3) and also as the coefficients of the given vectors in (4).

A point $\boldsymbol{\lambda}$ which satisfies the equation (4) is called a *feasible solution* of the problem ; it does not necessarily provide a maximum of (3). A point which also maximises (3) is called an *optimum feasible solution* of the problem and it is such a point which is sought. The general method of solution is to concentrate attention first on the set of feasible solutions and then on those feasible solutions which are optimal. It will be seen that feasible solutions make a convex set and that an optimum is to be sought among the extreme points of this set. The theory of convex sets is then of direct application.

As a convenient terminology, the association of the variables of the solution λ with the given vectors or points $\mathbf{p}$ in the equation (4) can be shown by saying that λ_s is the *weight* of the point $\mathbf{p}^{(s)}$ in the solution λ. This is in space of m dimensions. Since $\lambda_s \geqslant 0$, a solution can have some $\mathbf{p}^{(s)}$ with *positive weights* and the others with *zero weights*; this corresponds to some variables positive and the others zero in the solution. It is found important to distinguish between positive and zero weights.

Numbers of Variables and Side Relations. The standard form (1) of a linear programme has n variables and m side equations, i.e. the maximum of a linear function of n variables is to be found subject to m linear equations.

The general linear programme of 16.4 can be written in N variables subject to M linear inequalities. Suppose that *all* the side relations are inequalities, that there are no equations among them. Then, when put into standard form, it appears with $n = M + N$ variables (M being slack variables) and $m = M$ linear equations, see Ex. 2 below. Hence, in the standard form $m < n$. The same is true of the dual problem, see Ex. 3 below.

The importance of the fact that $m < n$, i.e. that solutions space is of greater dimensions than requirements space, is that feasible solutions for the variables satisfy fewer equations than there are variables. Consequently, it is generally true that there are many, indeed an infinite number of feasible solutions to a linear programme in standard form.

This may no longer be true if the general linear programme of 16.4 (with N variables subject to M side relations) has some or all of the side relations in the form of equations in the first place. Then, in standard form, the problem may have $m \geqslant n$ and feasible solutions come from a set of equations which is at least equal in number to the variables, see Ex. 4 below. There may be only one feasible solution (if the equations are consistent) or no feasible solution at all (if the equations are inconsistent).

To summarise : if a general linear programme is such that all the side relations are inequalities, then in standard form the number of side equations (m) is less than the number of variables (n) and an infinity of feasible solutions exists. This is the usual case. However, when the original problem has some or all of the side relations as equations, then it may happen that $m \geqslant n$. This is the exceptional case.

EXERCISES 16.6

1. Put the dual problem in two variables (16.3 above) into standard form (1) and show it has four variables, including two slack variables, and two side equations.

2. A general linear programme is to find N variables $\mathbf{x}$ such that $z = \mathbf{p'x} = \min$. subject to M relations $\mathbf{Ax} \geqslant \mathbf{b}$. Put into standard form of n variables subject to m equations. If *all* the original M relations are inequalities, show that $m = M$ and $n = M + N$ and hence that $m < n$.

3. The dual of the problem of the previous exercise is to find M variables $\boldsymbol{\xi}$ such that $\zeta = \mathbf{b'\xi} = \max$. subject to N relations $\mathbf{A'\xi} \leqslant \mathbf{p}$. Put into standard form of n' variables subject to m' equations and show that $m' = N$ and $n' = M + N$ if *all* the original relations are inequalities. Deduce that a linear programme and its dual, in standard form, have the *same* number of variables but *different* numbers of side equations.

4. Suppose that, in Ex. 2 above, the general linear programme in N variables has some equations among its original M side relations. Show that $m \geqslant n$ can arise in the standard form by considering the possibilities :

   (a) $M = N$ and all side relations as equations ($m = n$)
   (b) $M > N$ and N side relations as equations ($m = n$)
   (c) $M > N$ and more than N side relations as equations ($m > n$).

16.7 Some Properties of Convex Sets

The essential results in the theory of convex sets, as introduced in 12.5 above, are now set out. In addition, the concept of linear dependence of vectors or points, examined in 14.1 above, is relevant and the main results in this field can be given first.

Linear Dependence

There are n points $\mathbf{p}^{(1)}, \mathbf{p}^{(2)}, \dots \mathbf{p}^{(n)}$ in space of m dimensions ($n > m$). Any set of k of them, say the first k, are *linearly dependent* if coefficients μ_s not all zero can be found so that :

$$\sum_{s=1}^{k} \mu_s \mathbf{p}^{(s)} = \mathbf{0}$$

Then one point (corresponding to a non-zero μ) can be expressed as a linear combination of the other points. For example, if $\mu_1 \neq 0$, then :

$$\mathbf{p}^{(1)} = - \sum_{s=2}^{k} \frac{\mu_s}{\mu_1} \mathbf{p}^{(s)}$$

Otherwise the set is *linearly independent*, i.e. no one point is a linear combination of the others.

A basic result is :

(A) *Not more than m of the n points $\mathbf{p}^{(1)}, \mathbf{p}^{(2)}, \dots \mathbf{p}^{(n)}$ in m dimensions can be linearly independent.*

Hence, if there are $(m + 1)$ points, at least one of them *must* be linearly dependent, a linear combination of the others. However, even among m points, there *may* be linear dependence.

Suppose that exactly m points, say $\mathbf{p}^{(1)}$, $\mathbf{p}^{(2)}$, ... $\mathbf{p}^{(m)}$, are linearly independent. Then they form a *basis* of m-dimensional space in the sense that *every* other point in the space can be expressed as a linear combination of $\mathbf{p}^{(1)}$, $\mathbf{p}^{(2)}$, ... $\mathbf{p}^{(m)}$. More points will not serve as a basis since they are not linearly independent. Neither will fewer points serve since all other points cannot be expressed in terms of them. An example, and a very convenient one, of a basis is the set of m points at unit distance along the co-ordinate axes, obtained from the unit vectors $\boldsymbol{\epsilon}_r$ $(r = 1, 2, \ldots m)$:

$$(1, 0, 0 \ldots 0) \; ; \quad (0, 1, 0, \ldots 0) \; ; \quad \ldots \ldots$$

One application of the basic result of great use is the following. Out of the n points $\mathbf{p}^{(s)}$ $(s = 1, 2, \ldots n)$ select m which are linearly independent, say the first m, or $\mathbf{p}^{(r)}$ $(r = 1, 2, \ldots m)$. Then *every* point $\mathbf{p}^{(s)}$ can be expressed as a linear combination of the m points $\mathbf{p}^{(r)}$. Write the coefficients in the linear combination in the form x_{rs}. The result is obtained :

(B) *The points* $\mathbf{p}^{(r)}$ $(r = 1, 2, \ldots m)$ *are linearly independent. Any point* $\mathbf{p}^{(s)}$ $(s = 1, 2, \ldots n)$ *can then be expressed :*

$$\mathbf{p}^{(s)} = \sum_{r=1}^{m} x_{rs} \mathbf{p}^{(r)}$$

where x_{rs} *are certain coefficients* $(r = 1, 2, \ldots m \; ; \; s = 1, 2, \ldots n)$.

Note that this is not only true for $s > m$; it is also true if s is one of the first m and $\mathbf{p}^{(s)}$ is one of the linearly independent set. In this case, all the x_{rs} are zero except that $x_{rr} = 1$.

PROPERTIES OF CONVEX SETS

(i) *Given* $\mathbf{p}$ *and* $\mathbf{p}^{(s)}$ $(s = 1, 2, \ldots n)$ *in m dimensions, the points* $\boldsymbol{\lambda} = (\lambda_1, \lambda_2, \ldots \lambda_n)$ *which are non-negative* $(\lambda_s \geqslant 0)$ *and satisfy*

$$\sum_{s=1}^{n} \lambda_s \mathbf{p}^{(s)} = \mathbf{p}$$

comprise a convex set Γ *in n dimensions.*

Further, if $E^{(1)}$, $E^{(2)}$, ... are the *extreme points* of Γ, it is assumed in the application to linear programming that $E^{(1)}$, $E^{(2)}$ ... are finite (k) in number. The convex set Γ is then the *convex hull* (polyhedron) generated from $E^{(1)}$, $E^{(2)}$, ... $E^{(k)}$. The feasible solutions of a linear programme are the points of the convex hull Γ.

Proof : Let $\boldsymbol{\lambda}^{(1)}$ and $\boldsymbol{\lambda}^{(2)}$ be two distinct points of Γ, non-negative and satisfying the condition :

$$\sum_{s=1}^{n} \lambda_s^{(1)} \mathbf{p}^{(s)} = \mathbf{p} \qquad \sum_{s=1}^{n} \lambda_s^{(2)} \mathbf{p}^{(s)} = \mathbf{p}$$

Hence, for any μ $(0 \leqslant \mu \leqslant 1)$:

$$\sum_{s=1}^{n} \{\mu\lambda_s{}^{(1)} + (1-\mu)\lambda_s{}^{(2)}\}\mathbf{p}^{(s)} = \mathbf{p}$$

and

$$\mu\lambda_s{}^{(1)} + (1-\mu)\lambda_s{}^{(2)} \geqslant 0$$

So, if $\boldsymbol{\lambda}^{(1)}$ and $\boldsymbol{\lambda}^{(2)}$ belong to Γ, so does $\mu\boldsymbol{\lambda}^{(1)} + (1-\mu)\boldsymbol{\lambda}^{(2)}$. Hence Γ is convex.

(ii) *A linear function $f(\boldsymbol{\lambda})$ defined for the point $\boldsymbol{\lambda}$ of the convex set Γ has a maximum at an extreme point of Γ.*

Further, if $f(\boldsymbol{\lambda})$ is maximum at only one extreme point $E^{(1)}$, this is a unique maximum ; if $f(\boldsymbol{\lambda})$ is maximum at several extreme points $E^{(1)}$, $E^{(2)}$, ... , then there is an infinite number of maxima, at all points in the convex hull (part of Γ) generated by $E^{(1)}$, $E^{(2)}$, ... These two cases correspond to a unique and to an infinite number of optimum feasible solutions of a linear programme.

Proof : The function $f(\boldsymbol{\lambda})$ is taken as linear, the case used in linear programming. Suppose $f(\boldsymbol{\lambda})$ has maximum at a point $\boldsymbol{\lambda}$ which is *not* extreme. Then, by the definition of extreme points, $E^{(1)}$, $E^{(2)}$, ... $E^{(k)}$, of a convex set :

$$\boldsymbol{\lambda} = \sum_{r=1}^{k} \mu_r E^{(r)} \quad \text{for some} \quad \mu_r \geqslant 0, \quad \sum_{r=1}^{k} \mu_r = 1$$

So : Max. $f(\boldsymbol{\lambda}) = \sum_{r=1}^{k} \mu_r f(E^{(r)})$ \qquad since f is linear

$$\leqslant f(E^{(1)}) \sum_{r=1}^{k} \mu_r = f(E^{(1)})$$

if $E^{(1)}$ is the extreme giving the largest f.

Hence : \qquad\qquad\qquad Max. $f(\boldsymbol{\lambda}) \leqslant f(E^{(1)})$

The sign can only be " equals " and $f(\boldsymbol{\lambda})$ has a maximum at the extreme point $E^{(1)}$. The same kind of argument shows that, if there are several extremes $E^{(1)}$, $E^{(2)}$, ... having the same largest f, then they are all maxima of $f(\boldsymbol{\lambda})$ and so is any $\boldsymbol{\lambda}$ found as a convex linear combination of them.

(iii) *The point $\boldsymbol{\lambda} = (\lambda_1, \lambda_2, ... \lambda_n)$ is an extreme of Γ if and only if the $\mathbf{p}^{(s)}$ with positive weights $(\lambda_s > 0)$ form a linearly independent set among all $\mathbf{p}^{(s)}$ $(s = 1, 2, ... n)$. The other $\mathbf{p}^{(s)}$ have zero weights $(\lambda_s = 0)$.*

Further, by results (A) and (B) for linear dependence, an extreme point of Γ has not more than m positive weights, and at least $(n - m)$ zero weights ; if it has exactly m positive weights, then *any* $\mathbf{p}^{(s)}$ can be written :

$$\mathbf{p}^{(s)} = \sum_{r=1}^{m} x_{rs}\mathbf{p}^{(r)}$$

where $\mathbf{p}^{(r)}$ $(r = 1, 2, ... m)$ have the m positive weights.

Proof : Let λ be an extreme point of Γ with k positive weights, λ_1, λ_2, ... λ_k and other λ's zero. Then since λ belongs to Γ by (i) above :

$$\sum_{s=1}^{k} \lambda_s \mathbf{p}^{(s)} = \mathbf{p} \qquad \text{all } \lambda_s > 0 \quad \dots\dots\dots\dots\dots\dots(1)$$

Suppose that $\mathbf{p}^{(1)}$, $\mathbf{p}^{(2)}$, ... $\mathbf{p}^{(k)}$ are linearly dependent, so that :

$$\sum_{s=1}^{k} \mu_s \mathbf{p}^{(s)} = 0 \qquad \text{not all } \mu_s \text{ zero} \quad \dots\dots\dots\dots\dots(2)$$

Now, choose a small constant c so that $\lambda_s + c\mu_s$ and $\lambda_s - c\mu_s$ are both positive (like λ_s) for each $s = 1, 2, \dots k$. From (1) and (2) :

$$\sum_{s=1}^{k} (\lambda_s + c\mu_s)\mathbf{p}^{(s)} = \mathbf{p} \quad \text{and} \quad \sum_{s=1}^{k} (\lambda_s - c\mu_s)\mathbf{p}^{(s)} = \mathbf{p}$$

Hence, $\lambda^{(1)} = \lambda + c\mu$ and $\lambda^{(2)} = \lambda - c\mu$ both belong to Γ. But

$$\lambda = \tfrac{1}{2}\lambda^{(1)} + \tfrac{1}{2}\lambda^{(2)}$$

which is not possible since λ is an extreme point of Γ. Hence, $\mathbf{p}^{(1)}$, $\mathbf{p}^{(2)}$, ... $\mathbf{p}^{(k)}$ cannot be linearly dependent ; they must be linearly independent, as was to be proved.

Conversely, let $\mathbf{p}^{(1)}$, $\mathbf{p}^{(2)}$, ... $\mathbf{p}^{(k)}$ corresponding to the k positive weights of λ in Γ be linearly independent. Suppose that λ is a convex linear combination of two points $\lambda^{(1)}$ and $\lambda^{(2)}$ in Γ :

$$\lambda = \mu\lambda^{(1)} + (1-\mu)\lambda^{(2)} \qquad (0 \leqslant \mu \leqslant 1)$$

λ, $\lambda^{(1)}$ and $\lambda^{(2)}$ all have only k positive weights (the others being zero) and, since they all belong to Γ, then :

$$\sum_{s=1}^{k} \lambda_s \mathbf{p}^{(s)} = \mathbf{p} \; ; \quad \sum_{s=1}^{k} \lambda_s^{(1)}\mathbf{p}^{(s)} = \mathbf{p} \quad \text{and} \quad \sum_{s=1}^{k} \lambda_s^{(2)}\mathbf{p}^{(s)} = \mathbf{p}$$

Hence $\displaystyle\sum_{s=1}^{k} (\lambda_s - \lambda_s^{(1)})\mathbf{p}^{(s)} = 0 \quad \text{and} \quad \sum_{s=1}^{k} (\lambda_s - \lambda_s^{(2)})\mathbf{p}^{(s)} = 0$

which is not possible, the $\mathbf{p}^{(s)}$ being linearly independent, unless

$$\lambda = \lambda^{(1)} = \lambda^{(2)}$$

Hence λ cannot be a convex linear combination of two other points in Γ, i.e. λ is an extreme point of Γ, as was to be proved.

16.8 The Simplex Method of Solution

The general linear programme considered is arranged as in 16.6 above : To find non-negative $\lambda_s \geqslant 0$ ($s = 1, 2, \dots n$) such that

$$z = c_1\lambda_1 + c_2\lambda_2 + \dots + c_n\lambda_n = \text{max.} \quad \dots\dots\dots\dots\dots(1)$$

subject to $\qquad \lambda_1\mathbf{p}^{(1)} + \lambda_2\mathbf{p}^{(2)} + \dots + \lambda_n\mathbf{p}^{(n)} = \mathbf{p} \quad \dots\dots\dots\dots(2)$

A *feasible solution* satisfies (2) but not necessarily (1) as well. Such solutions form a convex set Γ, by 16.7, Property (i). Γ has extreme points $E^{(1)}, E^{(2)}, \ldots E^{(k)}$ and an *optimum feasible solution* which maximises z of (1) occurs at one or more of $E^{(1)}, E^{(2)}, \ldots E^{(k)}$, by 16.7, Property (ii). Hence, to solve the linear programme, attention must be concentrated on the extreme points from which Γ is generated. Two possibilities must be borne in mind ; *either* a maximum is attained at only one extreme point, in which case it is the unique solution of the problem, *or* maxima are obtained at several extreme points, in which case there is an infinite set of solutions at all λ of the convex hull of the several extreme points.

Property (iii) of 16.7 directs attention to another feature of the extreme points of Γ, i.e. the number of positive weights in the $\lambda = (\lambda_1, \lambda_2, \ldots \lambda_n)$ of an extreme point. This number may be less than m, in which case the $\mathbf{p}^{(r)}$ $(r = 1, 2, \ldots k)$ with the positive weights are linearly independent $(k < m)$. More useful is the case where the number is exactly m ; the linearly independent $\mathbf{p}^{(r)}$ $(r = 1, 2, \ldots m)$ then form a *basis* of m-dimensional space and so any $\mathbf{p}^{(s)}$ is to be written $\mathbf{p}^{(s)} = \sum_{r=1}^{m} x_{rs} \mathbf{p}^{(r)}$.

Suppose a *feasible solution* of the problem has been found which is an extreme point of Γ with exactly m positive weights, i.e. a solution :

$$\lambda = (\lambda_1, \lambda_2, \ldots \lambda_m, 0, 0, \ldots 0)$$

where $\lambda_r > 0$ $(r = 1, 2, \ldots m)$. Then $\mathbf{p}^{(r)}$ are linearly independent and so :

$$\mathbf{p} = \sum_{r=1}^{m} \lambda_r \mathbf{p}^{(r)} \qquad (\lambda_r > 0) \quad \ldots\ldots\ldots\ldots\ldots\ldots\ldots(3)$$

and
$$\mathbf{p}^{(s)} = \sum_{r=1}^{m} x_{rs} \mathbf{p}^{(r)} \qquad (s = 1, 2, \ldots n) \quad \ldots\ldots\ldots\ldots(4)$$

The corresponding value of z, not necessarily maximum, is :

$$z_0 = \sum_{r=1}^{m} c_r \lambda_r \quad \ldots\ldots\ldots\ldots\ldots\ldots\ldots\ldots\ldots\ldots\ldots(5)$$

Write
$$z_s = \sum_{r=1}^{m} c_r x_{rs} \qquad (s = 1, 2 \ldots n) \quad \ldots\ldots\ldots\ldots(6)$$

A *new feasible solution* at an extreme point of Γ is now sought by taking out $\mathbf{p}^{(r)}$ where r is one value selected from $1, 2, \ldots m$ and by adding in $\mathbf{p}^{(s)}$ where s is one value selected from $(m+1), (m+2), \ldots n$. The substitution is to be such that a *larger z* than z_0 results. In this way, working through the extreme points of Γ, an approach is made to maximum z, i.e. to the optimum feasible solution (or to one of the infinite number of optima).

The problem is : how to choose r for elimination and s for addition? Let θ be a constant coefficient. From (3) and (4) :

$$\mathbf{p} = \sum_{r=1}^{m} \lambda_r \mathbf{p}^{(r)} - \theta \mathbf{p}^{(s)} + \theta \mathbf{p}^{(s)}$$

$$= \sum_{r=1}^{m} (\lambda_r - \theta x_{rs}) \mathbf{p}^{(r)} + \theta \mathbf{p}^{(s)} \quad\ldots\ldots\ldots\ldots\ldots\ldots(7)$$

Take $\theta = \dfrac{\lambda_r}{x_{rs}}$ so that the rth term in (7) vanishes and only m terms are left.

Provided that $\lambda_r - \theta x_{rs} \geqslant 0$ and $\theta \geqslant 0$, the coefficients in (7) are a new feasible solution and the corresponding z, by (5) and (6), is :

$$z_0' = \sum_{r=1}^{m} c_r(\lambda_r - \theta x_{rs}) + \theta c_s = z_0 + \theta(c_s - z_s) \quad\ldots\ldots\ldots\ldots(8)$$

Hence, if $\theta > 0$ and $c_s > z_s$, then by (8) an improved solution $(z_0' > z_0)$ is obtained by the substitution. The choice of r and s must now satisfy :

$$\theta = \frac{\lambda_r}{x_{rs}} > 0 \quad \lambda_i - \theta x_{is} \geqslant 0 \quad \text{and} \quad c_s - z_s > 0 \quad\ldots\ldots\ldots\ldots(9)$$

where i is any value in $1, 2, \ldots m$ except r. Two conditions must be satisfied to permit a choice of r and s :

(i) At least one $c_s - z_s\,(s = m+1, m+2, \ldots n)$ must be positive, in which case select s for largest $c_s - z_s > 0$ and the last relation of (9) holds.

(ii) At least one $x_{rs}\ (r = 1, 2, \ldots m)$ must be positive, in which case select r for

$$\theta = \min \frac{\lambda_r}{x_{rs}} \quad \text{among} \quad x_{rs} > 0$$

and the two first relations of (9) hold.

Under these conditions, an improved solution is obtained by dropping $\mathbf{p}^{(r)}$ and adding $\mathbf{p}^{(s)}$ in the set of initial (linearly independent) points $\mathbf{p}^{(r)}$ $(r = 1, 2, \ldots m)$. Moreover, the new set is also linearly independent, again corresponding to an extreme point of Γ. To show this, suppose that the numbering is arranged so that $\mathbf{p}^{(1)}$ is omitted and $\mathbf{p}^{(m+1)}$ added, i.e. $r = 1$, $s = m+1$. Then by (4) :

$$\mathbf{p}^{(m+1)} = \sum_{r=1}^{m} x_{r(m+1)} \mathbf{p}^{(r)}$$

and

$$\mathbf{p}^{(m+1)} = \sum_{r=2}^{m} \mu_r \mathbf{p}^{(r)}$$

if the new set, $\mathbf{p}^{(2)}, \mathbf{p}^{(3)}, \ldots \mathbf{p}^{(m+1)}$, is linearly dependent.

Subtract :

$$x_{1(m+1)} \mathbf{p}^{(1)} = \sum_{r=2}^{m} (\mu_r - x_{r(m+1)}) \mathbf{p}^{(r)}$$

But the original set were linearly independent and $\mathbf{p}^{(1)}$ cannot be a linear combination of the others as now indicated. Neither can $x_{1(m+1)}=0$ since $r=1$ was selected from positive $x_{r(m+1)}$. Hence the new set is not linearly dependent; it is linearly independent.

The conclusion is that, if the conditions (i) and (ii) are satisfied, then the original λ and value z_0 can be improved; a new feasible solution is obtained, also an extreme of Γ, and a higher value of z_0. This provides a starting point for another application of the method. The whole process can be repeated, a process of iteration from an initially selected starting point; it never comes back to an earlier stage since the value of z is increased at every stage. The only stop sign (apart from a case of degeneracy referred to below) is that the conditions (i) and (ii) may fail to be satisfied at some stage. And this means that the maximum feasible solution has been reached. It is easily seen that *either* condition (ii) fails and all $x_{rs} \leqslant 0$ in which case the value of z becomes infinite *or* condition (i) fails and all $c_s - z_s \leqslant 0$, in which case a finite maximum of z has been recorded, i.e. the extreme point λ is an optimum feasible solution as sought.

The situation where the iterative method breaks down in practice occurs when there are not m positive weights in the feasible solution λ at some stage. This is the case of *degeneracy*. A solution of the difficulty, which permits the continued application of the Simplex Method, is suggested by Charnes (1952) and used in Charnes, Cooper and Henderson (1953).

Finally, note that the dual problem of any given linear programme can also be put in the standard " simplex " form of (1) and (2) above. Hence, it can be solved by another application of the Simplex Method. It is clear, however, that the original problem and its dual are so closely related (having the same maximised/minimised value for example) that it is to be expected that one application of the method will solve both problems. This is, in fact, the case; it is illustrated in the particular example of 16.9 below. In the final stage of the method on the given problem, when a finite maximum is obtained, all $c_s - z_s \leqslant 0$. The negatives of these values (i.e. $z_s - c_s$) finally obtained for the slack variables provide the optimal solution for the variables of the dual problem.

16.9 Solution of a Simple Linear Programme by Simplex Method

The method can be illustrated in practice in its application to a simple example, and the one selected is the dual problem already solved by graphical methods in 16.2 above and in the corresponding form of a game in 16.3 above. The same solution is now obtained by the Simplex Method; the advantages of this method, however, is that it can tackle more elaborate linear programmes not amenable to graphical solution or to solution of a corresponding game. A more elaborate problem is solved, and many other practical aspects of the Simplex Method are considered, in Charnes, Cooper and Henderson (1953). The Simplex Method is then seen to be designed for systematic machine computation.

The problem is to find non-negative ξ_1 and ξ_2 such that :

$$\zeta = 3\xi_1 + 4\xi_2 = \text{max.}$$

subject to

$$\xi_1 + \xi_2 \leqslant 6$$
$$2\xi_1 + 4\xi_2 \leqslant 21$$

To put into the standard form (16.6 above) for application of the Simplex Method, two slack variables are introduced, making four variables : $\lambda_1 = \xi_1$ and $\lambda_2 = \xi_2$ with λ_3 and λ_4 as slack variables. Then non-negative λ_s ($s = 1, 2, 3, 4$) are to be found such that :

$$z = 3\lambda_1 + 4\lambda_2 = \text{max.}$$

subject to

$$\lambda_1 + \lambda_2 + \lambda_3 = 6$$
$$2\lambda_1 + 4\lambda_2 + \lambda_4 = 21$$

Here requirements space is of two dimensions and contains five given points :

$$[\mathbf{p}^{(1)}\mathbf{p}^{(2)}\mathbf{p}^{(3)}\mathbf{p}^{(4)}\mathbf{p}] = \begin{bmatrix} 1 & 1 & 1 & 0 & 6 \\ 2 & 4 & 0 & 1 & 21 \end{bmatrix}$$

Solutions space is of four dimensions, containing the points

$$\boldsymbol{\lambda} = (\lambda_1, \lambda_2, \lambda_3, \lambda_4)$$

which are possible solutions of the problem. The given point $\mathbf{c} = (3, 4, 0, 0)$ which specifies the function z to be maximised is also in this space.

All feasible solutions $\boldsymbol{\lambda}$, satisfying the two side equations, comprise a convex set Γ in four dimensions. An initial feasible solution is to be selected, an extreme point of Γ with exactly two positive weights and two zero weights. A convenient solution of this kind is $\boldsymbol{\lambda} = (0, 0, 6, 21)$ which clearly satisfies the conditions ; the points $\mathbf{p}^{(3)} = \begin{bmatrix} 1 \\ 0 \end{bmatrix}$ and $\mathbf{p}^{(4)} = \begin{bmatrix} 0 \\ 1 \end{bmatrix}$

which have the positive weights are linearly independent. In fact, these points are the unit vectors (unit distances along the axes) of the two-dimensional space ; they form a simple basis of the space, all other points being linear combinations of them. This is why the initial feasible solution is selected.

The following Simplex Table is now built up stage by stage :

		c_s	λ	$\mathbf{p}^{(1)}$ 3	$\mathbf{p}^{(2)}$ 4	$\mathbf{p}^{(3)}$ 0	$\mathbf{p}^{(4)}$ 0
A	$\mathbf{p}^{(3)}$	0	6	1	1	1	0
	$\mathbf{p}^{(4)}$	0	21	2	4	0	1
	z_s			0	0	0	0
	$c_s - z_s$			3	4	0	0
B	$\mathbf{p}^{(3)}$	0	$\frac{3}{4}$	$\frac{1}{2}$	0	1	$-\frac{1}{4}$
	$\mathbf{p}^{(2)}$	4	$\frac{21}{4}$	$\frac{1}{2}$	1	0	$\frac{1}{4}$
	z_s			2	4	0	1
	$c_s - z_s$			1	0	0	-1
C	$\mathbf{p}^{(1)}$	3	$\frac{3}{2}$	1	0	2	$-\frac{1}{2}$
	$\mathbf{p}^{(2)}$	4	$\frac{9}{2}$	0	1	-1	$\frac{1}{2}$
	z_s			3	4	2	$\frac{1}{2}$
	$c_s - z_s$			0	0	-2	$-\frac{1}{2}$

Consider the first sector or tableau, A above ; this is the initial feasible solution. The first two rows are the points, here $\mathbf{p}^{(3)}$ and $\mathbf{p}^{(4)}$, with positive weights in $\lambda = (0, 0, 6, 21)$ and the positive weights are shown in the column headed λ. The other four columns throughout are the four points $\mathbf{p}^{(1)}$, $\mathbf{p}^{(2)}$, $\mathbf{p}^{(3)}$ and $\mathbf{p}^{(4)}$. Against rows and columns are shown the corresponding $\mathbf{c} = (3, 4, 0, 0)$. The main part of sector A is the set of entries in the two rows $\mathbf{p}^{(3)}$ and $\mathbf{p}^{(4)}$ and four columns $\mathbf{p}^{(1)}$, $\mathbf{p}^{(2)}$, $\mathbf{p}^{(3)}$ and $\mathbf{p}^{(4)}$. These are the coefficients x_{rs} in (4) of 16.8 above. They show how the point for each column is expressed as a linear combination of the selected basis $\mathbf{p}^{(3)}$ and $\mathbf{p}^{(4)}$. So :

$$\mathbf{p}^{(1)} = x_{31}\mathbf{p}^{(3)} + x_{41}\mathbf{p}^{(4)}$$

i.e.
$$\begin{bmatrix} 1 \\ 2 \end{bmatrix} = 1 \times \begin{bmatrix} 1 \\ 0 \end{bmatrix} + 2 \times \begin{bmatrix} 0 \\ 1 \end{bmatrix}$$

They are, in fact, the elements of the given matrix of the problem, see Ex. 1 below. The remaining two rows of A give two derived figures for each column :

$$z_s = c_3 x_{3s} + c_4 x_{4s} \quad (s = 1, 2, 3, 4) \quad \text{(6) of 16.8 above,}$$

and then $c_s - z_s$.

To pass to section B, one of $\mathbf{p}^{(3)}$ and $\mathbf{p}^{(4)}$ in the rows is to be replaced by one of $\mathbf{p}^{(1)}$ and $\mathbf{p}^{(2)}$. To decide on the substitution :

(i) Find the largest positive $(c_s - z_s)$; hence $\mathbf{p}^{(2)}$ is put in ;

(ii) For the column $\mathbf{p}^{(2)}$, find the smaller θ of $\dfrac{\lambda_3}{x_{32}}$ and $\dfrac{\lambda_4}{x_{42}}$ with positive x's.

Here the two values are $\frac{6}{1}$ and $\frac{21}{4}$ and $\mathbf{p}^{(4)}$ is taken out.

Section B is set up with rows $\mathbf{p}^{(3)}$ and $\mathbf{p}^{(2)}$, the new pair of linearly independent points with positive weights in the new feasible solution $\boldsymbol{\lambda}$. The elements of $\boldsymbol{\lambda}$ are seen by the relation (7) of 16.8 above; here $\boldsymbol{\lambda} = (0, \frac{21}{4}, \frac{3}{4}, 0)$. The positive weights are shown under $\boldsymbol{\lambda}$ in B. The coefficients x_{rs} of (4) in 16.8 above are then found and put in the table. For example :

$$\mathbf{p}^{(1)} = x_{31}\mathbf{p}^{(3)} + x_{21}\mathbf{p}^{(2)}$$

i.e.
$$\begin{bmatrix} 1 \\ 2 \end{bmatrix} = x_{31}\begin{bmatrix} 1 \\ 0 \end{bmatrix} + x_{21}\begin{bmatrix} 1 \\ 4 \end{bmatrix}$$

The values $x_{31} = \frac{1}{2}$, $x_{21} = \frac{1}{2}$ satisfy this relation, see Ex. 2 below. The rows for z_s and $(c_s - z_s)$ are then derived as before.

Section C is a further application of the same process. The pair $\mathbf{p}^{(3)}$, $\mathbf{p}^{(2)}$ which was the basis of B is replaced by the new basis $\mathbf{p}^{(1)}$, $\mathbf{p}^{(2)}$. First, $\mathbf{p}^{(1)}$ is put in, from the largest positive $(c_s - z_s)$ of B, indeed the only positive $(c_s - z_s)$ remaining. Then $\mathbf{p}^{(3)}$ is taken out, from the smaller θ of $\dfrac{\lambda_3}{x_{31}}$ and $\dfrac{\lambda_2}{x_{21}}$, i.e. of $\frac{3}{4}/\frac{1}{2}$ and $\frac{21}{4}/\frac{1}{2}$. Hence $\theta = \frac{3}{2}$ and the new $\boldsymbol{\lambda} = (\frac{3}{2}, \frac{9}{2}, 0, 0)$ from (7) of 16.8 above. The rest of C follows as before.

The end is now reached since all $(c_s - z_s) \leqslant 0$ and a finite maximum of z is obtained. The maximum feasible solution is $\boldsymbol{\lambda} = (\frac{3}{2}, \frac{9}{2}, 0, 0)$ for which :

$$z = 3\lambda_1 + 4\lambda_2 = 22\tfrac{1}{2}$$

This is the solution obtained (16.2 above), i.e. $\xi_1 = \frac{3}{2}$, $\xi_2 = \frac{9}{2}$ and $\zeta = 22\frac{1}{2}$. It is to be noted that the dual problem, or the nutrition problem of 16.1 above, has a solution which can be read off the Simplex Table above. It comes from the last row for $(c_s - z_s)$ with signs reversed and with variables and slack variables switched. Here it is $\boldsymbol{\lambda} = (2, \frac{1}{2}, 0, 0)$, i.e. $x_1 = 2$, $x_2 = \frac{1}{2}$, from which $z = 22\frac{1}{2}$.

EXERCISES 16.9

1. The vectors $\begin{bmatrix} 1 \\ 0 \end{bmatrix}$ and $\begin{bmatrix} 0 \\ 1 \end{bmatrix}$ are linearly independent and as points $(1, 0)$ and $(0, 1)$ form a basis of two-dimensional space. Any point (x_1, x_2) can be obtained as a linear combination of them. Show that the rule for finding the combinations is :

$$\begin{bmatrix} x_1 \\ x_2 \end{bmatrix} = x_1\begin{bmatrix} 1 \\ 0 \end{bmatrix} + x_2\begin{bmatrix} 0 \\ 1 \end{bmatrix}$$

2. A basis of two-dimensional space is provided by any pair of linearly independent vectors of order 2, and not only by the pair of the previous exercise. Take $\begin{bmatrix} 1 \\ 0 \end{bmatrix}$ and $\begin{bmatrix} 1 \\ 4 \end{bmatrix}$ as such a basis. Any point (x_1, x_2) is a linear combination of them :

$$\begin{bmatrix} x_1 \\ x_2 \end{bmatrix} = \lambda_1 \begin{bmatrix} 1 \\ 0 \end{bmatrix} + \lambda_2 \begin{bmatrix} 1 \\ 4 \end{bmatrix}$$

Show that the rule for finding the combination is here :

$$\lambda_1 = x_1 - \tfrac{1}{4} x_2 ; \quad \lambda_2 = \tfrac{1}{4} x_2$$

3. Solve the nutrition problem of 16.1 above directly by the Simplex Method. Hence derive the solution of its dual. Check from the direct solution of the dual above.

4. Solve the nutrition problem of 16.1, Ex. 5, and 16.2, Ex. 4, by the Simplex Method. Check with the solution obtained from the corresponding game (16.3, Ex. 3).

5. In the shipping problem of 16.1, Ex. 7. show that the five given points in requirements space (of two dimensions) are

$$[\mathbf{p}^{(1)}\mathbf{p}^{(2)}\mathbf{p}^{(3)}\mathbf{p}^{(4)}\mathbf{p}] = \begin{bmatrix} 1 & 1 & 0 & 0 & b_1 \\ 1 & 0 & 1 & 0 & b_2 \end{bmatrix}$$

How many pairs are linearly independent and how many linearly dependent?

6. Take a particular example of the shipping problem of 16.1, Ex. 7 :

$$z = x_1 + \tfrac{1}{2}(x_2 + x_3) = \min.$$
$$\text{subject to} \quad x_1 + x_2 = 10 \quad x_1 + x_3 = 20$$

Show directly that $z = 15$ for any feasible values of x_1, x_2 and x_3. Attempt to solve the linear programme (a) by graphical means, (b) from the solution of the corresponding game and (c) by the Simplex Method. Also examine the dual problem. Comment on these procedures and interpret the problem in terms of the number of ships required for the traffic and voyage times taken.

7. In the shipping problem of 16.1, Ex. 8, take the particular example where the matrix of amounts shipped between points, and the matrix of costs, are :

x_{11}	x_{12}	2
x_{21}	x_{22}	10
6	6	12

and $\begin{bmatrix} 3 & 2 \\ 5 & 4 \end{bmatrix}$

Show that the problem is to minimise a linear function of four variables subject to three linear equations. What does the Simplex Method give in this case? Compare with the result of the previous exercise. See Dantzig in Koopmans (1951), Chapter XXIII, for a more general analysis.

REFERENCES

Charnes (A.) (1952) : " Optimality and Degeneracy in Linear Programming ", *Econometrica*, **20**, 160–170.

Charnes (A.), Cooper (W. W.) and Henderson (A.) (1953) : *An Introduction to Linear Programming* (Wiley, 1953).

Chipman (J.) (1953) : " Computational Problems in Linear Programming ", *Review of Economics and Statistics*, **35**, 342–9.

Danø (S.) (1958) : *Linear Programming in Industry : Theory and Applications* (to appear).

Dantzig (G. B.) (1949) : " The Programming of Interdependent Activities : Mathematical Model ", *Econometrica*, **23**, 200–11.

Dorfman (R.) (1951) : *Application of Linear Programming to the Theory of the Firm* (California, 1951).

Dorfman (R.), Samuelson (P. A.) and Solow (R. M.) (1958) : *Linear Programming and Economic Analysis* (McGraw-Hill, 1958), Chapters 1–4 and 16.

Kemeny (J. G.), Snell (J. L.) and Thompson (G. L.) (1957) : *Introduction to Finite Mathematics* (Prentice-Hall, 1957), Chapter VI.

Koopmans (T. C.) (Editor) (1951) : *Activity Analysis of Production and Allocation* (Wiley, 1951).

Lomax (K. S.) (1952) : " Allocation and Programming in Modern Economics ", *Manchester Statistical Society* (1952), 1–48.

McKinsey (J. C. C.) (1952) : *Introduction to the Theory of Games* (McGraw-Hill, 1952), Chapter 14.

Morton (G.) (1950) : *Food Consumption Levels—Some International Comparisons* (London Ph.D. thesis, unpublished).

Morton (G.) (1951) : " Notes on Linear Programming ", *Economica*, **18**, 397–411.

Newman (P.) (1955) : " Some Calculations on Least-cost Diets using the Simplex Method ", *Bulletin of Oxford Institute of Statistics*, **17**, 303–20.

Stigler (G. J.) (1945) : " The Cost of Subsistence ", *Journal Farm Economics*, **27**, 303–14.

Vajda (S.) and others (1955) : " Symposium on Linear Programming ", *Journal Royal Statistical Society*, Series B, **17**, 165–203.

Vajda (S.) (1956) : *The Theory of Games and Linear Programming* (Methuen, 1956), Chapter IV–XI.

Waugh (F. V.) and Burrows (E. L.) (1955) : " A Short Cut to Linear Programming ", *Econometrica*, **23**, 18–29.

Wood (M. K.) and Dantzig (G. B.) (1949) : " The Programming of Interdependent Activities : General Discussion ", *Econometrica*, **17**, 193–99.

CHAPTER 17

PROGRAMMING OF ACTIVITIES; ALLOCATION OF RESOURCES

17.1 Introduction: General Economic Equilibrium

THE main thread of economic theory is now taken up again: static and dynamic models of general scope. Economic equilibrium is defined broadly in Chapter 10 and in very special form in Chapter 11; these apparently divergent lines of approach need to be pulled together. The Walrasian system of Chapter 10 allows for all possible inter-relations in what Robbins (1932) has described as *the* economic problem: the use of limited resources to obtain certain economic objectives. All this is far too general. Even with the ingenuity of Hicks or Samuelson, few results of empirical content can be derived. It is true that a count of equations shows that solutions are *possible*—but not that they *exist*, at least with non-negative prices and quantities.

These objections can be met by the double device of taking a *linear system* with equations replaced by *linear inequalities*. This is not very restrictive for linearity means fixed production coefficients, *not* linear demand or cost functions—and inequalities are required in any case, e.g. $p \geqslant 0$ for a price.

The *linear Walrasian system* of 10.2 above has fixed production co-efficients. For convenience here, simplify further by taking a fixed supply $\overline{X}_s$ of each of k factors ($s = 1, 2, \ldots k$) and m consumer goods ($t = 1, 2, \ldots m$) with no initial stocks. Equations (i) and (iii) of 10.2 give market demand functions X_t for consumer goods, each in terms of the prices of all consumer goods. Write a_{st} as the set of fixed technical coefficients, π_s for factor prices and p_t for prices of consumer goods. There remain two sets of linear equations, (ii) of 10.2:

(a) $\sum_t a_{st} X_t = \overline{X}_s$ ($s = 1, 2, \ldots k$)   (b) $\sum_s \pi_s a_{st} = p_t$ ($t = 1, 2, \ldots m$)

Since X_t are in terms of prices and $\overline{X}_s$ given, these are equations for market prices.

As suggested by Zeuthen (p. 317 above), if solutions are limited to *non-negative prices* ($\pi_s \geqslant 0$, $p_t \geqslant 0$), then the equations must be turned into inequalities. Set (a) must state, not that " given resources are used exactly ", but that " not more than given resources can be used ". Similarly, set (b) require negative or zero profits, not zero profits exactly. So :

(a) $\Sigma_t a_{st} X_t \leqslant \bar{X}_s$ $(s = 1, 2, \ldots k)$ (b) $\Sigma_s \pi_s a_{st} \geqslant p_t$ $(t = 1, 2, \ldots m)$

In full, the linear inequalities are :

(a) $a_{11} X_1 + a_{12} X_2 + \ldots + a_{1m} X_m \leqslant \bar{X}_1$ (b) $a_{11} \pi_1 + a_{21} \pi_2 + \ldots + a_{k1} \pi_k \geqslant p_1$
$a_{21} X_1 + a_{22} X_2 + \ldots + a_{2m} X_m \leqslant \bar{X}_2$ $a_{12} \pi_1 + a_{22} \pi_2 + \ldots + a_{k2} \pi_k \geqslant p_2$
....
$a_{k1} X_1 + a_{k2} X_2 + \ldots + a_{km} X_m \leqslant \bar{X}_k$ $a_{1m} \pi_1 + a_{2m} \pi_2 + \ldots + a_{km} \pi_k \geqslant p_m$

Now (as in game theory, property (iii) of 15.7 above) a *strict* inequality for factor s in (a) implies that the factor is not fully employed and its price π_s must be zero. Similarly, a *strict* inequality for good t in (b) means negative profits and output X_t must be zero. Here are the distinctions between free and scarce factors, between lines of production used and not used.

The linear Walrasian system is then similar to a linear programme with dual sets of inequalities. A basic result can now be proved, one that Walras and his followers never established. Under very simple conditions (e.g. continuous demand functions at all price configurations), *there exist solutions of the system* : one or more sets of non-negative prices. A simple proof is given by Dorfman, Samuelson and Solow (1958), Chapter 13, using the concept of a linear programme and its dual. This is a modified version of the original proof by Wald (1935, 1951). A more general approach is that of Arrow and Debreu (1954).

Two points are to be noticed. The Walrasian system in linear form has appropriate solutions ; the " no solution " case is out. There can still be multiple solutions, alternative sets of non-negative prices. More stringent conditions are required for a unique solution and, as Dorfman, Samuelson and Solow (1958) show, these have to do with the " revealed preferences " properties of the market demand functions. The other point is that the existence proof, as indicated here, applies to linear systems. But it is to be expected that solutions exist for other systems with continuous production functions, marginal products, and so on. General competitive equilibrium is not an idle exercise ; it does have solutions, established by linear programming methods. This represents the original achievement of Wald.

The Leontief system of Chapter 11 now fits well. It is a linear system with fixed input-output relations and it gets quickly to results of use in practice. It only needs a little tidying up, e.g. in the matter of the apparent lack of substitution possibilities in production. Neither of the linear systems of Walras and Leontief is a linear programme, but they are obviously related to linear programming. The theories of games and linear programming (Chapters 15 and 16) are going to have applications in the general problem of economic equilibrium and dynamics.

In a consolidated attack by linear programming methods on the broad economic problem of allocation of limited resources to attain given production objectives, the elements of the problem are :

(i) The technical conditions on productive possibilities specified (usually) in linear form as fixed coefficients making up a matrix.

(ii) The resources available specified (usually) as a vector of amounts of various primary factors which cannot be exceeded.

(iii) The objective specified in terms of final products and other desired commodities, together with the optimal procedure of selecting the most efficient allocation of resources under the given technical conditions.

With the emphasis so placed on the technical aspects of the problem, there seems to be no place for a consideration of the function of markets, of market prices, of profits. However, once a linear problem has been set up on the basis of technology, the dual problem can be written and examined and it is here that prices and profits are to be sought. The function of market prices and of profits then becomes clear, as guides to efficient allocation of technical resources and as means of allowing for varying degrees of centralisation or de-centralisation in combining activities. Linear programming then has an obvious and direct bearing on the economics of socialism and collectivist planning, see Mises (1935). The point is : no matter how far the price mechanism allows for de-centralisation, there remain some technical choices and decisions which *must* be taken by someone. Other decisions *may* also be made, e.g. by the state.

Hence, despite the apparent concentration on purely technical aspects, application of linear programming in general economic equilibrium does keep the necessary balance between technology and the market mechanism. Its advantage is that it allows for the inequalities inevitably present in a " real " problem. Its disadvantage is a simplification of technical conditions, inevitable when solutions to actual problems are required within the limits of computing practice. See Chipman (1953).

Linear programming has many fields of application varying from problems of shipping and military logistics to technical decisions within the firm. The particular application now considered is in the study of inter-industry relations—the allocation of resources in production, the programming of productive activities, in the context of general economic equilibrium. Applications to the theory of the firm and to consumers' behaviour are taken up in the following chapters.

17.2 Activity Analysis : Concepts and Definitions

The application of linear programming to the analysis of production in the broad is most easily interpreted in economic terms if the general concepts of " commodities " and " activities " used are first defined explicitly. The best account is that given in Koopmans (1951), Chapter III.

Commodities are defined in the sense of Chapter 10 above. They comprise :

(i) primary factors (such as labour and raw materials) available as resources from outside the system considered ;

(ii) intermediate products, produced and used within the system ;

(iii) final products, produced within the system and made available to meet the objectives of the system.

Hence primary factors are among the given resources ; final products are among the requirements or objectives ; intermediate products like pig iron or cotton yarn are neither. There is a complication in that some primary factors may themselves be " required " in the objectives, e.g. labour used directly to meet final demand. It is convenient, in meeting this difficulty, to assume either that no primary factors are amongst requirements or that all are.

Take m commodities, $r=1, 2, \ldots m$. Write x_r for the *output* of each $(r=1, 2, \ldots m)$; x_r is net output and it may be positive, negative or zero. If $x_r > 0$, the rth commodity is a final product, meeting final requirements. If $x_r < 0$ the rth commodity is an input, a factor used up. If $x_r = 0$, it is an intermediate product, what is produced is also used up in the system.

Activities are combinations of commodities, some being inputs used in fixed proportions to produce others as outputs in fixed proportions (as in 10.8 above). An activity is a quantitative concept ; it has a *level* and hence a *unit* size. A unit level of an activity (the sth) is represented by the vector of order m :

$$\mathbf{A}^{(s)} = \{a_{rs}\} = \begin{bmatrix} a_{1s} \\ a_{2s} \\ \ldots\ldots \\ a_{ms} \end{bmatrix}$$

where a_{rs} represents the amount (or rate of flow) of the rth commodity involved in the unit activity. If $a_{rs} < 0$, the rth commodity is among the inputs of the activity ; if $a_{rs} > 0$, it is an output. All are in fixed proportions because the a_{rs} are fixed and given constants. If $a_{rs} = 0$, the rth commodity does not enter the activity, except perhaps as an intermediate product.

Two assumptions are made, corresponding to the usual properties of vectors. *First*, two activities are additive without change in their structural coefficients. So, if a_{r1} and a_{r2} are the outputs of the rth commodity in two activities $\mathbf{A}^{(1)}$ and $\mathbf{A}^{(2)}$, then the combined activity produces $(a_{r1}+a_{r2})$. This is expressed :

$$\mathbf{A}^{(s)}+\mathbf{A}^{(t)}=\{a_{rs}\}+\{a_{rt}\}=\{(a_{rs}+a_{rt})\} \quad\text{...................(1)}$$

Second, the level of an activity is fixed by a scalar multiple λ of the unit activity. As the level increases, so each input or output (over all commodities) increases in proportion. This can be written, for any $\lambda \geqslant 0$:

$$\lambda\mathbf{A}^{(s)}=\lambda\{a_{rs}\}=\{\lambda a_{rs}\} \quad\text{.............................(2)}$$

The assumptions imply *constant returns* to scale both in combining activities and within one activity. Further, if the level is to vary continuously with a continuous multiple λ, an activity must be *perfectly divisible* ; all inputs and outputs must move together and continuously. In the light of the considerations of 10.8 above, it can be said that it is the first of these assumptions which is the more restrictive ; in practice, production processes may not be additive in the simple sense assumed here.

The two results (1) and (2) taken together serve to define a (positive linear) combination of any given set of k activities :

$$\sum_{s=1}^{k}\lambda_s\mathbf{A}^{(s)}= \sum_{s=1}^{k}\lambda_s\{a_{rs}\}=\{(\sum_{s=1}^{k}\lambda_s a_{rs})\} \quad (\lambda_s\geqslant 0) \quad\text{...................(3)}$$

The sum $\Sigma \lambda_s \mathbf{A}^{(s)}$ is itself an activity ; it is a column of m inputs and outputs in fixed proportions. Clearly there are many such activities for different non-negative λ_s, and for various activities $\mathbf{A}^{(s)}$ combined. Given a complete range of them, they can be classified into basic activities and those which are combinations of basic activities.

In a system of activities, the set of *basic activities* comprises those which are *not* (positive linear) combinations of other activities in the system. Let the basic activities be n in number :

$$\mathbf{A}^{(1)}=\begin{bmatrix} a_{11} \\ a_{21} \\ \cdots \\ a_{m1} \end{bmatrix} \mathbf{A}^{(2)}=\begin{bmatrix} a_{12} \\ a_{22} \\ \cdots \\ a_{m2} \end{bmatrix} \cdots \mathbf{A}^{(s)}=\begin{bmatrix} a_{1s} \\ a_{2s} \\ \cdots \\ a_{ms} \end{bmatrix} \cdots \mathbf{A}^{(n)}=\begin{bmatrix} a_{1n} \\ a_{2n} \\ \cdots \\ a_{mn} \end{bmatrix}$$

They can be put together into a matrix $\mathbf{A}$ which defines the *technology* of the system :

$$\mathbf{A}=\begin{bmatrix} a_{11} & a_{12} & \cdots & a_{1n} \\ a_{21} & a_{22} & \cdots & a_{2n} \\ \cdots & \cdots & \cdots & \cdots \\ a_{m1} & a_{m2} & \cdots & a_{mn} \end{bmatrix}$$

Any activity, the basic ones and all others, can then be written by (3) as a positive linear combination of $\mathbf{A}^{(s)}$ with various (non-negative) λ_s. The general activity $\Sigma \lambda_s \mathbf{A}^{(s)}$ is very wide in scope, since some of the λ's can be zero and the others can take any positive values whatever.

The technology $\mathbf{A}$ is a matrix of order $m \times n$. Read across a row, $\mathbf{A}$ gives the inputs or outputs of a given commodity in the n basic activities. Read down a column, $\mathbf{A}$ gives the inputs or outputs of m commodities for a given basic activity. It summarises all the technical possibilities. For example, consider ways of getting an output x_1 of the first commodity. There may be several positive entries in the first row of $\mathbf{A}$ and x_1 can be got by using any of the corresponding activities, alone or in combination. So x_1 is the first element in the vector $\Sigma \lambda_s \mathbf{A}^{(s)}$ where Σ extends over all columns in which the first entry is positive. The relative values of the λ's can be changed, so varying the allocation of resources ; the absolute value of the λ's can be changed, so altering the scale of production. At the same time, some other commodities may be jointly produced, since among the columns $\mathbf{A}^{(s)}$ with a first positive entry there may be columns with one other, two other, ... positive elements. An illustration is given in Ex. 4 below.

Activity analysis deals with production or transformation in the wide sense of 10.8 above. The technology $\mathbf{A}$ is designed to show up the alternative production processes available—to indicate why one is selected rather than another and what switching of processes follows any change in the given conditions of the economic problem. It leaves open all questions of managerial decision ; it does not assume away the technical choices facing the production manager.

The great range of application and interpretation of the technology $\mathbf{A}$ is clear. For example, it may express the nutrient/food relations of the problem of 16.1 above. Or, it may apply to various problems of transportation ; for example, in shipping a homogeneous product between port P and port Q, there are two " commodities ", the product at P and the same product at Q, and the shipment from P to Q is an " activity " with the first commodity as input and the second as output.

EXERCISES 17.2

1. Commodities and associated activities are here described for an " open " system, given resources coming in and final products going out. Show that the matrix $\mathbf{A}$ applies equally well to a " closed " system, a_{rs} being positive, negative or zero according to the uses of the rth commodities in the sth activity, but that all commodities are intermediate with $x_r = 0$. What kind of activity then has (e.g.) man-hours of work as its output?

2. Consider the treatment of labour as the rth commodity in an open system, the total amount of labour used ($-x_r$) being then a fixed amount $\bar{x}_r$ available. Is it convenient to have an activity " recreation " with one output " leisure " and one input " labour "? Or should only unskilled labour be the primary factor, with skilled labour as the " output " of the activity " training "?

3. In an open system, if the rth commodity is a primary factor limited in availability ($-x_r$) $\leqslant \bar{x}_r$, how should " free goods " available to the system be treated? Is it the same thing (i) to put $\bar{x}_r$ infinite, or (ii) to omit the commodity altogether, if the rth commodity is free?

4. Suppose that the columns of the technology A with positive entries in the first row (first commodity produced) are :

$$\begin{bmatrix} 1 & 1 & 1 \\ -1 & 2 & 1 \\ 0 & -1 & 2 \\ -1 & -3 & -4 \end{bmatrix}$$

Interpret and show that the first commodity may be produced alone, jointly with the second commodity, or jointly with the second and third commodities. Show that *all* the different ways of producing one unit of the first commodity can be shown in one combination of activities with variable multiples λ_1, λ_2 and λ_3 subject to $\lambda_1 + \lambda_2 + \lambda_3 = 1$. Write the net output (positive, zero or negative) of each of the other three commodities and examine under what conditions these are outputs or inputs.

17.3 Leontief's Open System as Linear Programming of Activities

The open form of Leontief's static model of inter-industry relations is formulated in 14.7 above. Take n industries and commodities, together with one primary factor (labour). The *given data* for the n industries ($r = 1, 2, \ldots n$) are :

$A = I - A^*$ where $A^* = [a_{rs}]$ is the $n \times n$ matrix of input coefficients (with $a_{rr} = 0$ by convention) ;

$\mathbf{b} = \{b_r\}$ a vector of labour input coefficients ;

$\mathbf{x} = \{x_r\}$ a vector of final demands for outputs of industries ;

$\mathbf{w} = \{w_r\}$ a vector of wage costs per unit output.

If w is a given wage rate (a scalar) for the primary factor, there is the relation between $\mathbf{b}$ and $\mathbf{w}$:

$$\mathbf{w} = w\mathbf{b}$$

The *variables* are :

$\mathbf{X} = \{X_r\}$ a vector of total outputs of industries ;

$\mathbf{p} = \{p_r\}$ a vector of prices of outputs.

A is a square matrix of order n ; all vectors are of order n.

The technology of Leontief's system is the matrix $\begin{bmatrix} A \\ \cdots \\ -\mathbf{b}' \end{bmatrix}$ of order

$(n+1) \times n$. The last row has entries which are all negative, labour input coefficients. The rest of the matrix is made up of rows and columns each of which has only one positive entry (unity). Each industry (activity) has a single and distinct product, and all other commodities are inputs or do not appear at all. Each commodity is produced in only one way in the appropriate industry, but can be used as an input in any other industry.

The *equilibrium conditions* of the system are :

$$\text{(i)} \quad \mathbf{AX}=\mathbf{x} \quad \text{and} \quad \text{(ii)} \quad \mathbf{A'p}=\mathbf{w}$$

to which should be added $\mathbf{X} \geqslant 0$ and $\mathbf{p} \geqslant 0$ since outputs and prices are non-negative. The condition (ii) is the transpose of the form $(\mathbf{p'A}=\mathbf{w'})$ in which it is written in 14.7 above.

Two scalar values can be defined from the variables $\mathbf{X}$ and $\mathbf{p}$. Total employment of the primary factor is $Y=\mathbf{b'X}$. Write $z=wY$ for the wage bill :

$$\text{Wage bill} \quad z=w\mathbf{b'X}=\mathbf{w'X}$$

a linear function of variable outputs $\mathbf{X}$. The variable prices $\mathbf{p}$ can be used to give total expenditure on final demand :

$$\text{Final expenditure} \quad \zeta=\mathbf{x'p}$$

The system can now be written as a particular linear programme together with its dual :

(i) $z=\mathbf{w'X}$ (ii) $\zeta=\mathbf{x'p}$

subject to $\quad \mathbf{AX}=\mathbf{x}$ subject to $\mathbf{A'p}=\mathbf{w}$

and $\quad\quad \mathbf{X} \geqslant 0$ and $\quad\quad \mathbf{p} \geqslant 0$

It is to be stressed that z and ζ are *not* maximum or minimum ; they are simply *given* in terms of $\mathbf{X}$ and $\mathbf{p}$. Why there are no optimal conditions in the linear programme becomes clear when the nature of the solution is examined. The clue is the number of variables and equations in (i) and (ii) ; there are n variables in both the linear programme and its dual and there are also n side equations. Hence, the equations being linear and $\mathbf{A}$ being assumed non-singular, if there is a feasible solution at all ($\mathbf{X} \geqslant 0$, $\mathbf{p} \geqslant 0$), then it is unique. There is, therefore, no room for any maximum or minimum of z or ζ ; there can be no optimal feasible solution. There is just one solution for $\mathbf{X}$ or $\mathbf{p}$ from the side equations and, corresponding to it, just one value for z or ζ. This fits into the general considerations of 17.1 above, if it is taken that, in allocating resources to meet final demand in Leontief's system, there is no need for anyone to make an optimal choice. In Leontief's system, there is no choice or substitution between activities ; why the activity used to produce a given product is chosen rather than others is assumed away in the formulation of the problem.

However, (i) and (ii) above are a linear programming problem and its dual ; they have a common and unique solution. It only remains to write the solutions and link them together as the same thing. The solution is by the inversion of the matrix A to A^{-1} :

$$\text{(i) } X = A^{-1}x \quad \text{and} \quad \text{(ii) } p = (A')^{-1}w \text{ or } p' = w'A^{-1}$$

In this way, variable outputs X are given in terms of final demands x and variable prices p are given in terms of wage costs w. The common element is that the wage bill z and the final expenditure ζ are equal in value. This is the expression of (i) and (ii) as dual problems in linear programming. To find the common value :

Wage bill $\qquad z = w'X = w'A^{-1}x$

Final expenditure $\qquad \zeta = x'p = p'x = w'A^{-1}x$

The primary factor is labour, the final demand is the demand of consumers who provide the labour ; in equilibrium, income and expenditure balance.

Here is the first illustration of a point made towards the end of 17.1 above. Leontief's open system can be expressed solely in terms of the linear programme (i). Hence total outputs are given in terms of final demands, $X = A^{-1}x$, and the wage bill is $z = w'A^{-1}x$. There is no reference at all to market prices or to expenditure. But these come in when the dual of the linear programming problem is written, as it always can be. Then, market prices are also given, $p = (A')^{-1}w$. The prices are such that everything squares up, e.g. final expenditure $= w'A^{-1}x =$ wage bill.

17.4 Substitution in Leontief's Open System

The assumptions of Leontief's open system are two-fold. First, it is taken that each industry produces one separate and distinct product with constant returns to scale. There is nothing to be done about this ; it is a simplifying assumption, of an empirical nature, which serves to describe the type of economy considered. The other assumption is of a different kind, i.e. that there is for each industry only one production process. The various industries contribute only one column each to the technology matrix. This seems to rule out all possibilities of substitution in production, or at least to eliminate any explanation of how the one process is chosen rather than other possible processes.

With Fig. 44 and 45 (pp. 335, 338 above) the second assumption is as follows. *Either* production in an industry is technically confined to the use of inputs in fixed proportions (Fig. 44b); *or* one production process is selected from a specified and limited number available (Fig. 45); *or* one line of production, with inputs in fixed proportions, is selected and runs across the constant product loci obtained from a continuous (linear homogeneous) production function (Fig. 44a). As long as the decision-taking factor is ignored—and constant returns to scale assumed—it is quite immaterial what is taken to lie behind the single process specified for the industry. The point, however, can be examined further, in more precise and algebraic terms.

Consider Leontief's system in terms of outputs and ignore the dual problem in prices; also write the equations with employment Y rather than the wage bill z. Then:

$$\mathbf{AX} = \mathbf{x} \quad \text{and} \quad -\mathbf{b'X} = -Y \quad \dots\dots\dots\dots\dots\dots(1)$$

are $(n+1)$ equations of the system with the technology matrix $\begin{bmatrix} \mathbf{A} \\ \dots\dots \\ -\mathbf{b'} \end{bmatrix}$

appearing as the coefficients on the left-hand side. If the final demands $\mathbf{x} = (x_1, x_2, \dots x_n)$ are given, the equations serve to determine the total outputs $\mathbf{X}$ and employment Y. In particular, Y is given as a linear expression in the x's:

$$Y = \mathbf{b'A^{-1}x} \dots\dots\dots\dots\dots\dots\dots\dots\dots(2)$$

Now suppose that $x_2, x_3, \dots x_n$ are still given, but not x_1, the final demand for the first good. Then the system (1) can be written:

$$\text{subject to} \quad \left. \begin{array}{l} x_1 = X_1 - a_{12}X_2 - \dots - a_{1n}X_n = \text{max.} \\ -a_{21}X_1 + \quad X_2 - \dots - a_{2n}X_n = x_2 \\ \dots\dots\dots\dots\dots\dots\dots\dots\dots\dots\dots \\ -a_{n1}X_1 - a_{n2}X_2 - \dots + \quad X_n = x_n \\ -b_1X_1 - b_2X_2 - \dots - b_nX_n = -Y \end{array} \right\} \quad \dots\dots\dots\dots(3)$$

The linear programme now has a maximum condition. There are n side equations which serve to express the X's in terms of Y. Hence x_1 appears as a function of Y to be maximised; if the programme has a feasible solution, this maximum of x_1 is restricted only by total labour available, being infinite otherwise. The final result is that the X's are all found, in terms of the given $x_2, x_3, \dots x_n$; the maximised value of x_1 is also found in terms of the same given elements.

The solution of (3) is much the same in nature as that of (1). The difference is mainly one of interpretation, i.e. x_1 is maximised, not given. In particular, the value of Y which is determined is still linear in all the

x's exactly as in (2); the difference is that x_1 as a maximum is to be expressed in terms of $x_2, x_3, \ldots x_n$ instead of being given like the others.

The form (3) can be generalised to apply to the case where the technical coefficients $a_{rs} = \dfrac{x_{rs}}{X_s}$ and $b_s = \dfrac{x_{n+1s}}{X_s}$ are not constants. Re-write (3) in the variables $x_{rs} =$ the amount of the rth commodity used as an input in the sth industry. So, with $x_{rr} = 0$:

$$
\left.
\begin{aligned}
x_1 = X_1 - \sum_{s=1}^{n} x_{1s} &= \text{max.} \\
\text{subject to} \qquad X_r - \sum_{s=1}^{n} x_{rs} &= x_r \quad (r = 2, 3, \ldots n) \\
\text{and} \qquad \sum_{s=1}^{n} x_{n+1s} &= Y
\end{aligned}
\right\} \quad \ldots\ldots\ldots\ldots\ldots (4)
$$

The $(n+1)$th commodity is labour, used as an input in all industries; there is no corresponding industry and hence no x_{n+1} or X_{n+1}.

The linear programme (4) is exactly the same as (3) provided that the technical coefficients are fixed. On the other hand, (4) remains a problem of restrained maximum even when the technical proportions are no longer constant. This is the problem to be explored.

The output X_1 of the first commodity is produced with inputs x_{r1} of the other commodities $(r = 2, 3, \ldots n)$ and with labour input $x_{n+1\,1}$. Assume that there is a production function of linear homogeneous form :

$$
\left.
\begin{aligned}
X_1 &= f_1(x_{21}, x_{31}, \ldots x_{n1}, x_{n+11}) \\
\lambda X_1 &= f_1(\lambda x_{21}, \lambda x_{31}, \ldots \lambda x_{n1}, \lambda x_{n+11})
\end{aligned}
\right\} \quad \ldots\ldots\ldots\ldots (5)
$$

such that

for any $\lambda > 0$. As a particular case, write $\lambda = \dfrac{1}{X_1}$ so that :

$$
f_1 \left(\frac{x_{21}}{X_1}, \frac{x_{31}}{X_1}, \ldots \frac{x_{n1}}{X_1}, \frac{x_{n+11}}{X_1} \right) = 1
$$

i.e. $\qquad f_1(a_{21}, a_{31}, \ldots a_{n1}, b_1) = 1$

where a's and b are technical coefficients as before. The difference is that the coefficients are variable and not fixed. In the Leontief system with technology $\begin{bmatrix} \mathbf{A} \\ \cdots \\ -\mathbf{b}' \end{bmatrix}$, the coefficients are fixed and they are to be read off the first column of the matrix, i.e. 1 as the first entry followed by $(-a_{21})$, $(-a_{31}), \ldots (-a_{n1}), (-b_1)$. Substitution between inputs is now possible, whereas in Leontief's system it is not.

Write (4) with production functions of the type (5) for all n commodities :

$$\left.\begin{aligned}
x_1 = f_1(x_{11}, x_{21}, \ldots x_{n+1\,1}) &- \sum_{s=1}^{n} x_{1s} &= \text{max.} \\
\text{subject to} \quad f_r(x_{1r}, x_{2r}, \ldots x_{n+1\,r}) &- \sum_{s=1}^{n} x_{rs} &= x_r (r=2, 3, \ldots n) \\
\text{and} \quad &\sum_{s=1}^{n} x_{n+1\,s} &= Y
\end{aligned}\right\} \quad \ldots\ldots\ldots(6)$$

where $x_{rr}\ (=0)$ is also written as a " variable " in the production functions to simplify the notation. There are $n(n+1)$ variables x_{rs} to be determined, for $r=1, 2, \ldots (n+1)$ and $s=1, 2, \ldots n$. A function of these variables is to be maximised subject to n side equations. There are n given values, $x_r\ (r=2, 3, \ldots n)$ and Y.

As a problem in the calculus, it can be shown that the conditions for maximum x_1 involve, not the $n(n+1)$ variables x_{rs}, but the n^2 ratios $c_{rs} = \dfrac{x_{rs}}{x_{n+1\,s}}$ for r and $s=1, 2, \ldots n$. Further, these ratios are determined irrespective of the values given to $x_2, x_3, \ldots x_n$ and Y. For a proof see Samuelson in Koopmans (1951), Chapter VII.

It follows that, no matter what values are assigned to $x_2, x_3, \ldots x_n$ and Y and no matter what maximum value is assumed by x_1, the ratios :

$$c_{rs} = \frac{x_{rs}}{x_{n+1\,s}} = \frac{a_{rs}}{b_s}$$

are fixed in value in the optimum position of (6). The problem (6) starts with *variable* technical coefficients. But, when the optimum position is reached, the technical coefficients are *fixed*, no matter what values are taken by the x_r and Y. Hence (6) has the same solution as in the Leontief system, which assumes from the beginning that the technical coefficients are fixed.

Finally, though Y is assumed given as well as $x_2, x_3, \ldots x_n$ in (6), this can now be offset in the optimum position by a relation which must exist, as in Leontief's system, between Y and the values of $x_1, x_2, \ldots x_n$ (the first maximised, the others given). The relation is linear and given by (2) above.

The conclusion is that Leontief's system and its solution can allow for substitution of inputs, according to some continuous production function of linear homogeneous form (constant returns to scale). The same result follows if the given process, with fixed technical coefficients, is assumed to be the only possibility, or if it is just one among many available. The point is that Leontief's system is not concerned with decision-taking (e.g. by the firm) and so substitution is incidental.

17.5 Representation of Technical Possibilities

The concept of a technology (17.2 above) is of very wide scope. A matrix of technical coefficients is given: $\mathbf{A} = [a_{rs}]$ of order $m \times n$. There are m commodities corresponding to the rows of $\mathbf{A}$ and n basic activities given by the columns. Reading across a row of $\mathbf{A}$ gives the various outputs or inputs of a certain commodity according to which of the activities is adopted. Reading down a column of $\mathbf{A}$ shows what outputs and inputs are involved in a given basic activity at the unit level. All this applies equally well to various systems, e.g. a firm, a defined sector of the economy, the whole economy (provided that it is open). The matrix does no more than specify the technical possibilities within the system, whatever it is.

Let $\mathbf{x} = \{x_r\}$ $(r = 1, 2, \dots m)$ be the outputs obtained by combining basic activities at levels $\boldsymbol{\lambda} = \{\lambda_s\}$ $(s = 1, 2, \dots n)$ where $\lambda_s \geqslant 0$. Then the *technical transformation* from levels of activity $\boldsymbol{\lambda}$ to outputs $\mathbf{x}$ is given simply by :

$$\mathbf{x} = \mathbf{A}\boldsymbol{\lambda} \quad (\boldsymbol{\lambda} \geqslant 0) \qquad \dots\dots\dots\dots\dots(1)$$

or in full by :

$$\left.\begin{aligned}
x_1 &= a_{11}\lambda_1 + a_{12}\lambda_2 + \dots + a_{1n}\lambda_n \\
x_2 &= a_{21}\lambda_1 + a_{22}\lambda_2 + \dots + a_{2n}\lambda_n \\
&\dots\dots\dots\dots\dots\dots\dots\dots\dots\dots\dots\dots\dots \\
x_m &= a_{m1}\lambda_1 + a_{m2}\lambda_2 + \dots + a_{mn}\lambda_n
\end{aligned}\right\} \qquad \dots\dots\dots\dots\dots(2)$$

All that is technically possible within the system is shown by (1) or (2). They represent all *feasible allocations* of a linear programme which has (1) as its side relations.

The implications of linearity, of constant returns to scale, must be borne in mind. If the level of each activity used is doubled so, by (1), is the output of any commodity ; and similarly for any constant proportion. It is convenient, therefore, to distinguish between the *relative* allocations of resources and the scale of production. A unit combination of basic activities can be defined by $\boldsymbol{\mu} = \{\mu_s\}$, where $\mu_s \geqslant 0$ and $\sum_{s=1}^{n} \mu_s = 1$, with corresponding outputs given by $\mathbf{x} = \mathbf{A}\boldsymbol{\mu}$. As the μ's vary, the relative allocation of resources is changed, always at the unit level. The scale of activity is then allowed for by applying a uniform factor κ to all activity levels. Any allocation or state of production is then given by

$$\boldsymbol{\lambda} = \kappa\{\mu_s\}, \quad \mathbf{x} = \mathbf{A}\boldsymbol{\lambda} = \kappa\mathbf{A}\{\mu_s\}.$$

The distinction between relative allocation $\boldsymbol{\mu}$ and scale κ applies in all cases. For example, if the first basic activity alone is used, then the relative allocation is fixed and $\mu = (1, 0, \ldots 0)$; the scale of production is given by the level λ_1 at which the activity is employed :

$$\mathbf{x} = \mathbf{A}\boldsymbol{\lambda} = \lambda_1 \begin{bmatrix} a_{11} \\ a_{21} \\ \ldots\ldots \\ a_{m1} \end{bmatrix}$$

where $\boldsymbol{\lambda} = (\lambda_1, 0, \ldots 0)$.

The coefficients a_{rs} can be positive, negative or zero according as the commodity is produced (an output), consumed (an input) or not used in the activity concerned. The elements in the output vector $\mathbf{x}$ are to be similarly interpreted by sign. In general, in any realistic system, it can be taken that there is one (or more) final product not available from outside for which $x_r > 0$, and that there is one (or more) primary factor provided from outside for which $x_r < 0$. There may also be intermediate products, $x_r = 0$, neither available from outside, nor produced for use outside the system. On the other hand, it is perfectly possible for a primary factor to be produced as an output in some activities as well as being available from outside, or for a final product to be consumed in some activities as well as being produced for use outside. This means simply that *any* row in $\mathbf{A}$ can contain both positive and negative coefficients. One further property can be taken, however, as characteristic of a realistic system, i.e. that there is at least one primary factor which is always consumed (and never produced). Such a factor can be thought of as " labour ", or at least as " unskilled labour " even if skilled labour is regarded as the product of the activity of " training ". All coefficients in the corresponding row of $\mathbf{A}$ are negative. Similarly, assume at least one final product which may be produced but never consumed in any activity, i.e. a row of $\mathbf{A}$ with all positive (or zero) coefficients.

The properties of the technology now indicated are particular cases. They are convenient for applications of the matrix $\mathbf{A}$ in realistic systems but they are not formally necessary and systems can be defined in which they do not hold. For convenience and simplicity (no more) the following assumptions are here made :

Assumption (i). There must be one commodity (taken as the first) which is made available as a final product for use outside the system and which is not provided as a primary factor from outside the system, or used as an input in any activity, so that $a_{1s} \geqslant 0$ and $x_1 > 0$.

Assumption (ii). There must be one commodity (taken as the last) which is provided as a primary factor from outside and which is used as an input in all activities, so that $a_{ms} < 0$ and $x_m < 0$.

The trivial case $\lambda = 0$, where no activities are used, is ignored throughout; otherwise x_1 and x_m could also be zero. Hence, when $\lambda \geqslant 0$ is written in (1) it must be interpreted as : all $\lambda_s \geqslant 0$ and some $\lambda_s > 0$.

A more general analysis, based on alternative and less restrictive assumptions than those above, is given in Koopmans (1951), Chapter III. One particular alternative assumption is considered and illustrated in Ex. 4 and 5 below.

A diagrammatic representation of the technical possibilities arising from the transformation (1) is useful in all cases, but particularly when the number of commodities m is not greater than 3. There are two spaces in which points λ and x respectively can be shown. *Activity space* of n dimensions contains points $\lambda = (\lambda_1, \lambda_2, \ldots \lambda_n)$, each of which represents a particular combination of activities ; since $\lambda \geqslant 0$ only the positive segment of this space needs to be taken. Even more useful is *commodity space* of m dimensions, containing points $x = (x_1, x_2, \ldots x_m)$, each of which represents a particular set of outputs. Various segments of this space must be considered since the x's can be positive (outputs) or negative (inputs) ; but, by the assumptions, only positive x_1 and negative x_m are here taken, a considerable simplification. The transformation (1) is then a " mapping " of the activity space onto the commodity space, and the mathematics of " topology " are of immediate application (see 12.5 above). The present analysis, however, avoids the more technical mathematical aspects ; it is confined to an examination of the cases $m = 2$, 3 with diagrammatic representation in two- or three-dimensional commodity space. More general results are stated only by analogy with those found for $m = 3$.

Take first the case of two commodities and two activities ($m = n = 2$) :

$$A = \begin{bmatrix} a_{11} & a_{12} \\ a_{21} & a_{22} \end{bmatrix}$$

The two basic activities are $A^{(1)} = \begin{bmatrix} a_{11} \\ a_{21} \end{bmatrix}$, $A^{(2)} = \begin{bmatrix} a_{12} \\ a_{22} \end{bmatrix}$. By the assumptions, a_{11} and a_{12} are non-negative, a_{21} and a_{22} negative. Since the choice of unit level of each activity is arbitrary, it is quite convenient to take $a_{21} = a_{22} = -1$, i.e. unit activity is that with a unit input of " labour ". The non-negative a_{11} and a_{12} then show the output of the final product x_1 per unit of " labour " on the two basic activities. In commodity space Ox_1x_2, plot the points $A^{(1)} = (a_{11}, -1)$ and $A^{(2)} = (a_{12}, -1)$. These represent output when one or the other basic activity is used at unit level. For any combination of the basic activities, still at unit level:

$$\left.\begin{array}{l} x_1 = a_{11}\mu + a_{12}(1-\mu) \\ x_2 = a_{21}\mu + a_{22}(1-\mu) = -1 \end{array}\right\} \quad (0 \leqslant \mu \leqslant 1)$$

as shown by a point P on the segment of line between $A^{(1)}$ and $A^{(2)}$ in Fig. 61. To allow for scale of production, the results for unit level can be

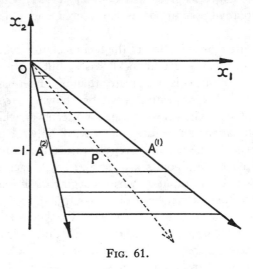

FIG. 61.

multiplied by any factor κ ($\kappa > 0$). In terms of Fig. 61, this means that any point on the half-line $OA^{(1)}$ gives output for the first activity at various levels, and similarly for $OA^{(2)}$ and in general for OP. So, any possible output $\mathbf{x} = \mathbf{A}\boldsymbol{\lambda} = \kappa\mathbf{A}\{\mu, 1-\mu\}$ is shown by some point on the half-line OP, where OP can swing between $OA^{(1)}$ and $OA^{(2)}$ inclusive. Hence all *feasible points* $\mathbf{x} = \mathbf{A}\boldsymbol{\lambda}$ lie in or on the boundary of the *cone $OA^{(1)}A^{(2)}$* shown shaded in Fig. 61. By the assumptions, this cone is pointed at O and lies in the quadrant: $x_1 > 0$, $x_2 < 0$. This is the diagrammatic equivalent of *feasible allocations* of resources or production, of feasible solutions in the sense of linear programming.

It is shown in Ex. 6 below that cases of two commodities and three or more activities ($m = 2$, $n > 2$) are not possible on the assumptions made. In any case, the two-commodity problem is not very interesting, one commodity being " labour " and the other a single final product. It is more important to turn to the case of three commodities ($m = 3$) with illustrations in three-dimensional commodity space. The number of activities can then vary from two upwards.

The case of three commodities, two activities ($m=3$, $n=2$) has

$$\mathbf{A}=\begin{bmatrix} a_{11} & a_{12} \\ a_{21} & a_{22} \\ a_{31} & a_{32} \end{bmatrix} \qquad \mathbf{A}^{(1)}=\begin{bmatrix} a_{11} \\ a_{21} \\ a_{31} \end{bmatrix} \qquad \mathbf{A}^{(2)}=\begin{bmatrix} a_{12} \\ a_{22} \\ a_{32} \end{bmatrix}$$

where a_{11}, $a_{12} \geqslant 0$ and a_{31}, $a_{32} < 0$ on the assumptions. This is illustrated in Fig. 62, again with unit levels taken for $a_{31}=a_{32}=-1$.

The two points $A^{(1)}$ and $A^{(2)}$ are plotted in space $Ox_1x_2x_3$ and any possible allocation is then represented by a point $\mathbf{x}$ in or on the boundary

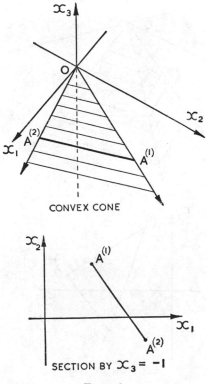

FIG. 62.

of the two-dimensional cone $OA^{(1)}A^{(2)}$. Again *feasible points* $\mathbf{x}=\mathbf{A}\boldsymbol{\lambda}$ lie in or on a two-dimensional cone, pointed at O, but in three dimensions. The section of the cone by the plane $x_3=-1$ (corresponding to unit level of activity, outputs per unit of " labour ") is also shown in Fig. 62. It is the line segment joining two points $A^{(1)}$ and $A^{(2)}$, which must lie somewhere to the right of the vertical (x_2) axis by the assumptions.

When there are three commodities, three activities ($m=n=3$):

$$\mathbf{A}=\begin{bmatrix} a_{11} & a_{12} & a_{13} \\ a_{21} & a_{22} & a_{23} \\ a_{31} & a_{32} & a_{33} \end{bmatrix} \quad \mathbf{A}^{(1)}=\begin{bmatrix} a_{11} \\ a_{21} \\ a_{31} \end{bmatrix} \quad \mathbf{A}^{(2)}=\begin{bmatrix} a_{12} \\ a_{22} \\ a_{32} \end{bmatrix} \quad \mathbf{A}^{(3)}=\begin{bmatrix} a_{13} \\ a_{23} \\ a_{33} \end{bmatrix}$$

and the position is shown in Fig. 63. Again a_{11}, a_{12}, $a_{13} \geqslant 0$, and $a_{31}=a_{32}=a_{33}=-1$ by choice of unit levels. The three points $A^{(1)}$, $A^{(2)}$

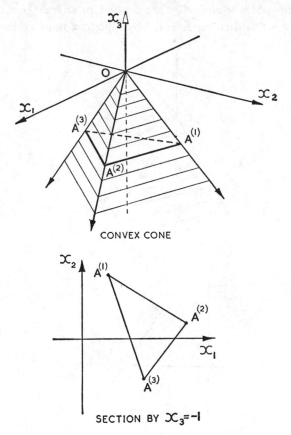

CONVEX CONE

SECTION BY $x_3=-1$

Fig. 63.

and $A^{(3)}$ in space $Ox_1x_2x_3$, and on the section by the plane $x_3=-1$, make up a triangle in two-dimensions. It is not possible for one of the points (e.g. $A^{(3)}$) to lie on the segment of line between the other two. If this were so, then activity $\mathbf{A}^{(3)}$ would be a combination of the activities $\mathbf{A}^{(1)}$ and $\mathbf{A}^{(2)}$; it would not be a basic activity and it would not qualify to appear in $\mathbf{A}$. Apart from this, the points $A^{(1)}$, $A^{(2)}$ and $A^{(3)}$

can lie anywhere in the plane to the right of the vertical (x_2) axis in the section by $x_3 = -1$. *Feasible points* $\mathbf{x} = \mathbf{A}\lambda$ lie in or on the three-dimensional cone $OA^{(1)}A^{(2)}A^{(3)}$, which is pointed at O.

If there are more than three activities, so that $\mathbf{A}$ contains more than three columns, i.e. more than three basic activities $\mathbf{A}^{(1)}$, $\mathbf{A}^{(2)}$, $\mathbf{A}^{(3)}$, ... , then the position is very similar as illustrated in Fig. 64. All that is

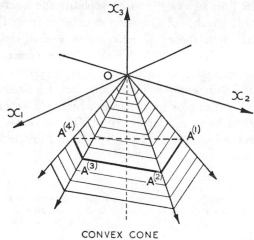

CONVEX CONE

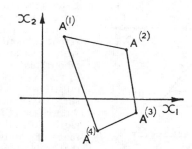

SECTION BY $x_3 = -1$

Fig. 64.

required, to allow for extra basic activities, is that the points $A^{(1)}$, $A^{(2)}$, $A^{(3)}$, ... in the section by $x_3 = -1$ should make up a plane figure and correspond to the extremes of a convex set. This is needed if the activities are to be basic, no one being a combination of any of the others.

Hence, for three commodities ($m = 3$), all technically possible allocations of resources are shown by points in three dimensions which lie on or in a cone pointed at O and the cone is " generated " from a figure in the plane $x_3 = -1$. The plane figure (section by $x_3 = -1$) is a *convex set* with extreme points $A^{(1)}$, $A^{(2)}$, $A^{(3)}$, ... The cone obtained from it has much the same proportions and it can be called a *convex cone*. A distinction can clearly be made between the *interior* and the *boundary* points either of the convex set or of the convex cone. For the cone, the boundary is made up of one or more *facets*, the triangular plane figures like $OA^{(1)}A^{(2)}$, together with the lines like $OA^{(1)}$ which separate the facets.

All this is clearly capable of extension to cases of more than three commodities and the whole theory of convex sets, and of the corresponding cones, is seen to apply (see 16.7 above). For m commodities, feasible allocations in the technology are shown by feasible points $\mathbf{x} = A\lambda$ in or on a convex cone in m dimensions. The cone will be denoted by (A); it has a point at O and one or more facets which are generally of $(m-1)$ dimensions but can be of still lower order. The cone (A) can always be examined in terms of the section by $x_m = -1$ and this is a convex set in $(m-1)$ dimensions.

EXERCISES 17.5

1. Examine the wider range of forms of the cone (A) when assumption (i) is not made while assumption (ii) is retained. If A is of order 2×2, show that the cone can be as in Fig. 65 and that this implies " wasteful " activities (inputs but no outputs).

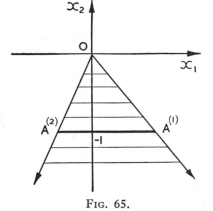

FIG. 65.

2. Extend the illustration of the previous exercise to the case where A is of order 3×3, using Fig. 63 above. Show that activities then exist for producing x_1 with x_2 as an input (in addition to labour) *and* conversely. Deduce that x_1 and x_2 can be final products but must both be available from outside such a system. In what sense is this " unrealistic "? Examine an alternative possibility, that of limiting the range of points λ in activity space so that at least one of x_1 and x_2 is not available from outside the system.

3. Abandon both assumptions (i) and (ii) and show that the cone (A), when A is of order 2×2, can take all kinds of forms, including the " solid " form (covering the whole plane) and the three types of Fig. 66. Extend to the case of A of order 3×3.

4. In place of (i) and (ii) make the two assumptions :

There is no $\lambda \geqslant 0$ such that (a) $\mathbf{x} = A\lambda = 0$ or such that (b) $\mathbf{x} = A\lambda \geqslant 0$

where " $\geqslant$ " excludes the possibility of all elements zero. Show that these are less restrictive than (i) and (ii), i.e. that they hold if (i) and (ii) hold, but not conversely. See Koopmans (1951), Chapter III.

5. In the assumptions of the previous exercise, interpret (a) as " production is not reversible " and (b) as " something cannot be got for nothing ". Show that,

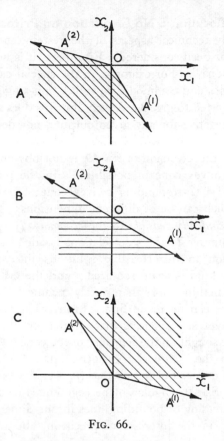

FIG. 66.

when **A** is of order 2×2, assumption (a) cuts out Fig. 66b and assumption (b) cuts out Fig. 66c, so that only cases like Fig. 66a are possible when both are satisfied. Compare with Fig. 61 and 65.

6. Show that the case of **A** of order 2×3 is not possible either on assumptions (i) or (ii) or on the assumptions of Ex. 4 above.

7. Draw diagrams like Fig. 63 when

$$(a) \ \mathbf{A} = \begin{bmatrix} 2 & 3 & 1 \\ 2 & 0 & 3 \\ -1 & -1 & -1 \end{bmatrix} \qquad (b) \ \mathbf{A} = \begin{bmatrix} 1 & 2 & 1 \\ 2 & 1 & 1 \\ -1 & -1 & -1 \end{bmatrix}$$

8. Draw the cones (A) and their sections by $x_3 = -1$ when

$$(a) \ \mathbf{A} = \begin{bmatrix} 2 & 2 & 1 \\ 2 & 1 & \frac{3}{2} \\ -1 & -1 & -1 \end{bmatrix} \qquad (b) \ \mathbf{A} = \begin{bmatrix} 2 & 1 & 1 \\ 3 & 1 & 2 \\ -1 & -1 & -1 \end{bmatrix}$$

and contrast with those of the previous exercise. In what sense can it be said that the first basic activity is obviously more " efficient " than the others in these cases?

17.6 Efficient Allocation : No Limitation on Primary Factors

Only the purely technical aspects of the system, as shown by $\mathbf{x} = \mathbf{A}\lambda$ $(\lambda \geqslant 0)$, have so far been considered. Even here, it is not just a matter of " counting equations ". For example, in the special case of $m = n$ (equal number of activities and commodities) and $\mathbf{A}$ non-singular, it is true that $\mathbf{x} = \mathbf{A}\lambda$ can be inverted to give $\lambda = \mathbf{A}^{-1}\mathbf{x}$. But this does not guarantee that the λ's are non-negative for any given outputs, nor does it serve to distinguish between the various λ's and x's which correspond. More generally $(m \neq n)$ even the inversion of $\mathbf{x} = \mathbf{A}\lambda$ is not obvious. What is given technically is a convex cone of possible λ's in the positive segment of activity space and a corresponding convex cone of possible x's in commodity space, which can be of different dimensions. It remains to proceed from the *technically feasible* to the *economically optimal* or *efficient*. In linear programming, to the side relations is added some minimum or maximum criterion to turn feasible solutions into optimal solutions. Something of the kind is again required ; and the criterion or objective taken must be something more than purely technical.

A general point can be made first. From what has been said (16.7 above) about convex sets suggests that optimal or efficient allocations of resources must be sought on the *boundary* of the cone (A) in m dimensions, as obtained from the technical transformation $\mathbf{x} = \mathbf{A}\lambda$. The boundary generally consists of *facets* of dimensions $(m - 1)$ or less ; when $m = 3$, for example, it comprises triangular plane segments in two dimensions together with the dividing or bounding lines in one dimension. Something needs to be said, in the interests of precision, about the facets of the boundary of (A).

In the three-dimensional cases of Figs. 63 and 64, the following represents the essentials. For three commodities, a facet like $OA^{(1)}A^{(2)}$ is of two dimensions ; it can be taken as *open* without the dividing lines $OA^{(1)}$ and $OA^{(2)}$ or it can be taken as *closed* with these lines. In the first case, the lines like $OA^{(1)}$ and $OA^{(2)}$ need to be considered as facets in themselves and they are of one dimension, open if O is excluded, closed if O is included. The algebraic representation of a facet is easily obtained. Take :

$$\mathbf{A} = \begin{bmatrix} a_{11} & a_{12} & a_{13} & a_{14} \\ a_{21} & a_{22} & a_{23} & a_{24} \\ a_{31} & a_{32} & a_{33} & a_{34} \end{bmatrix}$$

as in Fig. 64. The whole cone (A) is defined by the four columns $\mathbf{A}^{(1)}$, $\mathbf{A}^{(2)}$, $\mathbf{A}^{(3)}$ and $\mathbf{A}^{(4)}$ of $\mathbf{A}$ and the relation $\mathbf{x} = \mathbf{A}\lambda$. The facet defined by $OA^{(1)}A^{(2)}$ is obtained in exactly the same way from the two columns $\mathbf{A}^{(1)}$ and $\mathbf{A}^{(2)}$, i.e. it represents all possible allocations using only the first two basic activities. Hence the facet $(F) = OA^{(1)}A^{(2)}$ is defined :

$$\mathbf{x} = \mathbf{F}\lambda \quad (\lambda \geqslant 0) \quad \text{where} \quad \mathbf{F} = \begin{bmatrix} a_{11} & a_{12} \\ a_{21} & a_{22} \\ a_{31} & a_{32} \end{bmatrix} \quad \text{................(1)}$$

It is closed or open according as the basic activities $A^{(1)}$ and $A^{(2)}$ are included or not, i.e. according as $\lambda = (\lambda_1, 0)$ or $(0, \lambda_2)$ are permitted or not. Similarly, the one-dimensional facet $(F) = OA^{(1)}$ is defined :

$$\mathbf{x} = \mathbf{F}\lambda \quad (\lambda \geqslant 0) \quad \text{where} \quad \mathbf{F} = \begin{bmatrix} a_{11} \\ a_{21} \\ a_{31} \end{bmatrix} \quad \text{....................(2)}$$

Notice that, in (1), λ is a vector of two elements, while in (2) λ is a scalar of only one element. These results are generalised in an obvious way to the case of any number (m) of commodities.

A simple problem of efficient allocation is first considered. It is taken that there is no limitation on the availability of primary factors from outside the system, e.g. there is no limit on the amount of " labour " which can be used. If a primary factor is not desired in itself, i.e. if it does not appear among the requirements of the system, then it is a free good and it need not be considered at all. Hence, to have a " realistic " case, it is taken further that all primary factors are desired commodities and appear among the requirements. In addition, for convenience, it is taken that the technology $\mathbf{A}$ does not include intermediate products or that $\mathbf{A}$ has been reduced to eliminate such products.

The technical specification of the problem is :

> The technology is given by a matrix $\mathbf{A}$ of order $m \times n$. All m commodities are desired in themselves ; some are primary factors available without limit from outside the system and the others are final products not so available.

Commodity space is of m dimensions and, since all commodities are desired, the requirements of the system make use of all the dimensions.

It remains to define the objective to be attained and hence to select, from the feasible points of the cone (A), those which are optimal or efficient :

DEFINITION : A feasible allocation of resources $\mathbf{x} = \mathbf{A}\lambda$ is *efficient* if an increase in one output of $\mathbf{x}$ can be achieved only at the expense of a decrease in another output.

As before, output is here used in the net sense. Hence, at an efficient point $\mathbf{x}$, one final product can be increased only at the expense of reduced output of another final product or at the expense of increased use of some input. In the latter case, there is restricted use of the input commodity in its own desired capacity, e.g. more labour is required for production and so there is less " leisure ".

The analysis is now made in terms of the case of three commodities and at least three activities, the cone (A) of technically possible points being illustrated by Figs. 63 and 64. The boundary of (A) comprises closed facets of two dimensions such as $OA^{(1)}A^{(2)}$ or these facets taken as open together with facets like the half-line $OA^{(1)}$ in one dimension. A *normal* at a point $\mathbf{x}$ of (A) is a direction pointing out of (A) and at right angles to it at $\mathbf{x}$. Hence, a normal is defined only on the boundary of (A) and it is unique for a two-dimensional facet. It is not unique for a one-dimensional facet ; a normal to $OA^{(2)}$, for example, is anywhere between the normal to $OA^{(1)}A^{(2)}$ and that to $OA^{(2)}A^{(3)}$.

A point $\mathbf{x}$ of (A) is efficient if, and only if, there is *no* direction of change *within* (A) which is non-negative, and so some output must decrease. Hence there must be a *normal* at $\mathbf{x}$ in the positive direction. If such a normal exists, any movement from $\mathbf{x}$ is at an angle of a right angle or more to it and this is never in the positive direction. Hence :

> *A point $\mathbf{x}$ of the cone (A) is efficient if, and only if, $\mathbf{x}$ is on the boundary of (A) with a normal in the positive direction.*

Now consider a two-dimensional facet such as $OA^{(1)}A^{(2)}$ of the cone (A). If a point *within* the facet (not on its boundary) has a positive normal, the same positive normal applies at all points *in and on the boundary* of the facet. Hence the whole closed facet is efficient if one point of the open facet is efficient. Similarly for a facet like $OA^{(2)}$ in one dimension, a normal is anywhere between those of the adjacent facets $OA^{(1)}A^{(2)}$ and $OA^{(2)}A^{(3)}$. Even if these latter normals are not positive, it may still happen that there is a positive normal between them, i.e. a point on $OA^{(2)}$ is efficient and so all points on $OA^{(2)}$ equally.

It follows that attention is to be directed not so much to single efficient points of (A), but to *efficient facets* of the cone (A). In Fig. 63, as drawn, there is one efficient facet $OA^{(1)}A^{(2)}$ including the boundaries $OA^{(1)}$ and $OA^{(2)}$. In Fig. 64, there are two efficient facets $OA^{(1)}A^{(2)}A^{(3)}$ including the boundaries $OA^{(1)}$, $OA^{(2)}$ and $OA^{(3)}$. Further, either of these cones could be rotated so that no two-dimensional facet is efficient, and only one of the half-lines like $OA^{(1)}$ is efficient; hence, efficient points can be confined to a one-dimensional facet.

It remains to put these considerations into algebraic terms. In the three-commodity case, the technology is:

$$\mathbf{A} = \begin{bmatrix} a_{11} & a_{12} & \cdots & a_{1n} \\ a_{21} & a_{22} & \cdots & a_{2n} \\ a_{31} & a_{32} & \cdots & a_{3n} \end{bmatrix}$$

for any n (taken $\geqslant 3$). By (1) and (2) above, the one-dimensional facet $OA^{(1)}$ and the two-dimensional facet $OA^{(1)}A^{(2)}$ are defined respectively by:

$$\mathbf{F} = \begin{bmatrix} a_{11} \\ a_{21} \\ a_{31} \end{bmatrix} \quad \text{and} \quad \mathbf{F} = \begin{bmatrix} a_{11} & a_{12} \\ a_{21} & a_{22} \\ a_{31} & a_{32} \end{bmatrix} \quad \dots\dots\dots\dots(3)$$

and similarly for any other facet. Let $\mathbf{p} = (p_1, p_2, p_3)$ be any positive vector or direction; only the ratios $p_1 : p_2 : p_3$ need be specified, except that all p_1, p_2, p_3 must be positive ($\mathbf{p} > 0$). Suppose $OA^{(1)}$ is efficient and so has a positive normal $\mathbf{p}$. Hence $\mathbf{p}$ must be at right angles to the vector (a_{11}, a_{21}, a_{31}) but at an angle of a right angle *or more* to any other direction in the cone (A) and, in particular, to $OA^{(2)}$ with direction (a_{12}, a_{22}, a_{32}), to $OA^{(3)}$ with direction (a_{13}, a_{23}, a_{33}), and so on. Now, the cosine of the angle between $\mathbf{p}$ and (a_{11}, a_{21}, a_{31}) is proportional to $p_1 a_{11} + p_2 a_{21} + p_3 a_{31}$ and this must be zero (cosine of a right angle). The other angles are right angles or more, with similar expressions for their cosines, non-positive in sign. Hence $OA^{(1)}$ is an efficient facet if:

$$\left. \begin{array}{l} p_1 a_{11} + p_2 a_{21} + p_3 a_{31} = 0 \\ p_1 a_{12} + p_2 a_{22} + p_3 a_{32} \leqslant 0 \\ \cdots\cdots\cdots\cdots\cdots\cdots\cdots \\ p_1 a_{1n} + p_2 a_{2n} + p_3 a_{3n} \leqslant 0 \end{array} \right\} \quad \dots\dots\dots\dots(4)$$

Now suppose $OA^{(1)}A^{(2)}$ is an efficient facet, so that a positive normal $\mathbf{p}$ exists which must be at right angles to $OA^{(1)}$ and $OA^{(2)}$ but at a right angle or more to the other half-lines $OA^{(3)}$, ... Hence:

$$\left. \begin{array}{l} p_1 a_{11} + p_2 a_{21} + p_3 a_{31} = 0 \\ p_1 a_{12} + p_2 a_{22} + p_3 a_{32} = 0 \\ p_1 a_{13} + p_2 a_{23} + p_3 a_{33} \leqslant 0 \\ \cdots\cdots\cdots\cdots\cdots\cdots\cdots \\ p_1 a_{1n} + p_2 a_{2n} + p_3 a_{3n} \leqslant 0 \end{array} \right\} \quad \dots\dots\dots\dots(5)$$

The expressions (4) and (5) are the algebraic conditions for efficient facets, in one and in two dimensions respectively. All expressions on the left-hand side are non-positive ($\leqslant 0$) and those which correspond to half-lines in the facet are zero ($=0$). They can be summarised in matrix notation

$$\mathbf{p'F}=0 \quad \text{and} \quad \mathbf{p'A}\leqslant 0 \quad (\mathbf{p}>0) \quad\dots\dots\dots\dots\dots(6)$$

where $\mathbf{F}$ is the sub-matrix of $\mathbf{A}$ for the facet, as in (3) above. As long as a positive direction $\mathbf{p}$ ($\mathbf{p}>0$) exists for (6), the facet is efficient.

The development above is for the case of $m=3$ commodities. The result (6) is, however, quite general, as proved in Koopmans (1951), Chapter III. The conditions for efficient allocation of resources for any technology A of order $m \times n$ are :

Algebraic Formulation :

A closed facet (F) of the cone (A) is efficient if, and only if, there is a positive vector $\mathbf{p}$ such that

$$\mathbf{p'F}=0 \quad \text{and} \quad \mathbf{p'A}\leqslant 0 \quad (\mathbf{p}>0)$$

where $\mathbf{F}$ is the sub-matrix of $\mathbf{A}$ defining the facet.

Diagrammatic Formulation :

A closed facet (F), including its boundary, of the cone (A) is efficient if, and only if, there is one efficient point in the open facet, (F) without its boundary, i.e. if, and only if, there is a normal in the positive direction $\mathbf{p}$ to the open facet. The direction $\mathbf{p}$ is unique if (F) is of ($m-1$) dimensions, but not if (F) is of lower dimensions.

The solution of the problem is now complete. *Feasible allocations* of production are given by all points $\mathbf{x}=\mathbf{A}\boldsymbol{\lambda}$ of the cone (A). *Efficient allocations* on the definition of efficiency adopted are those given by the points of efficient facets of (A) and the conditions above determine these facets. With Figs. 63 and 64 as illustration, it is clear that there may be one or more efficient facets of ($m-1$) dimensions or of lower dimensions.

The practical problem is to find $\mathbf{p}$ for the condition (6). This is where the section of the cone (A) by the plane $x_3=-1$ helps, as illustrated in Figs. 63 and 64 ($m=3$). The whole cone (A) can be imagined by looking down on the boundary of the section from the point O, which lies above the plane. A normal $\mathbf{p}=(p_1, p_2, p_3)$ is to be found for each facet, i.e. for each side or corner of the section. Values of the ratios $p_1 : p_2 : p_3$ are to be found from the equations in (4) or (5), and the signs of p_1, p_2 and p_3 checked by the inequalities in these relations. If all the p's turn out to be positive, the facet is efficient. Each side or corner of the section can be taken in turn ; if it has a positive normal *in the plane of the section*, then the facet, joining up to O, *may* have a positive normal. It depends how the normal in the plane gets tilted when the facet is considered. Ex. 1–3 below provide practice in determining **p** for facets of actual cones.

EXERCISES 17.6

1. Consider the technology of 17.5, Ex. 7 (*a*). Show that $\mathbf{p}=(2, 1, 6)$ is normal to the facet $OA^{(1)}A^{(2)}$, $\mathbf{p}=(-3, -2, -9)$ to the facet $OA^{(2)}A^{(3)}$ and $\mathbf{p}=(1, 1, 4)$ to the facet $OA^{(1)}A^{(3)}$ of the cone (A). Hence show that the efficient allocations of production are given by points on two facets of (A).

2. In the technology of 17.5, Ex. 7 (*b*), show that there is only one efficient facet of the cone (A).

3. For the technology of 17.5, Ex. 8 (*a*), show that none of the three *two-dimensional* facets of (A) has a positive normal. Deduce that only $OA^{(1)}$ is efficient.

4. Examine the case where **A** is of order 3×2, illustrated in Fig. 62. Show that *either* the whole facet $OA^{(1)}A^{(2)}$ is efficient, *or* only one of the half-lines $OA^{(1)}$ or $OA^{(2)}$, according to the positions taken by $A^{(1)}$ and $A^{(2)}$.

17.7 Prices and the Dual Problem

In the problem of 17.6 above, efficient production depends on the existence of a positive vector **p** to satisfy the relations (6), written out in full in the form (4) or (5) above. Such a vector is interpreted in commodity space, i.e. as a normal to an efficient facet of the cone (A) representing technical possibilities $\mathbf{x}=\mathbf{A}\lambda$. The next step is to re-interpret **p** as a vector of *prices* and then to relate the problem of 17.6 to its dual.

The components of the positive vector **p** are taken as internal or *accounting prices*, and only their ratios are specified. There is, as yet, no relation with market prices ; indeed no market has been defined and there may be none. Take the case of three commodities and suppose that the cone (A) has an efficient facet $OA^{(1)}A^{(2)}$ in two dimensions. There is then a *unique* set of ratios $p_1 : p_2 : p_3$ as accounting prices and the relations (5) of 17.6 hold. The expression $(p_1a_{11}+p_2a_{21}+p_3a_{31})$ is the net profits obtained from the unit level of activity $A^{(1)}$ at these prices ; the a's are positive or negative (outputs and inputs) so that receipts are balanced against costs in arriving at net profits. Similarly $(p_1a_{12}+p_2a_{22}+p_3a_{32})$ is the net profits from the activity $A^{(2)}$ at unit level. By (5) of 17.6, both these net profits are zero. Hence, both the activities $A^{(1)}$ and $A^{(2)}$ produce zero profits, and so does any combination of the activities, i.e. any efficient allocation on the facet $OA^{(1)}A^{(2)}$. The remaining relations of (5) of 17.6, show that all other activities, i.e. $A^{(3)}$, $A^{(4)}$, ... or any combination involving them have profits which are zero or negative.

M.E.

This result can be generalised to m commodities. It will then cover the case where an efficient facet is either of dimensions $(m-1)$, or of lower dimensions (in which case the prices are not unique). For any efficient combination of activities, accounting prices are such that net profits are zero ; for any other combination of activities, net profits are negative (or at most zero). Hence the use of accounting prices can be described :

> At a set of accounting prices $\mathbf{p}(\mathbf{p}>0)$, which may or may not be unique, no activity in the technology $\mathbf{A}$ gives positive profits and any activity which is efficient at these prices gives zero profits.

The prices are indicators of efficient allocation of resources. It is broadly true that efficient allocations have zero profits and others negative profits ; but since there may be multiple sets of prices and various alternative sets of efficient allocations, allowance must be made for zero as well as negative profits outside the efficient production possibilities considered. It can always be said, however, that activities which are unprofitable (negative profits) are not efficient.

The accounting prices can now be interpreted in economic terms as rates of substitution. The substitution considered is between one efficient allocation and another efficient allocation on the same efficient facet of the cone (A). The facet must be taken of dimensions $(m-1)$; for example, when $m=3$, there are possibilities of substitution on a two-dimensional facet but not on a facet of one dimension, where only changes in scale and not in relative allocation are possible. Let $\boldsymbol{\lambda}^{(1)}$ and $\boldsymbol{\lambda}^{(2)}$ be two efficient allocations on the facet (F) and let $\mathbf{x}^{(1)}=\mathbf{F}\boldsymbol{\lambda}^{(1)}$ and $\mathbf{x}^{(2)}=\mathbf{F}\boldsymbol{\lambda}^{(2)}$ be the corresponding outputs. Since (F) is efficient, by (6) of 17.6 :

$$\mathbf{p}'\mathbf{x}^{(1)}=\mathbf{p}'\mathbf{F}\boldsymbol{\lambda}^{(1)}=0$$
and
$$\mathbf{p}'\mathbf{x}^{(2)}=\mathbf{p}'\mathbf{F}\boldsymbol{\lambda}^{(2)}=0$$
Hence
$$\mathbf{p}'\{\mathbf{x}^{(1)}-\mathbf{x}^{(2)}\}\mathbf{F}=0$$

Take the case where only the outputs of the first two commodities change so that :

$$p_1\{x_1^{(1)}-x_1^{(2)}\}+p_2\{x_2^{(1)}-x_2^{(2)}\}=0$$
i.e.
$$\frac{p_1}{p_2}=\frac{x_2^{(2)}-x_2^{(1)}}{x_1^{(1)}-x_1^{(2)}} \quad\dots\dots\dots\dots\dots\dots\dots\dots(1)$$

Since, by the definition of efficiency, $x_1^{(1)}>x_1^{(2)}$ implies $x_2^{(1)}<x_2^{(2)}$ and conversely, the ratio on the right-hand side of (1) is positive and measures the rate of substitution between outputs of the two commodities. For small changes, the price ratio can be described as the marginal rate of substitution ; but it is not necessary to think in marginal terms. Hence,

the price ratios $p_1 : p_2 : \ldots : p_m$ are the rates of substitution between outputs of the various commodities on the efficient facet (F). If there are two or more efficient facets, then there are discontinuities in switching between efficient allocations. The accounting prices are the same on one facet but change (discontinuously) from one facet to another and there is no rate of substitution defined between an efficient set of outputs on one facet and an efficient set on another.

Hence, in the solution of the technical problem of allocation of resources, given the technology $\mathbf{A}$ and the criterion of efficient allocation, sets of accounting prices are derived and serve to distinguish efficient from other allocations. There may be only one or there may be several sets of price ratios. If it happens that a non-efficient allocation is made, the evidence of the accounting prices being ignored, then there is a " dead loss " in the economy which can be measured. See the " coefficient of resource utilisation " of Debreu (1951).

The computation of the prices is a problem in the inversion of matrices. The efficient facet (F) considered is defined by $\mathbf{F}$, a submatrix of $\mathbf{A}$ and of order $m \times (m-1)$. The transpose $\mathbf{F}'$ is of order $(m-1) \times m$ and its rank can be taken as $(m-1)$; it can always be partitioned into the form $[\,\mathbf{B} : \boldsymbol{\beta}\,]$ where $\mathbf{B}$ is a non-singular square matrix of order $(m-1) \times (m-1)$ and $\boldsymbol{\beta}$ is a column vector. For example, if $\mathbf{F}$ is defined from the first $(m-1)$ activities in $\mathbf{A}$, then :

$$\mathbf{F}' = \begin{bmatrix} a_{11} & a_{21} & \cdots & a_{m-1\,1} & a_{m\,1} \\ a_{12} & a_{22} & \cdots & a_{m-1\,2} & a_{m\,2} \\ & & \cdots\cdots\cdots & & \\ a_{1\,m-1} & a_{2\,m-1} & \cdots & a_{m-1\,m-1} & a_{m\,m-1} \end{bmatrix} = [\,\mathbf{B}\mid\boldsymbol{\beta}\,]$$

The price ratios are to be found from $\mathbf{p}'\mathbf{F}=0$, i.e. $\mathbf{F}'\mathbf{p}=0$, which is a set of $(m-1)$ linear equations in the $(m-1)$ price ratios. Denote

$$\mathbf{q} = \left(\frac{p_1}{p_m}, \frac{p_2}{p_m}, \ldots \frac{p_{m-1}}{p_m}\right)$$

so that $\mathbf{F}'\mathbf{p}=0$ becomes :

$$\left.\begin{aligned} \mathbf{Bq} &= (-\boldsymbol{\beta}) \\ \mathbf{q} &= \mathbf{B}^{-1}(-\boldsymbol{\beta}) \end{aligned}\right\} \quad \cdots\cdots\cdots\cdots\cdots\cdots\cdots\cdots\cdots(2)$$

and so

The computation of price ratios then involves the inversion of $\mathbf{B}$.

For example, in the case $m=3$ and the efficient facet $OA^{(1)}A^{(2)}$, there are two equations for the price ratios $p_1 : p_2 : p_3$ given by (5) of 17.6 above :

$$p_1 a_{11} + p_2 a_{21} + p_3 a_{31} = 0$$
$$p_1 a_{12} + p_2 a_{22} + p_3 a_{32} = 0$$

The equations (2) are then

$$q_1 a_{11} + q_2 a_{21} = -a_{31} \; ; \quad q_1 a_{12} + q_2 a_{22} = -a_{32}$$

and
$$q_1 = \frac{a_{32} a_{21} - a_{31} a_{22}}{a_{11} a_{22} - a_{12} a_{21}} \qquad q_2 = \frac{a_{31} a_{12} - a_{32} a_{11}}{a_{11} a_{22} - a_{12} a_{21}}$$

These give the ratios $p_1 : p_2 : p_3$. The signs of the p's must be fixed to satisfy the inequalities of (5) of 17.6 above.

The solution of the problem can now be reviewed in terms of linear programming. One point needs to be stressed : the combination of the assumption of constant returns to scale in the technology A, and of the case of no limitation on primary factors, implies that relative allocation of resources and relative prices may be found, but neither the scale of production nor the level of prices. Only the *ratios* of λ and p are sought ; the *scale* of operations is not determined. It then follows that, as a linear programme, the problem has no maximum or minimum condition in the ordinary sense ; to maximise a linear function like $z = b'\lambda$ would require a determination of scale as well as of relative allocation.

A sub-matrix F of the technology A is sought so that $x = F\lambda$ represents efficient allocations within the wider range of possible allocations $x = A\lambda$ for $\lambda \geqslant 0$. Usually, if A is of order $m \times n$, then F is of order $m \times (m-1)$. Hence, feasible allocations λ are of order n, but efficient allocations λ only of order $(m-1)$; not all basic activities are used in efficient allocation. F is found from some positive price vector p of order m such that $F'p = 0$ (provided also that $A'p \leqslant 0$). As a linear programme and its dual, the problem is to find λ and p so that :

$$\left. \begin{array}{ll} F\lambda = x & \text{and} \quad F'p = 0 \\ \lambda > 0 & \qquad\quad p > 0 \end{array} \right\} \qquad \dots\dots\dots\dots\dots\dots(3)$$

This is a particular (and reduced) case of the more usual linear programme :

$$\begin{array}{ll} z = b'\lambda = \min. & \qquad\qquad \zeta = x'p = \max. \\ \text{subject to} \quad F\lambda \geqslant x & \text{subject to} \quad F'p \leqslant b \\ \lambda > 0 & \qquad\qquad\quad p > 0 \end{array} \left. \right\} \dots\dots(4)$$

Here b is some given vector, defined in activity space ; but no sense can be made of it in the present context. It is, however, only necessary to set $b = 0$ in (4) and the programme (3) is obtained (see Ex. 4 below).

EXERCISES 17.7

1. The cone (A) for $A = \begin{bmatrix} 1 & 2 & 1 \\ 2 & 1 & 1 \\ -1 & -1 & -1 \end{bmatrix}$ has one efficient facet $OA^{(1)}A^{(2)}$ (see

17.6, Ex. 2). Write the relations (5) of 17.6 in the form :

$$p_1 + 2p_2 - p_3 = 0 \; ; \quad 2p_1 + p_2 - p_3 = 0 \; ; \quad p_1 + p_2 - p_3 \leqslant 0$$

Show that $p_1 : p_2 : p_3 = 1 : 1 : 3$ from the first two, and that positive signs must be attached to p_1, p_2 and p_3 to satisfy the third.

2. If $\mathbf{A} = \begin{bmatrix} 2 & 3 & 1 \\ 2 & 0 & 3 \\ -1 & -1 & -1 \end{bmatrix}$, find the prices for the efficient facet $OA^{(1)}A^{(2)}$ and for the efficient facet $OA^{(1)}A^{(3)}$.

3. What set or sets of prices can be defined for efficient allocations when

$$\mathbf{A} = \begin{bmatrix} 2 & 2 & 1 \\ 2 & 1 & \frac{3}{2} \\ -1 & -1 & -1 \end{bmatrix}$$

4. Interpret the linear programme (4) above by taking **x** as a vector of outputs which must be at least obtained and **b** as a vector of net profits which cannot be exceeded in the various basic activities. Show that both z and ζ are then to be interpreted as aggregate net profits. Why does (4) fail to make sense in a problem of constant returns to scale and no limitations on resources, except in one case, i.e. **b** $= 0$?

17.8 Efficient Allocation : Limitations on Primary Factors

The essential results have been obtained, in 17.6 and 17.7 above, when no limitations exist on the availability of primary factors. Possible allocations of resources are shown in commodity space in or on a convex cone (A) defined from the technology matrix **A**. Certain points, or rather facets, of the boundary of (A) are efficient allocations. They are found by means of a system of accounting prices : allocations which are unprofitable (negative profits) are ruled out as not efficient, and all efficient allocations are characterised by the condition of zero profits, at the prices. The introduction of limitations on available primary factors does not change this ; it merely permits a determination of the optimal scale of production as well as the efficient allocation, and adds a maximum (minimum) condition to the corresponding linear programme.

The m commodities are now divided into two groups : primary factors not desired in themselves with net output $x_p \leqslant 0$, and final products such that net output $x_f \geqslant 0$. Let ξ_p be the amount of a primary factor available from outside the system, ξ_p being given and positive. So :

$$(-x_p) \leqslant \xi_p \quad \text{or} \quad x_p \geqslant (-\xi_p)$$

If it happens that $x_p = -\xi_p$, then all resources are used and an (accounting) price for the factor is sought. However, if $x_p > (-\xi_p)$, then there are unused resources, the primary factor is a " free good " and it is to be expected that its price is zero.

It is again assumed, for convenience, that there are no intermediate products (or that **A** has been reduced to eliminate them). This does not rule out the possibility that $x_f = 0$ (as opposed to $x_f > 0$) for some allocations of resources and a particular final product. It may just happen that it does not pay to produce one or more of the (possible) final products.

Two cases where there are three activities and commodities will be examined in diagrammatic terms. The first case arises when two final products x_1 and x_2, are obtained from one primary factor x_3 (labour). The units for measuring x_3 can be chosen so that $\xi_3 = 1$ (availability), i.e. so that $x_3 \geqslant -1$. The unit levels of activities can, as before, be so chosen that the last row in the technology matrix is written with elements (-1):

$$\mathbf{A} = \begin{bmatrix} a_{11} & a_{12} & a_{13} \\ a_{21} & a_{22} & a_{23} \\ -1 & -1 & -1 \end{bmatrix}$$

where all the a's can now be taken as positive. The possible cone (A), without regard to limitations on x_3, is of the form shown in Fig. 63 above,

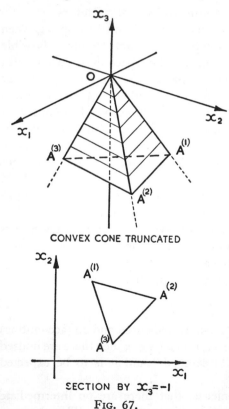

CONVEX CONE TRUNCATED

SECTION BY $x_3 = -1$

Fig. 67.

except that $A^{(1)}$, $A^{(2)}$ and $A^{(3)}$ are all in the positive quadrant of $Ox_1 x_2$. *Attainable* allocations are those, in the possible cone (A), which come within the fixed limits, here $x_3 \geqslant -1$. Hence the *attainable cone* (A) is simply the original cone, truncated by the plane $x_3 = -1$, as illustrated in Fig. 67. *Efficient points* or facets of the attainable cone (A) are sought, the definition of efficiency being the same as before (17.6 above) except that it is confined to final products. Hence, **x** is efficient if an increase in output of one final product can only be obtained at the expense of a decrease in another.

From Fig. 67 it is clear that the full amount, $x_3 = -1$, of the limiting factor must be used in an efficient allocation; otherwise both final products can be produced in greater output by use of more of the factor. Hence, efficient points are on the boundary of the two-dimensional convex set $A^{(1)}A^{(2)}A^{(3)}$ and must be on a segment, such as $A^{(1)}A^{(2)}$ in Fig. 67, which is negatively sloped to both x_1 and x_2 axes (see Ex. 1 below). At such a point, there is a positive normal in Ox_1x_2 space, defining a price vector (p_1p_2) for final products. Hence, there are prices p_1 and p_2 which are positive and which represent the rate of substitution between (efficient) outputs of x_1 and x_2. Further, the value of:

$$\zeta = p_1x_1 + p_2x_2 = \max.$$

when x_1 and x_2 are efficient outputs of all attainable outputs. (For an outline of a proof, see Ex. 2 below). This is the maximum condition to

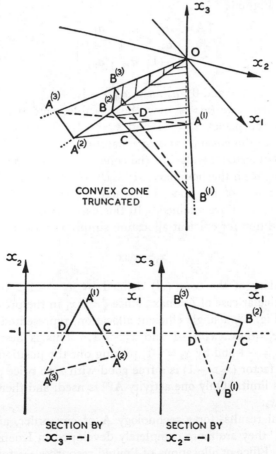

FIG. 68.

be added to the linear programme, (3) of 17.7 above ; it determines prices of final products and maximises receipts obtainable from their sale at the prices.

The second case, illustrated in Fig. 68, has one final product x_1 and two primary factors, x_2 and x_3, with units chosen so that the limiting conditions are $x_2 \geqslant -1$ and $x_3 \geqslant -1$. In the technology matrix **A**, the last two rows comprise negative elements and the unit level for each activity can be chosen so that the larger (numerically) of the two negative elements in the column of **A** is (-1). Hence, in each column of **A**, the last two elements are (-1) and a value between 0 and (-1), but the (-1) entry may appear in either position. For example, it may appear as the third position in $A^{(1)}$ but in the second position in $A^{(2)}$ and $A^{(3)}$, the case illustrated in Fig. 68 :

$$\mathbf{A} = \begin{bmatrix} a_{11} & a_{12} & a_{13} \\ a_{21} & -1 & -1 \\ -1 & a_{32} & a_{33} \end{bmatrix}$$

where $a_{11}, a_{12}, a_{13} > 0$ and $0 > a_{21}, a_{32}, a_{33} > -1$.

The *attainable cone* (A) is now the possible cone truncated in two directions by the planes $x_2 = -1$ and $x_3 = -1$. The cone is shown in Fig. 68 in three dimensions, and in its sections by $x_2 = -1$ and $x_3 = -1$ (i.e. the two truncated " ends " of the cone). *Efficient points* of (A) must clearly be sought on the boundary, $A^{(1)}CB^{(2)}B^{(3)}DA^{(1)}$ in Fig. 68, of the truncated " ends " of the cone, i.e. where either or both of the limits $x_2 = -1$ and $x_3 = -1$ are attained. In this case, with only one final product, the condition for efficient allocation simply reduces to :

$$x_1 = \text{max.}$$

on the boundary of the cone (A) defined by $x_2 = -1$ and by $x_3 = -1$. This is a particular case of $\zeta = \text{max.}$, since $\zeta = p_1 x_1$ in the present problem. There is, in Fig. 68, a single efficient allocation, represented by the point $B^{(2)}$, where $x_1 = \text{max.}$, $x_2 = -1$ and $x_3 > -1$. This is best seen in the sections by $x_3 = -1$ and by $x_2 = -1$, picking out the position for max. x_1. One primary factor $(x_3 > -1)$ is a free good with zero price ; the other is used up to its limit. Only one activity $\mathbf{A}^{(2)}$ is used, and there is only one scarce factor x_2.

The general results, for a technology **A** of any order, are now sufficiently clear ; they are more completely developed in Koopmans (1951), Chapter III. Efficient allocations of limited resources are found on those parts of the boundary of a truncated (attainable) cone (A) in commodity space which correspond to the attainment of the limits of one or more primary factors. The function of (accounting) prices remains ; unprofitable allocations are eliminated and efficient allocations characterised by zero profits. Prices of final products are still equal (in their ratios) to rates of substitution between efficient outputs of the final products. In addition, there is a maximum condition to be added to the linear programme, i.e. $\zeta = \mathbf{p}'_f \mathbf{x}_f = \text{max.}$, where ζ is the receipts from the outputs of final products at the (accounting) prices. The scale of production, and the level of prices, are thereby determined.

One aspect of the general results is particularly to be stressed. Among the primary factors, some are found to be used up to their limits, and others not, in efficient allocation. There are *scarce factors* with positive prices ; there may also be *free factors* with zero prices. The efficient allocation (on an efficient facet) is a combination of a number of activities ; hence some activities are used, and others not, in an efficient allocation. In this problem where primary factors are not desired in themselves, it can be said as a general rule that *the number of activities used is equal to the number of scarce primary factors.* The number of activities used (which is not greater than the total number n of basic activities) is therefore less than or equal to the total number of primary factors supplied from outside the system—" less than " if there are some free factors not used up to the limit, " equal to " if all factors are scarce and used up to the limit. This rule is modified in certain " degenerate " cases when the number of activities used can be less than the number of scarce factors ; see the basic result quoted in 16.6 above.

The set of prices is derived, in an accounting sense, from the technical aspects of the problem. The properties of prices as rates of substitution. and as the determinant of relative levels of profits in different activities, provide the clue to the wider interpretation of the price system. The prices are equivalent to market prices if there is a market and if competitive conditions are such as lead to the identification of market prices and rates of substitution. At the other extreme, in a planned or welfare economy, the prices (and profit margins which result) are available to the central " planners " as guides in their problems of allocation of resources and as means to de-centralise the taking of decisions. Moreover, since the problem is a linear programme with a maximum condition, the computational procedures developed for such programmes are available in the determination of the efficient allocation of resources and of the system of accounting prices.

EXERCISES 17.8

1. Re-draw Fig. 67 to cover various cases where the number of basic activities in A is greater than three (still with three commodities). Examine possible configurations of the points $A^{(1)}, A^{(2)}, \ldots$. Show that efficient allocations may be given (a) by one point such as $A^{(1)}$ only, (b) by one line segment such as $A^{(1)}A^{(2)}$ or (c) by several such line segments such as $A^{(1)}A^{(2)}A^{(3)}$.

2. In Fig. 67, let P be any point on an efficient line segment $A^{(1)}A^{(2)}$ and let Q be any other attainable point for which $x_3 = -1$. Show that the normal (p_1, p_2) to $A^{(1)}A^{(2)}$ is at right angles to PQ if Q is also an efficient point on the same segment as P, and at right angles or more to PQ for any other Q. Take x_1 and x_2 as outputs at P and $\bar{x}_1$ and $\bar{x}_2$ at Q. Deduce that, if P and Q are both efficient on $A^{(1)}A^{(2)}$:

$$\frac{p_1}{p_2} = \frac{\bar{x}_2 - x_2}{x_1 - \bar{x}_1} = \text{rate of substitution}$$

and that, if P is efficient but Q not :

$$p_1(\bar{x}_1 - x_1) + p_2(\bar{x}_2 - x_2) \leqslant 0$$

Hence show that $\zeta = p_1 x_1 + p_2 x_2 \geqslant p_1 \bar{x}_1 + p_2 \bar{x}_2$, i.e. that $\zeta = \max$.

3. Draw the attainable cone (A) and its appropriate sections, as in Fig. 68, for :

$$A = \begin{bmatrix} 2 & 3 & 2 \\ -\frac{1}{3} & -\frac{2}{3} & -1 \\ -1 & -1 & -\frac{1}{2} \end{bmatrix}$$

Examine from the point of view of efficient allocations. Show that both factors are used to the limit in efficient allocation.

17.9 Programmes over Time; von Neumann Growth Model

The analysis of the previous sections applies only under static or stationary conditions to a competitive or planned economy. Problems of monopolistic practices are not considered. Even more important, the analysis is not designed for a dynamic treatment of the problem. It can be extended, however, to provide the essential basis of any consideration of general equilibrium in a progressive economy, and to throw light on the features which are dominant in a dynamic model of broad scope.

The concept of the technology A is purely static ; the elements a_{rs} represent timeless outputs and inputs, i.e. flows per unit of time in a stationary state. The particular extension now considered takes a sequence of equally-spaced time periods, the tth period being from time $(t-1)$ to time t for $t = 1, 2, \ldots T$. The n basic activities (each involving m commodities) which make up to technology A now need to be timed, i.e. $A^{(s)}(t)$ rather than $A^{(s)}$ for $s = 1, 2, \ldots n$ and $t = 1, 2, \ldots T$. The timing may be no more than the same activity (i.e. the same input-output coefficients) shifted from one period to another ; or there may be changes over time in the structure of the activity. In any case, instead of the general combination of activities $\sum_{s=1}^{n} \lambda_s A^{(s)}$, a combination of all activities over time is now required: $\sum\limits_{s=1}^{n} \sum\limits_{t=1}^{T} \lambda_{st} \mathbf{A}^{(s)}(t)$ for any $\lambda_{st} \geq 0$. The coefficient λ_{st} is the level of the sth activity used in period t.

It is most convenient to take $\mathbf{A}^{(s)}(t)$ as consisting of a set of inputs at the beginning of the period, time $(t-1)$, followed by a set of outputs at the end of the period, time t. Only non-negative values need then be written for the input and output coefficients, and each commodity appears among inputs and among outputs (with the possibility of zero coefficients). Write:

$$\text{Inputs at} \quad \mathbf{A}_t^{(s)} = \begin{bmatrix} a_{1st} \\ a_{2st} \\ \cdots \cdots \\ a_{nst} \end{bmatrix} \quad \text{Outputs at} \quad \mathbf{B}_t^{(s)} = \begin{bmatrix} b_{1st} \\ b_{2st} \\ \cdots \cdots \\ b_{mst} \end{bmatrix}$$
$$\text{time } (t-1) \qquad\qquad\qquad \text{time } t$$

for $s = 1, 2, \ldots n$, $t = 1, 2, \ldots T$ and $a_{rst} \geq 0$, $b_{rst} \geq 0$. These can be put together into two matrices, representing the technology of period t:

$$\text{Inputs at} \quad \mathbf{A}_t = [a_{rst}] \qquad \text{Outputs at} \quad \mathbf{B}_t = [b_{rst}] \quad \ldots\ldots\ldots\ldots(1)$$
$$\text{time } (t-1) \qquad\qquad\qquad\quad \text{time } t$$

The level of the sth activity at period t is given by λ_{st}. Write the vector $\boldsymbol{\lambda}_t = \{\lambda_{st}\}$ of order n ($s = 1, 2, \ldots n$). A linear programme over time can be defined: to choose $\boldsymbol{\lambda}_t$ over time to maximise (minimise) a linear objective:

$$z = \sum \mathbf{c}_t' \boldsymbol{\lambda}_t$$

where $\mathbf{c}_t = \{c_{st}\}$ of order n ($s = 1, 2, \ldots n$) is a given vector. Apart from $\boldsymbol{\lambda}_t \geq 0$, there will be certain side relations, extensions of the relations like $\mathbf{A}\boldsymbol{\lambda} = \mathbf{x}$ in the stationary state. An obvious set of relations links the inputs of period t to the outputs of period $(t-1)$, as in (1), commodity by commodity; both are timed at the same point $(t-1)$. For the rth commodity:

$$\text{Input of period } t \qquad = \sum_{s=1}^{n} a_{rst} \lambda_{st}$$
$$\text{Output of period } (t-1) = \sum_{s=1}^{n} b_{rst-1} \lambda_{st-1}$$

Hence the net input of the rth commodity at the beginning of period t is:

$$\sum_{s=1}^{n} a_{rst} \lambda_{st} - \sum_{s=1}^{n} b_{rst-1} \lambda_{st-1} \qquad \begin{pmatrix} r = 1, 2, \ldots m \\ t = 1, 2, \ldots T \end{pmatrix}$$

i.e. $\qquad\qquad\qquad\qquad \mathbf{A}_t \boldsymbol{\lambda}_t - \mathbf{B}_{t-1} \boldsymbol{\lambda}_{t-1}$

The side relations impose definite restrictions on this vector of net inputs. For example, if the maximum net input (from outside the system) permitted in each period is specified as $\mathbf{x}_t = \{x_{rt}\}$ $(r...1, 2, ... m)$, then the linear programme over time, and its dual, are :

$$z = \Sigma\, \mathbf{c}_t'\boldsymbol{\lambda}_t = \text{max.} \qquad\qquad \zeta = \Sigma\, \mathbf{x}_t'\mathbf{p}_t = \text{min.}$$

$$\left.\begin{array}{ll} \text{subject to} \quad \mathbf{A}_t\boldsymbol{\lambda}_t - \mathbf{B}_{t-1}\boldsymbol{\lambda}_{t-1} \leqslant \mathbf{x}_t & \text{subject to } \mathbf{A}'_t\mathbf{p}_t - \mathbf{B}'_{t-1}\mathbf{p}_{t-1} \geqslant \mathbf{c}_t \\ \text{and} \qquad\qquad \boldsymbol{\lambda}_t \geqslant 0 & \text{and} \qquad\qquad \mathbf{p}_t \geqslant 0 \end{array}\right\} \quad ....(2)$$

The whole programme is over time, $t = 1, 2, ... T$. Such a programme might be used for investment in working capital over time, i.e. cost of inputs in one period *less* proceeds of outputs of the previous period.

Linear programmes of this kind, and of more general types in which continuous variations are permitted, are put in a general setting in Dantzig (1949). The problems of computation are of some interest, since the side relations of (2), taken for various t, involve very large matrices made up from (1) for $t = 1, 2, ... T$. If $\mathbf{B}_{t-1}$ is set as zero for $t = 1$ as an initial condition, the side relations in $\boldsymbol{\lambda}_t$ in (2) are :

$$\begin{array}{ll} \mathbf{A}_1\boldsymbol{\lambda}_1 & \leqslant \mathbf{x}_1 \\ -\mathbf{B}_1\boldsymbol{\lambda}_1 + \mathbf{A}_2\boldsymbol{\lambda}_2 & \leqslant \mathbf{x}_2 \\ \qquad\quad -\mathbf{B}_2\boldsymbol{\lambda}_2 + \mathbf{A}_3\boldsymbol{\lambda}_3 \leqslant \mathbf{x}_3 \end{array}$$

....

where the $\mathbf{A}$'s and $\mathbf{B}$'s are all matrices of order $m \times n$. If $\boldsymbol{\lambda}$ represents the whole set of λ's, and $\mathbf{x}$ the whole set of x's, over time, then the side relations are :

$$\mathbf{A}\boldsymbol{\lambda} \leqslant \mathbf{x}$$

for a large matrix of the decomposable type (of 13.9 above) :

$$\mathbf{A} = \begin{bmatrix} \mathbf{A}_1 & 0 & 0 \\ -\mathbf{B}_1 & \mathbf{A}_2 & 0 \\ 0 & -\mathbf{B}_2 & \mathbf{A}_3 \\ & & \end{bmatrix}$$

The computational problem is simplified by the grouping of the non-zero elements around the leading diagonal. There is generally over-lapping of these blocks of non-zero elements, by rows and by columns, so that one commodity appears in different periods and one activity uses commodities timed differently. In fact, if it were not for such over-lapping, the linear programme over time would break up into a sequence of independent programmes in successive periods.

All this is anticipated by a model of economic growth developed by von Neumann (1937, 1945). This cannot be called an " application " of linear programming since it came so much earlier (1937). But von Neumann was the first to use a linear model of production with *linear inequalities* and stressing the *dual problem*. The model has more recently been generalised by Kemeny, Morgenstern and Thompson (1956) to include (e.g.) Leontief's dynamic system as a special case. In (2), set $\mathbf{x}_t$ and $\mathbf{c}_t$ at zero : the maximum (minimum) conditions of the programme disappear to be replaced by a minimax type of objective for an expanding economy. Assume, further, that the technology ($\mathbf{A}_t$ and $\mathbf{B}_t$) does not change over time, so that the linear programme (2) is :

$$\left. \begin{array}{l} \text{(i)} \ \mathbf{A} \, \boldsymbol{\lambda}_t - \mathbf{B} \, \boldsymbol{\lambda}_{t-1} \leqslant 0 \quad \boldsymbol{\lambda}_t \geqslant 0 \\ \text{(ii)} \ \mathbf{A}' \mathbf{p}_t - \mathbf{B}' \mathbf{p}_{t-1} \geqslant 0 \quad \mathbf{p}_t \geqslant 0 \end{array} \right\} \ \dots\dots\dots\dots\dots\dots(3)$$

In the interpretation of (3), the broad and general assumptions made about the economy are : *first* that it is a closed system with constant returns to scale and *second* that there is no limit on the amounts of primary factors (land, unskilled labour) available in the system. The implications are many. For example, the services of labour are an output against inputs consisting of the consumption (in fixed proportions) of the commodities necessary to maintain (and, if necessary, to train) the workers. Further, constant returns to scale and no limits on resources imply technically (as in 17.6 and 17.7) that the scale of production and the level of prices are not determined. Only the *ratios* of $\boldsymbol{\lambda}_t$, and of $\mathbf{p}_t$, are to be found.

Conditions (i) of (3) then state that inputs at period t do not exceed outputs of the previous period ; these are technical conditions. A further and very familiar condition is now added : whenever a strict inequality holds for input-output in (3) (i), then the commodity is a free good and its price is zero. Conditions (ii) of (3) are in terms of (accounting) prices and state that net profits in each line of activity are never positive. A familiar condition is added : whenever an activity has negative profits so that " > " rather than " = " holds in (3) (ii), then the activity s is not used and $\lambda_s = 0$.

The requirements of an economy expanding at a constant rate are now, to be introduced. Let α be a constant expansion factor where $\alpha = 1 + \dfrac{r}{100}$ and expansion is at $r\%$ per period. Then $\boldsymbol{\lambda}_t : \boldsymbol{\lambda}_{t-1} = \alpha$. The dual of this in terms of prices is the rate of interest. Let β be the constant interest factor where $\beta = 1 + \dfrac{\rho}{100}$ and interest is at $\rho\%$ per period. Then $\mathbf{p}_t : \mathbf{p}_{t-1} = \beta$ since interest is applied between the beginning and the end of each period.

The programme (3) is written in amplified form as :

(i) *Technical* $\alpha A\lambda \leqslant B\lambda$ $\lambda \geqslant 0$

and whenever " $<$ " rules for any commodity the corresponding price is zero.

(ii) *Prices* $\beta A' p \geqslant B' p$ $p \geqslant 0$

and whenever " $>$ " rules for any activity the corresponding level is zero. Here the levels of activities (λ) and of prices (p) are given only as ratios. The trivial case $\lambda = p = 0$ is ruled out so that the inequalities " $\geqslant 0$ " on λ and p are to be interpreted as " all elements non-negative with some positive ". The conditions can be spelled out :

$$\left.\begin{array}{l}
\text{(i) } Technical \quad \alpha \sum_{s=1}^{n} a_{rs}\lambda_s = \sum_{s=1}^{n} b_{rs}\lambda_s \,; \quad p_r \geqslant 0 \quad \text{ for some } r \\[2mm]
\qquad\qquad \alpha \sum_{s=1}^{n} a_{rs}\lambda_s < \sum_{s=1}^{n} b_{rs}\lambda_s \,; \quad p_r = 0 \,; \quad \text{for other } r \\[2mm]
\text{(ii) } Prices \quad \beta \sum_{r=1}^{m} a_{rs}p_r = \sum_{r=1}^{m} b_{rs}p_r \,; \quad \lambda_s \geqslant 0 \,; \quad \text{for some } s \\[2mm]
\qquad\qquad \beta \sum_{r=1}^{m} a_{rs}p_r > \sum_{r=1}^{m} b_{rs}p_r \,; \quad \lambda_s = 0 \,; \quad \text{for other } s
\end{array}\right\} \quad \dots\dots\dots\dots(4)$$

Let $\bar{\lambda}$ and $\bar{p}$ be any levels of activity and prices which are not necessarily solution of (4). Define ϕ as a ratio of bilinear forms :

$$\phi(\bar{\lambda}, \bar{p}) = \frac{\sum\limits_{r=1}^{m} \sum\limits_{s=1}^{n} b_{rs}\lambda_s \bar{p}_r}{\sum\limits_{r=1}^{m} \sum\limits_{s=1}^{n} a_{rs}\lambda_s \bar{p}_r}$$

The vectors λ and p will now be used only for solutions of the programme (4). The function ϕ is to be used to pick out the solutions λ and p.

Take the technical conditions (i) of (4). They state that :

$$\alpha = \frac{\sum\limits_{s=1}^{n} b_{rs}\lambda_s}{\sum\limits_{s=1}^{n} a_{rs}\lambda_s} \text{ for some } r \quad \text{and} \quad \alpha < \frac{\sum\limits_{s=1}^{n} b_{rs}\lambda_s}{\sum\limits_{s=1}^{n} a_{rs}\lambda_s} \text{ for other } r$$
$$\qquad\qquad (p_r \geqslant 0) \qquad\qquad\qquad\qquad\qquad (p_r = 0)$$

i.e.
$$\alpha = \operatorname*{Min}_{r} \frac{\sum\limits_{s=1}^{n} b_{rs}\lambda_s}{\sum\limits_{s=1}^{n} a_{rs}\lambda_s}$$

Write $\dfrac{\sum\limits_{s=1}^{n} b_{rs}\lambda_s}{\sum\limits_{s=1}^{n} a_{rs}\lambda_s} = \alpha + \alpha_r$ where $\alpha_r = 0$ when $p_r > 0$
$$\qquad\qquad\qquad\qquad\qquad\qquad\qquad \alpha_r \geqslant 0 \quad \text{when} \quad p_r = 0$$

Then $\quad \phi(\lambda, \bar{\mathbf{p}}) = \dfrac{\sum\limits_{r=1}^{m} \bar{p}_r(\sum\limits_{s=1}^{n} b_{rs}\lambda_s)}{\sum\limits_{r=1}^{m} \bar{p}_r(\sum\limits_{s=1}^{n} a_{rs}\lambda_s)} = \dfrac{\sum\limits_{r=1}^{m} \bar{p}_r(\alpha+\alpha_r)(\sum\limits_{s=1}^{n} a_{rs}\lambda_s)}{\sum\limits_{r=1}^{m} \bar{p}_r(\sum\limits_{s=1}^{n} a_{rs}\lambda_s)}$

$$= \alpha + \frac{\sum\limits_{r=1}^{m}\sum\limits_{s=1}^{n} \alpha_r a_{rs}\lambda_s \bar{p}_r}{\sum\limits_{r=1}^{m}\sum\limits_{s=1}^{n} a_{rs}\lambda_s \bar{p}_r}$$

The second expression here is non-negative and it vanishes when $\bar{p}_r = p_r$ since either $\alpha_r = 0$ $(p_r > 0)$ or $p_r = 0$.

Hence $\qquad\qquad\qquad \phi(\lambda, \bar{\mathbf{p}}) \geqslant \phi(\lambda, \mathbf{p}) = \alpha$

and $\phi(\lambda, \bar{\mathbf{p}})$ has a minimum value (α) when $\bar{\mathbf{p}} = \mathbf{p}$.

Conditions (ii) can be analysed similarly and it follows that :

$$\phi(\bar{\lambda}, \mathbf{p}) \leqslant \phi(\lambda, \mathbf{p}) = \beta$$

i.e. $\phi(\bar{\lambda}, \mathbf{p})$ has a maximum value (β) when $\bar{\lambda} = \lambda$.

The solution $(\lambda, \mathbf{p})$ of (4) is thus to be sought as the saddle point :

$$\phi(\lambda, \mathbf{p}) = \alpha = \beta$$

of the function $\phi(\bar{\lambda}, \bar{\mathbf{p}})$ for any $\bar{\lambda}$ and $\bar{\mathbf{p}}$ which are non-negative. The solution of the problem reduces to a problem in the theory of games. It was proved by von Neumann (1937, 1945) that there may be several solutions for the ratios λ and $\mathbf{p}$ but that all solutions have unique and equal values of α and β. He assumes that every element of $\mathbf{A} + \mathbf{B}$ is positive, i.e. that every commodity appears (as input or output) in every process, a very restrictive assumption. It has been relaxed by Kemeny, Morgenstern and Thompson (1956) at the cost of having more than one equal pair of α and β.

It also follows that α is the *largest* expansion rate technically possible, being set by the commodity with the slowest rate of expansion. For, if $\bar{\alpha}$ is any other possible rate, and with any $\bar{\lambda}$ to correspond :

$$\bar{\alpha}\mathbf{A}\bar{\lambda} \leqslant \mathbf{B}\bar{\lambda}$$

Multiply each term by the corresponding term in $\mathbf{p}$ and add :

$$\bar{\alpha} \sum_{r=1}^{m}\sum_{s=1}^{n} a_{rs}\bar{\lambda}_s p_r \leqslant \sum_{r=1}^{m}\sum_{s=1}^{n} b_{rs}\bar{\lambda}_s p_r$$

i.e. $\qquad\qquad\qquad \bar{\alpha} \leqslant \phi(\bar{\lambda}, \mathbf{p}) \leqslant \phi(\lambda, \mathbf{p}) = \alpha$

Similarly, β is the *smallest* rate of interest possible with a price system yielding negative or zero profits in all activities. In short, though this closed system of equilibrium of an expanding economy has no minimum or maximum condition, its solution does correspond to a minimax position as in the theory of games, with α as the largest expansion rate and β as the smallest interest rate possible.

The conditions and the properties of the solution can be summarised in the following sequence of results ; see the comments by Champernowne (1945).

(i) *Free goods* : the technical conditions of the problem are that the input of any commodity cannot exceed the output of the previous period ; however, if the input is less than the output, the commodity is a free good with zero price.

(ii) *Unused (unprofitable) activities* : the conditions on (accounting) prices are that no activity has a positive profit ; however, if an activity has a negative profit, then it will not be used.

(iii) *Rate of expansion* of the system over time is the largest technically possible, i.e. the rate set by the commodity of which the rate of production expansion is the lowest in the whole system.

(iv) *Rate of interest* of the system is the smallest possible with price systems corresponding to no positive profits in any line of activity, i.e. set by the most profitable of all the activities of the system.

(v) *The equilibrium property* is that the (maximum) rate of expansion is the same as the (minimum) rate of interest ; these are uniquely determined.

This is an analysis of the basic problem of long-run economic equilibrium under conditions of steady growth over time. It is an analysis of a closed system under constant returns to scale and with no limits on availability of primary factors. It provides, therefore, no more than a basis on which to build in turning to more " realistic " problems, e.g. when there are consumer preferences and substitution, and in particular in passing to problems of the dynamics of change from or about long-run equilibrium.

However, the analysis does show up in high relief some of the essential features of economic equilibrium, e.g. the function of accounting prices and the choice between activities according as profits are zero or negative. See Dorfman, Samuelson and Solow (1958), particularly pp. 386–8. When the model is expressed in linear programming terms, the technical problem of efficient allocation of resources is matched by the dual problem of prices and profits. J. von Neumann was the pioneer in this field ; see Kuhn and Tucker (1958). The prices are only accounting prices ; they can be realised as market prices under suitably competitive conditions or they can be used by " planners " in a centralised or decentralised " welfare " system. It can be said that, whatever the system, if such accounting prices do not exist then it is necessary to invent them.

REFERENCES

Arrow (K. J.) and Debreu (G.) (1954) : " Existence of an Equilibrium for a Competitive Economy ", *Econometrica*, **22**, 265–90.

Cameron (B.) (1951) : " The Construction of the Leontief System ", *Review of Economic Studies*, **19**, 19–27.

Champernowne (D. G.) (1945) : " A Note on J. v. Neumann's Article ", *Review of Economic Studies*, **13**, 10–18.

Chipman (J.) (1953) : " Linear Programming ", *Review of Economics and Statistics*, **35**, 101–17 and 342–9.

Dantzig (G. B.) (1949) : " Programming of Interdependent Activities : Mathematical Model ", *Econometrica*, **17**, 200–11.

Debreu (G.) (1951) : " The Coefficient of Resource Utilisation ", *Econometrica*, **19**, 273–92.

Dorfman (R.), Samuelson (P. A.) and Solow (R. M.) (1958) : *Linear Programming and Economic Analysis* (McGraw-Hill, 1958), Chapters 9–10 and 13.

Georgescu-Roegen (N.) (1935) : " Fixed Coefficients of Production and Marginal Productivity Theory ", *Review of Economic Studies*, **3**, 40–9.

Kemeny (J. G.), Morgenstern (O.) and Thompson (G. L.) (1956) : " A Generalisation of the von Neumann Model of an Expanding Economy ", *Econometrica*, **24**, 115–35.

Kemeny (J. G.), Snell (J. L.) and Thompson (G. L.) (1957) : *Introduction to Finite Mathematics* (Prentice-Hall, 1957), Chapter VII.

Koopmans (T. C.) (Editor) (1951) : *Activity Analysis of Production and Allocation* (Wiley, 1951).

Kuhn (H. W.) and Tucker (A. W.) (1958) : " John von Neumann's Work in the Theory of Games and Mathematical Economics ", *American Mathematical Society*, **64** (3 II), 100–22.

Leontief (W. W.) (1951) : *The Structure of American Economy, 1919–1939* (Oxford, Second Ed., 1951).

Mises (L.) (1935) : " Economic Calculation in the Socialist Commonwealth ", in Hayek (F. A.) (Editor), *Collectivist Economic Planning* (Routledge, 1935).

Morgenstern (O.) (Editor) (1954) : *Economic Activity Analysis* (Wiley, 1954).

Neumann (J. von) (1937, 1945) : " A Model of General Economic Equilibrium ", *Review of Economic Studies*, **13**, 1–9, English translation of an earlier (1937) article in German.

Robbins (L. C.) (1932) : *The Nature and Significance of Economic Science* (Macmillan, 1932).

Wald (A.) (1935, 1951) : " On Some Systems of Equations in Mathematical Economics ", *Econometrica*, **19**, 368–403, English translation of an earlier (1935) article in German.

Wong (Y. K.) and Morgenstern (O.) (1957) : " A Study of Linear Economic Systems ", *Weltwirtschaftliches Archiv*, **79**, 222–39.

CHAPTER 18

THE THEORY OF THE FIRM

18.1 Marginal Analysis : Substitution of Factors in Production

THE mathematical tools are now available for a detailed analysis of production in the firm. The concept of a firm is simple, a matter of definition ; it is the effective decision-taking unit in whatever production activity is considered. In practice, this may be what is called an establishment or plant, or it may be a company. On the other hand, it may be a group of establishments or companies organised into some unit of effective control, an organisation like Unilevers or a nationalised industry. Whatever the organisation, however, it is assumed here that there is a decision-taking unit—for the particular activity and time period (short or long) considered —and the unit is called the firm as a matter of convenience.

The analysis of the firm is to be contrasted with that of the whole production system ; it is an analysis of the " micro " type. Attempts may be made to analyse some sector of the economy, not the whole but wider than a single firm. There seems to be little place for this ; there is no obvious resting place between the firm and the whole economy. An approximation may be made by a conventional and statistical grouping of firms into " industries ". Even so, it is not obvious how to answer questions like : " how many firms comprise an industry? " The question may be unimportant (if not meaningless) if the firms are identical in organisation and technology, if each firm is the industry in miniature. On the other hand, it may be framed in such terms as to make the answer an extremely awkward one of analysing expectations and conditions of entry.

As indicated in 10.8 above, the theory of the firm can proceed *either* in marginal terms following the " classical " or traditional pattern, *or* in the large by means of linear programming and activity analysis. The approaches are complementary rather than competitive ; both can be kept for use according to the nature of the problem. The present development uses both methods. In any case, the analysis is short-run (or moderately long-run) since the firm is regarded as having something fixed in its organisation and since the decisions taken are related to a (more or less) restricted time-horizon.

In the traditional marginal analysis, attention is concentrated on substitution between factors, between products or between a factor and a product. To isolate factor substitution, the first problem considered is that of a firm with one product and a number of factors. The case of two factors is sufficient to illustrate most of the problems. The production function is then :

$$y = f(x_1, x_2)$$

where y is the product and x_1 and x_2 are the factors used. It can be shown on a diagram as a system of constant product curves (10.7 above). Let $f_r = \dfrac{\partial y}{\partial x_r}$ and $f_{rs} = \dfrac{\partial^2 y}{\partial x_r \partial x_s}$ ($r, s = 1, 2$) be the partial derivatives at any point (x_1, x_2). The symmetric matrix :

$$\mathbf{F} = \begin{bmatrix} 0 & f_1 & f_2 \\ f_1 & f_{11} & f_{12} \\ f_2 & f_{12} & f_{22} \end{bmatrix}$$

is formed ; write F as the determinant value of $\mathbf{F}$, and F_r and F_{rs} as the co-factors of f_r and f_{rs} respectively.

Under *pure competition*, assume that the firm obtains factors at given prices p_1 and p_2 on the factor market and sells the product at a given market price π. The problem then is to find the combination (x_1 and x_2) of factors used and the scale of production (y) to maximise net revenue :

$$R = \pi y - (p_1 x_1 + p_2 x_2) \quad \text{where} \quad y = f(x_1, x_2)$$

The necessary conditions are $\dfrac{\partial R}{\partial x_1} = \dfrac{\partial R}{\partial x_2} = 0$, giving :

$$\pi f_1 - p_1 = \pi f_2 - p_2 = 0$$

Hence, the uses of the factors (x_1 and x_2) are obtained as functions of the prices (p_1, p_2 and π) from :

$$\frac{p_1}{f_1} = \frac{p_2}{f_2} = \pi \quad \dots\dots\dots\dots\dots\dots\dots\dots(1)$$

and the scale of production (y) from $y = f(x_1, x_2)$.

The first equation of (1) shows that, for equilibrium, the relative usage of factors is such that the marginal rate of substitution between them (ratio of marginal products $f_1 : f_2$) is equal to the given price ratio. The scale of production, i.e. the levels of x_1 and x_2 and hence of $y = f(x_1, x_2)$, is then given by adding the other equation of (1), written in the form :

$$p_1 = \pi f_1 \quad \text{and} \quad p_2 = \pi f_2 \dots\dots\dots\dots\dots\dots(2)$$

i.e. the scale is expanded until the value of each marginal product (at the given product price) becomes equal to the factor price.

The equilibrium represented by (1) or (2) can be reached in two stages. First, suppose that output y is given, as well as p_1 and p_2. The usage of factors (x_1 and x_2) is such that cost of production $C = p_1 x_1 + p_2 x_2$ is a minimum subject to $f(x_1, x_2) = y$ (given). By use of the Lagrange multiplier (Ex. 1 below) this is achieved by minimising :

$$Z = C - \lambda \{ f(x_1, x_2) - y \} \quad (y \text{ given}) \dots\dots\dots\dots(3)$$

so that x_1 and x_2 are given as functions of y, p_1 and p_2 by:

$$\frac{p_1}{f_1} = \frac{p_2}{f_2} = \lambda \quad \text{and} \quad f(x_1, x_2) = y \dots\dots\dots\dots(4)$$

The cost of production C is then also a function of y, p_1 and p_2.

The sufficient condition for a minimum of Z is $d^2 Z > 0$, where

$$d^2 Z = -\lambda (f_{11} \, dx_1^2 + 2 f_{12} \, dx_1 \, dx_2 + f_{22} \, dx_2^2) \quad \text{by (3)},$$

subject to $f(x_1, x_2) = y$ (given). Hence :

$$f_{11} \, dx_1^2 + 2 f_{12} \, dx_1 \, dx_2 + f_{22} \, dx_2^2 < 0 \quad \text{subject to} \quad f_1 \, dx_1 + f_2 \, dx_2 = 0$$

By the results for quadratic forms (14.5 above), the condition is :

$$F = \begin{vmatrix} 0 & f_1 & f_2 \\ f_1 & f_{11} & f_{12} \\ f_2 & f_{12} & f_{22} \end{vmatrix} > 0 \dots\dots\dots\dots(5)$$

The second stage is then : given the product price π, output y is fixed to maximise net revenue $(\pi y - C)$. A comparison of (1) and (4) shows that it is only necessary to put the multiple $\lambda = \pi$ in (4). Condition (5) must still hold for stability.

The advantage of the two-stage analysis is that the cost function, and the corresponding marginal and average cost, can be written and its variation as y, p_1 and p_2 vary can be determined. Differentiating equations (4) with respect to y, p_1 and p_2 in turn provides the information (see Ex. 2 and 3 below). It is found, first, that $\dfrac{\partial C}{\partial y} = \lambda = \pi$ when the optimum output is determined. Hence, in equilibrium, marginal cost equals product price. It is *not* required that the common value of marginal cost and product price is also equal to average cost (see Ex. 4 below).

Next, as p_1 varies (y and p_2 fixed), the demand for factors changes according to the rates:

$$\frac{\partial x_1}{\partial p_1} = \frac{1}{\lambda} \frac{F_{11}}{F} = -\frac{f_2^2}{\lambda F} < 0$$

and

$$\frac{\partial x_2}{\partial p_1} = \frac{1}{\lambda} \frac{F_{12}}{F} = \frac{f_1 f_2}{\lambda F} > 0$$

by the stability condition (5). Hence, as the price of a factor falls, the use of the factor increases and that of the other factor decreases. The factors are substitutes in production; complementarity can only arise when there are more than two factors.

Fig. 69 shows the first stage in the determination of equilibrium. The constant product curve $f(x_1 x_2) = y$ is given by the problem. There is a

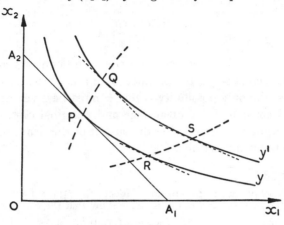

FIG. 69.

whole series of parallel cost lines ($p_1 x_1 + p_2 x_2 = C$, for various costs C) and the lowest of them (C a minimum) is sought. If the constant product curve is convex to O, the equilibrium factor usage is given by P where a cost line $A_1 A_2$ touches the constant product curve. The tangency condition is that the marginal rate of substitution equals the price ratio. Fig. 69 also shows the result of increasing output y (move from P to Q), of decreasing the price p_1 (move from P to R), or both (move from P to S). The corresponding variation in factor demand, x_1 and x_2, is read off the diagram.

The particular case of *constant returns to scale* is of interest. The production function is of linear homogeneous form so that, by Euler's Theorem as set out in Allen (1938), the relation :

$$y = f_1 x_1 + f_2 x_2$$

holds at every point. Hence, at the equilibrium point, by (2) :

$$\pi y = p_1 x_1 + p_2 x_2$$

and the product (by value) is completely distributed over the two factors. The maximised value of net revenue R is then zero. Any other usage of the factors than the equilibrium ratio gives a negative rate of profits. This result i.e. the " adding up " of marginal products and the zero profits, holds for any equilibrium position when there are constant returns to scale. It does not hold, except at special equilibrium points, for other production functions.

If the matter is pursued further, however, the case of constant returns to scale is seen to be of doubtful use in the theory of the firm. The cost function, at the first stage in the analysis, is found (Ex. 5 below) to be such that :

$$\frac{\partial C}{\partial y} = \frac{C}{y} = \lambda$$

i.e. marginal cost and average cost are equal and constant at all outputs. When, at the second stage, the product price π is introduced (equal to λ), it follows that the only possibility is that π must be given as equal to the common and constant value of average and marginal cost. With this π given, any output y will serve, i.e. the output of the firm (under constant returns to scale) is indeterminate.

EXERCISES 18.1

1. If $C = p_1 x_1 + p_2 x_2$ is a minimum subject to $f(x_1, x_2) = y$ (given), write $Z = C - \lambda\{f(x_1, x_2) - y\}$ and minimise Z. Show that the conditions are :

$$p_1 - f_1 \lambda = p_2 - f_2 \lambda = 0$$

2. Differentiate equations (4) with respect to y and obtain :

$$f_1 \frac{\partial x_1}{\partial y} + f_2 \frac{\partial x_2}{\partial y} = 1$$

$$f_1 \left(\frac{1}{\lambda} \frac{\partial \lambda}{\partial y}\right) + f_{11} \frac{\partial x_1}{\partial y} + f_{12} \frac{\partial x_2}{\partial y} = 0$$

$$f_2 \left(\frac{1}{\lambda} \frac{\partial \lambda}{\partial y}\right) + f_{12} \frac{\partial x_1}{\partial y} + f_{22} \frac{\partial x_2}{\partial y} = 0$$

Solve by Cramer's rule to give $\dfrac{\partial x_1}{\partial y} = \dfrac{F_1}{F}$ and $\dfrac{\partial x_2}{\partial y} = \dfrac{F_2}{F}$. Use the first equation above, and the equilibrium conditions, to show that $\dfrac{\partial C}{\partial y} = \lambda$.

3. Differentiate equations (4) with respect to p_1, obtain equations similar to those of the previous exercise, and solve to get $\dfrac{\partial x_1}{\partial p_1} = \dfrac{1}{\lambda} \dfrac{F_{11}}{F}$ and $\dfrac{\partial x_2}{\partial p_1} = \dfrac{1}{\lambda} \dfrac{F_{12}}{F}$.

4. Show that average cost is $\left(\pi - \dfrac{R}{y}\right)$, where R is (maximised) net revenue, and deduce that average and marginal cost are only equal if the maximised net revenue is zero.

5. For equilibrium with a linear homogeneous production function, show that

$$y = f_1 x_1 + f_2 x_2 = \frac{1}{\lambda} C.$$

Deduce that marginal and average cost are equal at each output y, and hence that each is constant as y changes.

18.2 Joint Production

The analysis so far assumes that the firm has only one product; joint production is not considered, in order that attention may be directed to substitution between factors in production. The general case is now taken where the firm produces any number of outputs and makes use of any number of factors. All kinds of substitution between factors and products are possible. The technical conditions are assumed, as before, to be represented by a single production function of continuous form, with continuous derivatives. One way of writing the relation, as in 10.7 above, is:

$$f(x_1, x_2, \dots x_r, y_1, y_2, \dots y_s) = 0$$

where r inputs (the x's) are used in the production of s outputs (the y's). The simple case of 18.1 arises when $r = 2$ and $s = 1$. Even this is not quite general, however, since it does not allow for the possibility that one commodity is an input in some production combinations and an output in others. In any case, it is preferable to denote the variable commodities in a uniform way, an input being a negative output. Write:

$$f(x_1, x_2, \dots x_n) = 0$$

as the production function, the outputs of n commodities being x_r ($r = 1, 2, \dots n$). If $x_r > 0$, the commodity is produced; if $x_r < 0$, it is a factor or input. Denote the partial derivatives by $f_r = \dfrac{\partial f}{\partial x_r}$ and $f_{rs} = \dfrac{\partial^2 f}{\partial x_r \partial x_s}$ for $r, s = 1, 2, \dots n$, and write the symmetric matrix:

$$\mathbf{F} = \begin{bmatrix} 0 & f_1 & f_2 & \cdots & f_n \\ f_1 & f_{11} & f_{12} & \cdots & f_{1n} \\ f_2 & f_{12} & f_{22} & \cdots & f_{2n} \\ \multicolumn{5}{c}{\dotfill} \\ f_n & f_{1n} & f_{2n} & \cdots & f_{nn} \end{bmatrix}$$

The determinant value is F and F_r and F_{rs} are the co-factors of f_r and f_{rs} in F.

Assume that, under pure competition, the prices of commodities (products and factors) are given to the firm as p_r ($r = 1, 2, \dots n$). The analysis follows Hicks (1939, 1946). The firm chooses the combination of inputs and outputs to maximise net revenue:

$$R = \sum_r p_r x_r$$

subject to
$$f(x_1, x_2, \dots x_n) = 0$$

Notice that R comprises positive terms (for products) and negative terms (for factors), i.e. R is the difference between receipts and costs. The equilibrium position is best determined by using a Lagrange multiplier λ and by maximising :

$$z = R - \lambda f$$

for the n variables x_r $(r = 1, 2, \ldots n)$. The necessary conditions are $\dfrac{\partial z}{\partial x_r} = 0$, giving :

$$
\left.
\begin{aligned}
p_r &= \lambda f_r \quad (r = 1, 2, \ldots n) \\
f(x_1, x_2, \ldots x_n) &= 0
\end{aligned}
\right\} \quad \ldots\ldots\ldots\ldots\ldots\ldots(1)
$$

and

as $(n+1)$ equations for the $(n+1)$ variables, the x's and λ.

The sufficient conditions, to ensure a maximum (rather than a minimum) of net revenue R, are that $d^2z < 0$ for any variation satisfying the production function. Since $d^2z = -\lambda\, d^2f$, the conditions are :

$$d^2 f = \sum_r \sum_s f_{rs}\, dx_r\, dx_s > 0$$

subject to

$$df = \sum_r f_r\, dx_r = 0$$

This must be the case for any variations from the equilibrium position. The stability conditions now assumed are designed to ensure that a (maximum) equilibrium position can exist for any prices :

$$\sum_r \sum_s f_{rs}\, \xi_r\, \xi_s > 0 \quad \text{subject to} \quad \sum_r f_r\, \xi_r = 0$$

for any ξ's not all zero (representing a direction of change from any point). The results for positive definite quadratic forms (14.5 above) apply and the stability conditions are that F and all its principal minors are negative. Another way of writing the conditions, generally more convenient, is that given at the end of 14.5 above ; it involves the elements of the inverse matrix $\mathbf{F}^{-1}$ and it can be written :

$$\sum_r \sum_s \frac{F_{rs}}{F} y_r y_s > 0 \ldots\ldots\ldots\ldots\ldots\ldots\ldots\ldots(2)$$

for any y's not all zero. F_{rs} is the co-factor of f_{rs} in F.

Equilibrium of the firm is given by (1), subject to stability conditions (2). The variables x_r are determined as functions of all the prices p_r, i.e. the demand functions for factors and supply functions for products. The effect of any specified change in the prices can be investigated, by differentiating (1) with respect to the prices varied and taking note of (2). This is a problem in comparative statics. Suppose only one price (say p_1) changes. Differentiate (1) and arrange the equations in the form :

$$\sum_s f_s \frac{\partial x_s}{\partial p_1} = 0$$

$$f_1\left(\frac{1}{\lambda}\frac{\partial\lambda}{\partial p_1}\right) + \sum_s f_{1s}\frac{\partial x_s}{\partial p_1} = \frac{1}{\lambda}$$

$$f_r\left(\frac{1}{\lambda}\frac{\partial\lambda}{\partial p_1}\right) + \sum_s f_{rs}\frac{\partial x_s}{\partial p_1} = 0 \quad (r=2, 3, \ldots n)$$

$$\Big\}\ldots\ldots\ldots\ldots(3)$$

The equations (3) make up a linear system in the variables $\left(\frac{1}{\lambda}\frac{\partial\lambda}{\partial p_1}\right)$ and $\frac{\partial x_s}{\partial p_1}$ ($s=1, 2, \ldots n$), to be solved by Cramer's rule. The first variable is not required and the others are obtained as $\frac{\partial x_s}{\partial p_1} = \frac{1}{\lambda}\frac{F_{1s}}{F}$. Generalise for a change in any one price (p_r):

$$\frac{\partial x_s}{\partial p_r} = \frac{F_{rs}}{\lambda F} \quad (r, s=1, 2, \ldots n) \ldots\ldots\ldots\ldots\ldots(4)$$

which shows the effect of one price change on the demand or supply of each commodity.

It remains to make use of the stability conditions in determining or limiting the signs of the expressions (4). The relations (2) now appear:

$$\sum_r \sum_s \frac{\partial x_s}{\partial p_r} y_r y_s > 0 \ldots\ldots\ldots\ldots\ldots\ldots\ldots(5)$$

for any y's not all zero. This follows since λ is positive, by (1). In particular, for all y's zero except y_r:

$$\frac{\partial x_r}{\partial p_r} > 0 \quad (r=1, 2, \ldots n) \ldots\ldots\ldots\ldots\ldots(6)$$

A further relation is to be derived from the determinant F and the equilibrium conditions (1), without reference to stability conditions. If the elements in the first row of F are multiplied by the co-factors of the elements in the $(r+1)$th row, the products add to zero by the expansion rule for determinants. Hence:

$$0 = \sum_s f_s F_{rs} = F \sum_s p_s\left(\frac{F_{rs}}{\lambda F}\right) = F \sum_s p_s \frac{\partial x_s}{\partial p_r}$$

by (1) and (4). It follows that:

$$\sum_s p_s \frac{\partial x_s}{\partial p_r} = 0 \quad (r=1, 2, \ldots n)$$

i.e.

$$\sum'_s p_s \frac{\partial x_s}{\partial p_r} = p_r\left(-\frac{\partial x_r}{\partial p_r}\right) < 0 \ldots\ldots\ldots\ldots\ldots(7)$$

where $\sum'_s$ is the summation for all $s \neq r$.

The results are now immediately interpreted. First, the equilibrium conditions (1) show that, for any two commodities (say $r = 1, 2$):

$$-\frac{dx_2}{dx_1} = \frac{f_1}{f_2} = \frac{p_1}{p_2}$$

where dx_1 and dx_2 are variations in the amounts of the two commodities (from the equilibrium position) according to the technical possibilities of the production function. The price ratio of two products ($x_1 > 0$, $x_2 > 0$) is in equilibrium equal to the marginal rate of substitution between the products in production, usages of factors fixed. The price ratio of two factors ($x_1 < 0$, $x_2 < 0$) is, as before, equal to the marginal rate of substitution between them (products fixed). The price ratio of a factor ($x_1 < 0$) and a product ($x_2 > 0$) equals the ratio of dx_2 the change in the product to $d(-x_1)$, the extra amount of the factor used; in other words, the price ratio is in equilibrium the marginal product of the factor.

Second, the direct effect of a price change, on the demand or supply of the commodity itself, is given by (6). For a product ($x_r > 0$), the condition is $\dfrac{\partial x_r}{\partial p_r} > 0$, i.e. a price increase raises the supply. For a factor ($x_r < 0$), the condition is $\dfrac{\partial(-x_r)}{\partial p_r} < 0$, i.e. a price increase reduces the demand.

Finally, the "cross" effects of price changes are given by (4) and restricted by (5) and (7). These are the effects of one price change on the demands or supplies of the other commodities. Since $\mathbf{F}$ is symmetrical and so $F_{rs} = F_{sr}$, the "cross" effects are also symmetrical, i.e. $\dfrac{\partial x_s}{\partial p_r} = \dfrac{\partial x_r}{\partial p_s}$. Then, for the effects of a change in one price p_r on various other commodities $\dfrac{\partial x_s}{\partial p_r}$ ($s \neq r$), the relation (7) shows that negative values must outweigh positive values. Hence, if p_r increases, the effect on other commodities will tend to be either to decrease the supply (of a product) or to increase the use (of a factor). As Hicks has shown, it can be taken generally that substitution dominates in product-factor relations; an increase in a factor price reduces supplies of products and an increase in a product price raises usages of factors. Against this there may be considerable relations of complementarity within the group of products (a price increase raising supplies), and within the group of factors (a price increase reducing their use).

In the particular case of *constant returns to scale* in production, the inputs and outputs can all be increased in the same proportion so that, if $f(x_1, x_2, \ldots x_n) = 0$, then :

$$f(\mu x_1, \mu x_2, \ldots \mu x_n) = 0 \quad \text{for any } \mu > 0$$

The function f is homogeneous (of degree zero) and by Euler's Theorem :

$$\sum_r f_r x_r = 0 \quad \ldots\ldots\ldots\ldots\ldots\ldots\ldots\ldots\ldots\ldots\ldots\ldots(8)$$

Hence, in equilibrium by (1) :

$$R = \sum_r p_r x_r = 0$$

The products are exactly distributed over the factors according to marginal productivity and the maximised net revenue is zero.

However, (8) holds at all points. It can be differentiated :

$$\frac{\partial}{\partial x_s}(\sum_r f_r x_r) = 0$$

i.e. $\qquad\qquad \sum_r x_r f_{rs} = -f_s \quad (s = 1, 2, \ldots n) \quad \ldots\ldots\ldots\ldots\ldots\ldots(9)$

This can be interpreted in terms of the determinant F. If the rows after the first are multiplied by $x_1, x_2, \ldots x_n$ and added to the first row $(0, f_1, f_2, \ldots f_n)$, the result by (8) and (9) is a row of zero elements. Hence $F = 0$. This is a serious matter; the stability conditions require $F \neq 0$, and if $F = 0$ they are not satisfied, nor can the effect of price changes (4) be written. The prices must assume particular given values and no one of them can be changed by itself without destroying equilibrium. The position is similar to that found (at the end of 18.1) in the simple case of one product. As long as a short-run view of the firm is taken, some element in its organisation is fixed and there are not constant returns to scale. The equilibrium position (subject to stability conditions) can be defined and varied; there is a (maximum) surplus of net revenue which is the return to the factors which are fixed. In the long-run, if all elements are variable and returns are constant, the analysis tends to break down, or to become inappropriate.

EXERCISES 18.2

1. The production function $f(x_1, x_2, \ldots x_n) = 0$ is not unique; any function of it, $\phi\{f(x_1, x_2, \ldots x_n)\} = 0$ will serve equally well in representing the firm's technology, provided that $\phi(f) = 0$ when $f = 0$. If $\phi(f)$ is substituted for f, show that neither the equilibrium equations (1) nor the stability conditions (2) are affected.

2. As a particular case of the stability conditions (5) show that :

$$\sum_{r=1}^{m} \sum_{s=1}^{m} p_r p_s \frac{\partial x_s}{\partial p_r} > 0 \quad \text{for } m \leqslant n$$

Use $\sum_{s=1}^{n} p_s \dfrac{\partial x_s}{\partial p_r} = 0$, as in (7), to deduce that :

$$\sum_{r=1}^{m} \sum_{s=m+1}^{n} p_r p_s \frac{\partial x_s}{\partial p_r} < 0$$

If commodities $r = 1, 2, \ldots m$ are factors and $s = m+1,\ m+2, \ldots n$ products, interpret this relation broadly in terms of increasing supply of a group of products when prices of a group of factors decrease.

3. A firm produces one product (y) with n factors ($x_1, x_2, \ldots x_n$) and the production function is $f(x_1, x_2, \ldots x_n, y) = 0$, all variables being positive. Assume that the factor prices and the product y (*not* the product price) are given. Find the necessary conditions for equilibrium (minimum cost), interpret and compare with (1) above.

4. In the problem of the previous exercise, differentiate the equilibrium equations with respect to one price, other prices and product (y) being fixed. Find an expression for $\dfrac{\partial x_s}{\partial p_r}$, i.e. the change in demand for the sth factor as the price of the rth factor increases. Write the stability conditions and show that they ensure that $\dfrac{\partial x_r}{\partial p_r} < 0$ but leave it open whether $\dfrac{\partial x_s}{\partial p_r} > 0$ (substitute factors) or $\dfrac{\partial x_s}{\partial p_r} < 0$ (complementary factors). Compare with the case examined in 18.1.

18.3 Marginal Analysis v. Linear Programming of the Firm

The marginal analysis of 18.2 above is framed to apply generally under certain conditions of pure competition, and specifically for factors which are available *without limit* to the firm at given market prices. The analysis can be re-worked, as Makower and Baumol (1950) show, when the factors are available to the firm only *within specified limits*. The factors may be all hired, and at given market prices, but a limit is imposed, at least, on the amount of cash or credit open to the firm for financing its operations. In addition to a basic cash limit, there may also be certain physical limits on particular factors, e.g. on owned and fixed factors such as land and buildings. The extended analysis takes account of the *given resources* of the firm. The theory can be further extended and adapted to allow for imperfect competition and for various forms of monopoly power, as in the familiar work of Chamberlin (1933) and Robinson (1933).

The advantages of the marginal analysis lie in the fact that it provides a clear exposition, leading to a variety of general results, of the actions of a firm when everything is capable of variation. The technology of the firm is summed up in a single relation of continuously variable form—the production function. There are no restrictions on the nature of the function and, in particular, there is no necessary assumption that the returns to scale are constant, or of any other precise specification.

The marginal technique, however, is not without its difficulties, both conceptual and mathematical. One objection is that the taking of decisions in the firm is essentially short-run in scope and hence that perfectly continuous variation or substitution is not a suitable basis of the theory. Another objection is that marginal analysis was designed historically to apply to the more " primitive " processes of (e.g.) agriculture and that it still draws its illustrations quite largely from this field. Highly developed industrial processes, it is maintained, are both more complex and far less flexible than marginal analysis assumes. It is not a matter of deciding on the optimum substitution between a range of factors—land, plant and labour of all kinds—but rather of fixing on a particular process with the relatively inflexible organisation which goes with it, e.g. the specialised labour to work a specialised plant. The smooth and comprehensive range of a production function seems an inadequate tool of analysis for a modern industrial firm.

It is no answer to these objections to say that, in the long-run, everything is variable and that it is worth while seeing how long-run decisions might be taken. For, as shown at the end of 18.2 above, the logical assumption in the long-run (constant returns to scale and a linear homogeneous production function) tends to lead to a break-down of marginal analysis. The scale of operations of a firm becomes indeterminate.

Marginal analysis, therefore, is one way of describing the decision-taking activities of a firm—on a simplified and approximate basis. It must be judged on its success or failure in handling relatively short-run problems. It provides a neat and tidy method of exposition, but it cannot pretend to produce answers to all kinds of questions on the behaviour of the firm. Alternative methods of analysis, to supplement rather than to replace the marginal approach, can be sought ; and it is here that the technique of linear programming and activity analysis would seem to be particularly relevant.

The basis of the linear programming approach to the theory of the firm is the specification of a technology in a way both more specific and more detailed than the production function of marginal analysis. Indeed, linear programming goes out of its way to stress the technical side of the decisions made by a firm. It starts from the assumption that the firm considers only a limited number of separate technical processes of production. In the short-run, there may be only a few processes worth considering ; in the longer-run, the number may be quite large but still finite. Not every process will be used ; on the contrary, the main object is to show how one process is selected and another rejected. Flexibility is introduced by the possibility that any one process can be used at various levels and that different processes can be combined, or used together, in various ways.

Put in this way, the linear programming approach seems very well adapted for application to decision-taking at the level of the firm. It deals easily with the kind of problem which is awkward in marginal analysis, when large (as well as small) changes in inputs and outputs are considered, and when there are limits on the availability of factors, e.g. the cash or credit limit imposed on the amounts which can be hired. It provides, through emphasis on technology, just the link required between the problems of interest to the economist and those which engage the attention of entrepreneur and engineers. Just as the inter-industry technique of Leontief applies best to the whole economy and to broad problems of (e.g.) governmental action, so linear programming finds its most profitable application in the more restrictive field of decisions taken within the firm.

As with marginal analysis, the technique of linear programming must simplify, and simplify very drastically, if only to keep the computations down to a manageable level. The usual simplification is the assumption that there are constant returns to scale in any one process so that, as in 10.8 above, the technology of the firm can be described by a matrix $A = [a_{rs}]$ for m commodities (factors or products) specified by $r = 1, 2, \ldots m$, and for n processes $s = 1, 2, \ldots n$. Reading down a column of A show. the fixed proportions in which inputs and outputs appear in one processs Reading across a row of A shows how one commodity appears in various processes as an input or an output. The linear assumption of constant returns to scale is partly a matter of defining processes in sufficient detail ; if a " process " seems to have non-constant returns to scale, it may be because it should be split into several more basic processes.

A linear programme of the activities of a firm requires, in addition to the specification of the technology, definite assumptions about the resources available to the firm and about the disposal of its products. Factors may be fixed in amount available, or they may be freely obtainable on a market ; for example, the firm may be assumed to have a given labour force or a certain plant, or it may be able to hire men or machines at given market prices, or both. Products may need to be supplied in certain fixed proportions, or they may be freely sold on a market, e.g. at given prices. All this needs to be specified.

The given data of a problem in linear programming of the firm are, firstly, the technical conditions under which it operates (the technology matrix A) and, secondly, the conditions on availability of resources and disposal of products. There are many types of problems which can be considered, varying according to the specification of the given conditions. The following development is not designed to provide a comprehensive survey of all the various problems which arise in the specific approach of linear programming. It attempts no more than some illustrations of the way in which linear programmes can be set up, and solved, for the firm ; and the programmes illustrated are of a kind which can conceivably be applied, when appropriately extended, in an empirical analysis of the decisions of a firm.

18.4 The Technology of the Firm

A problem in linear programming for a firm depends on the form assumed for the firm's technology, the matrix $\mathbf{A} = [a_{rs}]$ of order $m \times n$. This is not only a matter of giving the a's specific values, positive for outputs, negative for inputs. Essentially, it concerns the specification of the number and type of commodities, and of the number and type of basic processes, considered in the technology. There are, in general, m commodities and n processes, where m and n are finite but can be large.

Once $\mathbf{A}$ is fixed for the firm, the analysis of Chapter 17, in terms of the cone (A) of feasible allocation of resources, applies at once. If λ is the vector $(\lambda_1, \lambda_2, \ldots \lambda_n)$ of levels at which the n processes are used, then the vector $\mathbf{x}$ of outputs or inputs $(x_1, x_2, \ldots x_m)$ of the m commodities is given by :

$$\mathbf{x} = \mathbf{A}\lambda$$

i.e.
$$\left. x_r = \sum_{s=1}^{n} a_{rs}\lambda_s \right\} \quad \ldots\ldots\ldots\ldots\ldots\ldots\ldots\ldots\ldots\ldots\ldots\ldots(1)$$

is the output (or input if negative) of the rth commodity. For example, the output of the rth commodity is $a_{r1}\lambda_1$ if only one process (the first) is used, $(a_{r1}\lambda_1 + a_{r2}\lambda_2)$ if two processes (the first and the second) are used. If a_{r1} and a_{r2} are of opposite sign, the commodity is an output in one and an input in the other process.

There are two sets of units at choice in the representation of $\mathbf{A} = [a_{rs}]$: commodity units and unit levels for processes. The commodity units are familiar enough, e.g. man-years of labour used, or tons of coal produced. The unit levels of the processes are less obvious. For example, the first column of $\mathbf{A}$ consists of the vector $(a_{11}, a_{21}, a_{31}, \ldots a_{m1})$ which represents the fixed *proportions* between inputs and outputs in the first process. The a's can only be written if the level is fixed, e.g. the inputs for 1 ton of coal or the coefficients for the use of 100 man-years. Hence *both* the rows *and* the columns of **A** can be *normalised* in particular ways by choice of units. For example, as is often done, the unit level of the sth process can be fixed to make the output of one selected product $+1$ or the input of one factor -1. Even if this is done, it is still possible to fix the unit of each commodity in a convenient way, e.g. to make the total amount of the commodity available equal to unity.

It is useful to consider simple cases which can be represented on a diagram. When there are only three commodities, the matrix **A** is of order $3 \times n$ and the cone (A) given by (1) can be shown in three dimensions of commodity space. Figs. 63 and 64 above are illustrations of the possibilities when there are three and four processes respectively. It is not a very serious limitation to take, as in these diagrams, one commodity (x_1) as always an output, another commodity (x_3) as always an input, and the remaining commodity (x_2) as sometimes an input and sometimes an output. This will include as special instances both the two products/one factor case where x_1 and x_2 are the products, and the one product/two factors case where x_2 and x_3 are the factors.

The case of one product and two factors can be pursued further in diagrammatic terms, as in 10.8 above. Choose the unit process levels so that the output is $+1$ in each case. Then:

$$\mathbf{A} = \begin{bmatrix} 1 & 1 & \dots & 1 \\ a_{21} & a_{22} & \dots & a_{2n} \\ a_{31} & a_{32} & \dots & a_{3n} \end{bmatrix} = \begin{bmatrix} 1 & 1 & \dots & 1 \\ -\alpha_{21} & -\alpha_{22} & \dots & -\alpha_{2n} \\ -\alpha_{31} & -\alpha_{32} & \dots & -\alpha_{3n} \end{bmatrix}$$

where $\alpha_{rs} = -a_{rs}$ is written so that the negative a's can be replaced by positive α's for the inputs. The levels used in the process are shown by the nth order vector $\boldsymbol{\lambda} = (\lambda_1, \lambda_2, \dots \lambda_n)$. Hence the total output of the product (first commodity) is:

$$x_1 = \sum_s \lambda_s$$

and the corresponding inputs of the two factors are the positive values:

$$x_2 = \sum_s \alpha_{2s} \lambda_s \quad \text{and} \quad x_3 = \sum_s \alpha_{3s} \lambda_s \quad \dots\dots\dots\dots\dots\dots(2)$$

For various given values of the λ's, the values of x_2 and x_3 given by (2) can be plotted as the co-ordinates of a point P in Ox_2x_3 space of two dimensions (Fig. 70). All the feasible combinations can be shown and, by a process of weeding out inefficient combinations from the feasible ones, the efficient allocations of resources can be picked out.

Concentrate attention on unit output of the product, $x_1 = \sum \lambda_s = 1$.

This can be got by use of one process alone, the inputs being shown by the points P_1, P_2, P_3, ... in Fig. 70, where the co-ordinates of P_s are $(\alpha_{2s}, \alpha_{3s})$, as given by (2) with $\lambda_s = 1$ and other λ's zero. It is assumed that the processes are all different (independent) so that none of these points coincide. Unit output can be got also by use of two processes (e.g. the first two) in the proportion $\mu : 1 - \mu$, where $\lambda_1 = \mu$ and $\lambda_2 = 1 - \mu$ are the levels in (2). The inputs are then shown by points on P_1P_2 in Fig. 70, and similarly for any other pair of processes. The weeding out of inefficient combinations now proceeds ; single processes like P_5 can

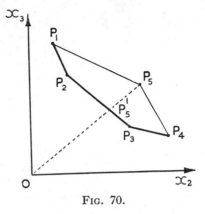

FIG. 70.

be eliminated, as can the combinations of pairs of processes like P_1P_3 (Fig. 70). For example, P_5' is a combination of P_2 and P_3 which is used in preference to P_5, since the factors are used in the same proportion but in smaller amounts for unit product. Finally, unit output can be got by using three or more processes in combination, but none of these is efficient and they can all be weeded out. For example, combinations of the first three processes correspond to points in the triangle $P_1P_2P_3$ of Fig. 70, but a point on P_1P_2 or on P_2P_3 (using two processes only) is to be preferred to any of them. The result is that, for unit product, any combination of factors shown by a point inside the figure $P_1P_2P_3P_4P_5$ of Fig. 70 is feasible, but only combinations on the convex segments $P_1P_2P_3P_4$ are efficient. All this is in line with 10.8 above and with the development of convex sets in 12.5 above.

With constant returns to scale, the representation of any level of output follows at once. Combinations of inputs for output x_1 are exactly the same as $P_1P_2P_3P_4$ increased (radially from O) in the ratio $x_1 : 1$. It is only a matter of enlarging or reducing the unit output combinations. So, in Fig. 71, the combinations for $x_1 = 2$ are $Q_1Q_2Q_3Q_4$, where $OQ_s = 2OP_s$ ($s = 1, 2, 3, 4$).

What is now obtained is something very similar to constant product curves. It is a system of constant product segments like $P_1P_2P_3P_4$, and to each is attached the level of output x_1 which corresponds. The differences, which are very important, are that the range of combinations of factors is confined within over-all limits (within the cone OA_1A_4 of Fig. 71) and that only linear combinations of specified proportions (processes) are allowed. In terms of the processes of **A**, the first stage is to eliminate some altogether (the fifth in the case considered in Fig. 70), and then to

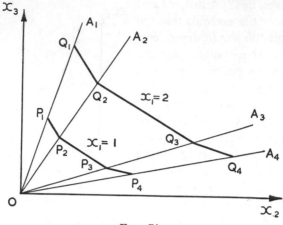

FIG. 71.

specify that only combinations of certain pairs of the others are efficient. The efficient pairs are shown by the adjacent lines (OA_1, OA_2), (OA_2, OA_3), (OA_3, OA_4) of Fig. 71. Hence, for efficient allocation of factors, the matrix **A** is very much circumscribed; the effective use of processes is confined either to a single process or to a combination of two adjacent processes. This is a particular application of the concept of efficient facets developed in 17.6 above.

It is to be noticed that the replacement of constant product curves by constant product segments is *not* a switch from continuous to discontinuous variation. There *is* a discontinuous element in the new formulation, i.e. only a finite number of processes are concerned which can be used singly or in adjacent pairs, so that the constant product loci have " kinks " at the points like P_2 and P_3 of Fig. 71. But the substitution of factors, though it may be made by finite jumps, can proceed continuously, within the range from P_1 to P_4 via P_2 and P_3 (for unit product). In fact, it is still assumed that the level of any one process can be varied continuously and that the proportions in which two processes are combined can change continuously.

The case where the firm's technology involves three commodities, one product and two factors, can be summarised in terms of a diagram like Fig. 71. It is assumed that, of the n processes, no one is dependent on, or identical with, any of the others, and that inefficient processes are eliminated. Hence, if $P_1 P_2 P_3 P_4 \ldots$ are the unit output points on the lines

$OA_1, OA_2, OA_3, OA_4 \dots$ representing processes, then no point is on a line joining any two others (nor does one coincide with any other) and no point lies above and to the right of any line joining two other points. The processes can be ordered in such a way that only a single process or a combination of two adjacent processes represents an efficient allocation of resources. This is what corresponds, in marginal analysis, to the property that constant product curves are downward sloping and convex to the origin.

Since only the technology is considered here, there is as yet no criterion as to what process or pair of processes is actually selected for use, and at what level. This depends on the other conditions of the problem.

18.5 Two Illustrative Linear Programmes

The first problem of the firm to be considered is effectively that of Dorfman (1951). Apart from a specification of the technology **A** of the firm, the conditions of the problem are *first* that the firm has m fixed factors available in given amounts and *second* that the products (and any other factors used) can be bought or sold at given market prices. In taking decisions, the firm ignores the fixed factors in any balancing of receipts and costs ; the factors are available at any prices they can get.

The factors and products appear in n processes, the columns of **A**, assumed to be independent of each other and with the inefficient ones eliminated. A further reduction of **A** can be made in the present problem. The uses of the m fixed factors are specified in **A** at the unit level (however selected) of each process, together with the corresponding amounts of outputs produced and of variable factors used. These latter amounts can be valued at the given prices and aggregated to obtain the net revenue from the process concerned at unit level. Let the vector $\mathbf{r} = \{r_s\}$ be the net revenues of the n processes ($s = 1, 2, \dots n$). It is convenient to take the technology **A** with signs reversed (inputs being positive). It can be restricted to the m rows of the fixed factors, with a row of net revenues added :

$$\begin{bmatrix} \mathbf{A} \\ \dots \\ \mathbf{r}' \end{bmatrix}$$

where $\mathbf{A} = [a_{rs}]$ is the matrix of non-negative inputs of m fixed factors in n processes ($r = 1, 2, \dots m$; $s = 1, 2, \dots n$).

The problem is to maximise the total net revenue of the firm, subject to the given amounts of m fixed factors and the given net revenues per unit of the n processes. The following two examples illustrate the problem and its solution. Though they happen to relate to agricultural commodities —usually the simplest to handle as a matter of exposition—they can be equally well interpreted in terms of industrial processes.

Ex. (*a*). Two products (corn and hogs) are produced with two fixed factors (labour and land) according to the technology :

$$
\begin{array}{lll}
\text{Labour} & \text{man-months} \\
\text{Land} & \text{acres} \\
\text{Corn} & \text{100 tons} \\
\text{Hogs} & \text{100 head}
\end{array}
\begin{bmatrix}
50 & 25 & 75 \\
5 & 50 & 60 \\
\tfrac{1}{2} & -1 & -1 \\
-1 & 0 & -\tfrac{1}{2}
\end{bmatrix}
$$

The first process has hogs as its final product, corn being used as an intermediate product for feeding hogs. The second process is for the growing of corn only and the remaining process has corn and hogs as joint products.

The available amounts of the fixed factors are : 50 man-months of labour and $52\tfrac{1}{2}$ acres of land. The corn and hog prices are £20 per ton and £20 per head respectively. The net revenues from the three processes (at unit levels shown) are then £1,000, £2,000, £3,000. Re-scale the technology matrix by taking the unit levels of the processes so that the net revenue is £2,000 in each case. The problem can then be expressed :

Input coefficients :

$$
\mathbf{A} = \begin{bmatrix} 100 & 25 & 50 \\ 10 & 50 & 40 \end{bmatrix}
$$

Receipts (£000) :

$$
2 \quad 2 \quad 2
$$

Resources :

50 man-months
$52\tfrac{1}{2}$ acres

Let the three processes be used at the levels represented by $\lambda = (\lambda_1, \lambda_2, \lambda_3)$. The problem is to find non-negative λ so that

Receipts (£000)

subject to

$$
\left.
\begin{array}{l}
z = 2(\lambda_1 + \lambda_2 + \lambda_3) = \text{max.} \\
100\lambda_1 + 25\lambda_2 + 50\lambda_3 \leqslant 50 \\
10\lambda_1 + 50\lambda_2 + 40\lambda_3 \leqslant 52\tfrac{1}{2}
\end{array}
\right\} \quad \dots\dots\dots\dots(1)
$$

This is a linear programme which can be solved graphically (Fig. 72).

Since the products of the three processes are expressed uniformly in value terms (unit : £2,000), the constant product loci of 18.4 above can be drawn in the form shown in Fig. 72a. For the unit locus, take P_1 as the point (100, 10), P_2 as (25, 50) and P_3 as (50, 40) referred to axes along which labour and land inputs are measured. It is seen that P_3 is above P_1P_2 and hence that the third process is never used, at the corn and hog prices specified. Hence $\lambda_3 = 0$ and the problem is simplified to the choice of λ_1 and λ_2. A combination of the first two processes is used ; it remains to determine in what proportions and at what level. This can be done on Fig. 72a, taking the series of constant product loci, effectively reduced to P_1P_2 at unit level (£2,000) and (e.g.) Q_1Q_2 at 1·25 level (£2,500). Let Q be the point (50, $52\tfrac{1}{2}$) so that the use of the fixed factors is restricted by (1) to the shaded rectangle shown. The problem is to find a point within this rectangle and on the highest constant product locus. This is the point Q dividing Q_1Q_2 in the ratio 4 : 1. The solution is then $\lambda_1 = 0.25$ and $\lambda_2 = 1.0$, as obtained from $100\lambda_1 + 25\lambda_2 = 50$ and $10\lambda_1 + 50\lambda_2 = 52\tfrac{1}{2}$ given by (1). The maximum of receipts is $z = 2(\lambda_1 + \lambda_2 + \lambda_3) = £2,500$, the level of the constant product locus Q_1Q_2.

With $\lambda_3 = 0$ determined, however, an even simpler graph can be drawn on the lines of 16.1 above, as shown in Fig. 72b. The axes measure the levels (λ_1 and λ_2) of the two processes used. The lines AP and BP intersecting in P represent the side relations of (1) as equations :

$$
100\lambda_1 + 25\lambda_2 = 50 \quad \text{and} \quad 10\lambda_1 + 50\lambda_2 = 52\tfrac{1}{2}
$$

A solution is confined to the shaded area and the maximum value of $z = 2(\lambda_1 + \lambda_2)$ is sought. The broken lines of Fig. 72b show :

$$\lambda_1 + \lambda_2 = \text{constant } (\tfrac{1}{2}z)$$

for increasing values of the constant (to be maximised). The solution is clear ; it is given by P so that :

$$\lambda_1 = 0.25, \quad \lambda_2 = 1.0, \quad \lambda_3 = 0 \quad \text{and} \quad z = \pounds 2,500$$

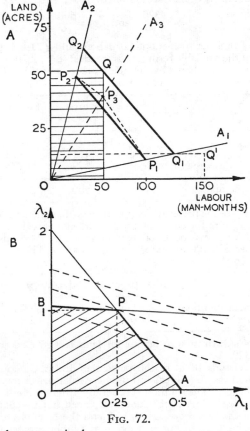

FIG. 72.

The solution can be summarised :

	Unit	First process	Second process	Total
Allocation : Labour	Man-months	25	25	50
Land	Acres	$2\tfrac{1}{2}$	50	$52\tfrac{1}{2}$
Production : Corn	Tons	-25	100	75
Hogs	Head	50	—	50
Receipts :	$\pounds$	500	2,000	2,500

The dual of the linear programme (1) can be written at once, in terms of the accounting prices (p_1 and p_2 in £) of the two fixed factors, labour and land. The third process is again ignored. So :

$$\zeta = 50p_1 + 52\tfrac{1}{2}p_2 = \text{min.}$$

subject to
$$\left.\begin{array}{l} 100p_1 + 10p_2 \geqslant 2,000 \\ 25p_1 + 50p_2 \geqslant 2,000 \end{array}\right\} \quad \dots\dots\dots\dots\dots\dots\dots\dots(2)$$

The solution is obtained when the side relations are equalities :

$$p_1 = \frac{320}{19} \quad \text{and} \quad p_2 = \frac{600}{19}$$

At these prices, £16·8 per man-month of labour and £31·6 per acre of land, the accounting cost of the available resources is smallest ($\zeta = £2,500$) and each process is operated at zero profit, as shown by the side equations of (2). The solution tabled above can then be valued at the (accounting) prices to give the transactions matrix :

Inputs	Price	First process	Second process	Total
		£	£	£
Labour	£16·8 per man-month	421	421	842
Land	£31·6 per acre	79	1,579	1,658
Receipts		500	2,000	2,500

Moreover, these are the prices which, in their ratio, equal the rate of substitution between the two factors for constant product in money value. To show this, in the table in quantity terms above, take an increase of £100 in use of the first process and a decrease of £100 in the use of the second. The shift in the allocation of resources is then :

	First process	Second process	Total
Labour (man-months)	+5·0	−1·25	+3·75
Land (acres)	+0·5	−2·5	−2·0

Hence the rate of substitution of labour for land is 3·75 : 2·0 and this is also the price ratio 600 : 320.

The solution depends both on the particular limiting amounts taken for the factors (50 man-months, $52\tfrac{1}{2}$ acres) and the particular prices for the products (£20 per ton, £20 per head). The solution is generally different if either or both of these given data is changed. The effect, moreover, need not be confined to a shift in the relative use of the two processes ($\lambda_1 : \lambda_2$) and the level of receipts (z). It may well involve the giving up of one process or the other ; indeed, it may result in the third process becoming efficient and being brought into use.

For example, suppose the limiting amounts of the factors are 150 man-months and $12\tfrac{1}{2}$ acres, the product prices being the same as before. Then, in Fig. 72a, the point Q shifts to Q' and the solution is given by Q_1 :

$$\lambda_1 = 1\cdot25, \quad \lambda_2 = 0 \quad \text{and} \quad z = £2,500$$

All resources are concentrated on the first (or land-saving) process. The full amount of land ($12\tfrac{1}{2}$ acres) is used, but only 125 of the 150 man-months of labour available. The product consists of 250 head of hogs (valued at £5,000), but against this 125 tons of corn (cost £2,500) must be bought on the market. The dual programme (2) in accounting prices then has solution :

$$p_1 = 200, \quad p_2 = 0 \quad \text{and} \quad \zeta = £2,500$$

The price of the scarce factor (land) goes to £200 per acre, and that of labour becomes zero.

As another example, a shift in the relative prices of corn and hogs can be taken and found to be even more drastic in its effect. Suppose that the price of corn remains at £20 per ton but that the price of hogs falls to £15 per head. It can then be shown (Ex. 3 below) that none of the three processes is then to be ruled out as inefficient and that, with the same limiting amounts of labour and land available, the actual production selected is a combination of the second and third processes. As compared with the solution above, the fall in the price of hogs results in more corn beir g produced and fewer hogs. The important point, however, is that this is achieved by switching from the first process to the third process, i.e. to a process which was not previously efficient at all.

An examination of the cases considered above, and of others specified in Ex. 2–5 below, indicates a relation between the number of processes used and the scarcity of the factors of production (see 17.8 above). The usual situation in the solution is that two of the three processes are used in combination and both the factors are employed to their limits, i.e. both are scarce and their accounting prices are positive. It can happen, however, that labour is so plentiful (at the given product prices) that the first process alone is used, production being concentrated on hogs ; or, alternatively, it can happen that land is plentiful and only corn is produced (by the second process). This is illustrated above and in Ex. 2 and 5 below. The characteristic of this situation is that only one process is used and only one factor employed to its limit ; the other factor is not scarce and its accounting price is zero. There is, finally, one possibility not covered—a kind of degenerate case. There are particular combinations of the amounts of the factors available such that both are used to their limits, and yet only one process is adopted ; for example, if the point Q happened to be at Q_1, in Fig. 72a (see Ex. 5 below). This is best regarded as an accidental case, which arises only if the availability of factors just happens to fit one process.

Ex. (b). A single product (corn) is produced with three fixed factors (labour, land and tractors) according to the technology :

Labour	man-months	$\begin{bmatrix} 25 & 5 & 4 \\ 50 & 100 & 125 \\ 20 & 3\frac{1}{2} & 0 \\ -1 & -1 & -1 \end{bmatrix}$
Land	acres	
Tractors	tractor-months	
Corn	100 tons	

The first process is highly mechanised and makes much use of the associated labour. The other two processes use little labour and less machinery.

The price of corn is given at £10 per ton, so that each process has receipts of £1,000 at the unit level.   Fixed amounts of the three factors are given according to the scheme :

Input coefficients :   Resources :

$$\mathbf{A} = \begin{bmatrix} 25 & 5 & 4 \\ .50 & 100 & 125 \\ 20 & 3\frac{1}{2} & 0 \end{bmatrix}$$

10 man-months
110 acres
10 tractor-months

Receipts (£000) :
$$\quad 1 \qquad 1 \qquad 1$$

If $\lambda = (\lambda_1, \lambda_2, \lambda_3)$ represents the levels used of the three processes, the problem is to find non-negative λ in the linear programme :

Receipts (£000) $z = \lambda_1 + \lambda_2 + \lambda_3 = \text{max.}$

subject to

$$\left.\begin{aligned} 25\lambda_1 + 5\lambda_2 + 4\lambda_3 &\leqslant 10 \\ 50\lambda_1 + 100\lambda_2 + 125\lambda_3 &\leqslant 110 \\ 20\lambda_1 + 3\tfrac{1}{2}\lambda_2 &\leqslant 10 \end{aligned}\right\} \quad \cdots\cdots\cdots\cdots(3)$$

The Simplex Method (16.8 above) gives the solution :

$$\lambda_1 = 0 \cdot 2, \quad \lambda_2 = 1 \cdot 0, \quad \lambda_3 = 0 \quad \text{and} \quad z = £1,200$$

A combination of the first two processes gives maximum receipts of £1,200 :

		Unit	First process	Second process	Total
Allocation :	Labour	Man-months	5	5	10
	Land	Acres	10	100	110
	Tractors	Tractor-months	4	$3\frac{1}{2}$	$7\frac{1}{2}$
Production :	Corn	Tons	20	100	120
Receipts :		£	200	1,000	1,200

The characteristic of this solution is that only two of the three processes are used. Against this, only two of the three factors are scarce and used to their limits ; the other factor (tractors) is not scarce and only $7\frac{1}{2}$ tractor-months are used though 10 tractor-months are available. The dual programme of (3) throws further light on this point. It can be written :

$$\zeta = 10p_1 + 110p_2 + 10p_3 = \min.$$

subject to

$$25p_1 + 50p_2 + 20p_3 \geqslant 1,000$$
$$5p_1 + 100p_2 + 3\tfrac{1}{2}p_3 \geqslant 1,000$$
$$4p_1 + 125p_2 \qquad \geqslant 1,000$$

$$\quad\quad\quad\quad\quad\quad\quad\quad\quad\quad\quad\quad\quad\quad(4)$$

The accounting prices (in £ per unit) of the three factors are such that the cost of the available amounts is a minimum, subject to the cost of each process being not less than the receipts. The Simplex Method of solving (3) also gives the solution of the dual (4) :

$$p_1 = \frac{200}{9}, \quad p_2 = \frac{80}{9}, \quad p_3 = 0 \quad \text{and} \quad \zeta = £1,200$$

The zero accounting price of tractors is a reflection of the fact that it is a free factor, not used to the full availability. The prices are such that the first two of the side relations in (4) are equalities, i.e. the two processes used are at zero profits on these accounting prices. The other side relation is $4p_1 + 125p_2 > 1,000$, and the third process, which is not used, is unprofitable. Costing by means of these prices picks out both the factor which is not scarce and the unprofitable process not used.

The prices are such that, in their ratio, they give the rate of substitution between labour and land for constant product (see Ex. 7 below). With the aid of the prices the solution given in quantity terms above can be written as a transactions matrix :

Inputs	Price	First process	Second process	Total
		£	£	£
Labour	£22·2 per man-month	111	111	222
Land	£8·9 per acre	89	889	978
Tractors		*	*	*
Receipts		200	1,000	1,200

* Not used to limit and not valued.

A graphical solution of the linear programme (3), or its dual (4), is not possible in two dimensions—except when something is guessed or known in advance about the solution. As a reasonable guess, take tractors as a non-scarce factor and eliminate it from the linear programme (3) by dropping the third side relation. Constant product loci can then be drawn and the limits for the two factors (labour and land) inserted. The result is shown in Fig. 73a, where $P_1P_2P_3$ is the locus for unit product (£1,000) and $Q_1Q_2Q_3$ for product 1·2 (or £1,200). The solution,

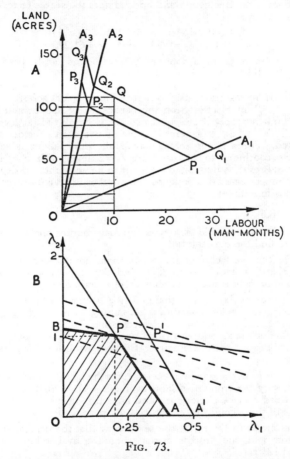

Fig. 73.

with maximum receipts of £1,200, is to combine the first two processes in the ratio 1 : 5 at the point Q, as obtained above. An alternative, also reasonable, is to guess that the third process is not used, writing $\lambda_3 = 0$ in the programme (3). The graphical method of 16.1 again applies and the result is shown in Fig. 73b. The third factor (tractors) is seen to be non-operative and, as before, it is found that $\lambda_1 = 0\cdot2$, $\lambda_3 = 1\cdot0$ at the point P.

The effect of changes in the given amounts of the three factors is to be found, in general, by re-solving (3) or (4) by the Simplex Method, after the insertion of the new given values in the side relations. However, if the third factor (tractors) can be eliminated as a free factor, or if the third process can be ignored as not used, then the changes can be traced in Fig. 73. Take the first two processes only, $\lambda_3 = 0$ in the programme (3), and represent their levels on Fig. 73b. There are three lines representing the side relations (as equations) ; these move parallel to themselves, upwards and to the right as the given amounts of the factors increase. For example, if the given amount of labour increases from 10 to (say) 15 man-months, then the line AP moves to the right to a position beyond $A'P'$ given by the limit of the third factor (10 tractor-months). The new solution is then obtained from P'. Labour is the free good, land and tractors the scarce factors. From (3), λ_1 and λ_2 are given by

$$50\lambda_1 + 100\lambda_2 = 110 \quad \text{and} \quad 20\lambda_1 + 3\tfrac{1}{2}\lambda_2 = 10$$

i.e. $\quad \lambda_1 = 0.35, \quad \lambda_2 = 0.93 \quad \text{and} \quad z = \pounds1,270$

A rather greater rate of profit is obtained when tractors can be used to the limit, labour being plentiful.

As another example, suppose that the given acreage increases from 110 acres, so that the line BP moves upwards. When the limit is 200 acres, BP is moved so far that BP and AP intersect at P on the vertical axis ; labour and land are still used to their limit but only the second process is employed (at level $\lambda_2 = 2$ with $z = \pounds2,000$). This is the " degenerate " case of two scarce factors and only one process adopted. For a larger acreage available, only labour is scarce and the second process continues to be used at $\lambda_2 = 2$ level with $z = \pounds2,000$. Once again, the general result is illustrated—except in an accidental or degenerate case, the number of processes used is equal to the number of scarce factors (here one or two out of a possible three).

EXERCISES 18.5

1. In Ex. (a), take the available factors as 150 man-months and $12\tfrac{1}{2}$ acres, re-draw Fig. 72b and find the new solution.

2. Take, in Ex. (a), the factor limits as $31\tfrac{1}{4}$ man-months and 75 acres. In Fig. 72a, show that Q moves beyond OA_2 and that Q_2 is the solution. Deduce that only one process is used and that there is only one scarce factor (labour).

3. The given prices in Ex. (a) are changed to £20 per ton for corn and £15 per head for hogs, the factor availability remaining as in the text above. Show that the third process is not to be rejected as inefficient and that the solution is a combination of the second and third processes. Deduce that some hogs are still produced despite the lower price. Illustrate with Fig. 72a. What happens to Fig. 72b?

4. Take the prices as in the previous exercise, fix the labour availability at 50 man-months but vary the amount of land available. How *little* land results in the use of the third process alone (corn and hogs produced)? How *much* land for the sole use of the second process (corn only produced)?

5. If the prices are as in Ex. (a) of the text, show that the degenerate case of two scarce factors and one process arises when the availabilities are 125 man-months and $12\tfrac{1}{2}$ acres.

6. Solve the linear programme (3) of Ex. (b) above by the Simplex Method. Obtain the solution of the dual (4) in the same process.

7. In the solution of Ex. (b) above, show that the rate of substitution between labour and land (product fixed) equals the factor price ratio (i.e. 2 : 5).

8. Ignore the third factor in Ex. (b) and use Fig. 73a above. Examine the various possibilities as the given amounts of labour and land are changed. Show that generally there are either two processes used and two scarce factors, or one process used and one scarce factor. What combinations give the degenerate case of one process used and two scarce factors?

18.6 Linear Programme : Fixed Factors and Given Product Prices

The problem illustrated in 18.5 above can be put in general terms. A firm has m fixed factors in amounts given by $\mathbf{b} = \{b_r\}$ for $r = 1, 2, \ldots m$. There are n processes and the net receipts at the given product (and variable factor) prices are obtained at the unit level of each process as $\mathbf{r} = \{r_s\}$ for $s = 1, 2, \ldots n$. If $\mathbf{A}$ is the $m \times n$ matrix of fixed factor inputs in the various processes, the given data of the problem can be arranged

Input coefficients :
$$\mathbf{A} = [a_{rs}]$$
Resources :
$$\mathbf{b} = \{b_r\}$$
Receipts :
$$\mathbf{r}' = [r_s]$$

The variable $\boldsymbol{\lambda} = \{\lambda_s\}$ for $s = 1, 2, \ldots n$ represents the levels at which the processes are used. The variable $\mathbf{p} = \{p_r\}$ for $r = 1, 2, \ldots m$ gives the accounting prices for each of the m fixed factors. The problem considered is then to find non-negative $\boldsymbol{\lambda}$ and $\mathbf{p}$ satisfying the linear programme and dual :

$$\left.\begin{array}{ll} \text{Receipts :} \quad z = \mathbf{r}'\boldsymbol{\lambda} = \text{max.} & \text{Cost :} \quad \zeta = \mathbf{b}'\mathbf{p} = \text{min.} \\ \text{subject to} \quad \mathbf{A}\boldsymbol{\lambda} \leqslant \mathbf{b} & \text{subject to} \quad \mathbf{A}'\mathbf{p} \geqslant \mathbf{r} \end{array}\right\} \quad \ldots\ldots\ldots(1)$$

The linear programme has a direct interpretation ; the firm chooses that combination of processes which maximises receipts from sales of products (less purchases of variable factors), subject to keeping within the given resources of fixed factors. The dual programme then follows automatically ; there are certain accounting prices for the fixed factors such that the (accounting) cost of the amounts available is a minimum provided that the (accounting) profits are not positive on any process. These prices are to be interpreted in their ratios as rates of substitution between the corresponding factors for a given level of receipts (see 17.7 above).

When the variables, the λ's and the p's, are found from the programme and its dual, the matrix $\mathbf{A}$ of input coefficients can be multiplied by columns by the λ's and by rows by the p's. The result is the *transactions matrix* of the solution, as illustrated in 18.5 above. The rows add across to the values of the limiting amounts of the factors (if they are fully employed) ; the columns add down to the receipts of the various processes (if they are used, at the zero profits level).

The solution of the problem is most easily seen—and computed by the Simplex Method—if m " slack variables " and a corresponding set of m " dummy processes " or " disposal processes " are added to the programme as in 16.6 above. Write :

$$\mathbf{B} = [\ \mathbf{A} \ \vdots \ \mathbf{I}\ ] \quad \text{of order } m \times (m+n)$$

where $\mathbf{I}$ is the mth order unit matrix. Similarly extend the nth order vectors $\mathbf{r}$ and $\boldsymbol{\lambda}$ by the addition of m zero elements and of m new variables respectively. Then:

$$\mathbf{v}=(r_1, r_2, \ldots r_n, 0 \ldots 0) \text{ and } \mathbf{x}=(\lambda_1, \lambda_2, \ldots \lambda_n, \mu_1, \ldots \mu_m)$$

are two vectors of order $(m+n)$, the first given and the second the variable levels for the n original and m dummy processes. The problem is to find non-negative $\mathbf{x}$ and $\mathbf{p}$ such that:

$$\left. \begin{array}{ll} z=\mathbf{v}'\mathbf{x}=\text{max.} & \zeta=\mathbf{b}'\mathbf{p}=\text{min.} \\ \text{subject to } \mathbf{Bx}=\mathbf{b} & \text{subject to } \mathbf{B}'\mathbf{p}\geqslant\mathbf{v} \end{array} \right\} \quad \ldots\ldots\ldots\ldots\ldots(2)$$

Notice that the linear programme has m side *equations* in $(m+n)$ variables x, but that the dual has $(m+n)$ side relations, still *inequalities*, in m variables p. If the solution of the first is obtained (e.g. by the Simplex Method), the solution of the other is given at the same time.

It remains to interpret the solution found for $\mathbf{x}$, i.e. for the λ's and for the μ's, in relation to the accounting prices $\mathbf{p}$. Consider the sth process, used at level λ_s. If $\lambda_s=0$ is found, the process is not used; if $\lambda_s>0$, the process is used in the optimum situation. Suppose that the number of positive λ's in $\mathbf{x}$ is N and the number of zero λ's is $(n-N)$. Then the number of processes used is $N\leqslant n$. Consider now the rth fixed factor, subject to the limit b_r. If $\mu_r=0$ is found, then the dummy or disposal process to get rid of the surplus of the rth factor is not in fact used, the factor is employed up to its limit and its price p_r is positive. If $\mu_r>0$ is found, the disposal process is used, the factor is not employed to its limit and its price p_r is zero. Suppose that the number of zero μ's in $\mathbf{x}$, equal to the number of positive p's in $\mathbf{p}$, is M; the number of positive μ's in $\mathbf{x}$ and zero p's in $\mathbf{p}$ is $m-M$.

The general result (17.8 above) is that $M=N$, i.e. the number of processes used is the same as the number of scarce factors employed (at positive accounting prices) up to their limits. As illustrated in 18.5 above, however, it is possible for an accidental combination of given resources to arise so that the number of processes used is less than the number of scarce factors. The first is the general or usual case; the second is a degenerate case.

The given data of the problem are shown either by the matrix $\mathbf{A}$ and vectors $\mathbf{b}$ and $\mathbf{r}$ in (1), or by the matrix $\mathbf{B}$ and vectors $\mathbf{b}$ and $\mathbf{v}$ in (2). It is easy to set up conditions limiting the matrix and vectors so that the technology is properly composed (i.e. no dependent or inefficient processes included) and so that the degenerate case is ruled out. For the first, the matrix $\mathbf{B}$ must be of rank m, equal to the number of rows, and the matrix

$$\begin{bmatrix} \mathbf{B} \\ \cdots\cdots \\ \mathbf{v}' \end{bmatrix}$$

must be of rank $(m+1)$, also equal to the number of rows. For the second, i.e. to cut out the degenerate case, the matrix $\mathbf{B}$ with any column replaced by the vector $\mathbf{b}$ must also be of rank m. This means that the availability vector $\mathbf{b}$ is not dependent on any $(m-1)$ columns of $\mathbf{B}$, or in particular on any $(m-1)$ columns of $\mathbf{A}$, i.e. the accidental " fit " of the availabilities to $(m-1)$ of the processes is ruled out. For example, when $m=2$ as in Ex. (a) of 18.5 above, what is ruled out is that the availability vector OQ of Fig. 72a agrees with one of the process vectors OA_1 or OA_2. This matter is pursued at some length by Dorfman (1951).

The solution of the linear programme, (1) above, gives the λ's for the use of processes (and hence for the products sold at market prices) and it gives the p's for the accounting prices of the fixed factors. The solution is generally different if any change is made in the given data $\mathbf{A}$, $\mathbf{b}$ and $\mathbf{r}$. The data can change in so many ways that it is worth while attempting to classify them. *First*, proportional changes can occur in all resources of fixed factors ($\mathbf{b}$) or in all unit receipts from processes ($\mathbf{r}$). For any positive multiple k, it is clear from (1) that :

Data ($\mathbf{A}$, $\mathbf{b}$, $\mathbf{r}$) changed to :	Solution (λ, $\mathbf{p}$) changed to :
$\mathbf{A}, k\mathbf{b}, \quad \mathbf{r} \equiv \frac{1}{k}\mathbf{A}, \quad \mathbf{b}, \frac{1}{k}\mathbf{r}$	$k\lambda, \mathbf{p}$
$\mathbf{A}, \quad \mathbf{b}, k\mathbf{r} \equiv \frac{1}{k}\mathbf{A}, \frac{1}{k}\mathbf{b}, \quad \mathbf{r}$	$\lambda, k\mathbf{p}$
$\mathbf{A}, k\mathbf{b}, k\mathbf{r} \equiv \frac{1}{k}\mathbf{A}, \quad \mathbf{b}, \quad \mathbf{r}$	$k\lambda, k\mathbf{p}$

A proportionate rise in all resources inflates the levels of use of processes (and the products) to the same extent. A proportionate rise in all unit receipts (i.e. in market prices) inflates the accounting prices of all fixed factors to the same extent. Either proportionate rise is equivalent to a proportionate reduction in the input coefficients of the technology. For example, if all resources are doubled, then twice as much of everything is produced ; the same result is obtained if resources do not change but all input coefficients are halved.

Second, there can be a change in only one of the resources, e.g. in b_1 for the first factor. The solution (λ, $\mathbf{p}$) will then be generally different ; the change will be not only in the general level but also in the relative uses of the processes and in the relative accounting prices. A proportionate change (in the opposite direction) in the first row of **A** has the same effect, i.e. a reduction in the input coefficients of the first factor in all uses is equivalent to a rise in the amount of the factor available. A similar result holds for a change in the unit receipts of one process or for the equivalent proportionate change in one column of **A**.

Third, there can be a change in the *relative* magnitudes of the input coefficients of A, across rows and down columns. This is not equivalent to any change in resources or in receipts. The consequence is again that the relative uses of processes, and the relative accounting prices of factors, are generally altered. As a matter of definition, this can be described as a *technological change*. In economic terms, the relative inputs of the factors in the various processes are changed by some technological process, and not just a different availability of resources or a different set of profitabilities in processes.

In one respect the result is very similar to that of marginal analysis : the supplies of products by the firm vary with the given resources available and with the market prices of the products. The difference is that it is now not only a matter of varying the proportions in which processes are used, but also of switching from one process to an entirely different one. A simple case illustrates the possibilities. In Ex. (*a*) of 18.5, suppose that the firm considers only the first two processes, that the resources of labour are b_1 man-months, of land b_2 acres, and that the market-prices are $£\pi_1$ per 100 tons of corn and $£\pi_2$ per 100 head of hogs :

$$\text{Input coefficients :} \qquad \text{Resources :}$$

$$\mathbf{A} = \begin{bmatrix} 50 & 25 \\ 5 & 50 \end{bmatrix} \qquad \begin{matrix} b_1 \\ b_2 \end{matrix}$$

Receipts : $\qquad (\pi_2 - \tfrac{1}{2}\pi_1) \quad \pi_1$

The linear programme is to find non-negative λ_1 and λ_2 so that :

Receipts : $\qquad z = (\pi_2 - \tfrac{1}{2}\pi_1)\lambda_1 + \pi_1\lambda_2 = \max.$

subject to : $\qquad 50\lambda_1 + 25\lambda_2 \leqslant b_1$

$\qquad\qquad\qquad 5\lambda_1 + 50\lambda_2 \leqslant b_2$

A representation on a diagram similar to Fig. 72*b* is possible. The point P is given by the side relations as equations :

$$\lambda_1 = \frac{2b_1 - b_2}{95} \quad \text{and} \quad \lambda_2 = \frac{10b_2 - b_1}{475} \quad\quad\dots\dots\dots\dots\dots(3)$$

The set of parallel lines for max. z are :

$$(\pi_2 - \tfrac{1}{2}\pi_1)\lambda_1 + \pi_1\lambda_2 = \text{constant} \quad\quad\dots\dots\dots\dots(4)$$

If both processes are to be used, with (3) as the solution, two conditions must be satisfied :

(i) P must be in the positive quadrant, so that by (3) :

$$\frac{1}{10} < \frac{b_2}{b_1} < 2 \quad \dots\dots\dots\dots\dots\dots\dots\dots\dots\dots(5)$$

which is a limiting (though wide) range for $b_2 : b_1$.

(ii) The lines (4) must have a slope intermediate between those of the side equations :

$$\frac{1}{10} < \frac{\pi_2 - \frac{1}{2}\pi_1}{\pi_1} < 2$$

i.e.

$$\frac{3}{5} < \frac{\pi_2}{\pi_1} < \frac{5}{2} \quad \dots\dots\dots\dots\dots\dots\dots\dots\dots(6)$$

which is a limiting (and fairly wide) range for $\pi_2 : \pi_1$.

Assume (5) and (6), so that both processes are used, at levels (3), and the outputs are :

Corn (100 tons) $\qquad \lambda_2 - \frac{1}{2}\lambda_1 = \dfrac{25b_2 - 12b_1}{950}$

Hogs (100 head) $\qquad \lambda_1 = \dfrac{2b_1 - b_2}{95}$

These outputs are influenced only by the values of b_1 and b_2, the factor limits within the range (5). Hogs are always produced, but the output of corn can be positive $\left(\dfrac{12}{25} < \dfrac{b_2}{b_1} < 2\right)$ or it can be negative $\left(\dfrac{1}{10} < \dfrac{b_2}{b_1} < \dfrac{12}{25}\right)$. If land is plentiful ($b_2 : b_1$ large), enough corn is produced both for feeding to hogs and for sale. If labour is plentiful ($b_2 : b_1$ small), the corn produced is not enough for feeding to hogs and extra supplies are bought.

The relative prices of corn and hogs have no influence, as long as they are in the range (6) and both processes are used. Where the prices are critical is in the decision as to which processes to use. If $\dfrac{\pi_2}{\pi_1} < \dfrac{3}{5}$, so that hogs fetch a low price, then only the second process (corn production) is used. If $\dfrac{\pi_2}{\pi_1} > \dfrac{5}{2}$, so that corn has a low price, then only the first process (hog production) is used. For price ratios in between, both corn and hogs are produced. Further, if other processes are available, as the third process of 18.5, Ex. (a), then the prices may be such that production is switched to one of them in preference to the two processes considered above.

EXERCISES 18.6

1. A firm has only one fixed factor (e.g. labour) and there are several processes involving products and variable factors available at given market prices. Show that only one process is used, that with the least use of the fixed factor (per £ of receipts).

2. An undertaking has the following simple technology:

Labour	man-months	$\begin{bmatrix} 25 & 10 \\ 50 & 100 \\ -1 & 0 \\ 0 & -1 \end{bmatrix}$
Land	acres	
Wheat	100 tons	
Hay	100 tons	

i.e. two separate production processes, one for wheat and one for hay. Given the resources, 50 man-months of labour and 260 acres of land, and given the prices, £20 per ton of wheat and £10 per ton of hay, solve graphically to show that both factors are fully employed and both wheat and hay produced. How high must the wheat price be (relative to that of hay) for wheat only to be produced? How low for only hay to be produced?

3. In the corn/hogs case of the text above, show that the dual programme is to find non-negative prices such that:

$$\zeta = b_1 p_1 + b_2 p_2 = \min.$$

subject to $50p_1 + 5p_2 \geqslant \pi_2 - \tfrac{1}{2}\pi_1$ and $25p_1 + 50p_2 \geqslant \pi_1$

Hence find the influence of product prices on the accounting prices of the factors. What product prices give one factor price zero, so that one factor is not fully used and production is concentrated on corn or on hogs?

4. In the linear programme of (1) above, prove the general result that the ratio of the accounting prices of two scarce factors equals the rate of substitution between the factors (receipts constant).

18.7 The Ricardo Effect

The linear programme of the firm is expressed in 18.6 above in simple form; it is capable of extension in a number of directions. One extension is to separate out, from the fixed factors and the products of the firm, a group of factors which are variable and obtainable at given market prices, i.e. the hired as opposed to the fixed factors. A restriction is then imposed on the hired factors, e.g. that they may be obtained up to a limit set by the amount of credit the firm commands. The given data are:

Input coefficients:			Resources:
Fixed factors	$\mathbf{A_1}$	0	$\mathbf{b}$
Hired factors	0	$\mathbf{A_2}$	

Cost of hired factors: $[\; \mathbf{0} \mid \mathbf{c'} \;]$ C

Receipts from products: $[\; \mathbf{r_1'} \mid \mathbf{r_2'} \;]$

Here there are m_1 fixed factors and n_1 processes, $\mathbf{A_1}$ being of order $m_1 \times n_1$. There are m_2 hired factors, which may include some or all of the factors which are also fixed, and they are used in combination in n_2 processes, A_2 being of order $m_2 \times n_2$. The row vectors for costs and receipts are obtained from the given market prices. The amount of credit available is C. The matrix of input coefficients is of order $(m_1 + m_2) \times (n_1 + n_2)$ and it is of the type known as decomposable (13.9 above). One particular case arises when the fixed and the hired factors are the same set of m factors, so that the n processes of the firm can be used with the fixed or with the hired factors, or in any combination. Then $A_1 = A_2$ and the input-coefficient matrix is of order $2m \times 2n$.

The linear programme is to find non-negative activity levels, given by $\lambda = \{\lambda_1 \mid \lambda_2\}$ of order $(n_1 + n_2)$, such that :

$$z = r_1'\lambda_1 + r_2'\lambda_2 - c'\lambda_2 = \max.$$

subject to
$$A_1\lambda_1 \leqslant b$$
$$c'\lambda_2 \leqslant C$$

The method of solution proceeds as before.

A further extension in the same direction is to take the hired factors (or the products) as obtainable, not at given market prices, but at prices which vary in a given way with the amounts demanded. One form of this, designed to show up the imperfection in the market for hired factors, is obtained when it is assumed that there are m factors, possessed by the firm in given amounts, hired up to certain other amounts at one set of prices, hired up to certain further amounts at a higher set of prices, and so on. When the firm exhausts its resources of factors, it can still obtain them, but at progressively higher prices, in certain specified blocks on the market for hired factors. The linear programme is of the type above, with the matrix of input coefficients :

$$\begin{array}{|ccc|}
\hline
A & 0 & 0 \\
0 & A & 0 \\
0 & 0 & A \\
\hline
\end{array}$$

The given n processes can be carried through with the fixed factors, equally with the first block of hired factors, and so on. The matrix is of order $km \times kn$, where k is the number of blocks of factors, and it is of the decomposable type.

The general feature of a linear programme, extended in suitable ways to give it an empirical content, is that it may involve a technology matrix of a large number of rows and columns. This multiplication of the size of the matrix raises problems of computation in practice, once it goes beyond a low order (such as 4×4). If a computational procedure has in any case to be devised, e.g. for the Simplex Method, it is just a matter of time and labour in computation, e.g. whether the matrix is of order 20×20 or of order 100×100. It is of some practical interest that the matrix is decomposable, containing blocks of zero elements, which make for easier computation.

A simple example illustrates a linear programme set up with a technology matrix of decomposable form. It involves the separation of fixed and hired factors, and also a further extension to allow for production in successive periods. It can be used to show (as at the end of 18.6 above) the effect of changes in the given market prices on the solution of the problem. The example is a version of one analysed in Makower (1957).

The given data for the firm are, all figures being per year :

Input coefficients :	Processes : a_1	b_1	a_2	b_2	A_1	B_1	A_2	B_2	Resources :
Owned : Labour (men)	10	12	10	12	0	0	0	0	100
Machines (no.)	5	2	5	2	0	0	0	0	60
Hired : Labour (men)	0	0	0	0	10	12	10	12	
Machines (no.)	0	0	0	0	5	2	5	2	
Cost of hired factors (£) :	[0	0	0	0	6,750	6,700	6,750	6,700]	33,500
Receipts from products (£)	[6,500	6,500	6,400	6,400	6,500	6,500	6,400	6,400]	

The product is made by either of two processes, one (a or A) being capital-intensive and the other (b or B) being labour-intensive. The product is also made either on a short process or on a long process (with the same proportionate use of factors). The short process, indicated by a subscript 1, gives the product in the same year as the inputs ; the long process, subscript 2, does not provide any product until the following year. Finally, all four processes are duplicated by allowing for hired factors, financed out of credit limited to £33,500. The prices of the hired factors are given as £500 a year for labour and £350 a year for machines. The price of the product, and the choice of unit process levels, are such that the receipts from the short process is £6,500. The long process has greater product, valued at £7,040, but this does not materialise until next year. The discounted value, at a given rate of interest of 10%, is £6,400, and this is shown as the receipts above.

With these data, on the graphical method already given, the choice is to concentrate all production on the first process a_1 (short, capital intensive, using owned resources). The level is 10, so that the full labour force is used but machines are unemployed. This is the familiar case of one scarce factor and one process used. The (maximised) receipts of the firm are £65,000. Notice that the way the model is framed excludes the possibility of using the surplus machines with hired labour.

The market prices (given) are the prices of the product, and those for labour (£500), for machines (£350) and the rate of interest (10%). If any of these is changed, then the solution of the linear programme varies, and it is to be expected that production will switch from the first process to one of the others, or to some combination of them. The switches in the firm's decision on which process to use can be investigated in various cases. Changes in the factor prices are examined in Ex. 3 below; here attention is concentrated on the product price and on the rate of interest.

(i) *Increase in product price* by 10%. The receipts vector becomes:

[7,150   7,150   7,040   7,040   7,150   7,150   7,040   7,040]

The first process is still used, to the limit of the labour supply. But, in addition, the hired processes are profitable and can be used up to the limit of the credit. The net receipts from unit use of the four hired processes are £400, £450, £290, £340 respectively. It is evident, and can be checked by graphical solution, that the second of these, the process B_1, is used. Hence, the solution is to use a_1 at level 10 to exhaust the labour resources (machines unemployed) and to use B_1 at level 5 to exhaust the firm's credit. Receipts are then £107,250 and the cost of the hired factors is £33,500, giving a net revenue (maximised) of £73,750. This is more than 10% above the previous level of £65,000, since the firm is now using hired factors and availing itself of its credit. The new process introduced is short, labour intensive, using hired resources, and it is added to the old process (short, capital intensive, using owned resources).

(ii) *Decrease in interest rate* from 10% to 4%. The receipts vector becomes:

[6,500   6,500   6,769   6,769   6,500   6,500   6,769   6,769]

since the product on the long process (receipts £7,040) is now discounted at 4% (to a value of £6,769). The solution now includes the full use of the owned labour resources (machines unemployed) but by process a_2 instead of a_1. Because of the fall in the rate of interest, the long process (still capital intensive) becomes the more profitable. In addition, however, two of the hired processes become profitable, i.e. the two long processes A_2 and B_2, with net receipts of £19 and £69 respectively. The decision is to use B_2 to the full extent of the credit. Hence the solution is to use a_2 at level 10 to exhaust labour resources and to use B_2 at level 5 to exhaust the credit. Receipts are £101,535, costs are £33,500 and net revenue is £68,035. The increase from £65,000 is partly due to the use of the fixed resources on the more profitable long process and partly due to the use of the credit available. The new solution is a combination of two processes; one is long, capital intensive, using owned resources, and the other is long, labour intensive, using hired resources. This is a complete switch from the old process (short, capital intensive, using owned resources). See also Ex. 2 below.

The main feature to be noticed in these results is the following. The original situation of the firm is that the rate of interest is high leading to a concentration on short processes, and that the price of machines is low relative to labour (see Ex. 5 below) with the consequent choice of a capital-intensive process. Moreover, the product price is such that it does not pay to make any use of the credit available ; the firm would lose by hiring factors. So only one process is used—short, capital-intensive and using owned resources. A fall in the rate of interest may have the expected result of switching production to a long process. Either a rise in the product prices or a fall in the interest rate may have the expected result of making the use of hired resources, of the firm's credit, possible. A new process involving hired factors is added to the original process in the owned factors. What is not obvious is the result, shown here to be at least a possibility, that the added process may be labour-intensive and not capital-intensive like the original process.

Hence, it is shown that, when a firm operates under the restrictions of limited credit on hired factors, it is *possible* for a rise in a product price to lead to greater use of labour-intensive processes. The prices of capital goods would need to be reduced to offset this—and not increased as the higher product price might suggest. This is the Ricardo Effect as analysed by Hayek (1942). Similarly, a fall in the rate of interest *may* mean greater employment of labour and relatively less of capital goods—and not greater use of capital equipment as the lower interest rate might suggest.

The analysis of such cases as the Ricardo Effect can proceed in marginal terms ; see Makower and Baumol (1950). The limitations on resources of the firm, and particularly the credit limit, which are essential to the Ricardo Effect, must be incorporated in the marginal analysis. However, all this is done both more naturally and more easily in terms of linear programming. The Ricardo Effect is not so much a matter of marginal adjustments as of choosing between one type of production process and another with due regard to the limitations, e.g. the credit open to the firm. Here is an example of the proper use of linear programming, of the method at its best.

EXERCISES 18.7

1. In the firm's original situation (above), confine the choice to the first two processes and apply the graphical method of solution of a linear programme to show that the first is selected.

2. Show that, in (ii) above, a fall in the interest rate from 10% to 6% shifts production from process a_1 to the long process a_2. Why is it still not profitable to use the credit available? How low does the rate have to fall to induce the switch to a long process, and how low to make hired resources profitable?

3. Find the solution of the problem when the price of machines falls to £300, the price of labour being unchanged. What is then the effect of an increase of 10% in the product price?

4. In the original problem, take the availability of machines at 50 and show that the factors are then fully used. Write the dual programme and solve for the factor prices (the first two processes alone being considered).

5. Show that, in the problem as set out originally, the relative productivity of labour to that of machines is 1·5, i.e. greater than the relative price of labour to that of machines (1·43). Show that the relation is reversed in the problem of Ex. 3 above and interpret the solution of this problem.

6. Any change in product price, factor prices and interest rate results in a change in the relative values of the rows for costs and receipts in the matrix of the problem. Hence indicate how the decision to switch from one process to another arises. Show also that a change in the interest rate affects the relation between columns in the matrix and indicate the effect of this on the firm's decisions.

18.8 Linear Programme : Fixed Demand Proportions

In a different problem from that of 18.6 above, the given data comprise the technology and the amounts of fixed factors available to the firm, together with the condition, not that products are sold at given market prices, but that they are demanded by the market in certain fixed proportions. This condition fixes the relative amounts produced of the various outputs ; what is to be maximised in the problem is then the scale of production.

The simplest way of handling the linear programme is to set up an additional or " dummy " process which disposes of the products of the processes of the technology in the given proportions. The technology of the firm is the matrix $\mathbf{A} = [a_{rs}]$ of order $(k+m) \times n$, where the first k rows correspond to k fixed factors and the last m rows to m products, and where the n columns are n production processes at choice. $\mathbf{A}$ is best written with inputs as positive elements. Add the extra process to give :

$$\mathbf{B} = [\ \mathbf{A}\ \vdots\ \mathbf{c}\ ]$$

where $\mathbf{c}$ is a vector comprising k zero elements followed by m entries representing the fixed proportions of the demand for products (e.g. scaled so that the entry for one product is unity). The vector $\mathbf{b}$ represents the given resources, i.e. a vector with k given amounts of the factors followed by m zero elements. If $\boldsymbol{\lambda}$ is the vector of the $(n+1)$ process levels, the linear programme is then to maximise λ_{n+1}, which can be expressed as the maximum of $z = \boldsymbol{\epsilon}'_{n+1}\boldsymbol{\lambda}$, where $\boldsymbol{\epsilon}_{n+1}$ is the unit vector with unity in the last place. Hence :

$$z = \boldsymbol{\epsilon}'_{n+1}\boldsymbol{\lambda} = \text{max.} \left.\begin{array}{l}\\ \\\end{array}\right\}$$

subject to $\qquad \mathbf{B}\boldsymbol{\lambda} \leqslant \mathbf{b}$ $\qquad\qquad\qquad$ ....(1)

Of the side relations in (1), the first k are *inequalities* for the factor limits ; the other m are *equations* and express the complete disposal of the products, in the given proportions on the market.

The m equations in (1) determine the main characteristic of the solution. Each equation is a linear expression in $\lambda_1, \lambda_2, \ldots \lambda_n$ equated to a multiple of λ_{n+1}, the multiples being given by $\mathbf{c}$. The equations give λ_{n+1} and $(m-1)$ of $\lambda_1, \lambda_2, \ldots \lambda_n$ in terms of the other $(n-m+1)$ λ's. If all n processes are used, or if the unused ones are first eliminated, take $n \geqslant m$, i.e. as many processes (at least) as products. Then the k inequalities in the side relations, which do not involve λ_{n+1}, reduce to k inequalities in $(n-m+1)$ of the λ's. To maximise λ_{n+1}, it is necessary to go to the limit as far as possible in these inequalities. The largest number which can be turned into equations by choice of the variable λ's is $(n-m+1)$ and the others remain " less than " inequalities. But an equation represents a scarce factor and a " less than " inequality a free factor. Hence, the number of scarce factors is generally $n - (m-1)$, i.e. $(m-1)$ less than the number of production processes used.

This result is important. In the previous case (18.6 above), the number of scarce factors is generally equal to the number of processes used. The reduction by $(m-1)$ in the present case is due to the restrictions of the market demand. The $(m-1)$ ratios given between m products imply that $n - (m-1)$ of the processes used are independent (and equal to the number of scarce factors) while the other $(m-1)$ follow to make good the demand restrictions. The simplest expression of the result for use in practice is that, when the technology matrix is reduced by eliminating unused processes and factors which are not scarce, then the number of rows is $n - (m-1)$ factors plus m products, i.e. $(n+1)$ rows in all ; the number of columns is also $(n+1)$, i.e. n used processes plus the consumption process. Hence, *the technology matrix, when reduced in the solution, is square.*

The dual programme is written in terms of the $(k+m)$ prices $\mathbf{p}$ of factors and products :

$$\left.\begin{aligned} \zeta = \mathbf{b'p} = \min. \\ \mathbf{B'p} \geqslant \boldsymbol{\epsilon}_{n+1} \end{aligned}\right\} \quad \dots\dots\dots\dots\dots\dots(2)$$

subject to

The expression minimised in (2) is the (accounting) cost of the fixed factors, a familiar condition. The first n side relations of (2) consist of inequalities with " $\geqslant 0$ " on the right-hand sides. They express the fact that the net costs (costs less receipts) of each process are not negative, i.e. profits are not positive. The last side relation is a purely formal one, that the cost of the amounts demanded in fixed proportions is unity ; this is a condition which simply scales the prices $\mathbf{p}$ and it can usually be ignored by considering only relative prices. When the price of a factor is found to be zero in (2), then the factor is not fully employed in the side relations of (1). When a process is found the be used in (1), then the profits are zero in the side relations of (2).

Once the levels $\boldsymbol{\lambda}$ and the prices $\mathbf{p}$ are determined, the technology matrix $\mathbf{A}$ can be multiplied by columns by the λ's and by rows by the p's to give the *transactions matrix* of the solution. This shows the value of each factor or product used or produced in each process. By the side relations of (1), the factor rows add to the value of the limiting amount of the factor (if fully employed) and the product rows add to the value of the product sales. By the side relations of (2), the columns add to zero, i.e. to zero profits, in all processes used.

Exactly as in 17.7. above, the price ratios determined by (2) are equal to the rates of substitution between factors and products, wherever the programme has sufficient flexibility for the necessary changes. There are now three kinds of substitution : between two factors, between two products and between a factor and a product. The general result for commodities r and s is :

$$\frac{p_r}{p_s} = \frac{\text{increase in } x_s}{\text{decrease in } x_r} \quad \text{(other } x\text{'s unchanged)}$$

where x_r and x_s are the total usages of the commodities (positive for factors, negative for products). With due allowance for the signs, the particular results are :

(i) Two factors : $\dfrac{p_r}{p_s} = \dfrac{\text{increase in use of } s\text{th factor}}{\text{decrease in use of } r\text{th factor}}$

$\qquad\qquad\qquad$ = rate of substitution between factors

$\qquad\qquad\qquad\quad$ (other factors and all products fixed)

(ii) Two products : $\dfrac{p_r}{p_s} = \dfrac{\text{decrease in output of } s\text{th product}}{\text{increase in output of } r\text{th product}}$

= rate of substitution between products

(other products and all factors fixed)

(iii) One factor, one product :

$\dfrac{p_r}{p_s} = \dfrac{\text{increase in output of } s\text{th product}}{\text{increase in use of } r\text{th factor}}$

= productivity of rth factor in terms of sth product (other factors and products fixed).

Two simple examples illustrate :

Ex. (*a*). The technology of the undertaking producing corn and hogs with two fixed factors (labour and land) is taken as in Ex. (*a*) of 18.5 above, together with the condition that the demands for corn and hogs are in the ratio $c : 1$ on the market. The given data are :

Technology :						Resources :
Labour	man-months	50	25	75	0	b_1
Land	acres	5	50	60	0	b_2
Corn	100 tons	$\frac{1}{2}$	-1	-1	c	0
Hogs	100 head	-1	0	$-\frac{1}{2}$	1	0

The linear programme is to maximise λ_4 subject to :

$$50\lambda_1 + 25\lambda_2 + 75\lambda_3 \leqslant b_1$$
$$5\lambda_1 + 50\lambda_2 + 60\lambda_3 \leqslant b_2$$
$$\tfrac{1}{2}\lambda_1 - \lambda_2 - \lambda_3 + c\lambda_4 = 0$$
$$-\lambda_1 - \tfrac{1}{2}\lambda_3 + \lambda_4 = 0$$

This can be solved by a computational process such as that of the Simplex Method (16.8 above). A simple graphical method is available, on the lines of Fig. 72*b* above, if it can be guessed or assumed that the third process is not used ($\lambda_3 = 0$). Two steps need to be taken. *First*, the side relations which involve the factor limits are :

$$50\lambda_1 + 25\lambda_2 \leqslant b_1 \quad \text{and} \quad 5\lambda_1 + 50\lambda_2 \leqslant b_2$$

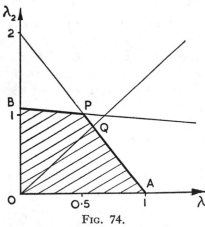

FIG. 74.

shown by the shaded area in the plane $O\lambda_1\lambda_2$ of Fig. 74. The line AP is the labour side relation as an equation and similarly BP for land ; any point on AP (or BP) represents full use of labour (or land). The point P, where both factors are fully used, is given by solving the equations as $\lambda_1 = \dfrac{2b_1 - b_2}{95}$ and $\lambda_2 = \dfrac{10b_2 - b_1}{475}$. The slope of OP is then $\dfrac{1}{5}\dfrac{10b_2 - b_1}{2b_1 - b_2}$. *Second*, the other side relations are equations which give:

$$\lambda_4 = \lambda_1 = \frac{\lambda_2 - \tfrac{1}{2}\lambda_1}{c}$$

Hence λ_1 is to be maximised subject to $\lambda_1 = \dfrac{1}{c}(\lambda_2 - \tfrac{1}{2}\lambda_1)$, i.e.

$$\frac{\lambda_2}{\lambda_1} = c + \tfrac{1}{2} = \text{constant}$$

The highest point is sought on the line OQ with slope $(c+\tfrac{1}{2})$ in Fig. 74. The solution is represented by λ_1 and λ_2 given by Q, which is on AP (labour scarce) if $c+\tfrac{1}{2} < \dfrac{1}{5}\dfrac{10b_2 - b_1}{2b_1 - b_2}$ and on BP (land scarce) if $c+\tfrac{1}{2} > \dfrac{1}{5}\dfrac{10b_2 - b_1}{2b_1 - b_2}$. Hence, both processes are used, but only one of the factors is used to the limit. However, there is only one independent process since the demand conditions fix the ratio of λ_2 to λ_1 at $(c+\tfrac{1}{2})$; this corresponds to only one scarce factor. Labour is scarce if c is small ; hogs are then in greater demand and requiring much labour. Conversely, land is scarce if corn is in greater demand (c large).

The case illustrated in Fig. 74 has :

$$b_1 = 50 \text{ man-months} ; \quad b_2 = 52\tfrac{1}{2} \text{ acres} ; \quad \text{and } c = 1.$$

The demand for hogs is sufficiently great, relative to that for corn, to make labour the scarce factor. The levels are $\lambda_1 = \tfrac{4}{7}$ and $\lambda_2 = \tfrac{6}{7}$.

The dual programme for the four accounting prices is :

$$\zeta = b_1 p_1 + b_2 p_2 = \min.$$

subject to
$$50 p_1 + 5 p_2 + \tfrac{1}{2} p_3 - p_4 \geqslant 0$$
$$25 p_1 + 50 p_2 - p_3 \qquad \geqslant 0$$

The other side relation (involving c, p_3 and p_4) is omitted as serving only to fix a (conventional) scale of prices. The solution in terms of relative prices (Ex. 3 below) in the numerical case as illustrated in Fig. 74 is :

$$p_1 : p_2 : p_3 : p_4 = 1 : 0 : 25 : 62 \cdot 5$$

This shows again that land is not fully employed in this particular case. The rate of substitution of corn for hogs is given by $62 \cdot 5 : 25$, i.e. it is the ratio 5 to 2. The productivity of labour is $1 : 25$ in terms of corn (i.e. 4 tons per man-month) and $1 : 62 \cdot 5$ in terms of hogs (i.e. $1 \cdot 6$ hogs per man-month). If one price is fixed, the ratios give the other prices ; for example, if corn is put at £10 per ton, then hogs are £25 per head and labour gets £40 per month.

The solution is shown up most clearly in the transactions matrix (with outputs positive), using the accounting prices (scaled to corn at £10 per ton) for costing :

		Price	First process	Second process	Total
			£	£	£
Factors used :	Labour	£40 per month	$-1,143$	-857	$-2,000$
	Land	—	*	*	*
Products :	Corn	£10 per ton	-286	857	571
	Hogs	£25 per head	$1,429$	—	$1,429$

* Not scarce ; the usage is $\tfrac{20}{7} + \tfrac{300}{7} = 45\tfrac{5}{7}$ acres $< 52\tfrac{1}{2}$ acres.

Ex. (b). The following example is based on one constructed by Cameron (1954). There is one fixed factor (labour, 300 man-months available) ; three products are obtained in three processes and demanded in the fixed proportions in tons : fresh fish 2, smoked fish 1, firewood 1. The given data are :

Technology :						Resources :
Labour	man-months	7	1	$\frac{1}{4}$	0	300
Fresh fish	tons	−1	2	0	2	0
Smoked fish	tons	0	−1	0	1	0
Firewood	tons	0	3	−1	1	0

It is to be noticed that the second (smoked fish) process uses fish and firewood produced in the other two processes. The linear programme is to maximise λ_4 subject to :

$$7\lambda_1 + \lambda_2 + \tfrac{1}{4}\lambda_3 \leqslant 300$$

and to :

$$-\lambda_1 + 2\lambda_2 + 2\lambda_4 = 0 \; ; \quad -\lambda_2 + \lambda_4 = 0 \; ; \quad 3\lambda_2 - \lambda_3 + \lambda_4 = 0$$

The latter give the ratios of the λ's :

$$\frac{\lambda_1}{4} = \lambda_2 = \frac{\lambda_3}{4} \quad (=\lambda_4)$$

which make the first side relation :

$$30\lambda_2 \leqslant 300$$

The maximum of $\lambda_4 = \lambda_2$ is obtained when $\lambda_2 = 10$ and labour is fully utilised. There is one scarce factor and one independent (and two dependent) process : $\lambda_1 = 40$, $\lambda_2 = 10$, $\lambda_3 = 40$.

The dual programme is to minimise p_1 subject to

$$\begin{aligned} 7p_1 - p_2 &\geqslant 0 \\ p_1 + 2p_2 - p_3 + 3p_4 &\geqslant 0 \\ \tfrac{1}{4}p_1 \quad\quad - p_4 &\geqslant 0 \end{aligned}$$

where the last side relation (scaling the prices) is again omitted. The ratios of the prices are obtained by taking all three relations as equations (all processes used, at zero profits level) :

$$p_1 : p_2 : p_3 : p_4 = 4 : 28 : 63 : 1$$

These give the rates of substitution between products and the productivity of labour. If the price of firewood is set at £5 per ton, then the other prices follow and the transactions matrix is :

	Price	First pro- cess	Second pro- cess	Third pro- cess	Total
		£	£	£	£
Factor used : Labour	£20 per month	−5,600	−200	−200	−6,000
Products : Fresh fish	£140 per ton	5,600	−2,800	—	2,800
Smoked fish	£315 per ton	—	3,150	—	3,150
Firewood	£5 per ton	—	−150	200	50

EXERCISES 18.8

1. In the simple technology of Ex. 2 of 18.6 above, take the given resources again as 50 man-months and 260 acres, assume that wheat and hay are demanded in tons in the fixed proportions $1 : c$. Show that labour or land is not fully employed according as $c > \frac{5}{3}$ or $c < \frac{5}{3}$ and interpret the solution. Find the accounting prices and interpret.

2. In Ex. (a) above, examine the case where $c + \dfrac{1}{2} = \dfrac{1}{5}\dfrac{10b_2 - b_1}{2b_1 - b_2}$ and interpret the results. Can this be called an accidental or " degenerate " case?

3. Obtain the solution (the prices) of the dual programme of Ex. (*a*), with $b_1 = 50$, $b_2 = 52\frac{1}{2}$ and $c = 1$. Put $p_4 = 1$, eliminate p_3 and get :

$$\zeta = 50(p_1 + 1 \cdot 05 p_2) = \text{min. subject to } 62 \cdot 5 p_1 + 30 p_2 \geqslant 1$$

Represent graphically in the plane $Op_1 p_2$ and find :

$$p_1 : p_2 : p_3 : p_4 = 1 : 0 : 25 : 62 \cdot 5$$

4. In Ex. (*b*) above, show that the rate of substitution of fresh for smoked fish is 28 tons to 63 tons and that the productivity of labour is approximately $0 \cdot 14$ ton of fresh and $0 \cdot 06$ ton of smoked fish.

18.9 An Example of Specialisation

The linear programme with fixed demand proportions is taken up later (19.7 below) in a wider setting. It has many applications; one is given here to illustrate a problem of specialisation analysed by Makower (1957).

Consider a firm with a simple technology ; two products are separately produced with two fixed factors and demanded in a given proportion :

Technology :   Resources :

$$\begin{bmatrix} a_{11} & a_{12} & 0 \\ a_{21} & a_{22} & 0 \\ -1 & 0 & c \\ 0 & -1 & 1 \end{bmatrix} \qquad \begin{matrix} b_1 \\ b_2 \\ 0 \\ 0 \end{matrix}$$

The linear programme is to find non-negative λ's to maximise λ_3 subject to :

$$a_{11}\lambda_1 + a_{12}\lambda_2 \leqslant b_1 \quad \text{and} \quad a_{21}\lambda_1 + a_{22}\lambda_2 \leqslant b_2$$
$$\lambda_1 = c\lambda_3 \quad \text{and} \quad \lambda_2 = \lambda_3$$

The solution is to be obtained, graphically in a numerical case, from a diagram like Fig. 74 above. The general result is that one of the two factors is scarce and the other unemployed. Now consider a second firm with the same technology, but with different amounts (b_3 and b_4) of the two fixed factors. A solution is again obtained, one factor scarce and unemployed resources of the second. It may well be that the scarce factor is different for the one firm and the other, that one has the first factor unemployed and the other the second factor. The question is : could the firms not get together and improve the combined result? The particular form of getting-together is not very relevant here ; it may be by agreement on a common decision as to production and on supplying the market together (not separately) with products in the proportion $c : 1$. Or it may be by a process of mutual trading, e.g. when the two firms are in different areas. The main point is that the fixed factors are not transferable and the supply of the products is made jointly, according to a combined technology as follows :

Technology :						Resources :
First firm's factors	a_{11}	a_{12}	0	0	0	b_1
	a_{21}	a_{22}	0	0	0	b_2
Second firm's factors	0	0	a_{11}	a_{12}	0	b_3
	0	0	a_{21}	a_{22}	0	b_4
Products	-1	0	-1	0	c	0
	0	-1	0	-1	1	0

The combined linear programme is then to find non-negative λ's to maximise λ_5 subject to :

$$a_{11}\lambda_1 + a_{12}\lambda_2 \leqslant b_1 \quad \text{and} \quad a_{21}\lambda_1 + a_{22}\lambda_2 \leqslant b_2 \quad\ldots\ldots\ldots\ldots\ldots(1)$$
$$a_{11}\lambda_3 + a_{12}\lambda_4 \leqslant b_3 \quad \text{and} \quad a_{21}\lambda_3 + a_{22}\lambda_4 \leqslant b_4 \quad\ldots\ldots\ldots\ldots\ldots(2)$$
$$\lambda_1 + \lambda_3 = c\lambda_5 \quad \text{and} \quad \lambda_2 + \lambda_4 = \lambda_5 \quad\ldots\ldots\ldots\ldots\ldots(3)$$

The last relations (3) serve to eliminate λ_4 and λ_5 :

$$\lambda_5 = \frac{1}{c}(\lambda_1 + \lambda_3) = \text{max.} \quad \text{and} \quad \lambda_4 = \frac{1}{c}(\lambda_1 + \lambda_3) - \lambda_2 \geqslant 0$$

There are then three λ's $(\lambda_1, \lambda_2, \lambda_3)$ to be found from the four inequalties (1) and (2) which express the factor limits of the two firms. Exactly how they are found is a matter of solving particular linear programmes. The general result, however, is that three of the relations (1) and (2) are taken as equations (factors to their limits) and one remains an inequality. The combined solution, therefore, has generally one unemployed resource ; one firm uses both factors to the limit and the other has one scarce and one unemployed factor. This is an improvement on the result obtained when the firms operate separately, i.e. when each firm had unemployed resources.

This is a general result. In particular cases, there may be no improvement. On the other hand, in some cases it may happen that the factor limits and the demand ratio are by accident just right—so that all the resources are fully used in the combined programme and not in the separate operation. This can be illustrated, to advantage, in a numerical case.

Ex. The technology of each firm is that of 18.6, Ex. 2, wheat and hay being produced with labour and land. The factor limits are different, one firm having more land and the other more labour. The demand is for wheat and hay in equal proportions. Take the combined position :

Technology :								Resources :
Labour	man-months	25	10	0	0	0		50
Land	acres	50	100	0	0	0		260
Labour	man-months	0	0	25	10	0		62
Land	acres	0	0	50	100	0		220
Wheat	100 tons	-1	0	-1	0	1		0
Hay	100 tons	0	-1	0	-1	1		0

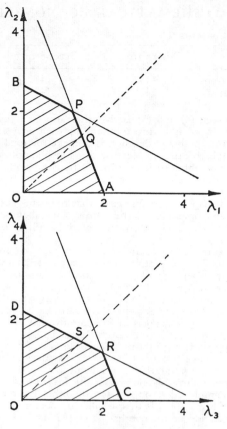

FIG. 75.

A graphical approach to the problem is made in Fig. 75, where λ_1 and λ_2 are the production levels for the first firm, λ_3 and λ_4 for the second.

Suppose, first, that the firms operate separately and sell products at given prices (e.g. equal prices) as in 18.6 above. Then the solutions for the separate firms are given by the points P and R in Fig. 75 :

$$\lambda_1 = 1\cdot2, \quad \lambda_2 = 2\cdot0, \quad \lambda_3 = 2\cdot0, \quad \lambda_4 = 1\cdot2 \quad \dots\dots\dots\dots\dots\dots(4)$$

The distribution of outputs is then :

	First firm	Second firm	Total
Wheat (tons)	120	200	320
Hay (tons)	200	120	320

There is no restriction on the proportions demanded ; the supplies just happen to be equal in total.

Next, suppose that the firms operate separately with demand proportions fixed for each as 1 : 1. This is the problem of 18.8 above and the solutions are given by the points Q and S of Fig. 75 :

$$\lambda_1 = \lambda_2 = \tfrac{10}{7} \quad \text{and} \quad \lambda_3 = \lambda_4 = \tfrac{22}{15} \quad \dots\dots\dots\dots\dots\dots(5)$$

with distribution of outputs :

	First firm	Second firm	Total
Wheat (tons)	143	147	290
Hay (tons)	143	147	290

The difference between (4) and (5) is that the ratio 1 : 1 just happens in (4) in total, but that in (5) it is imposed in total and on each firm separately.

The problem of the combined decision is to make the total supplies in the ratio 1 : 1, while allowing each firm to specialise in its own supplies. The question is : can the solution (4) be obtained instead of (5) by combined action? The answer here is that it can. The values (4) can be shown to satisfy the combined linear programme, (1), (2) and (3) above, and they can be checked to be the solution of this programme. It happens, in this case, that the firms operating separately as in (5) have both land unemployed (first firm) and labour unemployed (second firm) ; together they can employ all resources to the full as in (4). The output of wheat and hay alike is increased by 30 tons.

The accidental nature of this result—and the outline of a more general result— can be seen from Fig. 75. Separately the firms are restricted to Q and S, λ_1 and λ_3 being the wheat outputs and λ_2 and λ_4 being the hay outputs. If they get together and pool their decisions, the first firm can move from Q towards P, employing more land ; the second from S towards R, employing more labour. As they do so, the combined supplies must be kept in the ratio 1 : 1. It happens in this case, that both firms can reach their goals of full employment of resources ; this is the result of the accident that the given demand ratio 1 : 1 is identical with the combined result of supplies from fully-utilised resources. More generally, one firm (say the first) will achieve full employment of resources at P, while the other is still short of its goal, the point R. The second firm, even in the combined programme, has still unemployed labour. But the situation is much improved ; the first firm has no unemployed resources and the other has much less of its labour unemployed. Both firms are able to specialise in meeting the combined demand. This is the interpretation of the conditions (1), (2) and (3) above in the general case.

EXERCISES 18.9

1. Solve the combined linear programme, in the numerical case above, by the Simplex Method and show that it is (4).

2. Write and solve the dual programme in the numerical case and check that there are no unemployed resources.

3. Vary the numerical case by taking $c = \frac{4}{5}$, instead of $c = 1$, in the fixed demand proportions. Show that the solutions when the firms operate separately and when they combine are :

	Separate outputs			Combined outputs		
	First firm	Second firm	Total	First firm	Second firm	Total
Wheat (tons)	133	126	259	120	154	274
Hay (tons)	167	157	324	200	143	343

Show that only the second firm has unemployed resources (labour) when they combine in the output decisions.

REFERENCES

Allen (R. G. D.) (1938) : *Mathematical Analysis for Economists* (Macmillan, 1938), Chapter XIX.

Cameron (B.) (1954) : *The Determination of Production* (Cambridge, 1954).

Chamberlin (E. H.) (1933) : *The Theory of Monopolistic Competition* (Harvard, 1933).

Dorfman (R.) (1951) : *Application of Linear Programming to the Theory of the Firm* (California, 1951).

Dorfman (R.), Samuelson (P. A.) and Solow (R. M.) (1958) : *Linear Programming and Economic Analysis* (McGraw-Hill, 1958), Chapters 6 and 7.

Hayek (F. A.) (1942) : " The Ricardo Effect ", *Economica,* **9,** 127–52.

Hicks (J. R.) (1939, 1946) : *Value and Capital* (Oxford, First Ed. 1939, Second Ed. 1946), Chapters VI, VII and Appendix.

Makower (Helen) and Baumol (W. J.) (1950) : " The Analogy between Producer and Consumer Equilibrium Analysis ", *Economica,* **17,** 63–80.

Makower (Helen) (1957) : *Activity Analysis and the Theory of Economic Equilibrium* (Macmillan, 1957).

Robinson (Joan) (1933) : *The Economics of Imperfect Competition* (Macmillan, 1933).

Samuelson (P. A.) (1947) : *Foundations of Economic Analysis* (Harvard, 1947), Chapter IV.

Shephard (R. W.) (1953) : *Cost and Production Functions* (Princeton, 1953).

CHAPTER 19

THE THEORY OF VALUE

19.1 Utility : the Ordinal View

AN individual consumer is considered. There are n consumer goods $(X_1, X_2, \ldots X_n)$ so that the individual's consumption is shown by the vector :

$$\mathbf{x} = (x_1, x_2, \ldots x_n)$$

and hence by a point P in commodity space of n dimensions. Assume that the individual's level of satisfaction or utility is a function of his consumption :

$$u = u(x_1, x_2, \ldots x_n) \quad \ldots\ldots\ldots\ldots\ldots\ldots\ldots\ldots\ldots\ldots(1)$$

where u is taken to vary continuously, and with continuous derivatives of the first and second order. However, the relation of the utility level u to consumption $\mathbf{x}$ is taken in the ordinal sense, i.e. $u(x_1, x_2, \ldots x_n)$ is only one of many functions which can represent utility, and any other function which orders consumption in the same way will serve. This means that u is determined only up to an increasing (monotonic) transformation :

$$\text{utility} = \phi(u) \quad \ldots\ldots\ldots\ldots\ldots\ldots\ldots\ldots\ldots\ldots\ldots(2)$$

where ϕ is any function such that $\phi'(u) > 0$. For example :

$$au + b ; \quad au^2 ; \quad a \log u \quad (a > 0)$$

are all possible functions to represent ordinal utility.

The utility function (1) is represented by a hyper-surface in space of $(n+1)$ dimensions, i.e. the n dimensions of commodity space and the extra dimension, which can be called " vertical ", for utility levels. The " heights " of the hyper-surface show the varying utility of different commodity combinations in consumption. The contours of the hyper-surface are the n-dimensional loci of points P in commodity space with given levels of utility ; these make up the *indifference map* of the individual. So, if there are two commodities only, the utility function $u = u(x_1, x_2)$ is a surface in three dimensions referred to axes Ox_1x_2u. The indifference map is a system of curves referred to axes Ox_1x_2 in two dimensions of commodity space :

$$u(x_1, x_2) = \text{constant}$$

for various constant utility levels.

The form of the general (ordinal) utility function (2) depends on the ϕ chosen. The utility surface ($n=2$) or hyper-surface ($n>2$) depends also on which ϕ is chosen ; the " heights " can be changed at will, except that any change in consumption shown by increasing " height " (utility) on one surface or hyper-surface is also shown by increasing " height " on any surface. The contours are, therefore, completely unaffected by the ordinal property ; a contour of one surface or hyper-surface (unchanging utility) is a contour of any other. Only the constant utility levels marked as associated with a contour are affected. Hence, the indifference map of the individual is independent of the ordinal property of utility ; it is the same whatever ϕ is written in (2). Conversely, if the indifference map, as the loci of points representing indifferent combinations of commodities, is given for the individual, then the ordinal utility function (2) can be written immediately. It is only necessary to associate an ordered set of utility levels with the indifference loci and to write the set as some function $u=u(x_1, x_2, \ldots x_n)$; any increasing (monotonic) transformation $\phi(u)$ will then serve equally well.

The assumption of ordinal utility, therefore, can be expressed in two alternative and equivalent forms : a utility function $u=u(x_1, x_2, \ldots x_n)$ subject to monotonic transformation $\phi(u)$ where $\phi'(u)>0$, or an indifference map represented by $u(x_1, x_2, \ldots x_n)=$ constant. Limitations on the form of u or of the indifference map can then be added as further assumptions ; for example, it is usually assumed, as indicated later, that the indifference loci are downward sloping and convex to the origin, at least for the relevant ranges of the variable x's. The indifference map is related to utility in much the same way that the constant product loci are related to the production function.

At any consumption $(x_1, x_2, \ldots x_n)$, the utility function u has derivatives of the first two orders :

$$u_r = \frac{\partial}{\partial x_r} u(x_1, x_2 \ldots x_n) \quad \text{and} \quad u_{rs} = \frac{\partial^2}{\partial x_r \partial x_s} u(x_1, x_2, \ldots x_n)$$

for $r, s = 1, 2, \ldots n$. Write the matrix :

$$\mathbf{U} = [u_{rs}] = \begin{bmatrix} 0 & u_1 & u_2 & \ldots & u_n \\ u_1 & u_{11} & u_{12} & \ldots & u_{1n} \\ u_2 & u_{21} & u_{22} & \ldots & u_{2n} \\ \ldots\ldots\ldots\ldots\ldots\ldots\ldots\ldots \\ u_n & u_{n1} & u_{n2} & \ldots & u_{nn} \end{bmatrix}$$

which is defined at any consumption combination $(x_1, x_2, \ldots x_n)$ whatever. Since $u_{rs}=u_{sr}$, $\mathbf{U}$ is a symmetric matrix and it can be taken as non-singular, with determinant value $U=|\mathbf{U}|$. It is of order $(n+1)$ and u_{rs} can represent the general element if r and s range from $0, 1, 2, \ldots n$, with:

$$u_{00}=0 \quad \text{and} \quad u_{r0}=u_{0r}=u_r$$

by convention.

The derivatives u_r and u_{rs}, and the matrix $\mathbf{U}$, are not independent of the function ϕ used in the general expression (2). It is important to see what effect the choice of ϕ has. For the first derivatives :

$$\frac{\partial}{\partial x_r} \phi(u)=\phi'(u)u_r \dots\dots\dots\dots\dots\dots\dots\dots\dots(3)$$

and so the *ratios* of u_r are independent of ϕ. It is not possible to describe u_r as the " marginal utility " of the rth commodity. But the ratio $u_r : u_s$ is definite, independent of ϕ, and it can be defined as the *marginal rate of substitution* between the rth and sth commodities :

$$-\frac{dx_s}{dx_r}=\frac{u_r}{u_s}$$

for any changes $(dx_r$ and $dx_s)$ along an indifference locus.

For the second derivatives :

$$\frac{\partial^2}{\partial x_r \partial x_s} \phi(u)=\phi'(u)u_{rs}+\phi''(u)u_r u_s \dots\dots\dots\dots\dots\dots(4)$$

These depend on the form assumed for ϕ ; even the sign of a second derivative is not invariant. Equally, the matrix $\mathbf{U}$ is not independent of the form of ϕ taken. This is of little importance provided that the determinant value $U=|\mathbf{U}|$, and its various minors or co-factors, are not affected by the choice of ϕ. With any form of ϕ, the determinant becomes :

$$\Phi=|\ \{\phi'(u)u_{rs}+\phi''(u)u_r u_s\}\ | \quad r, s=0, 1, 2, \ldots n$$

as given by (3) and (4), provided that $u_{00}=0$ is taken by convention. This can be expressed as a sum, taking the two constituents of each element separately, but the only part of the sum which does not vanish is $|\ \phi'(u)u_{rs}\ |$ since all other parts have two rows or columns which are proportional. Hence:

$$\Phi=|\ \phi'(u)u_{rs}\ |=\{\phi'(u)\}^{n+1}|\ u_{rs}\ | \quad \dots\dots\dots\dots\dots(5)$$

It follows from (5) that, apart from a positive factor $\{\phi'(u)\}^{n+1}$ the determinant value $U=|\,u_{rs}\,|$ serves for all forms of the ordinal utility function. The same is true of any minor or co-factor of U.

As a particular case, if $\phi(u)=(au+b)$ is the utility function in general form, a and b being constant $(a>0)$, then by (3) and (4):

$$\frac{\partial}{\partial x_r}\phi(u)=au_r \quad \text{and} \quad \frac{\partial^2}{\partial x_r \partial x_s}\phi(u)=au_{rs}$$

The ratios of first and second derivatives are all invariant; u_r and u_{rs} alike are given apart from a constant (positive) multiple a. In this case, it is possible to speak of the " marginal utility " u_r and of definite signs for its derivatives u_{rs}, e.g. $u_{rr}<0$ can be taken as " decreasing marginal utility ". This is the case when u is determined up to a linear transformation $(au+b)$, i.e. only the unit and the zero level of u are at choice. It is this case which corresponds (19.5 below) to " measurable " or " cardinal " utility. It is a very special case, not assumed under ordinal utility.

This is the basis of a theory of consumer's behaviour in a non-monetary economy. There is nothing about the consumer's preferences (or demands) for money, cash and bonds, and no link with the macro-theory of liquidity preference (Chapter 2 above). Morishima (1952) shows that the theory can be extended to apply to a monetary economy under certain assumptions. The ordinary, and ordinal, utility function $u(x_1, x_2, \dots x_n)$ for n consumer goods is extended to:

$$\phi\{u(x_1, x_2, \dots x_n)\,;\ q(p_1, p_2, \dots p_n, M, B, p_b, L)\}$$

where p_1, p_2, $\dots p_n$ are the prices of the goods, M and B are the amounts of cash and bonds held by the consumer, p_b is the price of bonds, and L is an index of the future living standard desired by the consumer. Here q is the *probability* of the future living standard L, dependent on the consumer's present resources (M and B) and on present prices. The wider utility function ϕ, again ordinal, is written with the real and monetary phenomena separated one from the other. The essential assumption is that the marginal rate of substitution between two real goods does not depend on monetary features (prices, amounts of cash and bonds). Morishima proceeds to develop this into a theory of consumer's behaviour which incorporates the traditional (non-monetary) theory and which links with concepts of liquidity preference. For example, if saving increases with the interest rate, Morishima shows that the demands for real goods decrease (except for inferior goods) and that the demands for cash and bonds increase (apart from a substitution effect).

EXERCISES 19.1

1. Show that $U = |\mathbf{U}|$ is a quadratic form in the variables u_r, with coefficients involving only the second derivatives u_{rs}. Write it as :

$$U = -(u_{22}u_1^2 - 2u_{12}u_1u_2 + u_{11}u_2^2)$$

in the case of two commodities.

2. If $\frac{1}{2}u^2$ is taken as the measure of utility $\phi(u)$, given the function u, show that the determinant value $\Phi = u^{n+1}U$. Write it out in full in the case of two commodities.

3. Suppose $\log u$ is taken as an alternative measure of utility ; show that $\Phi = \dfrac{U}{u^{n+1}}$

and contrast with the result of the previous exercise.

19.2 Consumer's Demand

The individual consumer, with an ordinal utility function

$$u = u(x_1, x_2, \dots x_n),$$

has given money income M and can purchase the n commodities on a market at given prices $p_1, p_2, \dots p_n$. The problem is to determine his demands $(x_1, x_2, \dots x_n)$ for maximum utility, i.e. for max. u or equally for max. $\phi(u)$. The solution is that of restrained maximum ; the variable x's are to be determined for :

max. u subject to $\Sigma p_r x_r = M$

With a Lagrange multiplier λ, the condition is for :

max. $\{u - \lambda(\Sigma p_r x_r - M)\}$

Hence :

$$\left.\begin{aligned} u_r &= \lambda p_r \quad (r = 1, 2, \dots n) \\ \Sigma_r p_r x_r &= M \end{aligned}\right\} \quad \dots\dots\dots\dots\dots(1)$$

The equations (1) are the conditions for consumer equilibrium ; they are sufficient in number to determine λ and the n demands $(x_1, x_2, \dots x_n)$ in terms of the given prices and income of the consumer.

If the prices and income are treated as parameters, the conditions (1) give the demands of the consumer as functions of the p's and M. A proportional increase in all the p's and in M (and a similar decrease in λ) leaves (1) unaffected, i.e. consumer demand is not changed. The demand functions are homogeneous (of zero degree) in the variables. This is a characteristic feature of the problem ; only relative prices and income are concerned. Nothing is changed if, when all prices are (e.g.) doubled, the consumer's money income is also doubled. As an alternative, one commodity (the nth) can be taken *numéraire* and p_n put equal to unity. The demands of the consumer are then functions of $(n-1)$ prices and of income, and these functions are no longer homogeneous since $p_n = 1$ fixes relative prices (and income).

The parameter λ is introduced above as a matter of mathematical convenience. In equilibrium, according to (1), it is equal to the common value of the ratios $u_r : p_r$, i.e.

$$\lambda = \frac{u_1}{p_1} = \frac{u_2}{p_2} = \ldots = \frac{u_n}{p_n}$$

To the extent that the u_r can be thought of as " marginal utilities ", proportional to prices in equilibrium, the value of λ is the " marginal utility of money ". It is also a function of prices and income. More strictly, for ordinal utility, the equilibrium condition is that any marginal rate of substitution $(u_r : u_s)$ is equal to the corresponding price ratio $(p_r : p_s)$. Then the marginal rate of substitution of one commodity and money $(u_r : \lambda)$ is equal to the price ratio $(p_r : 1)$.

The equations (1) are the necessary conditions for maximum of u. Sufficient conditions are that :

$$d^2u = \sum_{r=1}^{n} \sum_{s=1}^{n} u_{rs}\, dx_r\, dx_s < 0$$

subject to

$$\sum_{r=1}^{n} p_r\, dx_r = 0$$

from the condition $\Sigma\, p_r x_r = M$. Since p_r is proportional to u_r in equilibrium, the conditions are :

$$\left.\begin{array}{l} d^2u = \displaystyle\sum_{r=1}^{n} \sum_{s=1}^{n} u_{rs}\, dx_r\, dx_s < 0 \\[2mm] du = \displaystyle\sum_{r=1}^{n} u_r\, dx_r = 0 \end{array}\right\} \quad \ldots\ldots\ldots\ldots\ldots\ldots(2)$$

subject to

These are the conditions for " stability " in the sense used by Hicks (1939, 1946). They are to hold for any variations (dx_r), not all zero, from any position $(x_1, x_2, \ldots x_n)$ whatever, to ensure that a genuine maximum can always be found, irrespective of the prices and income given.

The conditions (2) appear as the conditions for a quadratic form to be negative definite subject to a side relation, i.e.

$$Q = \sum_r \sum_s u_{rs}\, \xi_r\, \xi_s < 0$$

for all ξ_r (not all zero) subject to $\sum_r u_r\, \xi_r = 0$. These conditions are set out in 14.5 above. They are that :

$$\begin{vmatrix} 0 & u_1 & u_2 \\ u_1 & u_{11} & u_{12} \\ u_2 & u_{21} & u_{22} \end{vmatrix} > 0\,; \quad \begin{vmatrix} 0 & u_1 & u_2 & u_3 \\ u_1 & u_{11} & u_{12} & u_{13} \\ u_2 & u_{21} & u_{22} & u_{23} \\ u_3 & u_{31} & u_{32} & u_{33} \end{vmatrix} < 0\,; \quad \ldots\ldots\ldots\ldots(3)$$

i.e. that the principal minors of the determinant $U=|\mathbf{U}|$ are successively positive and negative. These conditions are independent of whatever utility function $\phi(u)$ may be taken (see Ex. 3 below).

A more convenient form of the conditions makes use of the result obtained at the end of 14.5 above, in terms of the corresponding quadratic form with the inverse matrix $\mathbf{U}^{-1}$. The stability conditions are then :

$$\sum_r \sum_s \frac{U_{rs}}{U} y_r y_s < 0 \quad\dots\dots\dots\dots\dots\dots\dots\dots\dots(4)$$

for any values of y_r and y_s, not all zero. Here U_{rs} is the co-factor of the element u_{rs} in the $(n+1)$th order determinant $U=|\mathbf{U}|$.

It is to be noticed that (3) and (4) are alternative ways of expressing the whole set of stability conditions. One particular condition, selected from the whole set, is obtained from the last two inequalities (3) :

$$\frac{U_{rr}}{U} < 0 \quad (r=1, 2, \dots n)$$

This is also obtained from (4) by taking all the y's zero except for y_r. But this is only one of many conditions, given in full by (3) and equally by (4).

EXERCISES 19.2

1. If the utility function is $u=\frac{1}{2}(a_{11}x_1{}^2 + 2a_{12}x_1x_2 + a_{22}x_2{}^2)$, show that the demands are given in terms of prices (p_1, p_2) and income (M) by :

$$a_{11}x_1 + a_{12}x_2 = \lambda p_1 \; ; \quad a_{12}x_1 + a_{22}x_2 = \lambda p_2 \; ; \quad p_1x_1 + p_2x_2 = M$$

Deduce that the demands are linear in M but not in p_1 and p_2. What is the equilibrium value of λ? Examine the conditions for downward sloping demand curves.

2. If the utility function is that of the previous exercise, show that for stability $a_{22}p_1{}^2 - 2a_{12}p_1p_2 + a_{11}p_2{}^2 < 0$ for any p_1 and p_2. Deduce that $a_{11}<0$, $a_{22}<0$, $a_{12}{}^2 < a_{11}a_{22}$. Check that the demand curves are then downward sloping. Indicate why the condition a_{11} and a_{22} negative implies that a quadratic utility function is not " realistic ".

3. Show that the stability conditions (3) are independent of the ordinal property of u.

19.3 The Income and Substitution Effects

The individual's demand functions, i.e. each of the x's in terms of the prices and income, are given by the equilibrium conditions :

$$u_r = \lambda p_r \quad \text{and} \quad \sum_r p_r x_r = M \quad (r=1, 2, \dots n) \dots\dots\dots\dots(1)$$

These $(n+1)$ equations can be differentiated with respect to any or all of the variables M and p_r $(r=1, 2, \dots n)$ to give the variation in demand as prices and income change.

First, take an increase in income M, prices unchanged. Differentiate equations (1) with respect to M and arrange :

$$\sum_s p_s \frac{\partial x_s}{\partial M} = 1$$

$$p_r \left(-\frac{\partial \lambda}{\partial M} \right) + \sum_s u_{rs} \frac{\partial x_s}{\partial M} = 0 \quad (r = 1, 2, \ldots n)$$

Substitute $p_r = \frac{1}{\lambda} u_r$, so that the equations are :

$$\left. \begin{array}{l} \sum_s u_s \dfrac{\partial x_s}{\partial M} = \lambda \\[2mm] u_r \left(-\dfrac{1}{\lambda} \dfrac{\partial \lambda}{\partial M} \right) + \sum_s u_{rs} \dfrac{\partial x_s}{\partial M} = 0 \quad (r = 1, 2, \ldots n) \end{array} \right\} \quad \ldots\ldots\ldots\ldots(2)$$

These can be solved, by Cramer's rule, for $\left(-\dfrac{1}{\lambda} \dfrac{\partial \lambda}{\partial M} \right)$ and the n variables $\dfrac{\partial x_s}{\partial M}$. The matrix of coefficients in (2) is $\mathbf{U}$; the determinant value is $U = |\mathbf{U}|$ with co-factors U_r and U_{rs}. The solution of (2) is :

$$\frac{\partial x_s}{\partial M} = \lambda \frac{U_s}{U} \quad (s = 1, 2, \ldots n) \quad \ldots\ldots\ldots\ldots\ldots\ldots(3)$$

together with a similar expression for $\left(-\dfrac{1}{\lambda} \dfrac{\partial \lambda}{\partial M} \right)$ which is not required.

The stability conditions of 19.2 above say nothing about the sign of U_s. Hence the variation of demand for increasing income, given by (3), can be in either direction. For some goods, demand may increase with income ; but for other (inferior) goods, the effect of increasing income is to reduce demand.

Next, take an increase in one price (say p_1), all other prices and income unchanged. Differentiate equations (1) with respect to p_1 and substitute $p_r = \frac{1}{\lambda} u_r$:

$$\left. \begin{array}{l} \sum_s u_s \dfrac{\partial x_s}{\partial p_1} = -\lambda x_1 \\[2mm] u_1 \left(-\dfrac{1}{\lambda} \dfrac{\partial \lambda}{\partial p_1} \right) + \sum_s u_{1s} \dfrac{\partial x_s}{\partial p_1} = \lambda \\[2mm] u_r \left(-\dfrac{1}{\lambda} \dfrac{\partial \lambda}{\partial p_1} \right) + \sum_s u_{rs} \dfrac{\partial x_s}{\partial p_1} = 0 \quad (r = 2, 3, \ldots n) \end{array} \right\} \quad \ldots\ldots\ldots\ldots(4)$$

The equations (4) can be solved by Cramer's rule for the n variables $\frac{\partial x_s}{\partial p_1}$, and for the variable $\left(-\frac{1}{\lambda}\frac{\partial \lambda}{\partial p_1}\right)$ which is not required :

$$\frac{\partial x_s}{\partial p_1} = -\lambda x_1 \frac{U_s}{U} + \lambda \frac{U_{1s}}{U} \quad (s=1, 2, \dots n)$$

The selected price can be any p_r (instead of the particular p_1), and so, on substitution of (3), the general result is :

$$\frac{\partial x_s}{\partial p_r} = -x_r \frac{\partial x_s}{\partial M} + X_{rs} \quad (r, s=1, 2, \dots n) \quad \dots\dots\dots\dots(5)$$

where $$X_{rs} = \lambda \frac{U_{rs}}{U} \quad (r, s=1, 2, \dots n) \quad \dots\dots\dots\dots\dots\dots(6)$$

By (5), the effect of a single price change on demand is in two parts : a term in $\frac{\partial x_s}{\partial M}$ and a term written X_{rs} by (6). This is the result first obtained by Slutsky (1915) and later by Hicks and Allen (1934).

The first term in (5) is the *income effect*. An increase in the price p_r corresponds to an effective reduction in income and hence to a fall in the demand for each and every commodity for which $\frac{\partial x_s}{\partial M} > 0$, and to a rise in the demand for any inferior commodity for which $\frac{\partial x_s}{\partial M} < 0$. To get rid of this effect, and hence to concentrate on the other (or substitution) effect, consider an increase dp_r in the price p_r accompanied by a *compensating increase* in income $dM = x_r\, dp_r$. The corresponding change in demand for any commodity is :

$$dx_s = \frac{\partial x_s}{\partial p_r} dp_r + \frac{\partial x_s}{\partial M}(x_r\, dp_r)$$

Hence, by (5), the *compensated variation* in demand is :

$$\frac{dx_s}{dp_r} = X_{rs}$$

This is the *substitution effect* ; it shows the result of the change in relative prices and the consequent substitution of commodities in consumption. The direction of change in the demand for x_s, for a compensated change in the price p_r, is shown by the sign of the expression X_{rs} given by (6). If $X_{rs} > 0$, the demand x_s rises with increasing price p_r ; the two goods are *substitutes*. If $X_{rs} < 0$, the demand x_s falls as p_r rises and the goods are *complementary*.

The stability conditions (4) of 19.2 above now come into play. They can be written in the form :

$$\sum_s \sum X_{rs} y_r y_s < 0 \quad\dotfill(7)$$

for any values of the y's, not all zero. In particular, taking all y's zero except y_r gives :

$$X_{rr} < 0 \quad (r = 1, 2, \dots n) \quad\dotfill(8)$$

There is, in addition, one further relation which always holds, irrespective of the stability conditions :

$$\sum_s X_{rs} p_s = \sum_s \lambda \frac{U_{rs}}{U} \frac{u_s}{\lambda} = \frac{1}{U} \sum_s u_s U_{rs} = 0$$

since the element of the first row of U are here multiplied by the co-factors of the corresponding elements of another row (the rth after the first) in U, and the results add to zero by the expansion rule for determinants. Hence :

$$\sum_s X_{rs} p_s = 0 \quad (r = 1, 2, \dots n) \quad\dotfill(9)$$

If the stability conditions are satisfied, then the substitution terms X_{rs} are restricted by the relations (7), (8) and (9). Many conclusions can be drawn ; the following are among the more important.

Since $\mathbf{U}$ is a symmetric matrix, $U_{rs} = U_{sr}$ and hence $X_{rs} = X_{sr}$, i.e. the substitution relation between two commodities is symmetrical. The direct effect of a compensated price change is $\dfrac{dx_r}{dp_r} = X_{rr} < 0$ by (8), i.e. demand falls as the price of the good rises. This is a compensated price rise, one accompanied by the appropriate rise in income. It does not follow that an uncompensated price rise causes demand to fall. In fact, by (5) :

$$\frac{\partial x_r}{\partial p_r} = x_r \left(-\frac{\partial x_r}{\partial M} \right) - (-X_{rr})$$

Here $(-X_{rr})$ is positive, but $\left(-\dfrac{\partial x_r}{\partial M} \right)$ can also be positive if the good is inferior and it is possible for this income effect to dominate, giving $\dfrac{\partial x_r}{\partial p_r} > 0$.

This is the well-known *Giffen effect* ; as the price of an inferior good rises it is possible (e.g. at low income levels) that more, rather than less, of the good is demanded.

For the " cross " effects of compensated price changes, all that can be said is that the sign of X_{rs}, and the substitute or complementary nature of the two goods, is the criterion. By (9):

$$\underset{s}{\Sigma'}\, X_{rs}p_s = (-X_{rr})p_r > 0$$

where $\underset{s}{\Sigma'}$ indicates summation for $s \neq r$. It is possible that all X_{rs} (given r, $s \neq r$) are positive, but not that all are negative. All goods can be substitutes, but not all can be complementary. There is a limit on the amount of complementarity in the system.

The importance of the restrictions (7), which make use of all the stability conditions, is seen in a consideration of *the demand for a group of goods* when the prices of all goods are changed in proportion. Take the first m goods as one group and let dp represent the proportionate price change so that $dp = \dfrac{dp_r}{p_r}$ ($r = 1, 2, \ldots m$). Write $v_r = p_r x_r$ for the expenditure on the rth good and take $v = \overset{m}{\underset{r=1}{\Sigma}}\, v_r$ for the group expenditure. Then, if the price of the rth good only varies $\left(\dfrac{dp_r}{p_r} = dp\right)$:

$$dv_s = \frac{\partial v_s}{\partial p_r}\, dp_r = p_s\, \frac{\partial x_s}{\partial p_r}\, dp_r$$

$$= \left(-p_s x_r\, \frac{\partial x_s}{\partial M} + p_s X_{rs}\right) p_r\, dp$$

i.e.

$$\frac{dv_s}{dp} = -v_r\, \frac{\partial v_s}{\partial M} + p_r p_s X_{rs}$$

If all prices change in proportion, sum the equations of this kind for all r and s from 1 to m and write $v = \Sigma\, v_r$:

$$\frac{dv}{dp} = -v\, \frac{\partial v}{\partial M} + \overset{m}{\underset{r=1}{\Sigma}}\, \overset{m}{\underset{s=1}{\Sigma}}\, p_r p_s X_{rs}$$

which is an equation for the group of exactly the same form as for a single member of the group. Moreover, the group substitution term for a proportionate price increase is:

$$\overset{m}{\underset{r=1}{\Sigma}}\, \overset{m}{\underset{s=1}{\Sigma}}\, p_r p_s X_{rs} < 0$$

by use of (7) with the first m y's taken as the prices and all other y's zero. There is a negative substitution term, exactly like X_{rr} for a single commodity, and the aggregate demand (in value) for the group falls when a proportionate (and compensated) price increase occurs. It is in this sense that a group of goods can be taken as a single good, as by Hicks (1939, 1946).

EXERCISES 19.3

1. Express the relation (5) above in elasticity form :

$$\frac{p_r}{x_s}\frac{\partial x_s}{\partial p_r} = -\frac{p_r x_r}{M}\left(\frac{M}{x_s}\frac{\partial x_s}{\partial M}\right) + \frac{p_r}{x_s}X_{rs}$$

Show that the coefficient of the income effect term is now the proportion of income spent on the commodity (with the price change) and examine the implication as regards the Giffen effect.

2. If there are only two goods, show that the only " cross " substitution term X_{12} must be positive and hence that no complementarity is possible. What is the extent of the complementarity possible when there are three goods?

3. From restriction (7) above, show that $\sum\limits_{r=1}^{m}\sum\limits_{s=1}^{n}X_{rs}p_r p_s < 0$ for any prices (not all zero) and for any $m \leqslant n$. Then use (9) above to deduce that $\sum\limits_{r=1}^{m}\sum\limits_{s=m+1}^{n}X_{rs}p_r p_s > 0$. Explain how this shows that, if all commodities are put into two groups, then one group is a substitute for the other and there can never be complementarity.

4. Consider the nutrient problem in linear programming (two foods, two nutrients) as set out in 16.3 and illustrated in Fig. 60 above :

$$z = p_1 x_1 + p_2 x_2 = \min. \quad \text{subject to} \quad \begin{aligned} a_{11}x_1 + a_{12}x_2 \geqslant b_1 \\ a_{21}x_1 + a_{22}x_2 \geqslant b_2 \end{aligned}$$

Show that the amounts bought ($\bar{x}_1$ and $\bar{x}_2$) remain fixed, both positive, for varying prices as long as $\dfrac{a_{11}}{a_{12}} > \dfrac{p_1}{p_2} > \dfrac{a_{21}}{a_{22}}$ assuming $a_{11}a_{22} > a_{12}a_{21}$ for convenience. The minimum expenditure $\bar{z}$ depends on the prices. Deduce that, as p_1 decreases (p_2 fixed), $\bar{z}$ decreases but $\bar{x}_1$ remains fixed until p_1 reaches a critical value and then $\bar{x}_1$ jumps to a higher value. Interpret as a substitution effect at the one critical value $\left(p_1 = \dfrac{a_{21}}{a_{22}}p_2\right)$. See Morton (1950).

19.4 Diagrammatic Representation

When there are two goods, the demands of a consumer are obtained by maximising $u(x_1, x_2)$ subject to the budget equation $px_1 + x_2 = M$, where p is the price of the first good (relative to that of the second, taken as unity) and M is income. The conditions are :

$$u_1 = pu_2 \quad \text{and} \quad px_1 + x_2 = M$$

giving x_1 and x_2 as functions of two variables, the relative price p and income M. For stability, $d^2u < 0$ for any variation such that $du = 0$.

The indifference map is a system of curves $(I_1, I_2, I_3, ...)$ in the plane Ox_1x_2 ; the equation is $u(x_1, x_2) = $ constant, for various values of the constant. The budget equation, $px_1 + x_2 = M$, is shown by a budget line A_1A_2 with slope $(-p)$ and with intercepts on the axes :

$$OA_1 = \frac{M}{p} \quad \text{and} \quad OA_2 = M$$

The vertical intercept is the consumer's income ; the horizontal intercept increases as the price p decreases. The equilibrium conditions are that the budget line touches an indifference curve (the slopes $-p$ and $-\dfrac{u_1}{u_2}$ being the same) at a point P whose co-ordinates are the equilibrium purchases. For stability, $d^2u < 0$ for any variation from P along the tangent to the indifference curve ($du = 0$), i.e. the tangent cuts lower indifference curves and the indifference curve at P is convex to O. This is shown in Fig. 76.

As p and M vary, the budget line A_1A_2 shifts, either in slope (variation of p) or in the vertical intercept (variation of M) or both. The equili-

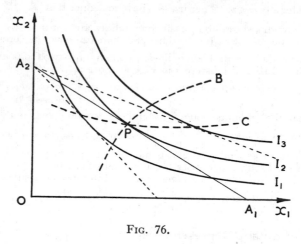

Fig. 76.

brium point P then moves across the indifference map, and the variation in its co-ordinates show the corresponding changes in demand (x_1 and x_2). If M increases (p fixed), A_1A_2 moves parallel to itself and P varies along an *income locus PB*, made up of points on various indifference curves with parallel tangents (given slope $-p$). If p decreases (M fixed), A_1A_2 swings around A_2, with A_1 moving to the right. The point P moves along a *price locus PC*, comprising points where the rotating budget line is tangential to indifference curves. The basic result of Slutsky is that a move from P along PC is the combination of two variations, one from P along the budget line (the substitution effect) and the other along the income locus PB (the income effect). The two goods must be substitutes, so that the substitution effect (p decreasing) must be to increase x_1 and to decrease x_2. However, the income effect is generally to increase both x_1 and x_2, so that the locus PC may show x_2 increasing or decreasing as x_1 increases.

This is for infinitesimal changes. It is convenient, however, to represent the variation diagrammatically in terms of small finite changes. This is done in Fig. 77. The price changes from p to $(p - \Delta p)$ with M fixed;

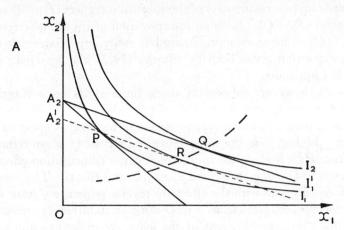

FIG. 77a.

the budget line swings from A_2P to A_2Q, the equilibrium point shifting from P to Q, on indifference curves I_1 and I_2. In Fig. 77a, the line $A_2'P$ is parallel to A_2Q and passes through P. As a budget line, $A_2'P$ has price $(p - \Delta p)$ and income sufficient to purchase the old amounts (at P) at this

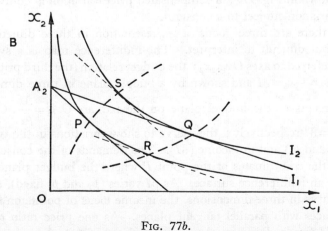

FIG. 77b.

price. The reduction in income (as compared with M) is $A_2'A_2 = x_1\Delta p$, where x_1 is the amount of the first good purchased at P. $A_2'P$ is tangential to some intermediate indifference curve I_1' at R, and the co-ordinates of

R show the purchases for the price decrease Δp, compensated by the appropriate income decrease of $x_1 \Delta p$. Hence, the price change (income fixed) results in a variation of demand shown by the move from P to Q. This is made up (approximately) of the substitution effect (P to R) and the income effect (R to Q). Such an interpretation of the Slutsky result, in terms of finite changes, is approximate but easily appreciated ; it agrees with the exposition given both by Slutsky (1915) and by Hicks (1939, 1946) in his Appendix.

There are, however, dangers in using finite shifts on a diagram to represent the infinitesimal changes of marginal analysis. As Mosak (1942) shows, Hicks used a different representation in his text, as opposed to his Appendix. In Fig. 77b, the same move from P to Q is split into two parts : from P to R along the indifference curve (substitution effect) and then from R to Q along an income locus (income effect). The move can be shown equally well with the effects in reverse sequence : from P to S along an income locus and from S to Q along an indifference curve. The point is that these two divisions of the move are different—and each of them differs from the previous interpretation of Fig. 77a. The ambiguity arises in the finite approximation. In the limit, for infinitesimal changes, all the representations come down to the same thing. In particular (see Ex. 2 below), the substitution effect taken along the budget line $A_2'P$ of Fig. 77a is in the limit the same as the effect along the indifference curve at P as shown in Fig. 77b ; a compensated price variation is equivalent to a price variation subject to u constant.

When there are three goods, a representation in three dimensions is possible but difficult to interpret. The indifference map is a system of surfaces referred to axes $Ox_1x_2x_3$; the budget relation (the third price unity) is $p_1x_1 + p_2x_2 + x_3 = M$ and shown by a budget plane in three dimensions. The intercepts of the budget plane on the axes are $OA_1 = \dfrac{M}{p_1}$, $OA_2 = \dfrac{M}{p_2}$ and $OA_3 = M$ respectively ; they serve to show variations in the two price ratios (p_1 and p_2) and in income (M). The demands of the consumer are given by the co-ordinates of the point P where the budget plane is tangential to an indifference surface. As M varies (p_1 and p_2 fixed), P moves along a curve in three dimensions, the income locus of points on indifference surfaces with parallel tangent planes. As one price ratio p_1 varies (p_2 and M fixed), P moves along a price locus obtained from points of tangency of a budget plane revolving around the line A_2A_3. It is this locus, and the similar one for varying p_2, which are difficult to visualise and interpret. The trouble is, not only to separate the substitution and income effects, but also to allow for the complementary relationship which can arise (as well as substitute relations) when there are three goods.

EXERCISES 19.4

1. In the case of two goods and a utility function $u(x_1, x_2)$, the stability condition ($d^2u < 0$ subject to $du = 0$) is

$$\begin{vmatrix} 0 & u_1 & u_2 \\ u_1 & u_{11} & u_{12} \\ u_2 & u_{12} & u_{22} \end{vmatrix} > 0$$

Write the slope of the tangent to an indifference curve as $\left(-\dfrac{dx_2}{dx_1}\right) = \dfrac{u_1}{u_2}$ numerically, obtain $\dfrac{d}{dx_1}\left(-\dfrac{dx_2}{dx_1}\right)$ in terms of the derivatives of u and interpret its sign by means of the stability condition. Hence show that the indifference curve must be convex to O for stability.

2. Use the method of 19.3 above (n commodities) to find the variation in demand when one price changes subject to $u = $ constant. Show that $\dfrac{\partial x_s}{\partial p_r} = X_{rs}$ and that the variation is equivalent to a compensated price change. See Mosak (1942).

3. When there are two goods, show that the Giffen effect arises when $\left(-\dfrac{\partial x_1}{\partial p}\right) < 0$, and $\dfrac{\partial x_1}{\partial M} < 0$, i.e. when the loci PB and PC of Fig. 76 both slope upwards and to the left. Draw an indifference map of a form appropriate to this (unusual) case.

19.5 Measurability of Utility

The assumption of the foregoing analysis is that the individual makes his decisions to maximise an ordinal utility function, to get as high as he can on his indifference map in commodity space. One question of some interest is side-stepped here. The ordinal concept of utility can be based on a single axiom, i.e. that any set of consumption situations $A, B, C, D, \ldots$ is arranged in a unique and consistent order of ascending preference. Suppose that the individual prefers B to A, that he prefers C to B, that he is indifferent between D and C, that he prefers E to D, and so on. Then, for consistency, it follows that C must be preferred to A, D must be preferred to both A and B, and so on. The utility levels are:

$$u_a < u_b < u_c = u_d < u_e \quad\ldots\ldots\ldots\ldots\ldots\ldots\ldots(1)$$

In terms of points in commodity space, C and D are on the same indifference locus which is lower than that on which E lies but above that of B (and still higher than that of A).

From this basic axiom it has not been yet established that there exists a utility function u subject only to a monotonic transformation $\phi(u)$, i.e. that there is an actual set of indifference loci (curves, surfaces, hypersurfaces) in commodity space. This is the question of "integrability", raised in such approaches to ordinal utility as Slutsky (1915) or Hicks and Allen (1934). The basic axiom gives an indifferent direction of change from any point (commodity combination), that specified by the marginal rate of substitution; it does not give a whole indifference locus unless the directions at various points can be "integrated" into such a locus. For this the marginal rates of substitution must satisfy a certain "integrability condition"; there is no apparent economic reason why they should, or indeed why they should not. However, the property of transitivity for preference or indifference, as summarised in (1) above, can be formed as an axiom to guarantee "integrability", and hence an ordered utility *function* and an indifference *map*. On this, see Georgesen-Roegen (1936).

An alternative approach, followed by Samuelson (1948, 1950) and Houthakker (1950), is through the concept of "revealed preference", based on the (ideally) observable behaviour of the individual as the consumption situation is changed. To guarantee "integrability", a "strong axiom" on transitivity is laid down: if A is revealed as preferable to B, B to C, ... and Y to Z, then A is revealed as preferable to Z. Z at the end of a chain of preferences cannot be preferred to A at the beginning. The position is summarised by Corlett and Newman (1952). The revealed preference concept is a useful supplement to the simple assumption of an ordinal utility function and indifference map.

A much larger question is whether, and under what conditions, ordinal utility can be taken also as measurable. There is a vast literature of increasingly mathematical content on this question. The following account is no more than the pursuit, in the simplest mathematical context, of one line of development. It is based on discussions with Dr. G. Morton, Dr. S. A. Ozga and other colleagues at the London School of Economics, and on such expositions as those of Alchian (1953), Ellsberg (1954), Marschak (1955) and Ozga (1956).

The point is whether the basic axiom of ordered preferences can be appropriately extended so that ordinal utility becomes measurable. In his "Interim Report" on the subject, Robertson (1951) asks why the word ordinal cannot carry "the connotation not only of being ordered but of being ordered in an orderly manner, i.e. with divisible spaces between any two ordered points?" (p. 129). Certainly there seems no *a priori* reason why such a position cannot be taken up, or why it should be hastily evacuated.

The basic axiom of ordered preferences arranges a set of consumption situations according to ascending utility as in (1). A second axiom is now added : that *increments* of utility, or degrees of preference, can also be ordered, i.e. that $(u_b - u_a)$, $(u_c - u_b)$, ... can be arranged in ascending order of preference as well as $u_a, u_b, u_c, \ldots$. In particular, a consumption situation B can be picked out, falling between A and C in the list of ordered preferences, so that the increment $(u_b - u_a)$ is judged equal to the increment $(u_c - u_b)$:

$$u_b - u_a = u_c - u_b \quad \text{or} \quad u_b = \tfrac{1}{2}(u_a + u_c) \quad \ldots\ldots\ldots\ldots\ldots\ldots(2)$$

When a result like (2) is added to the basic ordering of (1), utility becomes measurable, subject only to an arbitrary origin and unit of measurement. For (2) says that B falls exactly half way and not only somewhere between A and C, and that its utility level u_b is the mean of u_a and u_c.

The position can be illustrated by a numerical example of hypothetical changes in the individual's consumption of tea and coffee :

Commodity combination	lbs. per week		Ordinal utility	Measure of utility	
	Tea	Coffee		by increments	by risk-taking
A	2	—	1	1	1·5
B	2	1	2	2	2
C	2	2	} 3	2·5	2·5
D	3	—			
E	2	3	4	3	3
F	4	2	5	4	5

Using only the ordering of preferences (first axiom), suppose that the six combinations are arranged as shown in ascending order of preferences, C and D being indifferent. One set of (ordinal) utility levels is given in the fourth column of the table. This is only one of many such sets, and another (with $\log u$ instead of u) is :

$$0 \quad 0\cdot69 \quad 0\cdot92 \quad 1\cdot10 \quad 1\cdot39$$

Assume now that the increments of utility can be ordered (second axiom). For scaling, take $u_b = 2$ and $u_e = 3$, arbitrarily selecting the two combinations B and E for the purpose. Suppose :

(i) An increase of 1 lb. of coffee from situation B (2 lbs. of tea, 1 lb. of coffee) ranks equally with a similar increase from situation C (2 lbs. of tea, 2 lbs. of coffee). This means that the two successive increments of utility from B to C to E are ranked equal :

$$u_c - u_b = u_e - u_c \quad \text{or} \quad u_c = \tfrac{1}{2}(u_b + u_e) = 2\cdot5$$

Hence :
$$u_c = u_d = 2\cdot5$$

(ii) An increase of 1 lb. of coffee from situation A (2 lbs. of tea only) ranks equally with an increase of 2 lbs. of coffee from situation B (2 lbs. of tea, 1 lb. of coffee). There are equal increments from A to B to E:

$$u_b - u_a = u_e - u_b \quad \text{or} \quad u_a = 2u_b - u_e = 1$$

(iii) An increase of 1 lb. of tea from situation A (2 lbs. of tea) ranks equally with an increase of 2 lbs. of tea from situation C (2 lbs. of tea, 2 lbs. of coffee). The increments from A to D and from C to F are equal:

$$u_d - u_a = u_f - u_c \quad \text{or} \quad u_f = u_c + u_d - u_a = 4$$

Hence, given the three rankings (i), (ii) and (iii) of utility increments, and given the scale points set by u_b and u_e, the unique *measures* of utility of the fifth column of the table are derived. If different scale points are selected, the resulting figures in the column are different—but only in the sense that any measure depends on the origin and unit of measurement.

The three rankings suffice for the measurement of the five specified utility levels. A similar procedure would succeed no matter how many utility levels there are, provided only that the incremental rankings are increased to match. An essential point of the second axiom (as for the first) is that the rankings must be consistent. For example, the increases of 1 lb. of tea from A, 2 lbs. of coffee from A and 2 lbs. of tea from C must all be judged equal, the increment of utility being 1·5 in each case.

Two axioms on consistent ordering of preferences are sufficient for measurable utility. One relates to the ordering of original preferences, the other to the ordering of increments. If u is one representation of a utility level, the first axiom implies that u is an ordinal function with general form $\phi(u)$, where ϕ is monotonic (increasing). The second axiom then implies that u is a cardinal function (u measurable) and the general form is $(\alpha u + \beta)$ where α and β are constants for change of origin and unit of measurement. Ordered utility is determinated up to a monotonic (increasing) transformation, cardinal utility up to a linear transformation.

It is to be noticed that measurement in the physical sciences needs the same two constants for scaling. The height of an aircraft in flight, for example, can be measured in feet above London airport, or in metres above Le Bourget. Even when only one constant is apparently needed (as with weight in lbs. or grammes), it is only because there is some natural zero point (e.g. zero weight).

The two axioms are distinct and the second need not be added to the first. Either of them can be put up for testing or checking against observation. The first axiom may be taken as passing the test; it can be checked by observation, at least ideally. The second axiom is more suspect. For example, any check on the equal ranking of two increments such as those in (ii) implies first that a hypothetical situation B is compared with an existing situation A, and then that a second move is made from B to another hypothetical situation E. It is doubtful whether, from the point of view of empirical observation, it is possible to pile one hypothetical comparison upon another in this way. The Robertsonian position is defensible perhaps only as an act of faith.

Another and quite different line of development is opened up if consumer behaviour is viewed, not in relation to alternative but definite situations, but as decisions in the face of uncertainty. The introduction of risk-taking elements provides a possible way of avoiding the assessment of one hypothetical situation upon another, of getting back to what is observationally possible.

Let $A, B, C, D, \ldots$ be consumption situations, each regarded as certain or as a *sure outcome*. On the basic axiom they can be ordered to ascending preference as in (1). Suppose now that the individual is also faced with the *prospect* of two or more of the situations $A, B, C, D, \ldots$ with various probabilities, as when he buys a ticket in a lottery. The simplest kind of prospect is when there is a chance p of getting one combination A and a chance $1 - p$ of getting a second combination C. Here p is a *personal probability*, the individual's own estimate of his chance of A. It may or may not be the correct probability, e.g. in the outcome of the lottery. Define :

$$\text{Expected utility of prospect} = pu_a + (1 - p)u_c \ldots\ldots\ldots\ldots(3)$$

where u_a and u_c are the utilities of the sure outcomes A and C. (3) is the " expectation " in the mathematical or statistical sense ; it is the " moral expectation " of the eighteenth-century mathematician, Daniel Bernouilli. To the basic axiom of ordered preferences of sure outcomes, add a second axiom that the individual behaves in risk-taking situations so as to maximise expected utility (3). Comparisons of expected utilities, and the equation of expectations in risk-taking situations deemed indifferent, are then sufficient to make u measurable. Consider B lying between A and C in the preference order of sure outcomes. The prospect of A and C with chances $p : 1 - p$ may be deemed preferable, indifferent or worse than the sure outcome B. It all depends on the value of p. Pick out that p which makes the individual indifferent :

$$u_b = pu_a + (1 - p)u_c$$

Once p is determined, and once u_a and u_c are fixed (e.g. for scaling), the measure of u_b follows at once.

The numerical case of the table above can be used as illustration. Again take $u_b = 2$, $u_e = 3$ for scaling purposes. Suppose :

(a) The individual is indifferent between situation C (2 lbs. of tea, 2 lbs. of coffee) as a sure outcome and the prospect of B (2 lbs. of tea, 1 lb. of coffee) or E (2 lbs. of tea, 3 lbs. of coffee) with even chances. In other words, he is indifferent if he is faced with an equal chance of 1 lb. of coffee extra or 1 lb. less than he has. With $p = \frac{1}{2}$ in expected utility (3) :

$$u_c = \tfrac{1}{2}(u_b + u_e) = 2 \cdot 5$$

i.e. $$u_c = u_d = 2 \cdot 5$$

(b) The individual is indifferent between situation B (2 lbs. of tea, 1 lb. of coffee) and the prospect of A (2 lbs. of tea only) or E (2 lbs. of tea, 3 lbs. of coffee) with chances 2 : 1, i.e. he is willing to risk giving up his 1 lb. of coffee if he has a 1 : 2 against chance of getting 3 lbs. Put $p = \frac{2}{3}$ in expected utility:

$$u_b = \tfrac{2}{3}u_a + \tfrac{1}{3}u_e \quad \text{or} \quad u_a = 1 \cdot 5$$

(c) The individual is indifferent between situation B and the prospect of A (2 lbs. of tea only) or F (4 lbs. of tea, 2 lbs. of coffee) with chances 6 : 1, i.e. no better than a 6 : 1 against chance of the larger consumption F compensates him for the risk of losing his 1 lb. of coffee. Put $p = \frac{6}{7}$ in expected utility :

$$u_b = \tfrac{6}{7}u_a + \tfrac{1}{7}u_f \quad \text{or} \quad u_f = 5$$

In this way, a measure of utility is built up, as in the last column of the table above.

The two axioms, of ordered sure outcomes and of maximisation of expected utility for prospects, suffice to make utility measurable. This measurement of utility is of a different nature from the measurement which arises when the second axiom is that increments of utility are ordered. If it is assumed *both* that the individual orders increments of utility for sure outcomes *and* that he orders expected utility for prospects, then the same measure of utility can be written in each case, provided that the individual is consistent. But he may well be inconsistent as between his ordering of increments and his ordering of prospects. The high value $u_f = 5$ in the risk-taking measure (table above) arises because of the long chance (6 : 1) the individual is willing to take on getting the large consumption F in a lottery. It is possible that the individual is " lottery-minded " and that his views on increments of utility when consumption is certain give the value $u_f = 4$. See also Ex. 2 below.

To illustrate the position on a graph (Fig. 78), suppose that various consumer expenditures can be ordered in ascending preference according to the value $£x$ of the weekly income required. The variable x then serves as one index of ordinal utility. A cardinal measure of utility may be derived, on the axiom of ordered increments, e.g. in the form

$$u = \alpha \log (x + \beta)$$

for some scaling constants α and β, as shown as (A) in Fig. 78 scaling to $u = 0$ at $x = 0$ and $u = 100$ at $x = 20$. On the other hand, a cardinal measure, based on the axiom of ordered prospects in risk-taking situations, may be of the form $u = \lambda x^2 (\mu - x)$, where λ and μ are again scaling constants (see Ex. 3 below). Curve (B) of Fig. 78 is built up in this way, again scaling to $u = 0$ at $x = 0$ and $u = 100$ at $x = 20$. The two measures of utility (A) and (B) are quite different. (A) has the property of decreasing marginal utility ; (B) has not (except for large x). All that can be said is that one is obtained from the other by some monotonic (increasing) transformation.

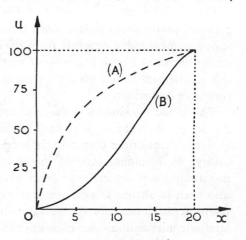

(A) $u = 32 \cdot 8 \log (x + 1)$

(B) $u = \frac{1}{80} x^2 (40 - x)$

Fig. 78.

The advantages of the measure derived from risk-taking situations lie in the facts that it is possible to envisage (under ideal conditions) that it can be checked empirically, and that it has an extensive field of application, in a world of uncertainty. One point must not be overlooked. This measure of utility depends on an assumption, implicitly made above, that personal probabilities can be defined and determined. Under empirical conditions, however, it is possible that personal probability is not observable. The very fact that an individual is asked about chances—or placed under observation—may make him change his expressed estimate of personal probability. He may be ashamed that he is " lottery-minded ".

The risk-taking approach to utility measurement can be developed. It need not be laid down as an axiom or hypothesis (accepted subject to empirical testing) that consumer decisions are consistent with maximum expected utility. Instead a more fundamental set of axioms on consumer behaviour can be devised from which the result of maximum utility can be deduced as a mathematical consequence. The whole approach stems from the work of Ramsey (1926) and von Neumann and Morgenstern (1947); it has been pursued by Marschak (1950, 1951), Samuelson (1952) and others. A precise formulation of the axioms is that of Herstein and Milner (1953). The critical point is the so-called " independence axiom " that, if A and B as sure outcomes are indifferent, so are the prospects $pA + (1 - p)C$ and $pB + (1 - p)C$ for any situation C whatever. Further, as Savage (1954) and Marschak (1954) show, it is not necessary to assume personal probabilities given ; both utility and personal probability can be scaled as measurable concepts from the axioms, alike consistent with consumer decisions on the principle of maximum expected utility. The only test is whether the axioms are an adequate, or convenient, description of consumer behaviour.

The broad conclusion is that the ordinal concept of utility, based on the simple hypothesis of ordinal preferences, remains the basis of the analysis of consumer demand. It is open to anyone to take a measurable utility, by assuming ordered increments, though by doing so he will inevitably move rather away from what is empirically observable. It is also open to anyone to take a measure of utility in the stochastic or risk-taking sense, a measure appropriate whenever an individual faces uncertain outcomes and assesses consumption possibilities according to degrees of personal or subjective probability.

EXERCISES 19.5

1. The second axiom in the risk-taking situation implies that the ordering of expected utilities is consistent. Illustrate in the numerical case of the table above by showing that the prospect of an equal chance of situations B and E must be ranked equally (indifference) with the prospect of A and F with chances $5 : 2$.

2. In the same numerical case, change the supposition (c) so that the chances of A and F in the prospect are reduced from $6 : 1$ to $3 : 1$. Then show that $u_f = 3 \cdot 5$ intead of 5.

3. Construct points on (B) of Fig. 78 for the following. Take $u(0) = 0$, $u(20) = 100$. Compare the sure outcome of $x = 10$ with the prospect of $x = 20$ or $x = 0$ with chances p, $(1 - p)$ and take $p = \frac{3}{8}$ for indifference. Hence get $u(10) = 37 \cdot 5$. Then compare a prospect of $x = 20$ or $x = 10$ with a sure $x = 16$, taking $p = 0 \cdot 6288$ for indifference. Hence get $u(16) = 76 \cdot 8$. Show that the four points (at $x = 0$, 10, 16, 20) lie on $u = \frac{1}{80} x^2 (40 - x)$.

19.6 Consumption Activities and Linear Programming

The analysis of consumer's demand (19.2 above) and the corresponding treatment of the firm (18.2 above) find their place in the wider setting of general market equilibrium. The strength of such an analysis, involving large numbers of individual firms and consumers, is that continuous sub-stitution is possible between competitive and complementary goods in production and consumption. The defect is that the analysis is too detailed ; it is difficult to see the wood for the trees. In attempts at simplification, to give the analysis an empirical content, the obvious device is to combine producers and consumers into broad groups with a corresponding grouping of commodities. This is accompanied by simplify-ing assumptions on the nature of the function involved, e.g. linear assump-tions of constant returns to scale. Such assumptions appear reasonable enough on the side of production, but far less so in consumption. The empirical facts of consumer's demand seem to be well described by relations of competition and complementarity among consumer goods ; there would appear to be no place for any assumption of constant returns to scale, in which goods are bought in fixed proportions.

Yet some drastic simplification must be made even on the side of con-sumption. In closed systems of equilibrium, such as those of Leontief (11.7 above) and von Neumann (17.9 above), the simplification may be carried to the extreme of lumping all consumption into one " activity " in which consumer goods are inputs in fixed proportions and labour services are outputs. The inter-dependence of production activities in the economy is then shown up clearly, but at the expense of ignoring the cor-responding relations between consumption activities. Something on a less sweeping scale, and with more attention to consumption, is needed. The method of linear programming suggests itself, a method which has been shown to be capable of handling quite large numbers of variables, while remaining manageable. The analyses of Leontief and von Neumann are special cases of linear programming, applied to the whole economy. The suggestion now is to limit the range to defined groups of producers and consumers and to employ the more usual forms of linear programming. The following analysis owes much to the work of Makower (1957) ; some of the examples devised by Cameron (1954) are also relevant.

The basic idea is to take a firm (or a group of producers) on one side and a group of consumers on the other, and to limit the analysis to defined groups of commodities produced by the firm and purchased by the con-sumers as the actual or potential customers of the firm. The producers' side is treated in Chapter 18 above ; it remains to incorporate the con-sumers' side in more detail. There are two points to consider, the group-ing of individual consumers and the selection of particular aggregative commodities. The second is something which can be accepted as a great simplification. As shown in 19.3 above, an assumption that the prices of commodities in a group move in proportion is sufficient for the group to be treated as a single composite commodity, obeying the same laws as an individual commodity. Moreover, goods can be grouped, with complementary items taken together, so that the relations between composite commodities are generally of the simplest substitution type.

The other point is more awkward and raises the question of interpersonal comparisons of utility. The question is here avoided rather than tackled. It is simply assumed that a group of consumers has an indifference map for the various products of a firm or group of producers, and that something measurable (called " utility " for convenience) can be attached to the sequence of ordered indifference loci. This is not an excursion into the economics of welfare ; no community indifference map for all consumers and all commodities is assumed, only a map for the consumers of particular goods produced by a firm. In practice, " utility " may be measured by market prices ; in any case, it is valued at defined accounting prices so that, in effect, " utility " is taken as some value measure of satisfaction.

The indifference map is then reduced to the matrix form relevant to linear programming. The process is similar to the replacement of constant product curves by constant product loci consisting of line segments, in the two-dimensional case of production in the firm. A finite number of basic consumption activities is assumed. Each activity has consumer

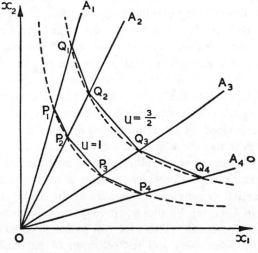

Fig. 79.

goods as inputs, in fixed proportions, but no outputs; it is rather like a dummy or disposal activity, as used in the Simplex Method for ease of computation. The assumptions are that there are constant returns to scale and that the level of the activity can be varied continuously. Further, it is taken that activities can be combined in a linear but continuous way, the addition assumption being again made (17.2 above). Finally, the unit level of each activity is specified by appropriate scaling of the fixed proportions, and a level of utility is assigned to each unit activity. Constant returns to scale then imply that, in one activity, the utility measure increases in proportion to the level of the activity.

When there are only two consumer goods (x_1 and x_2), the indifference map can be illustrated in two dimensions referred to axes Ox_1x_2 (Fig. 79). Take four consumption activities and show the fixed inputs of the two goods by a matrix in which the unit level of each activity is scaled to give utility $u=1$.

$$\text{Input coefficients}: \quad A = \begin{bmatrix} a_{11} & a_{12} & a_{13} & a_{14} \\ a_{21} & a_{22} & a_{23} & a_{24} \end{bmatrix}$$

$$\text{Utility level } (u): \qquad 1 \quad 1 \quad 1 \quad 1$$

The unit utility level of the indifference map is made up of the four points P_r with co-ordinates (a_{1r}, a_{2r}) for $r = 1, 2, 3, 4$, together with any combinations of them. It is assumed that no one P_r coincides with any other, or lies on any line joining two others; this ensures that the activities are independent, a basic set. It is also assumed no one P_r lies above and to the right of any line joining two other points; this cuts out activities which are inefficient and never used. The unit utility (or indifference) locus is of the form shown in Fig. 79. The points are ordered $P_1P_2P_3P_4$ and the choice is confined either to one activity or to a combination of adjacent activities. Other indifference loci, at other utility levels, are obtained by expansion or contraction of $P_1P_2P_3P_4$ radially from O. Fig. 79 shows the locus $Q_1Q_2Q_3Q_4$ at the level $u = \frac{3}{2}$. The particular map drawn in Fig. 79 fits the rectangular hyperbolas: $x_1x_2 = u^2$. Continuous indifference curves would be as shown by the broken lines; these are replaced by the line segments, such as P_1P_2, P_2P_3 and P_3P_4 for $u=1$. Hence, in this particular but fairly typical case, the input coefficients satisfy: $a_{1r}a_{2r} = 1$.

The *rate of substitution* between the two goods, at a given level of utility, is easily defined. If the rth and sth activities are used:

$$\text{Rate of substitution} = \frac{a_{1r} - a_{1s}}{a_{2s} - a_{2r}}$$

which is the decrease in x_1 per unit increase in x_2 for a shift from rth to sth activity (see Ex. 2 below). In the case illustrated in Fig. 79, there are only three different rates of substitution, the slopes of P_1P_2, P_2P_3 and P_3P_4 respectively, according to which of the activities are paired. This is true at any given utility level. Herein lies one of the main differences as compared with the continuous indifference map of marginal analysis. Both representations permit continuous changes in the combination of goods ; on activity analysis the changes are confined to particular line segments with a finite number of rates of substitution, whereas on marginal analysis the rate of substitution is defined marginally and subject to continuous change.

EXERCISES 19.6

1. What interpretation, in terms of consumers' utility, is to be placed on combinations of goods above OA_1 or below OA_4 in Fig. 79?

2. In the two goods case, show that any combination of the first two activities at unit utility level can be represented by

$$x_1 = \mu a_{11} + (1 - \mu)a_{12}, \quad x_2 = \mu a_{21} + (1 - \mu)a_{22} \quad (0 < \mu < 1)$$

Show that a *marginal* change is defined by varying μ, giving :

$$\left(-\frac{dx_1}{dx_2}\right) = \frac{a_{11} - a_{12}}{a_{22} - a_{21}} = \text{rate of substitution between } x_1 \text{ and } x_2 \text{ for the two activities.}$$

Interpret in terms of Fig. 79.

3. Write the matrix of input coefficients of order $3 \times n$, for 3 goods and n activities. Represent the indifference map in three dimensions and show that one locus (e.g. at unit utility level) consists of a set of plane segments, each formed by three points of a set $P_1P_2 \ldots P_n$. Show also that the whole system of indifference loci is defined by and bounded within a cone of radii from O. Interpret in terms of convex sets and cones.

4. When there are 3 goods, as in the previous exercise, show that points (and activities) of the indifference map are so ordered that the choice is between using one, two adjacent, or three adjacent activities, all other combinations giving less preferred results. Show that there is still only a finite number of different rates of substitution.

19.7 A Linear Programme of Technology-Tastes

The problem concerns a firm and the consumers who purchase its products. The firm makes m products using k fixed factors and a technology of n basic processes. The consumers have h basic consumption activities, in each of which the m products are taken in fixed proportions. The data make up a *technology-tastes matrix* of order $(k+m) \times (n+h)$:

$$\mathbf{A} = [a_{rs}]$$

$r = 1, 2, \ldots k$	for factors
$= k+1, k+2, \ldots k+m$	for products
$s = 1, 2, \ldots n$	for production processes
$= n+1, n+2, \ldots n+h$	for consumption activities

The coefficients a_{rs} are positive for inputs, negative for outputs.

The left-hand part of $\mathbf{A}$ is the firm's technology ($s=1, 2, \ldots n$). The right-hand part shows the consumers' tastes ($s=n+1, n+2, \ldots n+h$). The top part of $\mathbf{A}$ consists of rows for factors, with zero entries in the tastes section on the assumption that no factors are desired in themselves ($r=1, 2, \ldots k$). The bottom part of $\mathbf{A}$ has rows for products, mainly negative elements in the technology section, and all positive (or zero) elements in the tastes section ($r=k+1, k+2, \ldots k+m$).

The remaining data given in the problem are *first* the limiting amounts of the fixed factors available to the firm, and *second* the utility levels attached to the various consumption activities, each at whatever unit level is selected. From these data, write two vectors :

$$\mathbf{b}=\{b_1 \ b_2 \ldots b_k \ \ 0 \ \ 0 \ldots 0 \} \quad \text{of order } k+m$$
and $$\mathbf{c}=\{0 \ \ 0 \ldots 0 \ \ c_1 \ c_2 \ldots c_h\} \quad \text{of order } n+h$$

where the b's are the factor limits and the c's are the utility levels. Notice that the limits for *products* are all zero ; all products are disposed of in consumption. Similarly, the utility levels for *production processes* are all zero ; production is not an end in itself. Hence, the data of the problem are :

Technology-tastes :	Resources :
$\mathbf{A}=[a_{rs}]$	$\mathbf{b}$
Utility : $\mathbf{c}'$	

A particular case, though one which is general enough for many purposes, illustrates the formulation of the problem. There are two factors and two products, three production processes and three consumption activities. The data are arranged :

	Production			Consumption			Resources :
Technology-tastes :	a_{11}	a_{12}	a_{13}	0	0	0	b_1
	a_{21}	a_{22}	a_{23}	0	0	0	b_2
	$-a_{31}$	$-a_{32}$	$-a_{33}$	a_{34}	a_{35}	a_{36}	0
	$-a_{41}$	$-a_{42}$	$-a_{43}$	a_{44}	a_{45}	a_{46}	0
Utility :	0	0	0	c_1	c_2	c_3	

If the a's, b's and c's are taken as fixed (and usually all positive), then the units for processes or activities and for commodities can be chosen (e.g.) to make all b's and c's equal to unity, still with enough choice left over to put an entry ± 1 in each of the first three columns and in each of the last two rows. Putting the b's and the c's equal to unity is described as *normalising* the rows and columns concerned.

To complete the linear programme and its dual, write $\boldsymbol{\lambda}$ of order $(n+h)$

for the variable activity levels, and $\mathbf{p}$ of order $(k+m)$ for the corresponding prices. The linear programme is to maximise the utility level reached, i.e. $z=\mathbf{c}'\boldsymbol{\lambda}$. It is to find non-negative $\boldsymbol{\lambda}$ so that :

$$\text{Utility} \quad z=\mathbf{c}'\boldsymbol{\lambda}=\max. \left.\right\} \quad \text{.....................(1)}$$
$$\text{subject to} \qquad \mathbf{A}\boldsymbol{\lambda}\leqslant\mathbf{b}$$

The first k of the $(k+m)$ side relations express the factor limits. The last m of the side relations are equations with zero on the right-hand side (by the definition of $\mathbf{b}$); they require that all commodities produced are consumed.

The dual programme is to find non-negative $\mathbf{p}$ so that :

$$\text{Cost} \quad \zeta=\mathbf{b}'\mathbf{p}=\min. \left.\right\} \quad \text{........................(2)}$$
$$\text{subject to} \qquad \mathbf{A}'\mathbf{p}\geqslant\mathbf{c}$$

The variable ζ minimised is the cost of the fixed factors at the accounting prices. The first n of the $(n+h)$ side relations express the fact that costs are at least equal to receipts (non-positive profits) in each production process. The other side relations indicate that the product prices are scaled to make the utility level of each consumption activity equal to the value of the amounts consumed.

This linear programme of technology and tastes is an extension of the problem of the firm considered in 18.8 above. The latter can now be interpreted as the special case of (1) and (2) in which there is only one consumption activity, i.e. when the products must be consumed in certain fixed proportions. The extension now formulated allows for any number of consumption activities, and hence for substitution of goods in consumption as well as in production.

The general remarks made in 18.8 are again applicable, with certain extensions. Suppose that, in the programme (1), unused processes or activities are eliminated, so that n production processes and h consumption activities are used. It can be taken that $h\leqslant m$; it is not necessary to use more consumption activities than there are products to consume. Then, the m equations among the side relations of (1) determine $(m-h)$ of the process levels $\lambda_1, \lambda_2, \ldots \lambda_n$ and the h consumption activity levels which appear in z in terms of the other $(n-m+h)$ process levels. The k inequalities of (1) involve only the process levels $\lambda_1, \lambda_2, \ldots \lambda_n$ and so reduce to inequalities in $(n-m+h)$ of them. In maximising z, it is possible by choice of the variable λ's to make as many as $(n-m+h)$ of the inequalities into equations. In general, therefore, $(n-m+h)$ of the k factors are scarce and the others are free. The number of scarce factors is $(m-h)$

less than the number of production processes used, the reduction being due to the restrictions on consumption involved in using h sets of fixed ratios (used consumption activities) between m goods. This result, which is always subject to exceptions in " degenerate " cases, is much the same as before (18.8 above).

The practical form of the result is in terms of the technology-tastes matrix when reduced, in the solution, by eliminating all factors which are not scarce and all processes or activities which are not used. The number of scarce factors $(n - m + h)$ plus the number of products m give the number $(n + h)$ of the rows in the reduced matrix. This is also the number of the columns, i.e. the used processes n and consumption activities h. Hence, *the technology-tastes matrix, when reduced in the solution, is square.*

The accounting prices of (2) have the usual purpose ; a factor is free when its price is zero, and there are zero (as opposed to non-positive) profits in all used processes. The technology-tastes matrix $\mathbf{A}$ can be multiplied by λ down the columns and by $\mathbf{p}$ across the rows to give the *transactions matrix* :

$$\mathbf{V} = [v_{rs}]$$

This is square like the reduced $\mathbf{A}$; in fact, zero p's eliminate rows (non-scarce factors) and zero λ's eliminate columns (unused processes and activities) in the original $\mathbf{A}$. By virtue of the side relations of (1), $\mathbf{V}$ sums across to the values of the fixed factor limits and to zero values for products. From the side relations of (2), $\mathbf{V}$ sums down to zero for production processes (zero profits) and to utility levels for consumption activities.

Further, the prices determined by (2) have ratios which are equal to the various rates of substitution between goods. There are three kinds of substitution rates in production (as in 18.8 above), and there is now one further type of substitution, that between goods in consumption. The ratio of two product prices is equal both to the rate of substitution of these products in production and to their rate of substitution in consumption.

The linear programme (1) and its dual (2) between them give production, consumption and the accounting prices, all in terms of the given data : the technology-tastes matrix $\mathbf{A}$, the resources $\mathbf{b}$, and the consumers' indifference map $\mathbf{c}$. The solution varies as the given data are changed. This variation can arise in a large number of ways and the method of classifying changes in data, outlined in 18.6 above, is again useful. If one of the resources (say b_1) is increased in ratio k, then the same effect is obtained by decreasing all elements in the first row of $\mathbf{A}$ in the ratio $\dfrac{1}{k}$. As far as the solution for activity levels and accounting prices is concerned, there is no difference between an increase in availability of a factor and a reduced input of the factor in each production process (per unit product). Similarly, if tastes vary so that one utility level (say c_1) is increased in ratio k, then the same effect follows a reduction in all elements of one column (for the first consumption activity) of $\mathbf{A}$ in the ratio $\dfrac{1}{k}$. In particular, if *all* resources and *all* utility levels are increased in ratio k, equivalent to reducing *all* elements in $\mathbf{A}$ in ratio $\dfrac{1}{k}$, then it is evident from (1) and (2) that *all* activity levels and prices are alike increased in ratio k.

It is convenient, in view of this, to express all changes in data in terms of the technology-tastes matrix $\mathbf{A}$. A proportionate change across a row of $\mathbf{A}$ corresponds to a change in resources ; a similar change down a column of $\mathbf{A}$ represents a change in the strength of consumers' tastes. There remains a change in the relative magnitudes of the elements of $\mathbf{A}$ by rows or by columns. This can be described, as a matter of definition, as a change in the technology of production or in the structure of tastes.

With attention so concentrated on $\mathbf{A}$, the units of the k factors can be chosen so that there are unit resources available, i.e. $\mathbf{b}$ consists of the k unit values and m zero entries. Similarly, the unit levels of consumption activities can be chosen so that $\mathbf{c}$ consists of n zero values followed by h unit elements. This is the *normalised* form of the problem.

Problems in comparative statics are of the type : for specified changes in resources, in levels of consumers' utility, in production technology and in the structure of tastes, what variation occurs in production and consumption and how are accounting prices changed? When the linear programme (1) and its dual (2) are normalised, all problems in comparative statics reduce to tracing the effect of various changes in the matrix $\mathbf{A}$.

The illustrations of the following section are designed to show how a solution of a given linear programme can be obtained in numerical cases. They also indicate the method of treating problems in comparative statics. A general formulation of the problem has so many types of variation that a comprehensive view of its solution and answers to questions in comparative statics are almost impossible to obtain. Some simplification is needed, as in Ex. 2 below. What the following illustrations do is to simplify by taking only small numbers of factors and products—of production processes and consumption activities—and by assuming numerical values in the technology-tastes data.

EXERCISES 19.7

1. Interpret the linear programme (1) when the matrix **A** has non-zero values in the top right-hand corner (first k rows, last h columns) ; when the vector **b** has non-zero elements throughout ; when the vector **c** has non-zero elements throughout. Show that production is not necessarily cleared by consumption (with stocks changing), and that profits in production processes can be positive.

2. The linear programme (1), particularly when extended as in the previous exercise, is very wide in scope. Consider, compare and contrast the simplifications :

   (i) One consumption activity only, i.e. one composite commodity in consumption.
   (ii) One fixed factor only, e.g. resources such as labour or credit.
   (iii) Each product is never an input and an output of only one production process ; each production process with one product only.

3. Show that cases (i) and (ii) of the previous exercise have a dual relation and that the maximum of utility is sought under (i) and the minimum of factor cost under (ii).

4. In the case (iii) of Ex. 2, show that products and processes are equal in number (n) and that it can be arranged that the negative unit matrix ($-\mathbf{I}$) of order $n \times n$ can appear in the lower left-hand corner of **A**. Show that the simplification, in the dual programme, is that the side relations are : unit cost = product price for used processes, and unit cost > product price for other processes.

5. Take the numbers of factors and consumption activities as the same (m), with **A** having a negative unit matrix ($-\mathbf{I}$) of order $m \times m$ in the upper right-hand corner. Interpret and relate to the case of a closed economy in which labour services are outputs of activities with consumers' goods as inputs.

19.8 Some Illustrations

The main examples used to illustrate the solution of the linear programme of technology-tastes are extensions of those given in 18.8 above. Another and even simpler case is set out in Ex. 1 below. Though the field of application is again taken as production in agriculture and fisheries, the method applies equally well to industrial processes.

Ex. (a). Corn and hogs are produced with labour and land as fixed factors, and the products are demanded by consumers in various proportions, according to the technology-tastes matrix and given conditions :

Technology-tastes :

					Resources :
Labour	50	25	0	0	50 man-months
Land	5	50	0	0	$52\frac{1}{2}$ acres
Corn	$\frac{1}{2}$	-1	1	2	0
Hogs	-1	0	1	$\frac{1}{2}$	0
Utility :	0	0	1	1	

The linear programme is to find non-negative λ's so that :

$$\text{Utility} \quad z = \lambda_3 + \lambda_4 = \max.$$

subject to

$$\left. \begin{array}{l} 50\lambda_1 + 25\lambda_2 \leqslant 50 \\ 5\lambda_1 + 50\lambda_2 \leqslant 52\frac{1}{2} \end{array} \right\} \quad \dotfill (1)$$

$$\left. \begin{array}{l} -\frac{1}{2}\lambda_1 + \lambda_2 = \lambda_3 + 2\lambda_4 \\ \lambda_1 = \lambda_3 + \frac{1}{2}\lambda_4 \end{array} \right\} \quad \dotfill (2)$$

Notice that the consumption combinations are in agreement with the " rectangular hyperbola " case of Fig. 79. Each indifference locus has only one line segment and there is only one rate of substitution :

$$\frac{2-1}{1-\frac{1}{2}} = 2$$

i.e. 200 tons of corn compensate for the loss of 100 hogs.

The side relations of the linear programme fall into two pairs, (1) and (2), which are easily solved. The equations (2) give :

$$\lambda_3 = \tfrac{3}{2}\lambda_1 - \tfrac{1}{3}\lambda_2 \quad \text{and} \quad \lambda_4 = \tfrac{2}{3}\lambda_2 - \lambda_1 \quad \dots\dots\dots\dots\dots\dots\dots(3)$$

The maximum criterion can then be expressed in terms of λ_1 and λ_2 :

$$z = \tfrac{1}{2}\lambda_1 + \tfrac{1}{3}\lambda_2 = \text{max.} \quad \dots\dots\dots\dots\dots\dots\dots\dots\dots\dots(4)$$

Only those λ_1 and λ_2 are admissible which make $\lambda_3 \geqslant 0$ and $\lambda_4 \geqslant 0$, so that (3) gives :

$$\frac{\lambda_2}{\lambda_1} \leqslant \frac{9}{2} \quad \text{and} \quad \frac{\lambda_2}{\lambda_1} \geqslant \frac{2}{3}$$

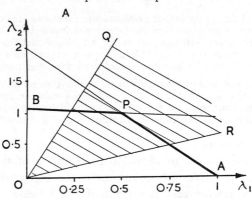

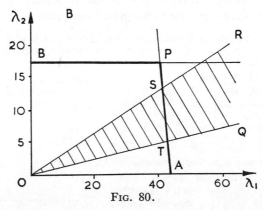

Fig. 80.

and the point with co-ordinates (λ_1, λ_2) must lie, in the plane $O\lambda_1\lambda_2$ of Fig. 80a, between the two lines :

$$OQ: \ \frac{\lambda_2}{\lambda_1}=\frac{9}{2} \quad OR: \ \frac{\lambda_2}{\lambda_1}=\frac{2}{3}$$

OQ corresponds to $\lambda_3=0$, first consumption activity not used, and similarly for OR. Between these lines, a set of parallel lines, $\frac{1}{2}\lambda_1+\frac{1}{3}\lambda_2=$ constant, is drawn; by (4), the problem is to reach the highest possible line in this set.

The side relations (1) are familiar, and they express the effect of the limiting amounts of labour and land respectively. The point with co-ordinates (λ_1, λ_2) must lie in the area $OAPB$ of Fig. 80a, where:

$$AP: \ 50\lambda_1+25\lambda_2=50 \quad \text{(for full employment of labour)}$$
$$BP: \ 5\lambda_1+50\lambda_2=52\tfrac{1}{2} \quad \text{(for full use of land)}$$

Hence the solution of the whole linear programme is the point P, which is both the intersection of AP and BP and lies on the highest of the parallel lines within the admissible areas of the figure. The solution is:

$$\lambda_1=\tfrac{1}{2}, \ \lambda_2=1, \ \lambda_3=\tfrac{5}{12}, \ \lambda_4=\tfrac{1}{6}, \ z=\tfrac{7}{12} \quad \text{(maximum)}$$

This happens to give the same allocation of resources as in Ex. (a) of 18.5 above but, in addition, the net production is distributed:

	Net product	Consumed	
		First activity	Second activity
Corn (tons)	75	42	33
Hogs (head)	50	42	8

The group of consumers takes part of the supplies in equal proportions (42 tons and 42 head) and part in the given unequal proportions (33 tons and 8 head).

This is the case where the matrix remains of order 4×4 in the solution. Other cases arise where the matrix reduces to order 3×3; only one factor is scarce and only one consumption activity is used. The solution is then given by the intersection of one of OQ and OR with one of AP and BP. Such cases are illustrated in Ex. 2 and 3 below.

Ex. (b). Fresh fish, smoked fish and firewood are produced with a single fixed factor (labour) and demanded in fixed proportions according to the scheme:

Technology-tastes: Resources:

Labour	man-months	7	1	$\tfrac{1}{4}$	0	0	300
Fresh fish	tons	−1	2	0	4	0	0
Smoked fish	tons	0	−1	0	0	2	0
Firewood	tons	0	3	−1	1	1	0
Utility:		0	0	0	1	1	

The linear programme is to maximise $z=\lambda_4+\lambda_5$ subject to:

$$7\lambda_1+\lambda_2+\tfrac{1}{4}\lambda_3 \leqslant 300 \quad\text{.....................................(5)}$$

$$-\lambda_1+2\lambda_2+4\lambda_4=0, \quad -\lambda_2+2\lambda_5=0 \quad \text{and} \quad 3\lambda_2-\lambda_3+\lambda_4+\lambda_5=0 \quad\text{......... (6)}$$

The equations (6) give:

$$\lambda_4=\tfrac{1}{4}\lambda_1-\tfrac{1}{2}\lambda_2; \quad \lambda_5=\tfrac{1}{2}\lambda_2; \quad \text{so that } z=\tfrac{1}{4}\lambda_1$$

and
$$\lambda_3=3\lambda_2+\tfrac{1}{4}\lambda_1$$

Hence the criterion is maximum λ_1 provided that $\lambda_1 \geqslant 2\lambda_2$ and $\lambda_2 \geqslant 0$ (for λ_4 and λ_5 non-negative). Substituting λ_3 in (5):

$$\tfrac{113}{16}\lambda_1+\tfrac{7}{4}\lambda_2 \leqslant 300$$

Since λ_1 is to be maximised, the solution is $\lambda_2 = 0$ and $\lambda_1 = \dfrac{4,800}{113}$, which satisfy $\lambda_1 \geqslant 2\lambda_2$ and $\lambda_2 \geqslant 0$. The other λ's can then be found from the results above to give the complete solution :

$$\lambda_1 = 42 \cdot 5 \quad \lambda_2 = 0 \quad \lambda_3 = 10 \cdot 6 \quad \lambda_4 = 10 \cdot 6 \quad \lambda_5 = 0$$

The original technology-tastes matrix is of order 4×5, so that a square matrix is obtained for solution only if (at least) one process or activity is eliminated as not used. The actual solution goes further ; it eliminates two columns, one process ($\lambda_2 = 0$) and one consumption activity ($\lambda_5 = 0$). At the same time, one commodity (smoked fish) disappears, since it is not produced. The square matrix obtained is of order 3×3 and the solution is :

		Production		Consumption *
		First process	Third process	
Fresh fis	tons	42·5	—	42·5
Firewood	tons	—	10·6	10·6
Labour used	man-months	297·4	2·6	—

* On first consumption activity.

Ex. (*c*). The problem of the previous example can be varied by eliminating the production process for firewood and by assuming instead that firewood is available (like labour) in given amount. Take the scheme :

Technology-tastes :						Resources
Labour	man-months	7	1	0	0	300
Firewood	tons	0	3	0	0	b
Fresh fish	tons	−1	2	1	3	0
Smoked fish	tons	0	−1	1	$\frac{1}{2}$	0
Utility :		0	0	1	1	

Here b is a constant (given resources of firewood) to which various values can be given, in observing the effect on the solution. Notice that the matrix is now square so that, in a solution, it is to be expected either that all processes and activities are used and both factors scarce, or that only one activity is used and only one factor scarce.

The linear programme is to find non-negative λ's for $z = \lambda_3 + \lambda_4$ to be a maximum subject to :

$$7\lambda_1 + \lambda_2 \leqslant 300 \qquad \text{and} \qquad 3\lambda_2 \leqslant b \quad \dots\dots\dots\dots(7)$$
$$-\lambda_1 + 2\lambda_2 + \lambda_3 + 3\lambda_4 = 0 \quad \text{and} \quad -\lambda_2 + \lambda_3 + \tfrac{1}{2}\lambda_4 = 0 \quad \dots\dots\dots\dots(8)$$

From (8) : $\lambda_3 = \tfrac{1}{5}(8\lambda_2 - \lambda_1)$; $\lambda_4 = \tfrac{2}{5}(\lambda_1 - 3\lambda_2)$; and $z = \tfrac{1}{5}(\lambda_1 + 2\lambda_2)$.

Hence the criterion for maximum is that the solution is the highest point on the parallel lines ($\lambda_1 + 2\lambda_2 = $ constant) within the cone OQR, where OQ is $\lambda_2 = \tfrac{1}{8}\lambda_1$ (for $\lambda_3 = 0$) and OR is $\lambda_2 = \tfrac{1}{3}\lambda_1$ (for $\lambda_4 = 0$), as shown in Fig. 80*b*. From (7), solutions for λ_1 and λ_2 must, according to the factor limits, lie within the area $OAPB$, where AP is the line $7\lambda_1 + \lambda_2 = 300$ and where BP is parallel to $O\lambda_1$ at height $OB = \tfrac{1}{3}b$. The point S has co-ordinates $\lambda_1 = \tfrac{450}{11}$, $\lambda_2 = \tfrac{150}{11}$; the point T has co-ordinates $\lambda_1 = \tfrac{800}{19}$, $\lambda_2 = \tfrac{100}{19}$. It is clear from Fig. 80*b* that the solution varies with b as follows :

(i) $b > \frac{450}{11}$; solution at S : $\lambda_1 = \frac{450}{11}$, $\lambda_2 = \frac{150}{11}$; $\lambda_3 = \frac{150}{11}$; $\lambda_4 = 0$.

(ii) $\frac{300}{19} < b < \frac{450}{11}$; solution at P (between S and T) :

$$\lambda_1 = \frac{1}{21}(900 - b), \quad \lambda_2 = \frac{1}{3}b, \quad \lambda_3 = \frac{1}{35}(19b - 300), \quad \lambda_4 = \frac{4}{105}(450 - 11b)$$

(iii) $b < \frac{300}{19}$; solution at T : $\lambda_1 = \frac{800}{19}$, $\lambda_2 = \frac{100}{19}$, $\lambda_3 = 0$, $\lambda_4 = \frac{200}{19}$

In case (i), firewood is plentiful and not used to the limit, i.e. there is only one consumption activity used (λ_3) and only one factor is scarce (labour) ; both products are produced but with some concentration on smoked fish. In case (iii), the situation is similar, except that firewood is scarce, labour unemployed, and the consumption activity used is that in which more fresh fish is demanded than smoked fish. The less extreme case (ii) is the one in which both factors are scarce and consumption follows the pattern of both activities.

As an exercise in comparative statics, in the problem of Ex. (a), write the technology (input-output) relations and the tastes with parameters instead of numerical values :

Technology-tastes :				Resources :
Labour	a_{11} a_{12}	0	0	1
Land	a_{21} a_{22}	0	0	1
Corn	$\frac{1}{2}$ -1	1	α	0
Hogs	-1 0	1	β	0
Utility :	0 0	1	1	

The four a's are all positive and $\alpha > 1$, $\beta < 1$. These parameters can be varied and the effect on the solution of the problem determined.

The matrix has been normalised. The units for labour and land are fixed as whatever amounts are available. The units for corn and hogs are chosen so that one unit of each are combined in the first consumption ratio. The unit levels of the two production processes are fixed so that one unit of each product (hogs and corn respectively) is the output. The unit consumption levels are taken so that unit utility is associated with each.

No attention is paid here to changing relations on the output side and these relations are fixed numerically, by the sub-matrix of elements $\begin{bmatrix} \frac{1}{2} & -1 \\ -1 & 0 \end{bmatrix}$. This is to permit concentration on changes in factors and in tastes, as indicated by the a's, and by α and β, respectively. For example, if a_{11} and a_{12} are decreased in proportion, then the effect of an increased amount of labour available follows. On the other hand, if a_{11} and a_{12} change in relative magnitude, then the effect studied is that of changing labour productivity in the two lines of production.

Ex. (*d*). The linear programme, with the data as specified above, is to find non-negative λ's so that

$$z = \lambda_3 + \lambda_4 = \max.$$

subject to
$$a_{11}\lambda_1 + a_{12}\lambda_2 \leqslant 1 \qquad a_{21}\lambda_1 + a_{22}\lambda_2 \leqslant 1$$
$$\tfrac{1}{2}\lambda_1 - \lambda_2 + \lambda_3 + \alpha\lambda_4 = 0 \qquad -\lambda_1 + \lambda_3 + \beta\lambda_4 = 0$$

The solution is shown on a diagram like Fig. 80a, where :

AP is $a_{11}\lambda_1 + a_{12}\lambda_2 = 1$ for full use of labour

BP is $a_{21}\lambda_1 + a_{22}\lambda_2 = 1$ for full use of land

P is $\lambda_1 = \dfrac{a_{22} - a_{12}}{A}$, $\lambda_2 = \dfrac{a_{11} - a_{21}}{A}$

for full use of labour and land

OQ is $\dfrac{\lambda_2}{\lambda_1} = \dfrac{\alpha}{\beta} + \dfrac{1}{2}$ for $\lambda_3 = 0$

OR is $\dfrac{\lambda_2}{\lambda_1} = \dfrac{3}{2}$ for $\lambda_4 = 0$

and the parallel lines (for maximum z) have slope :

$$-\frac{\alpha + \tfrac{1}{2}\beta - \tfrac{3}{2}}{1 - \beta}$$

Here $A = \begin{vmatrix} a_{11} & a_{12} \\ a_{21} & a_{22} \end{vmatrix} = a_{11}a_{22} - a_{12}a_{21}$, and the order of the two factors is so chosen

(as it always can be) that $A > 0$, i.e.

$$\frac{a_{11}}{a_{12}} > \frac{a_{21}}{a_{22}} \quad \text{and} \quad \frac{a_{11}}{a_{21}} > \frac{a_{12}}{a_{22}}$$

The solution is at the point P, where both factors are employed to the limit, and all four processes and activities are used, provided that the following conditions are all satisfied :

$$\left. \begin{array}{l} P \text{ in positive quadrant :} \quad \dfrac{a_{11}}{a_{21}} > 1 > \dfrac{a_{12}}{a_{22}} \\[2mm] P \text{ between } OQ \text{ and } OR : \dfrac{\alpha}{\beta} + \dfrac{1}{2} > \dfrac{a_{11} - a_{21}}{a_{22} - a_{12}} > \dfrac{3}{2} \\[2mm] \begin{array}{l}\text{Slope of parallel lines}\\ \text{between } AP \text{ and } BP :\end{array} \dfrac{a_{11}}{a_{12}} > \dfrac{\alpha + \tfrac{1}{2}\beta - \tfrac{3}{2}}{1 - \beta} > \dfrac{a_{21}}{a_{22}} \end{array} \right\} \quad \dots\dots\dots\dots(9)$$

If any of these fails to hold then the solution is the intersection of one of OQ and OR with one of AP and BP, e.g. OR and BP giving $\lambda_1 = \dfrac{2}{2a_{21} + 3a_{22}}$, $\lambda_2 = \dfrac{3}{2a_{21} + 3a_{22}}$. In such case, only one factor is scarce and only one consumption activity is used, i.e. land is scarce and the consumption is fixed in the ratio 1 : 1 in the case named.

The dual programme is to find non-negative p's so that :

$$\zeta = p_1 + p_2 = \min.$$

subject to
$$a_{11}p_1 + a_{21}p_2 \geqslant p_4 - \tfrac{1}{2}p_3 \qquad a_{12}p_1 + a_{22}p_2 \geqslant p_3$$
$$p_3 + p_4 = 1 \qquad \alpha p_3 + \beta p_4 = 1$$

As long as conditions (9) are satisfied, the values of λ_1 and λ_2 are as given for P, and the p's are all positive and found to be as follows :

$$\left. \begin{array}{ll} \lambda_1 = \dfrac{a_{22} - a_{12}}{A} & \lambda_2 = \dfrac{a_{11} - a_{21}}{A} \\[3mm] p_1 = \dfrac{(\alpha + \tfrac{1}{2}\beta - \tfrac{3}{2})a_{22} - (1 - \beta)a_{21}}{(\alpha - \beta)A} & p_2 = \dfrac{(1 - \beta)a_{11} - (\alpha + \tfrac{1}{2}\beta - \tfrac{3}{2})a_{12}}{(\alpha - \beta)A} \\[3mm] p_3 = \dfrac{1 - \beta}{\alpha - \beta} & p_4 = \dfrac{\alpha - 1}{\alpha - \beta} \end{array} \right\} \quad \dots\dots(10)$$

From (10), all the features of the solution can be found, e.g. the levels λ_3 and λ_4 of consumption, the maximum z of utility, the minimum ζ of cost, the outputs of the two products, and so on. The rates of substitution are of interest :

$$\frac{p_3}{p_4} = \frac{1-\beta}{\alpha-1} = \text{the single rate of substitution between products in consumption}$$

$$\frac{p_1}{p_2} = \frac{(\alpha + \frac{1}{2}\beta - \frac{3}{2})a_{22} - (1-\beta)a_{21}}{(1-\beta)a_{11} - (a + \frac{1}{2}\beta - \frac{3}{2})a_{12}} = \text{rate of substitution between factors}$$

$$\frac{p_1}{p_3} = \frac{1}{A}\left(\frac{\alpha + \frac{1}{2}\beta - \frac{3}{2}}{1-\beta}a_{22} - a_{21}\right) = \text{productivity of labour in terms of corn}$$

and similarly for other productivities.

Start now from a solution (10) assumed to be one of full employment of the factors. The effect of any change in the a's, or in α and β, can be traced from (10), provided that it is remembered that any violation of (9) results in one factor becoming unemployed and one consumption activity unused. Of the many possible changes, consider the following two.

Increase in the amount of labour available, i.e. a_{11} and a_{12} decrease in proportion. The immediate effect, from (10), is to increase λ_1 and to decrease λ_2, i.e. the output of hogs (λ_1) rises and of corn ($\lambda_2 - \frac{1}{2}\lambda_1$) falls. The increase may proceed so far that the middle condition of (9) fails (and later the first condition also). When this happens, $\lambda_2 = \frac{3}{2}\lambda_1$ and the outputs of corn and hogs are equal. Further increases, in labour available, leaves these outputs unchanged ; labour becomes unemployed and the consumption is fixed in the proportions 1 : 1. In terms of Fig. 80a, OQR is fixed but P has shifted and falls below OR.

Changes in tastes such that the utility of the $\alpha : \beta$ combination increases. This corresponds to a proportionate decrease in α and β and the rate of substitution $\frac{1-\beta}{\alpha-1}$ increases. The immediate effect, from (10), is no change whatever in λ_1 and λ_2, and hence in the output of corn and hogs. The change in tastes does not influence production. Its effect is to be sought in prices and in the maximum of utility (and minimum of cost) realised. Again from (10), p_3 increases relative to p_4, in line with the rate of substitution, i.e. corn becomes dearer since the $\alpha : \beta$ combination ($\alpha > 1$, $\beta < 1$) is more in demand. Further, p_1 decreases relative to p_2 and land (which is used heavily in corn production) becomes more highly priced. If the decrease in α and β becomes large, then the last condition of (9) fails. When this happens, λ_1 decreases, λ_2 increases so that $\frac{\lambda_2}{\lambda_1} = \frac{\alpha}{\beta} + \frac{1}{2}$; labour becomes unemployed and consumption is fixed in the preferred ratio $\alpha : \beta$. The price p_1 of labour falls to zero. In terms of Fig. 80a, P and the lines OQ and OR are fixed, only the numerical slope of the lines for maximum z gets smaller ; when this slope becomes equal to or less than that of BP, the solution shifts from P to the point where OQ intersects BP.

EXERCISES 19.8

1. Solve the linear programme for maximum utility, given :

Technology-tastes :				Resources :
Labour	25	10	0	0	50 man-months
Land	50	100	0	0	260 acres
Wheat	-1	0	1	2	0
Hay	0	-1	1	$\frac{1}{2}$	0
Utility :	0	0	1	1	

The units for wheat and hay are 100 tons. Show that only labour is scarce and that only the first consumption ratio is used. How small must the land resources be for land to become a scarce factor?

2. Take the resources as 30 man-months and 75 acres in the previous exercise. Solve the programme and show that only one factor is scarce. What can be said about the consumption ratios used?

3. In Ex. (a), write the lower right-hand corner of the matrix as $\begin{bmatrix} 1 & \alpha \\ 1 & \beta \end{bmatrix}$ for parameters $\alpha > 1$, $\beta < 1$. Solve in terms of α and β. In terms of Fig. 80a, show that the point P is inside the cone OQR (both factors scarce, both consumption ratios used) only if $\dfrac{\alpha}{\beta} > \dfrac{3}{2}$. Hence show that only one factor is scarce if $\dfrac{\alpha}{\beta} < \dfrac{3}{2}$. See Ex. ($d$) above.

4. Write the dual of Ex. (a) and solve : $p_1 : p_2 : p_3 : p_4 = 28 : 5 : 950 : 1900$

5. Formulate and solve the dual of Ex. (c), first for $b = 45$ tons and then for $b = 30$ tons. Interpret the price ratios found in terms of rates of substitution.

6. In Ex. (d), let a_{21} and a_{22} decrease in proportion and, hence, examine the effect of an increase in the amount of land available.

7. In Ex. (d), what are the interpretations and effects of :
  (i) increasing a_{11} and a_{21} in proportion
  (ii) increasing a_{12} and a_{22} in proportion
  (iii) changes in the relative magnitudes of a_{11} and a_{12}
  (iv) changes in the relative magnitudes of α and β?

REFERENCES

Alchian (A. A.) (1953) : " The Meaning of Utility Measurement ", *American Economic Review*, **43**, 26–50.

Cameron (B.) (1954) : *The Determination of Production* (Cambridge, 1954).

Corlett (W. J.) and Newman (P. K.) (1952) : " A Note on Revealed Preference and the Transitivity Condition ", *Review of Economic Studies*, **20**, 156–58

Dorfman (R.), Samuelson (P. A.) and Solow (R. M.) (1958) : *Linear Programming and Economic Analysis* (McGraw-Hill, 1958), Chapter 14 and Appendix A.

Ellsberg (D.) (1954) : " Classic and Current Notions of ' Measurable Utility ' " *Economic Journal*, **64**, 528–56.

Georgescu-Roegen (N.) (1936) : " The Pure Theory of Consumer's Behavior ", *Quarterly Journal of Economics*, **50**, 545–93.

Herstein (I. N.) and Milner (J.) (1953) : " An Axiomatic Approach to Measurable Utility ", *Econometrica*, **21**, 291–97.

Hicks (J. R.) and Allen (R. G. D.) (1934) : " A Reconsideration of the Theory of Value ", *Economica*, **1**, 52–76 and 196–219.

Hicks (J. R.) (1939, 1946) : *Value and Capital* (Oxford, First Ed. 1939, Second Ed. 1946), Chapters I–III and Appendix.

Hicks (J.R.) (1956) : *A Revision of Demand Theory* (Oxford, 1956).

Houthakker (H. S.) (1950) : " Revealed Preference and the Utility Function ", *Economica*, **17**, 159–74.

Makower (Helen) (1957) : *Activity Analysis and the Theory of Economic Equilibrium* (Macmillan, 1957).

Marschak (J.) (1950) : " Rational Behaviour, Uncertain Prospects, and Measurable Utility ", *Econometrica*, **18**, 111–41.

Marschak (J.) (1951) : " Why ' Should ' Statisticians and Businessmen Maximise ' Moral Expectation ' ", in *Second Berkeley Symposium on Mathematical Statistics and Probability* (California, 1951).

Marschak (J.) (1954) : " Scaling of Utilities and Probabilities ", in Shubik (M.) (Editor) : *Readings in Game Theory and Political Behaviour* (Doubleday, 1954).

Morishima (M.) (1952): " Consumer's Behaviour and Liquidity Preference ", *Econometrica*, **20**, 223–46.

Morton (G.) (1950) : *Food Consumption Levels—Some International Comparisons* (London Ph.D. thesis, unpublished).

Mosak (J. L.) (1952) : " On the Interpretation of the Fundamental Equation of Value Theory ", in Lange (O.), McIntyre (F.) and Yntema (T. O.) (Editors) : *Studies in Mathematical Economics and Econometrics* (Chicago, 1952).

Mosteller (F.) and Nogee (P.) (1951) : " An Experimental Measurement of Utility ", *Journal of Political Economy*, **59**, 371–404.

Neumann (J. von) and Morgenstern (O.) (1947) : *Theory of Games and Economic Behaviour* (Princeton, Second Ed. 1947).

Ozga (S. A.) (1956) : " Measurable Utility and Probability ", *Economic Journal*, **66**, 419–30.

Ramsey (F. P.) (1926) : " Truth and Probability ", paper written in 1926 and published in *The Foundations of Mathematics* (Ed. by R. B. Braithwaite, Kegan Paul, 1931), 156–98.

Robertson (D. H.) (1951) : " Utility and All That ", *Manchester School* (1951), 111–42.

Robertson (D. H.) (1954) : " Utility and All What? " *Economic Journal*, **64**, 665–78.

Samuelson (P. A.) (1948) : " Consumption Theory in Terms of Revealed Preference ", *Economica*, **15**, 243–53.

Samuelson (P. A.) (1950) : " The Problem of Integrability in Utility Theory ", *Economica*, **17**, 355–85.

Samuelson (P. A.) (1952) : " Probability, Utility, and the Independence Axiom ", *Econometrica*, **20**, 670–78.

Savage (L. J.) (1954) : *The Foundations of Statistics* (Wiley, 1954).

Slutsky (E.) (1915) : " Sulla teoria del Bilancio del Consumatore ", *Giornale del Economisti*, **51**, 1–26.

CHAPTER 20

THE AGGREGATION PROBLEM

20.1. The Problem

ECONOMIC models must be related to empirical data if they are to be of use either for explanatory or for predictive purposes. In the present state of computational procedures, they must involve relatively few aggregates like national income, consumption and investment, or inputs and outputs of broad groups of materials and products. This is certainly so for models of the whole economy, as in Hicks' trade-cycle theory (Chapter 7) or Leontief's input-output model (Chapter 11). It is also true of models, e.g. in linear programming, which apply to the operations of an industry or large concern. In most cases, a model must be confined to a few macro-relations between a few macro-variables.

Macro-economic models can be set up in their own right, as in the early chapters above, on the assumption that, at least approximately, aggregate variables are directly and simply related. However, this cannot be satis-factory to an economist, conscious that relations between aggregates are the resultant of many decisions by consumers and firms. It is natural to wish to go behind the macro-relations, to see how individual decisions lead to stable relations in the aggregate—if indeed they do so at all.

The picture is then completely changed. The economic theory of any model runs in micro-terms, based on decisions taken, e.g. by individual consumers or firms ; the macro-relations are derived constructions. There must be an explicit translation, through aggregation, from micro-relations to appropriate macro-relations. The translation may be, and often is, of the crudest kind. For example, if individual demand for tea is a function of the consumer's income, of the price of tea and of the prices of many related commodities, it may be laid down that, by analogy, market demand for tea is the same kind of function of national income, of the price of tea and of a general price index. Or the translation may involve more subtle (economic and statistical) considerations. The model is then based on *economic* theory in the form of many micro-relations between micro-variables, but expressed in terms of an *economic-statistical* construction of macro-relations between aggregate variables. The method of aggregation is vital, both in its economic aspect and in its statistical connotation in relation to available data.

A host of questions emerges. What kind of aggregation is needed? In the example of the market demand for tea, aggregation may be over a group of consumers, over a range of brands of tea, and over time to convert the " day " of the individual decision into the months or quarters of empirical data. Once aggregate variables are written, how are they to be related? The form in which the basic economic theory runs may determine this ; if individual demand functions are such that the price-elasticity for tea is constant, then market demand may also be taken with constant price-elasticity. What is the relation of the (statistical) coefficient of a macro-relation to the corresponding (economic) coefficients in the basic micro-relations? The market price-elasticity of demand for tea, for example, may be thought of as an average of the diverse individual price-elasticities. Is this appropriate and, if so, what kind of average is the aggregate coefficient? Such questions are clearly fundamental in economic model-building. They have been appreciated by economists in the past, e.g. by Tinbergen (1939, 1951), but they have only recently been explored at all systematically. It is not difficult to see why. The questions are not primarily economic, nor are they mainly statistical. The economist gets nowhere without statistical guidance ; the statistician has a few stock answers but needs more instruction from an economist than he is usually given. Some work has been done in particular fields, e.g. the economic basis of " cost-of-living " index numbers. But the general questions have remained unanswered, witness the lack of systematic treatment of index numbers either in texts on economic principles or in statistical theory.

The literature of the theory of aggregation is meagre. Almost the earliest serious discussion was in a series of articles by Klein and others in *Econometrica* in 1946. Considerable interest in the problem is evident among econometricians in France ; see Nataf (1948) and Roy (1952). The first systematic treatment, however, is to be found in a monograph by Theil (1954). The present account is based largely on the pioneer work of Theil.

The problem is examined here only in the case where a single macro-relation is derived by aggregation from a set of micro-relations. The complications which arise when a system of inter-related macro-equations come from the micro-relations have been examined by Theil (1954) ; they are not pursued here. Even in the simple case, the problem is a serious econometric exercise—neither pure mathematical economics nor just a matter of adding a statistical test of significance. It would indeed be excluded from the present text—which does not discuss econometric techniques—were it not for the fact that it is of basic economic interest.

The problem takes us back to the beginning ; it is " where we came in ".

Consider first the question of *consistency* between the three elements of the problem : micro-relations, aggregation of variables, macro-relation. One view, represented by Klein (1946), takes as given certain micro-relations thrown up by economic theory and an exact macro-relation of corresponding form. The question is : what aggregation from micro- to macro-variables is consistent with this set-up? The attempt to find a consistent method of aggregation is pursued in *approach* (i) in the following analysis.

In another view of consistency, one which appears to be taken by May (1946, 1947), it is assumed that the micro-relations and the form of aggregation are specified. The question is whether an exact macro-relation can then be written between the aggregates and, if so, what form it takes. Difficulties soon emerge in following this line of approach. Theil (1954) shows that consistency cannot be attained under all circumstances ; indeed it cannot even be expected as the usual case. He is then led to drop the requirement of consistency and, on his " analogy approach ", he adopts a statistical criterion instead. The question is : given the micro-relations and a method of aggregation, is it appropriate to fit a macro-relation of certain form by statistical methods? This is *approach* (ii) in the analysis below.

It is to be remembered that approach (i) concentrates on the *consistency* of an exact macro-relation with given micro-relations by choice of an appropriate aggregation. On the other hand, approach (ii) is based on the *statistical fitting* of a macro-relation to the given aggregates from given micro-relations.

The analysis is simplified by taking the micro-relations of the basic theory as linear, and by confining the macro-relation (either assumed or considered for statistical fitting) also to linear form. This can be regarded either as an important case or as a convenient approximation for small changes in the variables. In addition, the analysis is limited to the case of *linear aggregation*, i.e. the macro-variables are linear aggregates of the micro-variables. The aggregates may be unweighted or weighted (in the statistical sense) but they involve the micro-variables only in a linear form. In short, the analysis is concerned with the translation of linear micro-relations into a linear macro-relation by means of linear aggregates.

EXERCISES 20.1

1. Show that the question of consistency of the three-element problem can be viewed in a third way, i.e. by assuming that a given macro-relation holds between specified aggregates and by asking what micro-relations are consistent.

2. Indicate that this third view is appropriate on an empirical approach in which it is asserted that certain aggregates are related in a certain way. How does micro-economic theory fit in this picture?

20.2. Simple Example : Aggregation over Individuals

The demand of an individual consumer for a commodity (say, tea) is given by micro-theory as a (linear) function of a number of variables : the individual's income, the price of tea and the prices of all related commodities. It is required to construct a market demand relation for tea, the market consisting of n individual consumers. In all aggregation problems, it is important to be clear at the outset on how the micro-variables and relations are to be " boiled down " to the corresponding macro-variables and relations. Here then are n micro-relations of demand, one for each consumer on the market ; they are to be " boiled down " to one macro-relation for market demand. It is less easy to see how the variables are to be treated. If it is assumed that the same prices are paid by all consumers, then there is nothing to be " boiled down " here and the (common) prices can be easily handled (see Ex. 1 and 2 below). There remain variables such as family income, size and composition which vary from one consumer to another. It is these micro-variables which need to be replaced by aggregate variables : total income and population, and indicators of their distribution. In the present example, only income is taken as variable from one consumer to another.

There are n linear demand relations, one for each consumer :

$$y_s = a_s \mu_s + k_s \quad (s = 1, 2, \dots n) \quad \dots\dots\dots\dots\dots(1)$$

where y_s is the sth individual's demand for tea when his income is μ_s. The parameters (a_s and k_s) correspond respectively to the slope and intercept of the micro-relation when represented graphically as a straight line. The parameter a_s is of particular interest ; it is the individual's marginal propensity to consume tea.

So much for the micro-relations, given by the basic micro-theory of value. The rest depends on the approach to aggregation adopted.

Approach (*i*). It is assumed that the macro-relation is a linear dependence of aggregate demand y on aggregate income μ :

$$y = a\mu + k$$

where a and k are the corresponding macro-parameters, for slope and intercept respectively. The question is : how is the aggregation to be done? There is no difficulty about y ; aggregate demand is $y = \sum_s y_s$.

The problem concerns the n micro-variables for individual income, which are to be aggregated (somehow) into one macro-variable for total income. Summation of (1) gives :

$$y = \sum_s a_s \mu_s + \sum_s k_s$$

which states the obvious, i.e. total demand depends on *all* individual incomes. There is, as yet, no " boiling down " of μ_s into μ. There is just one aggregation which achieves the " boiling down " required. Write $\bar{a} = \frac{1}{n} \sum_s a_s$ for the mean value of the micro-slopes, i.e. the mean marginal propensity to consume tea, over all individuals. Now define the aggregation of individual incomes as : $\mu = \frac{1}{\bar{a}} \sum_s a_s \mu_s$, the sum of individual incomes μ_s, each weighted according to the individual's marginal propensity to consume a_s. Then :

$$\left. \begin{array}{l} y = a \mu + k \\[2mm] \text{where} \qquad a = \bar{a} = \frac{1}{n} \sum_s a_s \quad \text{and} \quad k = \sum_s k_s \\[2mm] \text{provided that} \qquad \mu = \frac{1}{\bar{a}} \sum_s a_s \mu_s \end{array} \right\} \quad \dots\dots\dots\dots\dots\dots\dots(2)$$

is the exact linear macro-relation, for total demand for tea, obtained from the n micro-relations (1).

The interpretation of (2) is simple ; as a macro-relation it is just what is required. The macro-slope a, the marginal propensity to consume in the aggregate, is the mean of the individual micro-slopes or marginal propensities to consume. The macro-intercept k is the sum of the individual micro-intercepts k_s. The difficulty with (2) is that it is not a " natural " aggregation to weight incomes with the individual marginal propensities to consume. Greater weight is given to those consumers on the market who expand their purchases most when income rises. What is even more disturbing about this weighted aggregation is that the aggregate μ is specific to the commodity (tea) considered. The " correct " aggregate income for another commodity (e.g. sugar or soap) is different, for the marginal propensities used as weights are different. In strict theory, there are as many measures of aggregate income μ as there are commodities. In practice, things may not be quite as bad as this, since the various measures are likely to move together (e.g. over time).

Approach (ii). It is assumed that simple aggregation is adopted :

$$y = \sum_s y_s \quad \text{and} \quad \mu = \sum_s \mu_s$$

The question is : can a linear macro-relation between y and μ be written at all, and if so what are the parameters? One point emerges at once. Except by accident, an exact linear relation between y and μ cannot be derived from the micro-relations (1). The macro-relation sought is a statistical, not an exact one ; consequently, it relates to a specific period of time (say $t = 1, 2, \ldots T$) and not simply to one time point. The course of y_s and μ_s over the time period must be given, and hence the course of the aggregates y and μ. There is a series of points (y, μ) given over the time period and a linear relation $y = a\mu + k + u$ (where u is a residual or disturbance) can be fitted by a statistical procedure such as least-squares. This is the most which can be achieved.

The least-squares fitting is done indirectly. For the time period considered ($t = 1, 2, \ldots T$), examine the relation of changes in an individual's income μ_s to the changes in aggregate income $\mu = \sum_s \mu_s$. Express the relation in the form of a regression equation, fitted by least squares :

$$\mu_s = A_s \mu + K_s + u_s$$

when A_s and K_s are coefficients found in the fitting, dependent on the course of μ_s and μ over time. Since $\sum_s \mu_s = \mu$, it follows that $\sum_s A_s = 1$ and $\sum_s K_s = 0$. The residual u_s has zero mean, minimised variance and no correlation with μ ; all that really matters in the present context is that u_s averages out to zero over the time period considered. Summation of (1) and substitution for μ_s give :

$$y = \sum_s a_s (A_s \mu + K_s + u_s) + \sum_s k_s$$
$$= (\sum_s a_s A_s)\mu + (\sum_s k_s + \sum_s a_s K_s) + (\sum_s a_s u_s)$$

which is of the form $y = a\mu + k + u$ required. Hence :

$$
\left.
\begin{array}{l}
y = a\mu + k + u \\
a = \sum_s a_s A_s \quad \text{and} \quad k = \sum_s k_s + \sum_s a_s K_s \\
\sum_s A_s = 1 \quad \text{and} \quad \sum_s K_s = 0
\end{array}
\right\} \quad \ldots\ldots\ldots\ldots\ldots(3)
$$

where and

is the statistical macro-relation, for total demand for tea, when simple aggregate demand (y) and income (μ) are taken. The residual or disturbance u has zero mean over the time period considered.

The result (3) can be compared with what might be expected—and indeed with what was achieved by the first approach to the problem. When simple aggregation is imposed, then the aggregate demand relation is generally found wanting. Not only is it of statistical (rather than exact) form ; it has coefficients which are not what are " naturally " expected.

Par for the course would be achieved by finding $a = \bar{a} = \dfrac{1}{n} \Sigma_s a_s$ and $k = \Sigma_s k_s$. In fact, the macro-slope a is a weighted average of the micro-slopes a_s, and the weights (A_s) depend on the course of the variables over time. The marginal propensity to consume in the aggregate is not the straight mean of the individual marginal propensities ; it is a weighted average with shifting weights from one time period to another. The situation for the macro-intercept is worse since k is influenced, not only by the course of the variables over time, but also by *both* the micro-intercepts and the micro-slopes.

Clearly simple aggregates introduce an *aggregation bias* in the macro-relation for total demand. This is quite apart from any statistical bias of estimation in the time period considered. It is useful to show the bias explicitly. It is seen in the correlation (over all individuals on the market) between the marginal propensities a_s and the coefficients (A_s or K_s) in the regression of individual income μ_s on aggregate income μ. Write the covariances :

$$\text{Cov}\,(a_s A_s) = \frac{1}{n} \Sigma_s (a_s - \bar{a}) \left(A_s - \frac{1}{n} \right) \qquad \left(\text{since mean } A_s = \frac{1}{n} \Sigma_s A_s = \frac{1}{n} \right)$$

$$= \frac{1}{n} \Sigma_s a_s A_s - \frac{1}{n} \bar{a} \qquad \left(\text{since } \frac{1}{n} \Sigma_s a_s = \bar{a}, \ \Sigma_s A_s = 1 \right)$$

and $$\text{Cov}\,(a_s K_s) = \frac{1}{n} \Sigma_s (a_s - \bar{a}) K_s \qquad \left(\text{since mean } K_s = \frac{1}{n} \Sigma_s K_s = 0 \right)$$

$$= \frac{1}{n} \Sigma_s a_s K_s \qquad \left(\text{since } \Sigma_s K_s = 0 \right)$$

The macro-parameters of (3) can thus be expressed :

$$\left. \begin{aligned} a &= \Sigma_s a_s A_s = \bar{a} + n \, \text{Cov}\,(a_s A_s) \\ k &= \Sigma_s k_s + \Sigma_s a_s K_s = \Sigma_s k_s + n \, \text{Cov}\,(a_s K_s) \end{aligned} \right\} \quad \cdots\cdots\cdots\cdots(4)$$

The results (4) show how, because of aggregation bias on the market, the macro-slope and macro-intercept of total demand can differ from the " natural " values, $\bar{a}$ and $\Sigma_s k_s$ respectively. Consider those individuals on the market with high marginal propensities to consume tea ($a_s > \bar{a}$). Suppose that, for these same consumers, individual incomes tend to increase rapidly when total income is growing over time. Then $A_s > 0$ can be quite large. Under these conditions, a_s and A_s are positively correlated, $\text{Cov}\,(a_s A_s) > 0$ and $a > \bar{a}$. The macro-slope of total demand for tea is larger than would be expected, i.e. larger than the mean of the separate micro-slopes. There can be a larger marginal propensity to consume in the aggregate than the average for the separate consumers.

In summary, therefore, the macro-parameters a and k are always " right " $(a = \bar{a}, k = \underset{s}{\Sigma} k_s)$ in approach (i) ; the aggregation of incomes is so weighted as to produce this result. On the other hand, with the simple aggregation of approach (ii), it is only by statistical accident that the macro-parameters are " right ".

EXERCISES 20.2

1. Write the individual demand relations for tea as :
$$y_s = a_s \mu_s + b_s p + k_s \quad (s = 1, 2, \ldots n)$$
where p is the price of tea, the same for all consumers. On approach (i), show that $y = a\mu + bp + k$ is the exact macro-relation if μ is defined as in the text above, and that :
$$a = \bar{a} ; \quad b = n\bar{b} ; \quad k = \underset{s}{\Sigma} k_s$$

2. In the problem of the previous exercise, using approach (ii), show that the method and results of the text apply, provided that a macro-relation
$$(y - bp) = a\mu + k + u$$
is fitted (with simple aggregation) to the n micro-relations written in the form $(y_s - b_s p) = a_s \mu_s + k_s$. Interpret.

3. An industry of n firms produces a single product ; micro-theory gives the demand of the sth firm for a factor (say, labour) as $y_s = a_s x_s + k_s$ $(s = 1, 2, \ldots n)$, where x_s is the firm's output. Show how a macro-relation $y = ax + k$ can be obtained for the industry. Also show how the factor price, the same for all firms, can be incorporated in the analysis.

20.3. Simple Example : Aggregation over Commodities

The micro-theory of value is used again, but there is now a single individual and his demands for each of m commodities are to be aggregated to his total demand for the commodity group. The group may be that of " beverages ", made up of various types and brands of tea, coffee, cocoa, soft drinks, etc. ; or the group may be wider still, e.g. consumption of food or of all commodities. Since the same consumer income appears in each demand relation (and can be easily handled, see Ex. 2 below), the variables to concentrate on, and to be aggregated, are the commodity prices. There are m micro-relations (the individual's demands for various commodities) to be " boiled down " to one macro-relation for total demand. There are m price variables, one for each commodity ; these are to be " boiled down " by aggregating or averaging into one group price. The present example simplifies by taking each micro-relation as involving only one commodity price (that for the commodity demanded) instead of the whole set of prices.

There are m linear demand relations, one for each commodity :

$$y_r = b_r p_r + k_r \quad (r = 1, 2, \ldots m) \quad \ldots\ldots\ldots\ldots\ldots\ldots\ldots(1)$$

where y_r is the individual's demand for the rth commodity (e.g. a brand of tea) when the price of the commodity is p_r. The parameters (b_r and k_r) are respectively the slope and intercept of the relation represented graphically as a straight line. The marginal effect of price on demand is shown by the b coefficient ; this would be the price-elasticity if y_r and p_r were measured logarithmically.

The m values y_r are to be aggregated into total demand y, and the m values p_r into an aggregate or average price p over all commodities. If there is no difficulty about units, then y_r and p_r for different commodities can be added. This is so if the commodities are, for example, different brands of tea ; total demand for tea (in lbs.) and the average price of tea (in d. per lb.) are sensible variables for a macro-relation. The results obtained are then exactly as before, i.e. results (2) of 20.2 above for the appropriate weighted aggregation of prices on approach (i), and results (3) and (4) for simple aggregation on approach (ii). Formally, aggregation over commodities and over individuals are equivalent processes. They differ only in interpretation and in practical applications.

When the commodity group is a " mixed bag ", commodity units and prices are not homogeneous and cannot be added. The difficulty is largely a practical one, overcome by applying the usual index-number techniques. It does, however, suggest an extension of the results which is both general and quite obvious but best introduced in the present connection.

The standard practice in constructing index numbers of quantity (or price) is to relate each quantity (or price) to a base or reference value. For the rth commodity :

$$\text{Quantity relative} = \frac{y_r}{y_{r0}} \; ; \quad \text{Price relative} = \frac{p_r}{p_{r0}}$$

These can be averaged as they stand, with or without weights. If index numbers of Laspeyres (base weighted) form are used :

$$\left.\begin{array}{c} y = \dfrac{\sum\limits_r w_{r0} \dfrac{y_r}{y_{r0}}}{\sum\limits_r w_{r0}} = \dfrac{\sum\limits_r p_{r0} y_r}{\sum\limits_r p_{r0} y_{r0}} \\[3em] p = \dfrac{\sum\limits_r w_{r0} \dfrac{p_r}{p_{r0}}}{\sum\limits_r w_{r0}} = \dfrac{\sum\limits_r p_r y_{r0}}{\sum\limits_r p_{r0} y_{r0}} \end{array}\right\} \quad \ldots\ldots\ldots\ldots\ldots\ldots(2)$$

where the weights are $w_{r0} = p_{r0} y_{r0}$ from the base values. Here y and p can be regarded as simple aggregation for non-homogeneous commodities, replacing $y = \sum_r y_r$ and $p = \sum_r p_r$ of the homogeneous case.

The micro-relations (1) can be re-formulated :

$$\frac{y_r}{y_{r0}} = b_r \frac{p_r}{p_{r0}} + k_r \quad (r = 1, 2, \ldots m) \quad \ldots\ldots\ldots\ldots\ldots\ldots(3)$$

where b_r is to be interpreted as the price-elasticity of demand at the base or reference point (see Ex. 3 below). The construction sought is to get from the m micro-relations (3), with the aid of weighted averages like (2), a single macro-relation of the form :

$$y = bp + k$$

The results (2) and (3) of 20.2 above are immediately applicable, once a transformation of variables is made :

$$y_r' = \left(\frac{w_{r0}}{\sum_r w_{r0}} \right) \frac{y_r}{y_{r0}} \quad \text{and} \quad p_r' = \left(\frac{w_{r0}}{\sum_r w_{r0}} \right) \frac{p_r}{p_{r0}}$$

The micro-relations (3) are then :

$$y_r' = b_r p_r' + k_r' \quad \text{where} \quad k_r' = \left(\frac{w_{r0}}{\sum_r w_{r0}} \right) k_r$$

and simple aggregation (2) is :

$$y = \sum_r y_r' \quad \text{and} \quad p = \sum_r p_r'$$

The result of approach (i) is that an exact macro-relation $y = bp + k$ is obtained when p is *not* of the simple (Laspeyres) form (2), but weighted with price-elasticities b_r in addition to the standard weights (w_{r0}). On approach (ii), the result of simple (Laspeyres) averaging is that a macro-relation $y = bp + k$ can only be obtained by statistical fitting over a period and that even so the parameters b and k have aggregation bias.

The general extension, suggested by this adaptation to practical index-number techniques, is that simple aggregation (e.g. $p = \sum_r p_r$) can be replaced by any *fixed-weight* aggregation :

$$p = \sum_r w_r p_r$$

where the weights w_r ($r = 1, 2, \ldots m$) are fixed and given in advance. It is only necessary to transform the variables :

$$p_r' = w_r p_r$$

The micro-relations $y_r = \dfrac{b_r}{w_r} p_r' + k_r$ $(r = 1, 2, \ldots m)$ are then to be aggregated by means of $p = \underset{r}{\Sigma} p_r'$. This is the process already considered under approach (ii).

EXERCISES 20.3

1. Write the micro-relations $y_r = b_r p_r + k_r$, where y_r is the logarithm of the demand for the rth commodity and p_r the logarithm of its price. The parameter b_r is then the price-elasticity of demand. Show that simple aggregation and a fitted macro-relation $y = bp + k$ apply as in the text, except that p is m times the logarithm of the geometric mean of prices, and similarly for y. Interpret b.

2. Show that, for aggregate demand, the macro-relation $y = a\mu + bp + k$ can be derived from the micro-relations $y_r = a_r\mu + b_r p_r + k_r$, where μ is the consumer's income. Interpret $a = ma$ in terms of marginal propensities to consume.

3. The micro-relations are written in form (3) above. Deduce that the price-elasticity of demand varies with price, with value b_r at the base point (price p_{r0}, quantity y_{r0}).

4. In producing a given output, a firm uses m inputs (factors of production). The demand for the rth input is $y_r = b_r p_r + k_r$ when the input price is p_r $(r = 1, 2, \ldots m)$. Show that a macro-relation $y = bp + k$ can be derived, where y is the firm's total input and where p is an average input price.

20.4. Contradictions between Micro- and Macro-Relations

The consequences of the use of simple aggregation are here pursued in terms of the example of aggregation over individuals (20.2 above). Results for aggregation over commodities are similar. The n micro-relations, $y_s = a_s\mu_s + k_s$ $(s = 1, 2, \ldots n)$, are aggregated $(y = \underset{s}{\Sigma} y_s,\ \mu = \underset{s}{\Sigma} \mu_s)$ into a single macro-relation of form $y = a\mu + k + u$, fitted statistically for a period of time. First, μ_s is related to μ over time by the regression equation :

$$\mu_s = A_s\mu + K_s + u_s \quad (\underset{s}{\Sigma} A_s = 1,\ \underset{s}{\Sigma} K_s = 0) \ \ldots\ldots\ldots\ldots\ldots\ldots(1)$$

Then the macro-parameters are determined :

$$\left.\begin{array}{l} a = \underset{s}{\Sigma}\, a_s A_s = \bar{a} + n\ \text{Cov}\ (a_s A_s) \\[2mm] k = \underset{s}{\Sigma} k\ + \underset{s}{\Sigma}\, a_s K_s = \underset{s}{\Sigma} k_s + n\ \text{Cov}\ (a_s K_s) \end{array}\right\} \ \ldots\ldots\ldots\ldots\ldots\ldots(2)$$

These involve, not only the micro-parameters a_s and k_s, but also the coefficients A_s and K_s which arise in fitting regression equations to the course of the variables over a particular period of time.

The difficulties in using such a macro-relation are two-fold. First, it is not true that one macro-parameter depends only on the *corresponding* micro-parameters. From (2), k is seen to depend on the corresponding

k_s, but also on the non-corresponding a_s from the micro-relations. It is an accident of the present simple case that a depends only on a_s; this is not carried over into the more complicated cases considered later. Secondly, there is the influence of the course of the variables over time, through the regression coefficients A_s and K_s of (1), on the macro-parameters. If the time period is changed, or if the variables happen to move differently, then the macro-parameters generally assume different values. This is summarised in the aggregation bias terms of (2).

These difficulties are to be expected to give rise to contradictions in the use of the micro- and macro-relations in prediction. This is the point to be pursued. Let μ_s increase by $\Delta\mu_s$ ($s=1, 2, \ldots n$), giving rise to an aggregate increase of $\Delta\mu = \Sigma\,\Delta\mu_s$ in μ. There are two ways of tracing the effect on aggregate demand $y = \Sigma\,y_s$. One is through the micro-relations:

$$\Delta_1 y = \Sigma\,\Delta y_s = \Sigma\,a_s\,\Delta\mu_s \quad\ldots\ldots\ldots\ldots\ldots\ldots\ldots(3)$$

The other is through the macro-relation (ignoring the residual):

$$\Delta_2 y = a\,\Delta\mu = a\,\Sigma\,\Delta\mu_s \quad\ldots\ldots\ldots\ldots\ldots\ldots\ldots(4)$$

In general, (3) and (4) are not the same; there is contradiction.

This is partly due to the fact that a, and hence $\Delta_2 y$, depends on movements in the time period considered—whereas $\Delta_1 y$ is quite independent of such movements. Even if all a_s are fixed (and so $\Delta_1 y$), differing movements of incomes over time can change a and hence the prediction $\Delta_2 y$ from the macro-relation. Some exploration of this situation is required. Take a particular but important case, that in which each μ_s varies in proportion to μ, either exactly or as an approximation. As aggregate income rises and falls, so does each individual income and in proportion (though the proportion can vary from one individual to another). Hence, in the regression equation (1), $K_s = 0$ and $A_s \neq 0$ fixes the proportion for the sth individual. *Averaging over the time period considered*, the proportion for the sth individual is given by (1):

$$A_s = \frac{\bar{\mu}_s}{\bar{\mu}} \quad \text{(since mean } u_s = 0\text{)}$$

The proportion by which individual income changes (in relation to aggregate income) is fixed by the individual's *mean income* $\bar{\mu}_s$ in the time period. So, from (2):

$$a = \frac{1}{\bar{\mu}} \Sigma_s\,a_s\,\bar{\mu}_s \quad\ldots\ldots\ldots\ldots\ldots\ldots\ldots(5)$$

The effect of the time period on a is only through mean incomes and the result seems sensible enough. To the extent that the grading of individuals from rich to poor is permanent, the time period chosen has little influence on the aggregate marginal propensity to consume a. The estimate of a, by aggregation from the individual marginal propensities, gives the rich greater weight than the poor.

Further, suppose that the increases taken in individual incomes are proportional to the level of the individual's income, as seems appropriate enough. Hence:

$$\frac{\Delta \mu_s}{\bar{\mu}_s} = \frac{\Delta \mu}{\bar{\mu}} \quad (s = 1, 2, \dots n)$$

and, by (3), (4) and (5):

$$\Delta_1 y = \frac{\Delta \mu}{\bar{\mu}} \sum_s a_s \bar{\mu}_s = a \Delta \mu = \Delta_2 y$$

There is no contradiction. The case considered appears to avoid, in large measure, the difficulties of the use of aggregation in prediction. The question, then, is transferred to the following: do individual incomes in fact tend to move over time in proportion to aggregate income? This seems likely, at least approximately in settled times. A " well-behaved " marginal propensity to consume in the aggregate is obtained by (5); the marginal propensities of individuals are weighted with their mean incomes.

There is evidence, quoted by Theil (1954), pp. 24–25, that the distribution of incomes is wider (the rich being relatively richer) in booms than in depressions. If this is so, individual incomes do *not* move in proportion to aggregate income; incomes of the rich increase more, and those of the poor less, during boom. The assumption $K_s = 0$ is not appropriate. In fact, the expression:

$$\frac{\mu_s}{\mu} = A_s + \frac{K_s}{\mu}$$

must increase with μ if the sth individual is rich, and decrease if he is poor. Hence $K_s < 0$ for the rich and $K_s > 0$ for the poor individual. Average the relation $\mu_s = A_s \mu + K_s + u_s$ over the time period for a rich individual ($K_s < 0$) and it follows that $\bar{\mu}_s < A_s \bar{\mu}$, i.e. that the weight of a_s in a given by (2) above is:

$$A_s > \frac{\bar{\mu}_s}{\bar{\mu}}$$

The macro-propensity to consume has a doubly-heavy contribution from marginal propensities of rich individuals—first because their average incomes are high and second because their incomes vary more over time.

On the other hand, some individuals (e.g. rentiers) may have unchanged incomes, even when other incomes are rising or falling. For such individuals it is not K_s but A_s which is zero. Their marginal propensities to consume have no influence whatever on the marginal propensity in the aggregate. Further, if real (rather than money) incomes are considered, the values of A_s for rentiers can be negative. The " weights " in the aggregate marginal propensity of (2) have the unconventional property that they can be negative. To the extent that negative " weights " occur, the aggregate marginal propensity can not only differ from the mean of individual propensities—it can actually be larger or smaller than any of them.

Turn now to another aspect of contradiction between $\Delta_1 y$ and $\Delta_2 y$ given by (3) and (4). The distribution of $\Delta\mu_s$ over individuals can be of any kind whatever, provided only that $\sum_s \Delta\mu_s = \Delta\mu$. Consequently $\Delta_1 y$ can vary in all kinds of ways, even when $\Delta\mu$ and $\Delta_2 y$ are fixed. It can only be under very special conditions that there is no contradiction irrespective of the distribution of a given increase in total income. It might be thought that $\mathrm{Cov}\,(a_s A_s) = \mathrm{Cov}\,(a_s K_s) = 0$ would turn the trick, for then a and k take their " best " values $\bar{a}$ and $\sum_s k_s$ respectively. This is not so, however, since an additional condition (that the income increase is equally distributed over individuals) is still required to avoid contradiction ; see Ex. 2 and 3 below.

In fact, when aggregation is of the simple kind, the condition for avoidance of all contradiction is very stringent indeed. There is no contradiction between macro-relation and micro-relations, whatever the distribution of an income increase, if and only if :

$$a_s = \bar{a} \quad \text{all } s = 1, 2, \dots n$$

i.e. all individuals have the same marginal propensity to consume. The proof of this result is as follows. First, if $a_s = \bar{a}$ for all s, then $\mathrm{Cov}\,(a_s A_s) = 0$ and the macro-parameter a is also equal to $\bar{a}$ by (2). Hence $\Delta_1 y$ and $\Delta_2 y$ are both equal to $\bar{a}\,\Delta\mu$; there is no contradiction. Second, if there is no contradiction, then $\sum_s a_s \Delta\mu_s = a \sum_s \Delta\mu_s$ however $\Delta\mu_s$ are distributed. Take $\Delta\mu_1 = -\Delta\mu_2 \neq 0$ and $\Delta\mu_s = 0$ $(s > 2)$. In this case the condition is

$$(a_1 - a_2)\,\Delta\mu_1 = 0, \quad \text{i.e.} \quad a_1 = a_2.$$

Similarly, all the other a_s are equal, i.e. $a_s = \bar{a}$ all s. This completes the proof.

The result does not seem very helpful : contradiction is avoided in a macro-model with simple aggregates if and only if everyone has the same marginal propensity to consume. But the important consequence of the result is still to be derived. Suppose that aggregation of incomes need not be of the simple (unweighted) kind, but that it can proceed by taking suitable weights fixed in advance. Contradiction in the macro-model can then always be avoided by appropriate selection of weights. Write $\mu = \sum_s w_s \mu_s$ for fixed weights w_s. As at the end of 20.3 above, transform the income variables :

$$\mu_s' = w_s \mu_s \quad (s = 1, 2, \ldots n)$$

so that the micro-relations :

$$y_s = \frac{a_s}{w_s} \mu_s' + k_s$$

aggregate by simple aggregation into $y = a\mu + k$ with $\mu = \sum \mu_s' = \sum w_s \mu_s$. There is no contradiction if and only if :

$$\frac{a_s}{w_s} = \text{constant} \quad (\text{all } s = 1, 2, \ldots n)$$

The weights w_s must be proportional to a_s. They can be written :

$$w_s = \frac{a_s}{\bar{a}} \qquad \left(\bar{a} = \frac{1}{n} \sum_s a_s \right)$$

so that the macro-parameter $a = \frac{1}{n} \sum_s \frac{a_s}{w_s} = \bar{a}$. Hence, the fixed-weight aggregation to adopt in avoiding contradiction is :

$$\mu = \frac{1}{\bar{a}} \sum_s a_s \mu_s \quad \ldots\ldots\ldots\ldots\ldots\ldots\ldots\ldots\ldots\ldots(6)$$

and the macro-relation is $y = \bar{a}\mu + \sum_s k_s$, as required.

The aggregation (6) is what Theil (1954) describes as *perfect aggregation*. It is the only weighting which avoids all contradiction in prediction between the (statistical) macro-relation and the individual micro-relations. The macro-relation also has the desired properties, e.g. the aggregate marginal propensity to consume is the mean of individual marginal propensities.

In the end, therefore, we come back to what was obtained by approach (i). It has now been established that the particular aggregation (6) gives an exact macro-relation ; also it cannot be avoided if there is to be no contradiction in the macro-model. Though not a " natural " aggregation, it is the *only* one which gives a macro-model free of contradiction in all circumstances.

In the simple case where individual demands for a commodity are aggregated into a single relation between total demand and aggregate income, the results can be expressed and interpreted :

(i) *an exact total demand relation is obtained by aggregating incomes with weights proportional to individua marginal propensities to consume ;*

(ii) *with simple aggregation, the total demand relation is determined statistically and its parameters generally depend on the movement of incomes over the time period considered ;*

(iii) *with simple aggregation, again, the only situation in which there is never contradiction in prediction between individual and total demand relations is when all individual marginal propensities to consume are equal ;*

(iv) *the only system of fixed weighting in aggregate income which leads to no contradiction in prediction is that where weights are proportional to individual marginal propensities to consume, as in* (i).

The perfect aggregation of incomes, to avoid all contradictions, involves weighting with marginal propensities to consume, a weighting system which varies from one commodity to another. The emphasis here is that contradiction in prediction *never* occurs. There are particular circumstances, even with simple aggregation, when the macro-relation gives the same prediction (at least approximately) as the individual micro-relations.

EXERCISES 20.4

1. The demand for a factor of production by an industry of n firms of various outputs is obtained as in 20.2, Ex. 3, above. Show that the model is substantially free from contradiction if each firm's output tends to vary over time in proportion to the industry's output. Is this a likely situation?

2. In the example of the text, take Cov $(a_s A_s) = 0$ so that $a = \bar{a}$. Show that $\Delta_1 y = \Delta_2 y$ only if $\sum_s a_s \Delta \mu_s = \frac{1}{n} \sum_s a_s \sum_s \Delta \mu_s$, i.e. only if $\Delta \mu_s$ are all equal.

3. Establish the converse of the previous exercise, i.e. take $\Delta \mu_s = \frac{1}{n} \Delta \mu$ (all s) and show that $\Delta_1 y = \Delta_2 y$ if Cov $(a_s A_s) = 0$.

4. Show that the condition $a_s = \bar{a}$ (all s) is more stringent than Cov $(a_s A_s) = 0$ by establishing that Cov $(a_s A_s) = 0$ when $a_s = \bar{a}$ but not conversely.

5. In perfect aggregation of incomes, show that some individual incomes can appear *negatively* in aggregate income, e.g. when a commodity is inferior for some and superior for other consumers.

20.5. Extension of the Simple Examples

The simplicity of the examples of 20.2 and 20.3 above is due to the facts that, *first*, only one independent variable (income or price) appears in each micro-relation and, *second*, no independent variable appears in more than one micro-relation. These limitations are removed, the first in the present section and the second in the next two sections. Each of the micro-relations, and the single macro-relation obtained from them, now include several independent variables; various cross-effects, hitherto ruled out, become important.

Suppose that individual consumers are in fact families of varying size and that, as far as the demand for a given commodity is concerned, family size can be represented by a single measure (e.g. by some equivalence scale). Write :

$$y_s = a_s\mu_s + b_s v_s + k_s \quad (s = 1, 2, \dots n) \quad \dots\dots\dots\dots\dots(1)$$

as the demand of the sth consumer when his income is μ_s and his family of size v_s. A macro-relation $y = a\mu + bv + k$ is sought, μ being some aggregate income and v some measure of total population.

Approach (*i*).   Assume that the summation of equations (1) :

$$y = \sum_s y_s = \sum_s a_s\mu_s + \sum_s b_s v_s + \sum_s k_s$$

leads to an exact macro-relation, which implies that μ and v are both weighted aggregates of the form already considered.   In fact :

$$\left.\begin{array}{c} y = a\mu + bv + k \\[6pt] \text{where} \quad a = \bar{a} = \dfrac{1}{n}\sum_s a_s ; \quad b = \bar{b} = \dfrac{1}{n}\sum_s b_s ; \quad k = \sum_s k_s \\[6pt] \text{provided that} \quad \mu = \dfrac{1}{\bar{a}}\sum_s a_s\mu_s \quad \text{and} \quad v = \dfrac{1}{\bar{b}}\sum_s b_s v_s \end{array}\right\} \quad \dots\dots\dots(2)$$

is the exact macro-relation to be obtained from the micro-relations (1).

Approach (*ii*).   With simple aggregation : $y = \sum_s y_s$, $\mu = \sum_s \mu_s$ and $v = \sum_r v_s$, a statistical macro-relation $y = a\mu + bv + k + u$ is to be fitted over a time period in which the courses of y_s, μ_s and v_s, and hence of y, μ and v, are given.   Fit the regression equations :

$$\left.\begin{array}{l} \mu_s = A_{as}\mu + B_{as}v + K_{as} + u_s \\ v_s = A_{bs}\mu + B_{bs}v + K_{bs} + v_s \end{array}\right\} \quad \dots\dots\dots\dots\dots\dots(3)$$

where $\sum_s A_{as} = \sum_s B_{bs} = 1$ and $\sum_s A_{bs} = \sum_s B_{as} = \sum_s K_{as} = \sum_s K_{bs} = 0$.

The six regression coefficients are dependent on the movements of the variables over time. Substitute (3) into (1), sum over all s, and get the statistical macro-relation for simple aggregation :

$$y = a\mu + b\nu + k + u$$

where

$$\left. \begin{aligned} a &= \sum_s a_s A_{as} + \sum_s b_s A_{bs} = \bar{a} + n \text{ Cov } (a_s A_{as}) + n \text{ Cov } (b_s A_{bs}) \\ b &= \sum_s a_s B_{as} + \sum_s b_s B_{bs} = \bar{b} + n \text{ Cov } (a_s B_{as}) + n \text{ Cov } (b_s B_{bs}) \\ k &= \sum_s k_s + \sum_s a_s K_{as} + \sum_s b_s K_{bs} = \sum_s k_s + n \text{ Cov } (a_s K_{as}) + n \text{ Cov } (b_s K_{bs}) \end{aligned} \right\} \quad ....(4)$$

Here u is a disturbance with zero mean and not correlated with μ and ν over time. The covariance terms on the right-hand sides of (4) represent the *aggregation bias* in the macro-parameters. They are derived exactly as before (see Ex. 1 below).

All this is familiar. The aggregation of approach (i) is simple but not the " natural " one. The statistical macro-parameters of approach (ii) depend on the micro-parameters and also on " history " in the particular time period selected. On this approach, contradictions generally arise in prediction. There are situations when contradiction is negligible, e.g. when individual incomes tend to move in proportion to aggregate income and individual family sizes with total population. But the only way of avoiding contradiction in all cases is to take μ and ν as weighted aggregates, with weights as given by (2), i.e. *perfect aggregation* for both variables.

The new feature is the cross-effects in the fitted macro-parameters of (4). The marginal propensity to consume a depends, not only on individual marginal propensities (a_s), but also on the influence of family size (b_s) in individual demands. The cross-effect is shown by the term

$$\sum_s b_s A_{bs} = n \text{ Cov } (b_s A_{bs})$$

in (4). The weights of b_s here have zero sum ($\sum_s A_{bs} = 0$), and it might be thought that the cross-effect is always small. This is by no means the case. If it happens that positive values of the regression coefficient A_{bs} arise for families with a large size effect (b_s), and negative A_{bs} with small b_s, then the cross-effect can be large.

The result is easily generalised to a set of micro-relations :

$$y_s = a_s x_{1s} + b_s x_{2s} + c_s x_{3s} + \ldots + k_s \quad (s = 1, 2, \ldots n)$$

aggregating into :

$$y = a x_1 + b x_2 + c x_3 + \ldots + k$$

The aggregation is done simply ; both for the y's and for each of the x's it is only necessary to sum down the list of n equations. The results of the aggregation process are exactly as in (2), (3) and (4) above, with more terms in each case. In particular, in (4), there is a greater range of terms representing cross-effects of one parameter on another. This is the case considered by Theil (1954) under his Theorem 1. It is illustrated in the following exercises.

EXERCISES 20.5

1. Get the aggregation bias terms in (4) by showing that :

$$\text{Cov}\,(a_s A_{as}) = \frac{1}{n} \underset{s}{\Sigma}\, a_s A_{as} - \frac{1}{n}\,\bar{a} \quad \text{and} \quad \text{Cov}\,(b_s A_{bs}) = \frac{1}{n} \underset{s}{\Sigma}\, b_s A_{bs}$$

2. If $y_s = a_s \mu_s + b_s \lambda_s + c_s \nu_s + k_s$ is the demand of a family of λ_s adults, ν_s children and income μ_s, show how to derive a total demand relation $y = a\mu + b\lambda + c\nu + k$. Interpret.

3. Some commodities appear in a group ($r = 1, 2, \dots n$) and others are left outside. Examine whether it is appropriate to aggregate the demands of an individual $y_r = a_r p_r + b_r q_r + k_r$ ($r = 1, 2, \dots n$) into $y = ap + bq + k$, where p is a price index for the commodity group (from p_r, $r = 1, 2, \dots n$) and where q is a price index of another set of commodities (from q_r, $r = 1, 2, \dots n$).

4. Show how the result of 20.2, Ex. 3, on the demand of an industry for labour, can be extended to the case where the industry (and its constituent firms) produces more than one product.

5. Examine the simplifications in result (4) when $\text{Cov}\,(b_s A_{bs}) = \text{Cov}\,(a_s B_{as}) = 0$ and analyse on the lines of 20.4 above. In particular, consider the case where the regression equations (3) are simply : $\mu_s = A_{as}\mu + u_s$ and $\nu_s = B_{bs}\nu + v_s$.

20.6. Summation over Individuals and over Commodities

The second limitation (20.5 above) is now removed. This is the assumption that no independent variable appears in more than one microrelation. How severe this limitation is can be seen by noting that microtheory generally gives an individual's demand for a commodity as dependent on the prices of many of the commodities ; or a firm's demand for a factor as dependent on the prices of many factors. In short, in the general case, the price of one commodity (factor) appears in many commodity (factor) demand relations.

The following examples show how important it is, in problems of aggregation, to lay out the relations and variables in such a way that the " boiling down " process is evident, i.e. the micro-relations into the macro-relations, and particularly what micro-variables are aggregated or averaged into the various macro-variables. The first two examples to be set out mark an intermediate case. The third example then introduces the more useful aggregation—a double summation, both over individuals and over commodities. This example leads to the general case treated in the following section.

Ex. (a). Individual demand for a group of commodities

The case considered in 20.3 was simplified by taking each commodity demand as dependent only on the price of the commodity concerned ; all cross-effects of inter-action, so important in the micro-theory of value, were ruled out. These cross-effects can now be introduced. Individual demand for the rth commodity is :

$$y_r = \begin{array}{l} b_{r1}p_1 + k_r \\ + b_{r2}p_2 \\ + \dots \\ + b_{rm}p_m \end{array} \qquad (r=1, 2, \dots m) \quad\dots\dots\dots\dots\dots\dots(1)$$

There are m such micro-relations and each contains the whole set of m commodity prices (though some b's can be zero where commodities are not related). The price terms in (1) are written in a column, to show how the aggregation proceeds The single macro-relation, individual demand for the commodity group, is :

$$y = bp + k$$

where $y = \sum_r y_r$ and where p is some average of $p_1, p_2, \dots p_m$. There are, in fact,

two rather different sums involved ; $y = \sum_{r=1}^{m} y_r$ covers the m micro-equations (1)

while $p = \sum_{\rho=1}^{m} p_\rho$ (or some weighted version) applies to each of the micro-relations.

For this reason, the macro-parameter b (which gives the price-elasticity) involves a double summation since it must come from the micro-parameters $b_{r\rho}$ for r and $\rho = 1, 2, \dots m$. It can be regarded as the reduction to some single value of the square matrix of order $m \times m$:

$$\mathbf{b} = [b_{r\rho}] = \begin{bmatrix} b_{11} & b_{21} & \dots & b_{m1} \\ b_{12} & b_{22} & \dots & b_{m2} \\ \multicolumn{4}{c}{\dots\dots\dots\dots\dots\dots} \\ b_{1m} & b_{2m} & \dots & b_{mm} \end{bmatrix}$$

It averages out, not only the price-effects for m different commodities, but also all the cross-effects between commodity prices in each individual demand relation. The matrix $\mathbf{b}$ is a very convenient way of arranging the micro-parameters. Reading down a column of $\mathbf{b}$ gives the parameters for one commodity demand ; reading across $\mathbf{b}$ picks out corresponding parameters from one demand relation to another.

Ex. (b). Firm's demand for a group of inputs

A given firm makes use of m inputs (factors) in producing k products. The firm's demand y_r for one input depends on *all* the outputs x_q $(q=1, 2, \dots k)$ and on *all* the input prices p_r $(r=1, 2, \dots m)$:

$$y_r = \begin{array}{l} a_{r1}x_1 + b_{r1}p_1 + k_r \\ + a_{r2}x_2 + b_{r2}p_2 \\ + \dots \quad + \dots \\ + a_{rk}x_k + \dots \\ \qquad\quad + b_{rm}p_m \end{array} \qquad (r=1, 2, \dots m) \quad\dots\dots\dots\dots\dots(2)$$

These m micro-relations are to be aggregated into the macro-relation :

$$y = ax + bp + k$$

where y is the firm's total input, x is some quantity index for output and p is some price index of inputs. The summations involved are : $y = \sum_{r=1}^{m} y_r$ over m micro-

relations, $x = \sum_{q=1}^{k} x_q$ (or some weighted form) over k output variables in each micro-relation, and $p = \overset{m}{\underset{\rho=1}{\Sigma}} p_\rho$ (or some weighted form) over m price variables in each micro-relation. The macro-parameter a for the effect of output on demand for inputs is a single value which corresponds to (and which might be expected to be derived from) the rectangular matrix of micro-parameters of order $k \times m$:

$$\mathbf{a} = [a_{rq}] = \begin{bmatrix} a_{11} & a_{21} & \cdots & a_{m1} \\ a_{12} & a_{22} & \cdots & a_{m2} \\ \cdots\cdots\cdots\cdots\cdots \\ a_{1k} & a_{2k} & \cdots & a_{mk} \end{bmatrix}$$

The macro-parameter b corresponds to a square $(m \times m)$ matrix $\mathbf{b}$ of exactly the same form as in Ex. (a). Each micro-relation (2) contributes one column to $\mathbf{a}$ and one column to $\mathbf{b}$.

Ex. (c). Market demand for a group of commodities

As an extension of Ex. (a), introduce the individual's income into each demand relation (the same income for each commodity) and then aggregate over the n individuals ($s = 1, 2, \ldots n$) on a market, as well as over the m commodities ($r = 1, 2, \ldots m$) on the market. The micro-relations are $m \times n$ demands (m commodities, n individuals) :

$$\begin{aligned} y_{rs} = a_{rs}\mu_s &+ {}_{rs}b_1p_1 + k_{rs} \quad (r = 1, 2, \ldots m) \dots\dots\dots\dots\dots\dots(3) \\ &+ {}_{rs}b_2p_2 \qquad\qquad (s = 1, 2, \ldots n) \\ &+ \cdots \\ &+ {}_{rs}b_mp_m \end{aligned}$$

The single macro-relation, for market demand, is :

$$y = a\mu + bp + k$$

For the aggregate demand the summation is now a double one, i.e. $y = \underset{r\ s}{\Sigma\ \Sigma}\, y_{rs}$. Each of the macro-variables, μ and p, is still a single summation : $\mu = \underset{s}{\Sigma}\, \mu_s$ over n individuals and $p = \underset{\rho}{\Sigma}\, p_\rho$ over m commodities. To show what micro-parameters correspond to the macro-parameters, replace the double summation for r and s by a single summation, with a subscript i running from $1, 2, \ldots$ up to $m \times n$ (i.e. through both individuals and commodities). The $m \times n$ micro-relations (3) are described by the subscript i. Then the parameter a corresponds to a row vector of micro-parameters, $m \times n$ in number : $\mathbf{a} = [a_i]$. The elements of $\mathbf{a}$ are the marginal propensities to consume each of m commodities by each of n individuals. The parameter b corresponds to a rectangular matrix of micro-parameters, of order m by $m \times n$: $\mathbf{b} = [{}_ib_\rho]$ for $i = 1, 2, \ldots m \times n$ and $\rho = 1, 2, \ldots m$. Each micro-relation (3) contributes one column of m elements to $\mathbf{b}$.

The consumption function of Keynesian-type, as used in simple macro-dynamic models, can be written in the present notation :

$$y = a\mu + \gamma$$

where y is total consumption and μ is some aggregate income. No time-lags are assumed and the usual linear form taken. It can be regarded as arising from the rather more general form:

$$y = a\mu + bp + k \dots\dots\dots\dots\dots\dots\dots\dots\dots\dots(4)$$

where p is some price index of consumers' goods, by taking p as given.

If (4) is to be based on the appropriate micro-theory of the decisions of individual consumers, then Ex. (*c*) above is relevant and (4) is the macro-relation from the $m \times n$ micro-relations (3).

This seems satisfactory enough as the basis of a consumption function —until the results so far obtained in the present chapter (and extended in 20.7 below) are brought into the picture. With simple aggregation ($\mu = \sum_s \mu_s$ and $p = \sum_p p_p$, or the appropriate Laspeyres index), (4) is a statistical relation and the parameters (a, b, k) involve both cross-effects and the influence of the courses of individual incomes and prices over time. There is also, in general, contradiction between the uses of (3) and (4) in prediction of y. The only case of simple aggregation free from all contradiction, with (4) taking the " best " form (*a* being the mean marginal propensity to consume), arises when all corresponding micro-parameters are equal. This implies that the basis of (4) is that everyone has the same marginal propensity to consume. Alternatively, special conditions for the time period need to be assumed, e.g. that everyone's income moves over time in proportion to national income. On the other hand, if simple aggregation is given up and some fixed-weight summation for μ and p allowed, then the search for perfect aggregation leads to weighting with micro-parameters, e.g. μ is weighted with individual marginal propensities to consume.

Clearly it is not permissible just to write (4) as the result of simple aggregation. The alternatives open are to ignore micro-theory, taking the consumption function (4) as the basic construction; or, on the other hand, to stick to micro-theory and to avoid a macro-relation like (4) except as a rough approximation or as appropriate to particular circumstances in particular time periods. Both cut across the grain. The economist wants simple macro-relations; and he wants them well-founded on micro-theory.

EXERCISES 20.6

1. Show that the construction of Ex. (*a*) can apply to the demand of a single firm for a group of inputs (factors). Compare and contrast with 20.3, Ex. 4, and with Ex. (*b*) above.

2. Show that Ex. (*b*) can be used for demand for a group of commodities by an individual having k different sources of income.

3. In Ex. (*b*), take y_r ($r = 1, 2, \ldots m$) as corresponding to a group of inputs (not all inputs) and let y_r depend on the prices p_s' ($s = 1, 2, \ldots n$) of other inputs, in addition to the variables already included. Show how to aggregate to
$$y = ax + bp + cp' + k$$
and interpret this macro-relation.

4. Set out the problem of aggregating industry demand for a group of m inputs ($r = 1, 2, \ldots m$), the industry being composed of n firms ($s = 1, 2, \ldots n$). Assume first that each firm produces one and the same product and show that the problem is similar to Ex. (c) above. Extend to the case of k products, the macro-relation being $y = a_1x_1 + a_2x_2 + \ldots + a_kx_k + bp + \text{constant}$. Can this be further reduced to $y = ax + bp + \text{constant}$?

20.7. General Case : One Macro-Relation

Micro-relations are given for each of a group of individuals, or commodities, or both. A single macro-relation is to be got by aggregation. All relations are linear ; no time-lags or aggregations over time are assumed. Let the subscript i represent a single micro-relation, so that Σ is the required aggregation over micro-relations. Generally, $\underset{i}{\Sigma}$ stands for a double-summation, e.g. over m commodities and n individuals. The problem depends on how the micro-variables are reduced to the macro-variables in the macro-relation, and turns on the derivation of the corresponding macro-parameters. Ex. (c) of 20.6 illustrates and suggests a notation.

Write the micro-relations, for various values of i :

$$
\begin{aligned}
y_i = \ & {}_ia_{11}x_{11} + {}_ia_{21}x_{21} + \ldots + {}_ia_{m1}x_{m1} + k_i \\
& + {}_ia_{12}x_{12} + {}_ia_{22}x_{22} + \ldots + {}_ia_{m2}x_{m2} \\
& + \ldots \\
& + {}_ia_{1n}x_{1n} + {}_ia_{2n}x_{2n} + \ldots + {}_ia_{mn}x_{mn}
\end{aligned}
$$

i.e. $$ y_i = \sum_{r=1}^{m} \sum_{s=1}^{n} {}_ia_{rs}x_{rs} + k_i \quad\ldots\ldots\ldots\ldots\ldots\ldots\ldots\ldots\ldots\ldots\ldots\ldots(1) $$

There are $m \times n$ micro-variables (x_{rs}) and the whole set appears in general in each micro-relation. Apart from a constant term (k_i), each micro-relation has a corresponding set of $m \times n$ micro-parameters (${}_ia_{rs}$). When a particular micro-variable does not appear in a micro-relation, the corresponding micro-parameter is set equal to zero ; but the general case requires everything to be retained.

The object of aggregation is to derive a single macro-relation :

$$ y = a_1x_1 + a_2x_2 + \ldots + a_mx_m + k = \sum_{r=1}^{m} a_rx_r + k \quad\ldots\ldots\ldots\ldots(2) $$

The summations proceed as follows. First, $y = \underset{i}{\Sigma} y_i$ over all micro-relations, generally a double summation. Then for each r ($r = 1, 2, \ldots m$), the macro-variables are : $x_r = \sum_{s=1}^{n} x_{rs}$; this is a single summation, running down a column in each micro-relation (1).

The critical point is to see how the m macro-parameters a_r in (2) are derived from the complex of micro-parameters $_ia_{rs}$ in (1). It is found, however, that a considerable simplification can be made in this complex of micro-parameters. In the results to be derived, $_ia_{rs}$ never appears by itself, but only in the sum $\Sigma \; _ia_{rs}$ obtained by picking out the micro-parameter in the same " cell " of each micro-relation and summing over all micro-relations. Hence define *derived micro-parameters*, one for each micro-variable x_{rs} :

$$a_{rs} = \Sigma \; _ia_{rs} \quad (r = 1, 2, \ldots m \; ; \; s = 1, 2, \ldots n)$$

The macro-parameter a_r (the coefficient of x_r) has a simple set of *corresponding* derived micro-parameters making up a column vector :

$$\mathbf{a}_r = \{a_{rs}\} = \begin{bmatrix} a_{r1} \\ a_{r2} \\ \ldots \\ a_{rn} \end{bmatrix}$$

Each micro-relation (1) contributes one column to an extended n-rowed matrix of micro-parameters :

$$[_ia_{rs}] = \begin{bmatrix} _1a_{r1} & _2a_{r1} & \cdots \\ _1a_{r2} & _2a_{r2} & \cdots \\ \cdots\cdots\cdots\cdots \\ _1a_{rn} & _2a_{rn} & \cdots \end{bmatrix}$$

Summing this matrix across rows gives $\mathbf{a}_r$. A desired property of the aggregation is that the macro-parameter a_r should depend only on the corresponding micro-parameters summarised in $\mathbf{a}_r$. This is desired but, as will again be seen, it is not always realised.

In the derivation of (2) from (1) by *approach (i)*, sum (1) :

$$y = \Sigma y_i = \sum_{r=1}^{m} \sum_{s=1}^{n} a_{rs} x_{rs} + \sum_i k_i$$

which is the same as (2) provided that the aggregation is :

$$x_r = \frac{1}{\bar{a}_r} \Sigma_s a_{rs} x_{rs} \quad \text{where} \quad \bar{a}_r = \frac{1}{n} \Sigma_s a_{rs} \quad\ldots\ldots\ldots\ldots\ldots(3)$$

and the macro-parameters are then :

$$a_r = \bar{a}_r = \frac{1}{n} \Sigma_s a_{rs} \quad \text{and} \quad k = \Sigma k_i \quad\ldots\ldots\ldots\ldots\ldots(4)$$

Both (3) and (4) are given for each r ($r = 1, 2, \ldots m$). The weighting of micro-variables, to give the macro-variable x_r in (3), is in proportion to the *corresponding* (derived) micro-parameters as in $\mathbf{a}_r$. This weighting, of course, varies from one parameter to another; there are as many different weighting systems as there are macro-parameters in the macro-relation (2). The macro-parameter a_r given by (4) is of the desired form; it comes from the *corresponding* (derived) micro-parameters $\mathbf{a}_r$ and indeed it is the simple mean of the n elements of $\mathbf{a}_r$.

In *approach* (ii), simple aggregation is specified, or any form of fixed-weight aggregation. Unless it happens that the particular aggregation (3) is selected in advance, the macro-relation (2) can only be obtained by statistical fitting over time. All the micro-variables are given time series and the result, in general, depends on their shape over time. The technique is the same as that already described. It is established formally by Theil (1954) in an even wider setting than the present. Fit the regression equations:

$$\left. \begin{array}{l} x_{rs} = {}_1A_{rs}x_1 + {}_2A_{rs}x_2 + \ldots + {}_mA_{rs}x_m + K_{rs} + u_{rs} \\ \qquad\qquad\qquad (r = 1, 2, \ldots m ; \;\; s = 1, 2, \ldots n) \\ \text{where} \quad \sum\limits_{s=1}^{n} {}_\rho A_{rs} = 1 \quad (\rho = r) \quad \text{and} \quad \sum\limits_{s=1}^{n} K_{rs} = 0 \\ \qquad\qquad = 0 \quad (\rho \neq r) \end{array} \right\} \quad \ldots\ldots(5)$$

The coefficients (A's and K's) in (5) all depend on the time series used. The macro-parameters of (2), fitted statistically, are:

$$\left. \begin{array}{l} a_r = \sum\limits_{\rho=1}^{m} \sum\limits_{s=1}^{n} a_{\rho s} \, {}_r A_{\rho s} \quad (r = 1, 2, \ldots m) \\ k = \sum\limits_{i} k_i + \sum\limits_{r=1}^{m} \sum\limits_{s=1}^{n} a_{rs} K_{rs} \end{array} \right\} \quad \ldots\ldots\ldots\ldots\ldots(6)$$

The result adds little to that obtained in the simpler cases (20.5 above) except in allowing for a greater variety of cross-effects. The values found for the macro-parameters in (6) can be checked against what is desired. They are found wanting in two respects. First, a_r is desired to come only from the *corresponding* micro-parameters of $\mathbf{a}_r$; whereas in fact it generally involves all the micro-parameters, corresponding and non-corresponding alike. Secondly, a_r depends on the particular time series used in estimation, as shown by the appearance in a_r of the regression coefficients (the A's) given by (5).

For the same reasons, prediction by the statistical macro-relation (2) generally gives contradictory results from that by the micro-relations (1).

There are special conditions, e.g. on the course of the variables over time, under which contradiction can be avoided. But all forms of contradiction are eliminated if and only if $a_{rs} = \bar{a}_r$ (all s) for each $r = 1, 2, \ldots m$. This is equivalent to weighting aggregates according to the system (3), i.e. to aggregation as found in approach (i) for an exact macro-relation of desired form. *Perfect aggregation* is that with the weighting system (3). It has the double property that it gives an exact and appropriate macro-relation ; and that it is the only fixed-weight aggregation which avoids all contradiction in the macro-model.

EXERCISES 20.7

1. Show that the macro-relations (1) can be adjusted so that the different micro-variables x_r are sums of different numbers (n_r) of micro-variables and that they are then :

$$y_i = \sum_{r=1}^{m} \sum_{s=1}^{n_r} {}_i a_{rs} x_{rs} + k_i$$

Show also that (1) of the text is still effectively the general case, with $n = \max n_r$ and with dummy variables (with zero coefficients) used to fill out the columns.

2. Exhibit Exs. (a) and (b) of 20.6 as particular cases of the present general case. What is subscript i in these cases?

3. A group of m bakers ($r = 1, 2, \ldots m$) supplies n consumers ($s = 1, 2, \ldots n$) with bread. The price charged by the rth baker is p_r ; the income of the sth consumer is μ_s. Show how micro-relations of demand for bread :

$$y_{rs} = a_{rs}\mu_s + \sum_{\rho=1}^{m} {}_{rs} b_\rho p_\rho + k_{rs}$$

can be aggregated to give total demand for bread : $y = a\mu + bp + k$, when $y = \Sigma \Sigma y_{rs}$, $\mu = \Sigma \mu_s$, $p = \Sigma p_\rho$. Compare 20.6, Ex. (c).

4. Show that Ex. (c) of 20.6, and the problem of the previous exercise, are particular cases of the general case above, by writing the micro-relations of Ex. (c) as :

$$\begin{aligned} y_i = \ & {}_i a_1 \mu_1 + {}_i b_1 p_1 + k_i \quad (i = 1, 2, \ldots m \times n) \\ & + {}_i a_2 \mu_2 + {}_i b_2 p_2 \\ & + \ldots \\ & + {}_i a_n \mu_n + {}_i b_m p_m \end{aligned}$$

Show that only one of the coefficients ${}_i a_s$ ($s = 1, 2, \ldots n$) is non-zero. Which is the coefficient and what is its meaning?

5. Arrange Ex. (c) of 20.6 as in the previous exercise, adopt simple aggregation and use (5) and (6) above to give the macro-parameters in $y = a\mu + bp + k$. Examine how the marginal propensity to consume in the aggregate depends on individual price-elasticities.

6. Follow up the previous exercise and distinguish commodities which are luxuries as opposed to necessities. If the rth commodity is a luxury, take $k_{rs} < 0$ and the constant in the regression for p_r also as negative (since p_r is likely to increase rapidly in boom). Deduce that luxuries are likely to have extra weight in the macro-parameter k and that the commodity group is likely to appear as a " luxury ".

M.E.

20.8. Welfare Economics

Problems of the aggregation of consumer's demand, over individuals or commodities or both, are to be carefully distinguished from the kind of problems arising in the economics of welfare. It is clear from the analysis above that aggregate demand is obtained *after* each consumer has made his decisions (e.g. to maximise utility). Though the distribution of consumer incomes is not without relevance, there is no question of comparing the utility levels of different consumers. In welfare economics, on the other hand, individual utilities are to be aggregated or compared in some way *before* an optimum position is looked for (e.g. maximum social welfare). A brief consideration of this second aggregation problem conveniently rounds off this text. It is brief partly because there is an extensive literature on the problem—a selection being given below—and partly because the mathematics are a relatively small part of the treatment of the problem.

Welfare economics also differs from the analysis of consumer demand in that there is no assumption made about the conditions of any market. For example, it is not assumed that there is pure competition among consumers, i.e. that market prices can be taken as parameters. On the contrary, one of the objects of welfare economics is to see if, and in what sense, pure competition can be regarded as a (social) optimal condition. It then goes on to consider optimal conditions, e.g. for income distribution, for taxation or for tariff policy, as in Hotelling (1938).

The simplest and most direct approach would seem to be an explicit assumption that individual utility is measurable (cardinal) and then to add the utilities of all individuals. In this addition, appropriate weighting can be adopted on the score that, though individuals may be all equal, some are more equal than others. Hence, a social welfare function $W = \sum_i w_i U_i$ can be written, the utility U_i of the ith individual being given the weight w_i. W is then a function of all inputs and outputs, of quantities of consumers' goods and of supplies of services. The (social) optimum is to be sought by maximising W subject to the given restraints of the problem.

There are two objections to this procedure. First, as seen in 19.5 above, individual utility is only to be taken as measurable (up to a linear transformation) in risk-taking situations. Secondly, and more important, even if cardinal utility is simply assumed, there is still no sense in aggregating utilities. As Kennedy (1954) and others have stressed, utility is indivisible—two utilities do not add to produce another utility. See Ex. 1 and 2 below.

Granted the validity of such objections, the essential question is how to avoid adding utilities in an analysis of welfare economics. There are at least two possibilities. One is to fix the list of situations open in the economy, to assume that each member of the community can order them according to his preferences (e.g. by an ordinal utility function), and finally to adopt the democratic or committee voting system to reduce the various orders to a single community order. The situation highest on the community order is then optimal in the social sense.

The difficulty here is the well-known fact that, even if every member of a committee or community is " rational " or " consistent ", the same is not necessarily true of majority decisions. And this is not just a matter of a remote possibility. Consider three individuals (1, 2, 3) faced with three situations (A, B, C). Assume each individual places the situations in a consistent order, say :

Individual	Order of preference
1	A, B, C
2	B, C, A
3	C, A, B

Consistency here simply means that, if A is preferred to B and B to C, then A must be preferred to C. As a committee of three, the individuals fix the social order of preference by the majority rule, taking each pair of situations in turn :

	Individuals	
Situations compared	For	Against
A preferred to B	1, 3	2
B preferred to C	1, 2	3
C preferred to A	2, 3	1

Hence the social preferences are inconsistent ; the committee of three is " irrational " in preferring C to A, after expressing a preference for A over B, and B over C. This is, indeed, the kind of situation which does arise when, for example, an American State votes for a social measure (like " Ham and Eggs ") on referendum and elects a Governor opposed to the measure, or conversely.

There is evidently a conflict of interests here, similar to the conflict treated in the theory of games (Chapter 15 above). This suggests that a solution to the welfare economics problem can be sought by applying game theory, a point noted by Arrow (1951).

Another approach to welfare economics is that of Samuelson (1947), following Bergson (1938) and Lange (1942). The first step is to work on the simplest principle that more is always preferred to less. On the production side, this gives a transformation relation (production function) between inputs and outputs ; on the side of individual supply and demand, it sets each marginal rate of substitution or ratio of marginal utilities as equal to the corresponding transformation rate in the production function. The result is a set of equations which falls short of the number of variables, by $(k-1)$ where k is the number of individuals. See Ex. 5, 6 and 7 below.

The next step is to provide the needed $(k-1)$ equations by separate consideration of social welfare. Kaldor (1939) and Hicks (1939) would work solely on the principle that there is an improvement only if someone gains while no-one loses by a change—provided that compensation is allowed to be paid. Samuelson (1947), however, looks for a *social welfare function* of the vector of k individual utility functions :

$$W = W(U_1, U_2, \ldots U_k)$$

W is ordinal like individual utility functions $U_i (i = 1, 2, \ldots k)$; it sets a *consistent* social ordering of all possible situations. He describes W as characterising " some ethical belief—that of a benevolent despot, or a complete egotist, or all men of good will . . ." (p. 221). A number of assumptions, all frequently made, is required for W. For example, each U_i must depend only on the individual's own consumption of goods and supply of services ; " conspicuous " expenditures designed to " keep up with the Jones' " are ruled out.

The set of $(k-1)$ equations required is found by the condition that W is a maximum subject to the restraints set by the rest of the system (see Ex. 8 below). All that is needed, for an optimum in welfare economics, is that W should be a given function, though still ordinal (i.e. defined up to a monotonic increasing transformation). It is not *necessary* that the separate U_i should ever be judged equal, or comparable, still less that they should be added or aggregated into any such form as $W = \sum_i w_i U_i$. The welfare economist need not be utilitarian ; but the utilitarian is still allowed in the field.

EXERCISES 20.8

1. Cardinal utility is measurable to a linear transformation, i.e. $U = \alpha u + \beta$, where u is one measure, α and β arbitrary constants. Show that the influence of β can be eliminated by adding only increments of utility. What of units of utility as fixed by α? Compare the situation with that of measuring temperature.

2. Instead of adding utilities as in $\sum U_i$, consider the possibility of treating U_i as

a vector and then of " compounding " utilities, as with forces in mechanics. Does this provide a useful concept of social welfare W? (See Lange (1942).)

3. Show that the inconsistency in the committee voting procedure (example above) can be seen alternatively : a consistent community order can be got if the committee stops after comparing two pairs of the three situations (since the third " vote " may be inconsistent) ; but different pairs can produce different orders.

4. In the simple voting example, show that the inconsistency arises because *each* situation is placed first by one individual and last by another, i.e. the order of preferences forms a " Latin Square ". Construct another such example.

5. Take k individuals ($i=1, 2, \ldots k$) and m commodities ($r=1, 2, \ldots m$) which may be outputs or inputs. Write $X_r = \underset{i}{\Sigma} x_{ir}$ for total output (input if negative) where x_{ir} is the amount for the ith individual. Show that technical production conditions (on the principle that more is preferred to less) give :

$$f(X_1, X_2, \ldots X_m) = 0$$

6. In the problem of the previous exercise, write individual utility (ordinal) as $U_i = U_i(x_{i1}, x_{i2}, \ldots x_{im})$ and show that, on the same principle of more rather than less :

$$\frac{\partial U_i}{\partial x_{ir}} : \frac{\partial U_i}{\partial x_{is}} = \frac{\partial f}{\partial X_r} : \frac{\partial f}{\partial X_s} \quad \text{for } i=1, 2, \ldots k \text{ and } r, s = 1, 2, \ldots m \ (r \neq s)$$

7. The number of variables x_{ir} in the previous exercises is km. Show that the number of independent equations is $k(m-1)$ from Ex. 6 and 1 from Ex. 5, i.e. $(k-1)$ short of km.

8. If the side conditions of the previous exercises reduce to $F(U_1, U_2, \ldots U_k) = 0$, show that $W = W(U_1, U_2, \ldots U_k) = $max. gives just $(k-1)$ independent equations : $\dfrac{\partial W}{\partial U_i} : \dfrac{\partial W}{\partial U_j} = \dfrac{\partial F}{\partial U_i} : \dfrac{\partial F}{\partial U_j} \ (i, j=1, 2, \ldots k, i \neq j)$. $\dfrac{\partial W}{\partial U_i}$ is called, by Lange (1942), the *marginal social significance* of the ith individual.

REFERENCES

Aggregation Theory

Klein (L. R.) (1946a) : " Macroeconomics and the Theory of Rational Behavior ", *Econometrica*, **14**, 93–108.

Klein (L. R.) (1946b) : " Remarks on the Theory of Aggregation ", *Econometrica*, **14**, 303–12.

May (K.) (1946) : " The Aggregation Problem for a One-Industry Model ", *Econometrica*, **14**, 285–98.

May (K.) (1947) : " Technological Change and Aggregation ", *Econometrica*, **51**, 51–63.

Nataf (A.) (1948) : " Sur la Possibilité de Construction de Certains Macro-modèles ", *Econometrica*, **16**, 232–44.

Roy (R.) (1952) : " Les Élasticités de la Demande relative aux Biens de Consommation et aux Groups de Biens ", *Econometrica*, **20**, 391–405.

Shou Shan Pu (1946) : " A Note on Macroeconomics ", *Econometrica*, **14**, 299–302.

Theil (H.) (1954) : *Linear Aggregation of Economic Relations* (North-Holland, Amsterdam, 1954).

Tinbergen (J.) (1939): *Statistical Testing of Business Cycle Theories* (Geneva, 1939).

Tinbergen (J.) (1951): *Econometrics* (Allen and Unwin, 1951), Chapter 2.

Wolff (P. de) (1941): " Income Elasticity of Demand, a Micro-Economic and a Macro-Economic Interpretation ", *Economic Journal*, **51**, 140–45.

Welfare Economics

Arrow (K. J.) (1951): *Social Choice and Individual Values* (Wiley, 1951).

Baumol (W. J.) (1952): *Welfare Economics and the Theory of the State* (Longmans, 1952).

Bergson (A.) (1938): " A Reformulation of Certain Aspects of Welfare Economics ", *Quarterly Journal of Economics*, **52**, 310–34.

Dorfman (R.), Samuelson (P. A.) and Solow (R. M.) (1958): *Linear Programming and Economic Analysis* (McGraw-Hill, 1958), Chapter 14.

Hicks (J. R.) (1939): " The Foundations of Welfare Economics ", *Economic Journal*, **49**, 696–712.

Hotelling (H.) (1938): " The General Welfare in Relation to Problems of Taxation and of Railway and Utility Rates ", *Econometrica*, **6**, 242–69.

Kaldor (N.) (1939): " Welfare Propositions in Economics ", *Economic Journal*, **49**, 549–52.

Kennedy (C.) (1954): " Concerning Utility ", *Economica*, **21**, 7–20.

Lange (O.) (1942): " The Foundations of Welfare Economics " *Econometrica*, **10**, 215–28.

Little (I. M. D) (1950): *A Critique of Welfare Economics* (Oxford, 1950).

Samuelson (P. A) (1947): *Foundations of Economic Analysis* (Harvard, 1947), Chapter VIII.

Scitovsky (T.) (1941): " A Note on Welfare Propositions in Economics ", *Review of Economic Studies*, **9**, 77–88.

Theil (H.) (1954): " Models and Welfare Maximisation ", *Weltwirtschaftliches Archiv*, **72**, 60–81.

THE ALGEBRA OF OPERATORS AND LINEAR SYSTEMS

1. Operational Methods

THE use of operators is a common device in applied mathematics. Operational methods are essentially practical; their justification is that they work. The basic idea is that a symbol, defined to indicate the performance of some operation on a variable, can be separated from its variable and treated as though it were an algebraic value in itself. For example, Dy denotes the result of differentiating the variable y with respect to an independent variable x, i.e. $Dy = \dfrac{dy}{dx}$. In operational methods, Dy is taken as D times y; D is then separated off and handled as an algebraic quantity. It is a matter of seeing whether symbols like D obey the ordinary rules of algebra, as in practice they do, with certain reservations and care in application.

Operational methods are used in the text above in a number of connections. They are applied in the solution of differential and difference equations (5.5 and 6.5) and they have particular relevance to the analysis of distributed lags (1.9, 5.8 and 8.7). Their major use, however, is in the treatment of closed-loop systems (Chapter 9), based on complex numbers or vectors representing sinusoidal motion (4.9 and 5.9).

The operators used are mainly D for differentiation and D^{-1} for the inverse process of indefinite integration. In addition, there are E and E^{-1} for the corresponding shift operation, as employed in difference equations, and Δ or ∇ for differences. The following account is a short and practical treatment of the use of these operators.

2. The Operators D and D⁻¹

A function $y = y(x)$ is given with derivatives to any desired order. In the notation for the first derivative, $\dfrac{dy}{dx} = \dfrac{d}{dx} y(x)$, it is convenient to write the operator " $\dfrac{d}{dx}$ " for differentiation by means of the symbol D and then to regard D as separable from y. The operation can be repeated:

$$\frac{dy}{dx} = Dy$$

$$\frac{d^2y}{dx^2} = \frac{d}{dx}\left(\frac{dy}{dx}\right) = D(Dy) = D^2y$$

$$\frac{d^3y}{dx^3} = \frac{d}{dx}\left(\frac{d^2y}{dx^2}\right) = D(D^2y) = D^3y$$

. . . .

$$\frac{d^ny}{dx^n} = \frac{d}{dx}\left(\frac{d^{n-1}y}{dx^{n-1}}\right) = D(D^{n-1}y) = D^ny \quad (n \text{ positive integer})$$

So far, this is just a matter of notation, of short-hand writing. For example, the equation $\frac{d^2y}{dx} - y = \sin \omega x$ is written $D^2y - y = \sin \omega x$. The question is whether, once D is taken as separable, the left-hand side of the equation can be written :

$$D^2y - y = (D^2 - 1)y = (D - 1)(D + 1)y$$

Further, if so, is it helpful to write the equation in this way? The answer to both questions is yes.

The point is that any expression in D, separated from the variable y to which it applies, can be handled according to the rules of algebra (13.1 above). The reservations are that only polynomial expressions in positive integral powers of D are admissible—subject to certain relaxations which come later—and that a variable or set of variables must be " tacked on " to follow the expression in D to give it any meaning. The rules to be considered first are :

Commutative : $a + b = b + a$ $ab = ba$

Associative : $a + (b + c) = (a + b) + c$ $a(bc) = (ab)c$

Distributive : $a(b + c) = ab + ac$

All these apply to positive integral powers of D. For example :

$$D^2 + D = D + D^2 \quad \text{since} \quad (D^2 + D)y = \frac{d^2y}{dx^2} + \frac{dy}{dx} = \frac{dy}{dx} + \frac{d^2y}{dx^2} = (D + D^2)y$$

$$D(D^2) = D^2(D) \quad \text{since} \quad D(D^2)y = \frac{d}{dx}\left(\frac{d^2y}{dx^2}\right) = \frac{d^3y}{dx^3} = \frac{d^2}{dx^2}\left(\frac{dy}{dx}\right) = D^2(D)y$$

$$D(D + 1) = D^2 + D \quad \text{since} \quad D(D + 1)y = \frac{d}{dx}\left(\frac{dy}{dx} + y\right) = \frac{d^2y}{dx^2} + \frac{dy}{dx} = (D^2 + D)y$$

It should be carefully noted, however, that such rules apply only to the D symbol itself ; they do not hold for D and y together. For example :

$$D^2y \neq DyD \neq yD^2$$

since the second and third expressions have no meaning allotted to them. Whenever an expression in D is written, it must be *followed* by some variable or other. One or two things can be done, apart from the manipulation of D itself. For example :

$$D(y+z)=Dy+Dz \qquad \text{(y and z two variables)}$$
$$D(ay)=a\,Dy \qquad \text{(y variable, a constant)}$$

The next question to be considered is whether a unit element and an inverse or reciprocal process exist, leading to the ordinary inverse rule of algebra: $a^{-1}=\dfrac{1}{a}$. The unit element $D^0=1$ is simple; when $D^0=1$ then $D^0y=y$, and $D^0=1$ implies no change in y. The inverse of D, or D^{-1}, is now defined as indefinite integration :

$$D^{-1}y=\int y\,dx$$

It then follows, since integration is the inverse of differentiation, that $D^{-1}=\dfrac{1}{D}$, i.e. that $DD^{-1}=1$. For :

$$DD^{-1}y=D(\textstyle\int y\,dx)=\frac{d}{dx}(\int y\,dx)=y$$

and so
$$DD^{-1}=1$$

A whole range of negative integral powers of D follows by repeated integration :

$$D^{-2}=\int(\textstyle\int y\,dx)dx, \quad D^{-3}=\int\{\int(\int y\,dx)\,dx\}\,dx, \text{ and so on.}$$

The rules of algebra, given above, extend to incorporate positive and negative integral powers of D ; for example :

$$D^{-1}(D^2+1)=\frac{D^2+1}{D}=D+\frac{1}{D}=D+D^{-1}$$

since $\quad D^{-1}(D^2+1)y=\displaystyle\int\left(\frac{d^2y}{dx^2}+y\right)dx=\frac{dy}{dx}+\int y\,dx=(D+D^{-1})y.$

This is the basis of the algebra of the operator D and its inverse D^{-1}. Only integral powers of D are admissible, but this is enough for successive differentiation and integration of any variable y.

3. Some Results for D

The expression for any sequence of differentiations and integrations performed on a variable y is $F(D)y$, where $F(D)$ denotes some polynomial in (positive or negative) integral powers of D. It is easily seen, however, that $F(D)$ can also be interpreted when it is the ratio of two such polynomials. Let y and z be two variables such that, for polynomials $F_1(D)$ and $F_2(D)$:

$$F_1(D)y = F_2(D)\, z$$

Then
$$z = \frac{F_1(D)}{F_2(D)}\, y$$

since applying $F_2(D)$ to z gives $F_2(D)\, \dfrac{F_1(D)}{F_2(D)}\, y = F_1(D)y$ as required.

The most common forms in which y appears in practice are as polynomial, exponential and circular functions. It is useful, indeed essential, to have some formulae for handling $F(D)y$, where $F(D)$ is the ratio of polynomials, and y is one of the particular functions. These are given and illustrated below, starting with the exponential form which turns out to be the simplest.

(i) *Exponential Functions.* The main result is :

$$F(D)e^{\alpha x} = F(\alpha)e^{\alpha x} \quad\dotfill(1)$$

and, more generally, for any function y :

$$F(D)ye^{\alpha x} = e^{\alpha x}F(D+\alpha)y \quad\dotfill(2)$$

For example :

Ex. (a). $\quad (D^2 - 1)e^{\alpha x} = (\alpha^2 - 1)e^{\alpha x}$

since $\qquad (D^2 - 1)e^{\alpha x} = \dfrac{d^2}{dx^2}\, e^{\alpha x} - e^{\alpha x} = \alpha^2 e^{\alpha x} - e^{\alpha x} = (\alpha^2 - 1)e^{\alpha x}$

Ex. (b). $\quad \dfrac{1}{D^2 - 1}\, e^{\alpha x} = \dfrac{e^{\alpha x}}{\alpha^2 - 1}$

which means that $(D^2 - 1)\left(\dfrac{e^{\alpha x}}{\alpha^2 - 1}\right) = e^{\alpha x}$, as is readily checked.

Ex. (c). $\quad (D^2 - 1)\, ye^{\alpha x} = e^{\alpha x}\{(D + \alpha)^2 - 1\}y = e^{\alpha x}(D^2 + 2\alpha D + \alpha^2 - 1)y$

since $\qquad (D^2 - 1)\, ye^{\alpha x} = \dfrac{d^2}{dx^2}\, (ye^{\alpha x}) - ye^{\alpha x}$

$$= \frac{d}{dx}\left(e^{\alpha x}\frac{dy}{dx} + \alpha e^{\alpha x}y\right) - ye^{\alpha x}$$

$$= e^{\alpha x}\frac{d^2y}{dx^2} + \alpha e^{\alpha x}\frac{dy}{dx} + \alpha e^{\alpha x}\frac{dy}{dx} + \alpha^2 e^{\alpha x}y - e^{\alpha x}y$$

$$= e^{\alpha x}(D^2 + 2\alpha D + \alpha^2 - 1)y$$

(ii) *Polynomial Functions.* The evaluation of $F(D)y$, where y is a polynomial expression in x, is straightforward in each case as long as $F(D)$ is a polynomial in D. If $F(D)$ is the ratio of polynomials, there is more difficulty. The trick is to express $F(D)$ in partial fractions, and to expand each in ascending powers of D. The method works because all higher derivatives vanish for a polynomial in x, i.e. each expansion has effectively only a finite number of terms. For example :

Ex. (d).
$$(D^2-1)(ax^2+bx+c) = \frac{d^2}{dx^2}(ax^2+bx+c) - (ax^2+bx+c)$$
$$= -(ax^2+bx+c-2a)$$

Ex. (e). $\dfrac{1}{D^2-1}(ax^2+bx+c)$

Here
$$\frac{1}{D^2-1} = \frac{1}{2}\left(\frac{1}{D-1} - \frac{1}{D+1}\right) = -\tfrac{1}{2}(1-D)^{-1} - \tfrac{1}{2}(1+D)^{-1}$$
$$= -\tfrac{1}{2}(1+D+D^2+\ldots +1-D+D^2-\ldots)$$
$$= -(1+D^2+\ldots)$$

Hence :
$$\frac{1}{D^2-1}(ax^2+bx+c) = -(1+D^2+\ldots)(ax^2+bx+c)$$
$$= -(ax^2+bx+c) - 2a$$
$$= -(ax^2+bx+c+2a)$$

As a check : the result implies that
$$(D^2-1)\{-(ax^2+bx+c+2a)\} = ax^2+bx+$$

which is so by the previous example.

Ex. (f). $\dfrac{D-1}{D(D+1)}(2x+3)$

Here $\dfrac{D-1}{D(D+1)} = \dfrac{2}{D+1} - \dfrac{1}{D} = 2(1+D)^{-1} - D^{-1} = 2(1-D+D^2-\ldots) - D^{-1}$

Hence $\dfrac{D-1}{D(D+1)}(2x+3) = 2(1-D+D^2-\ldots)(2x+3) - \int(2x+3)\,dx$
$$= 2(2x+3-2) - (x^2+3x)$$
$$= 2+x-x^2$$

(iii) *Circular Functions.* The main results are :
$$\left.\begin{array}{l} F(D^2)\sin\omega x = F(-\omega^2)\sin\omega x \\ F(D^2)\cos\omega x = F(-\omega^2)\cos\omega x \end{array}\right\} \quad\ldots\ldots\ldots\ldots\ldots\ldots(3)$$

These apply only when F involves even powers, but not odd powers, of D. If an odd power of D appears in the numerator of F, it can be applied directly to $\sin\omega x$ or $\cos\omega x$. However, if an odd power appears in the denominator, there is a device illustrated in Ex. (*i*) below to bring it up into the numerator. The following examples illustrate :

Ex. (g). $(D^2+1)\cos\omega x = (1-\omega^2)\cos\omega x$

since $(D^2+1)\cos\omega x = \dfrac{d^2}{dx^2}\cos\omega x + \cos\omega x = \dfrac{d}{dx}(-\omega\sin\omega x) + \cos\omega x$
$$= -\omega^2\cos\omega x + \cos\omega x$$
$$= (1-\omega^2)\cos\omega x$$

Ex. (h). $\dfrac{1}{D^2+1}\sin \omega x = \dfrac{\sin \omega x}{1-\omega^2}$

which implies that $(D^2+1)\left(\dfrac{\sin \omega x}{1-\omega^2}\right) = \sin \omega x$, as can be checked.

Ex. (i). $\dfrac{2D+1}{D(D+1)}\cos \omega x = \left(\dfrac{1}{D}+\dfrac{1}{D+1}\right)\cos \omega x$

$$= D^{-1}\cos \omega x + \dfrac{D-1}{D^2-1}\cos \omega x$$

$$= \int \cos \omega x \, dx + (D-1)\left(-\dfrac{\cos \omega x}{1+\omega^2}\right)$$

$$= \dfrac{1}{\omega}\sin \omega x + \dfrac{\omega \sin \omega x}{1+\omega^2} + \dfrac{\cos \omega x}{1+\omega^2}$$

Hence $\dfrac{2D+1}{D(D+1)}\cos \omega x = \dfrac{\sin \omega x}{\omega} + \dfrac{\cos \omega x + \omega \sin \omega x}{1+\omega^2}$

This can be checked by showing that $(2D+1)\cos \omega x$ equals $D(D+1)$ applied to the solution given.

4. Solution of a Differential Equation

The linear differential equation with constant coefficients in general form can be written :

$$a_0\dfrac{d^n y}{dx^n} + a_1\dfrac{d^{n-1}y}{dx^{n-1}} + \ldots + a_{n-1}\dfrac{dy}{dx} + a_n y = f(x)$$

or as : $$F(D)y = f(x)$$

where $$F(D) = a_0 D^n + a_1 D^{n-1} + \ldots + a_{n-1}D + a_n$$

$$= a_0(D-p_1)(D-p_2) \ldots (D-p_n)$$

Here, the n roots of $F(p)=0$ are $p_1, p_2, \ldots p_n$, real or complex.

Try $y=e^{px}$ as a solution of the homogeneous form $F(D)y=0$. Since :

$$F(D)y = F(p)e^{px}$$

by (1) above, any p which makes $F(p)=0$ gives $y=e^{px}$ as a solution. Hence the values of p are $p_1, p_2, \ldots p_n$ and the complementary function is :

$$y = \sum_{r=1}^{n} A_r e^{p_r x}$$

for arbitrary constants $A_1, A_2, \ldots A_r$. Notice that, for $y=e^{px}$, the operator $D=p$.

It remains to get a particular integral, i.e. any solution of $F(D)y=f(x)$. Such a solution is given by evaluating :

$$y = \dfrac{1}{F(D)}f(x)$$

If $f(x)$ involves exponential, polynomial or circular functions, then the results obtained above, and particularly (1), (2) and (3), apply to give the particular integral. In other cases, further devices or solution by trial and error need to be used. Two examples illustrate :

Ex. (*a*). $\dfrac{d^2y}{dx^2} - y = \sin \omega x$,   i.e. $(D^2 - 1)\, y = \sin \omega x$

The complementary function is obtained by solving :

$$F(p) = p^2 - 1 = (p - 1)(p + 1) = 0$$

and it is : $y = A_1 e^x + A_2 e^{-x}$ (A_1 and A_2 arbitrary)

The particular integral is :

$$y = \frac{1}{D^2 - 1} \sin \omega x = -\frac{\sin \omega x}{1 + \omega^2}$$ by (3) above.

The complete solution is then :

$$y = A_1 e^x + A_2 e^{-x} - \frac{\sin \omega x}{1 + \omega^2}$$

Ex. (*b*).   The following is the differential equation for Y lagged on Z, according to the continuously distributed (exponential) lag with speed of response λ, when Z has a given sinusoidal variation (5.8 above) :

$$(D + \lambda)\, Y = \lambda Z \quad \text{where} \quad Z = e^{\alpha t} \cos \omega t$$

The complementary function is $Y = A e^{-\lambda t}$ (A arbitrary)
The particular integral is :

$$Y = \frac{\lambda}{D + \lambda} (e^{\alpha t} \cos \omega t) = e^{\alpha t} \frac{\lambda}{D + \alpha + \lambda} (\cos \omega t) \quad \text{by (2) above}$$

$$= \lambda e^{\alpha t} \frac{D - (\alpha + \lambda)}{D^2 - (\alpha + \lambda)^2} (\cos \omega t)$$

$$= -\frac{\lambda e^{\alpha t}}{\omega^2 + (\alpha + \lambda)^2} \{D - (\alpha + \lambda)\} (\cos \omega t) \quad \text{by (3) above}$$

$$= \frac{\lambda e^{\alpha t}}{\omega^2 + (\alpha + \lambda)^2} \{(\alpha + \lambda) \cos \omega t + \omega \sin \omega t\}$$

$$= \rho e^{\alpha t} \cos (\omega t - \phi)$$

where $\rho = \dfrac{\lambda}{\sqrt{(\lambda + \alpha)^2 + \omega^2}}$ and $\tan \phi = \dfrac{\omega}{\lambda + \alpha}$

The complete solution is then :

$$Y = A e^{-\lambda t} + \rho e^{\alpha t} \cos (\omega t - \phi)$$

If $Y = 0$ when $t = 0$, the constant A is given :

$$A = -\rho \cos \phi$$

and $$Y = \rho e^{\alpha t} \cos (\omega t - \phi) - \rho \cos \phi\, e^{-\lambda t}$$

5. The Operators E and E⁻¹

The function y is now given for a discrete series $x=0, 1, 2, \ldots$ as :

$$y_0, y_1, y_2, \ldots y_x \ldots$$

The shift operator E is the process of going from y_x to y_{x+1} :

$$y_{x+1}=Ey_x$$

and the inverse E^{-1} is the reverse process :

$$y_{x-1}=E^{-1}y_x$$

Any positive or negative integral power of E can be obtained, e.g.

$$y_{x+2}=Ey_{x+1}=E(Ey_x)=E^2y_x$$
$$y_{x-2}=E^{-1}y_{x-1}=E^{-1}(E^{-1}y_x)=E^{-2}y_x$$

Generally :　　$y_{x+n}=E^ny_x$　　(n positive or negative integer)

The operator E and its inverse E^{-1} obey the rules of algebra in much the same way as do D and D^{-1}. For example :

$$E(E^2) \quad =E^2(E)=E^3 \text{ since } \quad E(E^2)y_x=Ey_{x+2}=y_{x+3}=E^3y_x$$
$$\text{and} \quad E^2(E)y_x=E^2y_{x+1}=y_{x+3}=E^3y_x$$

$$E(E+1)=E^2+E \quad \text{ since } E(E+1)y_x=E(y_{x+1}+y_x)=y_{x+2}+y_{x+1}$$
$$=(E^2+E)y_x$$

$$EE^{-1} \quad =1 \quad \text{ since } \quad EE^{-1}y_x=Ey_{x-1}=y_x$$

Consider $F(E)y_x$, where $F(E)$ is either a polynomial in E or a ratio of such polynomials. There are certain results for $F(E)y_x$ when y_x takes particular forms. The simplest form is $y_x=\alpha^x$ which corresponds in period analysis to the exponential function most easily managed by means of the operator D in continuous analysis. The results are :

$$\left. \begin{array}{l} F(E)\alpha^x \quad =F(\alpha)\alpha^x \\ F(E)y_x\alpha^x=\alpha^xF(\alpha E)y_x \end{array} \right\} \quad \ldots\ldots\ldots\ldots\ldots\ldots(4)$$

and

For example :

Ex. (a).　　$(E^2-1)\alpha^x=(\alpha^2-1)\alpha^x$

since　　　　$(E^2-1)\alpha^x=E^2\alpha^x-\alpha^x=\alpha^{x+2}-\alpha^x=(\alpha^2-1)\alpha^x$

Ex. (b).　　$\dfrac{1}{E^2-1}\alpha^x=\dfrac{\alpha^x}{\alpha^2-1}$

which implies $(E^2-1)\left(\dfrac{\alpha^x}{\alpha^2-1}\right)=\alpha^x$ as can be checked.

Ex. (c).　　$(E^2-1)y_x\alpha^x=\alpha^x(\alpha^2E^2-1)y_x$

since　　　　　　　　$(E^2-1)y_x\alpha^x=E^2y_x\alpha^x-y_x\alpha^x$
$$=y_{x+2}\alpha^{x+2}-y_x\alpha^x$$
$$=\alpha^x(\alpha^2E^2y_x-y_x)$$
$$=\alpha^x(\alpha^2E^2-1)y_x$$

When y_x is of polynomial form in x, it is best handled, as regards the shift operator, when the terms in the polynomial are written in :

$$x^{(n)} = x(x-1)(x-2) \dots (x-n+1)$$

rather than in powers x^n. The main result is :

$$Ex^{(n)} = (x+1)x^{(n-1)}$$

For : $$Ex^{(n)} = Ex(x-1)(x-2) \dots (x-n+1)$$

$$= (x+1)x(x-1) \dots (x-n+2) = (x+1)x^{(n-1)}$$

The shift operator E is closely connected with, and can be replaced by, the operator Δ used in the ordinary process of finite differences. This point needs to be investigated before the application to difference equations is considered.

6. The Operator Δ

The same function is given as a discrete series, y_x for $x = 0, 1, 2, \dots$. Successive differences, calculated forward from x, are denoted :

$$\Delta y_x = y_{x+1} - y_x$$
$$\Delta^2 y_x = \Delta(\Delta y_x) = \Delta y_{x+1} - \Delta y_x = y_{x+2} - 2y_{x+1} + y_x$$
$$\Delta^3 y_x = \Delta(\Delta^2 y_x) = \Delta^2 y_{x+1} - \Delta^2 y_x = y_{x+3} - 3y_{x+2} + 3y_{x+1} - y_x \quad \text{etc.}$$

Generally, for any positive integer n, define $\Delta^n y_x = \Delta(\Delta^{n-1} y_x)$ and so :

$$\Delta^n y_x = y_{x+n} - \binom{n}{1} y_{x+n-1} + \binom{n}{2} y_{x+n-2} - \binom{n}{3} y_{x+n-3} + \dots + (-1)^n y_x$$

where the coefficients $\binom{n}{r} = \dfrac{n!}{r!(n-r)!}$ are those of the Binomial expansion.

The difference operator is Δ, subject to the rules of algebra in the same way as D or E. For example :

$$\Delta(\Delta+1) = \Delta^2 + \Delta$$

for : $\Delta(\Delta+1)y_x = \Delta(\Delta y_x + y_x) = \Delta(y_{x+1}) = y_{x+2} - y_{x+1}$

and $(\Delta^2 + \Delta)y_x = \Delta^2 y_x + \Delta y_x = y_{x+2} - 2y_{x+1} + y_x + y_{x+1} - y_x = y_{x+2} - y_{x+1}$

The link between the operators E and Δ is simple. Write :

$$\Delta y_x = y_{x+1} - y_x = Ey_x - y_x = (E-1)y_x$$

Alternatively, write :

$$Ey_x = y_{x+1} = \Delta y_x + y_x = (\Delta+1)y_x$$

Hence the link is :

$$E - \Delta = 1$$

i.e. $$E = \Delta + 1 \quad \text{and} \quad \Delta = E - 1$$

It is, therefore, always possible to switch from E to Δ or conversely. Some examples can be given :

$$E^2 y_x = (\Delta + 1)^2 y_x = \Delta^2 y_x + 2\Delta y_x + y_x$$
$$\Delta^2 y_x = (E - 1)^2 y_x = E^2 y_x - 2E y_x + y_x$$
$$E(E+1)y_x = (\Delta + 1)(\Delta + 2)y_x = \Delta^2 y_x + 3\Delta y_x + 2y_x$$

Each of these pairs of equivalent expressions can be found in terms of the series of y's. The first pair equals y_{x+2}, the second $(y_{x+2} - 2y_{x+1} + y_x)$ and the third $(y_{x+2} + y_{x+1})$. In general, if $F(E)y_x$ is the result of a sequence of shift operators on y_x, then the same result in terms of differences is $F(\Delta + 1)y_x$. Similarly, $F(\Delta)y_x$ and $F(E-1)y_x$ correspond.

Backward differencing is sometimes adopted and the operator ∇ used to indicate the process :

$$\nabla y_x = y_{x-1} - y_x$$
$$\nabla^2 y_x = \nabla(\nabla y_x) = y_{x-2} - 2y_{x-1} + y_x \quad \text{etc.}$$

There is clearly a relation between ∇ and the inverse shift operator E^{-1}. It is the same as the relation between Δ and E :

$$\nabla y_x = y_{x-1} - y_x = (E^{-1} - 1)y_x$$

and so
$$E^{-1} - \nabla = 1$$
i.e.
$$E^{-1} = \nabla + 1 \quad \text{and} \quad \nabla = E^{-1} - 1$$

Since E and E^{-1} are inverse to each other $(EE^{-1} = 1)$, a relation between Δ and ∇ can be derived :

$$\begin{aligned} 1 = EE^{-1} &= (\Delta + 1)(\nabla + 1) \\ &= E(\nabla + 1) \\ &= (\Delta + 1)E^{-1} \end{aligned}$$

From these relations, it follows that $(\Delta + 1)$ and $(\nabla + 1)$ are inverse to each other, that $\nabla = -\Delta E^{-1}$ and that $\Delta = -E\nabla$.

7. Solution of a Difference Equation

The linear difference equation, with constant coefficients and equally spaced values of the independent variable, can be written :

$$a_0 y_{x+n} + a_1 y_{x+n-1} + \ldots + a_{n-1} y_{x+1} + a_n y_x = \phi(x)$$
i.e.
$$F(E)y_x = \phi(x)$$
where
$$\begin{aligned} F(E) &= a_0 E^n + a_1 E^{n-1} + \ldots + a_{n-1}E + a_n \\ &= a_0(E - p_1)(E - p_2) \ldots (E - p_n) \end{aligned}$$

Again $p_1\, p_2, \ldots p_n$ are the n roots, real or complex, of $F(p) = 0$.

The difference equation can also be expressed in terms of successive differences, i.e. Δy_x, $\Delta^2 y_x$, ... In terms of operators, since $E = \Delta + 1$, this second form can be written down at once:

$$F(\Delta + 1)y_x = \phi(x)$$

The complementary function is obtained by trying $y_x = p^x$ as a solution of the homogeneous equation $F(E)y_x = 0$. By (4) above:

$$F(E)y_x = F(p)p^x$$

in this case. Hence, any p such that $F(p) = 0$ gives $y_x = p^x$ as a solution. The complementary function is:

$$y = \sum_{r=1}^{n} A_r p_r^x$$

for arbitrary constants A_1, A_2, ... A_n.

The particular integral is any solution of $F(E)y_x = \phi(x)$, i.e.

$$y_x = \frac{1}{F(E)} \phi(x) \quad \dots\dots\dots\dots\dots\dots\dots\dots(5)$$

to be evaluated, by any practical devices available, in much the same way as for a differential equation.

The same difference equation can be written, as in 6.5 above, with y_x running backward instead of forward:

$$a_0 y_x + a_1 y_{x-1} + \dots + a_{n-1} y_{x-n+1} + a_n y_{x-n} = f(x)$$

where
$$f(x) = \phi(x - n) = E^{-n}\phi(x)$$

The equation is:

$$(a_0 + a_1 E^{-1} + \dots + a_{n-1} E^{-(n-1)} + a_n E^{-n})y_x = f(x)$$

i.e.
$$E^{-n}F(E)y_x = f(x)$$

The particular integral is now:

$$y_x = \frac{E^n}{F(E)} f(x) \quad \dots\dots\dots\dots\dots\dots\dots\dots(6)$$

Since $f(x) = E^{-n}\phi(x)$, the forms (5) and (6) are equivalent.

In the evaluation of (5) or (6), the simplest case arises when $f(x)$ or $\phi(x)$ involves a power of the form α^x; the results (4) above apply at once. The next simplest case has powers of x, i.e. x, x^2, x^3, ... , in the function $f(x)$ or $\phi(x)$. The trick is then to switch from E to Δ by writing $E = \Delta + 1$, to put:

$$\frac{1}{F(E)} = \frac{1}{F(\Delta + 1)}$$

into partial fractions, and finally to expand in ascending powers of Δ. The differences of x, x^2, x^3 ... are simple. For example :

$$\Delta x = 1 \quad \text{and} \quad \Delta^2 x = \Delta^3 x = \ldots = 0$$
$$\Delta x^2 = 2x + 1, \quad \Delta^2 x^2 = 2 \quad \text{and} \quad \Delta^3 x^2 = \ldots = 0$$

and so on. It is the vanishing of all the higher differences which makes the expansion method feasible. Two examples, sufficient to illustrate the practical technique, are given in 6.5 above.

8. Linear Equations and Transformations

The simplest of all equations is the *linear (algebraic) equation* obtained by equating to zero a polynomial of first degree in the variables concerned. One characteristic of such linear equations is that they have *unique solutions*, subject only to certain restrictions on the coefficients of the equations. A single linear equation has a unique solution for one of the variables in the equation (in terms of the others). A system of linear equations, with coefficients such that the equations are consistent and independent, has a unique solution for a set of variables equal in number to the number of equations (14.2 above).

The same property of uniqueness holds for *linear (algebraic) transformations*. For a linear transform from one variable x to another variable y : $y = ax + b$. This includes, and indeed combines, the two simpler relations of *proportionality* ($y = ax$) and of *shift* ($y = x + b$). There is a unique inversion of the transform, to give x in terms of y, subject only to $a \neq 0$. The property of *unique inversion* holds for a linear transformation which consists of a system of equations between two sets of variables, again subject only to certain restrictions on the coefficients of the system (14.3 above).

Linear equations and transformations have another characteristic ; they possess various *additive properties*. This can be illustrated in terms of :

$$ax + by + c = 0 \qquad \ldots\ldots\ldots\ldots\ldots\ldots\ldots\ldots(7)$$

a single equation (or transform) in two variables. If (7) is satisfied by two pairs of values (x_1, y_1) and (x_2, y_2), then it follows, by substitution into (7), that :

$$x = A_1 x_1 + A_2 x_2 ; \quad y = A_1 y_1 + A_2 y_2 \qquad \ldots\ldots\ldots\ldots(8)$$

also satisfy the equation for any constants A_1 and A_2. In geometric terms, given two points $P_1(x_1, y_1)$ and $P_2(x_2, y_2)$ on the straight line (7), then any other point on the line is given by (8).

These ideas can be extended at once to a *linear (ordinary) differential equation* as defined in 5.1. In general, it is of form (7) in a series of variables, i.e. Y and its successive derivatives $\dfrac{dY}{dx}, \dfrac{d^2Y}{dx^2}, \ldots$. The coefficients in the equation can involve the independent variable x; it is Y and its derivatives, and not x, which are related linearly. There is a sense in which a linear differential equation has a *unique solution*. If the equation is of order n, and if Y and its first $(n-1)$ derivatives are specified initially (say at $x=0$), there then is one, and only one, solution for Y in terms of x.

An equally important characteristic, which distinguishes linear differential equations from other types, is the *additive property*. By the rules of 5.2, if $y_1(x)$ and $y_2(x)$ are two solutions of the homogenous form of the linear differential equation, then $A_1y_1(x) + A_2y_2(x)$ is also a solution for any constants A_1 and A_2. Further, if $\overline{Y}(x)$ is any solution of the complete differential equation, then the general solution is :

$$Y = \overline{Y}(x) + A_1y_1(x) + A_2y_2(x) + \ldots$$

the number of terms with constants being equal to the order of the equation. The nature of the additive property is apparent.

There is a further group of transformations which can be described as linear, and the *Laplace Transform* is a leading example. There is again a unique relation both ways and the additive property holds. For the Laplace Transform :

$$\bar{y}(p) = \int_0^\infty e^{-pt} y(t)\, dt \quad \ldots\ldots\ldots\ldots\ldots\ldots\ldots(9)$$

on the assumption that the integral exists, there is a unique $\bar{y}(p)$ for given (t) and conversely (5.6 above). The additive property is : let $\bar{y}_1(p)$ be the Laplace Transform of $y_1(t)$ and $\bar{y}_2(p)$ of $y_2(t)$, then $A_1\bar{y}_1(p) + A_2\bar{y}_2(p)$ is the Laplace Transform of $A_1y_1(t) + A_2y_2(t)$ for any constants A_1 and A_2. This follows at once from the definition (9).

It is to be noticed (see 5.7) that the linear Laplace Transform converts derivatives, and hence differential equations, into purely algebraic terms. If $y(t)$ satisfies a linear differential equation with constant coefficients, then $\bar{y}(p)$ is given as an algebraic expression in p, usually the ratio of two polynomials in p. To solve the differential equation is now a matter of algebra, plus rules laid down for switching back and forth between a function and its Laplace Transform.

Similar properties hold for linear difference equations and the transforms designed to handle them. Consider the generating function of 6.8 :

$$\overline{Y}(s) = \sum_{x=0}^\infty Y_x s^x \text{ which transforms the sequence } Y_x(x=0, 1, 2, \ldots) \text{ into a}$$

function of a variable s. This is a linear transform, unique and additive. If $\overline{Y}_1(s)$ is the generating function of the sequence Y_{1x}, and $\overline{Y}_2(s)$ of the sequence Y_{2x}, then $A_1\overline{Y}_1(s) + A_2\overline{Y}_2(s)$ is the generating function of the sequence $(A_1Y_{1x} + A_2Y_{2x})$ for any constants A_1 and A_2.

9. Linear Models

A model or system comprises a set of relations between the variables $Y, Z, \ldots$ of the model. The model is *linear* if, for sinusoidal variation over time, all the variables of the model have the *same* damping and frequency. On the other hand, the amplitude and phase differ from one variable to another, as determined by extraneous conditions. A sinusoidal variation represented by the real part of $Ae^{i\epsilon}e^{pt}$ runs through the system with unchanged damping and frequency ($p = \alpha + i\omega$) but with amplitude and phase (given by A and ϵ) changing from one variable to another.

As indicated below, the change in amplitude and phase is a combination of a relation of *proportionality* for amplitude and one of *shift* for phase. There is a parallel here with the linear transformation of simple algebraic form. Further, from the results of 4.9, a linear model has the *additive property* that several variables of the system can be added to make another variable with the same damping and frequency, i.e. another variable consistent with the model. It is for reasons such as these that the term linear is appropriate to the model.

Consider one relation of the model relating Y as output to Z as input. The definition of the response of Y to Z may involve various derivatives and integrals, all kinds of lags and delays, without infringing the condition for a linear model. The response can be expressed in purely algebraic terms by the use of operators. If the sinusoidal variation concerned has $p = \alpha + i\omega$, write " delay θ " as $e^{-p\theta}$ and put $D = p$ for derivatives and integrals (4.9 above). The response of Y to Z then appears :

$$Y = F(p)Z$$

where $F(p)$ is the transfer function, depending on the p taken. Further, if the time-form of the response of Y to a unit step-change in Z is $f(t)$, then $F(p)$ is the Laplace Transform of $f(t)$ (see 9.3 above).

The value of $F(p)$ for any given p is a complex number or vector which can be written $\rho e^{i\theta}$. The change in the amplitude of the variation from Z to Y is given by ρ ; the shift in phase is given by ϕ. The relation of Y to Z is such that, as a sinusoidal variation of given damping and frequency passes from Z to Y, it undergoes a *proportional* change in amplitude given by ρ and a *shift* in phase given by ϕ.

The linear property of a model can be seen both for forced and for free oscillations in the system. If an input Z has a given (extraneous) oscillation, then another variable Y depending on Z has a *forced oscillation* of the same damping and frequency, with differing amplitude and phase. It all depends algebraically on the transfer function $F(p) = \rho e^{i\theta}$ for given p. For example, while the damping and frequency of oscillation of Y is exactly that introduced by Z, it may happen (ρ large) that its amplitude can be built up to such an extent that resonance results.

The structure of the linear model fixes the damping and frequency of each and every *free oscillation*, i.e. an oscillation which is self-supporting within the complete model. The determination of $p = \alpha + i\omega$ for free oscillations is a matter of algebra. Write $F(p) = 1$ where $F(p)$ is the feeds back transfer function of the model. If $p = \alpha + i\omega$ is any algebraic solution, then α is the damping and ω the frequency of a possible free oscillation, common to all variables of the model. The amplitude and phase of any variable remain to be fixed by extraneous conditions.

The simplicity of the linear model lies in these facts. For example, if one variable is damped so are all the others—but each variable takes its own amplitudes from extraneous circumstances. The same facts show up also the lack of " reality " of linear models as expressions of economic relations. It is only by accident ($\alpha = 0$ exactly) that a linear model has oscillations which neither explode nor die away ; and a linear model offers no explanation of why the amplitude of an oscillation is what it is.

Very similar properties are found for linear models in period terms, involving difference equations instead of differential equations. The reduction to algebra proceeds by the use of the shift operator E instead of the differential operator D.

THE ALGEBRA OF SETS, GROUPS AND VECTOR SPACES

1. The Concepts of Modern Algebra

There are references in the text to the basic concepts and results of modern algebra. This highly-developed branch of mathematics is characterised by abstract generality and by rigorous development from an axiomatic basis. As such, it should be of considerable interest to economists in their attempts to develop a structure of economic theory on sound foundations. Consider the axiomatic approach to a theory. The set of axioms laid down must be both consistent and independent : no axiom should conflict with another, no axiom should be the consequence of another. Once this is done, the development proceeds with the aid of a set of operational rules : the axioms and properties deducible from them. The two should not be confused ; the axioms give precisely what is needed as a basis and no more—the rules are a convenience for actual operation once the basis is firmly laid.

This Appendix must have a limited objective if it is to be short. The objects are to define the main algebraic concepts, to show what appears to be mathematicians' jargon may actually be useful, and to give some idea of the lines on which rigorous development can proceed. A complete treatment is not attempted ; some concessions are needed if modern algebra is to be related to what is familiar. The cart may sometimes be put before the horse, as when operational rules are written first—the superfluous being weeded out later to give a consistent and independent set of axioms. But the lines of rigorous development should be clear enough for the interested reader to pursue in the literature. A short and fairly simple account is in Littlewood (1949) ; a more comprehensive but still rather discursive treatment is in Birkhoff and MacLane (1941, 1953). An advanced text requiring great concentration is that of van der Waerden (1937–40, 1949–50). Some parts of modern algebra treated from special points of view are to be found in Courant and Robbins (1941), Murdoch (1957), Papandreou (1958) and in the excellent if somewhat advanced book by Thrall and Tornheim (1957).

One word of warning : the complexity of modern algebra is due to the fact that it deals with infinite collections of objects. This explains, not only why the subject is so fascinating, but also why it has such a range of applications. Finite mathematics is relatively simple, witness the beautiful treatment of Kemeny, Snell and Thompson (1957). But it is not enough. The number systems of mathematics, as used for the real and complex variables, are infinite. This is so even of the simplest case, the set of natural numbers or positive integers.

Moreover, some of the more remote corners of the algebraic field, where what seem to be very odd things happen, have turned out to have very practical applications in the modern world. Boolean algebra of sets and compound statements, and the algebra of sets of two elements (0 and 1, or even and odd), are abstract enough—but they apply in circuit theory and in the design and programming of computers.

REFERENCES

Birkhoff (G.) and MacLane (S.) (1941, 1953) : *A Survey of Modern Algebra* (Macmillan, New York, First Ed. 1941, Revised Ed. 1953).
Courant (R.) and Robbins (H.) (1941) : *What is Mathematics?* (Oxford, 1941).
Kemeny (J. G.), Snell (J. L.) and Thompson (G. L.) (1957) : *Introduction to Finite Mathematics* (Prentice-Hall, 1957).
Littlewood (D. E.) (1949) : *The Skeleton Key of Mathematics* (Hutchinson University Library, 1949).
Murdoch (D. C.) (1957) : *Linear Algebra for Undergraduates* (Wiley, 1957).
Papandreou (A. G.) (1958) : *Economics as a Science* (Lippincott, 1958).
Thrall (R. M.) and Tornheim (L.) (1957) : *Vector Spaces and Matrices* (Wiley, 1957).
van der Waerden (B. L.) (1937–40, 1949–50) : *Modern Algebra* (Frederick Ungar, two volumes 1949–50), English translation of the second (1937–40) German edition.

2. Sets and Boolean Algebra

The basic concept of all mathematics, as indeed of logic, is a *set* as a collection of well-defined objects, finite or infinite in number, and of any kind whatever. The objects are the *elements* of the set. Often a set has numbers as elements—sets of natural numbers, of integers (positive, negative and zero), of rationals, of real numbers and of complex numbers. The axiomatic basis and properties of these number systems of mathematics are taken for granted here. But this is by no means all. There are sets of other objects—for example : matrices, polynomials, transformations, or (as an example below shows) more every-day " objects ". There are also sets of sets. Indeed they are of very common usage ; since a matrix is an ordered set of elements (typically real numbers), a set of matrices is a set of sets.

A set comprises " well-defined " elements, so there must be a specification, achieved (i) by listing the elements and/or (ii) by providing a general description of all elements. As a matter of *notation* :

$$A = \{\text{listing}\} = \{a \mid a \text{ is } Q\} \text{ where } \text{``} a \text{ is } Q \text{''} \text{ is a description}$$

is a set A, and $a \, \epsilon \, A$ means " element a belongs to the set A ". Also as a matter of notation, write $A \subseteq B$ for A a *subset* of B in the sense that $a \, \epsilon \, A$ implies $a \, \epsilon \, B$. It is permissible that $A \subseteq B$ and $B \subseteq A$, which means that $A = B$, the two sets contain precisely the same elements. Finally, $A \subset B$ denotes A as a *proper subset* of B so that A is contained within B in the sense that $A \subseteq B$ but $A \neq B$.

Ex. (a). $\mathcal{J} = \{ \dots -2, \ -1, \ 0, \ 1, \ 2, \ \dots \} = \{a \mid a \text{ is an integer}\}$ with a variety of subsets, both infinite as :

$$N = \{1, \ 2, \ 3, \ \dots \} = \{a \mid a \text{ is a positive integer}\}$$

and finite as in the two following cases :

$$S_1 = \{1, \ 2, \ 3, \ 4\} = \{a \mid a \text{ is a positive integer less than 5}\}$$
$$S_2 = \{2, \ 3, \ 5, \ 7\} = \{a \mid a \text{ is a positive prime less than 10}\}$$

Ex. (b). A set consisting of 12 members of the particular family of three generations shown in the family tree of Fig. 81. The notation, made up for the occasion, is grandfather G ; sons and daughters S and D if married, Σ and Δ if unmarried ; grandsons and granddaughters s and d if married, σ and δ if unmarried. In addition, the subscript 1 indicates a spouse (if any) of the person denoted without subscript.

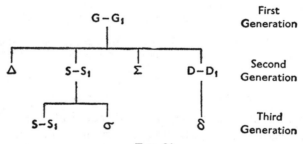

FIG. 81

Set theory has to do with relations between sets selected from a given totality of elements. Two special cases serve as *bounds*—the *empty set* ϕ consisting of no elements and the *universal set* U including all elements under consideration. Set theory then deals with subsets of U, including the bounds ϕ and U themselves :

$$\phi \subseteq A \subseteq U \qquad \text{for any set } A$$

Two operations on sets are now defined. Each involves two sets A and B and is thus of the type known as " binary " operations.

DEFINITION : The *union* of A and B, written $A \cup B$, is the set of those and
   only those elements which are either in A, or in B, or in both.
   The *intersection* of A and B, written $A \cap B$, is the set of those and
   only those elements which are both in A and in B.

The following properties or *operational rules* hold for sets A, B, C, ...

Rule	Union ($\cup$)	Intersection ($\cap$)
Closure	(1a) If A and B are sets of U, so is $A \cup B$	(1b) If A and B are sets of U, so is $A \cap B$
Idempotent	(2a) $\quad A \cup A = A$	(2b) $\quad A \cap A = A$
Associative	(3a) $A \cup (B \cup C) = (A \cup B) \cup C$	(3b) $A \cap (B \cap C) = (A \cap B) \cap C$
Commutative	(4a) $\quad A \cup B = B \cup A$	(4b) $\quad A \cap B = B \cap A$
Bounds $\{$	(5a) $\quad A \cup \phi = A$	(5b) $\quad A \cap U = A$
	(6a) $\quad A \cup U = U$	(6b) $\quad A \cap \phi = \phi$
Distributive†	$\cap$ over $\cup$: (7a) $\quad A \cap (B \cup C) = (A \cap B) \cup (A \cap C)$	
	$\cup$ over $\cap$: (7b) $\quad A \cup (B \cap C) = (A \cup B) \cap (A \cup C)$	

† By virtue of the commutative rules, (7a) also implies that $(A \cup B) \cap C = (A \cap C) \cup (B \cap C)$ and similarly for (7b).

The truth of these rules is illustrated in diagrams, called " Venn diagrams ", as in Fig. 82. For convenience, U is shown as all points inside a

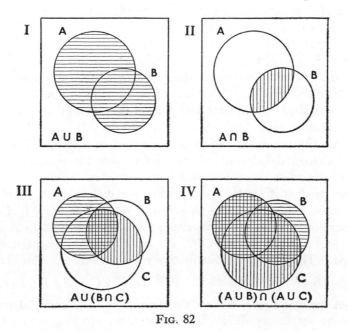

FIG. 82

square and sets A, B, C, ... as circles. Then $A\cup B$ is the area jointly covered by the circles A and B (I of the figure), $A\cap B$ the area common to the circles (II). As illustration, take rule (7b); then $A\cup(B\cap C)$ is the total area shaded in III and $(A\cup B)\cap(A\cup C)$ is the cross-hatched area in IV. The two are the same.

Now define a " unary " operation involving only one set A :

DEFINITION : The *complement* of A, written A', is the set of those and only those elements which are *not* in A.

The following *operational rules* follow and can be illustrated in Venn diagrams :

Rule	Union ($\cup$)	Intersection ($\cap$)
Complements $\Big\{$	(8a) $A\cup A'=U$ (9a) $(A\cup B)'=A'\cap B'$	(8b) $A\cap A'=\phi$ (9b) $(A\cap B)'=A'\cup B'$
Involution	(10) $(A')'=A$	

As a further example of set theory, the relation $\subseteq$ gives rise to other results, such as : if $A\cap B=\phi$, then $A\subseteq B'$. Each statement means that the sets A and B are *disjoint*, having no elements in common. There is no need to pursue the theory further here.

One feature of set theory is so remarkable that it is to be stressed, the feature of *duality*. In any one of the rules above, interchange the operations $\cup$ and $\cap$, and interchange the bounds ϕ and U, and another of the rules is found to result. The rules appear in pairs of duals, as shown in tabling them above. There are nine *pairs* of rules of set theory, and a tenth which is symmetrical.

That duality is a remarkable feature is seen in a comparison with the rules of elementary algebra. Most of the rules for sets correspond to familiar rules when union or logical sum is written $+$, when intersection or logical product is written $\times$, and when ϕ and U are written as 0 and 1. For example, (3a) becomes $A+(B+C)=(A+B)+C$ and (5b) is $A\times 1=A$. The idempotent rules are a departure from familiarity—$A+A=A$ and not $2A$; $A\times A=A$ and not A^2. An equally striking departure is the following. The two (dual) distributive rules for sets translate into :

$$A\times(B+C)=A\times B+A\times C \quad\text{and}\quad A+B\times C=(A+B)(A+C)$$

of which the first holds, but *not* the second, in elementary algebra. In fact, where set theory differs from elementary algebra, it is set theory which is simpler (no multiples or powers) and more symmetrical (never lacking duality).

To generalise, consider any set of objects A, B, C, ... subject to the relation $\subseteq$ and with bounds ϕ and U. Let operations $A \cup B$, $A \cap B$ and A' be defined so that the pairs of rules 1-9 and rule 10 are valid. Then the algebra of the set is a *Boolean algebra*. The algebra of all subsets of a given universal set is a Boolean algebra. So are other things, e.g. the system of " compound statements " in logic. Boolean algebra is simply the algebra of " and ", " or " and " not ", as represented here by inter-section, union and complement.

3. Relations : Functions, Mappings and Transformations

Consider two sets X and Y and let $x \in X$ and $y \in Y$ be any elements.

DEFINITION : The *Cartesian product* is the set of all ordered pairs (x, y) :

$$X \cdot Y = \{(x, y) \mid x \in X \text{ and } y \in Y\}$$

Ordering is essential: $X \cdot Y$ and $Y \cdot X$ are different. If X and Y are each the set of all real numbers, then the set $X \cdot Y$ is represented by all points in Cartesian space of two dimensions (a plane) referred to two fixed axes Ox and Oy at right angles.

DEFINITION : A *relation* R from set X to set Y is any proper subset of $X \cdot Y$, i.e. a proper subset of the set of all ordered pairs (x, y).

A relation can be defined by listing and/or description :

$$R = \{(x, y) \mid x \in X, y \in Y, yRx\}$$

where yRx describes the relation. Two examples illustrate.

Ex. (a). X and Y are sets of real numbers and $X \cdot Y$ can be visualised as a set of points on a plane. Consider the two relations :

$$R_1 = \{(x, y) \mid x \in X, y \in Y, y = x\} ; \quad R_2 = \{(x, y) \mid x \in X, y \in Y, y \leqslant x\}$$

The description of R_1 is the subset of $X \cdot Y$ given by " y has the same value as x " ; it can be visualised as the 45° line through O. R_2 is the subset such that " y is not greater than x ", visualised as all points on or below the 45° line through O—a relation between x and y like R_1.

Ex. (b). Various relations can be defined for the set of 12 family members of Ex. (b) of 2 above. They are algebraic relations—and actual family relationships. The following are two examples. If

$$X = \{G, S, \Sigma, D_1, s, \sigma\} \quad \text{and} \quad Y = \{G_1, \Delta, S_1, D, s_1, \delta\},$$

respectively the six males and the six females in the set, write :

$$R_1 = \{(x, y) \mid x \in X, y \in Y, y \text{ is wife of } x\} = \{(G, G_1) (S, S_1) (D_1, D) (s, s_1)\}$$

Here $X \cdot Y$ has 36 pairs ; R picks out the set of four married couples. Again, let X and Y each be the whole set of 12 members, and write :

$$R_2 = \{(x, y) \mid x \in X, y \in Y, y \text{ is of the same generation as } x\}$$

Here $X \cdot Y$ has 144 pairs ; R_2 is a subset, the 56 pairs of the same generation.

A relation is now written simply yRx, read "y is related by R to x". Each x in X need not have a y to correspond and the subset of X for which there *are* y's is called the *domain* of the relation. Similarly, each y in Y need not correspond to an x and those that *do* make up a subset of Y called the *range* of the relation. Further, yRx does not imply that there is only one y for each x in the domain—there may well be many. However, if there is only one y for each x, then the relation is a *functional* one. For example, $y=x$ is a functional relation, $y \leqslant x$ is not. Functions may or may not be analytical : $y=x$ is so, but the relation "$y=$ wife of x" is a perfectly proper function under monogamy.

DEFINITION :   A *functional relation* yFx from the set X to the set Y is a relation such that, if there exists a $y \epsilon Y$ for a given $x \epsilon X$, then y is unique. The function is defined on the *domain*

$$\{x \mid \text{there exists } y \text{ such that } yFx\}$$

and the *range* of the function is

$$\{y \mid \text{there exists } x \text{ such that } yFx\}.$$

The shorter term "function" is now used instead of "functional relation" and yFx is replaced by the more familiar $y=F(x)$. Strictly a function is a set of ordered pairs : $\{(x, y) \mid x \epsilon X, y \epsilon Y, y=F(x)\}$; but $y=F(x)$ is generally enough. The functions defined here are of the kind usually known as single-valued ; but multi-valued functions can be split into their single-valued branches to fit the present analysis.

Without serious loss of generality, take X as the domain of the function $y=F(x)$. Then $y=F(x)$ is defined on X and has a range which is a subset of Y. To each $x \epsilon X$, there is a unique $y=F(x)$ in the range. The converse is not true : to each y in the range of $y=F(x)$ there is at least one (not necessarily only one) x in X. For example, define $y_1=2x$ and $y_2=x^2$ on the domain X of all real numbers. The range of y_1 is the set of all real numbers and there is only one x for each y_1. But the range of y_2 is the set of non-negative real numbers and there are two x in X for each positive y_2.

The concept of a function can be viewed from a different angle and described in alternative and more "geometrical" terms :

DEFINITION :   The function $y=F(x)$ defined on X and with a subset of Y as range gives a *mapping* of the set X into the set Y, denoted $X \xrightarrow{F} Y$;

to each $x \epsilon X$ there is under F a unique *image* $y \epsilon Y$.

A mapping is the same thing as a function but often the more convenient concept. The reason is this : though a function is definable for sets of any kind whatever, it is usually associated with sets of numbers. There is no such connotation for a mapping, which can be between sets of any kind, e.g. from points in three dimensions to points in two dimensions, or from a set of integers into a set of polynomials with integral coefficients. All that $F(x)$ does is to lay down a *rule* of some kind for getting from $x \in X$ to its image $y \in Y$.

There are three distinctions to be made about a mapping F of X into Y;

(i) While x varies over the whole of X, its image y under F may well vary only over a *proper* subset of Y—the mapping is generally *into* Y. In the special case where the range is the *whole* of Y, the mapping is described as *onto* Y.

(ii) While each x in X has a unique image y, it can only be said that at least one x has a given y as image. There may well be many such x and the mapping is generally *many-one*. In the special case where only one x has a given image y, the mapping is *one-one* or biunique.

(iii) The sets X and Y are generally different. In the special case where they are the same set, the mapping is of X *into or onto itself*.

Ex. (c). Consider the two mappings : $F_1(x) = 2x$ and $F_2(x) = x^2$. If X is the set of positive integers, either F_1 or F_2 is a *one-one* mapping of X *into* itself. But, if X is the set of all real numbers, then F_1 is a *one-one* mapping of X *onto* itself while F_2 is a *two-one* mapping of X *into* itself. F_2 maps X *onto* the set of non-negative real numbers.

Ex. (d). Consider the mapping : $F(x) =$ wife of x for the set X of all married men (not widowers) in a monogamous tribe. If Y is the set of all women in the tribe, F is a *one-one* mapping of X *into* Y. If Y is the set of all married women (not widows), then F maps X *onto* Y. It is not possible for F to map X into itself. Vary the conjugal convention of the tribe and F has different interpretations. If it is polyandrous, then the mapping is *many-one*. Under polygamy, there is no mapping at all, since a man's image (wife) is not unique under F.

Ex. (e) The distinction between " into " and " onto " mappings can be eliminated by confining attention to the range of the mapping. This is often done. But the distinction is important as can easily be illustrated. Let A be the set $\{a\}$ of real numbers and P the set of all polynomials with real coefficients

$$(a_0 + a_1 x + a_2 x^2 + \dots)$$

Then A can be mapped *into* P by taking $F(a)$ as the polynomial with first coefficient a and the others zero. This particular mapping serves to identify real numbers with the constant terms in polynomials with real coefficients.

Ex. (f). The mapping of a *finite* set into itself is easily handled. Consider $X = \{0, 1, 2, 3, 4\}$ and map X into itself by $F(x) =$ remainder on division of x by 2. The mapping is *many-one* and *into* X, since 0, 2, 4 all map into 0 and 1, 3 into 1. It is easily seen, however, that any mapping of X *onto* itself must be *one-one* and so a permutation of the set.

There is still one further way of expressing and interpreting a functional relation or mapping. Given two sets X and Y, the relation $F(x) = y$ carries an element x of X into an element y of Y. This is a *transformation* F of the set X into the set Y. There is nothing new here; it is only a matter of terminology.

A final point concerns the importance of a *one-one correspondence*. If $y = F(x)$ is one-one, then a single-valued inverse function exists and can be written : $x = F^{-1}(y)$. The mapping $X \xrightarrow{F} Y$ can be inverted to $X \xleftarrow{F^{-1}} Y$ and both together can be shown $X \xleftrightarrow{F} Y$. The transformation $F(x) = y$ carrying x into y can be inverted to $F^{-1}(y) = x$ which carries y back to x.

4. Equivalence : Homomorphism and Isomorphism

A particular but very important relation is that of equivalence in a given set S. The definition is in general terms :

DEFINITION : *yRx is an equivalence relation in a set S if the rules*

    (1) *Reflexive* : xRx

    (2) *Symmetric* :   if *yRx*, then *xRy*

    (3) *Transitive* : if *zRy* and *yRx*, then *zRx*

are all satisfied for any x, y and z in S.

These rules are basic to all concepts of equivalence in logic and in mathematics. They hold for equality ($=$) but are of far wider application.† In particular, an equivalence relation serves to *partition* a set into a series of disjoint subsets, each comprising equivalent elements :

Given an equivalence relation yRx for x and y ∈ S, there is a partition of S into disjoint subsets S_i ($i = 1, 2, 3, \ldots$) such that x and y belong to the same S_i if and only if yRx.

The process of partitioning is exactly that described, in a particular example, in 13.8 above. The subsets of S are called *equivalence classes*; all equivalent (or congruent) members of S go into the same equivalence class. For many purposes, all the elements of S_i can be represented by one particular member x_i, selected for convenience. The representative x_i of the equivalence class S_i is called the *canonical form of S_i*.

† Equivalence relations are to be contrasted with other relations ; for example, those implying some kind of ordering of the elements of S. There is a *partial ordering* of S (relation $\leqslant$) if :

    (1) Reflexive : $x \leqslant x$

    (2) Anti-symmetric : if $x \leqslant y$ and $y \leqslant x$, then $x = y$

together with the usual transitive condition (3). Examples : the " less than or equal to " relation between numbers ; the inclusion relation ($\subseteq$) between sets. There is a stronger relation ($<$) of *linear ordering* if :

              Asymmetric : if $y < x$, then $x \not< y$

together with the transitive condition.

Ex. (a). Consider the relation " y is of the same generation as x " in the set of family members of Ex. (b) of **2** above. It is easily checked that this is an equivalence relation, all three rules being satisfied. It serves to partition the whole set into three subsets :

$$\{G, G_1\} \quad \{A, S, S_1, \Sigma, D, D_1\} \quad \{s, s_1, \sigma, \delta)$$

Each subset comprises equivalent persons (of the same generation). Representative members can be selected, e.g. the " senior " males G, S and s.

Let $X = \{x_1, x_2, x_3, \dots \}$ be a set in which some particular property is defined. The property might be an ordering of the elements of X, or it might be that the product of two elements of X also belongs to X. Let $Y = \{y_1, y_2, y_3, \dots \}$ be another set in which the same property holds.

DEFINITION : A *homomorphism* of X into Y is a mapping $X \xrightarrow{F} Y$ which preserves the defined property, i.e. if the property holds for x_1, x_2, ... of X, then it also holds for the images y_1, y_2, ... in Y. The mapping is an *isomorphism* of X onto Y in the particular case where F is one-one and of X onto Y.

Notice that it is the mapping, and not the pair of sets themselves, which is described as a homomorphism or isomorphism. However, if X and Y are related by a homomorphism, Y is the *homomorphic image* of X and Y is *homomorphic* with X. For the symmetric (biunique) mapping of an isomorphism, it is enough to say that the sets are *isomorphic*.

What has already been said about mappings applies at once to homomorphisms. The homomorphism may be many-one or one-one ; it may be " into " or " onto " ; it may relate different sets or one set into itself.†
The new feature is that a homomorphism preserves a defined property as elements of X are carried over to their images in Y. To make this clear, two particular examples can be taken :

(i) The property defined in X and Y is that of " less than " so that the homomorphism $X \xrightarrow{F} Y$ requires that, if $x_1 \longrightarrow y_1$ and $x_2 \longrightarrow y_2$, then $x_1 < x_2$ implies $y_1 < y_2$. This can be written more shortly :

$$\text{if } x_1 < x_2 \quad \text{then} \quad F(x_1) < F(x_2)$$

(ii) The property is that products are defined in X and Y so that the homomorphism $X \xrightarrow{F} Y$ requires that, if $x_1 \longrightarrow y_1$ and $x_2 \longrightarrow y_2$, then $x_1 \times x_2 \longrightarrow y_1 \times y_2$. More shortly :

$$F(x_1 \times x_2) = F(x_1) \times F(x_2)$$

† Different names are sometimes used for the various kinds of homomorphisms. A fairly complete range would include : monomorphism for one-one, X into Y ; epimorphism for many-one, X onto Y ; isomorphism for one-one, X onto Y ; endomorphism for many-one, X into X ; and automorphism for one-one, X onto X.

The important case where sets X and Y are isomorphic carries the implication that X and Y are not " substantially " different—in the sense that they have the same algebraic rules as far as the defined properties (preserved in the isomorphism) are concerned. Elements of X and Y can have different labels and they may have different uses and interpretations. But they behave in the same way, algebraically. For this reason, the notation $X \cong Y$ can be conveniently used for an isomorphism between sets X and Y. They can also be described as " equivalent up to an isomorphism ". Consider a series of temperatures; let X be the set of their measures in degrees centigrade and Y the set of corresponding measures in degrees fahrenheit. Then $X \cong Y$, equivalent up to an isomorphism, i.e. apart from the scale zero and unit.

The following example illustrates how very different sets can be brought into homomorphic or isomorphic relationship, provided only that the properties concerned—here addition and multiplication—are suitably defined :

Ex. (*b*). In the set $\mathcal{J} = \{ \ldots -2, -1, 0, 1, 2, \ldots \}$ of all integers, take yRx as "x and y have the same remainder on division by 2 ". This is an equivalence relation and it partitions $\mathcal{J}$ into two equivalence classes :

$$\mathcal{J}_0 \ (\text{mod } 2) = \{ \ldots -4, -2, 0, 2, 4, \ldots \} \text{ the set of even integers}$$
$$\mathcal{J}_1 \ (\text{mod } 2) = \{ \ldots -3, -1, 1, 3, 5, \ldots \} \text{ the set of odd integers}$$

Two integers are *congruent* (*modulo* 2) if they are in the same equivalence class, i.e. both even or both odd, with the same remainder on division by 2. The term " modulo 2 " indicates this particular relation. The representative member of $\mathcal{J}_0$ is 0 ; of $\mathcal{J}_1$ it is 1. In each case, it is the common remainder on division by 2 in the subset.

The sum (product) of two equivalence classes is now *defined* as the set of integers obtained by the addition (product) of an integer from one class and an integer from the other class. It is easily checked that the sum is itself an equivalence class :

$$\mathcal{J}_0 + \mathcal{J}_0 = \mathcal{J}_0 ; \quad \mathcal{J}_0 + \mathcal{J}_1 = \mathcal{J}_1 ; \quad \mathcal{J}_1 + \mathcal{J}_1 = \mathcal{J}_0$$

Similarly for the product of equivalence classes :

$$\mathcal{J}_0 \times \mathcal{J}_0 = \mathcal{J}_0 ; \quad \mathcal{J}_0 \times \mathcal{J}_1 = \mathcal{J}_0 ; \quad \mathcal{J}_1 \times \mathcal{J}_1 = \mathcal{J}_1$$

Consider the mapping $\mathcal{J} \xrightarrow{H} \{\mathcal{J}_0, \mathcal{J}_1\}$ where H sends each even integer of $\mathcal{J}$ into the element $\mathcal{J}_0$ and each odd integer into $\mathcal{J}_1$. The mapping preserves sums and products, as can be checked by examples :

Since	$2 \rightarrow \mathcal{J}_0$ and $3 \rightarrow \mathcal{J}_1$
then	$2 + 3 = 5 \rightarrow \mathcal{J}_1 = \mathcal{J}_0 + \mathcal{J}_1$
and	$2 \times 3 = 6 \rightarrow \mathcal{J}_0 = \mathcal{J}_0 \times \mathcal{J}_1$

Hence H is a homomorphism, preserving both sums and products. Now take the set $\{0, 1\}$ (mod 2) consisting of two elements, the representative members of $\mathcal{J}_0$ and $\mathcal{J}_1$. Agree to write congruent integers (mod 2) as equal and to replace them, for addition and multiplication, by their remainders (0 or 1) on division by 2. Sums and products can then be *defined* in the set $\{0, 1\}$, e.g. $1 + 1 = 2$ replaced by 0.

Consider the mapping $\{\mathcal{J}_0, \mathcal{J}_1\} \xleftrightarrow[I]{} \{0, 1\}$ where I sends $\mathcal{J}_0$ into 0 and $_1 \mathcal{J}$ into 1. This

is an isomorphism, since it is one-one and onto, and since it preserves sums and products. For example :

$$\mathcal{J}_1 + \mathcal{J}_1 = \mathcal{J}_0 \longrightarrow 0 = 1 + 1 \quad \text{and} \quad \mathcal{J}_1 \times \mathcal{J}_1 = \mathcal{J}_1 \longrightarrow 1 = 1 \times 1$$

Hence, the infinite set $\mathcal{J}$ has a homomorphic image, the finite set $\{\mathcal{J}_0, \mathcal{J}_1\}$ consisting of only two elements (each a subset), and this in its turn is isomorphic with the set $\{0, 1\}$ of two integers (mod 2).

There is an obvious generalisation of this example. Let m be a given positive integer. The equivalence relation " x and y have the same remainder on division by m " partitions $\mathcal{J}$, the set of all integers, into m equivalence classes $\mathcal{J}_r$ (mod m) for $r = 0, 1, 2, \dots (m-1)$. Here, $\mathcal{J}_0$ comprises 0 and all (positive and negative) multiples of m ; $\mathcal{J}_1$ is obtained by adding 1 to each member of $\mathcal{J}_0$; $\mathcal{J}_2$ by adding 2 to each member of $\mathcal{J}_0$; and so on. Two integers are *congruent* (*modulo* m) if they are in the same equivalence class $\mathcal{J}_r$, having the same remainder r on division by m. Representative members of the equivalence classes are $0, 1, 2, \dots (m-1)$, i.e. the common remainder in each case.

As a *definition*, write sums and products of equivalence classes :

$$\mathcal{J}_r + \mathcal{J}_s = \{j_r + j_s \mid j_r \,\epsilon\, \mathcal{J}_r, \ j_s \,\epsilon\, \mathcal{J}_s\} ; \quad \mathcal{J}_r \times \mathcal{J}_s = \{j_r \times j_s \mid j_r \,\epsilon\, \mathcal{J}_r, \ j_s \,\epsilon\, \mathcal{J}_s\}$$

The sum is the set of all integers obtained by adding an integer from $\mathcal{J}_r$ to an integer from $\mathcal{J}_s$; and similarly for the product. Now, on division by m, the integer j_r has remainder r, and j_s has remainder s. Hence, for some multiples p and q, write :

$$j_r = pm + r ; \ j_s = qm + s ; \quad \text{and} \quad j_r + j_s = (p+q)m + (r+s)$$

So $j_r + j_s$ has the remainder $(r+s)$ or $(r+s-m)$ on division by m, however the two integers of the sum are selected.† It follows that $\mathcal{J}_r + \mathcal{J}_s$ is the equivalence class which contains $(r+s)$ and this can be written $\mathcal{J}_{(r+s)}$. Similarly $\mathcal{J}_r \times \mathcal{J}_s$ is the equivalence class $\mathcal{J}_{(rs)}$ containing $(r \times s)$. The definition is such that the sum or the product of two equivalence classes is itself an equivalence class—as required.

On this basis, the result of the example (for mod 2) generalises at once to the following result for congruence (mod m) :

$$\mathcal{J} \xrightarrow{H} \{\mathcal{J}_0, \mathcal{J}_1, \mathcal{J}_2, \dots \mathcal{J}_{m-1}\} \xleftrightarrow{I} \{0, 1, 2, \dots (m-1)\} \ (\text{mod } m)$$

where H is a homomorphism and I an isomorphism, both preserving sums and products. Addition and multiplication in the set of m integers (mod m) proceeds on the agreement that all integers are replaced by their

† Since $0 \leqslant r, \ s < m$, so $0 \leqslant (r+s) < 2m$.

M.E.

remainders on division by m. This finite set of m members is isomorphic with (i.e. algebraically as good as) the set of m subsets $\mathscr{J}_r$. On jobbing backwards, it is also the homomorphic image of the whole (infinite) set of integers. All this is done by taking representative integers in a partition of $\mathscr{J}$ (mod m).

5. Binary and Other Operations

It is already clear that something needs to be said about operations performed on elements of a set. In **2** above, a set of subsets A, B, C, ... was considered, the elements being subjected to various operations. These include the unary operation of getting the complement A' of a given subset A, and the binary operations of writing the union (logical sum) and the intersection (logical product) of two subsets. Then, in **4** above, a different kind of sum (or product) of two sets was defined, the set of all sums (or products) of two elements selected one from each of the given sets :

$$A + B = \{(a+b) \mid a \in A, b \in B\} \quad \text{and} \quad A \times B = \{(a \times b) \mid a \in A, b \in B\}$$

A systematic treatment, on the lines of 13.1 above, is now required.

A set $S = \{a, b, c, ... \}$ is given ; the elements can be of any kind whatever. A *unary operation* which is *closed* in S is a rule of translation of any element of S to give another element of S. It is a mapping of S into itself. Nothing more needs to be said, in general, about this type of operation. A *binary operation* is a rule of combination (typically sum or product) of two elements of S, the elements being ordered. If *closed* in S, the binary operation on two elements gives another element of S ; it is a mapping of the Cartesian product $S . S$. into S. This is the kind of operation to be investigated in detail here. But the possibilities are still not exhausted. In view of the fact that the elements of S can be quite complicated entities, all kinds of operations may be performed on them. Indeed, one such operation—that of scalar multiplication—is essential to the development of vectors and matrices (13.1 above).

In every case, an explicit *definition* of an operation must be given, either by listing all possibilities, or by providing a general description, e.g. in terms of other operations. Addition and multiplication tables, as illustrated in 13.1 above, are examples of listing.

To maintain generality, a binary operation is now denoted by the neutral symbol $*$. Two elements a and b of S are combined to give $a * b$. To see what is going on, simply try the substitution of + or × for *. The desirable properties of the binary operation are :

(1) *Closure* : $a * b \in S$

(2) *Associative* : $a * (b * c) = (a * b) * c$

(3) *Commutative* : $a * b = b * a$

(4) *Identity* :   there is a unique identity $(e \in S)$ so that $a * e = e * a = a$
                         for each $a \in S$

(5) *Inverse* :   there is a unique inverse of a $(a^{-1} \in S)$ so that
                         $a * a^{-1} = a^{-1} * a = e$ for each $a \in S$

If these properties hold (except perhaps the commutative one), then it follows that † :

(5′) *Cancellation* :   if $a * b = a * c$, then $b = c$

The converse is not true. If (5) is replaced by (5′) in the list of properties, it does not follow that (5) holds. The set of integers provides an example. Hence, (5′) is a weaker form of (5).

When two binary operations * and o are defined in S, each may separately have the above properties. Further properties are needed in relating the two operations and the desirable ones are :

Distributive :

  * over o $a * (b \circ c) = (a * b) \circ (a * c)$ and $(a \circ b) * c = (a * c) \circ (b * c)$

  o over * $a \circ (b * c) = (a \circ b) * (a \circ c)$ and $(a * b) \circ c = (a \circ c) * (b \circ c)$

There are two distributive properties, one being the dual of the other, as in Boolean algebras (2 above).

Now drop the pretence that a binary operation is a neutral *. In most cases, it is + or × ; suitably defined sums and products exist in S. All the properties listed hold for sums and products of numbers (rational, real or complex), with one reservation and one exception. The reservation is that $a = 0$ must be excluded in writing reciprocals. The exception is that, unlike Boolean algebra, only one of the distributive properties holds, that of × over +. Hence the operational rules of Table 1A of 13.1 are obtained, all true for rational, real or complex numbers. For other sets, with suitably defined sums and products, the aim is to make as many of them valid as possible.

---

† For : $a * b = a * c$ implies $a^{-1} * (a * b) = a^{-1} * (a * c)$ since a^{-1} exists

i.e. $(a^{-1} * a) * b = (a^{-1} * a) * c$ by (2)

i.e. $e * b = e * c$ by (5)

i.e. $b = c$ by (4).

The rules are operational, not axiomatic. They are not put together in an " economical " way in the sense that some of the rules are superfluous, derivable from other rules. In a strict approach, a consistent and independent set of axioms is laid down ; any superfluous rules—and any not to be assumed in the particular system developed—must be first weeded out. A simple example illustrates :

Ex. (*a*). The second part of the distributive rule follows from the first part and the commutative rule for multiplication. The first part of the distributive rule states :

$$c \times (a+b) = c \times a + c \times b$$

So

$$(a+b) \times c = a \times c + b \times c$$

by the commutative rule. This is the second part of the distributive rule.

There are difficulties in handling zero, which relates to addition, in the operation of multiplication. A hint that difficulties exist is that $a=0$ must be omitted for reciprocals. But this is not all. Consider the set S in relation to the inverse and cancellation rules for products. Assume that all the other rules for sums and products are valid for S, except that it need not be commutative under multiplication, the rules being numbered as in Table 1A of 13.1. First :

$$a \times b + 0 = a \times b = a \times (b+0) = a \times b + a \times 0$$

by applying (A4) and (D). Hence, $0 = a \times 0$ by (A5'). Similarly $0 = 0 \times a$.

So

$$a \times 0 = 0 \times a = 0 \quad \dots\dots\dots\dots\dots\dots\dots\dots\dots\dots(1)$$

If the cancellation rule does hold for products, put $c=0$ in (M5') :

if $a \times b = a \times 0$ $(a \neq 0)$, then $b=0$

i.e. if $a \times b = 0$ $(a \neq 0)$, then $b=0$ by (1)

The cancellation rule thus implies a result which can be put in two equivalent forms :

$$\left. \begin{array}{l} \text{If } a \times b = 0, \quad \text{then} \quad \text{either } a=0 \text{ or } b=0 \\ \text{If } a \neq 0 \quad \text{and} \quad b \neq 0, \quad \text{then} \quad a \times b \neq 0 \end{array} \right\} \dots\dots\dots\dots(2)$$

On the other hand, if the cancellation rule does not hold, then the result (2) can fail. The possibilities are :

(i) S has reciprocals, rules (M5) and (M5') are valid, and (2) holds. No two non-zero members of S can multiply to zero. Example : the set of rational numbers.

(ii) S does not have reciprocals for all members (M5 not valid) but the cancellation rule (M5') holds. Hence (2) is still true. Though S

is lacking in reciprocals, it is a set *without zero divisors*, i.e. such that no non-zero elements multiply to zero. Example: the set of integers.

(iii) S neither has reciprocals for all members nor satisfies the cancellation rule (neither M5 nor M5′ valid). The result (2) can fail. Here S is a set *with zero divisors*, i.e. there are non-zero elements which multiply to zero. Example: certain sets of matrices.

Ex. (*b*). The set $\mathcal{J} = \{ \dots -2, -1, 0, 1, 2, \dots \}$ lacks reciprocals but is without zero divisors. Now consider products in the set of integers, modulo m. The multiplication tables for $m=3$ and 4 are:

$m=3$	0	1	2
0	0	0	0
1	0	1	2
2	0	2	1

$m=4$	0	1	2	3
0	0	0	0	0
1	0	1	2	3
2	0	2	0	2
3	0	3	2	1

Case $m=3$: the set $\{0, 1, 2\}$ (mod 3) has reciprocals for both its non-zero members. From the multiplication table, $1 \times 1 = 2 \times 2 = 1$; 1 is the reciprocal of itself and so is 2. The set satisfies the inverse and cancellation rules (M5 and M5′); it does better than $\mathcal{J}$ itself.

Case $m=4$: the set $\{0, 1, 2, 3\}$ (mod 4) lacks a reciprocal for the element 2. From the multiplication table, there is no a such that $2 \times a = 1$. The cancellation rule also fails and there are zero divisors. From the table, $2 \times 2 = 0$ and 2 is a divisor of zero. This peculiarity arises because 4 is not prime, i.e. $2 \times 2 = 4$ replaced by 0 (mod 4).

This last remark suggests what is in fact a general result for the multiplication of integers:

Set	Inverse rule	Cancellation rule
All integers	No	Yes
Integers (mod m):		
m prime	Yes	Yes
m not prime	No	No

The best-behaved set of integers is that modulo m, for m prime.

6. Groups

The set is the basic concept of logic and mathematics; but the sets of mathematics generally have the structure of a " group ". The definition is simple and general :

DEFINITION : A set $G=\{a, b, c, \ldots\}$ of elements of any kind, in which a binary operation $*$ is defined, is a *group* if :

Closure : $a*b \in G$
Associative : $a*(b*c)=(a*b)*c$
Identity :   there is an identity $(e \in G)$ so that $e*a=a$ for each $a \in G$
Inverse :   there is an inverse of a $(a^{-1} \in G)$ so that $a^{-1}*a=e$ for each $a \in G$

This is a strictly axiomatic definition. To fill it out, it can be *deduced*, by proofs which are tricky but not difficult, that :

(i) e is unique and $a*e=a$ $(=e*a)$
(ii) a^{-1} is unique and $a*a^{-1}=e$ $(=a^{-1}*a)$
(iii) if $a*b=a*c$, then $b=c$

Hence, a group has all the desired rules of operation, *except* the commutative rule. Elements of G commute, in general, only for particular cases such as e and a, or a and a^{-1}. A group which happens to satisfy the commutative rule for all elements is called a *commutative group*. In practice, the operation $*$ is either $+$ or $\times$. If the operation is $+$, it is commonly the case that the commutative rule is valid ; commutative groups under addition can be called *additive groups* for short. For them, all the rules (A1–5) hold. If the operation is $\times$, the commutative rule is often not satisfied, e.g. for the group of non-singular matrices. Of the rules (M1–5), all hold for commutative groups, and all except (M3) for non-commutative groups.

The following examples illustrate that a group can consist of elements of various kinds and that it may well comprise very few elements :

Ex. (a). The set of integers $\mathcal{J}$ is an additive group, the group operation being ordinary arithmetical addition. The set $\mathcal{J}$ is viewed from a different angle when the operation is multiplication. In fact, it is *not* a group under multiplication ; it has an identity (1) but no other elements have reciprocals (inverses).

Ex. (b). The set of integers, modulo m, is an additive group ; addition here is mod m. The negative of any element r is $(m-r)$, since these two add to m, replaced by 0 (mod m). When m *is prime*, the set is also a commutative group under the group operation of multiplication (mod m). The element 0 has here to be excluded from the group. The identity element is 1 and all elements have reciprocals. When m *is not prime*, the set is not a group under multiplication since it lacks reciprocals. This is illustrated, as in Ex. (b) of 5 above, by the sets $\{0, 1, 2\}$ (mod 3) and $\{0, 1, 2, 3\}$ (mod 4). The first of these is a group of three elements. There is also $\{0, 1\}$ (mod 2), a group of only two elements.

Ex. (c). Let F be a mapping (transformation) of X into Y, and G a mapping of Y into Z. The two mappings applied in succession, first F then G, give a mapping of X into Z :

$$F(x) = y \quad \text{and} \quad G(y) = z \quad \text{give} \quad G(F(x)) = z$$

Define this as the product GF. Now consider the set of all mappings F, G, H ... which are one-one and of X onto itself. Then GF is also one-one and of X onto itself (closure). Three mappings can be applied in succession and $H(GF)$ and $(HG)F$ give the same product mapping (associative). On the other hand, GF and FG are both product mappings but they need not give the same result (non-commutative). There is an identity mapping $I(x) = x$ which leaves the elements of X unchanged ; further, the product IF is the same mapping as F itself (identity). Finally, since the mappings are one-one, there is an inverse mapping F^{-1} which undoes what F does, i.e. $F^{-1}(F(x)) = x$ or $F^{-1}F = I$ (inverse). Hence, the set of all one-one mappings (transformations) of a set X onto itself is a non-commutative group under the operation of multiplication, a product being defined as the application of two mappings in succession. The concept of a group was, as a historical fact, first developed for transformations. Notice also that, if X happens to be a finite set, *all* transformations of X onto itself are one-one and form a group ; this is the group of permutations of the set X.

A group G has all kinds of subsets. The question is whether a given subset itself has the properties of a group ; it is then a subgroup.

DEFINITION : A subset K of a group G which itself satisfies the conditions for a group is called a *subgroup* of G. For this, it is enough : (1) if a, $b \in K$, then $a * b \in K$ and (2) if $a \in K$, then $a^{-1} \in K$.

The proof of the sufficient conditions, shown above, is easily provided. They boil down the full set of four conditions for a group in this case. Suppose (1) and (2) hold. (1) is closure and by two applications, if a, b, and $c \in K$, so do $a * (b * c)$ and $(a * b) * c$. Moreover, these are the same in G and hence in K also (associative). Further, if $a \in K$, then (2) says that $a^{-1} \in K$, and (1) that $a^{-1} * a \in K$. But $a^{-1} * a = e$, so that $e \in K$. This, with the fact that $a^{-1} \in K$, shows that the identity and inverse rules hold for K. Hence K is a group, a subgroup of G.

As a corollary, it has been established that :

A subgroup K of G must contain the identity (e) of G, which is also the identity of K. G has at least one subgroup, i.e. $\{e\}$.

On the subgroup $\{e\}$ of a single element, it is only necessary to note that $e * e = e$ so that e is the identity and its own inverse.

From the definitions of **4** above, write a *group homomorphism* $G \xrightarrow{F} G_1$ as mapping F of one group G into another group G_1 which carries the group operation $*$ over from G to G_1 : if $a \longrightarrow a_1$ and $b \longrightarrow b_1$, then $a * b \longrightarrow a_1 * b_1$ under F.[†] The homomorphism also carries the identity of G

† Even better : if there is a homomorphism of a group G into a *set* G_1, then it can be shown that G_1 is also a *group*, i.e. the homomorphic image of a group is another group.

into the identity of G_1, an inverse in G into an inverse in G_1, and a subgroup of G into a subgroup of G_1. The mapping is a *group isomorphism* in the particular case where it is one-one and of G onto G_1.

A main result in group theory is a " mapping theorem " which achieves two things : it is a partitioning of a group ; and it serves to make a new group out of an old group, one being mapped into the other. The result is developed here in the particular case of a *commutative group* G under the operation $*$, which may be $+$ or $\times$.†

G has at least one subgroup and it usually has many. Let K be any given subgroup of G. Suppose that $x^{-1} * y \in K$ for certain x and $y \in G$, so defining a relation yRx in G. It is easily checked that yRx is an equivalence relation and hence that it partitions G into disjoint subsets. Start with $e \in K$ and put into the first subset all y such that yRe, i.e. $e^{-1} * y \in K$. Since e is its own inverse : $e^{-1} * y = e * y = y$. Hence $y \in K$ and the first subset is K itself. Now take x_1 in G but not in K and form the second subset from all $y_1 \in G$ such that $y_1 R x_1$, i.e. $x_1^{-1} * y_1 \in K$ or $x_1^{-1} * y_1 = k$ for some element k of K. Hence :

$$y_1 = e * y_1 = (x_1 * x_1^{-1}) * y_1 = x_1 * (x_1^{-1} * y_1) = x_1 * k$$

The second subset is $\{x_1 * k\}$ where k ranges over K. Next, take x_2 in G but not in either of the first two subsets and the third subset is found similarly to be $\{x_2 * k\}$ where k ranges over K. This process continues until G is exhausted.

Hence the partitioning of G is into subsets :

$$K = \{e * k\} ; \quad S_1 = \{x_1 * k\} ; \quad S_2 = \{x_2 * k\} ; \quad \dots$$

where k ranges over K and where x_i ($i = 1, 2, 3, \dots$) is an element of G not in the subsets before S_i. The representative elements are e, x_1, x_2, $\dots$. The subsets are called *cosets* of K and a typical coset is denoted $x * K = \{x * k\}$. Note that K is a coset of itself since $K = e * K = \{e * k\}$. So G partitions into a set of cosets of K :

$$K = e * K ; \quad x_1 * K ; \quad x_2 * K ; \dots \quad \dots\dots\dots\dots\dots\dots(1)$$

† Essentially the same theorem holds when G is not commutative. The difference is that it does not work for any subgroup of G but only for a particular kind of subgroup called a *normal subgroup*. A subgroup K is normal if $k \in K$ implies that $x * k * x^{-1} \in K$ for all $x \in G$. Given x, the element $x * k * x^{-1}$ is the *conjugate* of k ; a normal subgroup is such that all conjugates of an element of K are also in K. The difficulty does not arise when G is commutative since $x * k * x^{-1} = x * x^{-1} * k = e * k = k$ and each element coincides with its conjugate. Note that $x * k * x^{-1}$ is $x + k + (-x)$ for addition, and $x \times k \times \dfrac{1}{x}$ for multiplication

The interpretation of this partition varies with the group operation :

(i) The operation $+$. The relation yRx is $(-x)+y \in K$ for x, $y \in G$. Since G is commutative, $(-x)+y=y+(-x)=y-x$. The relation is that the difference $(y-x) \in K$. The coset $x*K$ is $x+K=\{(x+k)\}$ where k ranges over K. Hence, to get a coset of K, simply add a fixed element x (not in K) to each element of K. In the partition of G, one subset differs from another only by a fixed addition to each element.

(ii) The operation $\times$. The relation yRx is $x^{-1} \times y \in K$ for x, $y \in G$. Since G is commutative, $x^{-1} \times y = y \times x^{-1} = y$ divided by x. The relation is that the ratio $y/x \in K$. The coset $x*K$ is $xK=\{x \times k\}$ where k ranges over K. Subsets in the partition of G differ only in that the elements of one are a constant multiple of the elements of another.

As a matter of *definition*, the group operation can be extended to apply to cosets. For addition, let x_1+K and x_2+K be two cosets, select an element from each (a_1 and a_2) and define the sum of the cosets as the set $\{(a_1+a_2) \mid a_1 \in x_1+K, a_2 \in x_2+K\}$. Now $a_1=x_1+k_1$ and $a_2=x_2+k_2$ for some k_1, $k_2 \in K$. So $a_1+a_2=(x_1+x_2)+k$ where $k=k_1+k_2 \in K$, since K is a subgroup. Hence (a_1+a_2) ranges over the coset $(x_1+x_2)+K$. There is a similar definition for the product of two cosets as another coset. Hence :

$$(x_1+K)+(x_2+K)=(x_1+x_2)+K \quad \text{and} \quad (x_1K) \times (x_2K)=(x_1x_2)K$$

i.e. $$(x_1*K)*(x_2*K)=(x_1*x_2)*K \dots\dots\dots(2)$$

The set of cosets (1) can be shown to be a group under the same group operation $*$ as in G, the operation applying to cosets as in (2). This is only a matter of checking the conditions for a group one by one. For example, the identity coset is $K=e*K$, since :

$$(e*K)*(x*K)=(e*x)*K=x*K$$

Similarly, $(x^{-1}*K)$ is the coset inverse to $(x*K)$. The group of cosets of K is called the *factor group* of G (mod K) and written G/K.

The final step is to link the original group G, first with the factor group G/K, and then with the group of representative elements of the cosets, making up G/K and shown in (1). This last group can be written $G_1 = \{e, x_1, x_2, \dots\}$. The result (2) shows how the group operation $*$ can be applied to the elements of the group G/K and also to those of G_1. Consider the mapping $G \xrightarrow{H} G/K$ where H sends each element of G into the coset to which it belongs, i.e. $H(x)=x*K$. By (2), H is a homomorphism which preserves the group operation $*$. Further, there is a mapping $G/K \longleftrightarrow G_1$ where I sends each coset of G/K into its representative element in G_1. This is an isomorphism and it also preserves the group operation. The *Mapping Theorem* now reached is as follows. If G is a given commutative group and K some subgroup of G, then a new group G/K can be constructed which is homomorphic with G; it is the factor group comprising K and all its cosets (a partition of G). Alternatively, the new group can be taken as $G_1 = \{e, x_1, x_2, \dots\}$ consisting of representative elements of K and its cosets. The relations can be summarised:

$$G \xrightarrow[H]{} G/K \xleftarrow[I]{} G_1$$

where H is a homomorphism and I an isomorphism, both preserving the group operation.

Ex. (d). For integers under the operation of *addition* only—ignoring multiplication at this stage—the results obtained in **4** above can be reviewed in the light of the fact that integers form additive groups. The set of integers $\mathcal{J}$, an additive group, has an additive subgroup in the form of the set $\mathcal{J}_0$ (mod m) comprising 0 and all multiples of m. That $\mathcal{J}_0$ (mod m) is itself a group is easily checked. Add 1 to each member of $\mathcal{J}_0$ and the coset $(1 + \mathcal{J}_0)$ is obtained; this is in fact $\mathcal{J}_1$ (mod m). Similarly, $\mathcal{J}_2, \mathcal{J}_3, \dots \mathcal{J}_{m-1}$ (all mod m) are the cosets $(2 + \mathcal{J}_0)$, $(3 + \mathcal{J}_0)$, $\dots (m - 1 + \mathcal{J}_0)$. Hence, on partitioning $\mathcal{J}$, the set of cosets $\{\mathcal{J}_0, \mathcal{J}_1, \dots \mathcal{J}_{m-1}\}$ is the factor group. This group is isomorphic with the group of representative elements $\{0, 1, \dots m - 1\}$, the integers (mod m). The mapping theorem simply states that $\mathcal{J}$ is homomorphic with either of these groups of m elements.

Take the case $m = 2$ as the simplest instance. The set $\mathcal{J}_0$ (mod 2) is that of all even integers; it is a subgroup of the group $\mathcal{J}$ of all integers under addition. There is only one coset, obtained by adding 1 to each member of $\mathcal{J}_0$ to give $\mathcal{J}_1$ (mod 2), the set of odd integers. Note that $\mathcal{J}_1$ is not itself a group—the addition of two odd integers is not another odd integer—but merely the coset of the subgroup $\mathcal{J}_0$. $\mathcal{J}$ is homomorphic with the group $\{\mathcal{J}_0, \mathcal{J}_1\}$ and with the group $\{0, 1\}$ (mod 2), both these groups being of two elements only.

Ex. (e). The set $\{e, a, a^2, \dots a^{n-1}\}$ is generated by a single element a, assumed to be such that $a^0 = e$ and $a^n = e$. It satisfies the conditions for a commutative group under the operation of multiplication, and with identity e; it is called a *cyclic group*. An example is the group of four elements $G = \{1, i, -1, -i\} = \{1, i, i^2, i^3\}$, where $i^2 = -1$ and $i^4 = 1$. G can be used to illustrate the mapping theorem as applied to cyclic groups generally.

$K = \{1, -1\}$ is a subgroup of G, with identity 1 and with -1 as its own reciprocal. The only coset of K is $iK = \{i, -i\}$, obtained from K by multiplying by i. The mapping theorem is:

$$G = \{1, i, i^2, i^3\} \xrightarrow[H]{} \{K, iK\} \xleftarrow[I]{} \{-1, i\} = G_1$$

where H is a homomorphism and I an isomorphism, preserving products. Notice that, of the two elements of G_1, -1 is representative of K and i of the coset iK. G is partitioned into two subsets and from this comes a new group G_1, the homomorphic image of G. The new group, like the old, is cyclic. The original group G is cyclic in i, with identity 1 and $i^4 = 1$. The new group G_1 has two elements only, cyclic in i, with identity -1 and $i^2 = -1$.

7. Fields and Rings

The elements of a group are subject to one binary operation only, generally *either* addition *or* multiplication. Group theory suffices for the algebra (e.g.) of sets where only products are defined, as for sets of mappings or transformations. But most of algebra deals with entities subject to two or more operations. A development is needed, based on group theory but extending it. Two lines are pursued here, both starting from an additive group, a set of elements " obedient " as regards addition. In one development, what is added is a product operation ; in the other, it is the operation of scalar multiplication.

In the first approach, the most useful concept is that of a field :

DEFINITION : A set F of elements a, b, c, ... of any kind, in which two binary operations (sums and products) are defined, is a *field* if the elements form a commutative group $(F+)$ under addition, if the non-zero elements form another commutative group $(F\times)$ under multiplication, and if the distributive rule holds :

$$a(b+c)=ab+ac$$

In short, a field combines in itself two commutative groups, one for sums and one for products, and it relates the two groups by the distributive rule. In practice, a field is a set which satisfies all the operational rules (A1–5, M1–5 and D). The most usual cases are the sets of numbers (rational, real or complex). The identity element is written as 0 for addition, and as 1 for multiplication. The $\times$ sign will now be dropped in writing products whenever there is no ambiguity.

A field is a very specialised set indeed, satisfying a long list of rules. There are other sets, with both sums and products, which satisfy most but not all of the rules ; examples : the set of integers, the set of square matrices. Here the wider concept of a ring enters :

DEFINITION : A set R of elements a, b, c, ... of any kind, in which two binary operations (sums and products) are defined, is a *ring* if the elements form a commutative group $(R+)$ under addition, if the non-zero elements $(R\times)$ under multiplication satisfy two conditions.

Closure : $ab \in R$ and Associative : $a(bc)=(ab)c$

as a minimum, and if the distributive rule holds :

$$a(b+c)=ab+ac \quad \text{and} \quad (a+b)c=ac+bc$$

Of the operational rules, (A1–5) and (D) hold but only (M1) and (M2) are specified for a ring ; the others (M3–5) are optional. Notice that both parts of the distributive rule need to be postulated; this is because it is not assumed that $(R \times)$ is commutative.

The following example shows how varied is the concept of a ring.

Ex. (*a*). Consider the Boolean algebra of a set of subsets (**2** above). The rules of the algebra, with union written $+$ and intersection $\times$, are familiar—but only in part. Can they be improved? The answer is yes—if sums are re-defined. Write $A + B$, not as the union of A and B, but as this union *less* the intersection of A and B. The sum is then the shaded area of Fig. 83I, replacing that of Fig. 82I. With this $A + B$ and with intersection still written $A \times B$, it is easily checked that the set of subsets A, B, C, ... satisfies all the conditions for a ring. For example, Fig. 83II illustrates that the associative rule holds for addition.

The ring is called a Boolean ring; it is commutative both for addition and for multiplication. Besides the familiar features, the ring has some rather strange ones. The identity elements are the *bounds*, ϕ for zero and U for unity. Since $A + A = \phi$, a set A is always its own negative. The ring lacks reciprocals and cancellation does not hold for products. In fact, it has zero divisors; $A \times B = \phi$ implies that A and B are disjoint, so that any disjoint sets divide zero ϕ.

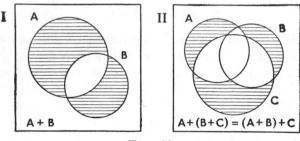

FIG. 83

A *field* is a special case of a ring, that in which all the optional rules (M3–5) are valid. An *integral domain* is another special case in which the rules are almost, but not quite, satisfied. An integral domain is a ring for which the rules (M3), (M4) and the weaker (M5') all hold, i.e. $(R \times)$ is commutative, with a unity and without zero divisors. All that an integral domain lacks is that the elements do not generally have reciprocals. The set of integers is the leading example of an integral domain; another is the set of polynomials with integral or rational coefficients.

The concept of a group homomorphism extends to that of a *ring homomorphism* $R \xrightarrow{F} R_1$. Here F is a mapping of the ring R into the ring R_1 which preserves both sums and products. A *ring isomorphism* arises when F is one-one and of R onto R_1. The *Mapping Theorem* for groups can be extended to rings, in the following way. Let R be a ring which is commutative (M3) and which has an identity (M4) under multiplication. This is the most important case in practice—including both integral domains and fields—though the result can in fact be somewhat generalised. The basic construction is for $(R+)$, the ring viewed as a commutative group under addition. Let K be a subset of R which is an additive sub-group. Then the mapping theorem for groups partitions R:

$$R \xrightarrow[H]{} R/K \xleftrightarrow[I]{} R_1 \dots\dots\dots\dots\dots\dots\dots\dots\dots\dots\dots\dots(1)$$

All three sets in (1) are additive groups and the mappings are H a group homomorphism and I a group isomorphism, preserving sums. R/K is the set of additive cosets $(x+K)$ and R_1 is the set of their representative elements. Now consider products in R and also in the other two sets of (1). It is *assumed* that K has a further property: if $k \in K$, then $rk \in K$ as r ranges over R. K is then called an *ideal* of R; it is an additive subgroup of R such that all multiples of an element of K also belong to K. It can then be deduced that the result (1), with exactly the *same sets* and the *same mappings*, holds for products as well as for sums. The sets are all rings; of the mappings, H is a ring homomorphism and I a ring isomorphism.

The result, not formally proved here, can be illustrated by $\mathcal{J}$, the set of all integers. $\mathcal{J}$ is a ring (integral domain) for sums and products. The analysis of **4** above, viewed from the angle of addition in Ex. (d) of **6** above, can now be completed. There is a partition of $\mathcal{J}$:

$$\mathcal{J} \xrightarrow[H]{} \{\mathcal{J}_0, \mathcal{J}_1, \mathcal{J}_2, \dots \mathcal{J}_{m-1}\} \xleftrightarrow[I]{} \{0, 1, 2, \dots m-1\} \pmod{m} \dots\dots\dots(2)$$

Where H is a homomorphism and I an isomorphism, preserving sums and products, suitably defined as in **4** above. Here:

$$\mathcal{J}_0 = \{ \dots -2m, -m, 0, m, 2m, \dots \}$$

which is an additive subgroup of $\mathcal{J}$ and which has the property that it contains all multiples of any given element. Hence, $\mathcal{J}_0$ is an ideal of the ring $\mathcal{J}$. All the sets of (2) are rings, related by ring homomorphisms. Though derived directly, (2) is in fact a case of the result (1).

In the mapping theorem, a new ring R_1 is constructed from an old one R. It would be good if the construction turned a *ring* into a *field*. This can be done, and in more than one way, as can be illustrated for the ring (integral domain) of integers. By suitably defining " ratios " of integers, this ring can be turned into the field of rationals. Another kind of field can be obtained from the mapping result (2). First, (2) shows that the finite set of integers (mod m) is a *ring* obtained, as a homomorphic image, from the ring of integers. Second, the results of Ex. (b) of **5** above show that the set of integers (mod m) is a *field*, provided that m *is prime*. Hence, the ring (integral domain) of integers has a series of finite fields as homomorphic images :

$$\{0, 1\} \,(\text{mod } 2) \; ; \quad \{0, 1, 2\} \,(\text{mod } 3) \; ; \quad \{0, 1, 2, 3, 4\} \,(\text{mod } 5) \; ; \; \ldots$$

and generally : $\{0, 1, 2, \ldots p-1\} \,(\text{mod } p)$ for p prime

Ex. (b).   Let a and b be any element of the field of integers (mod p) for p prime. Consider the cases of the smaller primes :

$p = 2 :$ $(a+b)^2 = a^2 + 2ab + b^2 = a^2 + b^2$ since $2 \equiv 0 \pmod 2$
$p = 3 :$ $(a+b)^3 = a^3 + 3a^2b + 3ab^2 + b^3 = a^3 + b^3$ since $3 \equiv 0 \pmod 3$
$p = 5 :$ $(a+b)^5 = a^5 + 5a^4b + 10a^3b^2 + 10a^2b^3 + 5ab^4 + b^5 = a^5 + b^5$
                                              since 5 and $10 \equiv 0 \pmod 5$

Generally, by expansion by the Binomial Theorem, the set of integers (mod p), for p prime, has the intriguing property : $(a+b)^p = a^p + b^p$.

8. Vector Spaces

A field is a very special set of elements, satisfying all the desirable properties for sums and products of the elements.   The usual number systems (rational, real or complex numbers) are fields ; they are used as such in the following.   When sets of more complicated elements are considered (e.g. polynomials or matrices), it is too much to expect that they are fields, though they may well be rings, for sums and products.   The second line of development (noted in **7** above) opens up more fruitful territory.   The starting point is again a set of elements forming an additive group ;   and again a second operation is defined to supplement addition. This second operation is multiplication of any element of the set, not by another element of the set, but by a scalar from a separate set of scalar elements.   The main set consists of elements of any kind, now identified as *vectors*.   The side set is a field, typically of rational, real or complex numbers.   The following definition is an abstract, though not perhaps the most general, formulation of a vector space over a field.   The rules specified are those of Table 1 of 13.1.

DEFINITION : V is a set of elements a, b, c, ... of any kind, in which the binary operation of addition is defined. F is a field of scalars λ, μ, v, ... such that the product $\lambda \,.\, a$ of any element a of V by any scalar λ of F is defined in V.   Then V is a *vector space over the field* F, and comprises *vectors*, if V is an additive group (rules A1–5) and if scalar multiplication satisfies the rules (S1–5).

Notice that the sets V and F are quite separate ; there is no requirement that V includes F.   There are then two distinct zero elements : the zero vector 0 of V which appears in the rules (A1–5) and the zero 0 of F which appears among the scalars λ, μ, ν, ... The same symbol is used; the context makes it clear which zero is intended in each case.

There is one particular case of a vector space which turns out to be most important. Write $a = (a_1, a_2, \ldots a_n)$ as an n-tuple of scalar components from the field F and consider, for given n, the set S of all such n-tuples as the components range over F. Define addition in S and scalar multiplication by λ of F:

$$a+b = (a_1+b_1, a_2+b_2, \ldots, a_n+b_n) \quad \text{and} \quad \lambda \cdot a = (\lambda a_1, \lambda a_2, \ldots, \lambda a_n)$$

each being another n-tuple of S. It is easily checked that the rules (A1–5) and (S1–5) are satisfied so that S is a vector space over F. S is called the *Cartesian space* of dimension n over F and denoted $V_n(F)$. Further, if the components of a are from the field of real numbers and if each a has a length $|a| = \sqrt{(a_1^2 + a_2^2 + \ldots + a_n^2)}$, then the set S is called the *Euclidean space* of dimension n over F and denoted $E_n(F)$.

The basic construction in a vector space is that of a linear combination of vectors, i.e. the sum of multiples of vectors. The two operations, addition and scalar multiplication, are here used together. Let $S_n = \{v_1, v_2, \ldots v_n\}$ be any subset of n vectors in V over F. Select scalars $\lambda_1, \lambda_2 \ldots, \lambda_n$ from F and write the *linear combination* of S_n:

$$v = \sum_{r=1}^{n} \lambda_r v_r = \lambda_1 v_1 + \lambda_2 v_2 + \ldots + \lambda_n v_n$$

Then v is itself a vector of V. Some, or indeed all, of the λ's can be zero. So, v_r is a linear combination of S_n (all λ's zero, except $\lambda_r = 1$) and the zero vector is a linear combination of S_n (all λ's zero).

The set S_n is *linearly independent* if *no* set of $\lambda_1, \lambda_2, \ldots, \lambda_n$ exist so that $\sum_{r=1}^{n} \lambda_r v_r = 0$. In this case, no one vector of S_n is a linear combination of other vectors of S_n. Conversely, if S_n is not linearly independent, then at least one vector of S_n is a linear combination of other vectors of S_n. The proof of these statements is simple. First, if S_n is linearly independent, suppose that v_1 (for example) were a linear combination of the others:

$v_1 = \sum_{r=2}^{n} \lambda_r v_r$. Then $\sum_{r=1}^{n} \lambda_r v_r = 0$ with $\lambda_1 = -1$. This is a contradiction.

Second, if S_n is not linearly independent, then $\sum_{r=1}^{n} \lambda_r v_r = 0$ for some λ's not all zero. Suppose that $\lambda_1 \neq 0$. Then $v_1 = \sum_{r=2}^{n} \left(\frac{\lambda_r}{\lambda_1}\right) v_r$ and v_1 is a linear combination of other vectors of S_n.

In the vector space V over F, look for a subset $S_n = \{v_1, v_2, \dots v_n\}$ such that *all* vectors of V are linear combinations of S_n. If there is no such S_n, no matter how large n, then V is said to be of *infinite dimension*. Infinite vector spaces are of interest ; the vector space of polynomials is one. But attention is concentrated here on finite vector spaces. If there is a subset S_n, such that all vectors of V are linear combinations of S_n, then V is of *finite dimension* and it is *spanned* by the set of vectors S_n.

DEFINITION :   The set $S_n = \{v_1, v_2, \dots v_n\}$ *spans* the vector space V over F if every vector v of V is a linear combination of S_n :

$$v = \sum_{r=1}^{n} \lambda_r v_r \quad \text{for some } \lambda_1, \lambda_2, \dots, \lambda_n \text{ in } F$$

Sets S_n can span V for various integral n. Pick out the *smallest* integer among them and denote by m. Then V is said to have *dimension m*.

Now let $S_k = \{v_1, v_2, \dots v_k\}$ be *any* set of k vectors in a vector space V of dimension m. It can be shown that † :

(i) If $k < m$, then S_k cannot span V, i.e. a set of fewer than m vectors may be linearly independent but it cannot span a vector space of dimension m.

(ii) If $k > m$, then S_k cannot be linearly independent, i.e. a set of more than m vectors may span the space but it cannot be linearly independent in a vector space of dimension m.

(iii) If $k = m$, then, when S_k spans V, it is also linearly independent ; and conversely, when S_k is linearly independent, it also spans V.

A set of vectors which is linearly independent *and* which spans V is called a *basis* for V. Hence, by the above results, a basis for V must consist of precisely m vectors, where m is the dimension of V. Further, in expressing a vector v of V as a linear combination of the basis (which spans V), the scalar coefficients are *unique*. For, suppose the basis $\{v_1, v_2, \dots, v_m\}$ is such that $v = \sum_{r=1}^{m} \lambda_r v_r = \sum_{r=1}^{m} \mu_r v_r$; then $\sum_{r=1}^{m} (\lambda_r - \mu_r) \, v_r = 0$. This is only possible if $\lambda_r = \mu_r$ since the basis is linearly independent. To summarise :

A basis $S_m = \{v_1, v_2, \dots, v_m\}$ of a vector space V over F of dimension m is a set of m linearly independent vectors which span V ; and any

---

† The results are reasonable enough, but only (i) follows at once, from the definition of dimension. The proof of (ii) is tricky and it is omitted here. Once (ii) is established, (iii) follows easily.

vector v of V is uniquely expressed as a linear combination of the basis :

$$v = \sum_{r=1}^{m} \lambda_r v_r \quad \text{for unique } \lambda_1, \lambda_2, ..., \lambda_m \text{ in } F \dots\dots\dots\dots(1)$$

The feature of a basis for V is that it is the *smallest* of all sets spanning V and the *largest* of all sets linearly independent in V. But there is not just one basis ; there can be, and usually are, many sets of m vectors which can serve as a basis for V.

Let V be a vector space of dimension m. A *subspace* W of dimension $n \leqslant m$ is a subset of vectors of V which is itself a vector space. W is not any subset, but that special kind of subset which itself satisfies the conditions for a vector space. It can easily be shown that, for this, it is enough that sums and scalar products are closed in W. A subspace can be generated as follows. Take any linearly independent set S_k of k vectors in V ($k \leqslant m$). Add to S_k all vectors of V which are linear combinations of S_k.

The result is then a subspace W. For : if $v = \sum_{r=1}^{n} \lambda_r v_r$ and $v' = \sum_{r=1}^{n} \lambda'_r v_r$ are

two such vectors contained in W, and if μ is any scalar, then :

$$v + v' = \sum_{r=1}^{k} (\lambda_r + \lambda'_r) v_r \quad \text{and} \quad \mu \cdot v = \sum_{r=1}^{k} (\mu \lambda_r) v_r \dots\dots\dots\dots(2)$$

and both of these are linear combinations of S_k, i.e. W is closed.

Ex. (*a*). $V_3(F)$ is the vector space of all $a = (a_1, a_2, a_3)$ with components from the scaler field F. Consider the subset S_3 of three vectors :

$$\epsilon_1 = (1, 0, 0) ; \quad \epsilon_2 = (0, 1, 0) ; \quad \epsilon_3 = (0, 0, 1)$$

S_3 is linearly independent since $\lambda_1 \epsilon_1 + \lambda_2 \epsilon_2 + \lambda_3 \epsilon_3 = (\lambda_1, \lambda_2, \lambda_3) = 0$ only if all the λ's are zero. Any other vector a is a linear combination of S_3 since $(a_1, a_2, a_3) = a_1 \epsilon_1 + a_2 \epsilon_2 + a_3 \epsilon_3$. Hence, $V_3(F)$ has dimension 3 and S_3 is a basis. There are other bases, e.g. the subset of three vectors $(1, 1, 0)$, $(1, -1, 0)$ and $(0, 0, 1)$ for which :

$$(a_1, a_2, a_3) = \tfrac{1}{2}(a_1 + a_2) (1, 1, 0) + \tfrac{1}{2}(a_1 - a_2) (1, -1, 0) + a_3(0, 0, 1)$$

There are various subspaces of $V_3(F)$ of dimension 2, each with a basis consisting of two vectors. For example, the vectors $(a_1, a_2, 0)$ form a subspace and a basis is the pair of vectors ϵ_1 and ϵ_2. All this can be represented geometrically ; the vectors of $V_3(F)$ are points in three-dimensional space and the vectors of a subspace of dimension 2 are points on a plane in the space.

Generally, the Cartesian space $V_n(F)$ of n-tuples $a = (a_1, a_2, a_3)$ of components from the scalar field F is a particular vector space of dimension n. A basis is provided by $S_n = \{\epsilon_1, \epsilon_2, ..., \epsilon_n\}$ where $\epsilon_r = (\delta_{r1}, \delta_{r2}, ..., \delta_{rn})$ in terms of the Kronecker delta δ_{rs}. Other linearly independent sets of n

vectors serve equally as bases for $V_n(F)$. Further, $V_n(F)$ has various subspaces of dimension m with bases of m linearly independent vectors $(m \leqslant n)$. The importance of $V_n(F)$ lies in the following result:

Any vector space V over F of dimension n is isomorphic with $V_n(F)$, the isomorphism preserving both addition and scalar multiplication.

Proof: let $S_n = \{v_1, v_2, ..., v_n\}$ be a basis for V. Hence, (1) holds, i.e. each v of V corresponds to an n-tuple $(\lambda_1, \lambda_2, ..., \lambda_n)$ of $V_n(F)$ and conversely. There is a one-one mapping of V onto $V_n(F)$:

$$v \longleftrightarrow \lambda = (\lambda_1, \lambda_2, ..., \lambda_n)$$

Further, if v and v' are two vectors of V, and if μ is a scalar, then:

if $v \longleftrightarrow \lambda$ and $v' \longleftrightarrow \lambda'$, then $v + v' \longleftrightarrow \lambda + \lambda'$ and $\mu \cdot v \longleftrightarrow \mu \cdot \lambda$

by (2) above, i.e. the mapping is an isomorphism.

As a consequence, a finite vector space of dimension n is algebraically equivalent to $V_n(F)$. Moreover, addition and scalar multiplication in $V_n(F)$ are operations performed solely on scalars of F. Hence, *any* finite vector space depends only on its dimension n and on scalars of F.

The vectors of the text (Chapter 12) form a special case of the vector spaces here defined. First, they are n-tuples in the finite-dimensional Cartesian space $V_n(F)$. By the last result, this is not a serious limitation. Second, F is taken as the field of real numbers, and not a general field. Third, the only basis taken for $V_n(F)$ is the obvious one: $\{\epsilon_1, \epsilon_2, ..., \epsilon_n\}$. Finally, where necessary, vectors are assumed to have length so that they are in Euclidean space $E_n(F)$. In these ways, each n-tuple vector

$$a = (a_1, a_2, ..., a_n)$$

can be represented by a point with co-ordinates $(a_1, a_2, ..., a_n)$ in ordinary geometrical space referred to fixed axes mutually at right angles. A change from one basis to another corresponds to a change in axes.

Ex. (b). As a variant of a vector space, consider the single operation of linear combination, without the separate operations of sums and scalar products. Let S be a set $\{A, B, C, ...\}$ (e.g. of consumption situations) in which *convex linear combination* is defined and closed:

$$\mu A + (1 - \mu)B \in S \quad \text{for any scalar } \mu \ (0 \leqslant \mu \leqslant 1)$$

The scalars μ are from the set Σ of real numbers in the closed interval $(0, 1)$. For any μ and ν in Σ, the following rules are assumed to hold:

(i) $\mu A + (1 - \mu)B = (1 - \mu)B + \mu A$
(ii) If $C = \nu A + (1 - \nu)B$ then $\mu C + (1 - \mu)B = \mu \nu A + (1 - \mu \nu)B$

Here (i) is an associative rule and (ii) states that, if C is a combination of A with B, then a combination of C with B is a " product " combination of A with B. The following is a result which can be established :

If there is a strong relation of linear ordering ($>$) in S such that just one of $A>B$, $A=B$, $B>A$ always holds and such that the transitive condition is satisfied ; further, if the ordering is such that :

(1) If $A>B$, then $A>\mu A+(1-\mu)B>B$ for all $\mu \in \Sigma$
(2) If $A>B>C$, then there exist $\mu \in \Sigma$ and $\nu \in \Sigma$ so that

$$\mu A+(1-\mu)C>B>\nu A+(1-\nu)C$$

then there is a real function u, defined on S uniquely up to a linear transformation, so that :

(a) If $A>B$, then $u(A)>u(B)$
(b) If A and B are any members of S, then

$$u\{\mu A+(1-\mu)B\}=\mu u(A)+(1-\mu)u(B) \quad \text{for all } \mu \in \Sigma$$

This is the result proved by von Neumann and Morgenstern for measurable utility under uncertainty. It can be varied to start from a " preference or indifference " ordering ($\geqslant$) instead of the stricter " preference " ordering ($>$). See 19.5 above.

A final extension of the concept of a vector space is appropriately considered here. Let A be a set of elements a, b, c, ... of any kind and F a field of scalars λ, μ, ν, ...

DEFINITION : If A is a vector space over F and if A has also the structure of a ring for an operation of multiplication defined in A, then A is a *linear algebra* over F.

The set $(A+)$ is an additive group since A is a vector space. What is new is that $(A\times)$ is defined with the minimum requirements of a ring, i.e. products in A are closed, associative and distributive. Other product rules (commutative, identity, inverse) are optional. As they are included in the ring structure, so the linear algebra A is built up to satisfy the whole system of operational rules of 13.1 above. A linear algebra is concerned with a very specialised set of elements for which a very comprehensive system of rules holds—rules on sums and products of the elements of the linear algebra, and on multiplication of these elements by scalars from an outside field.

9. Matrices and Linear Transformations

A *transformation* is an alternative term for a mapping of one set into another, as noted in **3** above. The important case to consider is that of a *linear transformation* with two special features : it is a mapping of one vector space into another, and it preserves the operations of addition and scalar multiplication. It is the homomorphic concept appropriate to vector spaces. The condition that addition and scalar multiplication are preserved is equivalent to the property that linear combinations are carried over in the mapping. Hence :

DEFINITION :   If $V=\{v_1,\ v_2,\ \dots\}$ and $V'=\{v'_1,\ v'_2,\ \dots\}$ are two vector spaces over a field of scalars $F=\{\lambda_1,\ \lambda_2,\ \dots\}$, then a *linear transformation* of V into V' is a mapping which carries a linear combination of vectors in V into the same linear combination of vectors in V' :

$$\sum_{r=1}^{k}\lambda_r v_r \longrightarrow \sum_{r=1}^{k}\lambda_r v'_r$$

where $v_r \longrightarrow v'_r$ and λ_r is any scalar $(r=1,\ 2,\ \dots,\ k)$.

This definition is both general and abstract.   It needs to be made specific and to be translated into concrete analytical terms.

Let V and V' be of finite dimensions, n and m respectively.   They can then be replaced by their isomorphic images, the Cartesian spaces $V_n(F)$ and $V_m(F)$.   Write $x=(x_1,\ x_2,\ \dots,\ x_n)$ as an n-tuple of $V_n(F)$ and $y=(y_1,\ y_2,\ \dots,\ y_m)$ as an m-tuple of $V_m(F)$.   A linear transformation T is then from the n-tuple x to the m-tuple y: $x \underset{T}{\longrightarrow} y$.

Take $\{\epsilon_1,\ \epsilon_2,\ \dots,\ \epsilon_n\}$ as the basis of $V_n(F)$ and $\{\epsilon_1,\ \epsilon_2,\ \dots,\ \epsilon_m\}$ as that of $V_m(F)$.   Under T, the images of $\epsilon_1,\ \epsilon_2,\ \dots,\ \epsilon_n$ as n vectors of $V_n(F)$ are certain vectors of $V_m(F)$.   Write them as :

$$\epsilon_1 \longrightarrow (a_{11},\ a_{21},\ \dots,\ a_{m1})$$
$$\epsilon_2 \longrightarrow (a_{12},\ a_{22},\ \dots,\ a_{m2})$$
$$\dots\dots\dots\dots\dots$$
$$\epsilon_n \longrightarrow (a_{1n},\ a_{2n},\ \dots,\ a_{mn})$$

where a_{rs} $(r=1,\ 2,\ \dots,\ m$ and $s=1,\ 2,\ \dots,\ n)$ are $m \times n$ fixed scalars of F given by T, and by the particular choices of the bases for the two vector spaces.   Now, each of these vectors in $V_m(F)$ can be written in terms of the basis for this vector space.   For example :

$$(a_{11},\ a_{21},\ \dots,\ a_{m1})=a_{11}\epsilon_1+a_{21}\epsilon_2+\dots+a_{m1}\epsilon_m$$

Generally :
$$\epsilon_s \to \sum_{r=1}^{m} a_{rs}\epsilon_r \ (s=1,\ 2,\ \dots,\ n)$$

So :
$$x=\sum_{s=1}^{n} x_s \epsilon_s \to \sum_{s=1}^{n} x_s \Big(\sum_{r=1}^{m} a_{rs}\epsilon_r\Big)=\sum_{r=1}^{m}\Big(\sum_{s=1}^{n} a_{rs}x_s\Big)\epsilon_r$$

But :
$$x \to y=\sum_{r=1}^{m} y_r \epsilon_r$$

Hence :
$$\sum_{r=1}^{m} y_r \, \epsilon_r = \sum_{r=1}^{m} \left(\sum_{s=1}^{n} a_{rs} x_s \right) \epsilon_r$$

i.e. the linear transformation T, referred to the selected bases, is :

$$y_r = \sum_{s=1}^{n} a_{rs} x_s \quad (r = 1, 2, \ldots, m)$$

$$\mathbf{y} = \mathbf{A} \, \mathbf{x}$$

where $\mathbf{x}$ of order $n \times 1$ is the column vector $(x_1, x_2, \ldots, x_n)$, $\mathbf{y}$ of order $m \times 1$ is the column vector $(y_1, y_2, \ldots, y_m)$, and $\mathbf{A}$ of order $m \times n$ is the matrix of given scalars $[a_{rs}]$.

The conclusion is that any linear transformation T from $V_n(F)$ to $V_m(F)$, with specific bases $\epsilon_1, \epsilon_2, \ldots, \epsilon_n$ and $\epsilon_1, \epsilon_2, \ldots, \epsilon_m$, can be represented by a matrix $\mathbf{A} = [a_{rs}]$ of $m \times n$ scalars from F. The set of all linear transformations T from $V_n(F)$ to $V_m(F)$ is isomorphic with the set of all $m \times n$ matrices $\mathbf{A}$ with components in F.† Hence, algebraically, it matters little whether we consider the set of linear transformations T or the set of $m \times n$ matrices $\mathbf{A}$. It is generally more convenient to operate with matrices, to take the set S_{mn} of all matrices of given order $m \times n$, as in 13.8 above.

Addition of matrices in the set S_{mn} satisfies all the rules (A1–5), i.e. S_{mn} is an additive group. Further, multiplication of matrices of S_{mn} by scalars of F satisfies the rules (S1–5), i.e. S_{mn} is a vector space over F. In this sense, matrices are extended forms of vectors. Indeed, a vector $(y_1 \, y_2, \ldots, y_m)$ can be written as a column vector $\mathbf{y}$, i.e. as a matrix of order $m \times 1$ in the set S_{m1}. There is an important equivalence relation in the set S_{mn} which serves to partition the set into equivalence classes $S_0, S_1, S_2, \ldots$. Equivalent matrices are of the same rank and the equivalence class S_r comprises all matrices of order $m \times n$ and rank r (13.8 above). This is about as far as we can go for rectangular matrices, of order $m \times n$ $(m \neq n)$. In particular, no products can be defined in the set S_{mn} $(m \neq n)$. Matrices can be multiplied, but only when their orders conform, e.g. a matrix from the set S_{mk} can be multiplied by one from the different set S_{kn}. Products exist *in* a set of matrices of fixed order *only* when the matrices are square.

Consider the set S_{nn} of all *square matrices* of fixed order $n \times n$. The corresponding set of linear transformations T then contains all cases where the vector space $V_n(F)$ is mapped into itself. The set S_{nn} is still a vector space ; but it is also closed under the operation of multiplication and the set

---

† If different bases are selected, then the linear transformation T appears as $\mathbf{y} = \mathbf{Bx}$ instead of $\mathbf{y} = \mathbf{Ax}$, where $\mathbf{B} = \mathbf{PAQ}$ is an equivalent matrix to $\mathbf{A}$. The matrices $\mathbf{P}$ of order $m \times m$ and $\mathbf{Q}$ of order $n \times n$ are determined by the particular change in basis assumed.

has the structure of a ring. The rules which are valid are (M1), (M2) and (M4), the identity being the unit matrix I of order $n \times n$. Generally, the set satisfies neither the commutative rule (M3) nor the inverse rule (M5)— and not even the weaker form, the cancellation rule (M5'). There can be zero divisors in S_{nn}; two non-zero square matrices can be multiplied to give a zero matrix (see 13.4, (v), above). However, the set S_{nn} has more than enough to qualify as a ring. If only addition and multiplication are considered, S_{nn} is a non-commutative ring with zero divisors. If scalar multiplication is included, then S_{nn} is a linear algebra; from this point of view, the set is described as a *total matrix algebra* and denoted $M_n(F)$.

Finally, consider an even narrower set of matrices L_n containing all *non-singular matrices* of fixed order $n \times n$. The corresponding set of linear transformations T then comprises all *one-one* mappings of the vector space $V_n(F)$ *onto* itself. For products, L_n is a non-commutative group, since all the rules (M1–5) hold except for the commutative rule (M3). In particular, a non-singular matrix **A** has an inverse $\mathbf{A}^{-1}$; the corresponding linear transformation $x \underset{T}{\longrightarrow} y$ has an inverse $y \underset{T^{-1}}{\longrightarrow} x$, both being one-one and onto. The group L_n of non-singular matrices of order $n \times n$, and the group of one-one linear transformations, are called *full linear groups*.

There is a loss which partly offsets the gain of greater " obedience " of products in L_n—the set is *not* closed under addition. Two non-singular matrices may well add to a singular matrix. Hence, L_n is a group under multiplication but not under addition; it is not a vector space and it is not a linear algebra over the field F. The analysis of non-singular matrices must be carefully confined to product operations.

The group L_n has various subgroups, each of which must contain the identity element I. One subgroup consists of all *orthogonal matrices* of order $n \times n$ (13.9 above). **A** is orthogonal if and only if $\mathbf{A}^{-1} = \mathbf{A}'$. It follows that, if **A** and **B** are orthogonal, so is the product **AB**. For :

$$(\mathbf{AB})^{-1} = \mathbf{B}^{-1}\mathbf{A}^{-1} = \mathbf{B}'\mathbf{A}' = (\mathbf{AB})'$$

Further, if **A** is orthogonal, so is $\mathbf{A}^{-1}$, since $(\mathbf{A}^{-1})' = (\mathbf{A}')^{-1} = (\mathbf{A}^{-1})^{-1}$. Hence, the set of orthogonal matrices (of fixed order) is closed for products and contains reciprocals; it satisfies the conditions for a subgroup (**6** above). The corresponding subgroup of orthogonal transformations are those which relate to rotation of axes in Euclidean space, distances and angles being preserved.

Another subgroup is that of all *permutation matrices* of order $n \times n$ (13.7 above). By the definition, the inverse of a permutation matrix, and the product of any two of them, are also permutation matrices. This sub-group is isomorphic with the group of permutations of a finite set of n elements $(1, 2, ..., n)$ amongst themselves.

10. Polynomials

The treatment of polynomials in the text, particularly in 4.6, is some-what cavalier. It is not at all easy to give a strict development in reasonably simple terms. This is because the subject is so basic to algebra and because it has so many and various ramifications.

Two general uses of polynomials are illustrated many times in the text. First, in algebra of the most elementary kind, a polynomial *equation* is written, e.g. $\frac{1}{2}x^2 + \frac{7}{4}x - 1 = 0$. Here, x is a fixed but *unknown* value ; the problem is to find it ($\frac{1}{2}$ or -4 in this case). Second, in analysis, a poly-nomial *function* is written, or a function which is the ratio of polynomials, e.g. $y = (x-1)/(x^2+x+1)$. Here x is a variable, the independent variable of the function.

This has become so familiar that it is all too easy to switch from one use to the other—though there is a real risk of confusion. One way of keeping the two uses in line is the following, with the general quadratic as illus-tration. Let x be a variable so that $y = ax^2 + bx + c$ is a polynomial *function*. Then say that the polynomial has a *root* α, a fixed value, if $a\alpha^2 + b\alpha + c = 0$. This *equation* can be written since both $a\alpha^2 + b\alpha + c$ and zero are fixed values.

The emphasis here is on the variable x or the root α of a polynomial. What of the coefficients of the polynomial? These may be specific as in $\frac{1}{2}x^2 + \frac{7}{4}x - 1$ or parameters as in $ax^2 + bx + c$. Usually these " values " are integers or rationals, sometimes real or even complex numbers. Apart from the case of integral coefficients, the coefficients can be taken as scalars from a field F, typically the field of rationals. From this point of view, the general quadratic $ax^2 + bx + c$ is a set (a, b, c) of scalars from F, the elements being kept separate by using powers of x (x^2, x, 1) as " place-markers ".

Ex. (a). Some particular quadratics illustrate :
  (i) $\frac{1}{2}x^2 + \frac{7}{4}x - 1$ with roots $\frac{1}{2}$ and -4
  (ii) $x^2 - 2$ with roots $\pm \sqrt{2}$
  (iii) $4x^2 - 8x + 13$ with roots $1 \pm \frac{3}{2}i$

Two points can be made. First, these are polynomials with rational coefficients and each can be written as a (rational) multiple of a similar polynomial with leading coefficient as 1, i.e. the leading coefficient can be " brought outside ". For example, (i) is $\frac{1}{2}(x^2 + \frac{7}{2}x - 2)$ and (iii) is $4(x^2 - 2x + \frac{13}{4})$. Second, though the poly-nomials have rational coefficients, the roots may be rational, real and irrational, or complex. To be sure of getting two roots for a quadratic, we have to go outside the field of rationals.

In the following, polynomials with rational coefficients are considered, i.e. polynomials over a field F of rationals.† When convenient, the polynomial is written with leading coefficient as 1. We have in mind to show that a polynomial of degree n has exactly n roots, but in the wider field of complex numbers. This is the " fundamental theorem of algebra " and we lead up to it by a series of digressions, interesting in themselves.

A first task is to define a polynomial so that it does not beg any questions about what x may be. The point of view is simply that x is *undefined* or *indeterminate*. The " place-marker " approach is the one to pursue. The parallel is the definition of a complex number $a+ib$, where i is a " place-marker " separating the ordered pair (a, b) and later interpreted as $i^2 = -1$. Hence :

DEFINITION : A *polynomial* with coefficients in a field F is a sequence of elements $(f_0, f_1, f_2, \dots)$ of F with a finite number of non-zero terms :

$$f_n \neq 0 \text{ for some integral } n \text{ and } f_m = 0 \text{ for all } m > n.$$

In the set of all polynomials, as the f's range over F and for any integral n, *define* sums and products :

$$(f_0, f_1, f_2, \dots) + (g_0, g_1, g_2, \dots) = (f_0+g_0, f_1+g_1, f_2+g_2, \dots) \quad \dots\dots(1)$$
and $\quad (f_0, f_1, f_2, \dots) \times (g_0, g_1, g_2, \dots) = (h_0, h_1, h_2, \dots)$
where $\quad h_m = f_0 g_m + f_1 g_{m-1} + \dots + f_m g_0 \qquad \Big\} \quad \dots\dots\dots\dots(2)$

These definitions are not arbitrary ; they reflect what happens to the coefficients when polynomials are added and multiplied in elementary algebra. From (1), the set of polynomials is seen to be an additive group with zero $(0, 0, 0, \dots)$; the rules (A1–5) hold. From (2), the set is seen to have $(1, 0, 0, \dots)$ as unity and to satisfy the rules (D) and (M1–4). Finally, if not all the f's and not all the g's are zero in (2), then not all the h's are zero, i.e. the product of two non-zero polynomials is a non-zero polynomial. The set is without zero divisors. Hence the polynomials form a ring, an *integral domain*, lacking reciprocals.

Introduce the *indeterminate* x as the particular polynomial $(0, 1, 0, \dots)$. Then, by repeated use of (2) :

$$x = (0, 1, 0, \dots) ; \quad x^2 = (0, 0, 1, 0, \dots) ; \quad x^3 = (0, 0, 0, 1, 0, \dots) ; \quad \dots\dots(3)$$

As a final convention, the polynomial $(f, 0, 0, \dots)$ can be identified as the

---

† This is the usual case in practice. But, for the most part, the results obtained are true of any field F. And the final " fundamental theorem " holds for polynomials with coefficients in any field of numbers (rational, real or complex).

element f of F; more strictly, the subset $(f, 0, 0, \ldots)$ of polynomials (for $f \in F$) is isomorphic with F. From (1), (2) and (3):

$$(f_0, f_1, f_2, \ldots) = (f_0, 0, 0, \ldots) + (0, f_1, 0, \ldots) + (0, 0, f_2, \ldots) + \ldots$$
$$= (f_0, 0, 0, \ldots) + (f_1, 0, 0, \ldots)(0, 1, 0, \ldots) + (f_2, 0, 0, \ldots)(0, 0, 1, 0, \ldots) + \ldots$$
$$= f_0 + f_1 x + f_2 x^2 + \ldots.$$

Hence, as a matter of notation, write a polymial of degree n as:

$$f(x) = f_0 + f_1 x + f_2 x^2 + \ldots + f_n x^n \quad (f_n \neq 0) \quad \ldots\ldots\ldots\ldots\ldots(4)$$

and denote the ring (integral domain) of polynomials $f(x)$ with coefficients in the field F by $F[x]$. Notice that the particular polynomials $f(x) = f_0$ =constant are identified as elements of F. Further, since F is a field in which division is possible, f_n can be brought outside the polynomial (4), all coefficients being divided by f_n. For most purposes, e.g. in writing factors or roots, this constant multiple can be ignored. The general polynomial can then be written with $f_n = 1$ and with the order of the terms reversed:

$$f(x) = x^n + f_{n-1} x^{n-1} + \ldots + f_1 x + f_0 \quad \ldots\ldots\ldots\ldots\ldots\ldots(5)$$

By the conventions adopted, x and its powers are themselves polynomials: $f(x) = x$ or x^2 or $x^3 \ldots$. Otherwise x is indeterminate. But one thing can be said, and it is basic. The definition of sums and products (1) and (2) is such that polynomials (4) can be handled under addition and multiplication exactly as they are in elementary algebra. Moreover, if an element $\alpha \in F$ is written for x in (4), the result is $f(\alpha)$, another element of F. Indeed, the same is true if $\alpha \in F_1$, where F_1 is some wider field containing F; sums and products for polynomials carry over when " numerical values " are substituted for x. Hence, if $f(x)$ is a polynomial defined in the field of *rationals* (i.e. with rational coefficients), then $y = f(x)$ can be written as a function over the field of *real numbers*, and $f(\alpha)$ can be put equal to zero in seeking a root α in the field of *complex numbers*.

Finally, scalar multiplication is a matter of definition:

$$af(x) = a(f_0 + f_1 x + f_2 x^2 + \ldots) = (af_0) + (af_1)x + (af_2)x^2 + \ldots$$

for any $a \in F$. The rules (S1–5) are then valid. Hence, in the end, polynomials $f(x)$ do satisfy all the operational rules with the single exception that they lack reciprocals.

So $F[x]$ is a *ring* (integral domain) for sums and products, and it is a *vector space* for sums and scalar multiplication—a vector space of infinite dimension with $(1, x, x^2, \ldots)$ as a basis. In short, $F[x]$ is an instance of a *linear algebra.* Even the one lack can be eliminated. Just as the integral domain of the integers can be extended, by proper definition of ratios, to the field of rationals, so the integral domain $F[x]$ of polynomials $f(x)$ can be extended to the *field* of rational fractions $\{f(x)/g(x)\}$ where $f(x)$ and $g(x)$ are in $F[x]$.

The property of polynomials to develop is that of *factorisation* ; from this come the *roots* of the polynomials. The guiding principle here is that polynomials are very like integers. Each forms an integral domain, lacking only reciprocals. The parallel between integers and polynomials turns out to be very remarkable indeed.

If m and n are integers ($m > n$), the following division processes are familiar. Divide m by n to give an integer q_1 and a remainder $r_1(< n)$: $m = q_1 n + r_1$. If $r_1 \neq 0$, divide n by r_1 to give : $n = q_2 r_1 + r_2$. This continues until the remainder is zero, as it must be sooner or later :

$$m = q_1 n + r_1 ; \quad n = q_2 r_1 + r_2 ; \quad r_1 = q_3 r_2 + r_3 ; \quad \ldots \quad r_{k-2} = q_k r_{k-1} + r_k$$

and finally $r_{k-1} = q_{k+1} r_k$. Then r_k is the H.C.F. (highest common factor) of m and n. Jobbing backwards through the divisions :

$$\begin{aligned} r_k = r_{k-2} - q_k r_{k-1} &= r_{k-2} - q_k(-q_{k-1} r_{k-2} + r_{k-3}) \\ &= -q_k r_{k-3} + (1 + q_k q_{k-1}) r_{k-2} = \ldots \\ &= (\text{integer})m + (\text{integer})n \quad \text{eventually} \end{aligned}$$

If c is the H.C.F. of m and n, there exist integers λ and μ so that :

$$c = \lambda m + \mu n \quad \ldots\ldots\ldots\ldots\ldots\ldots\ldots\ldots\ldots\ldots\ldots\ldots(6)$$

The process of repeated division leading to (6) is often called the *division algorithm*, or Euclid's algorithm, where " algorithm " simply means a rule for computation.

Define a *prime* integer as a positive integer $p > 1$ which has no factors other than 1 and p itself. The *Fundamental Theorem of Arithmetic* is :

Every positive integer $n > 1$ can be uniquely factored into a product of primes : $n = p_1 p_2 \ldots p_i$ *for some positive integer i.*

A negative integer is handled by multiplying the corresponding positive integer by (-1). The proof of the theorem is as follows.

First, a lemma : if prime p divides a product $m_1 \times m_2$, then either p divides m_1 or p divides m_2 or both. For, if p does not divide m_1, their H.C.F. is 1 and (6) gives

$$\lambda p + \mu m_1 = 1 \quad \text{for some integers } \lambda \text{ and } \mu$$

and so $\quad\quad\quad \lambda p m_2 + \mu m_1 m_2 = m_2$

But p divides pm_2 and it divides m_1m_2; it must divide m_2. Hence the lemma.

Second, the given integer n can certainly be factored until only prime factors appear; it must be shown that the factoring is unique. Suppose:

$$n = p_1p_2 \dots p_i = q_1q_2 \dots q_j \quad (p\text{'s and }q\text{'s prime})$$

Then p_1 divides n and so divides $q_1q_2 \dots q_j$. By the lemma, p_1 divides one of the q's and (by re-arrangement) this can be taken as q_1. Since p_1 and q_1 are prime, p_1 divides q_1 only if $p_1 = q_1$. This process continues with $p_2p_3 \dots p_i = q_2q_3 \dots q_j$ (dividing out $p_1 = q_1$) and each p is identified with a q until all are taken. Hence, $i = j$ and the p's and q's are the same set of primes. The theorem is proved.

Ex. (b). For $m = 105$ and $n = 12$, the division algorithm is:
$$105 = 8 \times 12 + 9; \quad 12 = 1 \times 9 + 3; \quad 9 = 3 \times 3$$
and the H.C.F. is 3. Further: $3 = (-1)105 + 9 \times 12$ and (6) has $\lambda = -1$ and $\mu = 9$ in this case. Finally, the unique factorisations are $105 = 7 \times 5 \times 3$ and $12 = 3 \times 2 \times 2$; the H.C.F. is again seen to be 3.

The development for integers can be repeated almost word for word for polynomials. If $f(x)$ of degree m and $g(x)$ of degree n are two polynomials of form (5) with $m < n$, then the *division algorithm* starts with $f(x) = q_1(x)g(x) + r_1(x)$ where $f(x)$ divided by $g(x)$ gives the polynomial $q_1(x)$ and remainder $r_1(x)$ of degree $< n$. It ends with a last remainder, the H.C.F. of $f(x)$ and $g(x)$. If $c(x)$ is this H.C.F., then there exist polynomials $\phi(x)$ and $\psi(x)$ so that:

$$c(x) = \phi(x)f(x) + \psi(x)g(x) \quad \dots\dots\dots\dots\dots\dots(7)$$

By adopting (5), all polynomials have 1 as leading coefficients, which makes for a concise statement of the following definition and result.

As a definition, a polynomial $p(x)$ of $F[x]$ is *irreducible* in the field F if it is of positive degree ($n \geqslant 1$) and such that it has no factors in F other than 1 and $p(x)$ itself. Then, as for integers, the result which follows from (7) is:

Every polynomial of positive degree $f(x)$ can be uniquely factored into a product of irreducible polynomials:

$$f(x) = p_1(x)p_2(x) \dots p_i(x) \quad \text{for some positive integer } i.$$

If the polynomial is of form (4), then constant factors must appear.

Ex. (c). For $f(x) = x^4 - 2x^3 + 2x^2 - 2x + 1$ and $g(x) = x^3 + x^2 + x + 1$, the division algorithm has two steps:
$$x^4 - 2x^3 + 2x^2 - 2x + 1 = (x - 3)(x^3 + x^2 + x + 1) + 4(x^2 + 1)$$
and
$$x^3 + x^2 + x + 1 = (x + 1)(x^2 + 1)$$
The H.C.F. is $(x^2 + 1)$, also seen from the unique factorisations:
$$f(x) = (x - 1)(x - 1)(x^2 + 1) \quad \text{and} \quad g(x) = (x + 1)(x^2 + 1)$$

As regards the roots of a polynomial, one simple result is evident: *The polynomial $f(x)$ has a root α if and only if $f(x)$ has a linear factor $(x - \alpha)$.* When $f(x)$ is uniquely factored into irreducible $p(x)$, some of the $p(x)$ can be of linear form $(x - \alpha)$, and so give roots of $f(x)$. But not all—as long as we are confined (as we are) to rationals. There are other irreducible polynomials such as $(x^2 - 2)$ and $(x^2 + 1)$. We must attempt to break out of the field of rationals; to follow up a hint already given, we must include the rational field in some larger over-field.

Much of the theory of fields is of the " Chinese Box " type. A given field F contains subfields, i.e. subsets which are themselves fields. There is always a smallest subfield, called a *prime field*, without further subfields.†
Conversely, a given field F, prime or not, can be embedded in larger fields —extension fields or over-fields. For example, the field of real numbers has a prime subfield, that of rationals; and it is contained within an over-field, that of complex numbers.

Consider a field F and an outside element x of any kind. The set of all elements of F *plus* x alone is not generally large enough to be a field or even a ring. To make it a ring, further elements are to be added—sums, differences and products (but not quotients) of x with elements of F. The ring so obtained is denoted $F[x]$, derived by *ring adjunction* of the single element x to F. The general element of $F[x]$ is clearly $(f_0 + f_1 x + f_2 x^2 + \ldots)$, a polynomial with coefficients in F. Hence, the ring of polynomials $F[x]$ is the ring adjunction of x to F. Now proceed further and make the set of F *plus* x into a field by adding all rational combinations (sums, differences, products *and* quotients) of x and elements of F. The field obtained by *field adjunction* of x to F is denoted $F(x)$. The general element of $F(x)$ is easily seen to be of the form $f(x)/g(x)$ where $f(x)$ and $g(x)$ are polynomials in $F[x]$. Hence, $F(x)$ is the field of rational fractions.

Take the case where an over-field F_2 is obtained by field adjunction of i (with $i^2 = -1$) to the field F_1 of real numbers. Any element of F_2 is:

$$\frac{f_0 + f_1 i + f_2 i^2 + \ldots}{g_0 + g_1 i + g_2 i^2 + \ldots} = \frac{a_0 + a_1 i}{b_0 + b_1 i} \qquad \begin{array}{l} \text{on substituting } i^2 = -1 \\ \text{and collecting terms} \end{array}$$

$$= \frac{(a_0 + a_1 i)(b_0 - b_1 i)}{(b_0 + b_1 i)(b_0 - b_1 i)} = \frac{a_0 b_0 + a_1 b_1}{b_0^2 + b_1^2} + \frac{a_1 b_0 - a_0 b_1}{b_0^2 + b_1^2} i$$

† If P is the prime field of a given field F, the basic result is that P is isomorphic with (substantially the same as) *either* the infinite field of rational numbers, *or* the finite field of the integers mod p for some prime p. In the former case, F is said to have *characteristic* 0 ; the field of complex numbers is an example. In the latter case, F has *characteristic* p ; the feature then is that $1 + 1 + 1 + \ldots$ (p times) $= 0$, where 0 and 1 are the identity elements of F.

for real numbers a_0, a_1, b_0, b_1. Hence the general element is of the form $(a + ib)$, as a and b range over the field of real numbers. The over-field F_2 is the field of complex numbers—by the adjunction of the single element i.

The application to roots of polynomials is immediate. The ring $F[x]$ of polynomials $f(x)$ has coefficients in the field F of rationals. Among irreducible $f(x)$ are those like $(x^2 - 2)$ which have real (but irrational) roots. Extend F to the over-field F_1 of real numbers and such $f(x)$, irreducible in F, become reducible further in F_1. There are still irreducible $f(x)$ even in F_1, e.g. $(x^2 + 1)$. It is now found that one more step is enough. Adjoin the element i to F_1 to give the over-field F_2 of complex numbers. Here, i is a root of the particular polynomial $(x^2 + 1)$, irreducible in F or F_1, but reducible in F_2 to $(x + i)(x - i)$. The final result is that F_2 contains *all* the roots of *all* polynomials $f(x)$.

The *Fundamental Theorem of Algebra* is :

If $f(x) = x^n + f_{n-1}x^{n-1} + \ldots + f_1x + f_0$ is any polynomial of degree n with rational coefficients, then $f(\alpha) = 0$ for some complex α.

One of the most remarkable things about this theorem is that, apparently, it is incapable of proof in purely algebraic terms. All available proofs involve topological concepts, see Courant and Robbins (1941), pp. 101–3 and 269–71. The following is a sketch of the proof, shorn of topological details. Let $\alpha = r(\cos \theta + i \sin \theta)$ be any complex number so that $f(\alpha)$ is also a complex number. Write it $\beta = \rho (\cos \phi + i \sin \phi)$. In an Argand diagram, α is a point P with polar co-ordinates (r, θ) and β a point $Q(\rho, \phi)$. The continuous function $\beta = f(\alpha)$ maps P into Q. Let P describe a circle of radius r (θ varying). Then Q describes some continuous curve in the diagram and let m be the number of counter-clockwise turns it makes about O. But m depends on r (i.e. on the circle chosen for P) and must vary continuously with r : $m(r)$ is a continuous function. P and Q are both single points when $r = 0$, i.e. $m(0) = 0$. It can be shown that m becomes a positive integer as r gets large ; indeed $m(r) \to n$ as $r \to \infty$. The curve described by Q, changing continuously as r increases, starts as a single point ($r = 0$) and finishes by winding round O ($r \to \infty$). It must sometime pass through O ($\beta = 0$). When it does, $f(\alpha) = 0$ and α is a complex root of $f(x)$.

The rest of the development of the final result is easy. Suppose α_1 is a complex root of $f(x)$ so that : $f(x) = (x - \alpha_1)g(x)$ for some $g(x)$, a polynomial of degree $(n - 1)$. Suppose α_2 is a complex root of $g(x)$, so that $(x - \alpha_2)$ is a factor of $g(x)$ and hence of $f(x)$. Proceeding :

$$f(x) = (x - \alpha_1)(x - \alpha_2) \ldots (x - \alpha_n) \ldots\ldots\ldots\ldots(8)$$

is finally obtained and $f(x)$ has exactly n roots α_1, α_2, ..., α_n in the complex field. Let $\alpha = a + ib$ be a root. If $b = 0$, the root is real; otherwise, both α and its conjugate $\alpha' = a - ib$ are roots. Consider the mapping of a complex number onto its conjugate and apply it to each side of (8). Since $f(x)$ has real (rational) coefficients, it is unchanged. On the other side, each α is carried into α'. Hence:

$$f(x) = (x - \alpha'_1)(x - \alpha'_2) \ldots (x - \alpha'_n)$$

i.e. the α''s are simply a re-arrangement of the α's, and the conjugate of any (non-real) root is also a root.

The final result can now be stated simply. A polynomial of degree n with rational coefficients has exactly n roots in the complex field. Some or all of the roots may be real. Other roots occur in conjugate complex pairs.

APPENDIX C

EXERCISES: SOLUTIONS AND HINTS

1.2 (p. 6)

1. Obtain $\alpha = \bar{X} - a\bar{P}$, $\beta = \bar{X} - b\bar{P}$, and substitute in (2). $\bar{X}$ and $\bar{P}$ must be positive ; hence $-\dfrac{b\alpha}{(-a)} < \beta < \alpha$. **2.** Solution : $p_t = p_0 c^t$ with $c = \dfrac{(-b)}{(-a)} > 0$. Distinguish case $(-b) > (-a)$ from case $(-b) < (-a)$. **3.** Model as in text, with a and b interchanged ; solution $p_t = p_0 \left(\dfrac{1}{c}\right)^t$ has damped variation if S is steeper than D.

4. Substitute $P_t = \lambda_0 + \lambda_1 t$ in (5) and find λ_0 and λ_1 by equating coefficient of t and constant term separately to zero.

1.3 (p. 8)

1. Write $c = \dfrac{(-b) - (-a)}{(-a_1)}$ and determine sign. **2.** Differential equation : $\dfrac{dp}{dt} = \gamma p$ where $\gamma = \dfrac{a-b}{b}$. In interpreting this case, consider a lag (of continuous exponential type) on demand side, as 1.9, Ex. 2. **3.** Differential equation : $\dfrac{dp}{dt} = \gamma p$ where $\gamma = \dfrac{b_0 - a_0}{a_1 - b_1}$. The coefficients a_1 and b_1 relate to speed of response in demand and supply.

1.6 (p. 14)

1. $p_t = 0, 1, -\frac{3}{8}, -\frac{15}{64}, \frac{117}{512}, \dots$. Here D is steeper than S ; price deviations have damped oscillation, converging slowly to zero. **2.** $p_t = 0, 1, -\frac{9}{8}, \frac{105}{64}, -\frac{1161}{512}, \dots$. Alternating and explosive.

1.7 (p. 19)

1. $(b-a) > 0$ when $(-b) < (-a)$, as text. When $(-b) > (-a)$, then $(b-a) < 0$ and $c > 1$ all positive λ, i.e. explosive case. **3.** $\lambda = 0$ gives $p_t = $ constant, irrespective of stocks. I is $p_t = p_{t-1}$. II is $p_t = 2p_{t-1} - p_{t-2}$. Each gives $p_t = p_0$ if initial prices are $p_0 = p_1$. $\lambda \to \infty$ gives $p_{t-1} = c p_{t-2}$ in both cases (setting coefficient of $1/\lambda$ equal to zero), i.e. simple cobweb. **4.** Much the same as Model I, see Ex. 1 above. **6.** $\lambda = 0$ gives $p(t) = $ constant. III is $\dfrac{dp}{dt} = 0$. IV is $\dfrac{d^2 p}{dt^2} = 0$ with $\dfrac{dp}{dt} = 0$ as an initial condition. $\lambda \to \infty$ gives differential equation as model of 1.3 above. Compare with period case of Ex. 2 and 3 above.

1.9 (p. 28)

1. Put $Y = 0$ in $\dfrac{dY}{dt} = -\dfrac{1}{T}(Y - Z_0)$ and show tangent is OA :

2. Equate demand and supply so that $(D + \lambda)(\alpha + aP) = \lambda(\beta + bP)$ and so on. Equation (1) of 1.3 above follows with $a = a_0$ and $\lambda = a_0/a_1$. **4.** Y given by

$$\frac{d^2 Y}{dt^2} + 4\lambda \frac{dY}{dt} + 4\lambda^2 Y = 4\lambda^2 Z_0 \quad \text{with} \quad Y = \frac{dY}{dt} = 0 \text{ at } t = 0$$

Solution (5.8 below) : $Y = \{1 - (1 + 2\lambda t)e^{-2\lambda t}\}Z_0$ a curve like (iii) of Fig. 3 but tangential to Ot at O. **5.** Note that integral of (8) is sum of two parts ; in one $Z(t - \tau) = Z_0 (\tau \leqslant t)$; in the other $Z(t - \tau) = 0 (\tau > t)$.

2.2 (p. 37)

1. Substitute in $Y - C = I$ and $L = M$; solve for Y and i. **2.** Differentiate Y and i with respect to β and take ratio of derivatives. Classical case : $\lambda_2 = 0$; Keynes special case : $\lambda_1 = 0$.

2.4 (p. 42)

1. Saving *ex ante* $= Y_{t-1} - C(Y_{t-1}) \neq Y_t - C(Y_{t-1}) = I(i_t)$. **2.** Saving and investment equal *ex ante*, not *ex post*. **4.** Stability condition : SI steeper than LM,

or $\dfrac{1 - c}{(-b)} > \dfrac{\lambda_1}{(-\lambda_2)}$.

2.6 (p. 48)

1. Taylor's expansion of $C(Y)$ for $(Y - Y_0)$ small :

$$\because \; C(Y) = C(Y_0) + \left(\frac{dC}{dY}\right)_0 (Y - Y_0) + \frac{1}{2}\left(\frac{d^2C}{dY^2}\right)_0 (Y - Y_0)^2 + \ldots$$

Substitute in $Y - C(Y) = A$ and note $Y_0 - C(Y_0) = A_0$.

2.7 (p. 52)

2. $(Y_t - Y_{t-1})$ is income lag : income earned *less* income for spending

$$Y_{t-1} - C(Y_{t-1})$$

is planned saving. **3.** Slope of OS is $\dfrac{1}{s}$; decreases as s increases. **4.** Linear

case : $\dfrac{dY}{dt} + (1 - c)Y = A$ with $\bar{Y} = \dfrac{A}{1 - c}$ as particular solution. Hence for

$y = Y - \bar{Y} : \dfrac{dy}{dt} + (1 - c)y = 0$ giving $y = $ constant $e^{-(1-c)t}$.

3.3 (p. 69)

1. In (ii) write $Z = Y - \dfrac{a_0}{1 - c}$ and adjust (1) accordingly. **3.** Write $Z = Y - \dfrac{a_0}{1 - c}$;

$\dfrac{dZ}{dt} = \dfrac{dY}{dt}$. Hence (1) equivalent to (4) : $\dfrac{dZ}{dt} = \rho\left(Z - \dfrac{A_0}{s}e^{rt}\right)$

5. Trend expansion : $\bar{Y} = \bar{Y}_0 e^{rt}$. With $y = Y - \bar{Y}$, (4) gives $y = y_0 e^{\rho t}$, as text. Proportional deviations are $\eta = \dfrac{Y - \bar{Y}}{\bar{Y}}$ and (4) gives $\eta = \eta_0 e^{(\rho - r)t}$. The first is shown graphically about a rising trend on a natural scale ; the second about a straight line trend on a semi-logarithmic scale.

3.4 (p. 72)

3. Exponential lag $\dfrac{dY}{dt} = -\kappa(Y - Z)$ with $\kappa = \lambda s$ and $Z = \dfrac{A}{s}$. **5.** Note that OA is tangent to curve (iii) at O ; 1.9, Ex. 1 above.

3.5 (p. 74)

2. At $t = 0$, $\dfrac{d^2Y}{dt^2} = (\kappa v - s)\lambda^2 A > 0$ usually. Hence path of Y is tangential to Ot but convex downwards at O. **4.** $\dfrac{d^3Y}{dt^3} + a\dfrac{d^2Y}{dt^2} + b\dfrac{dY}{dt} + cY = \kappa\lambda\gamma A$ where :

$$a = \kappa + \lambda + \gamma - \kappa\lambda v \; ; \quad b = \gamma(\kappa + \lambda s) + \kappa\lambda(1 - \gamma v) \; ; \quad c = \kappa\lambda\gamma s$$

This becomes (4) when $\gamma \to \infty$ (no consumption lag).

3.6 (p. 79)

1. Condition for investment plans realised : (*a*) Period model, no lags (this exercise) : $sY_t = v(Y_t - Y_{t-1})$. (*b*) Period model, lagged (3.6 above) :

$$sY_{t-1} = v(Y_t - Y_{t-1})$$

(c) Continuous model, no lags (3.3 above) : $sY = v\dfrac{dY}{dt}$. There is a warranted rate of growth in each case. **2.** If $v < s$, warranted rate of growth, in (a) of Ex. 1, is $\rho' = 1\Big/\left(\dfrac{v}{s} - 1\right) < 0$, c.f. $\rho = \dfrac{s}{v} > 1$ in (b) and (c).

3.7 (p. 83)

2. In (4) put $c_2 = 0$, $s = 1 - c = 0$. $Z_t = vZ_{t-1} + A$ has solution

$$Z_t = \frac{A}{1-v} + \text{constant } v^t \to \frac{A}{1-v} \quad (v < 1)$$

There is an equilibrium *growth* of income, not *level* of income. Note that the static multiplier level $\left(\dfrac{A}{s}\right)$ is infinite when $s = 0$. **3.** Same result with v reduced to $(v - c_2)$, as long as $v > c_2$. If $v < c_2$, then Z_t alternates.

3.8 (p. 85)

1. Substitute in $v - c_2 > (1 + \sqrt{s})^2$. A positive value of c_2 simply makes the critical value of v rather larger. **2.** If $s = 0$, one root of $R = 0$ is zero and the other positive if $v - c_2 > 1$. The curve of Fig. 8 goes through O.

3.9 (p. 89)

2. $R = s > 0$ at $r = 0$; $R \to \pm\infty$ as $r \to \pm\infty$. Hence curve cuts Or once to left of O. If it cuts Or again, there are *two* further crossings, *either* both to left, *or* both to right of O. Three cases follow.

4.2 (p. 96)

2. Values are same except for signs :

x	$\dfrac{\pi}{3}$	$\dfrac{2\pi}{3}$	$\dfrac{4\pi}{3}$	$\dfrac{5\pi}{3}$	$\dfrac{7\pi}{3}$
$\sin x$	+	+	−	−	+
$\cos x$	+	−	−	+	+
$\tan x$	+	−	+	−	+

3. Given $\cos x$ (Fig. 10b) there are two x in range $0 \leqslant x < 2\pi$, one giving $+$ for $\sin x$ and the other $-$. Similarly for $\tan x$. E.g. $\cos x = \frac{1}{2}$, then $x = \dfrac{\pi}{3}$ or $\dfrac{5\pi}{3}$; signs of $\sin x$ and $\tan x$ as in Ex. 2. **4.** Check :

$$\sin 0 = \sin x \cos x - \sin x \cos x = 0$$
$$\cos 0 = \sin^2 x + \cos^2 x = 1$$

6. $\dfrac{d}{dx}\left(\dfrac{\sin x}{\cos x}\right) = \dfrac{\sin^2 x + \cos^2 x}{\cos^2 x} = \dfrac{1}{\cos^2 x} \to \infty$ as $x \to \dfrac{\pi}{2}$

4.3 (p. 102)

3. By (1) : $(x_2 + x_1, y_2 + y_1) = (x_1 + x_2, y_1 + y_2)$. By (4) : $(x_2 x_1 - y_2 y_1, x_2 y_1 + x_1 y_2) = (x_1 x_2 - y_1 y_2, x_1 y_2 + x_2 y_1)$. **4.** Let $z = (x, y)$: $z_1 = zz_2 = (xx_2 - yy_2, xy_2 + x_2 y)$ i.e. $x_1 = xx_2 - yy_2$ and $y_1 = xy_2 + x_2 y$. Solve for x and y.

5. $\dfrac{x_1 + iy_1}{x_2 + iy_2} = \dfrac{(x_1 + iy_1)(x_2 - iy_2)}{x_2{}^2 + y_2{}^2} = $ etc., multiplying numerator and denominator by $(x_2 - iy_2)$. **6.** Show square of R.H.S. $= (x + iy)^2$

4.4 (p. 106)

1. Note : $e^0 = 1$. **2.** $OB' = e^{3/2 \, i\pi}$; $e^{2i\pi} = OA$ again. **3.** Multiply $(\cos x + i \sin x)$

2C

and $(\cos x - i \sin x)$. Then multiply $e^x = \cosh x + \sinh x$ and $e^{-x} = \cosh x - \sinh x$.

4. $2 \cos \left(\dfrac{\pi}{2} - x \right) = e^{i \left(\frac{\pi}{2} - x \right)} + e^{-i \left(\frac{\pi}{2} - x \right)} = i(e^{-ix} - e^{ix}) = $ etc.

4.5 (p. 110)

3. Quotient $= \dfrac{r (\cos \theta + i \sin \theta)}{r (\cos \theta - i \sin \theta)} = \dfrac{(\cos \theta + i \sin \theta)^2}{(\cos \theta - i \sin \theta)(\cos \theta + i \sin \theta)}$ and so on, using $\cos^2 \theta + \sin^2 \theta = 1$; $\cos^2 \theta - \sin^2 \theta = \cos 2\theta$; and $2 \sin \theta \cos \theta = \sin 2\theta$. **4.** $x^2 + y^2 = (x + iy)(x - iy) = (y + ix)(y - ix)$. **5.** Use

$$\cos 2\theta = \cos^2 \theta - \sin^2 \theta ; \quad \sin 2\theta = 2 \sin \theta \cos \theta$$

4.6 (p. 116)

3. Typical case : $f(x)$ has one max. or min. between a and b, i.e. one $f'(x) = 0$. Generally, an odd number of max. or min., with a point of inflexion where $f'(x) = f''(x) = 0$ counted as coincident roots of $f'(x) = 0$. If $f'(x) = 0$ has real roots at $x_1, x_2, \ldots x_{n-1}$ in ascending order and if $f(x)$ alternates in sign in the series $f(-\infty), f(x_1), f(x_2), \ldots f(x_{n-1}), f(\infty)$, then $f(x) = 0$ has n real roots separated by $x_1, x_2, \ldots x_{n-1}$. **4.** Here $f'(x) = 0$ at $x = \pm 1$. Signs :

x	$-\infty$	-1	$+1$	$+\infty$
$f(x)$	$-ve$	$(k+2)$	$(k-2)$	$+ve$

Hence three real and unequal roots if $-2 < k < 2$. **5.** If $a_n > 0$, no. of changes of sign (k) is even, and by graphical considerations no. of positive roots of $f(x) = 0$ is even. Similarly, if $a_n < 0$. It remains to show that no. of positive roots $\not> k$. Proof, see Durell and Robson (1937), based on result that, if $f(x)$ has k changes of sign, then $(x - a)f(x)$ has $(k+1)$ changes of sign for $a > 0$.

4.7 (p. 121)

1. Fig. 10 shows that $\sin x$ leads $\cos x$ by $\dfrac{\pi}{2}$.

2. $\cos \left(\omega x - \dfrac{\pi}{4} \right) = \cos \omega x \cos \dfrac{\pi}{4} + \sin \omega x \sin \dfrac{\pi}{4} = \dfrac{1}{\sqrt{2}} (\cos \omega x + \sin \omega x),$

and similarly, by addition formulae (4.2 above) and since $\cos 45° = \sin 45° = \dfrac{1}{\sqrt{2}}$.

3. Fig. 10 : $y = A \tan (\omega t + \epsilon)$ crosses Ot for $\omega t + \epsilon = n\pi$ (n integral). Hence period of $\dfrac{\pi}{\omega}$ and phase given by crossing at $t = -\dfrac{\epsilon}{\omega}$.

4.9 (p. 131)

1. Use $\cos (x + \pi) = \cos (x - \pi) = -\cos x$ for any x. **4.** $\dfrac{dy}{dt} = \rho A e^{\alpha t} \cos (\omega t + \epsilon + \eta).$

$\dfrac{d}{dt} y (t - \theta) = \rho(A e^{-\alpha \theta}) e^{\alpha t} \cos (\omega t + \epsilon + \eta - \omega \theta) = $ real part of $pe^{-p\theta} z$. Put $\alpha = 0$,

$\theta = \dfrac{\pi}{2\omega}$; so $\rho = \omega$, $\eta = \dfrac{\pi}{2}$, and $\dfrac{d}{dt} y \left(t - \dfrac{\pi}{2\omega} \right) = \omega A \cos (\omega t + \epsilon)$. **5.** $A e^{\nu \epsilon} = (\Sigma A_n) e^{i \epsilon}$

where ϵ is common phasing. Hence $A = \Sigma A_n$. Here OP_1 and OP_2 (Fig. 18) are the *same* direction, and so is OP; all sinusoidal oscillations with same phase and amplitude are simply added. **6.** From addition formulae (4.2 above):

$$\cos x + \cos y = 2 \cos \dfrac{x+y}{2} \cos \dfrac{x-y}{2} \text{ for any } x \text{ and } y.$$

Hence: $y = 2A e^{\alpha t} \cos \dfrac{\pi}{4} \cos \left(\omega t + \epsilon + \dfrac{\pi}{4} \right) = $ etc. $\left(\cos \dfrac{\pi}{4} = \dfrac{1}{\sqrt{2}} \right)$. In other case :

$y = 2Ae^{\alpha t} \cos \dfrac{\pi}{2} \cos \left(\omega t + \epsilon + \dfrac{\pi}{2} \right) = 0 \quad \left(\cos \dfrac{\pi}{2} = 0 \right)$. In Fig. 18, OP_1 and OP_2 of same length and at right angles (first case) or opposed (second case).

5.1 (p. 135)

2. Here x is multiple of $\dfrac{1}{n}$ and Y_x established by induction: If $Y_x = Y_0 \left(1 + \dfrac{r}{n} \right)^{nx}$,

then $Y_{x + \frac{1}{n}} = Y_x \left(1 + \dfrac{r}{n} \right) = Y_0 \left(1 + \dfrac{r}{n} \right)^{n\left(x + \frac{1}{n}\right)}$. As $n \to \infty$, note: $\left(1 + \dfrac{r}{n} \right)^{\frac{n}{r}} \to e$.

5.3 (p. 144)

1. $\dfrac{d}{dx} \left(\dfrac{a^x}{\log a} \right) = a^x$ for $a \neq 1$; hence solution. If $a = 1$, differential equation is $\dfrac{dY}{dx} = 1$ so that $Y = x + A$. **3.** Use $\sin (ax + b) = \cos \left(ax + b - \dfrac{\pi}{2} \right)$; $\cos (ax + b)$ $= -\sin \left(ax + b - \dfrac{\pi}{2} \right)$. **6.** Complementary function from Ex. 5. Check particular integrals: (i) $Y = x$ and (ii) $Y = \sin x$. Solutions are steady approach to (i) constant increase trend, (ii) oscillatory trend. **7.** Trend is $Y = \int f(x) dx$ as particular path of Y. Variation from trend is constant.

5.4 (p. 150)

2. Complementary functions from Ex. 1. Check particular integrals: $Y = x$ and $Y = e^{-x}$ respectively. **3.** $y = (A_1 + A_2 x)e^{-x}$ with $A_1 = A_2 = 1$ from initial conditions. **4.** Complementary function as Ex. 3; check $Y = x(1 - e^{-x})$ as particular integral; and find constants from initial conditions. **5.** Differential equations: $\dfrac{d^2 y}{dx^2} \pm 2 \dfrac{dy}{dx} + 2y = 0$. **6.** $A = 1$, $\epsilon = 0$; the same for both initial conditions, since with (i) it follows that $Y = \dfrac{\pi}{2}$ at $x = \dfrac{\pi}{2}$. **7.** Put $y = ue^{-\frac{1}{2}ax}$ in (6); so $\dfrac{d^2 u}{dx^2} = 0$, giving $u = A_1 + A_2 x$. **8.** If $(-a) < (-b)$, auxiliary equation $q^2 = \lambda(a - b)$ > 0; explosive case as Ex. 1 above. If $(-a) = (-b)$, $\dfrac{d^2 p}{dt_2} = 0$ and $p = A_1 + A_2 t$.

9. Oscillations only if $\lambda < \dfrac{4}{a^2}(b - a)$. R.H.S. here is positive $(a < 0, b > 0)$ but may be quite small, e.g. if a large numerically.

5.5 (p. 155)

2. Substitute $\dfrac{dy}{dx} = z(x)$ in L.H.S. of (i) and obtain L.H.S. of (ii); so $y = \int z(x) dx + A$.

3. Substitution in (8) gives linear equation in x, to hold for all x; hence put coefficient of x and constant term equal to zero separately, finding a and b.
4. Auxiliary equation is cubic with $(p - 1)$ as factor; e^x dominates, i.e. y has steady and oscillatory explosive elements.

5.6 (p. 161)

2. In "integration by parts" formula of Ex. 1, replace y by y' and by y''. **4.** Results are "integration by parts". Eliminate one of $\int e^{-pt} \sin \omega t \, dt$ and $\int e^{-pt} \cos \omega t \, dt$ and find the other. **7.** Any variable can appear in a definite integral, so that: $\bar{y}(p) = \displaystyle\int_0^\infty e^{-p\tau} y(\tau) \, d\tau$ and hence $\bar{y}\left(\dfrac{p}{\omega} \right) = \displaystyle\int_0^\infty e^{-\frac{p}{\omega}\tau} y(\tau) \, d\tau$.

5.7 (p. 166)

2. $-A_1 = A_2 = \frac{1}{2}$. **3.** Subsidiary equations : (i) $(p+1)^2\bar{y}(p) = \frac{2p+1}{p^2}$; (ii)

$(p+1)^2\bar{y}(p) = -\frac{p^3+2p^2-2p-1}{p^2}$. In (i), put $\frac{2p+1}{p^2(p+1)^2}$ into partial fractions and use standard forms to get from $y(p)$ to $y(t)$. Similarly (ii). **4.** Subsidiary equation : $\{(p+\frac{1}{2})^2+1\}\bar{y}(p) = \frac{4p+5}{4p^2}+p+\frac{3}{2}$. Solution is then $y = t + e^{-\frac{1}{2}t}\cos t$.

5.8 (p. 170)

1. $(D^3 + 9\lambda D^2 + 27\lambda^2 D + 27\lambda^3)\,Y = 27\lambda^3 Z$; auxiliary equation has three equal roots (-3λ). Try $Y = (A + Bt + Ct^2)e^{-3\lambda t}$; particular integral $Y = Z_0$. A, B and C from initial conditions. **2.** Auxiliary equation has two roots $(-\lambda_1)$ and $(-\lambda_2)$. Use initial conditions for solution : $Y = \left(1 + \frac{\lambda_2}{\lambda_1-\lambda_2}e^{-\lambda_1 t} + \frac{\lambda_1}{\lambda_2-\lambda_1}e^{-\lambda_2 t}\right)Z_0$.

3. (a) $Y = \left(\frac{n\lambda}{D+n\lambda}\right)^n Z$; (b) $Y = \frac{\lambda_1\lambda_2\cdots\lambda_n}{(D+\lambda_1)(D+\lambda_2)\cdots(D+\lambda_n)}Z$.

5.9 (p. 175)

2. Replace two terms in (4) : $\bar{y}(p) = \frac{A_1}{p-p_1} + \frac{A_2}{(p-p_1)^2} + \cdots$ giving :

$$y(t) = (A_1 + A_2 t)\,e^{p_1 t} + \cdots$$

Similarly for two equal pairs of conjugate complex roots. Resonance, with explosive element like $(A_1 + A_2 t)$, when inherent and forced variations coincide. **3.** Solution : $y = \frac{\cos \omega t}{1-\omega^2} + A\cos(t-\epsilon)$, i.e. forced + inherent oscillation. Resonance arises when $\omega \to 1$ and $y \to \infty$.

6.1 (p. 178)

3.
$$\begin{array}{lcccccc} y_x = & 1 & -1 & & 1 & -1 \ldots \\ \Delta y_x = & & -2 & 2 & -2 & \ldots \\ \Delta^2 y_x = & & & 4 & -4 & \ldots \end{array}$$

4. $\Delta y_x = y_{x+1} - y_x$; $\Delta^2 y_x = y_{x+2} - 2y_{x+1} + y_x$; $\Delta^3 y_x = y_{x+3} - 3y_{x+2} + 3y_{x+1} - y_x$. $y_{x+1} = \Delta y_x + y_x$; $y_{x+2} = \Delta^2 y_x + 2\Delta y_x + y_x$; $y_{x+3} = \Delta^3 y_x + 3\Delta^2 y_x + 3\Delta y_x + y_x$.

6.2 (p. 183)

2. General solution : $y_x = y_0(\frac{1}{2})^x$. **3.** $y_2 = y_1 - y_0$; $y_3 = -y_0$; $y_4 = -y_1$; $y_5 = -(y_1-y_0)$; $y_6 = y_0$; repeating each cycle in 6 intervals.

6.3 (p. 186)

3. Addition formulae give $(\sin x - \sin y)$ as in 4.9, Ex. 6. So :

$$\Delta(\sin ax) = \sin(ax+a) - \sin ax = \text{etc.}$$

5. $Y_{x+1} = Y_x + (x+1)^2$ gives ΔY_x. Use result of Ex. 4. **7.** For particular integral, try $Y_x = \mu a^x$ and show $\mu = \frac{\alpha}{\alpha-a}$. Case $\alpha = a$ is an example of resonance.

8. Try $Y_x = \mu_1 x + \mu_2$ as particular integral. Find constants μ_1 and μ_2 so that equation is true for all x ($= 0, 1, 2, \ldots$).

6.4 (p. 191)

1. Auxiliary equation gives $\lambda_1 = \frac{1}{2}$, $\lambda_2 = (-1)\frac{1}{2}$. **2.** Here $\lambda_1 = a$, $\lambda_2 = (-1)a$; damped if $a < 1$. **3.** Roots of auxiliary equation: (i) $\frac{1}{2}$ and 2; steady, explosive ; (ii) $\frac{1}{2}$ and $\frac{1}{2}$; steady, damped ; (iii) $\frac{1}{2}$ and $\frac{1}{4}$; steady, damped. **4.** Solution :

$$y = Ar^x \cos(\theta x - \epsilon) \text{ where } r = \frac{1}{\sqrt{2}}, \ \tan \theta = 1. \ \theta = \frac{\pi}{4}, \text{ period is 8.} \quad \text{Second}$$

equation similarly ; $\theta = \frac{3\pi}{4}$, period is $\frac{8}{3}$. **6.** Oscillations of constant amplitude

$(r=1)$ when $a^2<4$. Alternation (two real and *negative* values of λ) when $a^2>4$.
7. Try particular integrals: (i) $\bar{Y}=\mu\alpha^x$; (ii) $\bar{Y}=\mu x+\nu$. **8.** If $\lambda=0$, then $b=0$ and equation of first order. If $\lambda=1$, one term in (5) is an additive constant. **9.** Auxiliary equation $\lambda^2-\alpha\lambda-\beta=0$, gives oscillations if $\alpha^2+4\beta<0$. **10.** First order equation with solution: $u_t=u_0\alpha^t$. **11.** Auxiliary equation $\lambda^2-(a+b)\lambda+b=0$, oscillations if $a^2+2(a-2)b+b^2<0$. Orcutt case has $a=1$.

6.5 (p. 195)
1. Auxiliary equation has root $\lambda=1$. Difference is in constant term, steady and alternating respectively. **3.** Try $\bar{Y}=\mu x$ and find μ. Try $\bar{Y}=\mu x^2$ in further case. **4.** Use $x^{(2)}=x(x-1)$ and not x^2 (see 6.3 above). Extend by using $x^{(3)}$, $x^{(4)}$, ... **6.** Proceed as in 6.4 (second case).

6.6 (p. 200)
2. Auxiliary equation: $\lambda^2-c(1-\rho)\lambda-c\rho=0$ with $c=\dfrac{(-b)}{(-a)}<1$. $\rho=0$: $p_t=p_0c^t$ as simple cobweb. $\rho=1$: $p_t=c^{\frac{1}{2}t}\{A_1+-(1)^tA_2\}$ damped alternation. **3.** $\lambda>\dfrac{4}{b-a}$ gives $c>-1$ and $\mu_1=c-\sqrt{c^2-1}<-1$ dominates. Hence p_t alternating and explosive. $b-a<0$ if $(-b)>(-a)$, i.e. S downward and steeper than D, not realistic. **4.** Model II of 1.7, Ex. 2, has auxiliary equation

$$\mu^2-(2+\lambda a)\mu+(1+\lambda b)=0 \quad \text{with oscillatory case if} \quad 0<\lambda<\frac{4(b-a)}{a^2}.$$

6.7 (p. 206)
1. Case of delay of two periods, equivalent to a single lag. **2.** Dominant term is $y_t\to$constant (fixed by initial conditions). Check: *any* constant Y_t satisfies equation and saving is zero. **3.** λ_1 is a positive fraction and term $y_t=A_1\lambda_1{}^t$ dominates, i.e. sign of A_1 fixes whether $y_t\to0$ through positive or negative values. $(-\lambda_2)$ is positive and generally small, so that sign of y_1 is more important than that of y_0.

7.1 (p. 212)
1. $R>0$ all r when $R=0$ has complex roots; $R>0$ all positive r when $R=0$ has two real negative roots. Difficult case is $R=0$ with two positive roots; here r less than smaller of roots still gives $R>0$. **2.** (i) $0.5<v<2.5$, (ii) $0.7<v<1.5$. **3.** Yes. **4.** Oscillations if $1-\sqrt{s}<\sqrt{w}<1+\sqrt{s}$, i.e. $\sqrt{s}>1-\sqrt{w}$ (or $\sqrt{w}-1$). Hence $s>(1-\sqrt{w})^2$ for oscillations, e.g. $s>0.018$ for $w=0.75$.

7.2 (p. 216)
1. $y_t=A_1(0.96)^t+A_2(-0.01)^t\to0$ slowly. **3.** Auxiliary equation has real roots 1 and w. **4.** Auxiliary equation has two equal (real) roots. **6.** Regular oscillations in y_t: deviations from trend of constant amplitude; in η_t: % deviations from trend of constant amplitude (i.e. actual deviations increase in amplitude with the trend).

7.5 (p. 223)
2. $s>\dfrac{k}{1+k}$. **3.** Production for stock, replacement of stocks previously run down. Auxiliary equation has roots $c\pm i\sqrt{c(1-c)}$; $r=\sqrt{c}<1$. **4.** Write $Y_t=C_t+I_t$, $Y_{t-1}=C_{t-1}+I_{t-1}$ and so (Y_t-Y_{t-1}) in terms of Y and R. Then eliminate (R_t-R_{t-1}).

7.8 (p. 233)
1. Period $=\dfrac{2\pi}{\theta}=4$; damping $=r=\sqrt{-w}$, usually a small fraction, unless v is very weak and lagged consumption important. **2.** Graph of $f(\lambda)$ has maximum *below* $O\lambda$.

7.9 (p. 237)

1. Write $\dfrac{d}{d\lambda} g(\lambda) = 0$. If $w_2 < 0$, maximum and minimum reversed. **4.** $\lambda = 1$ gives

additive constant in y_t. Other roots $\lambda = \frac{1}{2}(w_1 \pm \sqrt{w_1^2 + 4w_2})$. Hence y_t oscillates if $w_1 < 2\sqrt{w_2}$. **5.** Auxiliary equation for z_t is $\lambda_t - w_1\lambda - w_2 = 0$, as Ex. 4. The additive constant of Ex. 4 disappears when difference z_t is taken. **7.** For $w_1 > 0$, $w_2 > 0$, graph $f(\lambda)$ like equation (3) of 6.7 above (see Fig. 20); graph of $g(\lambda)$ is a hyperbola like Fig. 25.

8.2 (p. 247)

2. If $K < \bar{K}$, initial point between A and B (moderate deficit) or to left of A (larger deficit). First step to B, then cycle $BCDA$ .... **3.** Autonomous outlays (consumption, investment) can be absorbed into term for technological progress.

8.5 (p. 258)

1. $b = a + k =$ small, so log b negative and numerically large. Hence $A > 1$; two real roots ρ exist (Fig. 31). **2.** Fig. 32 (for $A > 1$) shows that lowest $\omega > 2\pi$. **3.** $A = 0.405$ (log $1.1 = 0.095$). For ω see Fig. 32. **4.** $A = 0.857$ (log $0.7 = -0.357$). Smaller ω than Ex. 3.

8.6 (p. 261)

2. $P = \lambda Y + \mu$ for constant λ and μ. (1) is : $\lambda Y + \mu = \dfrac{I + A}{1 - c}$. (4) is :

$B = a(1 - c)(\lambda Y + \mu) + \dots$. (5) unchanged except for constants. **3.** If ϕ is

average lag, weighted by c: $Y(t - \phi) = \dfrac{Y(t) - cY(t - \psi)}{1 - c}$. Then (1) gives

$Y(t) = \dfrac{I(t + \phi) + A}{1 - c}$. Hence equation immediately before (5) becomes:

$I(t + \theta) = \dots$ expression in $I(t + \phi)$, i.e. $I(t + \theta - \phi) = \dots$ expression in $I(t)$. Lag in (5) reduced from θ to $\theta - \phi$.

8.7 (p. 268)

1. (3) can be written $\dfrac{1}{\lambda} D^2 Y + \left(s + \dfrac{\kappa}{\lambda} - \kappa v\right) DY + \kappa s Y = (D + \kappa)A$. $\lambda \to \infty$ and A

constant : $DY - \rho Y = -\rho \dfrac{A}{s}$ with solution shown. **2.** Turn radians into degrees, put $A = -1$. Use sin $(x - 90°) = -\cos x$. **3.** In (4), put p_1, $p_2 = 0.2 \pm i \, 0.98$.

8.9 (p. 279)

5. $D^3 Y + 18D^2 Y + 48DY + 288 Y = 64(D + 2)A$ with steady level $Y = \dfrac{4A}{9}$ as Ex. (a).

Roots of $p^3 + 18p^2 + 48p + 288 = 0$ graphically : $p = -16.13$, $-0.935 \pm i \, 4.12$. $Y(t)$ has heavily damped steady term and mildly damped oscillation ($\alpha = -0.935$) of period $\dfrac{2\pi}{4.12} = 1.5$. Less damped oscillation than Ex. (a).

6. $D^4 Y + 18D^3 Y + 48D^2 Y + 288DY + 256 Y = 64D(D + 2)A$ with steady level $Y = 0$ as Ex. (b). Roots $p = -1$, -16.06, $-0.47 \pm i \, 3.96$. $Y(t)$ has two damped steady terms and mildly damped oscillation ($\alpha = -0.47$) of period $\dfrac{2\pi}{3.96} = 1.6$. Less damped oscillation than Ex. (b).

9.3 (p. 295)

1. For $\rho = \dfrac{1}{\sqrt{\alpha^2 + \omega^2}}$ and $\tan \phi = \dfrac{\omega}{\alpha}$, $Y = \displaystyle\int_0^t Ae^{\alpha t} \cos (\omega t + \epsilon) \, dt$

$$= \text{real part of } \rho e^{-i\phi} Z = \frac{1}{p} Z.$$

Integration by parts is used (as 4.9 above). **2.** $f(t) = Y'(t) = \dfrac{1}{p_1 - p_2}(e^{p_1 t} - e^{p_2 t})$

with Laplace Transform : $F(p) = \dfrac{1}{p_1 - p_2}\left(\dfrac{1}{p - p_1} - \dfrac{1}{p - p_2}\right) = \dfrac{1}{p^2 + ap + b}$ as from

relation with $D = p$. **3.** Case of resonance. **4.** $F(p) = \dfrac{1}{(p+1)^2} = \dfrac{1}{(1 + i\omega)^2}$ for

$p = i\omega$ ($\alpha = 0$). Hence locus of point with co-ordinates $\dfrac{1 - \omega^2}{(1 + \omega^2)^2}$ and $-\dfrac{2\omega}{(1 + \omega^2)^2}$.

As ω varies, (iii) of Fig. 39 obtained. **6.** $Y = \dfrac{1}{2T}\displaystyle\int_{t-2T}^{t} Z\, dt$. Substitute

$Z = A \cos(\omega t + \epsilon)$ and integrate.

9.4 (p. 298)
1. Loop with unlagged multiplier has transfer function $F_1(p) = c$. **3.** At given point, $F(p)$ is different according to which loop it is computed for. But $F(p) = 1$ gives same equation ; here $F_1(p) + F_2(p) = 1$ is obtained in text and in this exercise.

9.5 (p. 302)
1. Cubic in p can have no more than one conjugate complex pair of roots, i.e. at most one oscillatory solution. **2.** For two oscillatory solutions, at least quartic equation in p.

9.7 (p. 308)
1. $\dfrac{F_1(p)}{1 - F_2(p)} \neq \dfrac{F_2(p)}{1 - F_1(p)}$ but same p obtained by putting either equal to unity

(see 9.4, Ex. 3). **2.** (1) with $(v - g)$ as power of accelerator has coefficient

$\dfrac{v}{s} - \dfrac{g}{s} = k - k'$ instead of k. (2) becomes $\alpha = 2(k - k' - 1)$, $\omega = 2\sqrt{(k - k')(2 - k + k')}$ and it is equivalent to (4).

10.1 (p. 317)
1. Equations (i) give

$$x_i = (b_i p - h_i)\frac{\bar{x}_i p + \bar{y}_i}{P_i} \; ; \quad y_i = (a_i - h_i p)\frac{\bar{x}_i p + \bar{y}_i}{P_i}$$

where $P_i = a_i - 2h_i p + b_i p^2$ ($i = 1, 2$). **2.** First equation of (ii) gives on substitution from result of Ex. 1 :

$$\frac{(b_1 p - h_1)(\bar{x}_1 p + \bar{y}_1)}{P_1} + \frac{(b_2 p - h_2)(\bar{x}_2 p + \bar{y}_2)}{P_2} = \bar{x}_1 + \bar{x}_2$$

Other equation is automatically satisfied. Since P_1 and P_2 are quadratics, equation appears to be fourth order in p. But p^4 term is found to be zero and p^3 term generally non-zero, i.e. equation is cubic. Product of roots

$$= -\frac{\text{constant term}}{p^3 \text{ coefficient}} = \frac{a_1 a_2(\bar{x}_1 + \bar{x}_2) + a_2 h_1 \bar{y}_1 + a_1 h_2 \bar{y}_2}{h_1 b_2 \bar{x}_1 + h_2 b_1 \bar{x}_2 + b_1 b_2(\bar{y}_1 + \bar{y}_2)} > 0$$

if a_1, a_2, b_1, b_2 negative, h_1 and h_2 small. At least one $p > 0$.

10.2 (p. 319)
2. One $Y_t = 0$, one equation dropped in (iii), i.e. one equation and one variable less ; consistent with equilibrium. **3.** p_u and Y_u appear *only* in two added equations, which serve to fix them, substituting p's and Y's from other equations.

10.3 (p. 322)

3. (ii) (a) give $-xp_x = -yp_y = ap_xp_y$; (ii) (b) gives $xy = az$. Hence $z = ap_xp_y$.

4. First individual $(u_1 = a_1x_1^2 + 2h_1x_1z_1 + b_1z_1^2)$ has demand :

$$x_1 = (b_1p_x - h_1)\frac{R + p_x\bar{x}}{P_1} ; \quad y_1 = 0 ; \quad z_1 = (a_1 - h_1p_x)\frac{R + p_x\bar{x}}{P_1}$$

where $P_1 = a_1 - 2h_1p_x + b_1p_x^2$. Similarly for second individual :

$$x_2 = 0 ; \quad y_2 = (b_2p_y - h_2)\frac{p_y\bar{y}}{P_2} ; \quad z_2 = (a_2 - h_2p_y)\frac{p_y\bar{y}}{P_2}$$

Market conditions $(x = x_1 - \bar{x}, y = y_2 - \bar{y})$ are two equations in p's. **5.** Equations (ii) : $\dfrac{y}{p_x} = \dfrac{x}{p_y} = -2az$ and $xy = az^2$. Hence $p_xp_y = \dfrac{1}{4a}$; $-xp_x = -yp_y = \frac{1}{2}z$.
Also $R = xp_x + yp_y + z = 0$.

10.5 (p. 329)

1. Write $\dfrac{d}{dp_1}(Y_1 - X_1) = a_{11} + a_{12}\dfrac{dp_2}{dp_1} + a_{13}\dfrac{dp_3}{dp_1} > 0$

$$\frac{d}{dp_1}(Y_2 - X_2) = a_{21} + a_{22}\frac{dp_2}{dp_1} + a_{23}\frac{dp_3}{dp_1} = 0$$

$$\frac{d}{dp_1}(Y_3 - X_3) = a_{31} + a_{32}\frac{dp_2}{dp_1} + a_{33}\frac{dp_3}{dp_1} = 0$$

Find $\dfrac{dp_2}{dp_1}$ and $\dfrac{dp_3}{dp_1}$ from equations ; substitute to get $\dfrac{d}{dp_1}(Y_1 - X_1)$ as ratio of

$$\begin{vmatrix} a_{11} & a_{12} & a_{13} \\ a_{21} & a_{22} & a_{23} \\ a_{31} & a_{32} & a_{33} \end{vmatrix} \text{ to } \begin{vmatrix} a_{22} & a_{23} \\ a_{32} & a_{33} \end{vmatrix}.$$ Latter is positive. **3.** Ratios of determinants

positive, not necessarily determinants themselves, is required by

$$\frac{d}{dp_1}(Y_1 - X_1) > 0$$

10.6 (p. 332)

2. Simpler to use determinants (12.9 and 14.2 below). If $A = |a_{rs}|$ and A_{rs} co-factors, $\dfrac{dp_1}{d\alpha} = -\dfrac{\partial}{\partial\alpha}(Y_1 - X_1)\dfrac{A_{11}}{A}$; $\dfrac{dp_2}{d\alpha} = -\dfrac{\partial}{\partial\alpha}(Y_1 - X_1)\dfrac{A_{12}}{A}$; etc.　Given

$\dfrac{\partial}{\partial\alpha}(Y_1 - X_1) > 0$, and $A_{11} > 0$, $A > 0$ (Hicksian stability), $\dfrac{dp_1}{d\alpha} < 0$ and $\dfrac{dp_2}{d\alpha}$ has

sign of $(-A_{12})$.　**3.** Neglect a_{23}, a_{31}, take $a_{33} > 0$ (stability) ; so $\dfrac{dp_2}{d\alpha} = $ sign of

a_{21}. But, if a_{23} and a_{31} large and of same sign, then $\dfrac{dp_2}{d\alpha}$ can be negative even

if a_{21} positive.　Similarly if a_{23} and a_{31} of opposite sign and a_{21} negative.

10.8 (p. 341)

1. $y_1 = \dfrac{a_1a_2}{a}$, $y = \dfrac{(\lambda a_1)(\lambda a_2)}{a} = \lambda^2 y_1$　**2.** $y_1 = \sqrt{\dfrac{a_1a_2}{a}}$, $y = \sqrt{\dfrac{(\lambda a_1)(\lambda a_2)}{a}} = \lambda y_1$

3. If f homogeneous of degree r : $f(\lambda x_1, \lambda x_2, \dots \lambda x_m, \lambda y_1, \lambda y_2, \dots \lambda y_n) = \lambda^r f = 0$
Then any one variable is linear homogeneous function of others.

11.3 (p. 351)

1. Show $c_1 = \dfrac{1}{k}\sqrt{\dfrac{p_2}{p_1}}$, $c_2 = \dfrac{1}{k}\sqrt{\dfrac{p_1}{p_2}}$.　**2.** For linear homogeneous production function, all constant product curves are similar radially from O (see 10.7 above).　**3.** (i) are relations between outputs and final demands; (ii) imply that given prices and wage rates must be consistent with technical conditions of production.

11.5 (p. 354)
1. R.H.S. is value of output distributed to other industries, see total output to industries of Table 1. **2.** Use totals from Table 1. **3.** Columns add to zero.

11.6 (p. 358)

1. $X_1 = \dfrac{x_1 + a_{12}x_2}{1 - a_{12}a_{21}}$; $X_2 = \dfrac{a_{21}x_1 + x_2}{1 - a_{12}a_{21}}$; similarly for p_1 and p_2.

2. $A = \begin{vmatrix} 1 & -a_{12} \\ -a_{21} & 1 \end{vmatrix} = 1 - a_{12}a_{21}$, $A_{11} = 1$, $A_{12} = a_{21}$, etc. See Ex. 1. **3.** Use result (12.9 below) for multiplying rows or columns of a determinant by constant multiples (here prices). **4.** Commodity price : wage rate = increase in employment : increase in final demand.

11.7 (p. 361)
1. Attempt to solve pairs of equations for X_1 and X_2, X_3 arbitrary. Results are inconsistent unless third-order determinant is zero. If second-order determinants also zero, X_1 and X_2 are indeterminate. **2.** Matrix adds to zero, across and down. **3.** From (i), $\Sigma\, \alpha_{rs}V_s = 0$, i.e. matrix adds across to zero when columns are multiplied by V_1, V_2, $\dots$.

11.9 (p. 369)

2. For (4): $A_1 = \dfrac{k_2 X_{10} - X_{20}}{k_2 - k_1}$, $A_2 = \dfrac{k_1 X_{10} - X_{20}}{k_1 - k_2}$. Similarly for (7) with $k_1 = \dfrac{1}{a_{12}}$, $k_2 = k$. **3.** $1 - a_{12}a_{21} = 0$ is a condition for homogeneous (closed) system, not otherwise. Put $1 - a_{12}a_{21} = 0$, i.e. $a_{12} = \dfrac{1}{a_{21}}$, so that $B_1 - a_{12}B_2 = c_1$ and $B_1 - a_{12}B_2 = -\dfrac{c_2}{a_{21}}$. Hence only $B_1 : B_2$ given, provided that $c_1 = -\dfrac{c_2}{a_{21}}$. **4.** Try $X_1 = B_1 + B_{11}t$, $X_2 = B_2 + B_{22}t$ and find the B's. **6.** Try $X_1 = B_{11}e^{\mu_1 t} + B_{12}e^{\mu_2 t}$, $X_2 = B_{21}e^{\mu_1 t} + B_{22}e^{\mu_2 t}$ and find the B's. **8.** $a_{12} = a_{21} = 0$: production of commodities without inputs. $b_{11} = b_{22} = 0$: no stocks of commodities in production. $b_{12} \neq 0$, $b_{21} \neq 0$: stocks of one commodity needed in production of other.

12.4 (p. 382)
1. $(2, 2, 2) > (1, 1, 1)$. Other relations $\geqslant$. **2.** $\mathbf{p} \geqslant 0$; non-negative prices, at least one positive. Not $\mathbf{p} \geq 0$ which allows all prices to vanish. **3.** OP and OP' are of same length and opposed direction, i.e. compound to O. If OP is $\mathbf{a}$, then OP' is $(-\mathbf{a})$.

12.5 (p. 387)
1. By elementary co-ordinate geometry, A_1A_2 has equation $x_1 + x_2 = 1$. Point (x_1, x_2) is on line between A_1 and A_2 if $x_2 = 1 - x_1$ where $0 \leqslant x_1 \leqslant 1$. Result follows by writing $x_1 = \mu$ $(0 \leqslant \mu \leqslant 1)$. **2.** P has co-ordinates
$$x_1 = \mu x_1^{(1)} + (1 - \mu)x_1^{(2)}, \quad x_2 = \mu x_2^{(1)} + (1 - \mu)x_2^{(2)}$$
So : $PP_1^2 = (1 - \mu)^2\{(x_1^{(1)} - x_1^{(2)})^2 + (x_2^{(1)} - x_2^{(2)})^2\}$
$PP_2^2 = \mu^2\{(x_1^{(1)} - x_1^{(2)})^2 + (x_2^{(1)} - x_2^{(2)})^2\}$
i.e. $P_2P : PP_1 = \mu : (1 - \mu)$

12.6 (p. 392)
1. (a) diagonal and scalar (see Ex. 2) ; (b) symmetric, obtained from $\mathbf{I}$ by interchange of rows (see Ex. 3) ; (c) skew-symmetric ; (d) orthogonal, for transformation rotating axes through $45°$. **5.** $\begin{bmatrix} a_1 & a_2 & b_1 & b_2 & b_3 \\ 1 & 0 & 0 & 0 & 0 \\ 0 & 1 & 0 & 0 & 0 \end{bmatrix}$. $\mathbf{I}$ of order 2,

$\mathbf{0}$ of order 2×3.

12.8 (p. 398)

5. Pick out coefficient of y_t in double sum $\sum\limits_{s=1}^{n} \sum\limits_{t=1}^{n} a_{rs}b_{st}y_t$.

12.9 (p. 402)

1. (a) 8 ; (b) -1 ; (c) 0 ; (d) 1. **3.** Determinant $=1-3a^2+2a^3=(1+2a)(1-a)^2=0$ when $a=-\frac{1}{2}$ or 1. **4.** Put $a=b$ and show determinant zero. So $(a-b)$ is a factor. **9.** If $\mathbf{A}$ symmetric, so is $[A_{rs}]$; $|A_{rs}|=A^2$ only for third order. **10.** Use properties (ii) and (vi) above.

13.1 (p. 407)

1. $\dfrac{p_1}{q_1}+\dfrac{p_2}{q_2}=\dfrac{p_1q_2+p_2q_1}{q_1q_2}=$ rational ; similarly for other processes. **2.** (a) division fails ; (b) division fails and no unit ; (c) addition, subtraction and division fail. **3.** Without commutative law $a(b+c)=ab+ac$ and $(b+c)a=ba+ca \neq ab+ac$. **4.** Sums and products of two such numbers are numbers of the same form ; similarly for subtraction and division.

13.2 (p. 411)

1. $\mathbf{xA}$ not defined ; no inner products. **3.** $\mathbf{AB}$ not defined. **4.** $\mathbf{BA}$ not defined.

13.3 (p. 414)

4. $\mathbf{A+B}=10\begin{bmatrix} 1 & 1 & 1 \\ 1 & 1 & 1 \\ 1 & 1 & 1 \end{bmatrix}$ and $\mathbf{A-B}=2\begin{bmatrix} -4 & -3 & -2 \\ -1 & 0 & 1 \\ 2 & 3 & 4 \end{bmatrix}$

5. $\lambda=p$: $p\mathbf{A}=\mathbf{A+A}+\ldots$ (p terms) ; $\lambda=\dfrac{p}{q}$: $q\left(\dfrac{p}{q}\mathbf{A}\right)=p\mathbf{A}$, etc.

13.4 (p. 421)

2. $\mathbf{BA}$ not defined $(m \neq n)$. **3.** $(\mathbf{B+C})\mathbf{A}=\mathbf{BA+CA}$ and $\mathbf{BA} \neq \mathbf{AB}$, $\mathbf{CA} \neq \mathbf{AC}$ (except in special cases). **4.** $\mathbf{AC}$, $\mathbf{AD}$, $\mathbf{BA}$, $\mathbf{CD}$, $\mathbf{DB}$ obtained ; e.g.

$\mathbf{AC}=\begin{bmatrix} -3 & -3 & -3 \\ 8 & 10 & 12 \end{bmatrix}$; $\mathbf{DB}=\begin{bmatrix} 34 & 40 \\ 71 & 86 \\ 94 & 118 \end{bmatrix}$ **5.** $\mathbf{CDB}=\begin{bmatrix} 458 & 566 \\ 1055 & 1298 \\ 1652 & 2030 \end{bmatrix}$

6. $\mathbf{ACDB}=\begin{bmatrix} -597 & -732 \\ 2110 & 2596 \end{bmatrix}$ either by multiplying $\mathbf{A}$ by $\mathbf{CDB}$ of Ex. 5 or by multiplying $\mathbf{AC}$ by $\mathbf{DB}$ from Ex. 4. $\mathbf{CDBA}$ and $\mathbf{DBAC}$ can be written, but not $\mathbf{CDAB}$. **9.** $\mathbf{B^2}=\begin{bmatrix} 0 & 0 & 1 \\ 0 & 0 & 0 \\ 0 & 0 & 0 \end{bmatrix}$. Then multiply by $\mathbf{B}$ again, to show $\mathbf{B^3}=0$.

10. $\mathbf{C}=a^2b\begin{bmatrix} 1 & \left(\dfrac{1}{a^2}+\dfrac{1}{b}\right) \\ 0 & 1 \end{bmatrix}$; $\mathbf{C}^n=a^{2n}b^n\begin{bmatrix} 1 & n\left(\dfrac{1}{a^2}+\dfrac{1}{b}\right) \\ 0 & 1 \end{bmatrix}$.

11. $(\mathbf{A+B})^2=(\mathbf{A+B})(\mathbf{A+B})=\mathbf{A}(\mathbf{A+B})+\mathbf{B}(\mathbf{A+B})=\mathbf{A^2}+\mathbf{AB}+\mathbf{BA}+\mathbf{B^2}$; etc. **13.** Use notation for partitioned matrices, 12.6 (viii) above ; check that products like $\mathbf{x'\beta}$ are conformable ; multiply $\mathbf{AB}$ to a matrix of order 3×3 in partitioned form $\begin{bmatrix} * & * & * \\ * & * & * \\ * & * & * \end{bmatrix}$.

13.5 (p. 424)

1. To prove (iii) : (rp)th element in $\mathbf{B'}=b_{pr}$

(ps)th element in $\mathbf{A'}=a_{sp}$

$\therefore$ (rs)th element in $\mathbf{B'A'}=\sum\limits_{p} b_{pr}a_{sp}=(rs)$th element in $(\mathbf{AB})'$.

3. AA′ = $\begin{bmatrix} 14 & 32 & 50 \\ 32 & 77 & 122 \\ 50 & 122 & 194 \end{bmatrix}$ =symmetric matrix.

13.6 (p. 428)

1. $\mathbf{xy'} = [(x_r y_s)]$ of order $n \times n$; $\mathbf{yx'}$ is its transpose. Yes : $\mathbf{xy'}$ and $\mathbf{yx'}$ of order $n \times m$ or $m \times n$. **2.** $\mathbf{xx'} = [(x_r x_s)]$ symmetric, of order $n \times n$. **3.** E.g.

$$\mathbf{x'C} = [\,14 \quad 16 \quad 18\,] \ ;$$

then $\mathbf{x'Cy} = 28$. **4.** $\mathbf{x'Ax} = \underset{r\ s}{\Sigma\ \Sigma}\ a_{rs} x_r x_s$; $\mathbf{x'Ix} = \underset{r}{\Sigma}\ x_r^2$.

5. $\{1\}\ [1] = \begin{bmatrix} 1 & 1 & \dots & 1 \\ 1 & 1 & \dots & 1 \\ \multicolumn{4}{c}{\dots\dots\dots\dots} \\ 1 & 1 & \dots & 1 \end{bmatrix}$; $[1]\ \{1\} = n$ (scalar)

$[1]\ \mathbf{I}\ \{1\} = [\underline{1}]\ \{1\} = n$; see also $\mathbf{x'Ix}$ of Ex. 4.

6. $\bar{\lambda}\mathbf{x} = \begin{bmatrix} (\lambda_1 x_1) \\ (\lambda_2 x_2) \\ \dots\dots \end{bmatrix}$; $\mathbf{x'}\bar{\lambda} = [(\lambda_1 x_1)(\lambda_2 x_2)\ \dots]$; $\lambda'\mathbf{x} = \mathbf{x'}\lambda = \underset{r}{\Sigma}\ \lambda_r x_r$, which is the sum

of elements in $\bar{\lambda}\mathbf{x}$ and in $\mathbf{x'}\bar{\lambda}$. **7.** $\bar{\lambda}$ must be of order $m \times m$ in $\bar{\lambda}\mathbf{A}$; of order $n \times n$ in $\mathbf{A}\bar{\lambda}$. **8.** Orders of $\mathbf{I}$ are 1, n and 1 respectively.

13.7 (p. 434)

1. $\mathbf{AB} = \begin{bmatrix} 5 & 4 \\ -1 & 1 \end{bmatrix}$; $\mathbf{BA}\ \begin{bmatrix} 3 & 3 \\ 0 & 3 \end{bmatrix}$; $\mathbf{AC} = \mathbf{CA} = \begin{bmatrix} 3 & 0 \\ 0 & 3 \end{bmatrix}$. All determinants = 9.

3. $\mathbf{B^{-1}} = \begin{bmatrix} 1 & -a & -b \\ 0 & 1 & 0 \\ 0 & 0 & 1 \end{bmatrix}$. **4.** Write $\mathbf{A^{-1}} = \mathbf{IA^{-1}} = \mathbf{BAA^{-1}} =$ etc.

13.8 (p. 439)

2. *First*: (second row − first row) and (third row − $\frac{3}{2}$ first row). *Second*: $\frac{1}{4}$ first row and $(-\frac{1}{3})$ second row. **3.** Each reduces to $\begin{bmatrix} 1 & 0 & 0 \\ 0 & 0 & 0 \\ 0 & 0 & 0 \end{bmatrix}$. **4.** Elementary operations always leave at least one non-zero element, *except* when starting from 0. **5.** Pick a non-zero element and its corresponding negative element ; get a sub-matrix $\begin{bmatrix} 0 & a \\ -a & 0 \end{bmatrix}$ with determinant value $= a^2 \neq 0$.

13.9 (p. 446)

1. Subtract first column from each of other two, getting $\mathbf{A}$ to $\mathbf{I}$; and then $\mathbf{I}$ to $\mathbf{A^{-1}}$. **2.** $0 = \mathbf{A^{-1}}0 = \mathbf{A^{-1}AB} = \mathbf{IB} = \mathbf{B}$, if $\mathbf{A}$ non-singular. Similarly, $\mathbf{A} = 0$ if $\mathbf{B}$ non-singular. But, if $\mathbf{A}$ and $\mathbf{B}$ both singular, $\mathbf{AB}$ can still be 0 and neither $\mathbf{A}$ nor $\mathbf{B}$ is 0. **3.** $\mathbf{AA'} = \begin{bmatrix} \cos\theta & \sin\theta \\ -\sin\theta & \cos\theta \end{bmatrix} \begin{bmatrix} \cos\theta & -\sin\theta \\ \sin\theta & \cos\theta \end{bmatrix} = \mathbf{I}$.

4. Use $\mathbf{AA'} = \mathbf{BB'} = \bar{\mathbf{I}}$.

7. $\begin{bmatrix} \dfrac{1}{\sqrt{2}} & \dfrac{1}{\sqrt{2}} \\ -\dfrac{1}{\sqrt{2}} & \dfrac{1}{\sqrt{2}} \end{bmatrix}$ is orthogonal ; its transpose and its inverse are the same matrix.

8. $\mathbf{A}_\pi$ obtained by *same* shuffling of rows as of columns, so that principal diagonal elements of $\mathbf{A}$ remain on principal diagonal in $\mathbf{A}_\pi$, and elements off principal diagonal remain off.

14.1 (p. 453)

1. Compound vectors as in Fig. 47 and use method of Fig. 50. 2. Show first that rank is 3 ; hence no linear dependence. 3. Rank is 2. Transpose also of rank 2 but two dependent rows and one dependent column. 4. Use $H_{(rs)}$ of 13.4.

14.2 (p. 460)

1. Only $x_2=0$ is consistent with equations. 2. First set : matrix of rank 3 and $m(=3)<n(=4)$. Solution exists : $x_1 = -2x_3$, $x_2=x_4=0$ (given x_3). Contrast Ex. (b). Second set : matrix of rank 3 and $m(=4)>n(=3)$. No solution. Last equation inconsistent, cf. Ex. (a). 4. Write out A^{-1} in terms of co-factors of A from definition. 5. Solution only if $a+b+c=0$. Substitute $c=-(a+b)$ and solve. 6. Third equation same as first ; drop one for : $x_3=1$, $x_1+2x_2+1=0$. (a) Solution changed in values, same form. (b) Augmented matrix rank 3, no solution ; third equation inconsistent with first. 7. Dropping first equation of Ex. 6 does not change solution ; gives two equations here. 8. Drop first or third equation and non-singular system obtained. Substitute solution of Ex. 6 in extra equation ($x_1+x_2+x_3=1$) to get $x_1=1$, $x_2=-1$, $x_3=1$.

14.3 (p. 467)

3. Drop y_3 or y_3; they are related $y_1=2y_1$ for consistency.

4. $\mathbf{z}=\begin{bmatrix} \frac{1}{2} & \frac{1}{2} & 0 \\ 1 & 1 & 1 \end{bmatrix}\begin{bmatrix} -1 & 1 & 1 \\ 1 & -1 & 1 \\ 1 & 1 & -1 \end{bmatrix}\mathbf{x}=\begin{bmatrix} 0 & 0 & 1 \\ 1 & 1 & 1 \end{bmatrix}\mathbf{x}$, i.e. $\begin{aligned}z_1&=x_3,\\ z_2&=x_1+x_2+x_3.\end{aligned}$

14.4 (p. 472)

1. $\lambda=0$ and 2 ; $\lambda=1$ and $1\pm\dfrac{1}{\sqrt{2}}$. 3. p_1 =sum of first-order determinants (principal diagonal) from A ; p_2 =sum of second-order determinants of same type.

4. Transpose of $A(A-\lambda I)'=(A-\lambda I)A'=-\dfrac{1}{\lambda}\left(A'-\lambda I\right)$. So

$$-\frac{1}{\lambda}A(A-\lambda I)'=\left(A'-\frac{1}{\lambda}I\right)'=A-\frac{1}{\lambda}I$$

14.5 (p. 479)

2. $Q=(x_1-x_2)^2=2y_1{}^2$. 3. Matrix $\begin{bmatrix} 0 & 1 \\ 1 & 0 \end{bmatrix}$ non-singular. 4. $\begin{bmatrix} 1 & 0 & -\frac{1}{2} \\ 0 & 1 & -\frac{1}{2} \\ -\frac{1}{2} & -\frac{1}{2} & 1 \end{bmatrix}$

has positive characteristic roots 1 and $1\pm\dfrac{1}{\sqrt{2}}$. (14.4, Ex. 1.) 5. Sum of roots $=p_1$; sum of products of pairs of roots $=p_2$; product of roots $=p_3$. All p's positive if roots positive, and conversely. Then express p's as in 14.4, Ex. 3.

14.6 (p. 483)

1, 2. See 14.4, Ex. 3, and 14.5, Ex. 5.

14.7 (p. 485)

1. Apply Cramer's rule, 14.2 above. 2. $p'A=w'$ with inverse $p'=w'A^{-1}$ as row vector, or $A'p=w$ with inverse $p=(A^{-1})'w$ as column vector. 4. Sum of rth row of $U=\sum_s w_s x_s \dfrac{A_{sr}}{A}=w_r X_r$ =value added (rth industry). See Ex. 1. Similarly, sum of sth column of $U=p_s x_s$ =value of sth final expenditure. Total transactions $=\sum_r w_r X_r=\sum_s p_s x_s$ =national income.

14.8 (p. 488)

2. Show $v_{rs}=p_r x_{rs}=p_r a_{rs}X_s=(rs)$th element in $\bar{p}A\bar{x}$. First condition : V sum. by rows to zero, i.e. $\bar{p}A\bar{x}\{1\}=0$. Pre-multiply by $\bar{p}^{-1}$ to get $AX=0$. Second

condition, similarly, from $[1]\bar{p}A\bar{x}=0$ post-multiplied by $\bar{x}^{-1}$. **3.** $A+B$ has zero elements in last column (nth). In matrix equation $AX=0$, add BX to each side.

14.9 (p. 491)
1. If $|A|=0$, it is immaterial whether a row of A is multiplied by its proper co-factors or by co-factors of another row ; the result is zero in any case (expansion rule, 12.9 above). **4.** Try $X=C$ where C is a vector to be found. Then show $C=A^{-1}c$. **5.** Particular integral is $X_t=X$ (constant over time) where X is : $X=CX+K$, i.e. $X=(I-C)^{-1}K$. This is ultimate output if variation is damped.

15.2 (p. 498)
5. Note that odds n : 1 are shown (by n's) in principal diagonal ; the other elements (-1) represent bets lost. **6.** Each player has nine strategies : (1,1) (2, 1) (3, 1) (1, 2) (2,2) (3, 2) (1, 3) (2, 3) (3,3). The 9×9 pay-off matrix is

$$\begin{bmatrix} 0 & -3 & -4 & 2 \ \cdots \\ 3 & 0 & 0 & 0 \ \cdots \\ \cdots\cdots\cdots\cdots\cdots \end{bmatrix}$$

15.3 (p. 501)
1. $E=4(x-\tfrac{1}{2})(y-\tfrac{1}{2})$. Cf. Ex. ($a$) with players reversed. **2.** For a, α, β positive, show $a_{22}<a_{21}<a_{11}$ and $a_{22}<a_{12}<a_{11}$. **3.** Pure strategies $x=1$, $y=1$ have $E(1,1)=a(\alpha+1)(\beta+1)+b>0$; etc. **4.** Odds : 2 : 1 on and evens.
$$E=\tfrac{7}{2}(x-\tfrac{4}{7})(y-\tfrac{4}{7})-\tfrac{1}{7}.$$

The last term in E is negative, ensuring that " bookie " wins (see 15.5 below), e.g. try $x=\tfrac{1}{2}$, $y=\tfrac{1}{2}$ and show $E<0$. **5.** $E=100y$ when $x=0$; $E=1$ when $x=1$. Equal : 1% chance of fire. **6.** $A=[a_{rs}]$ for $r=1,2$; $s=1,2\ldots n$.
$$E(x,s)=xa_{1s}+(1-x)a_{2s}.$$
Case of 15.2, Ex. (g) has $E(x,s)=7x-4\quad(s=1)$; $9x-5\quad(s=2)$;
$$5-9x\quad(s=3)\ ;\quad 6-11x\quad(s=4).$$

15.4 (p. 506)
1. Solution: pay-off 1 to A ; first strategy for A, second for B. **2.** If " punter " backs one horse, run of horses can always defeat him. **4.** A plays first or third, B plays first strategy, pay-off 1 to A. If B happens to play second strategy, A gains (pay-off 3 instead of 2) by playing third strategy, the " better optimal ". **6.** Surface has saddle point at P ($\tfrac{1}{2}$, $\tfrac{1}{2}$) but with AA' as trough and BB' as ridge lines, instead of other way about (Fig. 52a). E has wrong sign for player A, but appropriate for player B.

15.5 (p. 511)
1. E is (3) of 15.3. **2.** $E=(3x-2)(2y-1)+1$; value of game $=1$. **3.** $x^*=0$, $\tfrac{1}{2}\leqslant y^*\leqslant 1$; value of game $=1$. If A plays wild (and uses first strategy at all), B gains by concentrating on first strategy ($y^*=1$) which is " best optimum ".

4. Take $a_2>a_1$ (or switch columns in A). $\quad E=a-(a_2-a_1)x\left(y+\dfrac{a-a_2}{a_2-a_1}\right)$

If $a>a_2>a_1$: $x^*=0\quad 0\leqslant y^*\leqslant 1$ $\qquad E=a$

If $a_2>a>a_1$: $x^*=0\quad \dfrac{a_2-a}{a_2-a_1}\leqslant y^*\leqslant 1$ $\qquad E=a$

If $a_2>a_1>a$: $x^*=y^*=1$ $\qquad E=a_1$

15.6 (p. 516)
2. $x^*=\tfrac{2}{3}$, $y^*=\tfrac{1}{2}$, $E=1$ as Ex. (c). **4.** $x^*=0$, $\tfrac{1}{2}\leqslant y^*\leqslant 1$, $E=1$. **5.** Plot B_1B_1' ($E=2-y$) ; B_2B_2' ($E=-y$) : B_3B_3' ($E=3-2y$). Rule out B_2B_2', i.e. A does not play second strategy. Then $y^*=1$ from B_1B_1' and B_3B_3'. With reduced matrix $\begin{bmatrix} 1 & 2 \\ 1 & 3 \end{bmatrix}$ for A, graph gives $0\leqslant x^*\leqslant 1$, $E=1$. **6.** Graph for A gives four

lines in plane OEx. First and fourth lines give $x^* = \frac{5}{9}$, $E = -\frac{1}{9}$. But lines are close together around $x = \frac{1}{2}$ so that B's play is only a matter of fine distinctions.

15.7 (p. 522)

1. Vector $(x, 1-x)$ for $0 \leqslant x \leqslant 1$ is line segment $A_1 A_2$ (12.5 above). In a $2 \times n$ game, A's choice fixed by variable x, not vector $\mathbf{x}$. **2.** Plane is $x_1 + x_2 + x_3 = 1$, i.e. $x_3 = 1 - x_1 - x_2$. For side $A_1 A_2$ ($x_3 = 0$) x is $(x_1, 1 - x_1, 0)$ and A mixes first and second strategies only. **3, 4.** If $\mathbf{x}^{(1)}$ and $\mathbf{x}^{(2)}$ satisfy (1), so does $\mathbf{x}$. If P_1 and P_2 are in $A_1 A_2 A_3$ so is mid-point P (Fig. 59). Generally, any convex linear combination of points in X is also in X. **7.** Use property (i). If game has two values, v_1 and v_2, take $c = \dfrac{v_1}{v_2}$. A and cA have same value, so $c = 1$.

15.8 (p. 529)

2. First row redundant, dominated by mean of other two. First column redundant, dominates last. **3.** $\begin{bmatrix} 6 & 9 & 3 \\ 9 & 15 & 0 \\ 9 & 5 & 8 \end{bmatrix}$ has value $\frac{20}{3}$. **4.** $\begin{bmatrix} -2 & 0 & 0 \\ 0 & -2 & 0 \\ 0 & 0 & -2 \end{bmatrix}$ suggests value $v = -\frac{2}{3}$. Property (ii) (b) gives $-2x_1 \geqslant -\frac{2}{3}$, etc. Take all equals signs : $x_1 = x_2 = x_3 = \frac{1}{3}$ (and similarly y's). Original game : solution has equal frequencies of play and value $\frac{1}{3}$. **6.** Reduce to $\begin{bmatrix} 2 & 2 \\ 1 & 6 \\ 5 & 0 \end{bmatrix}$ with value $2(v+1)$; find $y^* = \frac{3}{5}$

graphically. A's optimum is $(0 \ \frac{1}{2} \ \frac{1}{2})$, after eliminating first strategy. **7.** Row minima : $-3, 0, -4$. Column maxima : $3, 3, 0, 1$. Hence pure strategies (second for A, third for B) and game is fair. **8.** Four saddle points (value $= \frac{1}{4}$). Any combination of first and third strategies for A, second and fourth for B is solution. Fair if A makes side payment of $\frac{1}{4}$ to B.

15.9 (p. 533)

1. See Ex. (a) above. Suggests $(\frac{1}{4}, \frac{1}{4}, \frac{1}{4}, \frac{1}{4})$ as each player's optimum, value $= \frac{5}{2}$. Test by applying B's play of $(\frac{1}{4}, \frac{1}{4}, \frac{1}{4}, \frac{1}{4})$ to each of A's pure strategies :
$$1 \times \tfrac{1}{4} + 2 \times \tfrac{1}{4} + 3 \times \tfrac{1}{4} + 4 \times \tfrac{1}{4} = \tfrac{5}{2}, \text{ etc.}$$
4. Value of game $= 0$. Test suggested optimum strategy for B against each of A's pure strategies (as Ex. 1 above) ; $v = 0$ is found for third, fifth and seventh, i.e. A's used strategies.

5. Relations :
$$\begin{aligned} x_1 + x_2 + x_3 &= 1 & y_1 + y_2 + y_3 &= 1 \\ 40x_1 + 150x_3 &\geqslant v & 40y_1 + 30y_2 + 20y_3 &\leqslant v \\ 30x_1 + 100x_2 + 50x_3 &\geqslant v & 100y_2 + 250y_3 &\leqslant v \\ 20x_1 + 250x_2 - 50x_3 &\geqslant v & 150y_1 + 50y_2 - 50y_3 &\leqslant v \end{aligned}$$
Successful attempt is to take : $20x_1 + 250x_2 - 50x_3 > v$ ($y_3 = 0$)
$40y_1 + 30y_2 + 20y_3 < v$ ($x_1 = 0$)
Optimum strategies : $(0, \frac{1}{2}, \frac{1}{2})$ and $(\frac{1}{4}, \frac{3}{4}, 0)$; $v = 75$. **6.** Graph the three lines : $E = 150(1-x)$; $E = 50(x+1)$; $E = 50(6x-1)$ and get $x = \frac{1}{2}$ and $E = 75$. **7.** Test $v = 0$ and A's play $(\frac{1}{4}, \frac{1}{4}, \frac{1}{4}, \frac{1}{4})$ against each of B's pure strategies and show result is zero for each. **8.** E.g. A plays $(1, 1)$, B plays $(2, 1)$, with pay-off which is half the sum of 3 (H at I) and 0 (T at I). **9.** $A(x, y) = -1$ ($x = y = 0$) ; $= 1$ ($x = 1, y = 0$) ; $= 1$ ($x = 0, y = 1$) ; and $= -1$ ($x = y = 1$). This gives matrix.

16.1 (p. 538)

1. (a) Slope of parallel (constant cost) lines $= -\frac{1}{4} =$ slope BP. Optimal purchases : any point on PB. (b) Slope of parallel lines numerically $= \frac{1}{5} <$ slope PB. Optimum at B. **2.** (a) Parallel (constant cost) lines are $x_1 + 2x_2 =$ constant, whether cheese price 12d. or bread price $= 10\frac{1}{2}$d. Similarly (b). **5.** Add extra row to table of data:

Carbohydrate (50 gr.)   5   1   8

Add to (1) another side relation : $5x_1 + x_2 \geqslant 8$ and a corresponding third line in Fig. 60. Shaded area is above and to right of all three lines. P is still solution.
6. Add extra column to table of date, for X_3 : 18
2
3

Problem : $z = 6x_1 + 21x_2 + 18x_3 = \min.$ Subject to $x_1 + 2x_2 + 2x_3 \geqslant 3$ and $x_1 + 4x_2 + 3x_3 \geqslant 4$. Requires three dimensions for graphical solution. **7.** Answers to queries (end of exercise) depend on whether ships can be partly loaded or not ; also if problem is to be generalised. **8.** One of four side relations follows from others, since $a_1 + a_2 = b_1 + b_2$.

16.2 (p. 541)

1. Plot lines $\xi_1 + \xi_2 = 6$, $2\xi_1 + 4\xi_2 = 21$ in $O\xi_1\xi_2$; feasible solutions *under and to left* of lines and optimum is *maximum* position of parallel lines $3\xi_1 + 4\xi_2 = \text{constant}$. Solution, at intersection of lines, is $\xi_1 = \frac{3}{2}$, $\xi_2 = \frac{9}{2}$, $\zeta = 22\frac{1}{2}$. **2.** For example, 16.1, Ex. 1 (a), has $\xi_1 + \xi_2 = 6$, $2\xi_1 + 4\xi_2 = 24$, $3\xi_1 + 4\xi_2 = \max.$ Second line is higher, cuts first on $O\xi_2$, giving $\xi_1 = 0$, $\xi_2 = 6$, $\zeta = 24$. True for any diet $(0-\frac{1}{2}$ lb. cheese, 4–2 lb. bread) with 4 protein units at 6d. **3.** Dual : $\zeta = 3\xi_1 + 4\xi_2 = \max.$ subject to $\xi_1 + \xi_2 \leqslant 6$; $2\xi_1 + 4\xi_2 \leqslant 21$ and $2\xi_1 + 3\xi_2 \leqslant 18$. Graphically : three lines giving same solution as Ex. 1. **4.** Dual : $\zeta = 3\xi_1 + 4\xi_2 + 8\xi_3 = \max.$ subject to $\xi_1 + \xi_2 + 5\xi_3 \leqslant 6$ and $2\xi_1 + 4\xi_2 + \xi_3 \leqslant 21$. Requires three dimensions, as 16.1 Ex. 6. **5.** Interpret ξ_1 and ξ_2 in terms of time ships loaded (cf. empty).

16.3 (p. 544)

1. Dual : $\zeta = b_1\xi_1 + b_2\xi_2 + b_3\xi_3 = \max.$ subject to $a_{11}\xi_1 + a_{21}\xi_2 + a_{31}\xi_3 \leqslant p_1$ and $a_{12}\xi_1 + a_{22}\xi_2 + a_{32}\xi_3 \leqslant p_2$. Problem has 3 side relations in 2 dimensions ; dual has 2 side relations in 3 dimensions.

2. Matrix $=$
$$\begin{bmatrix} 0 & 0 & a_{11} & a_{21} & a_{31} & -p_1 \\ 0 & 0 & a_{12} & a_{22} & a_{32} & -p_2 \\ -a_{11} & -a_{12} & 0 & 0 & 0 & b_1 \\ -a_{21} & -a_{22} & 0 & 0 & 0 & b_2 \\ -a_{31} & -a_{32} & 0 & 0 & 0 & b_3 \\ p_1 & p_2 & -b_1 & -b_2 & -b_3 & 0 \end{bmatrix}$$

3. Game matrix $=$
$$\begin{bmatrix} 0 & 0 & 1 & 1 & 5 & -6 \\ 0 & 0 & 2 & 4 & 1 & -21 \\ -1 & -2 & 0 & 0 & 0 & 3 \\ -1 & -4 & 0 & 0 & 0 & 4 \\ -5 & -1 & 0 & 0 & 0 & 8 \\ 6 & 21 & -3 & -4 & -8 & 0 \end{bmatrix}.$$
Optimum $(\frac{4}{19}, \frac{1}{19}, \frac{3}{19}, \frac{9}{19}, 0, \frac{2}{19})$

Linear programme of 16.1, Ex. 5, has $x_1 = 2$, $x_2 = \frac{1}{2}$. Dual of 16.2, Ex. 4. has $\xi_1 = \frac{3}{2}$, $\xi_2 = \frac{9}{2}$, $\xi_3 = 0$.

4. $z = p_1 x_1 + p_2 x_2 + p_3 x_3 = \min.$
$\qquad a_{11}x_1 + a_{12}x_2 + a_{13}x_3 \geqslant b_1$
$\qquad a_{21}x_1 + a_{22}x_2 + a_{23}x_3 \geqslant b_2$

$\zeta = b_1\xi_1 + b_2\xi_2 = \max.$
$a_{11}\xi_1 + a_{21}\xi_2 \leqslant p_1$
$a_{12}\xi_1 + a_{22}\xi_2 \leqslant p_2$
$a_{13}\xi_1 + a_{23}\xi_2 \leqslant p_3$

Matrix $=$
$$\begin{bmatrix} 0 & 0 & 0 & a_{11} & a_{21} & -p_1 \\ 0 & 0 & 0 & a_{12} & a_{22} & -p_2 \\ 0 & 0 & 0 & a_{13} & a_{23} & -p_3 \\ -a_{11} & -a_{12} & -a_{13} & 0 & 0 & b_1 \\ -a_{21} & -a_{22} & -a_{23} & 0 & 0 & b_2 \\ p_1 & p_2 & p_3 & -b_1 & -b_2 & 0 \end{bmatrix}$$

16.6 (p. 553)

1. $\zeta = b_1\mu_1 + b_2\mu_2 =$ max.   subject to $a_{11}\mu_1 + a_{21}\mu_2 + \mu_3 = p_1$
$$a_{12}\mu_1 + a_{22}\mu_2 + \mu_4 = p_2$$

2. M slack variables in $n = M + N$; $m = M$ inequalities become equations.
3. In dual, N slack variables in group of $n' = M + N$, turning $m' = N$ inequalities into equations.   Programme and dual, same number of variables $(M + N)$. Equations (and numbers of slack variables), M for programme ; N for dual.

16.9 (p. 562)

2. $\lambda_1 \begin{bmatrix} 1 \\ 0 \end{bmatrix} + \lambda_2 \begin{bmatrix} 1 \\ 4 \end{bmatrix} = \begin{bmatrix} (\lambda_1 + \lambda_2) \\ 4\lambda_2 \end{bmatrix}$.   So $\lambda_1 + \lambda_2 = x_1$ and $4\lambda_2 = x_2$.   **3.** In last section

of Simplex table, λ column is $(2, \frac{1}{2})$ and the row for $c_s - z_s$ is $(0, 0, -\frac{3}{2}, -\frac{9}{2})$.
4. Dual is easier : $\zeta = 3\lambda_1 + 4\lambda_2 + 8\lambda_3 =$ max.

subject to $\lambda_1 + \lambda_2 + 5\lambda_3 + \lambda_4 = 6$ and $2\lambda_1 + 4\lambda_2 + \lambda_3 + \lambda_5 = 21$

Requirements, space of two dimensions $\begin{bmatrix} 1 & 1 & 5 & 1 & 0 & 6 \\ 2 & 4 & 1 & 0 & 1 & 21 \end{bmatrix}$

Start with $\mathbf{p}^{(4)}$ and $\mathbf{p}^{(5)}$ with weights 6 and 21.   Finish with :

$$\lambda_1 = \tfrac{3}{2}, \ \lambda_2 = \tfrac{9}{2}, \ \lambda_3 = \lambda_4 = \lambda_5 = 0$$

So : $\xi_1 = \tfrac{3}{2}, \ \xi_2 = \tfrac{9}{2}, \ \xi_3 = 0$ (16.2, Ex. 4).   For programme itself, last row for $c_s - z_s$ is $(0, 0, 0, -2, -\frac{1}{2})$;   so $x_1 = 2, x_2 = \frac{1}{2}$.
5. Drop $\mathbf{p}^{(4)} = \begin{bmatrix} 0 \\ 0 \end{bmatrix}$.   Then any *pair* of $\begin{bmatrix} 1 & 1 & 0 \\ 1 & 0 & 1 \end{bmatrix}$ linearly dependent ; also

$\begin{bmatrix} b_1 \\ b_2 \end{bmatrix}$ with any one of others, provided $b_1 \neq 0, b_2 \neq 0, b_1 \neq b_2$.   **6.** Infinite number

of solutions : $x_2 = 10 - x_1$ and $x_3 = 20 - x_1$ for any x_1 $(0 \leqslant x_1 \leqslant 10)$.   Dual : $\zeta = 10\xi_1 + 20\xi_2 =$ max., subject to $\xi_1 + \xi_2 = 1, \ \xi_1 = \frac{1}{2}, \ \xi_2 = \frac{1}{2}$.   This fixes ξ_1 and ξ_2 at $\frac{1}{2}$ and ζ at 15.   Methods of solution break down (unnecessary).
7. $z = 3x_{11} + 2x_{12} + 5x_{21} + 4x_{22} =$ min. ; $x_{11} + x_{12} = 2$; $x_{11} + x_{21} = 6$ and $x_{12} + x_{22} = 6$
Take $x_{11} = \lambda$.   So : $x_{12} = 2 - \lambda, \ x_{21} = 6 - \lambda, \ x_{22} = 4 + \lambda$. $z = 50$, independent of λ. Infinite number of solutions $(0 \leqslant \lambda \leqslant 2)$.   Simplex method breaks down (unnecessary).

17.2 (p. 570)

4. For example $x_2 = -\lambda_1 + 2\lambda_2 + \lambda_3 = 1 - 2\lambda_1 + \lambda_2$ $(\lambda_1$ and λ_2 positive fractions). Output if $\lambda_2 > (2\lambda_1 - 1)$.

17.5 (p. 584)

1. Compare Fig. 65 with Fig. 61.   Activities in cone (A) between $OA^{(2)}$ and vertical :   both commodities are inputs (no output).   **8.** Point $A^{(1)}$ is higher and at least as far to right as others, i.e. with unit input of " labour ", more of x_2 can be got from first activity with no sacrifice of x_1.

17.6 (p. 591)

1. $OA^{(1)}A^{(2)}$, $OA^{(1)}A^{(3)}$ efficient.   **2.** $OA^{(1)}A^{(2)}$ only efficient.   **3.** $\mathbf{p}_1 = (1, 0, 2)$ is normal to $OA^{(1)}A^{(2)}$, $\mathbf{p}_2 = (-1, 2, 2)$ to $OA^{(1)}A^{(3)}$.   Positive $\mathbf{p}$, e.g. $\mathbf{p} = (\frac{1}{2}, \frac{1}{2}, 2)$, between $\mathbf{p}_1$ and $\mathbf{p}_2$.   **4.** Fig. 62 as illustrated has $OA^{(1)}A^{(2)}$ efficient.   If $A^{(2)}$ is to left of $A^{(1)}$, then only $OA^{(1)}$ is efficient.

17.7 (p. 594)

2. For $OA^{(1)}A^{(2)}$: $2p_1 + 2p_2 - p_3 = 0$ giving $p_1 : p_2 : p_3 = 2 : 1 : 6$.
$$3p_1 \qquad - p_3 = 0$$
$$p_1 + 3p_2 - p_3 \leqslant 0$$

Similarly for $OA^{(1)}A^{(3)}$: $p_1 : p_2 : p_3 = 1 : 1 : 4$.   **3.** See 17.6, Ex. 3

17.8 (p. 600)

3. Efficient allocation at point like C of Fig. 68 but lying between $A^{(2)}$ and $A^{(3)}$ and between $B^{(2)}$ and $B^{(3)}$, i.e. on facet $OA^{(2)}A^{(3)}$ where $x_2 = x_3 = -1$ and both factors used to limit.

18.1 (p. 612)

2. Write (4): $f = y$; $p_1 = \lambda f_1$; $p_2 = \lambda f_2$. Differentiate with respect to y, noting that λ (as well as x_1 and x_2) varies with y. Then:

$$\frac{\partial C}{\partial y} = p_1 \frac{\partial x_1}{\partial y} + p_2 \frac{\partial x_2}{\partial y} = \lambda \left(f_1 \frac{\partial x_1}{\partial y} + f_2 \frac{\partial x_2}{\partial y} \right) = \lambda.$$

5. In $y = f_1 x_1 + f_2 x_2$ (Euler's Theorem) put $f_1 = \frac{1}{\lambda} p_1$ and $f_2 = \frac{1}{\lambda} p_2$. Note that $\frac{\partial C}{\partial y} = \lambda$, Ex. 2 above.

18.2 (p. 617)

1. Derivatives of $\phi(f)$ are $\phi'(f) f_r$ and $\phi'(f) f_{rs} + \phi''(f) f_r f_s$. Ratios of first derivatives given as $f_1 : f_2 : \dots$. Substitute in F, split each row (after first) into two parts, one of which (being proportional to first row) gives a zero determinant. Hence F has only a multiple $\{\phi'(f)\}^{n+1}$. **3.** $C = \Sigma p_r x_r =$ max. for

$$f(x_1, x_2, \dots x_n, y) = 0.$$

Find max. $z = C - \lambda f$ for variable x's, given p's and y. $\dfrac{\partial z}{\partial x_r} = 0$ gives $p_r = \lambda f_r$ which is same as (1), but for factors only. **4.** Analysis and results similar to text, equations (3).

18.5 (p. 632)

1. Take $\lambda_3 = 0$ and re-draw AP and BP from :

$$100\lambda_1 + 25\lambda_2 = 150 \quad \text{and} \quad 10\lambda_1 + 50\lambda_2 = 12\tfrac{1}{2}$$

These intersect *below* $O\lambda_1$. Solution confined to area under first line, i.e. where it cuts $O\lambda_1$ ($\lambda_1 = 1 \cdot 5$, $\lambda_2 = 0$).

3. $A = \begin{bmatrix} 200 & 25 & 60 \\ 20 & 50 & 48 \end{bmatrix}$ 50 man-months $52\tfrac{1}{2}$ acres

£000   2   2   2

Fig. 72a now shows constant product loci with two efficient segments $P_1 P_2 P_3$ and Q between OA_2 and OA_3. Since OA_3 used, hogs are produced. Fig. 72b with $\lambda_1 = 0$ has two lines :

$$25\lambda_2 + 60\lambda_3 = 50. \quad \text{So} : \lambda_2 = \tfrac{5}{12}, \ \lambda_3 = \tfrac{95}{144}$$
$$50\lambda_2 + 48\lambda_3 = 52\tfrac{1}{2}$$

4. Vary constant on R.H.S. of second equation of Ex. 3 (Fig. 72b). If 40 acres, $\lambda_2 = 0$ and only third process used. If 100 acres, $\lambda_3 = 0$, second process used. **5.** Solution at Q_1 of Fig. 72a ; first process only, both factors fully used. **6.** Note : one slack variable (turning third side relation into equation) has the non-zero value $2\tfrac{1}{2}$. **7.** First process increased, second decreased, by £100 :

	First	Second	Total
Labour (man-months)	$+2\tfrac{1}{2}$	$-\tfrac{1}{2}$	$+2$
Land (acres)	$+5$	-10	-5

Ratio 2 : 5, as prices. **8.** Two scarce factors and two used processes if ratio of land (acres) to labour (man-months) between 125 : 4 and 50 : 25. Otherwise, if more land, only A_3 process (labour scarce), and similarly if less land. Exception : land to labour ratio exactly $125:4$, or $100:5$, or $50:25$ (degenerate cases).

18.6 (p. 638)

1. Unit levels for receipts of £1. $\mathbf{A} = [a_{11}\ a_{12}\ ...]$ (row vector). Problem is max. $z = \Sigma_s \lambda_s$ for $\Sigma_s a_{1s}\lambda_s \leqslant b$. Solution : a_{1m} minimum of row of $\mathbf{A}$, $\lambda_m = \dfrac{b}{a_{1m}}$ and other λ's zero.

2. $\mathbf{A} = \begin{bmatrix} 12\frac{1}{2} & 10 \\ 25 & 100 \\ \hline £000 \quad 1 & 1 \end{bmatrix}$ $\begin{array}{l} 50 \text{ man-months.} \\ 260 \text{ acres} \end{array}$ Solution : $\lambda_2 = 2$, $\lambda_1 = 2\cdot4$.

Full factor use with output of 200 tons wheat, 160 tons hay. If prices are £$10p$ for wheat, £10 for hay, then $\mathbf{A} = \begin{bmatrix} \dfrac{25}{p} & 10 \\ \dfrac{50}{p} & 100 \end{bmatrix}$. Wheat only produced ($\lambda_2 = 0$) if

slopes $AP \leqslant 1$ numerically (Fig. 72b), i.e. $p \geqslant 2\cdot5$ (wheat price £25 per ton). Similarly, £5 per ton for hay only produced. **3.** If $\pi_2 \geqslant \frac{5}{2}\pi_1$, two lines

$$50p_1 + 5p_2 = \pi_2 - \tfrac{1}{2}\pi_1 \quad \text{and} \quad 25p_1 + 50p_2 = \pi_1$$

intersect below Op_1. Solution $p_2 = 0$, land not fully used, only hogs produced Similarly, $\pi_2 \leqslant \frac{3}{5}\pi_1$, solution $p_1 = 0$, labour not fully used, only corn produced.

18.7 (p. 643)

1. $\mathbf{A} = \begin{bmatrix} 10 & 12 \\ 5 & 2 \\ \hline £6500 \quad 1 & 1 \end{bmatrix}$ $\begin{array}{l} 100 \text{ men} \\ 60 \text{ machines} \end{array}$ $\begin{array}{l} z = \lambda_1 + \lambda_2 = \max. \\ \text{subject to } 10\lambda_1 + 12\lambda_2 \leqslant 100 \\ 5\lambda_1 + 2\lambda_2 \leqslant 60 \end{array}$

Graphical solution : $\lambda_1 = 10$, $\lambda_2 = 0$.

2. 6 % interest rate leaves discounted receipts $\left(£\dfrac{7,040}{1\cdot06} = £6,640\right)$ below cost of hired factors. If rate is $100r$ %, switch to long process if $\dfrac{7,040}{1+r} \geqslant 6,500$, i.e. rate $\leqslant 8\cdot3$ %. Switch to hired factors if $\dfrac{7,040}{1+r} \geqslant 6,700$, i.e. rate $\leqslant 5\cdot1$ %. **3.** Row for cost of hired factors :

$$[0 \quad 0 \quad 0 \quad 0 \quad 6,500 \quad 6,600 \quad 6,500 \quad 6,600]$$

Any switch to hired factors is to A's not B's. Product prices increased by 10 %, switch to A_1, added process like original. **4.** In Ex. 1 change second side relation to $5\lambda_1 + 2\lambda_2 \leqslant 50$. Show machines also fully used, though $\lambda_1 = 10$, $\lambda_2 = 0$ again. Dual : $\zeta = 100p_1 + 50p_2 = \min.$ subject to $10p_1 + 5p_2 \geqslant 1$, $12p_1 + 2p_2 \geqslant 1$. Solution : $p_1 = \frac{3}{40}$, $p_2 = \frac{1}{20}$. **5.** Price ratios of dual (Ex. 4) give productivity of labour to machines $= p_1 : p_2 = \frac{3}{40} : \frac{1}{20} = 1\cdot5$. Original problem has labour relatively under-priced, and switch is to labour-intensive processes. Reverse is case in Ex. 3 above.

18.8 (p. 648)

1. $\mathbf{A} = \begin{bmatrix} 25 & 10 & 0 \\ 50 & 100 & 0 \\ -1 & 0 & 1 \\ -0 & -1 & c \end{bmatrix}$ $\begin{array}{l} 50 \text{ man-months.} \\ 260 \text{ acres} \\ 0 \\ 0 \end{array}$ $\begin{array}{l} \text{Point } P : \lambda_1 = 1\cdot2,\ \lambda_2 = 2 \\ \text{i.e. } \dfrac{\lambda_2}{\lambda_1} = \dfrac{5}{3} \\ \text{(as Fig. 74).} \end{array}$

Other side relations ($-\lambda_1 + \lambda_3 = 0$ and $-\lambda_2 + c\lambda_3 = 0$) give $\dfrac{\lambda_2}{\lambda_1} = c$ and max. $\lambda_1 = \lambda_3$ is sought. Situation of Fig. 74 (land unused, price of land zero) if $c < \frac{5}{3}$. **2.** Accidental case where OQ coincides with OP (Fig. 74). **4.** Rate of substitution $= p_2 : p_3 = 28 : 63$. Productivity of labour $= p_1 : p_2 = 4 : 28 = 0.14$ tons of fresh fish per man-month, and similarly for smoked fish.

19.1 (p. 658)

2. $\phi(u) = \frac{1}{2}u^2$; $\phi'(u) = u$; $\phi''(u) = 1$. For two commodities :

$$\Phi = \begin{vmatrix} 0 & uu_1 & uu_2 \\ uu_1 & uu_{11} + u_1{}^2 & uu_{12} + u_1 u_2 \\ uu_2 & uu_{21} + u_1 u_2 & uu_{22} + u_2{}^2 \end{vmatrix} = u^3 \begin{vmatrix} 0 & u_1 & u_2 \\ u_1 & u_{11} + \dfrac{u_1{}^2}{u} & u_{12} + \dfrac{u_1 u_2}{u} \\ u_2 & u_{21} + \dfrac{u_1 u_2}{u} & u_{22} + \dfrac{u_2{}^2}{u} \end{vmatrix} = u^3 U$$

all other determinants being zero (columns in proportion). **3.** As Ex. 2 but with $\phi(u) = \log u$; $\phi'(u) = \dfrac{1}{u}$; $\phi''(u) = -\dfrac{1}{u^2}$.

19.2 (p. 660)

1. $x_1 = \dfrac{M}{P}(a_{22}p_1 - a_{12}p_2)$; $x_2 = \dfrac{M}{P}(a_{11}p_2 - a_{12}p_1)$; $\lambda = \dfrac{M}{P}(a_{11}a_{22} - a_{12}{}^2)$ where

$$P = a_{22}p_1{}^2 - 2a_{12}p_1 p_2 + a_{11}p_2{}^2$$

Differentiate x_1 and x_2 :

$$\frac{\partial x_1}{\partial p_1} = -\frac{M}{P^2}\{p_2{}^2(a_{11}a_{22} - a_{12}{}^2) + (a_{22}p_1 - a_{12}p_2)^2\}$$

So $\dfrac{\partial x_1}{\partial p_1} < 0$, certainly if $a_{11}a_{22} > a_{12}{}^2$. **2.** P as in solution of Ex. 1. From first condition (3) above :

$$U = \begin{vmatrix} 0 & u_1 & u_2 \\ u_1 & u_{11} & u_{12} \\ u_2 & u_{21} & u_{22} \end{vmatrix} = \lambda^2 \begin{vmatrix} 0 & p_1 & p_2 \\ p_1 & a_{11} & a_{12} \\ p_2 & a_{21} & a_{22} \end{vmatrix} = -\lambda^2 P > 0$$

Hence $P < 0$ and, by results for quadratic forms, a_{11} (and a_{22}) < 0 and $a_{11}a_{22} > a_{12}{}^2$. Note : under these conditions, u_1, u_2 and λ are negative (see Ex. 1), i.e. " marginal utility " is negative. **3.** Use result (5) of 19.1 above.

19.3 (p. 665)

2. From (8) and (9), three goods : $X_{12}p_2 + X_{13}p_3 > 0$; $X_{12}p_1 + X_{23}p_3 > 0$; and $X_{13}p_1 + X_{23}p_2 > 0$. Not more than one of X_{12}, X_{23}, X_{13} negative ; not more than one pair of goods complementary. **4.** Take p_1 decreasing, p_2 fixed. As p_1 passes critical value $\left(p_1 = \dfrac{a_{21}}{a_{22}}p_2 \right)$, purchase shift from P to B in Fig. 60 (i.e. $\bar{x}_2$ becomes zero). This is a substitution of first good for second. Otherwise, purchases fixed in quantity.

19.4 (p. 669)

1. $\dfrac{d}{dx_1}\left(-\dfrac{dx_2}{dx_1} \right) = \dfrac{\partial}{\partial x_1}\left(\dfrac{u_1}{u_2} \right) + \dfrac{\partial}{\partial x_2}\left(\dfrac{u_1}{u_2} \right)\dfrac{dx_2}{dx_1} = -\dfrac{1}{u^3}\begin{vmatrix} 0 & u_1 & u_2 \\ u_1 & u_{11} & u_{12} \\ u_2 & u_{21} & u_{22} \end{vmatrix} < 0$

Indifference curve less steep to right, i.e. convex to O. **3.** $\left(-\dfrac{\partial x_1}{\partial p} \right)$ and $\dfrac{\partial x_1}{\partial M}$

negative : x_1 *decreases* for price decreasing (along PC) and for income increasing (along PB), i.e. loci backward sloping at P. Indifference curves must be close together and steep for small x_1 ; far apart and flat for large x_1.

19.6 (p. 680)
1. Above OA_1 : x_2 surplus to requirements or too little x_1. 2. $dx_1 = (a_{11} - a_{12})d\mu$ and $dx_2 = -(a_{22} - a_{21})d\mu$. Hence $\left(-\dfrac{dx_1}{dx_2} \right)$, given by slope of P_1P_2 in Fig. 79.
4. Finite number of plane segments, each with only one slope (rate of substitution) for a given pair of goods.

19.7 (p. 685)
1. Some factors consumed directly (desired in themselves) ; some products not exactly consumed with limits set on stock-building ; some production processes with " utility " in themselves. 2. (i) as 18.8 above : max. utility from one consumption activity ; (ii) as 18.8, Ex. (*b*), above, but with several consumption activities : dual is min. cost ·of the single factor ; (iii) **A** in lower left-hand section has principal diagonal of (-1) and zero values elsewhere.

19.8 (p. 691)
1. In graph (Fig. 80*a*) : $z = \frac{1}{3}(\lambda_1 + 2\lambda_2) = \text{max.}$
$\quad AP \quad 25\lambda_1 + 10\lambda_2 = 50 \quad$ (labour fully used)
$\quad BP \quad 50\lambda_1 + 100\lambda_2 = 260 \quad$ (land fully used)
$\quad OQ \quad \lambda_2 = \lambda_1 \quad (\lambda_4 = 0,$ first consumption ratio only)
$\quad OR \quad \lambda_2 = \frac{1}{4}\lambda_1 \quad (\lambda_3 = 0,$ second consumption ratio only)
Solution : $\lambda_1 = \lambda_2 = \lambda_3 = \frac{10}{7}$, $\lambda_4 = 0$, where AP cuts OQ. So only labour fully used, only first consumption ratio used. Cf. 18.8, Ex. 1. If $\dfrac{1,500}{7} = 214$ acres or less, land also scarce. 2. P falls below OR (Fig. 80*a*); land scarce, labour unemployed. BP parallel to lines for $z = \text{constant}$ and λ's indeterminate in ranges : $\frac{1}{4} \leqslant \dfrac{\lambda_2}{\lambda_1} \leqslant 1$, $\lambda_3 \geqslant 0$, $\lambda_4 \geqslant 0$. 5. $b = 45$ has $p_1 : p_2 : p_3 : p_4 = 1 : 0 : 7 : 15$ (to be scaled by $p_3 + p_4 = 1$). $b = 30$ has $p_1 = \frac{1}{7} p_3$ and $p_2 = \frac{1}{21}(7p_4 - 15p_3)$; if $p_3 + p_4 = 1$ and $3p_3 + \frac{1}{2}p_4 = 1$ also used, then $p_1 : p_2 : p_3 : p_4 = 3 : 13 : 21 : 84$.
6. λ_1 decreases relative to λ_2 until $\dfrac{\lambda_2}{\lambda_1} = \dfrac{\alpha}{\beta} + \dfrac{1}{2}$. Thereafter $\alpha : \beta$ ratio only and land unused. P goes above OQ (Fig. 80*a*). 7. (i) and (ii) : proportionate decline in productivity of land and labour in first (second) production process. (iii) : Relative change in labour productivity between two processes. (iv) : Change in structure of tastes. Analyse effect as in text and Ex. 6.

20.1 (p. 696)
2. See Theil (1954), pp. 5–6.

20.2 (p. 701)
3. On approach (i), $a = \bar{a} = \dfrac{1}{n} \underset{s}{\Sigma} a_s$ and $k = \Sigma k_s$ provided that $x = \dfrac{1}{\bar{a}} \Sigma a_s x_s = \text{weighted}$ mean of output of firms, weights equal to marginal propensities to use factor.

20.3 (p. 704)
1. b is aggregate price-elasticity, but with respect to a price index of geometric mean form. 2. As 20.2, Ex. 1 and 2. Marginal propensity to consume commodity group is sum of marginal propensities to consume constituent commodities. 3. $\dfrac{p_r}{y_r} \dfrac{dy_r}{dp_r} = b_r \dfrac{p_r}{p_{r0}} \Big/ \dfrac{y_r}{y_{r0}} = b_r$ at base point.

20.4 (p. 709)

1. See evidence to the contrary quoted by Theil (1954), p. 25.

3. $\Delta_1 y = \left(\dfrac{1}{n} \sum_s a_s\right) \Delta\mu = \bar{a}\, \Delta\mu$; $\Delta_2 y = a\, \Delta\mu$. Equal if $a = \bar{a}$, i.e. if Cov $(a_s A_s) = 0$.

4. Cov $(a_s A_s) = 0$ when $a_s =$ constant but also under other circumstances.

20.5 (p. 712)

1. Use $\sum\limits_s A_{as} = 1$, $\sum\limits_s A_{bs} = 0$. **3.** Index q covers prices of commodities within and outside group ; only outside prices if the group comprises commodities not interrelated. **5.** a depends on a_s only and b on b_s only ; it is possible to avoid contradictions in the particular case specified if income increases are proportional to mean income levels.

20.6 (p. 715)

1. Assume firm has a single (given) output. **2.** Take x_q $(q = 1, 2, \ldots k)$ as the amounts of income from different sources. **4.** See also Ex. (b) extended by summing over firms.

20.7 (p. 719)

2. $i = 1, 2, \ldots m$ over commodities or inputs. **3.** See Theil (1954), p. 29. **4.** If y_i relates to rth commodity, sth individual, then $_i a_s \neq 0$ is his marginal propensity to consume commodity.

20.8 (p. 722)

Interpret condition as $X_1 =$ max. for given X_r $(r = 2, 3, \ldots m)$. **6.** Condition is $U_i =$ max. for $f(X_1, X_2, \ldots X_m) = 0$. **7.** For each i, conditions of Ex. 6 are :
$$\frac{\partial U_i}{\partial x_{i1}} : \frac{\partial U_i}{\partial x_{i2}} = \frac{\partial f}{\partial X_1} : \frac{\partial f}{\partial X_2}$$
and similarly for other pairs of commodities. There are only $(m - 1)$ independent ratios ; others follow. Check for 3 and 4 commodities. **8.** Only $(k - 1)$ independent equations, as in Ex. 7.

INDEX

Numbers refer to pages, and those in italics to exercises appended to the various sections

SUBJECTS

AUTHORS

See also references at the end of each chapter